S0-ARM-797

GENERAL INDEX

AUTOMATIC TRANSMISSION SERVICING
Section 1

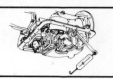

AUTOMATIC TRANSMISSIONS
Section 2

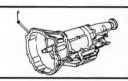

AUTOMATIC TRANSAXLES
Section 3

MANUAL TRANSMISSION SERVICING
Section 4

MANUAL TRANSMISSIONS
Section 5

MANUAL TRANSAXLES
Section 6

OVERDRIVES & TRANSFER CASES
Section 7

CLUTCHES
Section 8

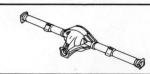

DRIVE AXLES
Section 9

CAUTION

LATEST CHANGES & CORRECTIONS
Blue Pages

PREFACE

This is the 1980 edition of Mitchell Manuals'
Transmission Service and Repair Manual for Imported Cars and Trucks.
This book, like the many Mitchell publications which have preceded it,
represents our commitment to professionalism
in the automotive service market.

The automotive industry advances every year,
and Mitchell Manuals pledges to advance and improve its products
as we maintain the quality and usefulness of all Mitchell Manuals' publications.

We cordially acknowledge the good will
and mutual goals that exist in the automotive business,
and it is in this spirit that we thank the automotive manufacturers,
distributors, dealers and the entire automotive industry
for their fine cooperation and assistance
which have made this publication possible.

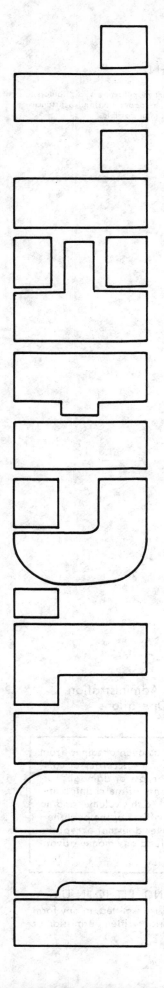

1980 IMPORTED CARS & TRUCKS TRANSMISSION SERVICE & REPAIR

National Service Data
Manuals For The Automotive Professional

Published By:
MITCHELL MANUALS, INC.
A Cordura Company
P.O. BOX 26260
SAN DIEGO, CA 92126

ISBN 0-8470-5770-4

ACKNOWLEDGEMENT

Mitchell Manuals thanks the automotive and equipment manufacturers, distributors, dealers and the entire automotive industry for their fine cooperation and assistance which makes the publication of this manual possible.

MITCHELL MANUALS, INC.

A Cordura Company

Vice President and Publisher
Richard M. Harris

Managing Editor
Kenneth A. Young

Ass't. Managing Editor
Daniel M. Kelley

Composition Manager
Doris J. Williams

Art Director
Eloise S. Stiverson

Technical Editors
Gary L. Haley
Daryl F. Visser
Robert B. Johnson
Steven L. Hansen
Michael Roeder
Terry L. Blomquist
Thomas L. Landis
Daniel D. Fleming
Philip G. Wallan
Alan M. Salo

PUBLISHED BY

MITCHELL MANUALS, INC.
9889 Willow Creek Road
P.O. Box 26260
San Diego, California 92126

a subsidiary of
CORDURA PUBLICATIONS, INC.
C.L. Kobrin, President
John Opelt, Vice President of Finance & Administration
Malcolm Ferrier, Vice President of Operations

ISBN 0-8470-5770-4

Introduction

You now have the most complete and up-to-date Service and Repair Manual currently available to the professional mechanic. Our staff of experts have spent many hundreds of hours gathering and processing service and repair information from sources throughout the automotive world. More than 150 separate articles provide specific, step-by-step testing, adjusting and repair procedures for 1980 Imported Cars and Trucks.

To use this manual in the most efficient and profitable way possible, please take the time to read the following section, "How to Find the Information". This will enable you to quickly locate the model car, and the mechanical procedure you desire, without wasting precious time thumbing through unnecessary pages.

HOW TO FIND THE INFORMATION
3 Quick Steps

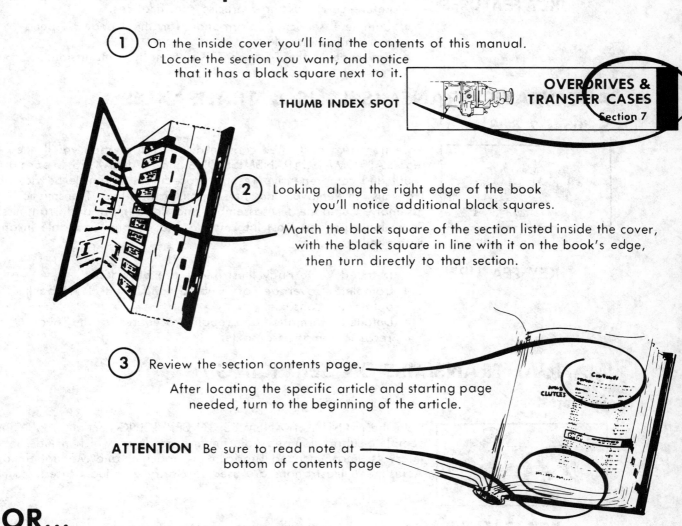

① On the inside cover you'll find the contents of this manual. Locate the section you want, and notice that it has a black square next to it.

THUMB INDEX SPOT

OVERDRIVES & TRANSFER CASES
Section 7

② Looking along the right edge of the book you'll notice additional black squares.

Match the black square of the section listed inside the cover, with the black square in line with it on the book's edge, then turn directly to that section.

③ Review the section contents page.

After locating the specific article and starting page needed, turn to the beginning of the article.

ATTENTION Be sure to read note at bottom of contents page

OR...

Go directly to the GENERAL INDEX located at the front of the book.
Use this alphabetical index as you would any type of reference index.

Section Highlights

GENERAL INDEX

This section of the Imported Transmission manual is a quick, easy reference to help you locate the information you need. It is arranged alphabetically and is broken down into all of the vehicle's major components and then divided into models under component headings.

AUTOMATIC TRANSMISSION SERVICING

Section 1

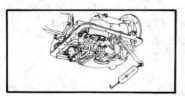

The AUTOMATIC TRANSMISSION SERVICING section of this book is broken down into individual models, and each servicing article contains two basic sections: a Lubrication section and an Adjustment section. The Lubrication section contains factory specified Service Intervals, Fluid Level Checking, Recommended Fluids, Capacities and Draining and Refill instructions. The Adjustment section contains instructions for Band Adjustment, Throttle and Kickdown Linkage Adjustment and Neutral Safety Switch Adjustment.

KEY FEATURES

- Reference charts show precise specifications.
- Complete servicing information for the Honda 3-speed automatic transaxle.
- Coverage of the Triumph TR8 automatic transmission.

AUTOMATIC TRANSMISSIONS & TRANSAXLES

Sections 2 & 3

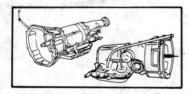

Sections two and three contain all the information you'll need to repair AUTOMATIC TRANSMISSIONS and TRANSAXLES. In each article, you'll find comprehensive Testing procedures, In-Vehicle Service and Transmission Removal and Installation. In addition, Transmission Disassembly, Component Disassembly and Reassembly and Transmission Reassembly are the most informative and graphic available in any repair manual.

KEY FEATURES

- Detailed Valve Body Illustrations are provided.
- Complete coverage of Champ and Colt Hatchback automatic transaxle.
- Detailed information and repair procedures for the Toyota Tercel automatic transaxle.

MANUAL TRANSMISSION SERVICING

Section 4

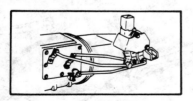

In the MANUAL TRANSMISSION SERVICING section, you'll find complete Lubrication and Adjustment procedures, which include Service Intervals, Recommended Lubricants, Capacities and Manual Linkage Adjustment. Illustrations are used to clarify detailed procedures.

KEY FEATURES

- Shift Linkage adjustment procedures are provided.
- All Service Intervals are included.
- Complete servicing information for the Porsche 924 Turbo manual transaxle.

MANUAL TRANSMISSIONS & TRANSAXLES
Sections 5 & 6

KEY FEATURES

In the MANUAL TRANSMISSIONS & TRANSAXLES section you'll find comprehensive articles covering Removal, Installation and Overhaul procedures for all Manual Transmissions covered in this book. Descriptions of transmissions used in individual models are placed at the front of the articles.

- Numerous Cut-Away and Exploded View Illustrations are provided.
- Coverage of the BMW 320i 5-speed manual transmission.
- Complete information on the Toyota Tercel manual transaxle.

OVERDRIVES & TRANSFER CASES
Section 7

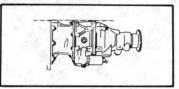

KEY FEATURES

This section covers OVERDRIVES & TRANSFER CASES used in most imported cars. Overdrive component manufacturers are included for precise repair. Comprehensive In-Vehicle Servicing, Removal and Installation and Overhaul procedures are complete and easy to understand. All Specifications and Tolerances are included to make precise repairs of these components.

- Trouble Shooting and Diagnostic information.
- Component Diagrams and Illustrations are included.
- Detailed information on the Datsun four-wheel-drive Pickup transfer case.

CLUTCHES
Section 8

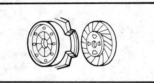

KEY FEATURES

In the CLUTCH section you'll find complete Removal and Overhaul procedures for Clutch Plates, Master Cylinders, Slave Cylinders and Release Bearings. Also with each article is the information needed to do complete adjustment and bleeding of Clutch systems.

- Diagrams and Illustrations of Clutch systems.
- Complete coverage of the Peugeot 505 clutch system.
- Information and repair procedures for the Volkswagen Jetta clutch system.

DRIVE AXLES
Section 9

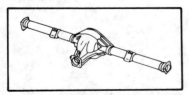

KEY FEATURES

Within this section you will find complete and detailed procedures for Removal, Installation, Overhaul and Adjustment of DRIVE AXLES. All Specifications and Clearances along with Illustrations are included. Please NOTE that vehicles with transaxles will not be found in this section, but are located in the Automatic or Manual Transaxles sections.

- All Tolerances clearly spelled out.
- Description and Identification of all units.
- Complete information on Locking Hubs used on Datsun, LUV and Toyota four-wheel-drive models.

LATEST CHANGES and CORRECTIONS

This section is printed on blue paper and contains information on changes and corrections from the car manufacturers which arrived too late to be included in the regular articles. This information may also refer to previous model automobiles which were covered in prior editions of Mitchell's Imported books.

GENERAL INDEX

The first step in using these pages is to locate the listed component that you require information on. Go down the list under the specific component heading to the model or engine size of the vehicle you are working on. On the righthand side of the column will appear the corresponding page number of the article, specification, or wiring diagram you require.

General Index

NOTE — ALSO SEE INDIVIDUAL SECTION CONTENTS PAGE.

NOTE – ALSO SEE INDIVIDUAL SECTION CONTENTS PAGE.

General Index

NOTE — ALSO SEE INDIVIDUAL SECTION CONTENTS PAGE.

NOTE – ALSO SEE INDIVIDUAL SECTION CONTENTS PAGE.

NOTE – ALSO SEE INDIVIDUAL SECTION CONTENTS PAGE.

NOTE – ALSO SEE INDIVIDUAL SECTION CONTENTS PAGE.

NOTE – ALSO SEE INDIVIDUAL SECTION CONTENTS PAGE.

NOTE — ALSO SEE INDIVIDUAL SECTION CONTENTS PAGE.

NOTE – ALSO SEE INDIVIDUAL SECTION CONTENTS PAGE.

Section 1

AUTOMATIC
TRANSMISSION
SERVICING

CONTENTS

NOTE — ALSO SEE GENERAL INDEX.

AUDI

4000
5000

LUBRICATION

SERVICE INTERVALS

All Models — Check fluid in automatic transmission and final drive every 15,000 miles. Change fluid in transmission every 30,000 miles.

CHECKING FLUID LEVEL

NOTE — *When checking fluid levels, be sure vehicle is level, place selector lever in "N" position and apply parking brake. Run engine at idle until fluid is lukewarm.*

Auto. Trans. Fluid, All Models — Pull out dipstick and wipe clean. Reinsert dipstick, making sure ring of dipstick handle is parallel to engine when fully seated. Fluid level should be between the two marks, but not above or below marks.

NOTE — *It takes approximately 1 pint of ATF to bring level from lower to upper mark on dipstick.*

Final Drive, All Models — When checking final drive, remove fill plug on side of assembly and note fluid level. It should be even with bottom of plug hole. If fluid level in final drive is higher than filler plug, it indicates ATF has possibly entered the final drive. If too low, hypoid oil may have entered transmission. If level is too high, hypoid oil in final drive must be changed.

RECOMMENDED FLUID

Auto. Trans. Fluid — USE ATF Dexron or Dexron II.

Final Drive Fluid — Use hypoid oil SAE 90 (MIL-L-2105B).

CAPACITY

NOTE — *Transmission capacities listed below are approximate, and correct fluid level should be determined by mark on dipstick rather than by amount added. Make periodic checks of fluid level when approaching "full" to help avoid overfilling.*

Transaxle Refill Capacities		
Application	Capacity (Pts.)	
	5000	4000
Auto. Trans.		
Dry	11.2	12.8
Refill	6.4	6.4
Final Drive	2.2	1.6

DRAINING & REFILLING

Transmission — After removing plug and draining fluid, pan should be removed and thoroughly cleaned with lint-free cloths. Reinstall pan using new gasket, tightening bolts in a criss-cross pattern. Tighten to 14 ft. lbs. (2 mkg), checking torque twice at 5-10 minute intervals as gasket settles. Add 5

pints of specified ATF, start engine and select all shift lever positions while keeping vehicle stationary. Drive a short road test until fluid is lukewarm. Check fluid level and top off so that level is between upper and lower marks on dipstick.

Final Drive — Remove drain plug and allow hypoid gear oil to drain. Replace drain plug and fill housing to proper level. *See Checking Fluid Level.*

ADJUSTMENT

SECOND GEAR BAND

Loosen lock nut and tighten adjusting screw to about 7 ft. lbs. (1 mkg). Loosen, and tighten again to 4 ft. lbs. (.5 mkg). Now turn adjusting screw out EXACTLY 2½ turns and tighten lock nut.

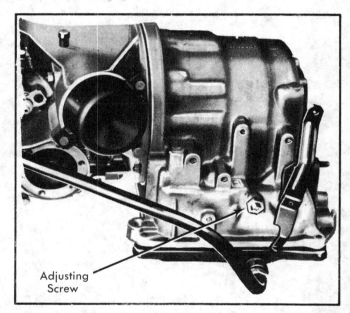

Adjusting Screw

Fig. 1　Location of Second Gear Band Adjusting Screw

THROTTLE LINKAGE

Ensure that throttle is in idle position and loosen clamping bolt on push rod at transmission end. Hold transmission selector lever in end position (neutral) and tighten bolt. Remove stop and intermediate piece under accelerator pedal. Attach 2 nuts onto M 8X135 bolt so that distance from top of bolt to bottom of nuts is 4⅞" (124 mm). Install bolt in place of pedal stop so bottom of pedal rests on bolt head. Adjust slack out of accelerator cable with adjusting screw on transmission bracket. Replace accelerator pedal stop.

NEUTRAL SAFETY SWITCH

Remove console and shift selector into "P". Loosen cable clamp nut and move lever on transmission into position Park to stop. Tighten cable clamp nut to 6 ft. lbs. (.8 mkg). Adjust neutral safety switch by moving forward or rearward so that engine can only be started in "N" or "P" positions and tighten mounting screws. Reinstall console.

BMW

320i
528i
633CSi
733i

TRANSMISSION IDENTIFICATION

Application	Transmission Model
All Models	ZF 3HP 22

LUBRICATION

SERVICE INTERVALS

Check fluid level at least at every oil change. Drain and refill transmission every 30,000 miles.

CHECKING FLUID LEVEL

Transmission must be at normal operating temperature with vehicle on a level surface, engine at idle and gear selector in Park. Fluid level should be between the "MAX" and "MIN" marks on the dipstick. Distance between marks represents .5 pint.

CAUTION — *DO NOT overfill.*

RECOMMENDED FLUID

Use only fluids labeled Dexron Automatic Transmission Fluid.

CAPACITY

NOTE — *Refill capacity is approximate, to be used as a guide when refilling after service. Actual fluid level should be checked by level on dipstick rather than by amount added.*

Transmission Refill Capacities	
Application	**Capacity (Pts.)**
320i	12.8
Refill	4.2
528i	5.0
Refill	4.2
633CSi	5.8
Refill	4.8
733i	5.8
Refill	4.8

DRAINING & REFILLING

1) With transmission at normal operating temperature, remove drain plug and allow fluid to drain. Remove oil pan bolts and tap on pan to break it loose. Remove oil screen and clean or replace as necessary. Clean oil pan.

2) Reinstall filter screen and oil pan. Fill transmission with new transmission fluid of the correct type.

ADJUSTMENT

SHIFT LINKAGE

All Models — 1) Check tightness of bearing bracket before adjusting. Disconnect selector rod from selector lever at adjustment pin.

2) Move transmission shifter lever to "O" (neutral) position. Press shifter against shift gate stop.

3) Alter length of selector rod with adjusting pin until adjusting pin aligns with hole in selector lever.

4) Shorten selector rod by one turn of adjusting pin. Attach selector rod, adjusting pin and selector lever together.

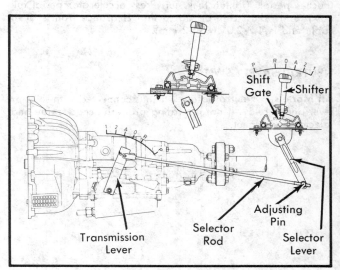

Fig. 1 BMW Shift Linkage Adjustment on All Models

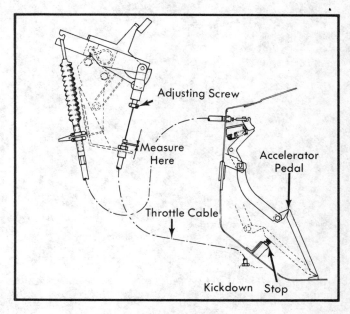

Fig. 2 Throttle Cable Adjustment on 320i Models

BMW (Cont.)

THROTTLE CABLE & KICKDOWN STOP

320i — With accelerator cable properly adjusted and transmission in neutral, turn adjusting screw until throttle cable clearance is .010-.030" (.25-.75 mm). Depress accelerator to kickdown stop. Clearance should now be 1.71-2.20" (43.5-51.5 mm). If not, adjust kickdown stop screw. *See Fig. 2.*

528i, 633CSi & 733i — Adjust accelerator pull rod length to 16.93" (430 mm). With throttle at idle, adjust cable housing nuts to give .010-.030" (.25-.75 mm) clearance between seal and cable housing end. Loosen kickdown stop nut and screw stop in as far as it will go. Depress accelerator pedal until transmission pressure point is felt, then loosen stop until it just touches pedal. Tighten lock nut. Press accelerator pedal full down and adjust control rod so that clearance from seal to cable end is 1.7-2.0" (43-52 mm).

NEUTRAL SAFETY SWITCH

All Models — Neutral safety switch is connected with selector lever and a relay. If not operating properly, check relay and selector adjustment.

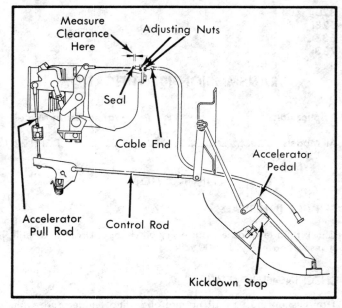

Fig. 3   Throttle Cable and Kickdown Stop Adjustment (528i, 633CSi and 733i Models)

CHRYSLER CORP. IMPORTS

Arrow   Colt
Arrow Pickup   D50 Pickup
Challenger   Sapporo
Champ

TRANSMISSION IDENTIFICATION

Application	Transmission Model
Champ & Colt Hatchback	Mitsubishi KM170
All Others	Torqueflite MA904A

LUBRICATION

SERVICE INTERVALS

Torqueflite — Under normal usage, fluid and filter change, and band adjustment are not required. Under severe usage, change fluid and filter, and adjust bands every 30,000 miles. Fluid level should be checked every 6 months.

KM170 — Under normal conditions, change fluid and filter and adjust bands every 30,000 miles. With more than 50% operation in heavy city traffic at temperatures over 90° F (32° C), service more frequently.

CHECKING FLUID LEVEL

Torqueflite and KM170 — With vehicle parked on level area, fluid at normal operating temperature, parking brake engaged and engine idling, select each gear momentarily. Place selector in "N" (neutral) position and clean area around dipstick tube. Check fluid level between lower and upper marks, but never over upper mark. Add or drain fluid as necessary.

CAUTION — If severe darkening of the fluid and a strong odor is noted, fluid and filter should be changed and bands adjusted.

RECOMMENDED FLUID

Use only fluids of the type labeled "Dexron II" Automatic Transmission Fluid.

CAPACITY

NOTE — Transmission capacity listed below is approximate, and correct fluid level should be determined by mark on dipstick, rather than by amount added.

Transmission Refill Capacities	
Application	Capacity (Pts.)
Torqueflite	14.4
KM170	
Dry	12.0
Fluid Change	9.6

DRAINING & REFILLING

Torqueflite — Carefully remove oil pan and drain fluid. Install new filter on bottom of valve body. Clean oil pan, replace gasket and install oil pan. Pour 8 pints of specified fluid through filler tube. Start engine and allow to idle for two minutes. Shift transmission into each position, ending in "N". Check fluid level with engine running at idle and add sufficient fluid to bring level to "ADD 1 PINT" mark. Recheck fluid level after transmission is at normal operating temperature. See *Checking Fluid Level.*

KM170 — 1) Remove drain plugs from both differential and pan and drain fluid. If replacing filter, remove bolts and lower oil pan. Install new filter on bottom of valve body and replace pan and install new gasket. Tighten differential plug to 22-25 ft. lbs. (3.0-3.4 mkg) and pan plug to 18-21 ft. lbs. (2.5-2.9 mkg). Ensure that dipstick hole area is clean and pour in approximately 8 pints of specified fluid.

2) Run engine for 2 minutes at idle, then shift transmission to each position, ending in "N". Add sufficient fluid to reach lower mark. After reaching normal operating temperature, fluid should be between upper and lower marks of "HOT" range.

NOTE — Since converter is not drained, it will only require 9.6 pints of fluid to refill transmission.

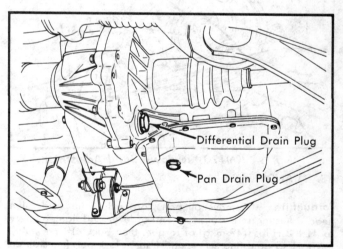

Fig. 1 KM170 Drain Plug Locations

ADJUSTMENT

FRONT (KICKDOWN) BAND

Torqueflite — Front (kickdown) band adjuster screw is located on left side of transmission case. To adjust band, loosen and back off lock nut about five turns. Check that adjuster screw turns freely. Using wrench (C-3380-A) with adapter (C-3705), tighten band adjuster screw to 47-50 INCH lbs. (54-58 cmkg). If adapter C-3705 is not used, tighten adjuster screw to 72 INCH lbs. (83 cmkg), which is the true torque. Back off adjusting screw three turns, hold adjuster screw and tighten lock nut.

CHRYSLER CORP. IMPORTS (Cont.)

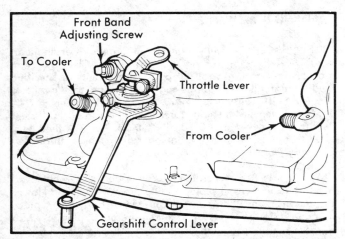

Fig. 2   Torqueflite Front Band Adjusting Screw Location

KM170 — Clean all dirt from kickdown servo cover and remove snap ring. Remove cover and loosen lock nut. Hold servo piston from turning and tighten adjusting screw to 7 ft. lbs. (1.0 mkg) and back it off. Repeat this twice to seat kickdown band against drum. Tighten adjusting screw to 3.5 ft. lbs. (.5 mkg) and back off 3.5 turns. Hold screw and tighten lock nut. Install cover and snap ring.

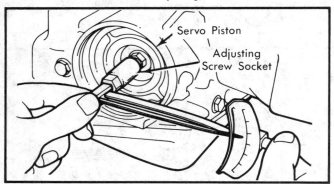

Fig. 3   KM170 Kickdown Band Adjustment

REAR BAND

Torqueflite — Remove oil pan. Loosen lock nut and Allen head adjusting screw at servo end of lever and tighten screw to 41 INCH lbs. (47 mkg) of torque, then back off screw 7½ turns. Hold adjusting screw and tighten lock nut. Reinstall oil pan.

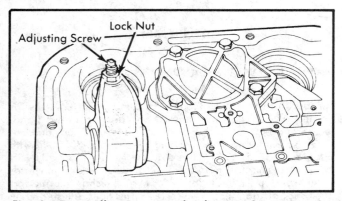

Fig. 4   Torqueflite Rear Band Adjusting Screw Location

TRANSMISSION THROTTLE CONTROL ADJUSTMENT

Torqueflite — With engine at normal operating temperature and idle speed set correctly, loosen bolt securing throttle rod "C" to "B". Lightly push throttle rod "A" or the transmission throttle lever and rod toward idle stop and set rods to idle position. Tighten bolt securing rod "B" to "C". Open throttle to wide open position and make sure that transmission lever moves from idle to wide open position (total movement 45° to 54°). Some play should still exist in throttle lever stroke at wide open throttle.

NOTE — *Choke must be in fully open position.*

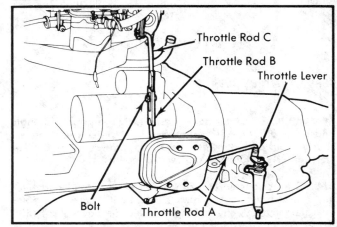

Fig. 5   Torqueflite Throttle Rod Adjustment

KM170 — Open throttle to wide open position and loosen lower cable bracket mounting bolt. Move bracket until distance between nipple and top of cover "A" on throttle cable is 2.019-2.059" (51.3-52.3 mm). With throttle lever still in wide open position, pull cable upward to ensure freedom of cable movement.

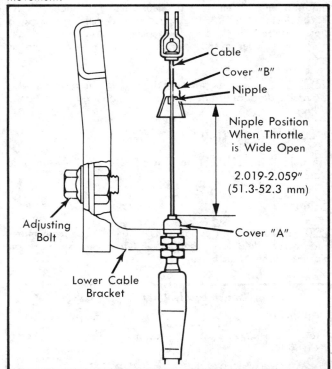

Fig. 6   KM170 Throttle Cable Adjustment

CHRYSLER CORP. IMPORTS (Cont.)

SHIFT LINKAGE

Torqueflite — Remove shift handle by loosening set screw and pulling off handle. Place selector lever in "N" and turn adjusting cam in top of lever until surface "A" of cam is flush with end of selector lever "B" (Fig. 7). Loosen lock nut at connection of rod and arm at transmission. Place transmission lever arm in neutral. Place selector lever in neutral and tighten lock nut to adjust control rod length.

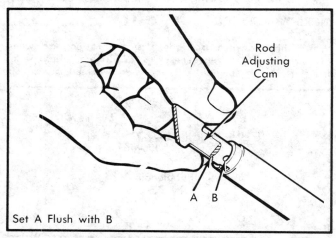

Set A Flush with B

Fig. 7   Adjusting Selector Rod Cam (Torqueflite)

KM170 — Place selector in "N" position and loosen set screw holding handle to lever. Depress selector knob and turn handle to give .008-.035" (.2-.9 mm) clearance between selector lever end pin and detent plate (Fig. 8). When knob is on driver's side, tighten set screw. With selector lever and neutral safety switch in neutral position, turn adjusting nuts at cable end until slack is removed from control cable.

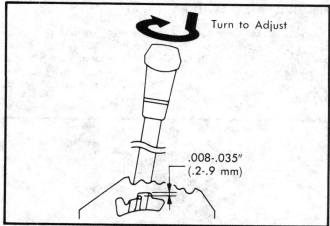

Turn to Adjust

.008-.035" (.2-.9 mm)

Fig. 8   Adjusting Selector Lever (KM170)

NEUTRAL SAFETY SWITCH

Torqueflite — Switch is located under shift lever console and is operated by shift lever. In addition to the neutral safety switch function, switch also operates back-up lights and seat belt warning system. To adjust switch, place selector lever in "N" position and slide switch back and forth to measure contact range of "N" position. Place switch in center of contact range and adjust so that there is .06" (1.5 mm) side clearance between selector lever and switch. Tighten attaching screws.

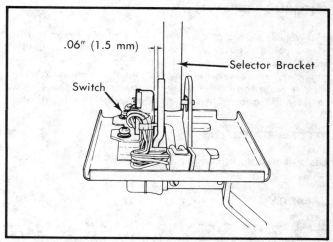

.06" (1.5 mm)

Selector Bracket

Switch

Fig. 9   Adjusting Torqueflite Neutral Safety Switch

KM170 — Place transmission control lever in neutral and loosen switch attaching bolts. Turn inhibitor switch body so that aligning hole end of lever overlaps switch body flange and tighten attaching bolts.

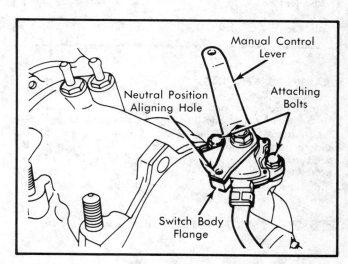

Manual Control Lever

Neutral Position Aligning Hole

Attaching Bolts

Switch Body Flange

Fig. 10   Adjusting KM170 Neutral Safety Switch

COURIER

Pickup

LUBRICATION

SERVICE INTERVALS

Automatic transmission fluid level should be checked every 2000 miles. Replace transmission hoses every four years.

CHECKING FLUID LEVEL

With vehicle standing level, run engine at idle speed (if cold, run at fast idle for several minutes, then slow to normal idle). Shift transmission through all gears and return to "P". With engine still on, clean area around dipstick, pull out dipstick, wipe it clean, and push all way back in. Level should read between "L" and "F" marks on appropriate side of dipstick.

RECOMMENDED FLUID

Use automatic transmission fluid (ATF) type "F".

CAPACITY

NOTE — *Transmission capacities listed below are approximate, and correct fluid level should be determined by mark on dipstick, rather than by amount added.*

Transmission Refill Capacities	
Application	**Capacity (Pts.)**
All Models	13.3

DRAINING & REFILLING

Loosen oil pan bolts and allow ATF fluid to drain. Remove oil pan and filter screen and thoroughly clean them. Using a new oil pan gasket, install filter screen and oil pan. Add six pints of fluid to transmission through filler tube. Run engine at idle speed for approximately two minutes, then run it at fast idle (1200 RPM) until it reaches normal operating temperature. Shift selector through all ranges and place in "N" or "P" position. Check fluid level and add as required.

CAUTION — *Do NOT race engine while warming up. Do NOT overfill transmission.*

ADJUSTMENT

BAND

Remove three servo cover bolts on right front of transmission and remove servo cover. Loosen lock nut and tighten adjusting screw to 9-11 ft. lbs. (1.2-1.5 mkg). Back off the adjusting screw two turns. Holding the adjusting screw, tighten lock nut to 22-29 ft. lbs. (3-4 mkg). Replace servo cover.

Fig. 1 *Showing Band Adjusting Screw*

KICKDOWN SWITCH

With ignition switch on, adjust switch to engage when accelerator pedal is between $\frac{7}{8}$-$\frac{15}{16}$" (22-24 mm) of full pedal travel. Downshift solenoid will click when switch engages.

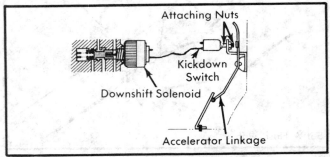
Fig. 2 *Schematic of Kickdown Switch*

SHIFT LINKAGE

Place shift lever in "N" position and disconnect clevis pin from transmission selector lever. Move transmission selector lever to "N" position (third detent from the rear) and adjust control rod so that clevis pin engages selector lever. Check that transmission correctly engages all selector positions.

NEUTRAL SAFETY SWITCH

1) Place transmission selector lever in "N" position (third detent from rear). Remove lever attaching nut. Loosen three switch mounting bolts. Remove screw from alignment pin hole at bottom of switch. Rotate switch and insert a .079" (2 mm) diameter pin through alignment pin hole and hole of internal rotor.

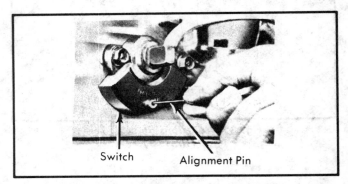
Fig. 3 *Making Neutral Safety Switch Adjustment*

2) Tighten switch attaching bolts and remove alignment pin. Install alignment pin screw in switch body. Position selector lever on shaft and tighten attaching nut. Check switch operation to see that engine will start in "N" or "P" position only.

DATSUN

200SX	510
210	810
280ZX	Pickup

TRANSMISSION IDENTIFICATION

Application	Trans. Model
All Models	Jatco 3N71B

LUBRICATION

SERVICE INTERVAL

Inspect fluid level every 3,000 miles. Periodic draining and refilling is not necessary.

CHECKING FLUID LEVEL

Check fluid with engine and transmission at normal operating temperatures (this is reached after several minutes of driving). With vehicle standing level and at idle, shift transmission through all positions and return to "P" (parking brake should be applied). Clean area around dipstick, remove stick, wipe clean, insert, and withdraw. Level should be between "H" and "L" marks. If not, add as necessary.

NOTE — *Normal fluid should be clear with a pink color and should not have a strong odor. If fluid has a strong, burned odor or is dark in color, overheating and internal wear may be indicated. If milky in appearance, moisture from cooling system or road may have entered the system. Foamy or excessively bubbled fluid indicates overfilling and aeration. DO NOT OVERFILL.*

RECOMMENDED FLUID

Use automatic transmission fluid type Dexron.

CAPACITY

NOTE — *Capacity listed below is approximate, and to be used as guide if refilling of transmission case is required (such as after on-car service or overhaul). Final "full" level should be checked by level on dipstick, as previously described. Do not rely entirely on amount added to achieve proper full level.*

Transmission Refill Capacities	
Application	Capacity (Pts.)
All Models	
Transmission Case	11.7
Torque Converter	5.7

DRAINING & REFILLING

Loosen oil pan bolts and allow ATF to drain. Remove oil pan and clean pan and screen thoroughly. Install pan using a new gasket. Add approximately 6 pints of fluid through filler tube.

Run engine at idle speed for about two minutes, then at fast idle (1200 RPM) for several more minutes, until normal operating temperatures are reached. Shift transmission through all gears and return to "P". Check fluid level and add to obtain appropriate level.

ADJUSTMENT

BAND

Loosen piston stem lock nut and tighten piston stem (adjusting screw) to 8.7-11 ft. lbs. (1.2-1.5 mkg). Back off piston stem two turns and tighten lock nut to 11-29 ft. lbs. (1.5-4.0 mkg).

SHIFT LINKAGE

Starting in "P" range, shift through all positions to "Range 1". If detents cannot be felt or pointer is improperly aligned, linkage must be adjusted. Place shift lever in "D" range and loosen lock nuts on rod. Turn lock nuts until pointer aligns properly and all detents can be felt. Tighten lock nuts and recheck positions, ensuring that full detent is felt in "P" position. If unable to adjust, grommets at ends of rod may worn or damaged and require replacment.

KICKDOWN SWITCH

Kickdown switch is located at top of accelerator pedal post. A "click" should be heard just before accelerator bottoms out when depressed. If not, loosen lock nut on switch and adjust. Do NOT allow switch to close too soon, or downshift will occur at part throttle.

NEUTRAL SAFETY SWITCH

Switch operates back-up lights and prevents starting except in "P" or "N" range. To adjust, ensure that transmission is in "N" position with lever at transmission in vertical position. Remove alignment hole screw at bottom of switch and loosen mounting bolts. Move switch until alignment pin can be inserted in rotor. Tighten mounting bolts and replace alignment hole screw.

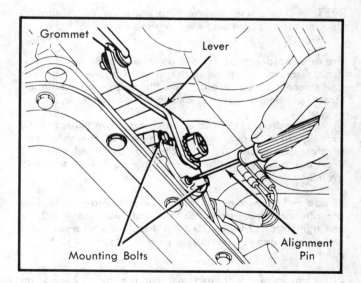

Fig. 1 Adjusting Neutral Safety Switch

FIAT

Brava
Spider 2000
Strada

LUBRICATION

SERVICE INTERVALS

Check automatic transmission fluid level every 3,000 miles. Change fluid every 30,000 miles or 2 years.

CHECKING FLUID LEVEL

With engine running at normal operating temperature, place transmission in "N" or "P". Clean area around dipstick, remove, wipe clean, insert to fully-seated position. Remove and note level: it should be between "MIN" and "MAX". Add fluid if necessary, taking care not to overfill.

RECOMMENDED FLUID

Use only fluids labeled "Dexron" Automatic Transmission Fluid.

CAPACITY

NOTE — *Refill capacity is approximate, to be used as a guide when refilling after service. Actual fluid level should be checked by level on dipstick rather than by amount added.*

Transmission Refill Capacities	
Application	**Capacity (Pts.)**
All Models	
Refill — Fluid Change	6.0
Refill — Overhaul (Dry)	12.0

DRAINING & REFILLING

NOTE — *Do not use any cleaning materials which may introduce lint or paper into the transmission.*

Brava & Spider — 1) Remove drain plug and allow fluid to drain. Remove oil pan and filter. Discard gasket. Clean pan and screen thoroughly and dry with compressed air. Install screen, position new gasket and install oil pan.

2) Replace drain plug. Add approximately two-thirds of refill capacity. Start engine and bring to normal operating temperature. Complete fluid level check as described and add necessary amount, constantly checking fluid level to avoid overfilling.

Strada — 1) Loosen oil pan and allow oil to drain, remove oil pan after draining. Remove oil filter and clean. Install oil filter and tighten to 2.2 ft. lbs. (.3 mkg). Install new oil pan gasket and tighten pan-to-transmission case screws to 14 ft. lbs. (2 mkg).

2) Fill transmission with fluid until fluid is between 2 marks on dipstick. Start engine, drive vehicle to bring transmission oil to operating temperature. Recheck fluid using above procedure and add as necessary.

ADJUSTMENT

BRAKE BAND

Brava & Spider — 1) Drain transmission oil. Remove pan and gasket, then servo brake cover. Loosen adjusting screw lock nut, then tighten adjusting screw to 40 INCH lbs. (46 cmkg). Back adjusting screw off exactly 5 turns. Hold screw in this position and tighten lock nut to 12-15 ft. lbs. (1.7 -2.1 mkg).

2) Install servo cover, new gasket, and tighten cover bolts to 17-19 ft. lbs. (2.3-2.6 mkg). Install oil pan with new gasket, tightening bolts to 7-9 ft. lbs. (1.0-1.3 mkg). Refill transmission fluid.

Strada — Loosen lock nut and unscrew a few turns. Tighten adjusting screw to 7.5 ft. lbs. (1 mkg). Totally loosen adjusting screw and retighten to 42 INCH lbs. (47 cmkg), then back off 2½ turns.

SHIFT LINKAGE

Brava & Spider — 1) Disconnect selector rod from lower end of relay lever and pull selector rod so that transmission selector lever (on side of casing) is in "P" detent (all the way back). Selector lever in passenger compartment should also be set in "P". Use adjusting nut on end of selector rod to adjust as required to obtain a free pin fit into end of relay lever.

2) Pull lower gear selector handle up and move gear selector through all six positions — a definite click should be felt in each position. Set selector (with lower handle still pulled up) into position "1". Release lower handle: the stop tooth should engage into the selector gate causing selector lever to be shifted from position. Repeat this check in all other gear positions. Make any necessary adjustments on selector rod as previously described

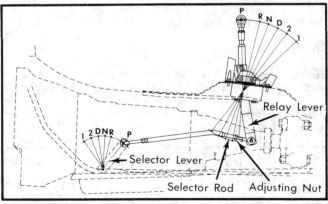

**Fig. 1   Shift Linkage Adjustment
Brava & Spider**

NOTE — *Indicator plate may also be shifted to align proper gear positions once all adjustments have been properly set.*

Strada — Remove shift name plate by squeezing, then remove 2 screws to remove center console. Place transmission in "P". Remove pin attaching shift cable to gearshift selector. Make sure gearshift selector is in "P" position. Loosen lock nut on shift cable, adjust clevis until pin can be freely installed, then tighten lock nut. Reinstall console and shift name plate.

FIAT (Cont.)

THROTTLE LINKAGE

Brava & Spider — 1) Disconnect telescoping link from control lever. Push accelerator pedal down until ball end on kickdown cable is just touching cable pin. Push pedal to stop and check that kickdown cable has extended .276-.354" (7-9 mm). If not, make correction with adjusting nuts on cable housing.

2) Push pedal to stop. Hold control lever in full throttle position and extend telescoping link .315-.393" (8-10 mm). Check that telescoping link can be connected to control lever when extended. If not, loosen nuts on both ends of link an even amount.

3) Release accelerator pedal until ball end is just touching cable pin. Move control lever to full throttle position and check that telescoping link can be connected to control lever without extending. Adjust nuts on link as required. Also note that kickdown valve moves properly when accelerator pedal is fully depressed.

Strada — Depress accelerator fully, check to see that throttle plate is open fully and that cable is pulled from its stop ½" (13 mm). If adjustment is necessary, adjust 14 mm nuts until proper adjustment is achieved. *See Fig. 3.*

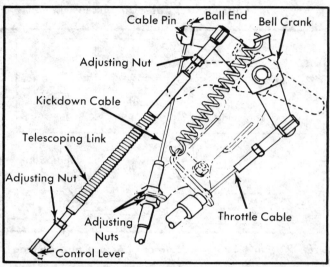

*Fig. 2   Components for Adjusting Throttle Linkage
Brava & Spider*

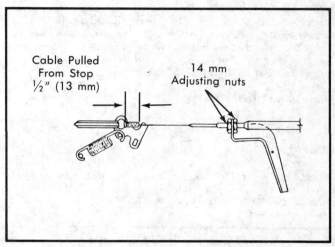

*Fig. 3   Throttle Linkage Adjustment
Strada*

HONDA

Accord
Civic
Prelude

LUBRICATION

SERVICE INTERVALS

Check fluid level at every oil change. Transmission fluid should be changed at 15,000 miles, then every 30,000 miles. No filter service or band adjustment is required.

CHECKING FLUID LEVEL

With vehicle on level area and at normal operating temperature, turn off engine. Clean area around dipstick and unscrew dipstick. Remove dipstick and wipe clean, then insert into hole but do not screw down. Remove dipstick and check level: It should be between upper and lower marks. Add as necessary but DO NOT OVERFILL.

RECOMMENDED FLUID

Use only Dexron type automatic transmission fluid.

CAPACITY

NOTE — *Capacities shown below are approximate and to be used as a guide when refilling; however, final "full" level should be determined by reading on dipstick rather than by amount added.*

Transaxle Refill Capacities	
Application	**Capacity (Pts.)**
All Models	5.2

DRAINING & REFILLING

Ensure that operating temperature is up to normal and remove transmission drain plug. Use new gasket and replace drain plug when fluid is drained. Fill with about 4 pints of fluid through dipstick hole and check level. Add fluid to bring to upper mark on dipstick.

NOTE — *Refill capacity will always be slightly less than specified capacity due to fluid remaining in recesses of housing and converter.*

ADJUSTMENT

SHIFT CONTROL CABLE

Civic — Ensure that reverse gear engages and remove center console. Place shift lever in "R" and remove lock clip and control cable pin. Check that hole in cable end is perfectly aligned with holes in selector lever arm. If not, loosen lock nuts on control cable and adjust as required. Tighten lock nuts and install pin with lock clip. If pin does not go in easily, further adjustment is required. Check gear operation.

Accord & Prelude — Ensure that reverse gear engages and remove center console. Place shift lever in "R" and remove lock pin from cable adjuster. Check alignment of hole in adjuster and hole in shift cable. If not perfectly aligned, loosen lock nut and adjust as required. Install lock pin and check for normal operation.

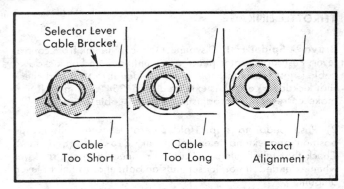

Fig. 1　Shift Control Cable Alignment (Civic)

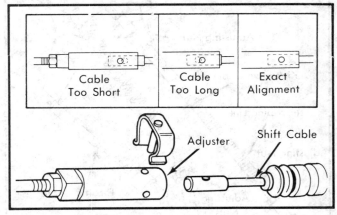

Fig. 2　Shift Cable Adjustment (Accord and Prelude)

THROTTLE CONTROL CABLE & BRACKET

Accord & Prelude Only — Ensure that engine is warmed up to normal operating temperature and cable securing clamps (3) are in position. Disconnect control cable from lever and lay end on top of shock absorber tower. Using special tool (07974-6890300), adjust cable control bracket so that distance between bracket and lever is 3.29" (83.5 mm). Depress accelerator until there is no slack in carburetor throttle cable. Adjust distance between control cable end and nut "A" to 3.37" (85.5 mm). Install cable and tighten lock nut "B", ensuring that lock nut "A" does not turn. See Fig. 3.

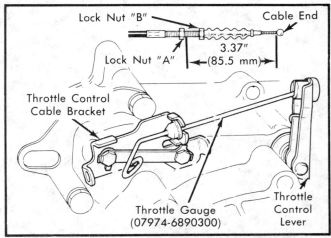

Fig. 3　Transmission Throttle Cable and Bracket Adjustment (Accord and Prelude)

JAGUAR

XJ6

TRANSMISSION IDENTIFICATION

Application	Transmission Model
XJ6	Borg-Warner Type 66

LUBRICATION

SERVICE INTERVALS

Check fluid every 6000 miles. It is recommended that the automatic transmission fluid and filter be changed at 30,000 miles.

CHECKING FLUID LEVEL

Transmission dipstick is located on left side of engine. With vehicle level and transmission at normal operating temperature, apply handbrake and position gear selector in all ranges and return to "P". With engine running at idle, withdraw and wipe dipstick, immediately check fluid level. If necessary, add fluid to reach "MAX" level on "HOT" side of dipstick. After adding, repeat checking procedure to make sure overfilling has not occurred.

RECOMMENDED FLUID

Use only fluids labeled Type F Automatic Transmission Fluid.

CAPACITY

NOTE — *Refill capacity is approximate, to be used as a guide when refilling after service. Actual fluid level should be checked by level on dipstick rather than by amount added.*

Transmission Refill Capacities	
Application	Capacity (Pts.)
Type 66	15.0

DRAINING & REFILLING

Place suitable drain pan under transmission and disconnect oil cooler lines. Detach dipstick/filler tube and remove pan. Remove and discard filter and gasket. Ensure that oil pan is clean and install filter and pan, using new gaskets. Replace dipstick/filler tube and add approximately 4 pints. Proceed as in *Checking Fluid Level*. DO NOT overfill.

NOTE — *Since converter is not drained, fluid required will be less than specified capacity.*

ADJUSTMENT

FRONT BAND

Remove nut securing selector lever to selector shaft and remove lever. Push left seat fully to rear and lift carpet from left footwell. Remove console side casing, then transmission access plate. Loosen lock nut securing band adjuster screw and loosen adjuster 2 or 3 turns. Tighten adjuster to 5 ft. lbs. (.8 mkg) torque, then back off screw ¾ turn. Tighten lock nut while holding adjuster and replace covers and carpet.

REAR BAND

Loosen lock nut and rear band adjusting screw 2 or 3 turns, ensuring that adjusting screw rotates freely in case. Tighten adjusting screw to 5 ft. lbs. (.8 mkg) torque, then back off ¾ turn. Tighten lock nut while holding adjusting screw.

TRANSMISSION THROTTLE CABLE

1) Engine must be correctly tuned before attempting transmission throttle adjustment. Lift carpet from left side of transmission tunnel and remove access plate. Using Allen wrench, remove plug from transmission and connect pressure gauge to transmission with adapter.

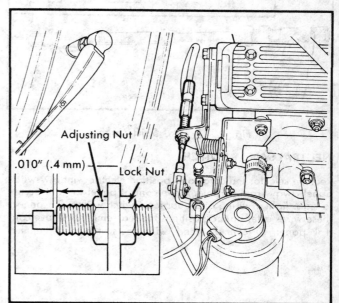

Fig. 1 Transmission Throttle Cable Adjustment

2) Feed gauge hose through hole in tunnel, keeping hose clear of exhaust pipe. Run engine to normal operating temperature. Block wheels and apply hand and foot brake. Select "D" position; pressure gauge should read 60-75 psi (4.2-5.3 kg/cm²) at idle speed. Increase engine speed to 1200 RPM; gauge should now read 85-95 psi (5.9-6.7 kg/cm²). If correct pressure is not obtained, switch engine off and place transmission in "N". Loosen lock nut on downshift cable, and adjust nut on outer cable to alter pressure. When pressure is correct, tighten cable lock nut, reinstall plug and cover plate using new sealing compound. Replace carpeting and road test vehicle.

NOTE — *Increasing length of cable increases pressure; decreasing length decreases pressure. Ferrule crimped on inner cable should be .010" (.4 mm) from threaded portion of outer cable.*

SHIFT LINKAGE

Remove console and place selector lever in position "1". Unscrew shift knob and remove indicator plate. Remove cotter pin and washer securing cable to bracket on lever. Ensure transmission lever is in "1" position. Adjust front and rear lock nuts until cable can be connected without selector or transmission lever being disturbed. Tighten lock nuts and secure cable with new cotter pin. Reinstall selector plate and shift knob.

JAGUAR (Cont.)

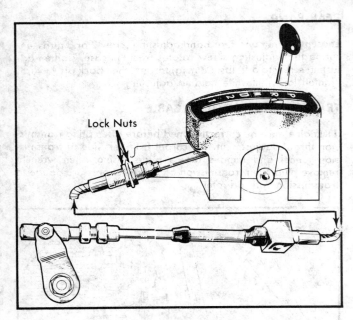

Fig. 2   Typical Shift Linkage

NEUTRAL SAFETY SWITCH

Remove selector indicator and position electric window switch panel away from console. Move control panel to gain access to cigar lighter wiring and door lock switch wiring. Disconnect these wires after noting positions for reassembly. Remove control panel. Disconnect feed wire to switch and connect powered test light to terminal. Place selector lever in "N" position and loosen lock nuts which secure the switch. Adjust switch until test light operates. Tighten switch lock nuts and check that light remains on with lever in "P", and goes off with lever in any driving position. Remove test light, reconnect feed wire, and reinstall all removed parts.

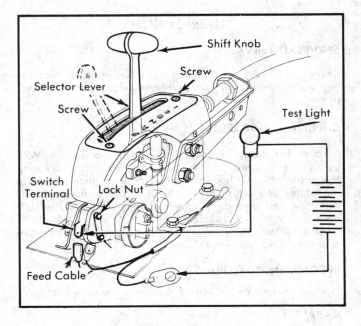

Fig. 3   Neutral Safety Switch Adjustment

LUV

Pickup

LUBRICATION

SERVICE INTERVALS

Check fluid at every oil change. Under normal conditions, replace fluid and filter every 60,000 miles. Under severe conditions, change fluid and filter at 15,000 mile intervals.

CHECKING FLUID LEVEL

Vehicle should be at normal operating temperature which is obtained after at least 15 miles of highway or equivalent city driving. Park vehicle on level surface with transmission selector in "P" position with engine idling and parking brake applied. Fluid level should be at full ("F") mark. If checking at ambient temperature, operate selector through each range with engine idling and immediately check fluid level with transmission selector in "P" position. Fluid should be $1/8$" to $3/8$" (3 to 10 mm) below "ADD" mark on dipstick. Refill as required but DO NOT OVERFILL.

RECOMMENDED FLUID

Use only automatic transmission fluid labeled Dexron II.

CAPACITY

NOTE — *The capacities listed are approximate and to be used only as a guide for refilling. Final "full" level should be determined by reading on dipstick rather than by amount added.*

Transmission Refill Capacities	
Application	Capacity (Pts.)
THM 200	
Fluid Change	6.0
Refill from Dry	12.8

DRAINING & REFILLING

If draining and refilling is required for any on-car service or because of overhaul, remove pan bolts and allow fluid to drain. Remove pan and gasket; discard gasket. Clean pan and screen thoroughly and reinstall with new gasket. Add fluid, checking level with dipstick to avoid overfilling.

ADJUSTMENT

SHIFT LINKAGE

Loosen control rod lock nuts. Turn manual shaft of transmission (viewed from left side of transmission) counterclockwise as far as it will go, then back shaft off three stops to neutral position. Hold shaft in this position and move shift lever to neutral position. Holding both levers in this position, push the shift control lower lever rearward to remove play. Tighten lock nuts. Check for proper shift lever movement.

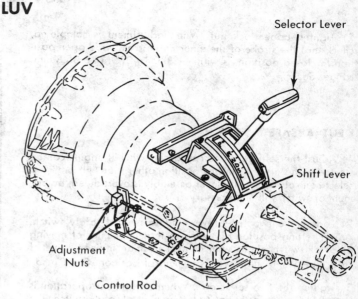

Fig. 1   Shift Linkage Adjustment

THROTTLE VALVE CABLE

1) Check carburetor lever and throttle valve cable bracket for distortion. Loosen cable adjusting nuts. Bring carburetor lever to wide open position, and adjust the setting of inner cable by turning lower adjusting nut on outer cable by hand so inner cable is provided with a play of .04" (1 mm).

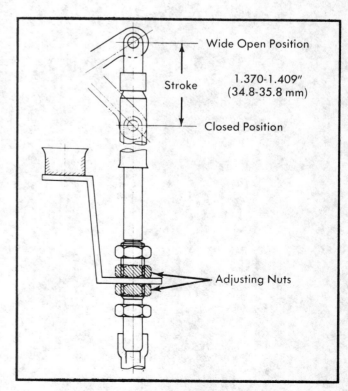

Fig. 2   Throttle Valve Cable Adjustment

LUV (Cont.)

2) Tighten upper lock nut. When adjustment is completed, check that the stroke of the inner cable from wide open position to closed position, is within 1.370-1.409" (34.8-35.8 mm) range. See *Fig. 2.*

NEUTRAL SAFETY SWITCH

1) Adjust the setting of neutral safety switch if engine can be started with shift lever in any position other than "N" or "P". If select control rod or shift lever assembly is overhauled, adjustment of switch will be necessary also.

2) Loosen the two set screws holding neutral safety switch. Adjust setting position of switch so that the center of moving piece of switch aligns with neutral position indicator line of steel case when shift lever is in neutral position. See *Fig. 3.*

3) Tighten the two set screws. When adjustment operation is completed, make a continuity test on neutral safety switch with the shift lever set in each gear position. If improper operation still exists, replace switch.

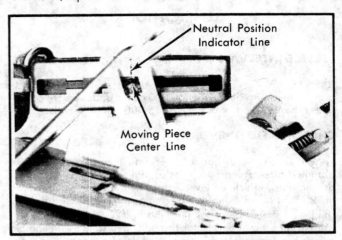

Fig. 3   Adjusting Neutral Safety Switch

MAZDA

GLC
626
RX7

LUBRICATION

SERVICE INTERVALS

Inspect automatic transmission fluid level every 7,500 miles, or 7½ months.

CHECKING FLUID LEVEL

Check fluid with vehicle on level surface. Apply parking brake firmly and run engine approximately two minutes at 1200 RPM. With engine running at normal idle, move selector lever through all gears, pausing at each gear to allow for engagement. Return to "P" and leave engine running. Wipe area around dipstick filler tube and remove dipstick. Wipe it clean, reinsert, withdraw, and note reading. If between "L" and "F" marks, level is satisfactory. If not, add fluid. DO NOT OVERFILL.

RECOMMENDED FLUID

Use only fluids labeled Type F Automatic Transmission Fluid.

CAPACITY

NOTE — *Refill capacity is approximate, to be used as a guide when refilling after service. Actual fluid level should be checked by level on dipstick rather than by amount added.*

Transmission Refill Capacities	
Application	Capacity (Pts.)
GLC	12.0
626 & RX7	13.2

DRAINING & REFILLING

If draining and refilling is required for any operation, remove pan bolts and allow fluid to drain. Remove pan and gasket; discard gasket. Clean pan thoroughly and reinstall new gasket, tightening pan bolts to 3.5-5.0 ft. lbs. (.5-.7 mkg). Add fluid, making sure not to overfill.

ADJUSTMENT

BRAKE BAND

NOTE — *Oil pan must be removed on GLC & 626 to adjust brake band.*

Loosen servo piston stem lock nut and back off a few turns. Using a torque wrench, tighten servo piston stem to 9-11 ft. lbs. (1.2-1.5 mkg), then back off piston stem exactly 2 turns. Hold piston stem in this position and tighten lock nut to 11-29 ft. lbs. (1.5-4.0 mkg).

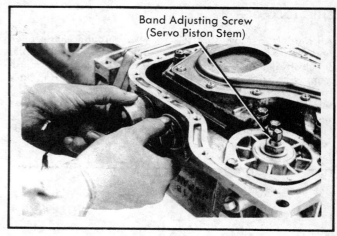

Fig. 1   Brake Band Adjustment (GLC & 626)

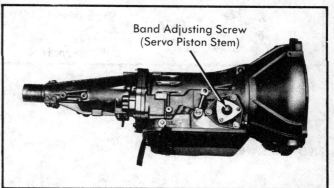

Fig. 2   Brake Band Adjustment (RX7)

KICKDOWN SWITCH & DOWNSHIFT SOLENOID

All Models — Depress accelerator pedal to limit. Near wide-open throttle, click should be heard from solenoid. Switch must operate at or after ⅞ of pedal travel. If not, loosen switch attaching nut and adjust switch to engage when pedal is at ⅞ of its full travel, tighten attaching nut and check solenoid.

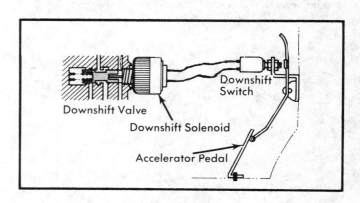

Fig. 3   Schematic of Kickdown Switch and Downshift Solenoid

MAZDA (Cont.)

SHIFT LINKAGE

All Models — Move shift selector lever through entire range and feel for clicks in all positions. When click is felt, pointer should be lined up with correct indicated position. If adjustment is not correct, disconnect "T" joint on lower rod. Place range select lever (on transmission) in "N" position (slot of selector shaft point straight up and detent engages). Position shift selector lever in "N" position and adjust "T" joint so linkage will reconnect with no looseness. Recheck setting in all ranges.

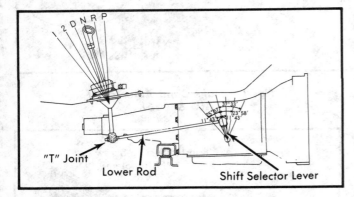

Fig. 4   Schematic of Shift Linkage

NEUTRAL SAFETY SWITCH

GLC & RX7 — 1) After checking and adjusting shift linkage, place the transmission lever in the "N" position. Remove transmission manual lever retaining nut. Loosen 3 inhibitor switch attaching bolts and remove screw from alignment pin hole at bottom of switch.

2) Rotate switch and insert a .078" (2.0 mm) diameter alignment pin through the alignment hole and into hole of internal rotor. Tighten 3 switch attaching bolts and remove alignment pin.

3) Reinstall alignment pin hole screw. Reinstall transmission manual lever and check operation of switch. The engine should only start in "N" or "P" position.

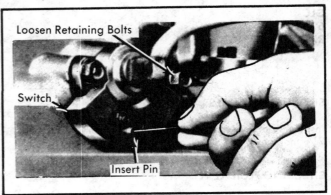

Fig. 5   Adjusting Neutral Safety Switch (GLC & RX7)

626 — 1) Shift the selector lever to "N" position and loosen switch attaching screws. Insure that selector lever is in the neutral position; adjust if necessary.

2) Move switch so that the identification marks on the switch body and sliding plate are aligned. Tighten switch attaching screws. Check operation of switch in the "N" and "P" position to insure proper operation. The engine should only start when the selector lever is in "N" or "P" position.

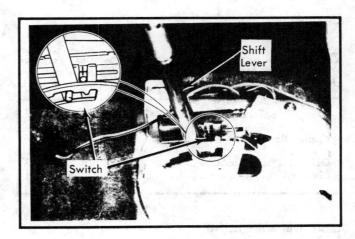

Fig. 6   Adjusting Neutral Safety Switch (626)

MERCEDES-BENZ

240D
280 Series
300 Series
450 Series

TRANSMISSION IDENTIFICATION

Application	Transmission Type
240D	W4B025
280 Series	W4B025
300 Series	W4B025
450 Series	W3A040

LUBRICATION

SERVICE INTERVALS

All Models — Check transmission fluid level at every oil change. Add as required. Change fluid and make any necessary adjustments every 30,000 miles. In severe service conditions, change fluid and make any necessary adjustments every 15,000 miles.

CHECKING FLUID LEVEL

Transmission at Room Temperature — Fluid level can be determined more accurately in a cold transmission with temperature between 68-86° F (20-30° C). With vehicle on a level surface, apply parking brake and place selector lever in "P". With engine at normal idle, check fluid. Fluid must be 1.18" (30 mm) below minimum marking. Add (or remove) fluid as necessary to reach this level. DO NOT OVERFILL.

Transmission at Operating Temperature — With vehicle on level ground and transmission in "P", idle engine for at least two minutes to make sure torque converter is filled. At this time, fluid level should be between upper and lower marks on the dipstick. Add (or remove) fluid as necessary to reach this level. DO NOT OVERFILL. Difference between the two marks represents approximately 0.6 pint. After adding fluid, shift gear selector through all ranges and recheck fluid.

RECOMMENDED FLUID

Use only fluids labeled Dexron Automatic Transmission Fluid.

CAPACITY

NOTE — *Refill capacity is approximate, to be used as a guide when refilling after servce. Actual fluid level should be checked by level on dipstick rather than by amount added.*

Transmission Refill Capacities (Pts.)		
Application	Refill (Dry)	Refill (Fluid Change)
240D	12.8	10.2
280 Series	14.0	11.2
300 Series		
SD	14.0	11.2
All Exc. SD	12.8	10.2
450 Series	18.8	16.8

DRAINING & REFILLING

All Models — Remove filler tube and allow fluid to drain. Rotate engine until drain plug in torque converter is accessible through hole in bottom of torque converter housing. When all fluid has drained, remove pan and oil filter screen. Install new screen, new gasket, then install pan. Replace plug in torque converter. Attach filler tube to oil pan and add fluid. When majority of fluid is added, start engine, idle for about two minutes, place selector in each gear and return to "P". Check fluid level and adjust as necessary. DO NOT OVERFILL.

ADJUSTMENT

TRANSMISSION THROTTLE ROD

240D Models — 1) Turn rotary knob of cable control for idling speed adjustment completely to the right. Disconnect throttle rod linkage, throttle rod, and accelerator rod from intermediate lever. Attach adjusting gauge with idle speed detent to intermediate lever. With throttle valve against idle speed stop and throttle linkage pulled back, adjust throttle rod linkage length for a free fit on ball socket of intermediate lever. Push control lever to idle position, then adjust accelerator rod length for a free fit over ball socket on intermediate lever. *See Fig. 1.*

2) Remove adjusting gauge idle detent from intermediate lever. Press accelerator pedal to kickdown position, adjusting

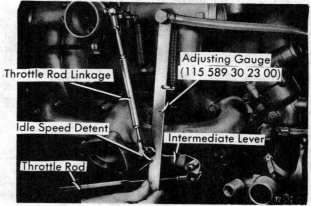

IDLE SPEED SETTING

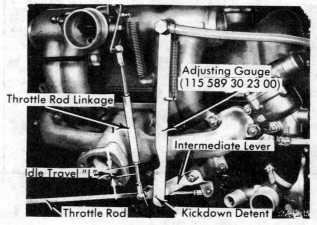

KICKDOWN SETTING

Fig. 1 Throttle Rod Adjustment (240D)

MERCEDES-BENZ (Cont.)

gauge full-throttle detent should fit freely into intermediate lever. If not, adjust length of accelerator rod for a free fit. With adjustments made, check that travel "L" of throttle rod linkage from full throttle position to kickdown position is approximately .236" (6 mm). If not, adjust ball socket in oblong hole of intermediate lever. When adjustments are correct, remove adjusting gauge.

280 Series — Disconnect throttle rod from lever and push lever toward rear. Push throttle rod rearward against stop and adjust length until throttle rod will fit freely over ball socket on lever. Tighten lock nut on throttle rod.

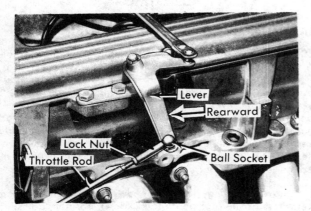

Fig. 2   *Throttle Rod Adjustment (280 Series)*

300 Series — During adjustment, accelerator must be in full-throttle position (depress pedal). Disconnect control pressure rod. In the full throttle position (kickdown position), the control lever must rest against full-throttle stop. If not, control shaft has to be adjusted by loosening screw on bellcrank. Pull control pressure rod forward to full-throttle position and adjust length on ball socket so that rod can be reconnected without tension.

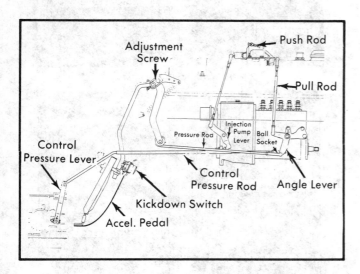

Fig. 3   *Throttle Rod Adjustment (300 Series)*

450 Series — Disconnect throttle rod from ball socket on intermediate lever. Push throttle lever and intermediate lever to idle

position. Push throttle rod rearward against stop then adjust length of rod for a free fit over ball socket on intermediate lever. Tighten lock nut.

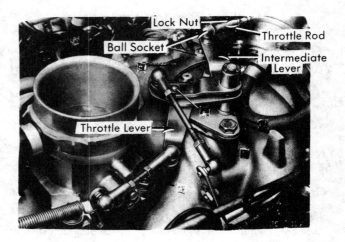

Fig. 4   *Throttle Rod Adjustment (450 Series)*

NEUTRAL SAFETY SWITCH

All Models — Place control lever in "N" position and disconnect shift rod from selector lever. Loosen adjusting screw and insert pin through selector lever into locating hole in shift housing. Tighten adjusting screw and connect shift rod to selector lever. Check that engine starts only in "N" and "P". See *Fig. 5*.

NOTE — *If shift rod does not fit freely in selector lever see Shift Linkage Adjustment in this article.*

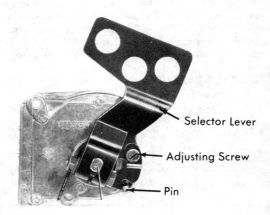

Fig. 5   *Neutral Safety Switch Adjustment*

SHIFT LINKAGE

Floor Shift (All Models) — Disconnect shift rod from selector lever. Place selector lever and control lever in "N" position. Make sure there is approximately .039" (1 mm) clearance between control lever and the "N" position stop on console. Adjust shift rod length for a free fit in selector lever. Tighten lock nut.

PEUGEOT

**504
505
604**

TRANSMISSION IDENTIFICATION

Application	Transmission Model
504 & 505	ZF 3HP 22
604	GM Automatic

LUBRICATION

SERVICE INTERVALS

Check transmission level at every oil change. Drain and refill transmission every 25,000 miles or 2 years whichever comes first. In severe driving conditions change fluid at 12,500 miles.

NOTE — *604 should have band adjusted at 25,000 mile oil change.*

CHECKING FLUID LEVEL

Position vehicle on level surface and have engine at operating temperature. Apply parking brake, move selector lever through all positions ending in "P". Remove dipstick and wipe with a clean lint free cloth. Reinstall dipstick and check fluid level. "MAX" mark is maximum hot level. "MIN" mark is minimum cold level. "MIDDLE" mark is minimum hot level or maximum cold level.

RECOMMENDED FLUID

Use only fluids marked Dexron B or D Automatic Transmission Fluid.

CAPACITY

NOTE — *Transmission capacity listed below is approximate, correct fluid level should be determined by mark on dipstick.*

Transmission Refill Capacities	
Application	**Capacity (Pts.)**
504 & 505	
Fluid Change	4.25
Refill from Dry	11.0
604	
Fluid Change	3.2
Refill from Dry	12.0

DRAINING & REFILLING

Have engine at normal operating temperature. Remove drain plug from transmission oil pan, allow all fluid to drain and install drain plug. Pour approximate amount of fluid as listed in above table in transmission. Start and run engine at normal idle. Shift selector lever through all positions, check fluid level, add fluid as needed.

ADJUSTMENT

BRAKE BAND

604 — Remove oil pan, servo cover, and seal. Loosen lock nut, then tighten adjusting screw to 4-5 ft. lbs. (.6-.7 mkg). Back off adjusting screw 5 turns and hold while tightening lock nut. Install servo cover, seal and oil pan. Refill transmission fluid to proper level.

KICKDOWN CABLE

504 & 505 — With throttle control drum in normal hot idle position, adjust cable housing to give maximum clearance of .020" (.5 mm) between end of cable housing and clip on cable.

604 — Place throttle control drum in fully open position and hold it open with screwdriver. Loosen cable mounting bolts at bracket. Pull on cable sheath to increase tension on cable. Screw nut "2" to within .039" (1 mm) of bracket and tighten nut "1". See *Fig. 1*.

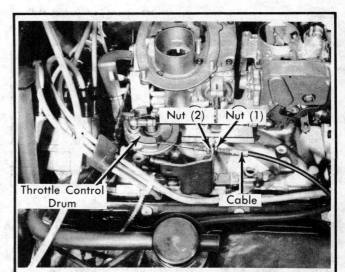

Fig. 1   604 Kickdown Cable Adjustment

SHIFT LINKAGE

All Models — Disconnect selector rod at transmission lever. Place transmission lever in neutral position. Place gear selector lever in "N" and adjust rod length to fit both levers without tension.

NEUTRAL SAFETY SWITCH

504 & 505 — Engine should start in "N" or "P" positions only. To adjust, install or remove shims at base of switch until proper operation is achieved.

604 — Place selector lever in "N" position. Loosen attaching screws and adjust switch so that detent ball and alignment marks coincide. Tighten switch in position and ensure that engine will only start in "P" or "N" positions. Back-up lights should work in "R" position.

PORSCHE

924
928

LUBRICATION

SERVICE INTERVALS

Check fluid level every 15,000 miles. Change fluid every 30,000 miles.

CHECKING FLUID LEVEL

With vehicle on level surface, run engine until normal operating temperatures are reached. Shift selector lever to "N" position. Oil level must be between both marks of filler container. Difference between upper and lower marks is approximatly 1 pint.

RECOMMENDED FLUID

Use automatic transmission fluid labeled "DEXRON" or "DEXRON II"

CAPACITY

NOTE — *Capacities shown are approximate, and correct fluid level should be determined by marks on filler.*

Transaxle Refill Capacities	
Application	Capacity (Pts.)
Fluid Change	
924	6
928	11
Overhaul (Dry)	
924	12.7
928	12.7

ADJUSTMENT

SELECTOR LEVER

924 — 1) Move selector lever to "P" position. Loosen nut on clamping sleeve for selector lever cable. Move operating lever on transmission to "P" position (against stop). See *Fig. 1.*

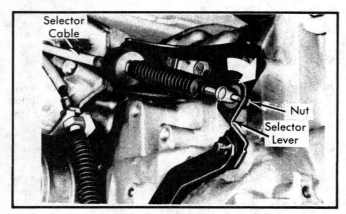

Fig. 1   Selector Lever Adjusting Point
924

2) Tighten nut on clamping sleeve. Move selector through all positions with engine running, engagement should be felt after 5 seconds.

928 — Place selector lever in "N" position. Detach cable from operating lever on transmission. Place selector lever (on transmission) in "N" position. Adjust cable so that socket attaches to operating lever without tension and reattach cable to lever. See *Fig. 2.*

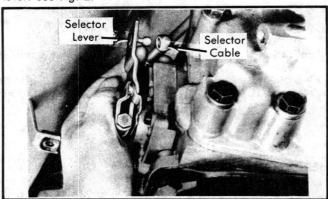

Fig. 2   Selector Lever Adjusting Point
928

NEUTRAL SAFETY SWITCH

924 — Starter should operate only in positions "P" or "N". If starter operates in any other position, remove selector lever gate and loosen mounting bolts on safety switch. Adjust switch as necessary.

928 — Move selector lever to "N" position. Loosen adjusting screw, insert .157" (4 mm) pin through drive dog into hole in case. Tighten adjusting screw and remove locating pin. Check to see that engine starts in "N" or "P" only.

THROTTLE PRESSURE CABLE

924 — 1) Screw in cable sleeve mounting nut on transmission bracket and tighten to specifications. Push roller holder in slot forward as far as possible and tighten bolts. Completely loosen short cable at firewall and long cable at roller holder.

2) Turn roller so that operating lever is forward. Hold roller in this position and mount throttle valve push rod without tension. Place cable around roller and adjust long cable sleeve until cable locator just rests in opening without tension.

928 — Detach cable at transmission lever. Adjust lever with adjusting bolt "A" after loosening bolt "B" so that cable can be attached without tension or free play. See *Fig. 3.*

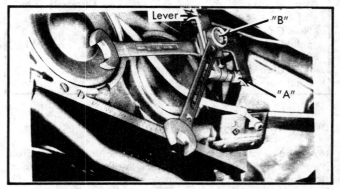

Fig. 3   Throttle Cable Pressure Adjustment
928

PORSCHE (Cont.)

BRAKE BANDS

All Models — Loosen lock nut, tighten adjusting screw to 7 ft. lbs. (1 mkg). Back off adjusting screw and retighten to 4 ft. lbs. (.5 mkg). Loosen adjusting screw 2½ turns and tighten lock nut.

NOTE — *928 models have 2 additional bands to adjust and are adjusted with pins as follows:*

1) Measure distance of free play for piston No. 2 by applying air pressure to No. 2 release port. See *Fig. 4.* Now, check distance at "B", then apply air pressure to No. 2 apply port and recheck distance "B". The difference of both distances is the free play.

2) Brake band No. 1 is checked by measuring the distance at "A". Now apply air pressure to No. 1 apply port and recheck distance "A". The difference of both measurements is the free play.

NOTE — *Free play of both bands should be .118-.157" (3-4 mm). Adjustments are made with adjustment pins.*

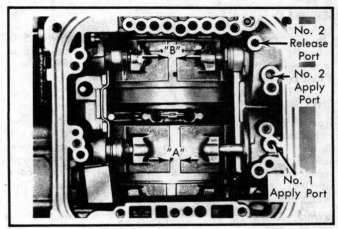

**Fig. 4   Brake Band Measurement
928**

SAAB

900

LUBRICATION

SERVICE INTERVALS

Check fluid level in transmission and differential every 7,500 miles. A one-time change of automatic transmission fluid is recommended at 15,000 miles when bands and cables are adjusted and filter cleaned.

CHECKING FLUID LEVEL

Transmission — With vehicle parked on level surface, engine idling and transmission in "P" position, remove and wipe off dipstick using lint free cloth or paper. Insert and remove dipstick. Fluid level should be between the maximum and minimum marks on the dipstick. Be sure to read hot or cold markings on dipstick, depending on transmission oil temperature.

CAUTION — *Do not overfill transmission.*

Final Drive — Remove final drive filler plug and make sure fluid level is to bottom of filler plug hole.

RECOMMENDED FLUID

Automatic Transmission — Use automatic transmission fluid to Ford specification M2C-33F or M2C-33G at each change. For topping up, type A, Suffix A or Dexron can be used.

Final Drive — Use only SAE 80 EP gear oil.

CAPACITY

NOTE — *Transmission capacity listed below is approximate, and correct fluid level should be determined by the mark on dipstick, rather than by amount added.*

Transaxle Refill Capacities	
Application	**Capacity (Pts.)**
Transmission	17
Final Drive	2.6

DRAINING & REFILLING

Automatic Transmission — Remove drain plug from transmission oil pan and drain fluid. DO NOT confuse engine and transmission drain plugs. A special wrench is required for the transmission plug. It is recommended that oil pan and filter be removed and cleaned when changing fluid. Adjustments should also be checked at this time. Replace drain plug and fill with ATF to correct level.

Final Drive — Remove drain plug and allow fluid to drain. Replace drain plug and refill until fluid level is to bottom of oil filler plug hole.

ADJUSTMENT

FRONT BAND

Drain fluid and remove pan. Place a ¼" (6.35 mm) thick spacer tool (8790073) between adjusting screw and boss on servo piston. Tighten adjusting screw to 10 INCH lbs. (11.5

cmkg). Check that gap between self-adjusting spring and lever is 1.5-2 screw threads.

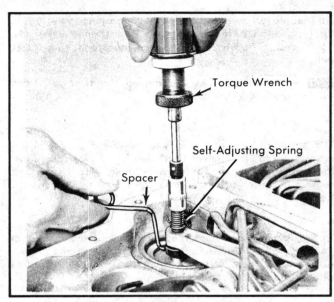

Fig. 1   Adjusting Front Band

REAR BAND

Rear band adjusting screw is located outside transmission housing on left side. To adjust band, loosen lock nut a few turns and tighten adjusting screw to 9-10 ft. lbs. (1.3-1.4 mkg). Back screw off ¾ turn and hold in position while tightening lock nut.

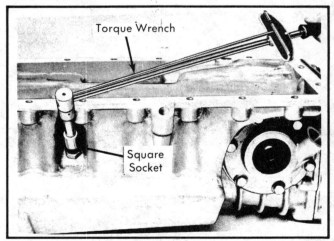

Fig. 2   Left Side View of Automatic Transmission Case Showing Rear Band Adjustment Point

TRANSMISSION THROTTLE CABLE

Connect tachometer to engine and pressure gauge to transmission. Apply parking brake, start engine and ensure that idle speed is to specification. Move transmission selector to "D" position. Pressure should read 50-70 psi (3.5-4.9 kg/cm²). Increase engine speed 500 RPM above idle. Pressure should increase 10-20 psi (.7-1.4 kg/cm²). If pressure is too low, adjust throttle cable outward. If pressure rise is too high, adjust cable inward.

SAAB (Cont.)

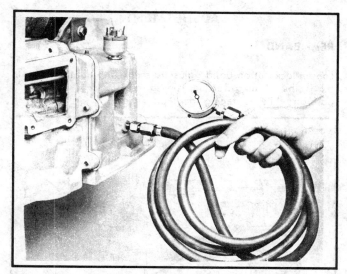

Fig. 3   Pressure Gauge Connecting Point for Throttle Pressure Test

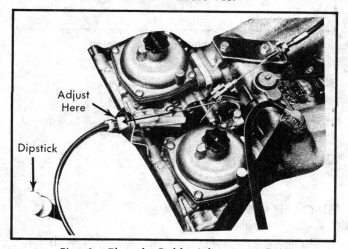

Fig. 4   Throttle Cable Adjustment Point

SHIFT LINKAGE

To check linkage adjustment, depress pawl button and move lever slightly back and forth until a click can be heard and you feel the selector valve lock in the neutral position. Release pawl button and selector lever should now be in "N" position. To adjust, loosen cable attachment at lever with Allen wrench and

extension while selector valve is locked in neutral. Move lever to position pawl in notch on selector segment and tighten cable set screw.

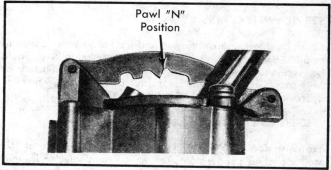

Fig. 5   Shift Selector Segment with "N" Detent

NEUTRAL SAFETY SWITCH

Disconnect wires from switch. With transmission in "D", loosen switch and connect self-powered test light to neutral safety switch terminals. Test light should operate. Screw switch in until light goes out and mark position. Move test light probes to back-up switch (wide) terminals and light should go out. Screw in switch and count turns until light goes on, then unscrew half way between these positions and secure switch lock nut. DO NOT overtighten lock nut or switch may be damaged.

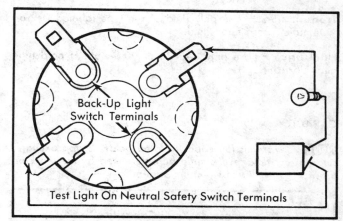

Fig. 6   Neutral Safety Switch Testing Points

SUBARU

1800

LUBRICATION

SERVICE INTERVALS

Check fluid level in transmission and final drive every 3 months or 3000 miles, whichever comes first. Transmission fluid should be changed every 30,000 miles and band adjusted as necessary. Drain and refill final drive after first 1000 miles of operation, then every 30,000 miles thereafter.

CHECKING FLUID LEVEL

Transmission — With vehicle parked on level surface at normal operating temperature, set transmission selector lever in "P" position with engine idling. Remove dipstick and clean with lint-free cloth. Insert and quickly remove dipstick. Note fluid level and add through dipstick hole to bring to full mark.

NOTE — *Normal operating temperature for fluid is 122-176° F (50-80° C) and is reached after driving for 10 minutes or idling for 25 minutes. When filling transmission, DO NOT overfill.*

Final Drive — Remove filler plug and check that fluid level is to bottom of filler plug hole.

RECOMMENDED FLUID

Transmission — Use only fluid of the type labeled Dexron Automatic Transmission Fluid.

Final Drive — Use only SAE 80 or 90 weight Hypoid type gear lubricant.

CAPACITY

NOTE — *Transmission capacity listed below is approximate, and correct fluid level should be determined by the mark on dipstick, rather than by amount added.*

Transaxle Refill Capacities	
Application	**Capacity (Pts.)**
Transmission	11.8-12.7
Final Drive	1.8-2.6

DRAINING & REFILLING

Transmission — Remove drain plug and drain fluid. Replace drain plug and fill transmission with about 8 pints of specified fluid. Start engine and check fluid level with engine idling. Add fluid as necessary.

Final Drive — Remove drain plug and drain oil. Replace drain plug and fill final drive with specified gear oil.

ADJUSTMENT

REAR BAND

Loosen lock nut on band adjusting screw and tighten screw to 6.5 ft. lbs. (.9 mkg) torque. Loosen screw 2 turns and hold in position while tightening lock nut.

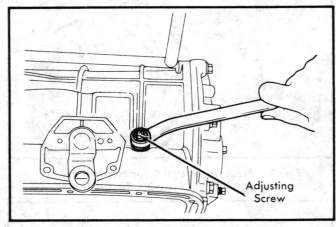

Fig. 1   Rear Band Adjustment

KICKDOWN SWITCH

Switch on ignition and depress accelerator fully. A "click" should be heard just as accelerator bottoms out. Adjust switch inward or outward for proper operation.

NOTE — *If switch operates too soon, downshift will occur at part throttle.*

SHIFT LINKAGE

Shift selector lever from "P" to "1" position. Lever should set into each position with a "click". At each position, check that

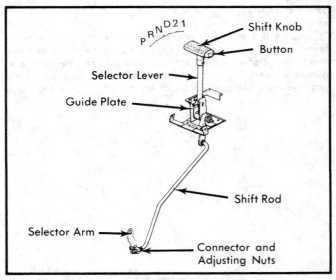

Fig. 2   Shift Linkage Adjustment

SUBARU (Cont.)

selector dial gives proper indication of gear position. If linkage is out of adjustment, make sure that selector lever does not move below "1" position, then shift to "D" position. Adjust length of linkage so that position of lever corresponds with detent of manual valve and that indicator is correctly lined up. Recheck in all positions.

NEUTRAL SAFETY SWITCH

Switch is mounted on right side of selector lever plate. To adjust, remove switch from plate and insert .08" (2 mm) diameter pin in alignment hole on switch. Ensure that selector lever is in "N" position, pushed lightly toward "P". Match locator to bracket hole and moving plate pin to arm hole. Tighten mounting bolts in position and remove alignment pin.

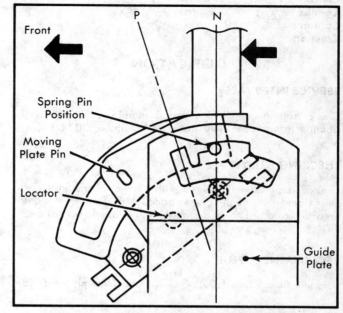

Fig. 3   Neutral Safety Switch Adjustment

TOYOTA

Celica	**Pickup**
Corolla	**Supra**
Corona	**Tercel**
Cressida	

LUBRICATION

SERVICE INTERVALS

Check transmission fluid every 6 months or 7,500 miles. Change transmission fluid every 24 months or 30,000 miles.

CHECKING FLUID LEVEL

Check transmission fluid level with engine idling. Shift each gear from "P" through "L" and back to "P". Fluid level should be within cold or hot ranges marked on dipstick. Do not overfill.

RECOMMENDED FLUID

Use only fluid labeled Type F Automatic Transmission Fluid.

CAPACITY

NOTE — *Refill capacity is approximate, to be used as a guide when refilling after servce. Actual fluid level should be checked by level on dipstick rather than by amount added.*

Transmission Refill Capacities	
Application	**Capacity (Pts.)**
Tercel	
Refill (Fluid Change)	4.6
Refill (Dry)	9.6
All Other Models	
Refill (Fluid Change)	5.0
Refill (Dry)	13.4

DRAINING & REFILLING

1) Remove drain plug, then bolts attaching oil pan. Remove oil pan and filter screens. Clean filter screens and dry with compressed air.

2) Install screens, oil pan and a new pan gasket. Tighten oil pan bolts to 53-78 INCH lbs. (60-90 cmkg) on Tercel or 34-43 INCH lbs. (40-50 cmkg) on all other models. Repeat tightening several times until torque remains constant, taking care not to over tighten bolts.

3) Replace drain plug and fill transmission with approximately 4 pints of fluid. Start engine and select all gears. Check fluid level and add additional fluid as necessary. Do not overfill.

ADJUSTMENTS

SHIFT LINKAGE

Column Shift Models — **1)** Inspect bushing between control shaft and manual valve lever for damage or deterioration.

2) Loosen nut on connecting rod swivel and move shift lever to verify that position indicator shows ranges corresponding to shift lever ranges. Check that position indicator is indicating "N" when control shaft lever is in "N".

3) Position transmission manual valve lever in "N" position. Adjust length of control first rod so position of indicator is in "N". Tighten lock nut at connecting rod swivel.

4) Check shift lever selectiveness, making sure position indicator registers correctly, and that vehicle moves correctly in ranges selected.

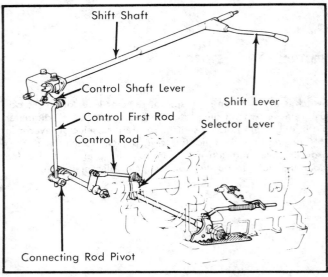

*Fig. 1   Shift Linkage Assembly
(Column Shift Models)*

Floor Shift Models — Place transmission shift lever in "N" position and adjust shift rod until shift lever indicates "N" position correctly. Tighten lock nuts and check that all ranges are correctly engaged.

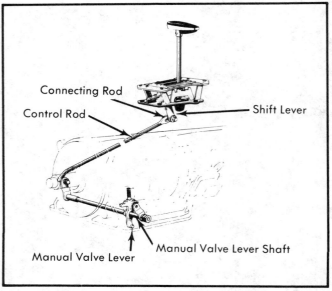

*Fig. 2   Shift Linkage Assembly
(Floor Shift Models)*

TOYOTA (Cont.)

THROTTLE CABLE (EXCEPT TERCEL)

Bellows Type — Remove air cleaner. Check throttle cable bracket and linkage for looseness or bending. Pull back rubber boot from outer cable. Open throttle valve wide-open. Adjust cable housing so distance between end of housing and stopper collar is 2.05" (52 mm). Tighten lock nut and secure rubber boot.

Straight Boot Type — Remove air cleaner. Check throttle cable bracket and linkage for looseness or bending. Open throttle valve wide-open. Adjust cable housing so distance between rubber boot end and inner cable stopper is .04" (0-1.0 mm). Tighten lock nut.

THROTTLE LINK (TERCEL)

Remove air cleaner. Check throttle cable bracket and linkage for looseness or bending. Open throttle valve wide open. Adjust linkage by turning turnbuckle until throttle valve lever indicator lines up with mark on transmission case. Tighten lock nut.

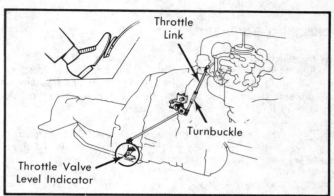

Fig. 4   View of Throttle Link Adjustment

NEUTRAL SAFETY SWITCH

Loosen adjusting bolt. Position shift lever in "N" position. Align switch shaft groove to neutral basic line. Tighten adjusting bolt.

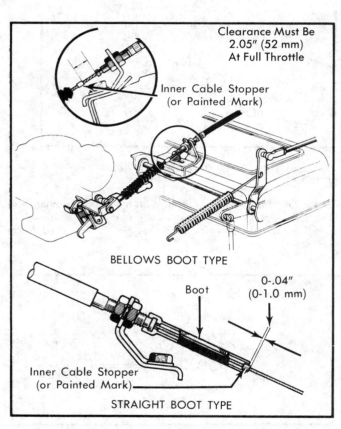

Fig. 3   View of Throttle Cable Adjustment

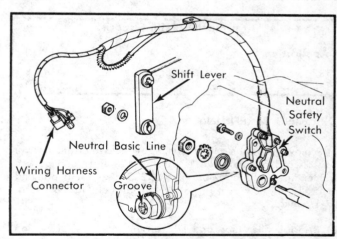

Fig. 5   Neutral Safety Switch

TRIUMPH

TR7
TR8

LUBRICATION

SERVICE INTERVALS

Check fluid level every 7500 miles. Replace fluid and filter every 30,000 miles.

CHECKING FLUID LEVEL

With vehicle on a level surface, start engine, let idle 2 or 3 minutes. Place selector lever through all positions, ending in "P". Remove dipstick and wipe clean with a lint free cloth. Replace dipstick making sure it is fully seated. Remove dipstick and read level. Add fluid as necessary.

NOTE — *Dipstick has 2 sets of markings, use "COLD" side for cold engine and "HOT" side if vehicle has been driven 20 miles or more.*

RECOMMENDED FLUID

Use only fluids marked Type F Automatic Transmission Fluid.

CAPACITY

NOTE — *Refill capacity is approximate, to be used as guide when refilling after service. Actual fluid level should be checked by level on dipstick rather than by amount added.*

Transmission Refill Capacity	
Application	Capacity (Pts.)
TR7	11.4
TR8	14.9

DRAINING & REFILLING

1) Remove filler tube and oil pan. Allow fluid to drain. Remove and discard filter and gasket. Install new filter and gasket. Tighten filter bolts to 1.7-2.5 ft. lbs. (.2-.3 mkg). Clean pan and reinstall with new gasket, tightening pan bolts to 5-8 ft. lbs. (.7-1.1 mkg).

2) Reinstall filler tube and fill transmission to "COLD" high mark on dipstick. Drive vehicle until transmission is at normal temperature (20 miles) and recheck fluid level. Add fluid as needed.

ADJUSTMENT

FRONT & REAR BAND

TR7 — Loosen lock nut and back off a few turns. Tighten adjusting screw to 3 ft. lbs. (.4 mkg), then back off adjusting screw ¾ turn. Tighten lock nut to 22 ft. lbs. (3.1 mkg).

TR8 — Loosen lock nut and back off a few turns. Tighten adjusting screw to 5 ft. lbs. (.7 mkg), then back off adjusting screw ¾ turn. Tighten lock nut to 35 ft. lbs. (4.8 mkg).

KICKDOWN CABLE

1) Apply hand brake and block wheels, start engine and place selector lever in "D". Adjust idle speed to 750 RPM, then turn off engine. Loosen locknut on kickdown cable at engine mounting bracket. Adjust outer cable to ¹⁄₁₆" (1.5 mm) from stop. See *Fig. 1*.

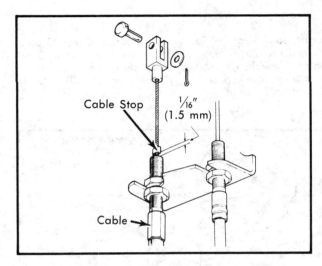

Cable Stop
¹⁄₁₆" (1.5 mm)
Cable

Fig. 1 Kickdown Cable Adjustment

2) Remove transmission oil pan. With the aid of another person, fully depress accelerator pedal and check that downshift cam is in the kickdown position. See *Fig. 2*. Adjust cable as necessary.

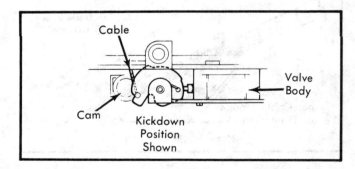

Cable
Valve Body
Cam
Kickdown Position Shown

Fig. 2 Checking Downshift Cam Position

SHIFT LINKAGE

1) Position selector lever in "N" on TR7 or in "P" on TR8. Apply hand brake. Loosen lock nuts at shift rod adjuster nut. Disconnect shift rod from transmission lever and check that transmission shift lever is in "N" position on TR7 or in "P" position on TR8.

2) To adjust, loosen or tighten adjusting nut so that shift rod will attach to transmission shift lever without tension. Tighten lock nuts and check that all ranges are correct.

VOLKSWAGEN

Dasher   Rabbit Pickup
Jetta   Scirocco
Rabbit   Vanagon

LUBRICATION

SERVICE INTERVALS

Automatic Transmission — Check fluid level every 6000 miles. Change fluid every 30,000 miles under normal conditions, or every 15,000 miles under heavy duty conditions.

CHECKING FLUID LEVEL

Automatic Transmission — With transmission warm and engine idling in neutral, check that ATF fluid is between marks on dipstick.

NOTE — *The ring shaped handle should be in a vertical position when checking level. The difference in fluid quantity between upper and lower marks is only .85 pt.*

RECOMMENDED FLUID

For automatic transmission use only DEXRON automatic transmission fluid. For final drive use only SAE 90W multipurpose gear lubricant.

CAPACITY

NOTE — *Transmission capacities listed below are approximate, and correct fluid level should be determined by the mark on dipstick, rather than by amount added.*

Transaxle Refill Capacities	
Application	**Capacity (Pts.)**
Automatic Transmission	
All Models	6.4
Final Drive	
Vanagon	3.0
All Others	1.6

DRAINING & REFILLING

Automatic Transmission — 1) Remove drain plug from oil pan and allow as much fluid to drain as possible. Remove oil pan and filter screen. Clean screen and air dry with compressed air.

NOTE — *To prevent lint from being introduced into transmission, DO NOT use cleaning rags to dry filter screen.*

2) Replace oil pan and screen using new gaskets. Tighten oil pan bolts to 14 ft. lbs. (1.9 mkg) in a diagonal pattern. Wait 5 minutes for gasket to compress and retighten bolts. Repeat several times until bolts remain at proper torque value.

CAUTION — *Do not overtighten bolts.*

3) Fill transmission with 5 pints of fluid. Warm up transmission fluid and top-up to proper level. See *Checking Fluid Level.*

ADJUSTMENT

BRAKE BAND

NOTE — *The transmission has to be in a horizontal position when band is adjusted or brake band may jam.*

Tighten 2nd gear brake band adjusting screw to 7 ft. lbs. (1.0 mkg). Loosen adjusting screw, then tighten again to 4 ft. lbs. (.5 mkg). Back off screw 2½ turns, then tighten lock nut to 14 ft. lbs. (2.0 mkg).

Second Gear Band
Adjusting Screw

Fig. 1   Brake Band Adjusting Location

KICKDOWN SWITCH

Dasher — Adjust kickdown switch (located below accelerator pedal) so that solenoid in transmission will pull in with an audible click when pedal is fully depressed.

Vanagon — Rotate throttle lever open until there is a gap of .040-.060" (1.0-1.5 mm) between lever and stop. Adjust position of switch so it operates with throttle lever in this position.

SELECTOR LEVER CABLE

Dasher — Place transmission in "P". Remove shift knob, indicator plate and console. Loosen nut for cable clamping bolt so cable is free to slide in clamping pin. Temporarily install indicator plate and move selector lever to "P" position so indicator for "P" is illuminated. Remove indicator plate. Tighten cable clamping nut to 6 ft. lbs. (.8 mkg). Replace indicator plate and shift through all gear positions making sure correct gear is aligned with correct mark on indicator plate. Replace console and shift knob.

Jetta, Rabbit & Scirocco — Place transmission in "P". Loosen nut for clamping pin which holds selector cable to operating lever on transaxle. Ensure that selector lever and operating lever are in "P" position. Tighten cable clamping nut to 6 ft. lbs. (.8 mkg).

Vanagon — Place transmission lever in "P". Loosen bolt which holds shift rod to operating lever on transaxle. Ensure that selector lever and operating lever are in "P" position. Push shift rod to rear and tighten bolt.

NEUTRAL SAFETY SWITCH

Neutral safety switch is located in shift console. Remove console cover and adjust switch so that it makes contact only in "P" and "N" positions.

VOLVO

DL
GL
GT

GLE
Coupe
Diesel

LUBRICATION

SERVICE INTERVAL

Under normal use it is not necessary to change the transmission fluid. Transmission fluid should be checked every 7,500 miles or twice a year. For vehicles in heavy duty service, transmission fluid should be changed every 25,000 miles.

CHECKING FLUID LEVEL

Position vehicle on level surface. Apply parking brake and shift selector lever into "P". Start engine and let idle. Shift selector lever through all gears pausing 4-5 seconds for engagement at each position. Return selector lever to "P". Wait two minutes then remove dipstick. Wipe dipstick off with lint free cloth and reinsert. Withdraw dipstick and check reading. Level must be between "MIN" and "MAX" marks. If not, add (or remove) fluid to obtain correct level.

RECOMMENDED FLUID

Use only fluids of the type labeled Type F Automatic Transmission Fluid.

CAPACITY

Transmission Refill Capacities	
Application	Capacity (Pts.)
All Models	14.6

ADJUSTMENT

THROTTLE & KICKDOWN CABLES

Transmission cable should be stretched in idle position. Distance between clip and sheath should be .010-.040" (.25-1.0 mm). See Fig. 1. Pull transmission cable out by hand approximately .39-.59" (10-15 mm), and release. A distinct "click" should be heard from transmission, indicating cable moves freely and throttle cam returns to initial position. Depress accelerator pedal completely. The transmission cable should travel 2.008" ±.016" (51 mm ±.4 mm), from idle position to full throttle position. See Fig. 1.

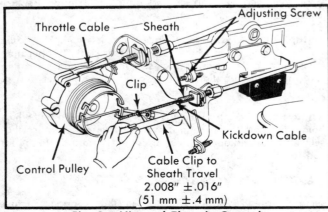

Fig. 1   View of Throttle Controls
(B21 F Engine Shown)

GEAR SELECTOR

Press on gear selector and check that clearance from "D" to stop is approximately the same as from "2" to stop. If clearance is incorrect, control rod needs adjustment. Adjustment is made by turning clevis in or out on control rod. Maximum visible thread length permitted is 1.1 " (28 mm). Increasing rod length reduces position "D" clearance. Decreasing rod length increases position "D" clearance. Shift to position "1" then to position "P" for recheck. See Fig. 2.

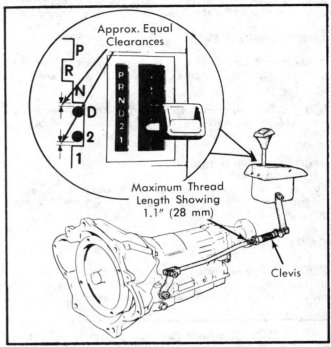

Fig. 2   Gear Selector Adjustment

NEUTRAL SAFETY SWITCH

NOTE — *Switch is located at and directly controlled by the gear shift control lever.*

Place selector lever in "P" position. Adjust neutral safety switch to set "P" mark at center of switch lever. Place selector lever in "N" position. Confirm "N" mark is at center of switch lever. Move selector lever from "P" to "1" and back again. Check that control pin does not slide out of switch lever. See Fig. 3. Check that engine only starts in "P" and 'N", and that the back-up lights illuminate in position "R" only.

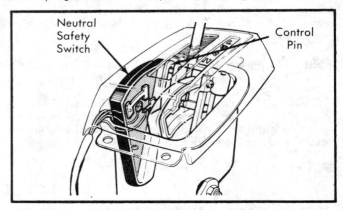

Fig. 3   Adjusting Neutral Safety Switch

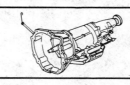
Section 2

AUTOMATIC TRANSMISSIONS

CONTENTS

NOTE — ALSO SEE GENERAL INDEX.

Automatic Transmissions

BORG-WARNER & AISIN-WARNER MODEL 55

Volvo
DL   **GLE**
GL   **Coupe**
GT   **Diesel**

TRANSMISSION IDENTIFICATION

Transmissions may be identified by a plate attached to left side of transmission case. Plate shows vendor (Borg-Warner or Aisin-Warner), transmission model number, and transmission serial number.

DESCRIPTION

Transmissions are fully automatic three-speed units consisting basically of a three-element torque converter, a compound planetary gear set, two multiple-disc clutches, two one-way roller clutches, and three multiple-disc brakes. A hydraulic system, pressurized by a gear type pump, provides the working pressure required to operate the automatic controls.

LUBRICATION & ADJUSTMENTS

See AUTOMATIC TRANSMISSION SERVICING Section.

TROUBLE SHOOTING

NOTE — *Almost any transmission problem will show up in one or more of the following tests: Check for proper fluid level, gear selector adjustment, throttle cable adjustment, line pressure, stall speed, or governor pressure. These tests show the condition of the most importment transmission components and should be checked to arrive at a proper diagnosis of the reported complaint.*

NO MOVEMENT IN "D" OR SLIPS IN "D"

Manual linkage out of adjustment. Faulty rear clutch, intermediate brake, one-way clutch for planetary gear set, front clutch, or valve body assembly.

NO MOVEMENT IN "R" OR SLIPS IN "R"

Manual linkage out of adjustment. Faulty rear clutch, intermediate brake, oil pump, or valve body assembly.

NO MOVEMENT IN ANY RANGE

Manual linkage out of adjustment. Parking pawl jammed or defective. Faulty torque converter, valve body assembly, or oil pump. Multiple unit damage. Shaft and/or spline damage.

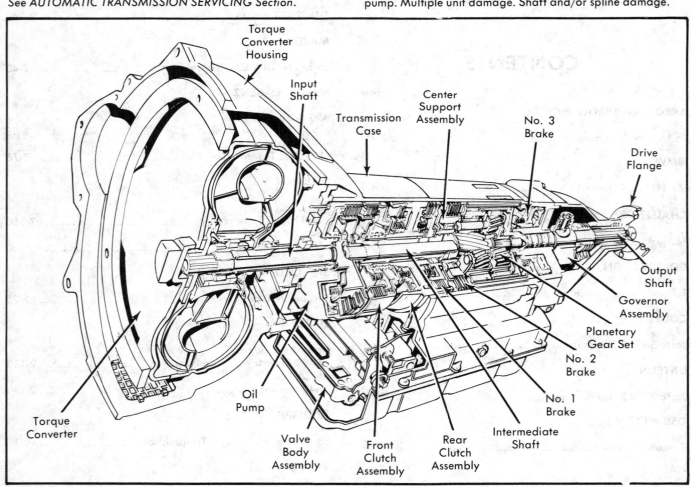

Fig. 1 Cutaway View of Borg-Warner and Aisin-Warner Model 55 Automatic Transmission

BORG-WARNER & AISIN-WARNER MODEL 55 (Cont.)

HARSH SHIFT FROM "N" TO "D" OR "R"

Accumulator pistons for front clutch or rear clutch seized or leaking.

HARSH 1-2 OR 2-1 SHIFT

Second speed brake accumulator piston seized or leaking. Valve body assembly intermediate coast shift valve seized.

HARSH 2-3 OR 3-2 SHIFT

Rear clutch accumulator piston seized or leaking. Defective valve body assembly. Check intermediate coast modulator valve.

SLIP ON 1-2 UPSHIFT

Valve body assembly intermediate coast shift valve seized, thereby not engaging No. 1 brake. Defective No. 1 brake. Defective No. 2 brake. Center support one-way clutch defective.

SLIP ON 2-3 UPSHIFT

Defective rear clutch or its oil circuit. Faulty valve body assembly (2-3 shift valve, etc.).

NO ENGINE BRAKING IN "1"

Defective No. 3 brake. Valve body assembly low coast modulator valve seized or low coast valve frozen in top position.

NO ENGINE BRAKING IN "2"

No. 1 brake or its oil circuit defective. Valve body assembly intermediate coast modulator valve seized.

NO 2-1 SHIFT IN "1"

Defective No. 3 brake. Valve body assembly low coast modulator valve or low coast shift valve seized.

VEHICLE STARTS OUT IN "2"

Governor pressure inaccurate (should be 0 with vehicle stationary). Valve body assembly 1-2 shift valve seized.

TRANSMISSION NOISE

Growling On Acceleration — Low fluid level. Defective torque converter.

NOTE — *If torque converter is replaced, oil cooler and lines must be cleaned.*

Gear Noise — Torque converter-to-drive plate bolts loose. Faulty coupling of one-way clutches. Faulty planetary gear sets. Worn thrust needle bearings or bushings.

Whining or Humming Noise — Defective torque converter (noise may disappear in "N"). Defective oil pump (noise varies with engine speed).

TESTING

ROAD TEST

1) Before road testing, ensure that fluid level and condition, and control linkage adjustments have been checked and corrected as necessary. During test, transmission should upshift and downshift at approximately the speed shown in Shift Speeds chart. All shifts may vary somewhat due to production tolerances or tire size. The important factor is the quality of the shifts. All shifts should be smooth, responsive, and with no slippage or engine speed runaway.

2) Slippage or engine runaway in any gear usually indicates clutch or brake problems. The slipping unit in a particular gear can usually be identified by noting transmission operation in other selector positions and comparing which internal units are applied in those positions. See *Clutch and Brake Application Chart.*

3) This process of elimination can be used to detect any unit which slips, and to confirm proper operation of good units; however, the actual cause of the malfunction usually cannot be easily decided. Practically any condition can be caused by leaking hydraulic circuits or sticking valves. Therefore, unless an obvious condition exists, do not disassemble transmission until hydraulic pressure tests have been made.

Shift Speed Specifications①	
Application	**MPH**
DL, GL, GT②	
1-2 Upshift	39-48
2-3 Upshift	62-71
3-2 Downshift	56 (Min.)
3-1 Downshift	22-35
GLE, Coupe, Diesel③	
1-2 Upshift	39-48
2-3 Upshift	66-78
3-2 Downshift	63 (Min.)
3-1 Downshift	24-35
① — At full (kick-down) throttle.	
② — Borg-Warner and Aisin-Warner.	
③ — Borg-Warner.	

STALL SPEED TEST

Stall Test Precautions — Before making a stall speed test ensure that line pressure is correct. If line pressure is too low when performing a stall test, transmission can be damaged. Also, during stall test do not hold throttle open for more than 5 seconds at a time.

Stall Test Procedure — 1) Remove front pressure plug from transmission and connect a pressure gauge. Connect a tachometer to engine. Position tachometer and pressure gauge so that they can be read from drivers seat.

2) Set parking and servicing brakes. Start engine and place selector lever in "D". Depress accelerator pedal completely and note maximum RPM and line pressure obtained. RPM and line pressure should be approximately as shown in Stall Test chart.

BORG-WARNER & AISIN-WARNER MODEL 55 (Cont.)

CLUTCH AND BRAKE APPLICATION CHART (ELEMENTS IN USE)

Selector Lever Position	Front Clutch	Rear Clutch	No. 1 Brake	No. 2 Brake	No. 3 Brake
D — DRIVE					
First	X				
Second	X		X	X	
Third	X	X		X	
2 — SECOND					
First	X				
Second	X		X	X	
1 — LOW	X				X
R — REVERSE		X			X

NEUTRAL OR PARK — All clutches and brakes released and/or ineffective.

3) Place selector lever in "N" and allow engine to idle for a while in order to cool off transmission. Then, place selector lever in "R" and repeat stall test. Stall RPM and line pressure should be approximately as shown in Stall Test chart.

Stall Speed Specifications

Application	Stall Speed RPM	Line Pressure Psi (kg/cm²)
Borg-Warner 55		
In "D"	①2400-2650	159-195 (11.2-13.7)
In "R"	①2400-2650	220-280 (15.4-19.6)
Aisin-Warner 55		
In "D"	2400-2650	135-170 (9.5-12.0)
In "R"	2400-2650	192-241 (13.5-17.0)

① — 2150-2400 RPM for GLE, Coupe and Diesel.

Stall Test Results — 1) If stall test RPM is approximately 600 RPM lower than specifications, torque converter one-way clutch is slipping and torque converter should be replaced. If stall RPM is approximately 300 RPM lower than specifications, engine performance may be unsatisfactory.

2) If stall test RPM is approximately 300 RPM above specifications in "R", rear clutch or No. 3 brake is slipping. If RPM is approximately 300 RPM above specifications in "D", front clutch is slipping. If stall speed is approximately 300 RPM above specifications, and no clutch or brake is slipping, fluid level is incorrect or valve body oil strainer is clogged.

LINE PRESSURE TEST

1) Connect a pressure gauge to front plug on transmission and place gauge so that it is visible from drivers seat. Connect a tachometer to engine.

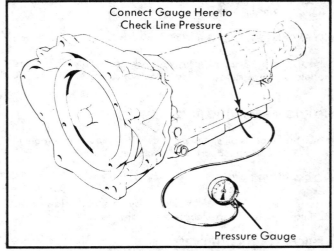

Fig. 2   Side View of Transmission Case Showing Line Pressure Test Port

2) Start engine and if necessary, adjust idle speed to 900 RPM. Depress brake pedal and place selector lever in "D". Note line pressure reading on gauge. Pressure should be approximately as shown in Line Pressure chart.

3) Repeat line pressure test with selector lever in "R". Pressure should be approximately as shown in Line Pressure chart.

Line Pressure Specifications

Application	Psi (kg/cm²)
Borg-Warner 55	
In "D"	75-90 (5.3-6.3)
In "R"	104-129 (7.4-9.1)
Aisin-Warner 55	
In "D"	57-64 (4.0-4.5)
In "R"	82-97 (5.8-6.8)

BORG-WARNER & AISIN-WARNER MODEL 55 (Cont.)

LINE PRESSURE TEST RESULTS

Pressure Too High — If pressure is too high, check throttle cable adjustment. If cable is correctly adjusted and pressure is still high, valve body assembly primary regulator valve or throttle valve may be seized.

Pressure Too Low — If line pressure is too low, check for seizing of the primary regulator valve or throttle valve in the valve body. If valves are not seized, check pressure relief valve and oil pump assembly for damage.

NOTE — A defective oil pump assembly will usually make noise.

GOVERNOR PRESSURE TEST

NOTE — Governor pressure is a "modified" line pressure. Therefore, governor pressure will be incorrect if line pressure is incorrect. Line pressure must be correct before checking governor pressure.

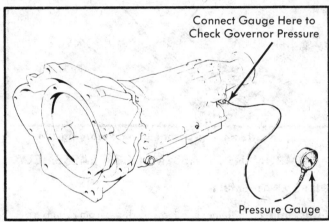

Connect Gauge Here to Check Governor Pressure

Pressure Gauge

Fig. 3 Side View of Transmission Case Showing Governor Pressure Test Port

Testing Procedures — Connect a pressure gauge to rear pressure port on transmission case and position gauge so that it is visible from drivers seat. Test drive vehicle in "D" and note pressure readings. Pressures should be approximately as shown in Governor Pressures chart.

Governor Pressure Specifications	
Vehicle Speed	**psi (kg/cm²)**
Borg-Warner 55	
DL, GL, GT	
17-19 MPH	14-18 (1.0-1.3)
31-35 MPH	23-38 (1.6-2.0)
30-67 MPH	53-62 (3.7-4.4)
GLE, Coupe, Diesel	
20 MPH	14-18 (1.0-1.3)
35 MPH	21-27 (1.5-1.9)
Aisin-Warner 55	
DL, GL, GT	
17-19 MPH	13-21 (.9-1.5)
31-35 MPH	23-31 (1.6-2.2)
60-67 MPH	58-75 (4.1-5.3)

SERVICE (IN VEHICLE)

NOTE — The following units can be removed from transmission without removing transmission from vehicle: Oil Pan, Valve Body Assembly, Accumulator Pistons, Parking Pawl, Rear Extension Housing and Oil Seal, Speedometer Driven Gear, and Governor Body. See procedures given in Transmission Disassembly and Transmission Reassembly.

TRANSMISSION REMOVAL & INSTALLATION

Removal — 1) Remove air cleaner, then disconnect throttle cable at pulley and cable sheath at bracket. Remove two upper bolts attaching transmission to engine.

2) Raise vehicle and support with safety stands. Disconnect oil filler pipe from oil pan and drain transmission fluid. Remove vehicle splash guard.

3) Disconnect muffler from hanger. Disconnect propeller shaft from drive flange on rear of transmission. Remove exhaust pipe clamps from bracket. Remove transmission support member attaching bolts, then pull member back, twist and lift out. Remove rear transmission mount and exhaust pipe bracket.

4) Disconnect speedometer cable from transmission. Disconnect oil cooler lines from transmission and oil cooler, then remove from vehicle. Disconnect gear shift control rod from transmission.

5) Remove torque converter cover plate. Remove starter motor attaching bolts and starter motor cover. Remove torque converter-to-drive plate attaching bolts.

6) Support transmission with a suitable transmission jack. Remove the two lower bolts attaching transmission to engine. Use a screwdriver and separate torque converter from drive plate. Lower transmission from vehicle.

Installation — Reverse removal procedure and note the following: Tighten all nuts and bolts evenly. After installation, fill transmission with fluid. Adjust throttle linkage and shift control linkage.

TORQUE CONVERTER

NOTE — Torque converter is a sealed unit and cannot be disassembled for service. Replace if found defective.

TRANSMISSION DISASSEMBLY

NOTE — Clean outside of transmission thoroughly before disassembly to prevent dirt or foreign material from entering transmission.

1) Pull torque converter from transmission. Place transmission in a suitable holding fixture. Remove attaching bolts and separate converter housing from transmission case. Remove speedometer driven gear assembly retaining bolt and pry assembly from transmission case using a screwdriver.

BORG WARNER & AISIN WARNER MODEL 55 (Cont.)

2) Hold output shaft drive flange stationary and remove flange bolt. Using a suitable puller, pull drive flange from transmission. Remove attaching bolts and lift off extension housing. Slide speedometer driving gear and spacer ring from output shaft. Remove retaining clip and pull governor assembly off shaft.

3) Invert transmission case so that oil pan is facing up, then remove oil pan and gasket. Remove attaching bolts and lift oil strainer and particle magnet from transmission case. Remove valve body-to-case attaching bolts, then lift valve body slightly and disconnect throttle cable from valve body cam. Lift valve body assembly from case.

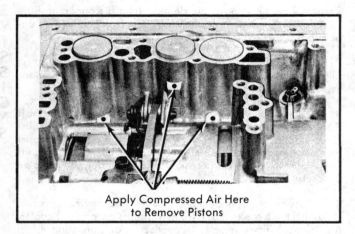

Fig. 4 Accumulator Pistons and Springs Removal

4) Apply compressed air to holes under accumulator pistons and force pistons from case bores, then remove piston springs. Invert transmission case so that oil pump faces up, then remove oil pump attaching bolts. Remove oil pump assembly from case using a suitable puller.

5) Pull front clutch assembly from case, then remove bearing and race from clutch. Remove rear clutch bearing and race, then pull rear clutch assembly from case. Remove center support bolts, then lift center support assembly from case.

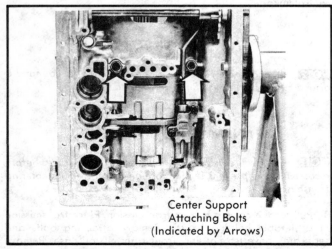

Fig. 5 Bottom View of Transmission Case Showing Location of Center Support Attaching Bolts

6) Remove large snap ring from groove in case, then lift No. 3 brake disc pack and planetary gear assembly from case as a unit. Remove brake apply tube, thrust bearing and races from transmission case.

7) Turn transmission so that rear face of case is up. Remove attaching screws and lift governor oil duct cover from case. Note position for reassembly reference, then remove oil cooler line nipples from case. Remove governor and line pressure plugs.

8) Turn transmission so that oil pan attaching face is up. Remove parking pawl rod plate attaching bolts, then remove plate and rod. Using a drift, drive detent lever lock pin out of lever and shaft, then pull shaft out of lever and transmission case. Lift up parking pawl, press out shaft and spring, then lift parking pawl from case.

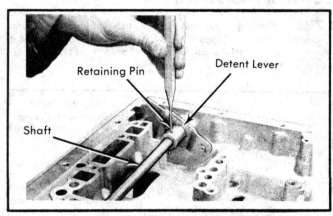

Fig. 6 Removing Detent Lever Retaining Pin

COMPONENT DISASSEMBLY & REASSEMBLY

OIL PUMP ASSEMBLY

Disassembly — Remove oil seals rings from pump cover. Remove attaching bolts and separate cover from pump housing. Remove large "O" ring from housing. Mark pump drive and driven gears for reassembly in same position, then remove them from pump housing. Pry oil seal from housing.

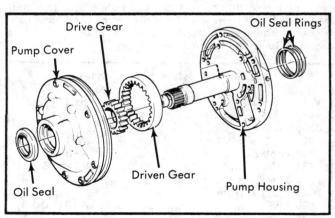

Fig. 7 Exploded View of Oil Pump Assembly

Inspection — Clean all parts thoroughly and dry with compressed air. Inspect all parts for wear, cracks, or scoring, and replace as necessary.

BORG-WARNER & AISIN-WARNER MODEL 55 (Cont.)

NOTE – *If pump housing, cover, drive gear or driven gear requires replacement, complete oil pump assembly must be replaced as they are a matched set.*

Reassembly – **1)** Install drive and driven gear into housing and ensure that marks made at reassembly are aligned. Using a feeler gauge measure clearance between pump driven gear and pump housing. Clearance should be .003-.012" (.07-.30 mm); if not replace oil pump assembly.

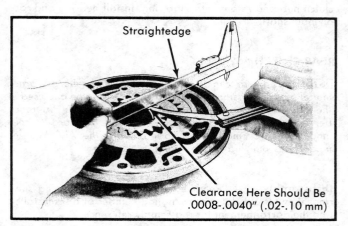

Fig. 8   Using a Feeler Gauge to Measure Housing-to-Gear Face Clearance

2) Next, check clearance between driven gear and crescent. Clearance should be .004-.020" (.11-.50 mm); if not, replace oil pump. Finally, using a straightedge and feeler gauge, check pump housing face to gear face clearance. Clearance should be .0008-.0040" (.02-.10 mm); if not replace oil pump assembly.

3) Lubricate all parts with automatic transmission fluid. Press new oil seal into pump housing. Assemble pump cover to housing, then install attaching bolts finger tight. Fit centering tool (5077) around housing and cover, then tighten centering tool clamp screw to align housing and cover. Tighten attaching

bolts and remove tool. Lubricate large "O" ring and install into groove on pump housing, then lubricate and install oil seal rings on pump cover.

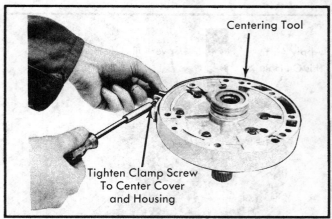

Fig. 9   Using Special Centering Tool to Align Oil Pump Housing and Cover

FRONT CLUTCH ASSEMBLY

NOTE – *The front clutch assembly used in the Borg-Warner model 55 transmission is slightly different from the one used in the Aisin-Warner transmission. The main difference between the two clutch assemblies is that the Borg-Warner model uses 18 small return springs while the Aisin-Warner model uses one big return spring.*

Disassembly – **1)** Remove bearing and race from input shaft. Remove snap ring and lift input hub from clutch assembly. Pull front clutch hub from clutch drum, then remove bearing and races.

2) Lift clutch discs from drum, noting number used and the order in which they are installed for reassembly reference. Compress return spring(s) retainer, then remove snap ring and lift out retainer and return spring(s).

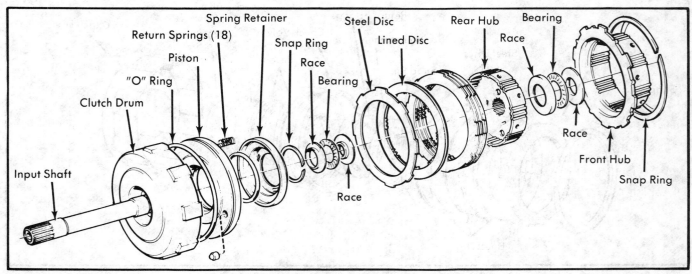

Fig. 10   Exploded View of Front Clutch Assembly (Borg-Warner Model Shown – Aisin-Warner Model Similar)

BORG-WARNER & AISIN-WARNER MODEL 55 (Cont.)

3) Place clutch drum with input shaft facing up. Apply compressed air to one oil hole on inside of drum while covering the other hole with finger and force piston from drum. Remove "O" rings from clutch piston.

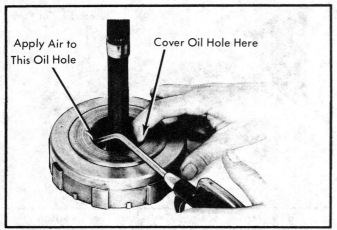

Apply Air to This Oil Hole

Cover Oil Hole Here

Fig. 11 Removing Front Clutch Piston from Drum Using Compressed Air

Inspection — Clean all parts (except discs) with clean solvent and dry with compressed air. Inspect clutch disc, discs should be flat, not burned, cracked or deformed. Minimum thickness of discs is .08" (2.1 mm). Inspect all other parts for wear or damage. Check clutch piston to ensure that check ball is not stuck. Replace any part found defective.

Reassembly — **1)** Coat all friction surfaces with automatic transmission fluid (Type F). Install new "O" rings on clutch piston. Install piston into clutch drum, then install return spring(s) and retainer.

2) Using a suitable compressor tool, compress return spring(s) and install retaining snap ring. Remove compressor tool. Apply compressed air to one oil hole while covering the other, and

check operation of piston. When air is applied, a "plop" should be heard as piston is applied.

3) Install clutch discs into clutch drum starting with a steel disc and alternating lined and steel discs until the same number of discs have been installed as were removed.

4) Install bearing and races onto top of return spring retainer, then install front clutch hub and ensure that hub meshes with clutch discs. Invert clutch assembly and install input (rear) clutch hub and retain with snap ring. Install bearing and race on input shaft.

REAR CLUTCH ASSEMBLY

NOTE — *The rear clutch assembly used in the Borg-Warner model 55 transmission is slightly different from the one used in the Aisin-Warner model 55 transmission. The main difference between the two clutch assemblies is that the Borg-Warner model uses 18 small return springs while the Aisin-Warner model uses one big return spring.*

Disassembly — **1)** Remove clutch disc pack retaining snap ring, then lift out clutch discs, noting number of discs installed and their arrangement for reassembly reference.

2) Using a suitable compressor tool, compress return spring(s) and remove retaining snap ring. Remove compressor tool. Lift retainer and clutch return spring(s) from drum. Apply compressed air to one oil hole in clutch drum while covering the other oil hole, and force piston from drum. Remove "O" rings from piston.

Inspection — Clean all parts (except discs) in clean solvent and dry with compressed air. Inspect clutch discs for signs of burning and wear. Check thickness of clutch discs. Minimum thickness is .08" (2.1 mm). Inspect all other parts for wear or other damage. Shake piston to ensure that check ball is not stuck. Replace any part found defective.

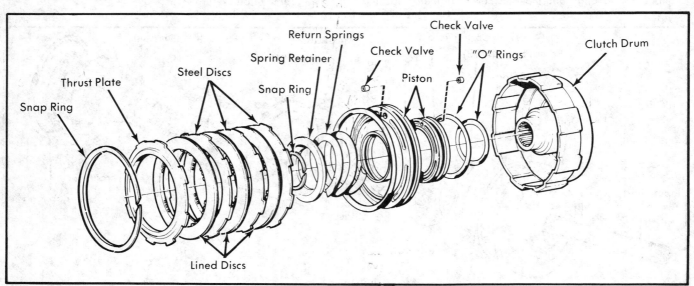

Snap Ring
Thrust Plate
Steel Discs
Spring Retainer
Return Springs
Snap Ring
Check Valve
Check Valve
Piston
"O" Rings
Clutch Drum
Lined Discs

Fig. 12 Exploded View of Rear Clutch Assembly (Aisin-Warner Model Shown — Borg-Warner Model Similar)

BORG-WARNER & AISIN-WARNER MODEL 55 (Cont.)

Fig. 13   Using Compressed Air to Remove Rear Clutch Piston from Drum

Reassembly — 1) Lubricate all friction surfaces with automatic transmission fluid (type F) before reassembly. Lubricate and install new "O" rings on clutch piston, then install piston into drum. Install return spring(s) on piston, then install retainer over spring(s). Compress return spring(s) and install retaining snap ring.

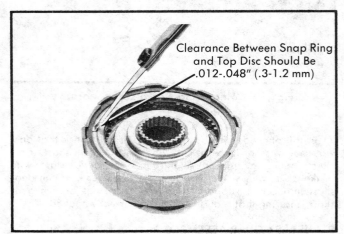

Fig. 14   Measuring Rear Clutch Clearance

2) Check operation of piston by applying compressed air to one oil hole while blocking the other. When air is applied, a "plop" should be heard as piston is activated.

3) Install clutch discs into clutch drum starting with a thin steel thrust disc (bevelled side facing out) and alternating lined and steel clutch discs until the same number of discs are installed as were removed. Install clutch pack retaining snap ring.

4) Using a feeler gauge, measure clearance between retaining snap ring and top clutch disc. Clearance should be .012-.048" (.3-1.2 mm).

CENTER SUPPORT ASSEMBLY

Disassembly — 1) Remove snap ring from sun gear shaft, then pull center support from shaft. Remove snap ring, then lift No. 1 brake discs from center support. Invert center support, remove retaining snap ring, then lift No. 2 brake discs from center support.

2) Using a suitable compressor tool, compress No. 2 brake return spring retainer and remove snap ring. Remove tool and lift return springs and retainer from center support. Repeat procedure on No. 1 brake, then remove return springs and retainer.

3) Use compressed air and force No. 2 brake piston and No. 1 brake piston from center support. Slide one-way clutch hub from sun gear shaft. Remove the 3 oil seal rings from center support hub. Remove the 2 oil seal rings from sun gear shaft. Remove "O" rings from brake pistons.

Inspection — Clean all parts (except discs) in clean solvent and dry with compressed air. Inspect all parts for wear or other damage and replace as necessary. Check thickness of all brake discs. Replace discs if thickness is less than .08" (2.1 mm).

Reassembly — 1 Lubricate all moving parts with automatic transmission fluid (type F). Install new oil seals and "O" rings on center support hub, sun gear shaft and clutch piston.

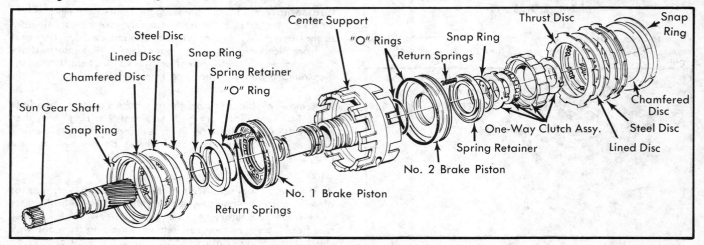

Fig. 15   Exploded View of Center Support Assembly

BORG-WARNER & AISIN-WARNER MODEL 55 (Cont.)

2) Lubricate "O" rings, then install No. 2 brake piston into center support using care not to damage "O" rings. Install 12 return springs into position on piston, then place retainer on return springs. Compress return springs and install snap ring. Repeat procedure for No. 1 brake piston and return springs.

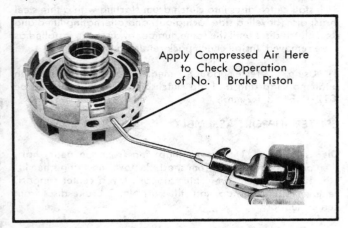

Fig. 16   Using Compressed Air to Check Operation of No. 1 Brake Piston

3) Use compressed air and check operation of both the No. 2 brake piston and No. 1 brake piston. When air is applied to their respective oil holes, a distinct clicking should be heard.

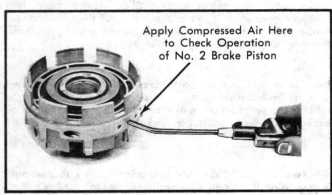

Fig. 17   Using Compressed Air to Check Operation of No. 2 Brake Piston.

4) Install No. 1 brake disc into center support in the following order: First install steel brake disc, then lined brake disc, and

Fig. 18   View Showing Correct Installation of Brake Discs Retaining Snap Ring

finally the chamfered disc (with chamfered side up). Install No. 1 brake pack retaining snap ring into center support so that snap ring opening is between openings on center support.

5) Install No. 2 brake discs into center support in the following order: First the thrust disc, then alternately install lined and steel brake discs until all discs are installed, and finally install chamfered disc (with chamfered side up). Install No. 2 brake pack retaining snap ring so that snap ring opening is between openings on center support.

6) Using a feeler gauge, measure clearance between No. 2 brake disc retaining snap ring and top brake disc. Clearance should be .012-.048" (.3-1.2 mm). Repeat measurement on No. 1 brake assembly. Clearance should be the same as No. 2 brake clearance.

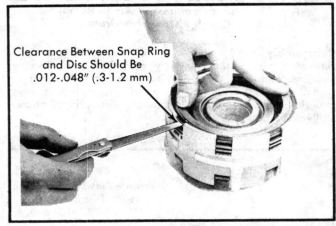

Fig. 19   Measuring Brake Disc Clearance (No. 2 Brake Shown)

7) Install one-way clutch on sun gear shaft. Check that one-way clutch is not loose or stiff when installed on shaft, if so, clutch should be replaced. Align splines of one-way clutch with brake discs splines, then install one-way clutch and sun gear shaft into center support. Install oil seal rings on sun gear shaft, ensuring that seal ring ends are correctly hooked.

PLANETARY GEAR ASSEMBLY

Disassembly — 1) Separate front planetary gear set and No. 3 brake discs from output shaft assembly. Invert shaft assembly so that assembly is resting on shaft. Compress snap ring and lift front planetary ring gear from assembly. Pull intermediate shaft and rear planetary gear set from output shaft housing, then remove bearing and race from housing.

2) Remove plastic and steel thrust washers from intermediate shaft. Pull rear planetary gear set from rear ring gear, then remove bearing and race. Remove snap ring and slide rear ring gear from intermediate shaft, then slide rear bearing race from shaft.

3) Remove oil seal rings from output shaft. Remove steel thrust plate from front planetary gear set, then lift No. 3 brake discs from around planetary gear set. Remove one-way clutch inner hub from planetary gear set. Remove snap ring from one-way clutch and remove both bearing cages, one-way clutch and plastic ring from gear set.

BORG-WARNER & AISIN-WARNER MODEL 55 (Cont.)

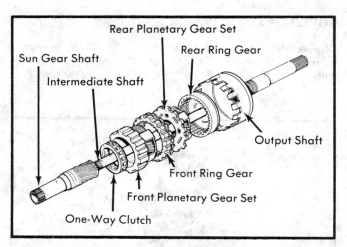

Fig. 20   Exploded View of Planetary Gear Set

Labels: Sun Gear Shaft, Intermediate Shaft, Rear Planetary Gear Set, Rear Ring Gear, Output Shaft, Front Ring Gear, Front Planetary Gear Set, One-Way Clutch

Snap Ring Ends Must Sit in Recess Indicated by Arrow

Fig. 21   Installation of Front Ring Gear Retaining Snap Ring

Inspection — Clean all parts (except discs) with clean solvent and dry with compressed air. Inspect all parts for wear, cracks, or other damage and replace as necessary. Check thickness of each brake disc. Replace discs if thickness is less than .08" (2.1 mm).

Reassembly — **1)** Lubricate all moving parts with automatic transmission fluid (type F). Install plastic ring and lower bearing cage into front planetary gear set, then install one-way clutch (with arrow on side of clutch pointing down) into gear set. Install one-way clutch upper bearing cage on top of clutch and retain with snap ring.

2) Install one-way clutch and front planetary gear set into front ring gear. With one-way clutch installed in front ring gear, it should be possible to rotate front planetary gear set in a counterclockwise direction only. Also, clutch must rotate freely and must not stick. Assemble No. 3 brake discs to front planetary gear set.

3) Install new oil seal rings on output shaft and ensure that ring ends are properly hooked. Position rear race on intermediate shaft, then slide rear ring gear onto shaft and secure with snap ring. Position bearing and front race into rear ring gear, then install rear planetary gear set into ring gear.

4) Position thrust bearing and race in housing on output shaft, then assemble intermediate shaft to output shaft. Install front ring gear into output shaft housing and secure in housing with snap ring.

NOTE — *Front ring gear retaining snap ring must be installed in housing with ring ends in recess of housing as shown in Fig. 21.*

5) Place plastic thrust washer into front ring gear so that it rests on top of rear planetary gear set. Place steel thrust washer on front planetary gear set and retain with vaseline. Assemble front gear set to output shaft housing.

NO. 3 BRAKE PISTON

Removal — **1)** To remove No. 3 brake piston from transmission case, attach compressor tool (5073) to transmission case as shown in *Fig. 22*. Tighten tool bolts alternately until snap ring on piston return spring retainer is free of tension, then use a screwdriver and pry off snap ring. Remove compressor tool.

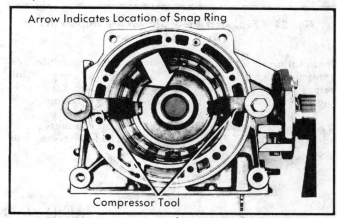

Arrow Indicates Location of Snap Ring

Compressor Tool

Fig. 22   Positioning of No. 3 Brake Piston Compressor Tool

2) Lift return spring retainer and 16 return springs from transmission case. Apply compressed air to hole shown in *Fig. 23* and force piston from its seat in case, then lift piston out of case.

Apply Compressed Air to Hole Indicated to Force Piston from Case

Fig. 23   No. 3 Brake Piston Removal

Automatic Transmissions

BORG-WARNER & AISIN-WARNER MODEL 55 (Cont.)

Disassembly & Reassembly — Pull front and rear No. 3 clutch pistons from piston sleeve, then remove "O" rings from pistons. Clean and inspect all parts and replace as necessary. Install new "O" rings on pistons, then assemble front and rear pistons to piston sleeve after coating all parts with automatic transmission fluid.

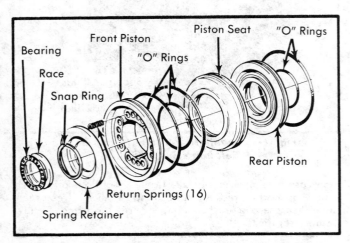

Fig. 24   Exploded View Showing Components of No. 3 Brake Piston.

Installation — 1) Carefully install piston assembly into transmission case using care not to damage "O" rings. Install return springs onto piston and use vaseline to hold springs in place on pistons. Install spring retainer on top of springs.

2) Using compressor tool used at removal, compress piston springs and install retaining snap ring. Remove compressor tool.

GOVERNOR ASSEMBLY

Disassembly — Remove retaining clip from governor assembly. Remove "E" clip from end of governor shaft, then withdraw shaft along with governor valve, spring and weight.

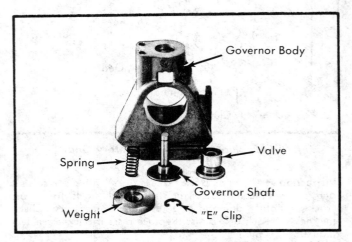

Fig. 25   Disassembled View of Governor Assembly

Inspection — Clean all parts with solvent and dry with compressed air. Inspect all parts for wear or damage.

Reassembly — Lubricate all parts with automatic transmission fluid (Type F). Install spring and valve on shaft, then install shaft into governor body. Place weight on shaft, then install "E" clip to retain parts. Install retaining clip on governor housing.

AISIN-WARNER MODEL 55

VALVE BODY SPRING IDENTIFICATION				
Valve Spring	Length In. (mm)	Diameter In. (mm)	Number Of Coils	Wire Thickness In. (mm)
Secondary Throttle Valve	1.693 (43.0)	.429 (10.9)	15.5	.047 (1.2)
Primary Throttle Valve	.756 (19.2)	.339 (8.6)	8	.028 (.7)
Detent Regulator Valve	1.197 (30.4)	.350 (8.9)	13	.035 (.9)
Inter. Coast Mod. Valve	1.394 (35.4)	.346 (8.8)	14	.035 (.9)
Reverse Clutch Sequence Valve	1.449 (36.8)	.358 (9.1)	15	.043 (1.1)
Governor Modulator Valve	1.421 (36.1)	.358 (9.1)	17	.028 (.7)
Low Coast Modulator Valve	1.669 (42.4)	.362 (9.2)	15	.031 (.8)
Inter. Coast Shift Valve	1.382 (35.1)	.350 (8.9)	12.5	.031 (.8)
Secondary Regulator Valve	2.945 (74.8)	.661 (16.8)	15	.063 (1.6)
Primary Regulator Valve	3.209 (81.5)	.697 (17.7)	15	.063 (1.6)
Cooler Bypass Valve	1.209 (30.7)	.543 (13.8)	7	.051 (1.3)
Pressure Relief Valve	1.264 (32.1)	.516 (13.1)	11	.079 (2.0)
Low Coast Shift Valve	1.362 (34.6)	.295 (7.5)	13	.024 (.6)
Reverse Gear Pilot Valve	1.480 (37.6)	.362 (9.2)	14.5	.047 (1.2)

BORG-WARNER & AISIN-WARNER MODEL 55 (Cont.)

BORG-WARNER MODEL 55

VALVE BODY SPRING IDENTIFICATION				
Valve Spring	Length In. (mm)	Diameter In. (mm)	Number Of Coils	Wire Thickness In. (mm)
Secondary Throttle Valve	.787 (20.0)	.343 (8.7)	7	.032 (.8)
Primary Throttle Valve	1.693 (43.0)	.431 (10.95)	14	.055 (1.4)
Detent Regulator Valve	1.429 (36.3)	.358 (9.1)	12	.030 (.76)
Inter. Coast Mod. Valve	1.413 (35.9)	.390 (9.9)	13.5	.035 (.9)
Reverse Clutch Sequence Valve	1.654 (42.0)	.354 (9.0)	15.5	.055 (1.4)
Governor Modulator Valve	1.421 (36.1)	.356 (9.1)	12	.026 (.7)
Low Coast Modulator Valve	1.413 (35.9)	.390 (9.9)	13.5	.035 (.9)
Inter. Coast Shift Valve	1.425 (36.2)	.402 (10.2)	11	.035 (.9)
Secondary Regulator Valve	1.949 (49.5)	.650 (16.5)	11	.083 (2.1)
Cutback Valve	.709 (18.0)	.142 (3.9)	19	.014 (.36)
Primary Regulator Valve	2.720 (69.1)	.669 (17.0)	13.5	.071 (1.8)
Cooler Bypass Valve	1.169 (29.7)	.543 (13.8)	7	.059 (1.5)
Pressure Relief Valve	1.264 (32.1)	.516 (13.1)	9	.079 (2.0)
Low Coast Shift Valve	1.165 (29.6)	.213 (5.4)	13	.024 (.6)

VALVE BODY ASSEMBLY

NOTE — *The valve body assemblies used on Borg-Warner transmissions and Aisin-Warner transmission are slightly different. These differences will be called out in the following procedures.*

Disassembly — **1)** Remove attaching bolt and lift off detent spring assembly, then pull manual valve out of valve body bore. Remove front and rear upper valve body attaching bolts from top of lower valve body, then invert valve body assemblies and remove retaining bolts from bottom of lower valve body. Carefully lift lower body off both upper bodies, then place lower body aside with gasket up.

2) To disassemble front upper valve body, place valve body on a work bench with cored face up. Remove check ball and throttle valve retaining plate. Using a screwdriver, push out cutback valve retainer, then remove cutback valve and spring.

NOTE — *The Aisin-Warner valve body is not equipped with a cutback valve spring.*

3) Remove attaching bolt, then remove throttle cam, spring and spacer sleeve from front upper valve body. Pull out throttle valve, kickdown valve, spring and spacers, and note the number of spacers removed with throttle valve, as an equal amount of spacers must be reinstalled for proper throttle valve adjustment. Remove secondary regulator valve cover plate, then remove regulator valve.

CAUTION — *Use care when removing secondary regulator valve cover plate as plate is under spring tension.*

4) To disassemble rear upper valve body, place body on a work bench with cored face up. On Borg-Warner transmissions, remove 2 check balls from valve body passages. On Aisin-Warner transmissions, remove 3 check balls. On both models, push in intermediate coast shift valve and remove retainer, then slide coast valve and spring for 2-3 shift valve out of valve body. Remove 2-3 shift valve retainer, then remove shift valve.

5) Using a small screwdriver, push out detent regulator valve retainer, then remove valve and spring. Remove remaining cover plate from rear upper valve body, then remove the following valves and springs from valve body bores: Low coast modulator valve, governor modulator valve, reverse clutch sequence valve, and intermediate coast modulator valve.

6) To disassemble lower valve body, lift off spacer plate and gaskets, then remove cooler bypass valve and spring. On Borg-Warner transmissions, remove 4 check balls from valve body passages. On Aisin-Warner transmissions, remove 2 check balls from valve body passages.

7) On all transmissions, push in 1-2 shift valve retainer and allow retainer to drop out of valve body, then remove 1-2 shift valve. Remove cover plate, then slide low coast shift valve and reverse gear pilot valve and spring from valve body.

NOTE — *The Borg-Warner transmission valve body is not equipped with a reverse gear pilot valve.*

8) Remove pressure relief ball retainer, then lift out relief ball and spring. Remove primary regulator valve train retainer, then slide valve train and spring out of valve body.

Automatic Transmissions

BORG-WARNER & AISIN-WARNER MODEL 55 (Cont.)

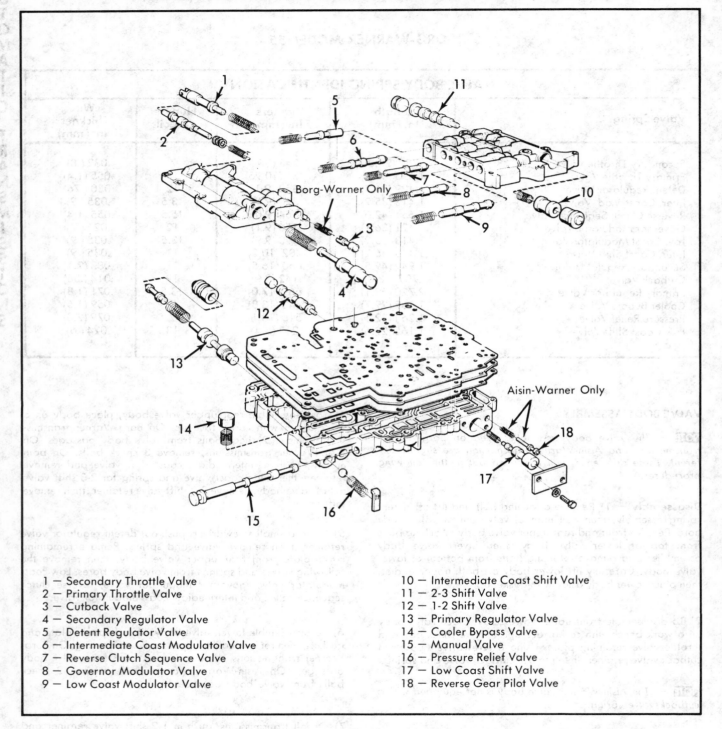

Fig. 26 Exploded View of Valve Body Assemblies Showing Component Installation

1 — Secondary Throttle Valve
2 — Primary Throttle Valve
3 — Cutback Valve
4 — Secondary Regulator Valve
5 — Detent Regulator Valve
6 — Intermediate Coast Modulator Valve
7 — Reverse Clutch Sequence Valve
8 — Governor Modulator Valve
9 — Low Coast Modulator Valve

10 — Intermediate Coast Shift Valve
11 — 2-3 Shift Valve
12 — 1-2 Shift Valve
13 — Primary Regulator Valve
14 — Cooler Bypass Valve
15 — Manual Valve
16 — Pressure Relief Valve
17 — Low Coast Shift Valve
18 — Reverse Gear Pilot Valve

Inspection — 1) Thoroughly clean all parts in clean solvent, then use compressed air to dry parts and to blow out all channels and passages in valve bodies.

2) Check spacer plate to ensure all holes are open. Check all valves and valve bores for wear and damage. With valves cleaned and lubricated with automatic transmission fluid, they must slide freely in their bores.

Reassembly — 1) Reverse disassembly procedures and note the following: Lubricate all valves and valve bores with automatic transmission fluid (Type F) before reassembly. Ensure that all check balls are installed in the correct valve body passages. *(See Fig. 27).*

2) When installing throttle valve in front upper valve body, install the same number of spacers that were removed to ensure that throttle valve is correctly adjusted.

BORG-WARNER & AISIN-WARNER MODEL 55 (Cont.)

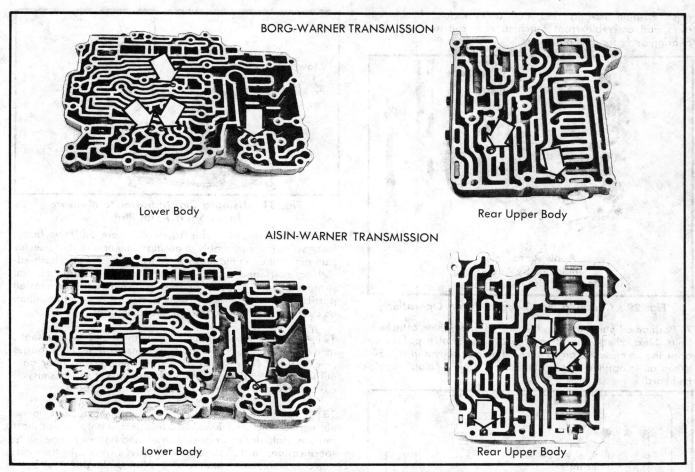

BORG-WARNER TRANSMISSION

Lower Body

Rear Upper Body

AISIN-WARNER TRANSMISSION

Lower Body

Rear Upper Body

Fig. 27   View of Valve Bodies Showing Check Ball Installation

TRANSMISSION REASSEMBLY

1) Install new "O" rings on oil cooler line nipples, then install nipples in transmission case ensuring that they point in same direction as when removed. Install new "O" rings on line pressure and governor pressure plugs, then install plugs in case.

2) Install governor oil ducts cover on transmission case using a new gasket. Install throttle cable in case. Install parking pawl, spring and shaft to case, then install detent lever and shaft. Drive detent lever retaining pin through lever and into shaft. Fit parking pawl rod to pawl and detent lever, then install parking pawl cam plate.

3) Invert transmission case so that case opening is up. Install rearmost bearing and race. Install No. 3 brake apply tube into case so that lower lugs on tube are on the inside of No. 3 brake piston and parking pawl pin is in the middle of drum recess.

4) Install planetary gear and No. 3 brake disc assembly into transmission case so that recess in reaction plate is facing oil pan. Install planetary assembly retaining snap ring in groove of case, and ensure that snap ring ends are between splines as shown in *Fig. 28*. Check operation of No. 3 brake piston by applying compressed air to oil holes shown in *Fig. 29*. When air is applied an audible "plop" should be heard.

Snap Ring Ends
Must be Between
Disc Splines

Fig. 28   Interior View of Transmission Case Showing Planetary Assembly Snap Ring Installation

5) Hold sun gear shaft and lower center support assembly into transmission case until it mates with planetary gear assembly. Install center support bolts by hand into case to avoid any damage to threads, then tighten bolts in four stages until specified torque is obtained.

6) Ensure discs on center support are aligned, then install rear clutch assembly into transmission case. If rear clutch is properly assembled, clutch splines and sun gear shaft splines should

BORG-WARNER & AISIN-WARNER MODEL 55 (Cont.)

mesh. Position bearings and races on rear clutch hub. Align discs and assemble front clutch to rear clutch, then install bearing and race on input shaft.

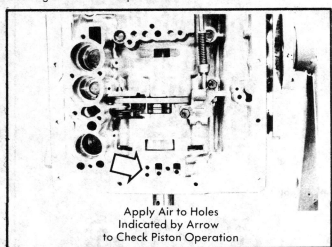

Fig. 29 Checking No. 3 Brake Piston Operation

Apply Air to Holes
Indicated by Arrow
to Check Piston Operation

7) Position oil pump in case, then install and tighten attaching bolts. Next, check operation of brake and clutch pistons by applying compressed air to each oil hole as shown in *Fig. 30*. When air is applied to each oil hole, a distinct "plop" should be heard.

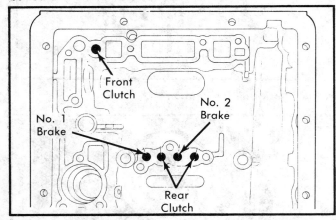

Fig. 30 Checking Clutch and Brake Piston Operation

8) Mount a dial indicator on transmission so that indicator tip is in contact with end of input shaft. Zero dial indicator. Move input shaft up and down and note maximum dial indicator reading. This reading is input shaft axial play. Input shaft axial play should be .009-.020" (.22-.53 mm). Also, rotate input shaft and ensure that it does not jam.

9) Attach torque converter housing to transmission case. Install converter housing-to-transmission case attaching bolts and tighten them to specified torque.

10) Rotate transmission on holding fixture until oil pan mounting face is up. Install accumulator piston springs into case bore. **NOTE** — *The short accumulator piston spring is installed in center bore and the two longer springs in the outer bores.* Install new "O" rings on accumulator pistons, then install pistons into bores. **NOTE** — *Install the small piston in center bore. The two large pistons are different sizes and cannot be incorrectly installed.*

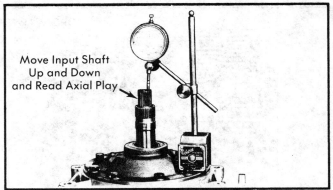

Move Input Shaft
Up and Down
and Read Axial Play

Fig. 31 Using a Dial Indicator to Measure Input Shaft Axial Play

11) Connect throttle cable to throttle cam on valve body. Place valve body assembly in position and ensure that selector cam pin is fitted in manual valve recess. Install valve body attaching bolts and tighten them to specified torque. Install strainer on valve body and tighten attaching bolts, then install particle magnet and oil pan gasket. Place oil pan into position on case, then install and tighten attaching bolts.

12) Align governor retaining clip with hole in output shaft, then slide governor onto shaft and ensure that clip engages hole in shaft. Slide spacer ring and speedometer gear onto output shaft. Position extension housing gasket on transmission case, then install housing and tighten attaching bolts.

13) Install drive flange on rear of output shaft. Coat flange nut with Loctite (or equivalent), then install onto output shaft threads. Hold drive flange stationary and tighten flange nut to specifications. Install speedometer driven gear into transmission case bore, then install retainer plate and tighten bolt.

14) Position torque converter on input shaft, then turn converter slowly and slide it onto input shaft splines and oil pump drive. Place a straightedge across converter housing, then measure distance from top surface of straightedge to converter face ring. Distance should be .64-.77" (16.2-19.6 mm). Transmission assembly is now complete.

TIGHTENING SPECIFICATIONS

Application	Ft. Lbs. (mkg)
Converter Hsg.-to-Engine	30-37 (4.1-5.1)
Converter Hsg.-to-Transmission Case	
M10 Bolts	19-29 (2.6-4.0)
M12 Bolts	35-43 (4.8-5.9)
Converter-to-Drive Plate	
Gas Engines	30-37 (4.1-5.1)
Diesel Engine	13-20 (1.7-2.8)
Oil Pump Cover-to-Housing	4-7 (.6-1.0)
Oil Pump-to-Trans. Case	16-21 (2.2-2.9)
Center Support Bolts	
Stage 1	5 (.7)
Stage 2	10 (1.4)
Stage 3	15 (2.1)
Final Stage	18-21 (2.5-2.9)
Governor Oil Ducts Cover	4-7 (.6-1.0)
Extension Hsg.-to-Case	19-29 (2.6-4.0)
Drive Flange Nut	30-37 (4.1-5.1)
Valve Body-to-Case	6-9 (.8-1.2)
Lower-to-Upper Valve Bodies	4-7 (.6-1.0)

BORG-WARNER MODEL 65

Jaguar
XJ6
Triumph
TR7
TR8

DESCRIPTION

Transmission is a fully automatic three speed unit consisting basically of a three element torque converter and a compound planetary gear set. Two multiple-disc clutches, one roller clutch, and two brake bands provide the friction elements required to obtain the desired function of the planetary gear set. A hydraulic control system, pressurized by a gear-type oil pump, provides the working pressure required to operate the automatic controls. Transmission kickdown is actuated by cable, attached to accelerator assembly and a cam internal in case.

LUBRICATION & ADJUSTMENT

See AUTOMATIC TRANSMISSION SERVICING Section.

TROUBLE SHOOTING

ROUGH INITIAL ENGAGEMENT

Engine idle speed too high. Throttle cable out of adjustment. Valve body assembly faulty, valves sticking or worn.

NO ENGAGEMENT

In Any Position — Incorrect fluid level. Manual linkage out of adjustment. Throttle cable out of adjustment. Input shaft broken. Primary regulator valve sticking. Front pump worn.

In Forward Gears — Governor valve stuck or damaged. Output shaft seal rings or governor pressure tube seals worn or faulty. Also check front clutch, stator support shaft bearing, and front seal rings on sun gear shaft.

In First Gear in "D" — One-way clutch faulty or installed backwards.

In Second Gear — Front band faulty or out of adjustment. Front servo piston or seals worn or damaged. Oil pipes loose, damaged, or missing. Foreign matter or damage in valve body.

In Third Gear — Foreign matter in valve body or governor. Check rear clutch feed pipes, rear clutch, and piston rings in hub of intermediate shaft.

No Overrun Braking in "1" — Rear band out of adjustment or worn. Rear servo seals or feed pipes damaged or missing.

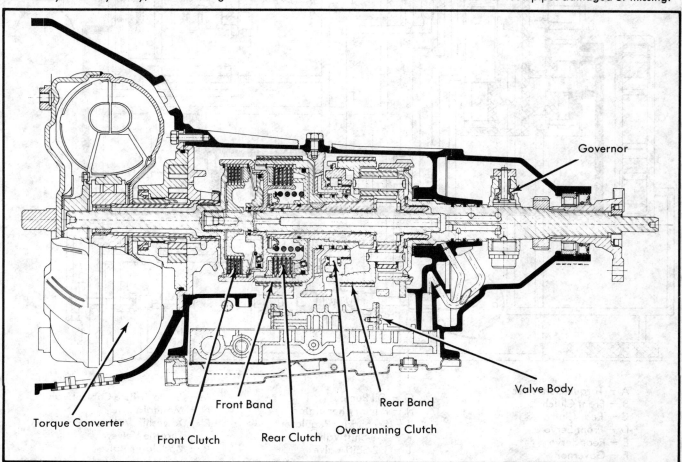

Fig. 1   Cross-Sectional View of Borg-Warner Model 65 Automatic Transmission

Automatic Transmissions

BORG-WARNER MODEL 65 (Cont.)

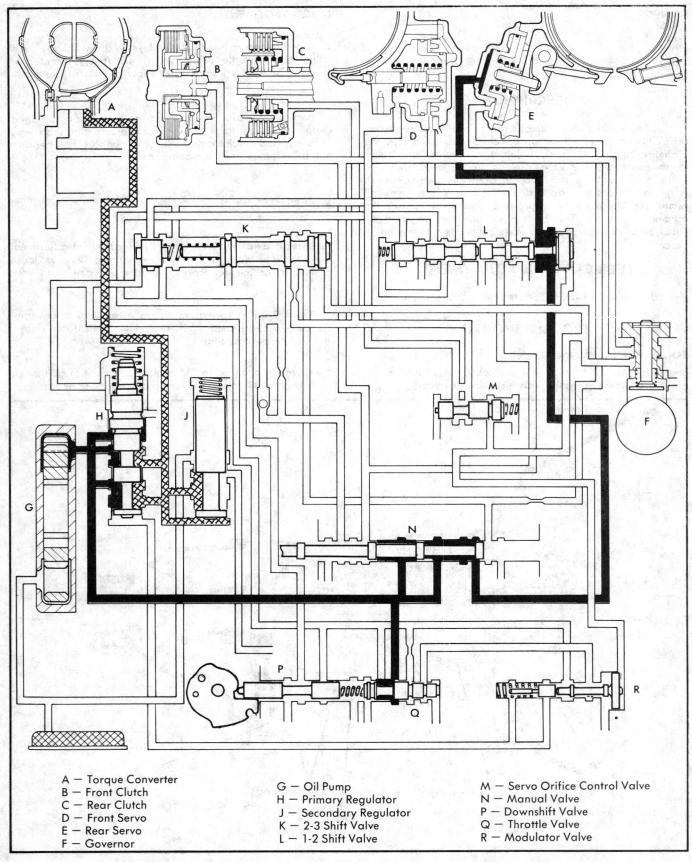

A — Torque Converter
B — Front Clutch
C — Rear Clutch
D — Front Servo
E — Rear Servo
F — Governor

G — Oil Pump
H — Primary Regulator
J — Secondary Regulator
K — 2-3 Shift Valve
L — 1-2 Shift Valve

M — Servo Orifice Control Valve
N — Manual Valve
P — Downshift Valve
Q — Throttle Valve
R — Modulator Valve

Fig. 2   Borg-Warner Model 65 Automatic Transmission Hydraulic Circuits Diagram

BORG-WARNER MODEL 65 (Cont.)

SLIPPING OR LATE SHIFTS

Throttle cable out of adjustment. Main pressure not within specifications (check oil pump and seals on pump tubes). Governor faulty. Valve body faulty. Check output shaft oil seal rings and governor tubes for wear or damage. Check front and rear bands and servos for wear or damage.

TRANSMISSION NOISE

Whine In and Out of Second Gear — Front band out of adjustment. Front servo parts worn or damaged. Oil pipes loose. Front band worn or damaged. Valve body faulty.

Whine In and Out of Third Gear — Rear clutch, feed pipe, or seals worn or damaged. Valve body faulty.

Whining Noise With Engine Running — Oil pump gears worn or damaged. Bushing worn in torque converter.

Irregular Noise (All Except Third Gear) — Planetary gear set defective.

TESTING

ROAD TEST

Drive vehicle on the road, allowing transmission to shift through all ranges. Note transmission performance under varying load conditions: light throttle, full throttle, and kickdown. Transmission should operate smoothly but firmly, with no apparent slipping or engine speed flare-up. Compare transmission shift points with figures given in Shift Speeds chart.

NOTE — *Shift speeds may vary slightly due to production tolerances, rear axle ratio, or tire size.*

Triumph Shift Speed Specifications		
Shift Condition	**TR7 (MPH)**	**TR8 (MPH)**
Part Throttle		
1-2 Upshift	8-12	9-13
2-3 Upshift	12-16	13-17
Full Throttle		
1-2 Upshift	38-44	37-46
2-3 Upshift	65-71	67-76
Full Throttle Kickdown		
3-2 Downshift	58-66	56-70
3-1 Downshift	30-38	24-39
Part Throttle Kickdown		
3-2 Downshift	30-40	44 Max.

OIL PRESSURE TEST

NOTE — *Before making pressure test, be certain that fluid level and condition, and control linkage adjustments have been checked and corrected as necessary. Connect a tachometer to engine and a pressure gauge to main pressure take-off point on rear of transmission. See Fig. 3.*

1) Apply service and parking brake, place transmission selector lever in "D" position, and with engine at idle (750 RPM), check main pressure. Main pressure should be 60-75 psi (4.2-5.3 kg/cm²) for XJ6 and TR7 or 50-65 psi (3.5-4.6 kg/cm²) for TR8.

2) Next, increase engine speed to 1000 RPM for TR7 and TR8 or 1200 RPM for XJ6. Again check pressure gauge. Pressure should be 75-95 psi (5.3-6.7 kg/cm²) for TR7, 70-91 psi (4.9-6.4 kg/cm) for TR8, or 85-95 psi (5.9-6.7 kg/cm²) for XJ6.

Jaguar Shift Speed Specifications	
Shift Condition	**XJ6 (MPH)**
Part Throttle	
1-2 Upshift	8-12
2-3 Upshift	13-18
Full Throttle	
1-2 Upshift	41-51
2-3 Upshift	73-81
Full Throttle Kickdown	
3-2 Downshift	63-73
3-1 Downshift	25-35
Part Throttle Kickdown	
3-2 Downshift	32-42
Closed Throttle Kickdown	
2-1 Downshift	5-10

CLUTCH AND BAND APPLICATION CHART
(ELEMENTS IN USE)

Selector Lever Position	Front Clutch	Rear Clutch	Front Band	Rear Band	One-Way Clutch
D — DRIVE					
First Gear	X				X
Second Gear	X		X		
Third Gear	X	X			
2 — INTERMEDIATE Second Gear	X		X		
1 — LOW	X			X	
R — REVERSE		X		X	
NEUTRAL OR PARK — All clutches and bands released and/or ineffective.				X	

BORG-WARNER MODEL 65 (Cont.)

3) If pressures are not within specified limits, first check adjustment of transmission throttle cable. See *AUTOMATIC TRANSMISSION SERVICING* Section.

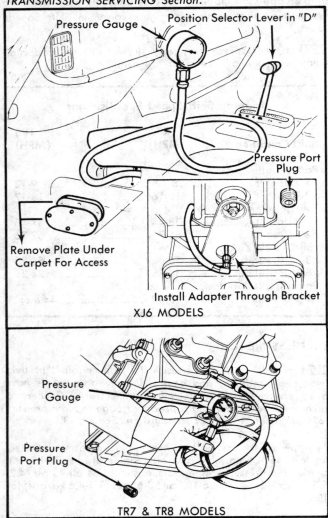

Fig. 3 Hydraulic Pressure Test Hook-Up

STALL TEST

1) With engine and transmission at normal operating temperature, tachometer installed, and parking and service brakes applied, place transmission selector lever in "D" for XJ6 or in "1" or "R" for TR7 and TR8. Press accelerator pedal to the floor and read maximum engine speed obtained.

CAUTION — *To prevent damage to transmission by overheating, DO NOT stall test for more than 10 seconds at a time.*

2) Stall speed should be 2200 RPM for TR7, 1800-2000 RPM for TR8, or 1950-2100 RPM for XJ6. If stall speed is considerably less than specified, check for insufficient engine output or one-way clutch slippage in torque converter. If stall speed is higher than specified, clutch or band slippage is indicated.

TRANSMISSION REMOVAL & INSTALLATION

NOTE — *On XJ6 models, engine and transmission are removed together.*

Removal (XJ6) — **1)** Remove hood and disconnect battery. Discharge air conditioning system. Disconnect and cap refrigerant lines. Remove fuel lines from cooler and plug fuel inlet line. Remove fuel cooler mounting screws and secure cooler, receiver-drier, refrigerant lines and fuel lines away from engine.

2) Remove fender brace rods. Remove air cleaner, then remove radiator. Disconnect coolant hoses to expansion tank. Remove both engine mount-to-bracket nuts. Drain power steering fluid. Disconnect power steering lines then slacken pump mounting bolts and move pump as close to engine as possible.

3) Pull connectors from alternator. Separate connector plug from engine harness. Disconnect brake vacuum pipe at manifold and secure out of way. Release pipe clip and pull heater-A/C operating vacuum pipe from non-return valves; secure away from engine. Remove exhaust manifolds.

4) Remove starter cable and solenoid cable. Disconnect heater hoses at firewall connectors. From fuel injection system, disconnect the following: Thermotime switch, cold start injector, throttle switch, oxygen sensor, auxiliary air valve, water temperature sensor and throttle linkage. Disconnect hoses from charcoal canister.

5) Position suitable lifting device and attach to rear lifting eye on engine. Remove nut at center of rear transmission mounting. Unscrew nuts securing bracket on transmission. Remove heat shield. Position jack to support mounting plate of transmission and unscrew mounting bolts. Lower jack and remove mounting plate along with spring washers and rubber rings.

6) Remove special nuts securing propeller shaft to output flange. From transmission unit selector lever, remove nut to release ball peg on inner selector cable. Remove set screw and spring washer securing outer selector cable clamp. Disconnect speedometer cable from transmission.

7) From front of vehicle, position jack to support transmission assembly below oil sump. Support engine on lifting assembly. Lift front of engine while lowering rear and withdraw engine/transmission assembly forward and upward.

CAUTION — *Use extreme care when withdrawing engine to prevent damage to air conditioning expansion valve.*

8) To separate transmission from engine, disconnect throttle from retaining bracket and throttle linkage. Remove dipstick tube and cover on front of converter housing. Disconnect oil cooler lines from transmission case and plug lines.

9) Remove all converter housing-to-engine bolts, position starter out of way, and separate transmission from engine. Remove 4 bolts retaining torque converter on drive plate and remove converter.

NOTE — *Converter bolts are accessible through starter hole in engine block.*

Installation — Install transmission to engine, fit insulating material across transmission and reverse removal procedure to complete installation.

Removal (TR7 & TR8) — **1)** Disconnect downshift cable from throttle linkage. Raise vehicle on suitable lifting device. Remove front exhaust pipe. Disconnect dipstick tube from transmission

BORG-WARNER MODEL 65 (Cont.)

sump, selector lever from shaft and breather hose from transmission.

2) Disconnect starter inhibitor/reverse light wiring at switch. Disconnect cooler lines, speedometer cable and driveshaft. Remove torque converter bolts. Place adjustable jack under transmission, remove center bolt and plate from rear crossmember, remove 4 bolts from crossmember-to-frame and remove crossmember.

3) Detach cooler lines from retaining clips, remove upper radiator mounts, loosen 4 bolts securing lower radiator and push radiator forward. Remove exhaust support bracket. Lower transmission with adjustable jack and remove all the bolts and nuts securing bell housing and starter to engine. Lower and remove transmission from vehicle.

Installation — Reverse removal procedure and note the following: Make sure transmission input splines and converter splines are correctly aligned when installing transmission. After engine and transmission assembly has been installed in vehicle, fill transmissn with fluid and adjust manual linkage and throttle cable.

TORQUE CONVERTER

NOTE — *Torque converter is a sealed unit and cannot be disassembled for service. If defective, converter must be replaced. In addition, do not attempt to clean converter, either internally or externally with flammable fluids.*

TRANSMISSION DISASSEMBLY

1) Remove bolts, nuts and washers retaining converter housing to transmission and remove housing. If not previously done, remove dipstick and breather from case, and drain transmission fluid. Place transmission on bench with oil pan facing upward and place selector lever in park position. Remove retaining bolts and withdraw speedometer driven gear assembly from extension housing, then remove and discard sealing "O" ring.

2) Remove bolt or nut securing flange to output shaft and withdraw flange using a puller if necessary. Remove bolts and nuts securing extension housing to case, then withdraw housing and discard gasket. If necessary, remove and discard oil seal from extension housing. Slide speedometer drive gear off output shaft. Remove oil pan-to-case bolts and washers, remove oil pan, and discard gasket.

3) Note installed positions of oil tubes for reassembly reference, and using a screwdriver, pry out the five oil tubes connected to valve body. **CAUTION** — *Do not attempt to remove the oil tube partially covered by valve body.* Disconnect throttle cable from throttle cam, remove valve body-to-case bolts, and withdraw valve body (take care not to lose manual valve). Remove two remaining oil tubes from valve body area of case. Remove bolts retaining oil pump tube plate and withdraw plate and tubes.

4) Scratch alignment marks on oil pump housing and transmission case, remove pump-to-case bolts, and withdraw oil pump. Remove and discard pump-to-case gasket and pump-to-front clutch thrust washer. At rear end of transmission, remove plug and spring washer retaining governor to output shaft, note installed position of governor, and remove from shaft. Using a screwdriver, carefully pry oil tubes from case and governor support.

5) Loosen both band adjusting screw locknuts, remove adjusting screws from case, then withdraw both band struts. Withdraw front clutch and input shaft assembly from case, remove bronze and steel thrust washers, then withdraw rear clutch assembly. Compress ends of front band together and remove from case. Withdraw forward sun gear shaft from case, along with small needle thrust bearing from front end of shaft and large needle thrust bearing and race from rear end of shaft.

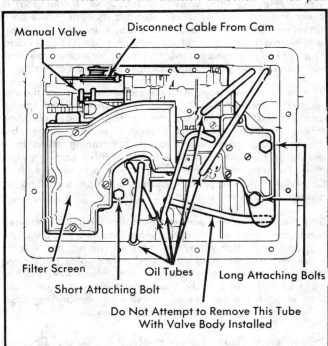

Fig. 4 Removal of Valve Body Assembly and Related Components

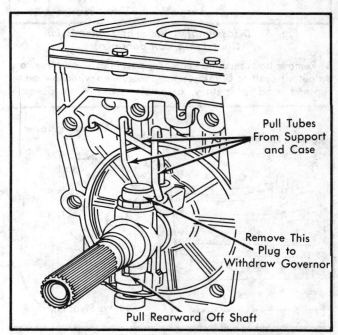

Fig. 5 Removal of Governor and Oil Tubes

BORG-WARNER MODEL 65 (Cont.)

VALVE BODY SPRING IDENTIFICATION

Valve Spring	Length In. (mm)	Diameter In. (mm)	Number Of Coils	Color
Secondary Regulator Valve	2.593 (65.8)	.480-.490 (12.2-12.4)	23	Blue
Primary Regulator Valve	2.94 (74.6)	.604-.610 (15.3-15.5)	14	Blue
Servo Orifice Control Valve	1.005 (25.5)	.198-.208 (5.0-5.3)	17	Yellow
2-3 Shift Valve	1.59 (40.4)	.275-.285 (6.9-7.2)	22.5	Yellow
1-2 Shift Valve	1.094 (27.7)	.230-.240 (5.8-6.1)	13	Plain
Throttle Return Valve	.807 (20.5)	.136-.146 (3.4-3.7)	28	Yellow
Modulator Valve	1.069 (27.1)	.150-.160 (3.8-4.1)	19	Plain
Throttle Valve	1.180 (29.9)	.230-.240 (5.8-6.1)	18	Green
Dump Ball Valve	.70 (17.7)	.210-.230 (5.3-5.8)	16	Plain/White

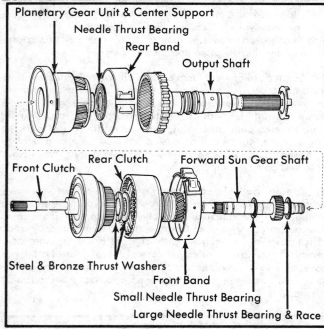

Fig. 6   Disassembled View of Transmission Gear Train Components

6) Remove bolts securing center support in case, push forward on output shaft to break support loose, then withdraw center support and planetary assembly from case. Remove

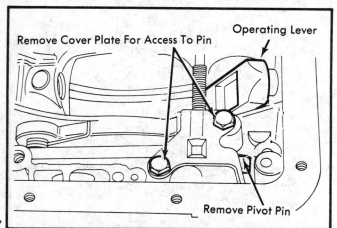

Fig. 7   Removing Rear Servo Operating Lever

planetary-to-output shaft needle thrust bearing, then separate support and planetary. Move output shaft back into original position, compress ends of rear band together, and remove band from case. Remove output shaft assembly from case along with output shaft-to-case thrust washer.

7) Remove bolts securing front servo cover to case, remove cover, and withdraw servo piston, rod and spring. Scribe alignment marks on rear servo cover and transmission case, remove bolts attaching servo cover, then remove rear servo cover, piston, rod and spring from case. Remove retaining bolts from plate covering parking pawl, withdraw pivot pin, and remove rear servo operating lever.

COMPONENT DISASSEMBLY & REASSEMBLY

VALVE BODY ASSEMBLY

Disassembly — 1) Remove manual valve from body. Remove screws retaining filter screen (and adapter if equipped) to body and remove filter screen. Remove six upper valve body retaining screws from lower valve body, invert valve body, and remove four screws retaining upper body and cam mounting arm. Remove cam mounting arm, withdraw downshift valve and spring, then separate upper body from assembly.

2) Remove screws securing end plates to upper body and remove plates. Remove 1-2 shift valve, plunger and spring, and 2-3 shift valve, plunger and spring. Remove retaining screws and lift transfer plate off main valve body. Loosen, but do not remove, governor pressure plate retaining screws. Hold separator plate in contact with main valve body, remove governor pressure plate retaining screws, and remove plate. Carefully remove separator plate from main body, noting position of ball valve and spring.

3) From main valve body, remove following parts: Retainer, spring, and servo orifice control valve; retaining pin, plug, spring, and modulator valve; two retainers, spring, and throttle valve. Remove retaining screw and detent roller and spring assembly. Remove screws securing regulator valve retaining plate to main valve body, slowly release pressure on plate, then withdraw plate, spring, sleeve and primary regulator valve, and spring and secondary regulator valve.

Inspection — Clean all parts in solvent and air dry. Check all valves, plugs, and sleeves for wear, burrs, and scoring. Make sure all valves and plugs move freely in valve body bores. Also check all valve springs for distortion or collapsed coils.

BORG-WARNER MODEL 65 (Cont.)

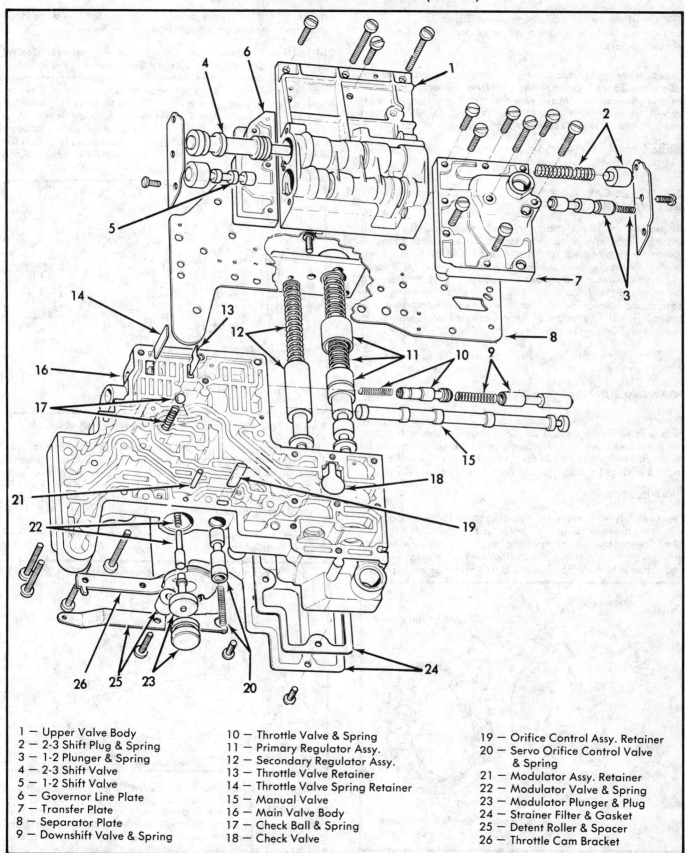

1 — Upper Valve Body	10 — Throttle Valve & Spring	19 — Orifice Control Assy. Retainer
2 — 2-3 Shift Plug & Spring	11 — Primary Regulator Assy.	20 — Servo Orifice Control Valve
3 — 1-2 Plunger & Spring	12 — Secondary Regulator Assy.	& Spring
4 — 2-3 Shift Valve	13 — Throttle Valve Retainer	21 — Modulator Assy. Retainer
5 — 1-2 Shift Valve	14 — Throttle Valve Spring Retainer	22 — Modulator Valve & Spring
6 — Governor Line Plate	15 — Manual Valve	23 — Modulator Plunger & Plug
7 — Transfer Plate	16 — Main Valve Body	24 — Strainer Filter & Gasket
8 — Separator Plate	17 — Check Ball & Spring	25 — Detent Roller & Spacer
9 — Downshift Valve & Spring	18 — Check Valve	26 — Throttle Cam Bracket

Fig. 8 *Exploded View of Valve Body Assembly*

BORG-WARNER MODEL 65 (Cont.)

NOTE — *If any valve body component is damaged or worn, entire valve body assembly must be replaced; parts are not serviced separately.*

Reassembly — Reverse disassembly procedure and note the following: Coat all components with transmission fluid before installing into bodies. Make sure check ball and spring are installed in correct main body passage (see *Fig. 8*). Always use a new strainer filter gasket when assembling.

CAUTION — *Do not overtighten valve body attaching bolts and screws.*

PLANETARY CARRIER & ONE-WAY CLUTCH

Inspection — Check planetary gear teeth for chipping or scoring (light scoring is acceptable). Make sure all gears rotate freely by hand, and that end play of gears is not excessive. Inspect bushing in hub of planetary carrier for wear. If any part of carrier is worn or damaged, complete carrier must be replaced. Withdraw one-way clutch roller assembly from carrier and inspect for worn or broken rollers and damage to outer race. If any one-way clutch component is damaged, replace roller and outer race assembly.

NOTE — *When installing roller assembly into outer race (in carrier), make sure lip of roller cage faces outward.*

FORWARD SUN GEAR SHAFT

Inspection — Check oil passages in shaft for obstructions; clear out with compressed air only. Inspect splines, seal ring grooves, and gear teeth for damage (minor damage may be removed with a fine abrasive). Check large and small needle thrust bearings for damage and replace as necessary.

REAR CLUTCH

Disassembly — Remove clutch pack retaining snap ring, then withdraw pressure plate, five steel clutch plates, and five lined discs. Using a suitable compressor tool, compress piston return spring, remove snap ring, then withdraw tool, spring retainer, and piston return spring. Remove clutch piston by applying air

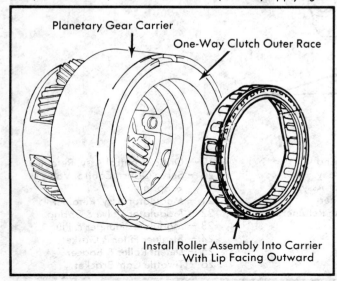

Fig. 9 Disassembled View of Planetary Carrier and One-Way Clutch Assembly

pressure to fluid supply passage in clutch hub. Remove inner seal from clutch drum and outer seal from piston.

Inspection — Check clutch drum for scoring or wear and all fluid passages for obstructions. Clear passages with compressed air only. Inspect piston for damage and free operation of check ball. Check all lined discs for wear and distortion; all lined discs must be flat. Check steel clutch plates for scoring or burrs; replace any plates found damaged. Also check steel plates for coning; plates must be coned at least .010" (.25 mm). Inspect needle roller bearing in clutch hub for wear. If bearing is worn or damaged, replace complete clutch housing.

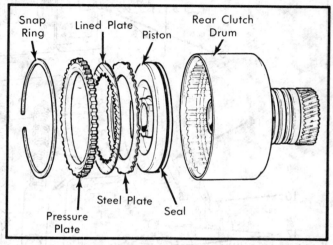

Fig. 10 Exploded View of Rear Clutch Assembly

Reassembly — 1) Coat new piston seals with petroleum jelly and install onto piston and clutch hub. Position a suitable piston installing tool into clutch drum, coat piston with transmission fluid, and install into bottom of drum. Position piston return spring and retainer on top of piston, compress assembly, and install retaining snap ring.

NOTE — *If new lined discs are used, soak in transmission fluid before installation.*

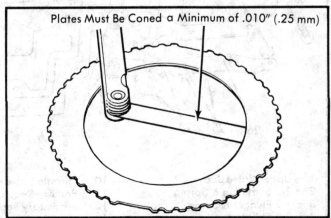

Fig. 11 Checking Rear Clutch Steel Plate Coning

2) Install clutch pack into drum, starting with steel plate and alternating lined discs and steel plates until correct number are installed (TR7 and TR8 use 4 steel and 3 lined, XJ6 uses 5 steel and 5 lined). Make sure all steel plate cones are facing in same direction. Install pressure plate into clutch drum (flat side downward) and install clutch pack retaining snap ring.

BORG-WARNER MODEL 65 (Cont.)

3) Install new sealing rings onto clutch drum hub and lock ends (if used). Install new seal rings onto forward sun gear shaft, then position shaft in a holding fixture with long end of shaft upward. Coat small needle thrust bearing with petroleum jelly and install over shaft and against sun gear. Coat sun gear shaft with transmisison fluid, then install rear clutch assembly onto shaft and against thrust washer. Place assembly to the side.

FRONT CLUTCH

Disassembly — Remove clutch pack retaining snap ring and withdraw turbine shaft, thrust washer, clutch hub, and clutch pack from drum. Remove large retaining snap ring and diaphragm return spring. Remove clutch piston by applying air pressure to fluid supply passage in clutch hub. On models so equipped, remove spring washers from clutch drum. On all models, remove seals from clutch hub and piston.

Inspection — Check clutch drum for scoring or wear and all fluid passages for obstructions. Clear passages with compressed air only. Inspect piston for damage and free operation of check ball. Check diaphragm release spring for cracks or distortion and replace as necessary. Inspect all clutch plates for wear or other damage. Make sure all plates are flat; coned plates are used in rear clutch only. Check bushing in turbine shaft for wear; if damaged, replace.

Reassembly — **1)** Coat a new seal with petroleum jelly and install onto clutch piston. On models with an "O" ring type seal on clutch hub, coat seal with petroleum jelly and install. On all other models, install spring washers into bottom of piston and follow with inner seal. **NOTE** — *Open end of seal should face out of piston.* On all models, position a suitable piston installing tool into clutch drum, coat all parts with transmission fluid, and install piston into drum. Install diaphragm spring into drum with cone facing upward, then install retaining snap ring.

2) With rear clutch and sun gear shaft assembly again positioned on bench, install steel backing washer and bronze thrust washer over sun gear shaft and against rear clutch. Make sure seal ring gaps on sun gear shaft are staggered, and that rear clutch lined disc splines are aligned, then install forward clutch drum and piston assembly into rear clutch.

NOTE — *Make sure all parts are fully mated.*

3) Install pressure plate into front clutch drum and against diaphragm spring snap ring. Follow with clutch pack, starting with a lined plate and alternating steel and lined plates until all plates are installed (TR7 and TR8 use 4 steel and 4 lined, XJ6 uses 4 steel and 5 lined).

4) Align inner splines of lined plates and install clutch hub, making sure it fully engages all plates. Position a new thrust washer into recess of hub. Install turbine shaft and snap ring, making sure ring is correctly seated in groove of clutch drum.

CAUTION — *With all parts assembled, do not allow front and rear clutches to separate as damage to seal rings on sun gear shaft may occur.*

OIL PUMP

Disassembly — Remove bolts and screw retaining pump housing to cover, then separate cover and housing. Mark mating surfaces of pump drive and driven gears with a die marker for reassembly reference. **CAUTION** — *Do not punch or scribe marks in gears.* Remove "O" ring seal from outer diameter of pump housing, and converter lip seal from front of pump housing.

Inspection — Check surfaces of housing and cover, gears, splines, and bushings for scoring, wear or other damage. If

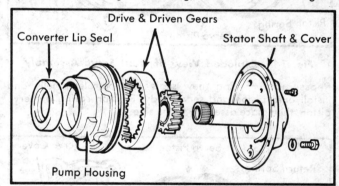

Fig. 13 Exploded View of Oil Pump Assembly

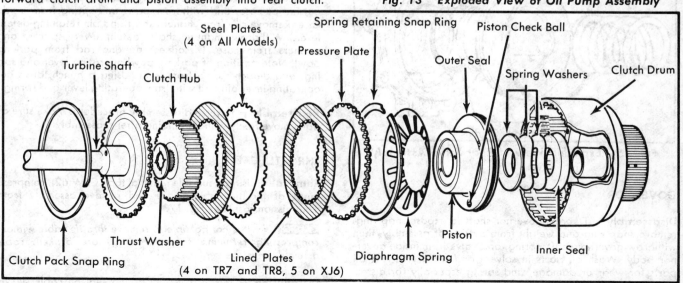

Fig. 12 Exploded View of Front Clutch Assembly

BORG-WARNER MODEL 65 (Cont.)

any part shows evidence of wear, entire assembly must be replaced; parts are not serviced separately.

Reassembly — Soak new converter lip seal and housing "O" ring seal in transmission fluid and install into pump housing. Install drive and driven gears into housing, aligning marks made at disassembly. Install cover into housing, align bolt and screw holes, then install and tighten attaching bolts and screw. Rotate pump gears to check for freedom of movement.

FRONT & REAR SERVOS

Disassembly — Remove spring from servo piston, then withdraw piston from servo body. Remove seals from piston and body, then clean all parts in solvent. Blow dry with compressed air, clearing out all lubrication passages.

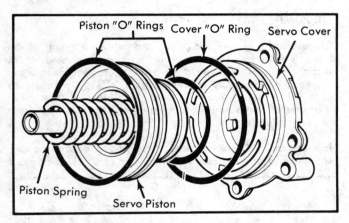

Fig. 14   Exploded View of Front Servo Assembly

Reassembly — Coat new seals with petroleum jelly and install onto piston and servo body. Position spring on servo piston, then place assembly to the side.

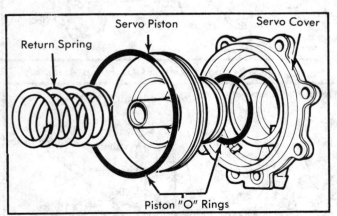

Fig. 15   Exploded View of Rear Servo Assembly

GOVERNOR

Disassembly — Depress governor shaft to expose snap ring, remove snap ring and weight from outside of assembly, then withdraw governor shaft, spring, and valve from inside governor body. Wash all parts in solvent and air dry. Check all parts for wear or damage, and spring especially for distortion. If any part of governor is found to be damaged, entire governor assembly must be replaced.

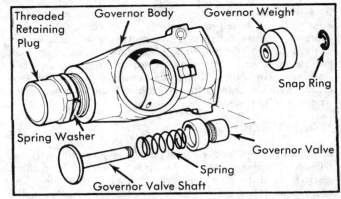

Fig. 16   Exploded View of Governor Assembly

Reassembly — Lubricate all parts with transmission fluid. Install governor valve, spring, and shaft into body, position weight on shaft, then install snap ring. Check all parts for freedom of movement. If governor shaft shows signs of sticking, governor assembly must be replaced.

OUTPUT SHAFT & RING GEAR

Disassembly — Remove seal rings from groove in output shaft. Remove large retaining snap ring and withdraw output shaft from ring gear.

Inspection — Check all passages in output shaft for obstructions and clear using compressed air only. Inspect splines, seal ring grooves, and gear teeth of shaft and ring gear for burrs, scoring, or other damage (minor damage may be removed with a fine abrasive). If any part is worn or damaged, replace.

Reassembly — Position output shaft in ring gear and install retaining snap ring. Install new seal rings into grooves of output shaft, taking care to stagger ring gaps.

MANUAL LINKAGE

Disassembly — Note position of parking pawl spring, then detach spring from pawl. Remove parking pawl shaft from outside of case, and withdraw pawl and spring from inside case. Remove clip from manual shaft and pin retaining detent lever. Withdraw manual shaft, detent lever, spacer, and washers from case. Disconnect parking rod from parking pawl. Note position of parking pawl operating lever and spring, and detach spring from lever. Using a punch, drive out operating lever pin and withdraw operating lever and spring.

Reassembly — Reverse disassembly procedure. Make sure all parts move freely without binding after reassembly.

THROTTLE CABLE

Removal — Using a suitable removal tool (CBW.62), compress tangs of throttle cable sleeve and remove assembly from transmission case. See Fig. 17.

CAUTION — It is not possible to remove throttle cable without compressing retaining tangs; if tangs are broken, cable assembly must be replaced.

Installation — Install a new "O" ring seal on cable sleeve, and push cable assembly into case until sleeve locks into place.

BORG-WARNER MODEL 65 (Cont.)

TRANSMISSION REASSEMBLY

1) Coat large tabbed thrust washer with petroleum jelly and install into case, making sure tabs engage slots in case. Install output shaft and ring gear assembly into case and through thrust washer, making sure washer is not displaced. Place front and rear bands in position in case. While holding clutch assemblies (previously assembled), install large needle thrust bearing and race onto sun gear shaft, with flange facing away from clutches.

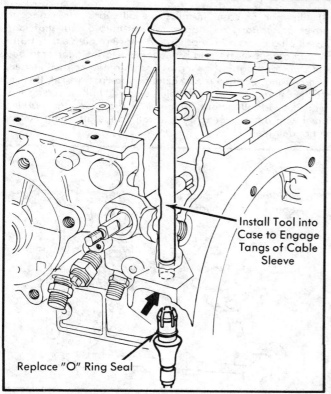

Install Tool into Case to Engage Tangs of Cable Sleeve

Replace "O" Ring Seal

Fig. 17 *Using Special Tool to Remove Throttle Cable*

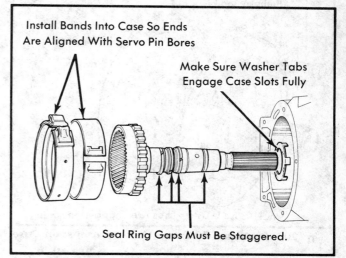

Install Bands Into Case So Ends Are Aligned With Servo Pin Bores

Make Sure Washer Tabs Engage Case Slots Fully

Seal Ring Gaps Must Be Staggered.

Fig. 19 *Installation of Output Shaft Into Transmission Case*

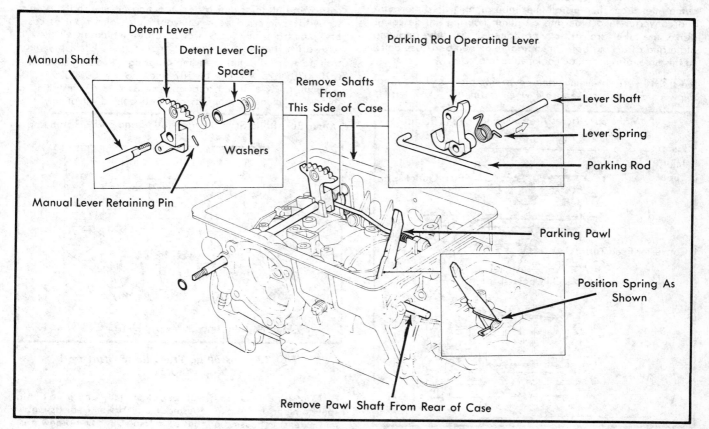

Manual Shaft

Detent Lever

Detent Lever Clip

Spacer

Washers

Manual Lever Retaining Pin

Remove Shafts From This Side of Case

Parking Rod Operating Lever

Lever Shaft

Lever Spring

Parking Rod

Parking Pawl

Position Spring As Shown

Remove Pawl Shaft From Rear of Case

Fig. 18 *Exploded View of Manual Linkage Components*

Automatic Transmissions

BORG-WARNER MODEL 65 (Cont.)

2) Install center support, clutch and sun gear assembly into planet carrier. Rotate center support until holes on outer diameter are in approximate alignment with center support bolt holes in case, then install entire assembly (clutches, planetary carrier, and support) into transmission case.

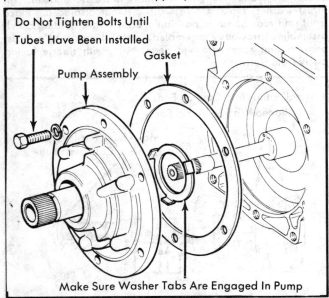

Fig. 20   Installing Oil Pump Onto Transmission Case

3) Position a new thrust washer and gasket onto rear of oil pump, mount oil pump to transmission case, and install but do not tighten attaching bolts. Install a new "O" ring seal on pump inlet tube, then install inlet tube along with outlet tube and converter feed tube into oil pump housing (inside case). Make sure tubes are correctly positoned, install tube retaining plate and attaching bolts, then tighten oil pump-to-case bolts. At this time, also install oil cooler tube into case.

CAUTION — *To prevent damage to internal parts, do not allow components to separate when installing.*

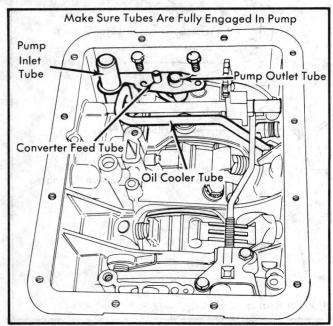

Fig. 21   Installing Oil Tubes Into Case

4) On rear of case, install three oil tubes into case and governor support. Slide governor unit onto output shaft and install plug and spring washer, making sure plug enters **blind** hole in output shaft. Install speedometer drive gear onto output shaft and against governor. Install a new seal into extension housing, position a new extension-to-case gasket, then install housing onto case, tightening nuts and bolts in a diagonal sequence. Install output flange onto shaft, engage parking pawl with parking gear, then install flange attaching bolt or nut and tighten.

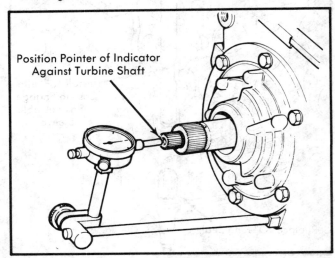

Fig. 22   Measuring Gear Train End Play Using a Dial Indicator

5) Position a dial indicator assembly on front of transmission case with button of indicator contacting turbine shaft. With a screwdriver inserted between front clutch and front of case, pry gear train fully rearward. Zero dial indicator. Next, with screwdriver between parking gear and rear clutch, pry gear train forward and note reading on gauge. Reading should be .010-.030" (.25-.75 mm) on TR7 and TR8, or .008-.029" (.20-.73 mm) on XJ6; if not, repeat steps **3)** and **4)**, installing a thicker or thinner washer as required behind oil pump.

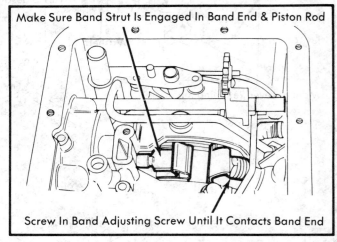

Fig. 23   Installing Front Band Strut and Adjusting Screw

6) Coat a new "O" ring with petroleum jelly and install onto speedometer driven gear housing. Install driven gear assembly into extension housing and install retainer. Position a new gasket on front servo, mount servo on case, and install and tighten

BORG-WARNER MODEL 65 (Cont.)

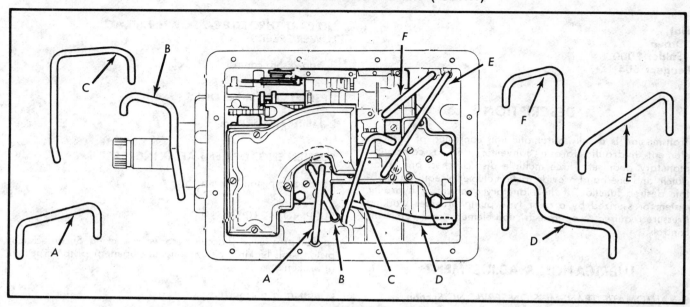

Fig. 24   Valve Body-to-Case Oil Tube Installation

attaching bolts. Install front band strut into servo rod and band, then screw in front band adjusting screw until it engages band end, do not tighten screw or lock nut at this time.

7) If removed, install rear servo operating lever in transmission case. Install new "O" rings and gasket on rear servo body, and mount servo on case, making sure servo rod engages operating lever. Install rear band strut between band end and operating lever, screw in band adjusting screw until contact is just made with band, then tighten servo body-to-

case bolts. At this time, install the one oil tube which will be partially covered by valve body (tube "D" in *Fig. 24*).

8) Install valve body into case, making sure manual valve engages detent lever and that valve body fully engages oil pump tubes. Install valve body-to-case bolts, noting that shortest bolt is installed at front. Connect kickdown cable to cam, then install valve body oil tubes (see *Fig. 24* for positioning). Install oil pan using a new gasket. Install converter housing, oil filler tube, and breather. To complete assembly, adjust both bands as follows: Tighten band adjusting screw to 5 ft. lbs. (.7 mkg), back out screw ¾ of a turn, hold in position and tighten adjusting screw lock nut.

Install Strut Between Band End and Operating Lever

Screw In Adjuster Until It Contacts Band

Servo Operating Lever

Fig. 25   Installing Rear Band Strut and Adjusting Screw

TIGHTENING SPECIFICATIONS

Application	Ft. Lbs. (mkg)
Transmission-to-Engine	
M-8 Bolts	20 (2.7)
M-12 Bolts	40 (5.5)
Oil Pan-to-Case	6 (.83)
Frt. & Rear Servo Cover-to-Case	19 (2.6)
Oil Pump Cover-to-Housing	
Screw	2.5 (.35)
Bolts	19.5 (2.7)
Oil Pump-to-Case	19 (2.6)
Pressure Test Plug	7 (1.0)
Drain Plug	11 (1.5)
Valve Body-to-Case	7 (1.0)
All Other Valve Body Screws	2 (.3)
Oil Pump Tube Plate	2 (.3)
Adjusting Screw Lock Nuts	35 (4.9)
Extension Housing-to-Case	43 (5.9)
Parking Pawl Plate	5 (.7)
Output Flange	35-50 (4.8-6.9)
Governor-to-Output Shaft	17 (23)

Automatic Transmissions

GM AUTOMATIC

Fiat
  Brava
  Spider 2000
Peugeot 604

DESCRIPTION

Transmission is a fully automatic unit consisting of a three-element hydraulic torque converter and a compound planetary gear set. Three multiple disc clutches, one sprag clutch, and one band provide friction elements required to obtain desired function of the planetary gear set. A hydraulic system pressurized by a gear type pump provides working pressure required to operate friction elements and automatic controls.

LUBRICATION & ADJUSTMENT

See AUTOMATIC TRANSMISSION SERVICING Section

TROUBLE SHOOTING

NO DRIVE

In Any Range — Low oil level. Clogged suction screen. Inner manual valve linkage or shift linkage disconnected. Input shaft broken. Pressure regulator stuck in open position. Defective oil pump.

In Forward Ranges Only — Worn band or band servo piston jamming. Band servo seal ring cracked.

No Drive in "D" or "2" ("1" and "R" OK) — Input sprag installed backwards or input sprag faulty.

No Drive in "R" (All Other Ranges OK) — Reverse clutch failure.

LOW OIL PRESSURE

Low oil level. Clogged suction screen. Leak in pump section circuit or internal leak in pressure circuit. Priming valve sticking. Pressure regulator failure.

HIGH OIL PRESSURE

Broken or disconnected vacuum line to transmission. Vacuum modulator failure. Leak in engine or accessory vacuum system. Pressure regulator failure.

NO SHIFT AT ANY SPEED

Governor valves sticking. 1-2 shift valve sticking in downshift position. Large leak in governor pressure passage.

UPSHIFTS ONLY AT PART THROTTLE

Detent pressure regulator valve sticking. Detent cable broken or out of adjustment.

NO PART THROTTLE 3-2 DOWNSHIFT AT LOWER SPEEDS

3-2 downshift control valve sticking.

UPSHIFTS FROM 1-2 ONLY

2-3 shift valve sticking.

SUDDEN ENGAGEMENT AFTER INCREASE IN RPM

Band servo piston binding.

SLIPPING 1-2 UPSHIFTS

Low oil pressure. 1-2 accumulator valve sticking. Second clutch piston seals leaking, check ball stuck open, or piston cracked or broken.

SLIPPING 2-3 UPSHIFTS

Low oil pressure. Third clutch piston seals leaking, check ball stuck open or piston cracked or broken. Input shaft bushing worn.

HARSH 1-2 UPSHIFT

High oil pressure. 1-2 accumulator valve sticking. Governor valve sticking.

HARSH 2-3 UPSHIFT

High oil pressure. Governor valve sticking.

HARSH 3-2 FORCED DOWNSHIFT AT HIGH SPEED

High speed downshift timing valve sticking open.

HARSH 3-2 COAST DOWNSHIFT

Low speed downshift timing valve sticking open.

TESTING

ROAD TEST

Oil Pressure Test — 1) Connect a tachometer to engine and a pressure gauge to transmission. Connect a vacuum gauge in line to modulator. Place gauges in position where they can be read while driving.

2) With engine and transmission at normal operating temperatures, place selector in "D". Allow engine to idle at 750-850 RPM. Oil pressure should be 61-70 psi (4.3-4.9 kg/cm^2).

3) With selector still in "D" position, press accelerator pedal down past "kickdown" position. Transmission should upshift when oil pressure is 108-119 psi (7.5-8.4 kg/cm^2). Vacuum gauge should read .86 in. Hg.

GM AUTOMATIC (Cont.)

4) Stop vehicle and place selector in "1" position. Oil pressure should now read 98-109 psi (6.9-7.7 kg/cm²) with approximately 12 in. Hg of vacuum.

Stall Test — With pressure gauge and tachometer still installed in vehicle. Place selector in "1" or "R" position, apply brakes and run engine to stall speed. **CAUTION** — *Do not keep engine at stall speed for more than a few seconds to avoid overheating transmission.* Oil pressure should be 156-160 psi (10.9-11.7 kg/cm²).

NOTE — *Stall speed is maximum speed engine can obtain with brakes applied and accelerator pressed to maximum. Stall speed should be 2200-2300 RPM.*

TRANSMISSION REMOVAL & INSTALLATION

Removal (Fiat) —1) Remove dipstick and tube. Disconnect battery. In driver's compartment, remove center console. Disconnect transmission switch connector and push connector through opening in floor.

2) Raise vehicle. Remove drain plug and allow transmission to drain. Remove starter bolts and place starter out of way. Remove speedometer cable connector safety wire then disconnect speedometer cable.

3) Remove cooling lines clamp and disconnect cooling lines from transmission. Remove exhaust pipe bracket. Disconnect vacuum hose from modulator valve. Disconnect vacuum tube from spring clip on transmission. Remove bracket for kickdown cable and disconnect kickdown cable from kickdown valve.

NOTE — *Bolt for kickdown cable bracket is located above the modulator valve at rear of transmission.*

4) Remove nut holding lever to control rod in transmission, then disconnect lever. Remove propeller shaft.

5) Support transmission with suitable jack, then remove transmission support bolts. Remove flywheel cover, then turn flywheel to gain access to bolts holding flywheel to converter and remove bolts. Remove transmission to engine mounting

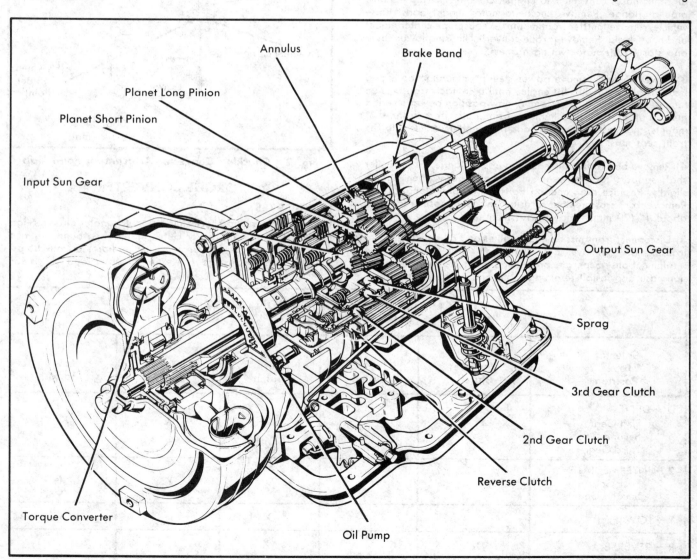

Annulus
Brake Band
Planet Long Pinion
Planet Short Pinion
Input Sun Gear
Output Sun Gear
Sprag
3rd Gear Clutch
2nd Gear Clutch
Reverse Clutch
Torque Converter
Oil Pump

Fig. 1 Cutaway View Showing Major Components of GM Automatic Transmission

AUTOMATIC TRANSMISSIONS

GM AUTOMATIC (Cont.)

bolts, then tip rear of transmission down, to prevent converter from falling out. Slide transmission back and remove from vehicle.

Installation — To install, reverse removal procedure and note the following: Feed connector for transmission switch through floor before positioning transmission. After attaching transmission to engine, push converter against flywheel flange and check that gap between boss and attachment point is .008-.048" (.2-1.21 mm). If clearance is not correct, replace flywheel.

NOTE — *On Peugeot vehicles, transmission has to be removed together with engine.*

Removal (Peugeot) — **1)** Drain cooling system. Remove engine compartment hood. Remove air cleaner and attachments. Disconnect negative battery terminal, radiator hoses and fan motor wiring. Remove radiator shroud and radiator.

2) Disconnect carburetor linkage, electrical connections and all other hoses connected to engine. Disconnect front exhaust pipe at flange. Remove engine-to-motor mount bolts. Raise vehicle, remove muffler front mount, exhaust pipe center mount and heat shield. Remove torque converter housing lower cover and starter/alternator wiring harness.

3) Lower vehicle, remove power steering mounting bolts and belt. Install engine lift, lift engine until it contacts transmission tunnel, then lower it 3/8" (10 mm), now position power steering pump out of the way. Remove front bolts from front seat mounts, then install screwed rods from under vehicle into the front seat nuts.

4) Remove bolt at flexible coupling upper flange. Fit propeller shaft support tool between muffler and body, then tighten slightly. Replace rear steering bolts with slightly longer ones. Remove front crossmember securing bolts and loosen rear bolts about 1" (30 mm) to lower crossmember.

5) Disconnect transmission cooling lines and all switch leads to transmission. Remove propeller shaft tube-to-transmission retaining bolts. Seperate propeller shaft tube from transmission case and install retaining plate and secure with 2 bolts.

Lower vehicle and install suitable engine lifting device, remove engine and transmission from vehicle.

6) Lower engine on suitable engine stand. Remove torque converter side cover plate, starter and transmission oil pan. Disconnect kickdown cable from transmission, and governor pipe. Remove torque converter-to-drive plate bolts. Remove bell housing-to-transmission bolts and separate transmission from engine.

Installation — To install, reverse removal procedure.

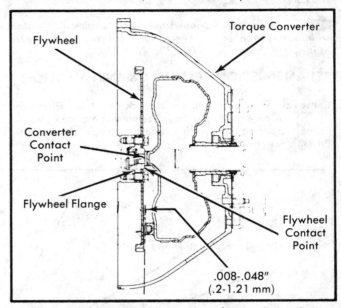

Fig. 2　Checking Converter Attachment Point Gap

TORQUE CONVERTER

LEAKAGE TEST

Drain converter and check fluid for clutch material or foreign matter. If foreign matter or clutch material is found, replace converter. Install test tool on converter and pressurize to 85 psi (5.8 kg/cm²). Submerge converter in water and check for leaks.

CLUTCH AND BAND APPLICATION CHART (ELEMENTS IN USE)

Selector Lever Position	Reverse Clutch	Second Clutch	Third Clutch	Sprag Clutch	Low Band
D — DRIVE					
First Gear				X	X
Second Gear		X			X
Third Gear		X	X		
2 — INTERMEDIATE					
First Gear				X	X
Second Gear		X			X
1 — LOW (First)			X		X
R — REVERSE	X		X		
NEUTRAL OR PARK — Band & Clutches released and/or ineffective.					

GM AUTOMATIC (Cont.)

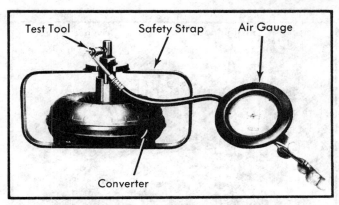

Fig. 3 Tool Set-Up for Torque Converter Leak Test

TRANSMISSION DISASSEMBLY

1) Drain transmission, if not already drained. Place transmission in suitable holding fixture. Remove speedometer driven gear and gasket. Turn transmission over and remove bolts holding oil pan, then remove pan and gasket.

2) Remove detent roller and spring, then remove bolts and lift off oil filter and gasket. Remove bolts and transfer plate reinforcement, then remove servo cover. Remove remaining bolts and carefully remove valve body, gasket and transfer plate. Hold manual valve link and disconnect it from selector lever. Remove check balls from oil passages.

3) Using suitable compressor tool (23075), compress servo piston assembly and remove retaining snap ring. Loosen compressor tool slowly since servo piston assembly is under high spring pressure, then remove tool and piston assembly from case.

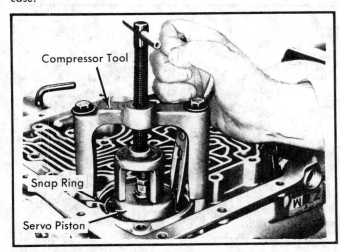

Fig. 4 Using Compressor Tool to Compress Servo and Remove Snap Ring

4) Remove vacuum modulator, gasket and modulator plunger. Remove valve and sleeve for modulator assembly. Carefully, remove retaining pin holding kickdown valve assembly, then remove kickdown sleeve, valve, spring seat and spring case.

5) On Fiat, remove output flange. Remove extension housing. Remove snap ring and slide collar and speedometer gear off shaft.

NOTE – The speedometer drive gear retainer has been modified. It is retained with a collar and snap ring.

6) On Peugeot, remove speedometer drive pinion sleeve retaining bolt and remove drive pinion sleeve. Remove extension housing. Using a suitable puller, remove speedometer drive gear.

7) Remove attaching bolts and slide governor assembly from output shaft. Remove governor hub snap ring and slide hub off output shaft.

8) On all models, turn transmission on work stand so converter housing faces up. Lift converter out, then remove converter housing attaching bolts and remove housing with oil pump. Lift third clutch assembly and second clutch drum from case. Remove selective washer from input shaft. Remove reverse clutch plates and planetary carrier with output shaft from case being careful not to lose needle bearing and inner race.

9) Pull reaction sun gear and drum with needle bearing and outer race from rear of case. Slightly compress low band and pull band from case. Remove nut and retaining pin, then remove selector lever and shaft from case.

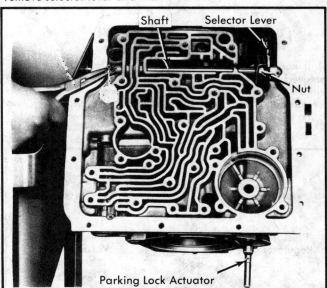

Fig. 5 Removing Selector Lever and Shaft

COMPONENT DISASSEMBLY & REASSEMBLY

CONVERTER HOUSING, OIL PUMP & REVERSE CLUTCH

Disassembly – 1) Remove second clutch assembly and selective washer from oil pump shaft. Remove outer oil seal from oil pump. Remove attaching bolts and separate oil pump from converter housing, then remove oil pump wear plate. Remove converter housing oil seal, and if necessary, remove housing bushing using suitable driver. Mark relative location of oil pump gears and remove gears from oil pump body.

2) Using suitable compressor tool, compress reverse clutch piston return springs and remove snap ring. Loosen compressor tool and remove clutch retaining ring and the 24 piston return springs, then remove piston. If necessary remove priming valve assembly from oil pump body using a drift inserted through hole at rear of oil pump.

GM AUTOMATIC (Cont.)

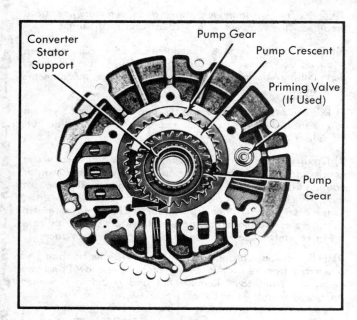

Fig. 6   Oil Pump Gears

3) If necessary, pressure regulator valve assembly may be removed from oil pump by using a pair of wire cutters to remove retaining pin. With retaining pin removed, lift out pressure regulator boost valve sleeve, boost valve, spring, two spring seats and pressure regulator valve.

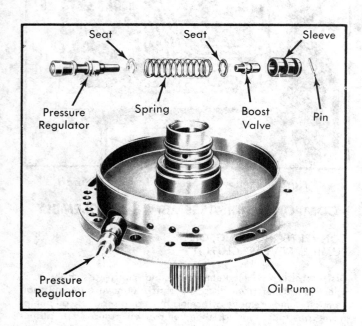

Fig. 7   Pressure Regulator Valve Assembly

Inspection — 1) Wash all parts in clean solvent and blow dry with compressed air. Inspect all parts for wear, damage or scoring and replace as necessary. Install gears into pump body and check pump body-to-gear face clearance using a feeler gauge and straightedge; clearance should be .0005-.0015" (.013-.038 mm). If clearance is not within specifications, replace complete oil pump assembly. See Fig. 8.

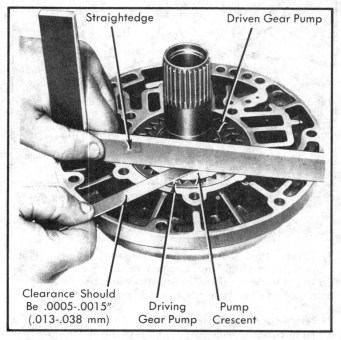

Fig. 8   Checking Pump Body-to-Gear Face Clearance Using a Feeler Gauge

2) Install aligning tool on oil pump drive gear-to-center gear. Measure clearance between drive gear and pump crescent while rotating gears through 360°. Use feeler gauge. If clearance is not between .0053-.0093" (.135-.235 mm), replace pump assembly. See Fig. 9.

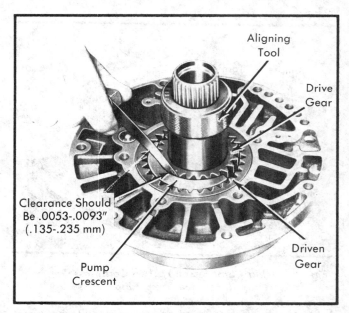

Fig. 9   Measuring Clearance Between Drive Gear and Pump Cresent

3) Measure clearance between outside of driven gear and pump housing. Rotate gear through 360° while measuring. If clearance is not within .0027-.0065" (.069-.165 mm), replace pump assembly. See Fig. 10.

GM AUTOMATIC (Cont.)

4) Measure clearance between inside of driven gear and pump crescent. Rotate gear through 360°. If clearance is less than .005" (.125 mm), replace pump assembly.

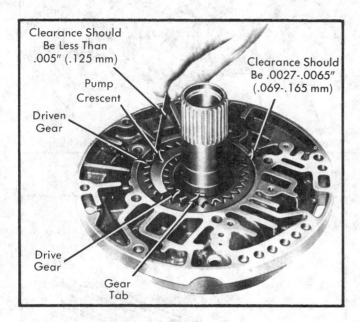

Fig. 10 *Measuring Clearance Between Outside of Driven Gear and Pump Housing*

Oil Pump Hub Bushing Replacement — **1)** To remove, thread a standard pipe tap into bushing, then using a drift on tap, press bushing from pump hub with an arbor press.

2) To install, position oil pump with pump shaft hole facing downward (See Fig. 11), then scribe an alignment mark on oil pump shaft inner diameter at center of oil groove to right of Hole "A". Scribe mark on outer edge of bushing through the centers of small and large drilled holes "B". Place bushing into pump shaft with small hole UP, and align scribe mark on bushing with mark in pump shaft. Use arbor press to drive bushing into pump shaft until firmly seated in bore.

Reassembly — **1)** If removed, coat pressure regulator valve assembly with transmission fluid, then install pressure regulator valve, spring seats, spring, boost valve and sleeve into pump body bore. Depress boost valve sleeve until back end lines up with pin hole and insert new retaining pin.

2) Install new oil seals on reverse clutch piston, then install piston onto rear face of oil pump. Install the 24 piston return springs and spring retaining seat. **NOTE** — *If any springs are damaged, replace entire set.* Using same compressor tool as was used for disassembly, compress return springs and install retaining snap ring.

NOTE — *DO NOT air check reverse clutch as clutch is not complete and damage to return spring seat may occur.*

3) Turn oil pump and reverse clutch assembly so that oil pump face is up. Install oil pump gears using location mark made at

disassembly. If removed, install converter housing bushing using suitable driver until bushing is flush with front face of housing. Lubricate and install new converter housing oil seal.

NOTE — *The remaining reassembly procedure will be performed at Transmission Reassembly.*

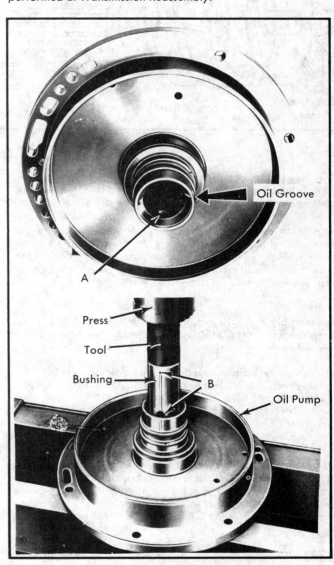

Fig. 11 *Installation of Pump Hub Bushing Showing Alignment of Hub Passage and Bushing Holes*

SECOND CLUTCH ASSEMBLY

Disassembly — **1)** Remove retaining ring and lift out second clutch ring gear. Remove clutch spacer plate retaining ring and remove spacer plate. Remove clutch steel and composition plates from clutch drum. **NOTE** — *Record number and sequence of plates for reassembly reference.* Remove clutch assembly thrust washer.

2) Install suitable compressor tool (J23078 Fiat or KMJ 23078 Peugeot) and adapter on clutch piston return spring retainer. Compress piston return springs, then remove retainer snap

GM AUTOMATIC (Cont.)

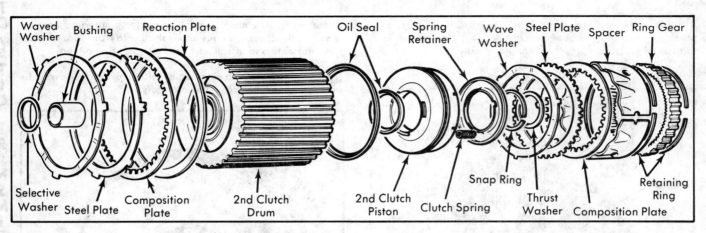

Waved Washer — Bushing — Reaction Plate — Oil Seal — Spring Retainer — Wave Washer — Steel Plate — Spacer — Ring Gear

Selective Washer — Steel Plate — Composition Plate — 2nd Clutch Drum — 2nd Clutch Piston — Clutch Spring — Snap Ring — Thrust Washer — Composition Plate — Retaining Ring

Fig. 12   Exploded View of Second Clutch Assembly

ring. Remove retainer seat and 22 piston return springs, then lift out clutch piston. Remove oil seals from piston. If necessary, remove clutch hub bushing using suitable driver.

Inspection — Inspect piston for damage. If piston is damaged or check ball falls out or is stuck, replace piston. Inspect piston return springs. If any spring is damaged, replace complete set. Inspect thrust washer and clutch plates for wear, damage, or heat marks. Replace clutch pack if damaged.

Reassembly — **1)** If removed, install new clutch hub bushing using suitable tool (J23130) until tool bottoms on bench. Install new oil seals on piston.

2) Coat oil seal, piston and drum with transmission fluid. Place suitable tool (J23080 Fiat or KMJ 23080 Peugeot) on piston to protect oil seal and install piston and tool in drum, then remove tool. Install 22 piston return springs and retaining seat onto clutch piston, then using compressor tool, compress springs and install retaining snap ring.

3) Install thrust washer so that tang seats in slot of clutch hub; retain washer with petroleum jelly. Lubricate clutch plates with transmission fluid and install them into clutch drum starting with wave washer, then alternating steel and composition plates. Install spacer plate in drum, then install retaining snap ring.

NOTE — *If plate slides in without pressure, expand plate by using screwdriver in plate slot. Make sure spacer seats tightly in drum.*

Second Clutch Plate Usage Chart

Application	Steel Plates	Composition
All Models	①4	3

① — Plus 1 Waved steel plate.

4) Install ring gear in drum, then secure ring gear with snap ring. Apply air to oil hole in drum to check that clutch piston moves. If piston does not move, disassemble clutch and check seal rings.

Drum

Oil Hole

Fig. 13   Applying Air Pressure to Second Clutch to Check Operation

THIRD CLUTCH ASSEMBLY

Disassembly — **1)** Compress retaining ring holding third clutch sprag race and retainer in drum. Remove input sun gear with clutch hub. Remove sprag race and retainer from clutch hub, then push sprag race out of retainer.

2) Remove 3rd clutch plates from drum, keeping plates in same order for later reassembly. Remove thrust bearing and washer from input shaft. Using suitable compressor and arbor press, compress piston return springs and remove retaining snap ring. Remove spring seats and 12 return springs, then lift out clutch piston. Remove oil seals from piston and input shaft, in clutch drum.

Inspection — Inspect piston for damage, if check ball is missing or falls out, replace piston. Clean and inspect clutch drum and thrust washer. Replace if scored or damaged. Inspect piston return springs. If any spring is damaged, replace complete set. Inspect clutch plates for wear, damage, or heat marks. Replace clutch pack if damaged. Check sprag assembly for wear, damage, or sprags that fall out of cage.

GM AUTOMATIC (Cont.)

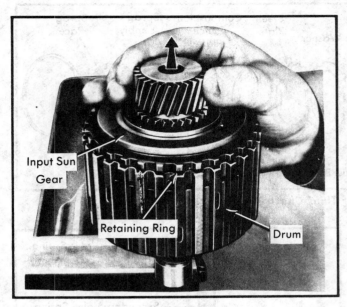

Fig. 14   Third Clutch Assembly

Reassembly — 1) Coat new oil seals for piston and input shaft with transmission fluid. Lubricate inside of drum with transmission fluid. Install oil seals, then install piston into drum with suitable tool (23084 Fiat or KMJ 23084 Peugeot). If tool is not available, push piston down until it reaches inside drum. Use a .020" (.5 mm) feeler gauge to guide oil seal into drum.

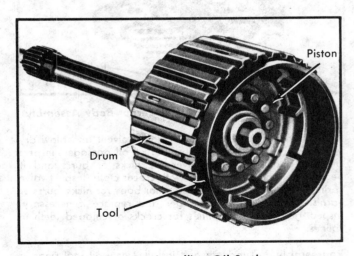

Fig. 15   Installing Oil Seals

2) Install 12 piston return springs and spring seat, then compress return springs and install retaining snap ring.

3) Install thrust washer and needle thrust bearing onto input shaft and retain them in place with petroleum jelly. Install sprag onto clutch hub with groove on sprag cage outer diameter toward input sun gear. Install sprag race and retainer assembly over sprag assembly. Check sprag lock up by holding sun gear stationary and turning sprag race in direction of arrow "A" (see Fig. 16). Sprag should lock up. Turn sprag race in opposite direction. Arrow "B" and sprag should rotate freely.

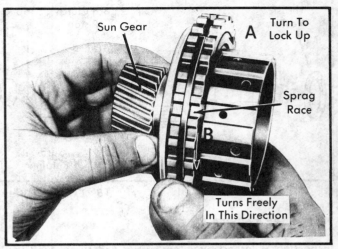

Fig. 16   Checking Sprag Operation

4) Lubricate clutch plates with transmission fluid, then starting with a waved washer, alternately install steel and composition clutch plates into drum.

NOTE — *Be sure to install same number of clutch plates as were removed.*

Third Clutch Plate Usage Chart		
Application	**Steel Plates**	**Composition**
Fiat	①4	3
Peugeot	①5	4
① — Plus 1 Waved steel plate.		

5) Align clutch plates and install clutch hub to index with clutch plate splines. **NOTE** — *Input sprag, race and retainer assembly must also spline into clutch drum.* Compress retaining ring and seat input sprag race assembly into clutch drum. Air check operation of third clutch assembly (See Fig. 17).

Fig. 17   Using Air Pressure to Check Operation of Third Clutch

Automatic Transmissions

GM AUTOMATIC (Cont.)

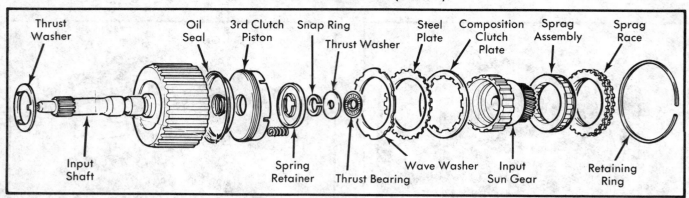

Thrust Washer — Oil Seal — 3rd Clutch Piston — Snap Ring — Thrust Washer — Steel Plate — Composition Clutch Plate — Sprag Assembly — Sprag Race — Input Shaft — Spring Retainer — Thrust Bearing — Wave Washer — Input Sun Gear — Retaining Ring

Fig. 18 Exploded View of Third Clutch Assembly

PLANETARY CARRIER ASSEMBLY

Inspection — Inspect planetary carrier and output shaft for distortion or damage. Inspect planetary pinions for excessive wear or damage. Check end clearance of all pinions with a feeler gauge at points "A" and "B" (see Fig. 19). Clearance should be .005-.035" (.13-.89 mm). Replace entire planetary carrier assembly if damage or excessive wear is noted.

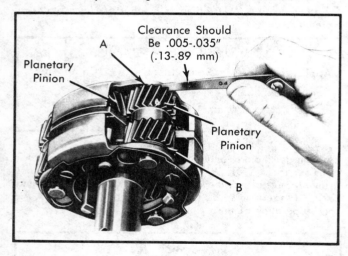

Fig. 19 Planetary Pinion End Play Check Locations

REACTION SUN GEAR & DRUM

Inspection — Inspect sun gear for chipped or nicked teeth, wear, damage or scoring and replace if necessary. Inspect drum for wear or scoring and replace as necessary. Inspect drum bushing and if necessary, replace using suitable driver. When installing new bushing, ensure it is flush with rear face of drum hub.

GOVERNOR ASSEMBLY

Disassembly — Depress secondary valve spring and remove valve spring retainer. Remove secondary valve spring, secondary valve, primary valve and roll pin from governor body. Remove the three oil seal rings and oil screen from governor hub.

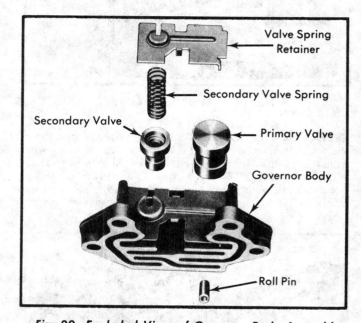

Valve Spring Retainer — Secondary Valve Spring — Secondary Valve — Primary Valve — Governor Body — Roll Pin

Fig. 20 Exploded View of Governor Body Assembly

Inspection — Wash all parts in clean solvent and blow dry with compressed air, then blow out all oil passages. Inspect primary and secondary valves for nicks or burrs and if necessary, remove small burrs with crocus cloth. Inspect valve spring for distortion. Inspect governor body for nicks, burrs or varnish build-up in oil passages and replace if necessary. Inspect governor hub splines for cracks or chipped teeth in splines.

Reassembly — Lubricate and install 3 new oil seal rings in grooves on governor hub, then install oil screen. Install roll pin flush to .010" (.25 mm) below front face of governor body. Lubricate and install primary valve, small end first, into governor body. Lubricate and install secondary valve, small spool portion first, into body, then install valve spring. Depress valve spring and install retainer.

SERVO PISTON ASSEMBLY

Disassembly — Remove servo piston apply rod. Hold servo piston sleeve at flat portion, then loosen and remove adjusting bolt lock nut. Depress piston sleeve and remove sleeve retaining ring. Push sleeve through piston and remove cushion spring and spring retainer. Remove piston ring.

GM AUTOMATIC (Cont.)

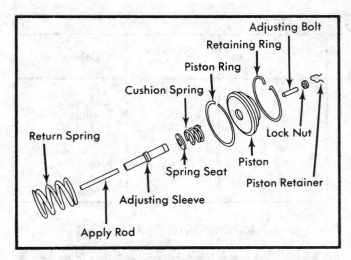

Fig. 21 Exploded View of Servo Piston Assembly

Inspection — Inspect cushion spring, adjusting bolt, and sleeve for damage. Inspect piston for damage and piston ring for side wear and replace if necessary.

Reassembly — To reassemble, reverse disassembly procedure.

VALVE BODY ASSEMBLY

NOTE — *As valve trains are removed from each valve body bore, place individual parts in correct order and in relative position to valve body to simplify reassembly.*

CAUTION — *Valves and springs are not interchangeable; all parts must be installed in correct order in proper valve body bore. See Fig. 22.*

Disassembly - 1) Remove manual valve and valve link from valve body. Turn valve body so that transfer plate is facing up, then remove the 2 attaching bolts and lift off transfer plate and gasket. Using a small "C" clamp, compress accumulator piston and remove retaining ring, then remove accumulator piston, oil ring and spring.

2) Remove retaining pin, then remove 1-2 shift control valve sleeve, control valve, 1-2 shift valve spring and valve. Remove retaining pin, then remove 2-3 shift control valve, spring seat, spring and 2-3 shift valve. Remove retaining pin, then remove 3-2 control valve plug, spring and control valve.

3) Remove retaining pin, then remove detent pressure regulator valve spring and valve. Remove retaining pin and remove high speed downshift timing valve spring and valve, then from the same bore, remove downshift timing valve plug

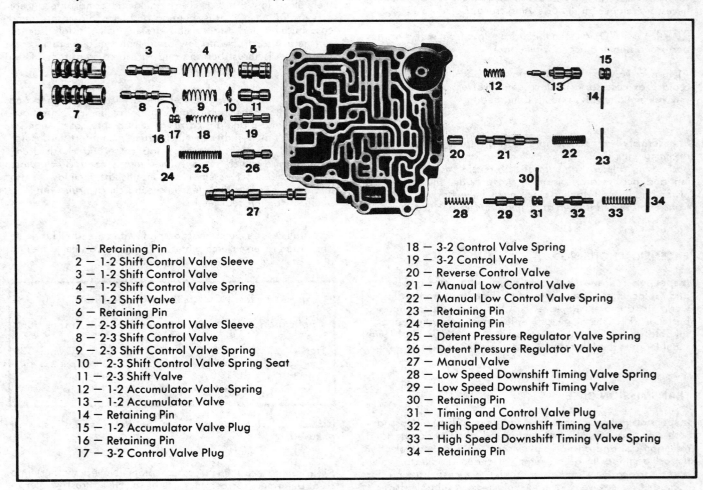

1 — Retaining Pin
2 — 1-2 Shift Control Valve Sleeve
3 — 1-2 Shift Control Valve
4 — 1-2 Shift Control Valve Spring
5 — 1-2 Shift Valve
6 — Retaining Pin
7 — 2-3 Shift Control Valve Sleeve
8 — 2-3 Shift Control Valve
9 — 2-3 Shift Control Valve Spring
10 — 2-3 Shift Control Valve Spring Seat
11 — 2-3 Shift Valve
12 — 1-2 Accumulator Valve Spring
13 — 1-2 Accumulator Valve
14 — Retaining Pin
15 — 1-2 Accumulator Valve Plug
16 — Retaining Pin
17 — 3-2 Control Valve Plug

18 — 3-2 Control Valve Spring
19 — 3-2 Control Valve
20 — Reverse Control Valve
21 — Manual Low Control Valve
22 — Manual Low Control Valve Spring
23 — Retaining Pin
24 — Retaining Pin
25 — Detent Pressure Regulator Valve Spring
26 — Detent Pressure Regulator Valve
27 — Manual Valve
28 — Low Speed Downshift Timing Valve Spring
29 — Low Speed Downshift Timing Valve
30 — Retaining Pin
31 — Timing and Control Valve Plug
32 — High Speed Downshift Timing Valve
33 — High Speed Downshift Timing Valve Spring
34 — Retaining Pin

Fig. 22 Exploded View of Valve Body Assembly

GM AUTOMATIC (Cont.)

VALVE BODY SPRING IDENTIFICATION				
Valve Spring	Length In. (mm)	Diameter In. (mm)	Number Of Coils	Color
1-2 Shift Valve	2.15 (54.6)	.....	7	None
2-3 Shift Valve	1.76 (44.7)	.....	7	White
3-2 Control Valve	1.38 (35.1)	.....	9	Red
Detent Pressure Regulator Valve	1.72 (43.6)	.....	1½	Silver
Reverse & Low Control Valve	1.34 (34.0)	.....	7	Green
Low Speed Timing Valve	1.43 (36.3)	.....	9½	Violet
High Speed Timing Valve	1.35 (34.3)	.....	9½	White
Accumulator Piston	2.70 (68.6)	.....	6	None

retaining pin and remove plug, low speed downshift timing valve and spring.

4) Remove manual low and reverse control valve retaining pin, then remove spring, manual low control valve and reverse control valve. Remove retaining pin, then remove 1-2 accumulator valve plug, valve and spring.

Inspection — 1) Inspect each valve for free movement in its respective bore in valve body. Inspect valves for burrs and if necessary remove small burrs using crocus cloth.

NOTE — *DO NOT remove the sharp edges from valves as they perform a cleaning action within bore.*

2) Inspect valve springs for distortion or collapsed coils and replace as necessary. Replace entire valve body assembly if any valve on the valve body is damaged.

Reassembly — Reassemble valves, springs, plugs and retaining pins in their proper location and order into valve body using a liberal amount of transmission fluid. Install spring and accumulator piston in valve body, then compress piston and install retaining ring. Install valve body gasket and transfer plate and tighten attaching bolts to specifications.

EXTENSION HOUSING

Inspection — Inspect extension housing for wear or damage and replace if necessary. Inspect parking pawl and spring for wear or damage. Remove oil seal and inspect housing bushing. If bushing needs replacement, remove using a suitable driver. Install new bushing until it is flush with shoulder of extension housing. Install new oil seal.

TRANSMISSION CASE

Inspection — Inspect case for damage and clean oil passages with cleaning solvent and compressed air. Check for good retension of band anchor pins. Inspect all threaded holes for thread damage. Inspect detent valve and modulator valve bores for scratches and scoring. Inspect case bushing for damage or excessive wear and replace using suitable driver if necessary.

TRANSMISSION REASSEMBLY

1) Install new selector lever shaft oil seal, then install selector lever shaft using care not to damage oil seal. Install spring pin to secure shaft in case. Guide selector lever over shaft and retain with lock nut. Insert parking pawl actuator rod from front of case and through hole at rear of case, then install retaining ring.

2) Turn transmission case so that front of case is facing up, then place low band in case and locate band onto anchor pins. Install needle thrust bearing and race into case around case bushing and retain with petroleum jelly. Install reaction sun gear and drum into low band with sun gear facing up. Install needle thrust bearing and race onto front face of sun gear and retain with petroleum jelly.

3) Install input sun gear-to-planetary carrier washer and bearing into carrier and retain with petroleum jelly. Insert output shaft and planetary carrier assembly into case. Align second clutch drive plates in clutch drum, then insert third clutch drum and input shaft through top of second clutch drum, seating third clutch drum splines into second clutch plate splines. Hold clutch assemblies by input shaft, then lower them into case, indexing ring gear in second clutch drum with long planetary pinion gear teeth.

4) Install reverse clutch reaction plate into case, then lubricate and install reverse clutch plates, starting with a steel plate and alternately steel and composition plates.

Reverse Clutch Plate Usage Chart		
Application	Steel Plates	Composition
Fiat	①4	3
Peugeot	①5	4
① — Plus 1 Waved steel plate.		

NOTE — *Install same number of clutch plates as were removed.*

5) Install reverse clutch cushion plate (waved washer) into case. Determine correct thickness of selective thrust washer to be installed using the following procedure:

GM AUTOMATIC (Cont.)

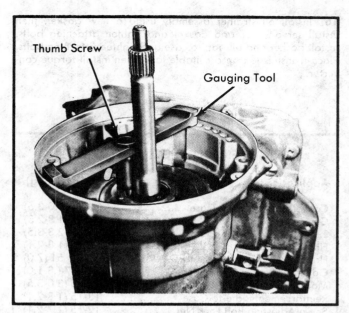

Fig. 23   Tool Set-Up for Determining Correct Selective Thrust Washer

6) Place suitable gauging tool (23085) on case flange and against input shaft. Loosen thumb screw on tool to allow inner shaft to drop on second clutch drum hub, then tighten thumb screw and remove tool. Place selective washer removed from transmission against inner shaft of tool. Selective washer should be flush with top face of shaft; if not flush, select next larger or smaller washer until correct size is obtained. Selective washers are available in the following thicknesses:

Selective Washer Thicknesses	
Color Code	In. (mm)
Yellow	.070-.074 (1.78-1.88)
Blue	.076-.080 (1.93-2.03)
Red	.081-.085 (2.06-2.16)
Brown	.086-.090 (2.18-2.28)
Green	.091-.095 (2.31-2.41)
Black	.097-.101 (2.46-2.56)

7) Install wear plate on oil pump, then insert guide pin into oil pump for alignment of converter housing and lower housing into pump. Install new oil seal washers on converter housing-to-oil pump attaching bolts, then loosly install bolts into converter housing. Use a suitable aligning tool to align converter housing to oil pump, then tighten attaching bolts and remove tool.

8) Install new converter housing-to-case oil seal and new oil pump flange gasket. Place end play selective washer, previously determined, onto oil pump shaft and retain with petroleum jelly. Install two guide pins in case and lower converter housing and oil pump into case. Install new oil seal washers on housing-to-case attaching bolts, then install and tighten bolts. Check for correct assembly by turning input shaft by hand and making sure assembly rotates freely.

9) Turn transmission so that bottom of case is facing up. Lubricate oil seal rings and install governor hub onto output shaft, then install retaining snap ring. Install governor body

gasket, then install governor body to governor hub and tighten attaching bolts.

NOTE — *Make sure governor valves move freely after governor body bolts are tightened.*

10) Slide speedometer drive gear and collar into position on shaft, install snap ring. Install new gasket, then slide extension housing over output shaft and align holes. Align parking pawl shaft into extension housing, then install and tighten housing-to-case attaching bolts.

11) Install speedometer driven gear into extension housing and install retainer. Lubricate and install detent valve, sleeve, spring and spring seat into case bore, then depress spring and install retaining pin into sleeve hole.

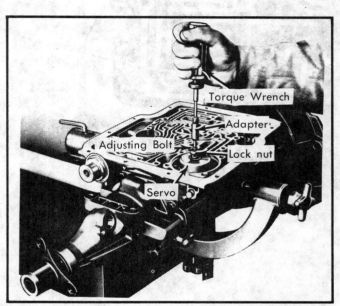

Fig. 24   Bottom View of Transmission Showing Adjustment of Servo Apply Rod

NOTE — *Install sleeve with slots facing oil pan.*

12) Install modulator valve (small end first) and sleeve into case. Use a new gasket and install modulator plunger, then thread modulator assembly into case and tighten to specifications.

13) Lubricate and install servo assembly apply rod, spring and piston into case. Compress piston spring using a suitable tool, lightly tapping piston while compressing, until piston is seated to avoid damage to oil seal ring, then install retaining ring and remove tool. To adjust servo apply rod, use a 3/16" hex head wrench and tighten adjusting bolt to 40 INCH lbs. (46 cmkg), then back off 4 full turns. Hold adjusting bolt and sleeve stationary and tighten lock nut.

14) Install two check balls into oil passages in transmission case (see Fig. 25), then install new transfer plate gasket. Install guide pins into case to insure correct alignment of valve body and transfer plate. Lubricate and install manual valve into

GM AUTOMATIC (Cont.)

valve body bore, then install long side of manual valve link into valve. Install small end of valve link into selector lever, then install valve body and transfer plate assembly over guide pins. Install selector lever roller spring and retainer.

15) Install and tighten valve body attaching bolts, starting at center of valve body and working outward. Install reinforcement plate and tighten attaching bolts.

16) Install oil strainer assembly using a new gasket, then install servo cover and gasket and tighten attaching bolts. Install gasket and oil pan to case and tighten attaching bolts. Place transmission on a suitable jack, then install torque converter.

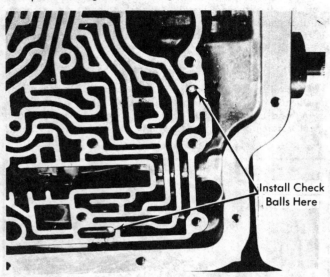

Install Check Balls Here

Fig. 25   Bottom View of Transmission Showing Check Ball Positions in Oil Passages

TIGHTENING SPECIFICATIONS

Application	Ft. Lbs. (mkg)
Converter Housing-to-Case	22-26 (3.0-3.6)
Converter Housing-to-Oil Pump	13-17 (1.8-2.3)
Extension Housing-to-Case	20-25 (2.8-3.5)
Filter-to-Case Bolt	13-15 (1.8-2.1)
Flange Nut	51 (7.0)
Governor Body-to-Governor	6-7 (.8-1.0)
Modulator Assembly	22-25 (3.0-3.5)
Reinforcement Plate-to-Case	13-15 (1.8-2.1)
Servo Adjusting Bolt Lock Nut	12-15 (1.7-2.1)
Servo Cover-to-Body	17-19 (2.3-2.6)
Transfer Plate-to-Valve Body	6-8 (.8-1.1)
Valve Body-to-Case	13-15 (1.8-2.1)

Application	INCH Lbs. (cmkg)
Servo Adjusting Bolt	40 (46)

JATCO 3N71B & R3A

MODEL 3N71B
  Courier
  Datsun
  Mazda GLC & 626
MODEL R3A
  Mazda RX7

TRANSMISSION IDENTIFICATION

Transmission type may be identified by a group of characters stamped into transmission case casting on left side; characters will correspond to transmissions type: 3N71B or R3A. Transmission model may be identified by a metal plate attached to right side of transmission. Plate lists model code and serial number. Type R3A may be identified from type 3N71B as follows: Type R3A servo cover is mounted on right front exterior corner of transmission case; Type 3N71B servo cover is internal in transmission case.

DESCRIPTION

The JATCO (Japan Automatic Transmission Company) 3N71B and R3A transmissions are three speed units, consisting basically of a three element torque converter and two planetary gear sets. Two multiple disc clutches, one multi-disc brake, one brake band, and a one-way clutch provide the friction elements required to obtain the desired function of the planetary gear set. A hydraulic system, pressurized by a gear-type pump, provides working pressure required to operate friction elements and automatic controls.

LUBRICATION & ADJUSTMENT

See AUTOMATIC TRANSMISSION SERVICING Section.

TROUBLE SHOOTING

ENGINE WILL NOT START WITH SELECTOR LEVER IN "N" OR "P"

Check ignition system. Adjust selector lever linkage. Check inhibitor switch and wiring.

ENGINE STARTS IN POSITIONS OTHER THAN "N" OR "P"

Check selector lever linkage and inhibitor switch and wiring.

SHARP SHOCK FROM "N" TO "D" SHIFT

High engine idle RPM. Check vacuum diaphragm and hoses. Faulty throttle valve. Check transmission oil pressure. Faulty manual control valve or rear clutch.

VEHICLE HAS "2", "1", AND "R", BUT NO "D"

Check selector lever linkage. Faulty throttle pressure valve, manual control valve, or one-way clutch.

VEHICLE HAS "R", BUT NO FORWARD GEARS. TRANSMISSION SLIPS BADLY, POOR ACCELERATION

Check oil level and adjust selector lever. Faulty throttle pressure valve, manual control valve, rear clutch, or oil passage leak.

NO MOVEMENT IN ANY RANGE

Check oil level. Adjust selector lever linkage. Faulty throttle pressure valve, manual control valve, rear clutch, or oil passage leak. "P" linkage failure.

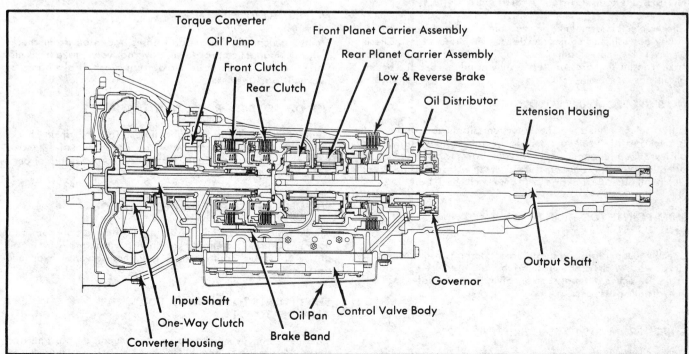

**Fig. 1   Cutaway View of Jatco Models 3N71B & R3A Automatic Transmission Assembly
(Long Extension Housing Model Shown)**

JATCO 3N71B & R3A (Cont.)

SLIPPAGE OF CLUTCHES OR BRAKES WHEN STARTING AWAY

Check oil level. Faulty throttle valve pressure, manual control valve, vacuum diaphragm and hoses, oil pump, or oil passage leak.

VEHICLE MOVES IN "N" OR "P"

Adjust selector linkage. Check oil level. Faulty manual control valve or rear clutch.

POOR ACCELERATION, VEHICLE WILL NOT ATTAIN TOP SPEED

Check oil level and selector lever linkage. Faulty throttle pressure valve. Incorrect stall RPM. Faulty band servo, manual control valve, engine or brakes, low and reverse brake, band brake, rear clutch, front clutch or oil pump.

VEHICLE BRAKED BY SHIFTING INTO "R"

Check oil level and transmission pressure. Faulty band servo, rear clutch, band brake, or "P" linkage.

VEHICLE HAS EXCESSIVE "CREEP"

Adjust idle RPM.

VEHICLE WILL NOT "CREEP"

Check oil level and selector lever adjustment. Adjust engine idle RPM. Faulty manual control valve, oil pump, oil passage leakage, rear clutch, or front clutch.

NO SHIFT FROM "2nd" TO "3rd"

Check selector lever linkage, vacuum diaphragm and hoses. Faulty downshift solenoid, kickdown switch and wiring. Check oil level. Defective manual control valve, or governor valve. Take transmission pressure test. Faulty band servo, band brake or oil passage leak.

NO SHIFT FROM "D1" TO "D2"

Adjust selector linkage. Check vacuum diaphragm and hose. Inspect downshift solenoid, kickdown switch and wiring. Check oil level. Faulty manual control valve, governor valve, or inadequate transmission pressure. Defective band servo, front clutch, oil passage leakage, or front clutch check ball.

SHIFT POINTS TOO HIGH IN "D1" TO "D2" AND "D2" TO "D3"

Check vacuum diaphragm and hoses, and downshift solenoid, kickdown switch and wires. Faulty oil pressure. Check oil drain. Defective manual control valve, governor valve, or leak in hydraulic passages.

SHIFTS FROM "D" TO "D3" SKIPPING "D2"

Check oil drain. Faulty manual control valve. Take transmission air check. Faulty governor valve, band brake or leak in hydraulic passages.

SHIFTING SHOCK FROM "D" TO "D2"

Faulty vacuum diaphragm and hoses. Excessive engine RPM. Check oil quantity. Faulty manual control valve, band servo, or band brake.

SHIFTING SHOCK FROM "D2" TO "D3"

Faulty vacuum diaphragm and hoses. Defective downshift solenoid, kickdown switch and wiring. Oil pressure. Faulty manual control valve, band servo and check oil level.

LITTLE OR NO SHIFT SHOCK, EXCESSIVE SLIPPAGE FROM "D1" TO "D2"

Check oil level. Adjust selector lever. Check vacuum diaphragm and hoses. Faulty oil pressure. Make oil drain check. Faulty manual control valve, take transmission air check. Faulty band servo, brake band, or hydraulic passage leakage.

LITTLE OR NO SHIFT SHOCK, EXCESSIVE SLIP AND ENGINE RUNAWAY FROM "D2" TO "D3"

Check oil level, adjust selector lever, check vacuum diaphragm and hoses. Faulty oil pressure. Check drain plug. Faulty manual control valve. Take transmission air check. Defective band servo, front clutch, hydraulic passage leaks, or front clutch check ball.

VEHICLE IS BRAKED ON "D1" TO "D2" SHIFT

Make oil drain check. Faulty manual control valve, low & reverse brake, front clutch, or one-way clutch in power train.

NO "D3" TO "D2" CHANGE

Faulty vacuum diaphragm and hoses. Make oil drain check. Defective manual control valve, governor valve, take transmission air check. Faulty band servo, front clutch, brake band, or hydraulic passage leaks.

NO "D2" TO "D1" OR "D3" TO "D1" CHANGE

Faulty vacuum diaphragm and hoses. Take oil drain check. Defective manual control valve or governor valve. Make transmission air check. Faulty band servo, brake band, or one-way clutch in power train.

SHIFTING SHOCK FELT ON DECELERATION

Check selector lever linkage. Faulty vacuum diaphragm and hoses, downshift solenoid, kickdown switch and wiring, oil pressure, manual control valve, governor valve, or hydraulic passage leak.

SHIFT POINTS TOO HIGH IN "D3" TO "D2" AND "D2" TO "D1"

Check selector lever linkage. Faulty vacuum, diaphragm and hoses, downshift solenoid, kickdown switch and wiring, oil pressure, manual control valve, governor valve, or hydraulic passage leak.

JATCO 3N71B & R3A (Cont.)

NO KICKDOWN AT NORMAL SPEEDS IN "D3"

Faulty downshift solenoid, kickdown switch and wiring, vacuum diaphragm and hoses. Make oil drain check. Defective manual control valve, governor valve, brake band, or hydraulic passage leak.

EXCESSIVE ENGINE RPM WHEN ACCELERATING IN "D3" ABOVE KICKDOWN SPEED

Check selector lever linkage, vacuum diaphragm and noses. Faulty oil pressure. Check oil drain. Defective manual control valve or governor valve. Take transmission air check. Faulty front clutch, or hydraulic passage leak.

ENGINE SLIP OR RUNAWAY ON "D3" TO "D2" KICKDOWN

Check vacuum diaphragm and hoses. Defective oil pressure. Check oil drain. Faulty manual control valve, band servo, brake band or leak in hydraulic passages. Take transmission air check. Check front clutch and front clutch check ball.

NO ENGINE BRAKING IN "1" RANGE

Check selector lever linkage. Faulty oil pressure. Make oil drain check. Defective manual control valve. Take transmission air check. Faulty low & reverse brake, or hydraulic passage leak.

TRANSMISSION OVERHEATS

Check oil level. Faulty rear lubrication or oil pressure. Incorrect engine stall speed. Make oil drain check. Defective manual control valve. Take transmission air check. Faulty band servo, front clutch, band brake, low & reverse brake, oil pump. Possible hydraulic passage leaks. Defective one-way clutch in torque converter, or planetary gear.

TRANSMISSION NOISY IN "P" AND "N"

Check fluid level. Faulty oil pressure or oil pump.

TRANSMISSION NOISY IN "R" AND ALL "D" RANGES

Check fluid level. Faulty oil pressure, rear clutch, oil pump, one-way clutch in power train, or planetary gear.

TESTING

ROAD TEST

NOTE — *References made to "D1", "D2", and "D3" indicate first, second, and third gears in selector position "D".*

1) Check upshift and downshift against ranges specified in shift point table. With selector lever placed in "D" and vehicle accelerated at wide open throttle, shifts should occur at points specified.

2) With engine at constant speed in "D3", check for correct operation of kickdown of "D3" to "D2". Continue kickdown until speed is reached where transmission will no longer kick down to lower gear, note speeds attained. Repeat test for "D2" to "D1" shift.

3) With vehicle at road speed of more than 45 MPH, place selector lever from "D" into "1". Note vehicle speed when final downshifts in "1" gear occur at closed or minimum throttle.

NOTE — *Avoid shifting into "1" at speeds above capacity of gear to avoid damage to transmission.*

4) With transmission selector lever in "2" position, transmission should not shift out of "2".

5) Shift points should be smooth without conspicuous shock. No excessive 'creep' should be noted, a slight 'creep' in each range is acceptable.

SHIFT SPEED CHART (MPH)								
	Kickdown				Half-Throttle		Closed Throttle	
Application	D1-D2	D2-D3	D3-D2	D2-D1	D1-D2	D2-D3	D3-D1	1_2-1_1 ①
Courier	31-43	55-71	64-50	32-22	8-17	16-37	.....	34-26
Datsun								
210	32-37	58-62	57-52	29-24	12-17	34-38	22-17	29-25
510	36-41	63-68	62-57	31-26	14-19	37-42	24-19	32-27
810	34-39	60-65	60-55	30-25	13-18	35-40	23-18	30-25
200SX	38-42	66-71	65-60	33-28	14-19	39-44	25-20	33-29
280ZX	38-43	65-70	64-59	34-29	12-17	34-42	26-21	34-29
Pickup	33-38	59-63	58-54	29-25	13-17	37-42	44-37	30-25
Mazda								
GLC	29-41	51-69	60-45	31-20	7-17	14-36	12-6	31-23
626	30-40	53-68	59-46	30-20	8-16	16-35	13-6	31-24
RX7	32-45	59-77	65-51	30-14	9-12	18-40	12-6	33-24

① — Obtained by shifting to "1" range from "D".

JATCO 3N71B & R3A (Cont.)

CLUTCH AND BAND APPLICATION CHART (ELEMENTS IN USE)

Selector Lever Position	Front Clutch	Rear Clutch	Low-Reverse Brake	Brake Band	One-Way Clutch
P — PARK			X		
R — REVERSE	X		X		
N — NEUTRAL①					
D — DRIVE First		X			X
Second		X		X	
Direct	X	X			
2 — SECOND		X		X	
1 — LOW First		X	X		
Second		X		X	

① — Band and all clutches released and/or ineffective.

HYDRAULIC PRESSURE TESTS

Line Pressure Tests — 1) Make sure transmission fluid is at correct level and operating temperature. Connect pressure gauges to line pressure test ports at front and rear of transmission. See Fig. 2.

NOTE — Front port is used to check pressure in "R" range, rear port is used for forward ranges.

2) Block front and rear wheels and securely set parking brake, place selector lever in range to be checked, and note pressure reading on gauge at idle. Gradually increase throttle opening until wide open, then again check pressure reading, pressure should correspond with figures given in Line Pressure chart.

NOTE — Front port is used to check pressure in "R" range, rear port is used for forward ranges.

CAUTION — Do not hold throttle open longer than five seconds at a time.

Governor Pressure Test — Connect a pressure gauge to governor pressure port on transmission case. See Fig. 2. Read pressure with vehicle running at speeds indicated in Governor Pressure chart. If pressures are not within specifications, disassemble and clean governor assembly.

NOTE — Governor pressure is tested only when shift points are different than those listed in Shift Speeds chart.

Line Pressure Specifications (Courier & Mazda)

Application	psi (kg/cm²)
At Idle Speed	
In "R"	57-100 (4.0-7.0)
In "D"	43-57 (3.0-4.0)
In "2"	114-171 (8.0-12.0)
In "1"	43-57 (3.0-4.0)
At Stall Speed	
In "R"	228-270 (16.0-19.0)
In "D"	128-156 (9.0-11.0)
In "2"	114-171 (8.0-12.0)
In "1"	128-156 (9.0-11.0)

Line Pressure Specifications (Datsun)

Application	psi (kg/cm²)
At Idle Speed	
In "R"	
280ZX	74-101 (5.2-7.1)
All Others	60-80 (4.2-5.6)
In "D"	
All Models	46-54 (3.2-3.8)
In "2"	
280ZX	112-196 (7.9-13.8)
All Others	85-166 (6.0-11.7)
In "1"	
All Models	46-54 (3.2-3.8)
At Stall Speed	
In "R"	
280ZX	303-347 (21.3-24.4)
All Others	203-230 (14.3-16.2)
In "D"	
280ZX	164-185 (11.5-13.0)
All Others	141-158 (9.9-11.1)
In "2"	
280ZX	175-196 (12.3-13.8)
All Others	145-166 (10.2-11.7)
In "1"	
280ZX	164-185 (11.5-13.0)
All Others	141-158 (9.9-11.1)

JATCO 3N71B & R3A (Cont.)

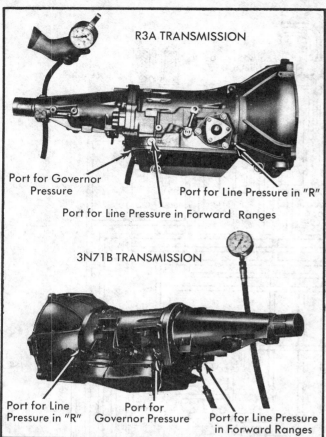

Fig. 2 Hydraulic Pressure Test Port Locations

R3A TRANSMISSION

Port for Governor Pressure
Port for Line Pressure in "R"
Port for Line Pressure in Forward Ranges

3N71B TRANSMISSION

Port for Line Pressure in "R"
Port for Governor Pressure
Port for Line Pressure in Forward Ranges

Governor Pressure Specifications

Application	psi (kg/cm²)
Courier	
At 20 MPH	12-18 (.8-1.3)
At 35 MPH	24-33 (1.7-2.3)
At 55 MPH	45-60 (3.2-4.2)
Mazda	
GLC	
At 20 MPH	11-20 (.8-1.4)
At 35 MPH	26-36 (1.8-2.5)
At 55 MPH	51-70 (3.6-4.9)
626	
At 20 MPH	13-20 (.9-1.4)
At 35 MPH	26-34 (1.8-2.4)
At 55 MPH	52-66 (3.7-4.7)
RX7	
At 20 MPH	11-18 (.8-1.3)
At 35 MPH	23-33 (1.6-2.3)
At 55 MPH	44-60 (3.1-4.2)

STALL TEST

1) Check engine and transmission for proper lubricant levels, bring engine to normal operating temperature. Attach suitable tachometer to engine and position so that dial is visible from driver's compartment. Block front and rear wheels, apply hand brake firmly.

2) Place one foot firmly on brake pedal and position selector lever in "D" range. Gradually accelerate engine to wide open throttle, when speed is constant, take reading from

tachometer and decelerate engine. **NOTE** — *Do not hold engine at wide open throttle for more than five seconds.*

3) Move shift lever to "N" or "P" position and run engine at 1200 RPM for one minute or so to cool automatic transmission fluid. Repeat same procedure for "2", "1", and "R" ranges.

Stall Speed Specifications

Application	Stall RPM
Courier	1950-2200
Datsun	
210	1850-2150
510	1900-2200
810	1650-1950
200SX	1650-1950
280ZX	1950-2250
Pickup	1750-2050
Mazda	
GLC	1900-2150
626	2000-2250
RX-7	2300-2550

TRANSMISSION REMOVAL & INSTALLATION

Removal — 1) Disconnect battery ground, remove torsion shaft from accelerator linkage (if equipped). Hoist vehicle off ground and support with safety stands. Remove any mounting brackets or bolts holding exhaust system to transmission case. Remove propeller shaft, using suitable output shaft plug to prevent oil leakage from rear of transmission.

2) Remove speedometer cable from extension housing. Disconnect all electrical and vacuum leads from engine to transmission. Take off fluid cooler lines and transmission filler tube. Support engine with suitable wooden block between oil pan and jack stand.

3) Take off engine rear plate or rubber plug for access to converter bolts. **NOTE** — *Some rotary engine models may require removal of starter motor at this time to gain access to bolts.* Place paint or scribe marks on torque converter and drive plate to ensure alignment at reassembly. Remove converter bolts.

4) With transmission supported by transmission jack, remove rear engine mount and crossmember. Remove starter motor (if not already done). Take out bolts securing converter housing to engine, lower and remove transmission.

Installation — 1) Before installing transmission, check run out of torque converter drive plate. Acceptable run out is .012" (.3 mm), if run out exceeds .020" (.5 mm), replace drive plate. Position transmission in vehicle for installation.

2) Line up notch in torque converter with same notch in oil pump. On Datsun models, torque converter is correctly positioned when distance from converter to face of converter housing is .542" (13.8 mm) on 210 models or .846" (21.5 mm) on all other Datsun models. *See Fig. 5.* Align marks of torque converter and drive plate, install transmission on engine, then install and tighten converter-to-drive plate bolts, making sure marks are still aligned.

3) Rotate crankshaft several times to ensure that transmission turns freely and is not binding. Reconnect all electrical, vacuum, and coolant leads and lines to transmission. Replace

Automatic Transmissions

JATCO 3N71B & R3A (Cont.)

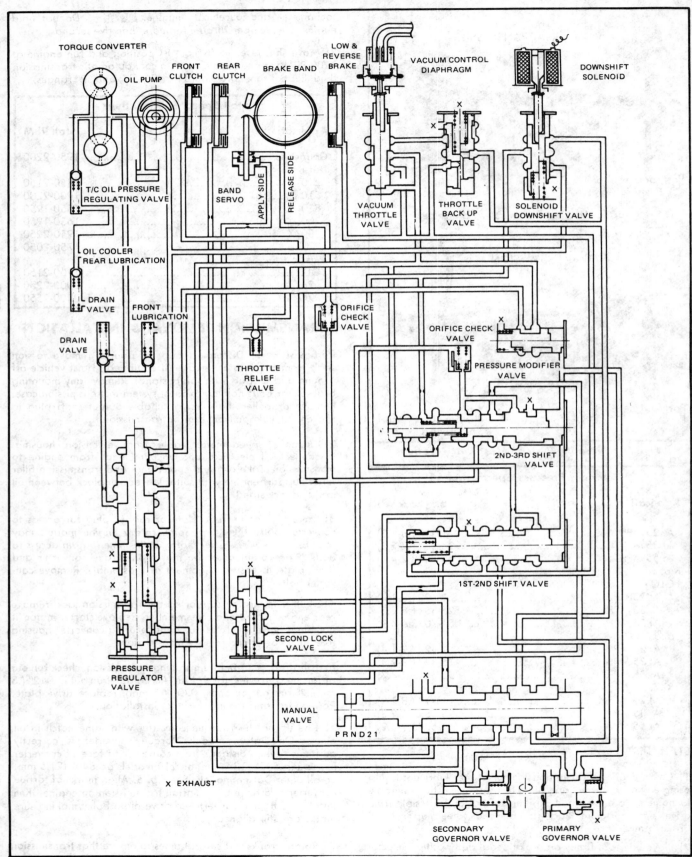

Fig. 3 *Jatco Automatic Transmission Hydraulic Circuits Diagram
(Courier & Mazda Models)*

JATCO 3N71B & R3A (Cont.)

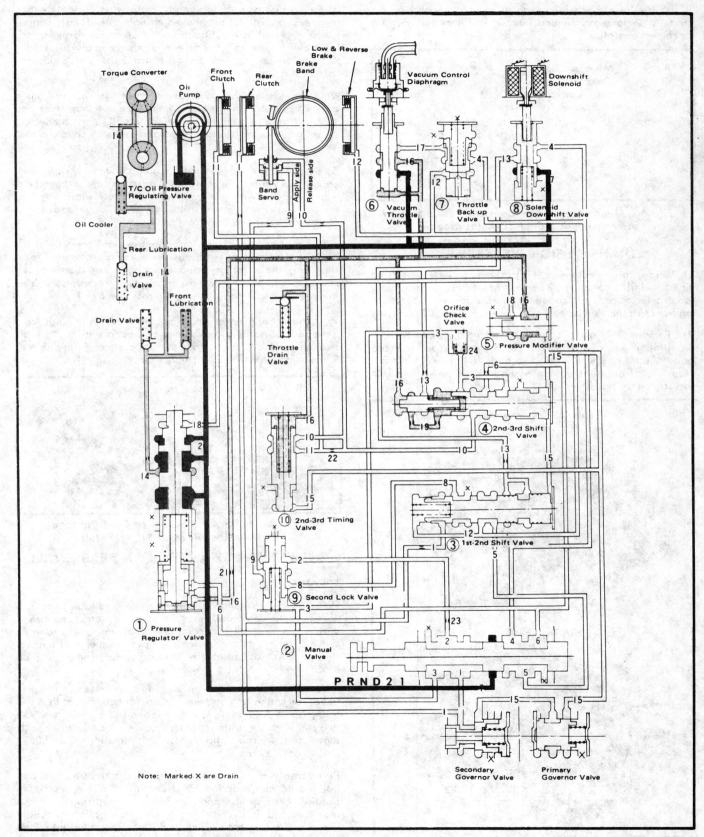

Fig. 4   Jatco Automatic Transmission Hydraulic Circuits Diagram
(Datsun Models)

JATCO 3N71B & R3A (Cont.)

all other related parts in reverse of removal procedure. Fill transmission to recommended fluid level. Check all functions for correct operation.

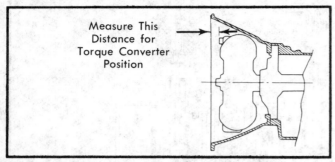

Fig. 5　Measuring Torque Converter Engagement in Transmission Case (Datsun Models)

TRANSMISSION DISASSEMBLY

1) Remove torque converter, tilt transmission case and drain oil into suitable container. Remove transmission dipstick tube, range selector rod, and counter shaft. Detach converter housing from transmission case.

2) Remove oil pan, downshift solenoid, and vacuum diaphragm with operating rod. Remove valve body-to-case bolts (*Fig. 6*) and withdraw valve body from case. Withdraw input shaft from front pump. Loosen lock nut on servo band, then tighten piston stem.

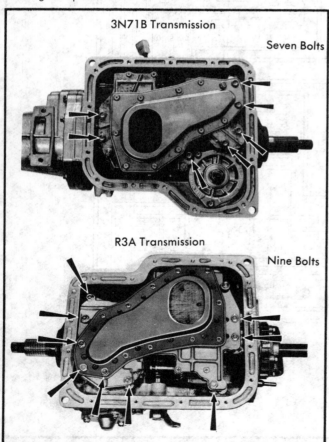

Fig. 6　Bottom View of Transmission Case Showing Valve Body-to-Case Bolt Locations

3) Pull out oil pump using equal leverage on opposite edges of pump so that unit is removed straight out of case. Loosen piston stem and take out band strut, then remove brake band, front clutch assembly, and rear clutch assembly as a unit. Remove connecting shell, rear clutch hub, and planetary carrier as a unit.

4) Remove snap ring and take connecting drum and inner gear of planetary carrier as a unit. Take out snap rings and pull out rear planetary carrier, internal gear, connecting drum, one-way clutch outer race and one-way clutch, in that order.

5) Detach and remove rear extension housing, parking pawl, spring and washer. Pull output shaft rearward, remove oil distributor along with governor valve. Pry off snap ring and remove low-reverse brake retaining plate, drive and driven plates, and dished plate from case.

6) On rear of transmission case, remove eight one-way clutch attaching bolts, then withdraw one-way clutch inner race, snap ring, piston return spring and support ring. Remove low-reverse brake piston from case by applying compressed air to low-reverse brake apply passage in case (see *Fig. 7*).

7) Remove band servo attaching bolts. Pry snap rings from both ends of parking brake lever and remove lever. Back off manual shaft lock nut, remove manual plate and parking rod. Remove inhibitor switch and manual shaft.

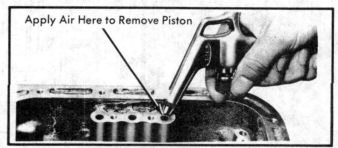

Fig. 7　Applying Air Pressure to Case Passage to Remove Low-Reverse Brake Piston

COMPONENT DISASSEMBLY & REASSEMBLY

FRONT CLUTCH

Disassembly — Remove snap ring using suitable tool and take out retaining plate, inner plates, outer plates, and dished plate. Take out coil spring retainer snap ring using suitable clutch spring compressing tool, remove retainer and ten coil springs. Force out piston by blowing compressed air into oil hole.

Inspection — Inspect inner plates for undue wear or fatigue. Check coil spring retainer, replace if deformed. Ensure that coil spring has not lost tension, inspect seal around piston and "O" ring inside clutch drum for damage. Replace all parts which show undue wear or fatigue. Standard plate thickness is .059-.065" (1.5-1.65 mm).

Reassembly — **1)** Coat new seals with transmission fluid and install onto piston and clutch drum. Install piston into drum, position return springs and retainer on top of piston, compress assembly and install retaining snap ring. Install dished plate into drum, follow with a flat steel plate, then alternate lined and steel plates until all clutch plates are installed (see *Front Clutch Plate Chart*). Position retaining ring in drum, then install clutch pack snap ring.

JATCO 3N71B & R3A (Cont.)

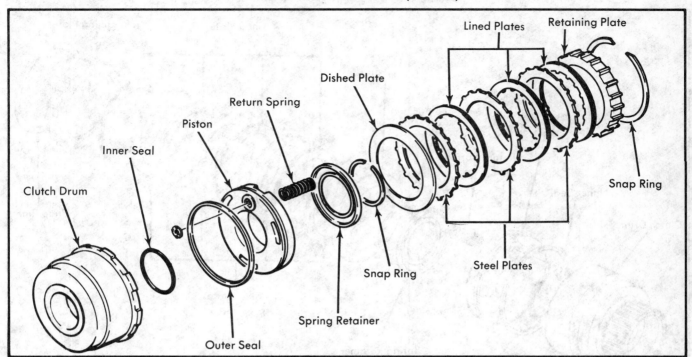

Fig. 8 Exploded View of Front Clutch Assembly

2) Using a feeler gauge, measure clearance between clutch pack retaining snap ring and retaining plate in drum. Clearance should be .063-.071" (1.6-1.8 mm). If clearance is not within specifications, adjust by installing a selective thickness retaining plate, available in the following thicknesses: For 3N71B transmission, from .417" (10.6 mm) to .457" (11.6 mm) in increments of .008" (.2 mm); For R3A transmission, from .283" (7.2 mm) to .323" (8.2 mm) in increments of .008" (.2 mm).

Front Clutch Plate Chart

Application	Lined Plates	Steel Plates
Courier	4	4
Datsun		
All Models	3	3
Mazda		
All Models	3	3

REAR CLUTCH

Disassembly — Remove snap ring, retaining plate, outer plate, inner plate, and dished plate in same order used for front clutch. Remove coil spring retainer using suitable compressing tool, take out retainer and ten coil springs. Remove piston by blowing compressed air into oil hole.

Inspection — Make same inspection of components as for front clutch. Replace any parts showing undue wear or fatigue.

Reassembly — **1)** Coat new seals with transmission fluid and install onto piston and clutch drum. Install piston into drum, position return springs and retainer on top of piston, compress assembly and install retaining snap ring. Install dished plate into drum, follow with a flat steel plate, then alternate lined

and steel plates until all plates are installed (see *Rear Clutch Plate Chart*). Position retaining plate in drum, then install clutch pack snap ring.

2) Using a feeler gauge, measure clearance between clutch pack retaining snap ring and retaining plate in drum. Clearance should be .031-.063" (.8-1.6 mm). If clearance is not within specifications, check all clutch components for wear and replace as necessary.

Rear Clutch Plate Chart

Application	Lined Plates	Steel Plates
Courier	5	5
Datsun		
210	3	3
200SX	5	5
810	6	6
280ZX	5	5
All Others	4	4
Mazda		
All Models	3	3

LOW & REVERSE BRAKE

NOTE — *Low-Reverse brake is removed and installed in case as part of Transmission Disassembly and Transmission Reassembly.*

Inspection — Check lined, steel, and retaining plate surfaces for wear, scoring, or other damage and replace parts as necessary. Inspect piston release spring for distortion or cracks and replace if found damaged. Check piston for damage and replace if required.

JATCO 3N71B & R3A (Cont.)

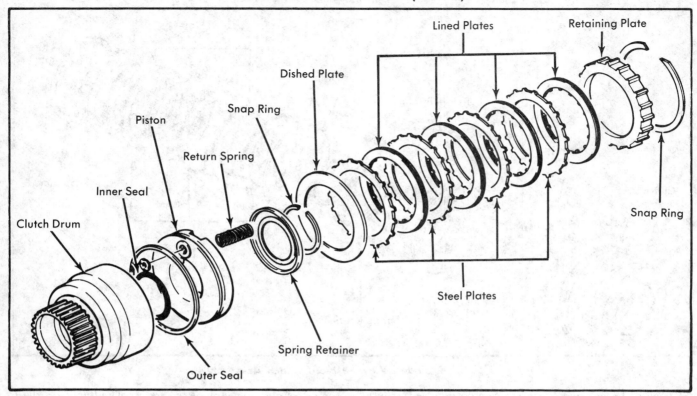

Fig. 9   Exploded View Showing Components of Rear Clutch Assembly

BAND SERVO PISTON

Disassembly — Remove three bolts attaching band servo retainer to transmission case. Take out retainer and servo piston. Lift out return spring. If servo retainer is difficult to free from case, remove by forcing compressed air into oil hole on piston release side. Blow compressed air into oil hole on apply side of servo piston to remove piston from retainer.

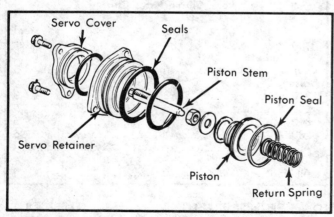

Fig. 10   Exploded View of Band Servo Assembly (Mazda Model Shown — Others Similiar)

Inspection — Ensure that two "O" rings on servo retainer and rubber seal on servo piston are not damaged. Check all parts for undue wear or fatigue, inspect return spring for adequate tension and brake band lining for excessive wear or damage. Replace any parts needed.

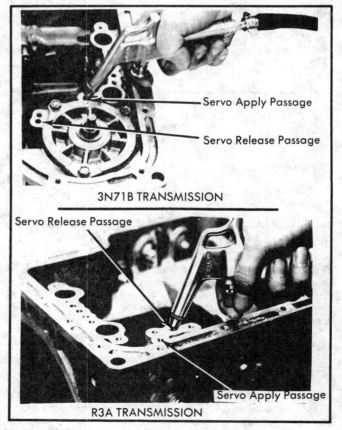

Fig. 11   Using Compressed Air to Check Band Servo Operation

JATCO 3N71B & R3A (Cont.)

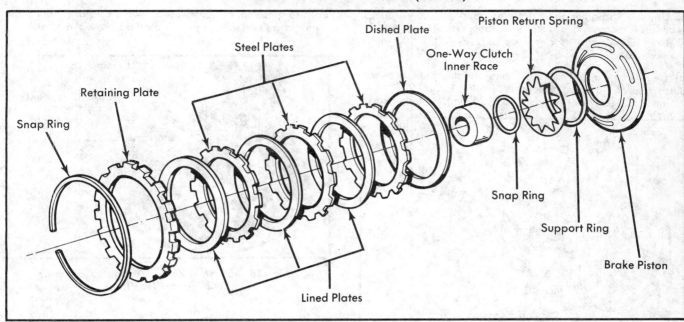

Fig. 12 *Exploded View Showing Components of Low-Reverse Brake Assembly*

Reassembly — Coat all parts with automatic transmission fluid and reassemble in reverse order of disassembly. To check for correct operation of component, blow compressed air into oil hole on servo piston apply side to ensure piston operates correctly. Back off three attaching bolts slightly and apply compressed air to oil hole on servo release side, if retainer rises by same amount as bolts are backed off, release is normal. Retighten bolts to specified torque.

GOVERNOR VALVE ASSEMBLY

Disassembly — Separate governor from oil distributor by removing four bolts. Remove secondary governor retainer plate, then remove spring and secondary governor valve from body. If primary governor valve is to be disassembled for any purpose, remove spring seat, primary governor valve, spring, and spring seat.

Inspection — Check valve and body for valve sticking or catching. Ensure that spring has not lost tension or that

retainer plates are not deformed. Check side clearance between sealing ring and groove. Correct clearance is .002-.006" (.04-.16 mm).

Reassembly — Coat all parts with automatic transmission fluid and reassemble in reverse order of disassembly. Be careful not to confuse primary valve with secondary valve. Ensure that governor spring is straight and there are no sticking or catching places in governor valve movement. Tighten governor to oil distributor with four bolts at specified torque.

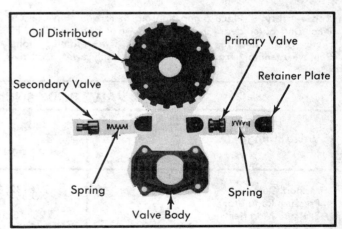

Fig. 14 *Exploded View Showing Governor Assembly*

OIL PUMP ASSEMBLY

Disassembly — Take pump cover off pump housing by removing five bolts. Mark inner and outer gears with quick-drying ink or paint for reassembly reference, then remove gears from housing. Remove large seal ring from outside diameter of pump housing, and seal rings from stator support.

Inspection — 1) Check for undue wear or damage to gear teeth. Replace rubber ring if worn to any extent. Check the following oil pump clearances:

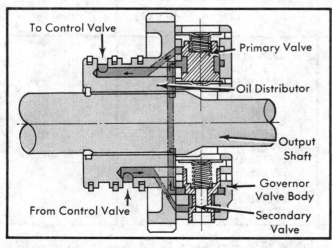

Fig. 13 *Cutway View of Governor Showing Hydraulic Circuits*

JATCO 3N71B & R3A (Cont.)

2) Using a straightedge and feeler gauge, measure pump gear face-to-cover clearance. Clearance should be .0008-.0016″ (.02-.04 mm). If clearance exceeds .003″ (.08 mm), replace gears.

3) Next, using a feeler gauge, measure clearance between outer gear and crescent. Clearance should be .006-.008″ (.14-.21 mm). If clearance exceeds .010″ (.25 mm), replace gears.

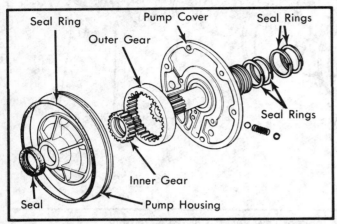

Fig. 15　Exploded View of Oil Pump Assembly

4) Finally, measure clearance between outer gear and pump housing using a feeler gauge. Clearance should be .002-.008″ (.05-.20 mm). If clearance exceeds .010″ (.25 mm), replace gears.

5) Check all parts for wear or fatigue, replace any defective part(s) found. Ensure that oil seal rings of oil feed grooves are not damaged, and still have tension, check side clearance of oil ring, .002-.006″ (.04-.16 mm) is acceptable.

Reassembly — Place pump housing in torque converter, fit inner and outer gears in housing as when disassembling. Fit pump cover and temporarily tighten five retaining bolts. Remove assembly from converter and finally tighten all five

bolts to specifications. Install seal rings on stator support, and a new large seal ring on pump housing outside diameter.

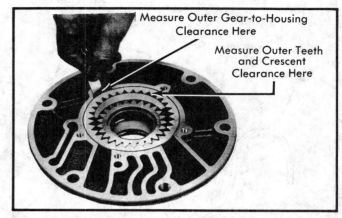

Fig. 16　Using a Feeler Gauge to Measure Oil Pump Clearances

PLANETARY CARRIER

NOTE — *Planetary carrier is one-piece unit, only check is for clearance between pinion washer and carrier. Standard clearance is .008-.028″ (.20-.70 mm), if clearance exceeds .031″ (.80 mm), replace carrier.*

VALVE BODY ASSEMBLY

Disassembly — 1) Remove oil screen attaching bolts and oil screen. Remove bolts attaching upperbody to lower body, then separate upper body and separator plate from lower body, taking care not to lose check valves and springs in lower body. Slide manual valve out of body. Remove shift valve cover plate from body and remove following parts: 1-2 shift valve and spring, 2-3 shift valve, plug, and spring, and also modulator valve and spring.

① VALVE BODY SPRING IDENTIFICATION				
Valve Spring	**Length** In. (mm)	**Diameter** In. (mm)	**Number Of Coils**	**Color**
Manual Detent	1.276 (32.4)	.236 (6.0)	15	.....
Pressure Regulator	1.693 (43.0)	.413 (10.5)	13	.....
Pressure Modifier	.728 (18.5)	.315 (8.0)	5	.....
1-2 Shift	1.260 (32.0)	.236 (6.0)②	16③	.....
2-3 Shift	1.614 (41.0)	.244 (6.2)	18	.....
2-3 Shift Timing	1.280 (32.5)	.217 (5.5)	15	.....
Throttle Back-Up	1.417 (36.0)	.256 (6.5)	14	.....
Solenoid Downshift	.866 (22.0)	.197 (5.0)	12	.....
Second Lock	1.319 (33.5)	.197 (5.0)	16	.....
Throttle Relief	1.055 (26.8)	.221 (5.6)	14	.....
Orifice Check	.610 (15.5)⑤	.188 (4.77)	12④	.....
Primary Governor	.858 (21.8)	.327 (8.3)	5	.....
Secondary Governor	.992 (25.2)	.335 (8.5)	5.5	.....

① — Courier specifications not available.　② — Mazda diameter is .258″ (6.55 mm).　③ — Mazda number of coils is 16.7.
④ — Mazda number of coils is 15.　⑤ — Mazda free length is .847″ (21.5 mm).

JATCO 3N71B & R3A (Cont.)

2) Remove downshift cover plate from body and withdraw following parts: downshift valve and spring, throttle back-up valve and spring, throttle valve, and on Datsun models only, the 2-3 timing valve and spring. Remove pressure regulator cover plate from body and withdraw following parts: pressure regulator valve sleeve, plug, spring seat, spring, pressure regulator valve, second lock valve and spring.

Inspection — Check all parts for any problem which may cause components to stick. Inspect all valve springs and check valve springs for adequate tension. Ensure that no damage has occured to oil strainer. Look over separator plate for any abnormal oil passages, check for same defects in oil passages of valve body. Replace any parts showing abnormal wear or fatigue.

Reassembly — Replace all parts in reverse order of removal procedure after coating parts with automatic transmission fluid. Use illustration to confirm location and position of small valves and springs. Do not force any part which seems difficult to place or insert. Use light straight pressure to fit parts. Tighten all bolts to torque standards specified.

INPUT SHELL & SUN GEAR ASSEMBLY

Disassembly & Reassembly — Remove external snap ring from sun gear, withdraw thrust washer, then remove sun gear from shell. Remove internal snap ring from sun gear. Coat all parts with transmission fluid and reverse disassembly procedure.

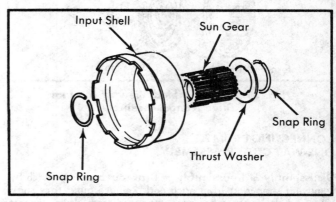

Fig. 18   Exploded View of Input Shell and Sun Gear Assembly

INTERNAL DRIVE FLANGE ASSEMBLY

Disassembly & Reassembly — Remove snap ring and disconnect flange from internal gear. Inspect parts for wear or fatigue. Coat parts with automatic transmission fluid and assemble in reverse of disassembly procedure.

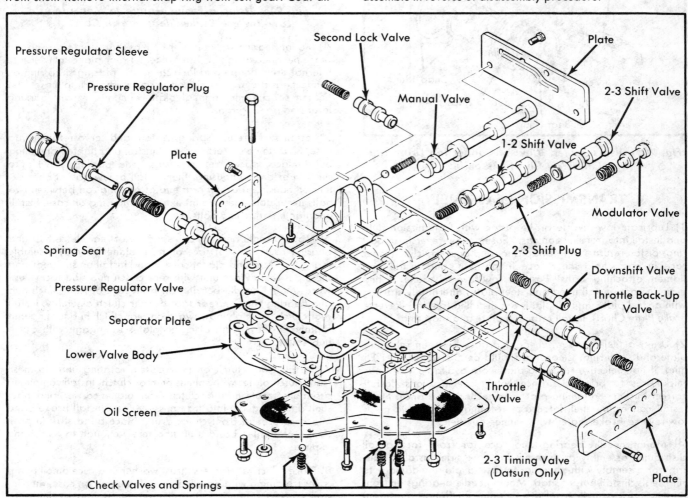

Fig. 17   Exploded View of Valve Body Assembly

JATCO 3N71B & R3A (Cont.)

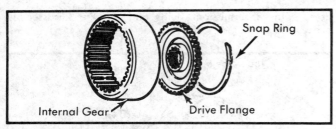

Fig. 19 Disassembled View of Internal Drive Flange Assembly

CONNECTING DRUM & ONE-WAY CLUTCH ASSEMBLY

Disassembly & Reassembly — Draw out one-way clutch by removing snap ring from each end. Remove outer race snap ring and draw out outer race rearward from drum. Inspect one-way clutch for undue wear or damage, also check contacting surfaces of inner and outer races. When reassembling one-way clutch, ensure that arrow mark is fitted toward front of vehicle.

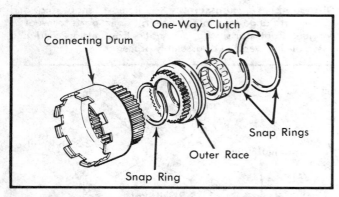

Fig. 20 Disassembled View of Connecting Drum and One-Way Clutch Assembly

TRANSMISSION REASSEMBLY

1) Lubricate low-reverse brake piston with transmission fluid and install into transmission case. Position low-reverse support ring, piston return spring, snap ring, and one-way clutch inner race in case, hold inner race in position, and install and tighten attaching bolts. Position low-reverse brake dished plate in case, install lined and steel plates alternately starting with a steel plate until all plates are installed (see Low-Reverse Brake Plate Chart). Install retaining plate and snap ring.

2) Using a feeler gauge, check clearance between retaining plate and snap ring. Clearance should be .031-.049" (.8-1.25 mm), if not, selective retaining plates are available in various thicknesses to bring clearance within specifications. Install correct thickness retaining plate and recheck clearance. Next, install connecting shell into case, rotating clockwise to mesh low-reverse brake plates with splines on shell.

3) Mount needle bearing and race for front face of oil distributor assembly on transmission case side. Install oil distributor assembly with governor to case, avoid any damage to ring seals. Install output shaft. Mount needle bearings on front and rear faces of internal drive flange, fit flange on output shaft and lock in place with snap ring.

Low-Reverse Brake Plate Chart		
Application	Lined Plates	Steel Plates
Courier	4	4
Datsun		
210	3	3
810 & 280ZX	5	5
510, 200SX & Pickup	4	4
Mazda		
GLC	3	3
All Others	4	4

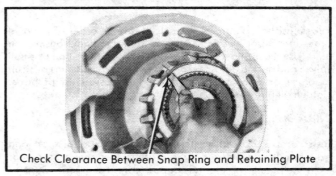

Check Clearance Between Snap Ring and Retaining Plate

Fig. 21 Using a Feeler Gauge to Measure Low-Reverse Brake Clearance in Case

4) Mount bearing race on rear face of rear planet carrier and place needle bearing on front face. Fit rear planet carrier into internal drive flange and lock carrier by placing snap ring on connecting drum. Push in on manual shaft into case and tighten spacer and manual plate with nut. Mount parking lever and parking rod.

5) Install servo return spring, piston, and servo retainer into case, hold down on retainer, and install and tighten attaching bolts. Place spacer, return spring, and parking pawl onto shaft in extension housing, then install a new gasket onto extension housing face. Fit rear end of parking rod between two balls in support, then mount extension housing on case. Install and tighten attaching bolts.

6) Mount needle bearing on rear face of rear clutch hub and bearing race on front face of front planet carrier, assemble rear clutch hub and planet carrier and install on sun gear and the input shell. Place unit with rear clutch hub side facing upward. Mount needle bearing on front face of rear clutch hub and bearing race on rear face of rear clutch assembly, install rear clutch assembly downward on rear clutch hub turning unit slightly to allow teeth of clutch plates to engage with clutch hub spline.

7) Install front clutch on rear clutch, rotating units to mesh front clutch plates with splines on rear clutch. Install completed assembly (front and rear clutch, front planet carrier, and input shell and sun gear) into transmission case. Install brake band into case around front clutch drum, place band strut in position, then tighten band adjusting screw enough to hold band in place.

8) Place selective thickness thrust washer and race on oil pump cover (retaining with Vaseline), position pump on case, then install converter housing. Install input shaft into assembly.To check pump cover-to-front clutch drum end play, insert a

JATCO 3N71B & R3A (Cont.)

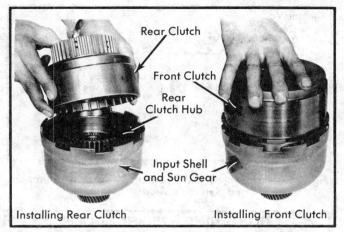

Fig. 22 Assembling Front and Rear Clutch Units

10) To adjust band, tighten servo piston stem to 8.6-11 ft. lbs. (1.2-1.5 mkg), loosen stem exactly two turns, hold stem in position and tighten lock nut. Install valve body on transmission case, tightening attaching bolts evenly. Install vacuum unit push rod into case. **NOTE** — *If transmission case, valve body, or diaphragm unit has been replaced, measure distance from edge of case to bottom of hole in throttle valve (valve completely compressed in bore). Select correct length rod as indicated in Diaphragm Rod Chart.* Install vacuum unit, downshift solenoid, and oil pan.

feeler gauge between front clutch drum and input shell. Clearance should be .020-.032" (.5-.8 mm); if not, select a different selective thrust washer that will bring clearance to specification. Thrust washers are available in thicknesses from .059" (1.5 mm) to .106" (2.7 mm) in .008" (.2 mm) increments.

9) To measure total end play of transmission assembly, place a dial indicator on front end of transmission with indicator button contacting input shaft. Push input shaft fully rearward and zero dial indicator. Insert a screwdriver behind input shell forcing gear train forward, then read resulting play on gauge. End play should be .010-.020" (.25-.50 mm); if not, select correct thickness thrust washer race to bring play within specifications. Races are available from .047" (1.2 mm) to .087" (2.2 mm), in .008" (.2 mm) increments.

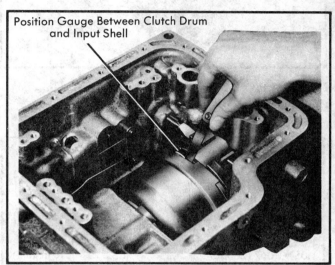

Fig. 24 Using a Feeler Gauge to Measure Pump Cover-to-Front Clutch Clearance

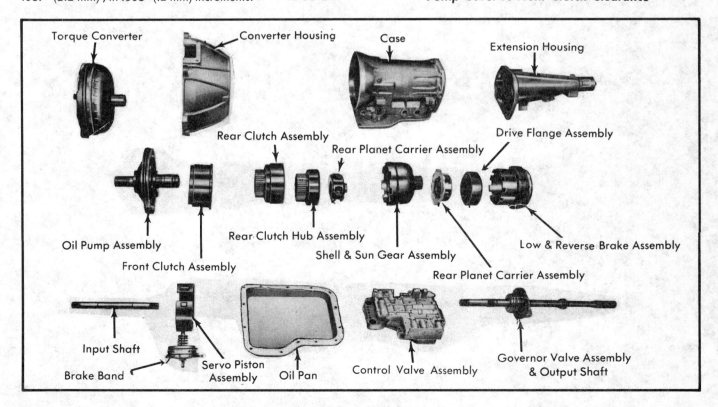

Fig. 23 Exploded View Showing Major Components of Jatco Automatic Transmission Assembly

Automatic Transmissions

JATCO 3N71B & R3A (Cont.)

Move Connecting Shell Forward

Dial Indicator

Fig. 25   Using a Dial Indicator to Measure Total End Play of Transmission

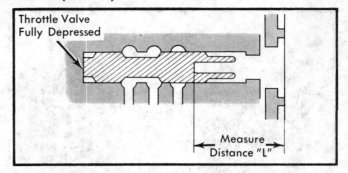

Throttle Valve Fully Depressed

Measure Distance "L"

Fig. 26   Cutaway View Showing Vacuum Diaphragm Rod Selection Measurement

Diaphragm Rod Selection Chart

If Distance "L" Is In. (mm)	Use This Rod In. (mm)
Under 1.008 (25.6)	1.142 (29.0)
1.012-1.028 (25.7-26.1)	1.161 (29.5)
1.032-1.047 (26.2-26.6)	1.181 (30.0)
1.051-1.067 (26.7-27.1)	1.201 (30.5)
Over 1.071 (27.2)	1.222 (31.0)

TIGHTENING SPECIFICATIONS

Application	Ft. Lbs. (mkg)
Convertor Hsg.-to-Engine	25-36 (3.5-5.0)
Convertor Hsg.-to-Trans. Case	
Mazda 626	22-36 (3.0-5.0)
All Others	33-40 (4.6-5.5)
Drive Plate-to-Crankshaft	
Courier	54-64 (7.5-8.8)
Datsun	101-116 (14.0-16.0)
Mazda	
GLC	60-69 (8.3-9.5)
626	112-118 (15.5-16.3)
RX-7	30-46 (4.1-6.4)
Drive Plate-to-Converter	
Datsun	29-36 (4.0-5.0)
Courier & Mazda	25-36 (3.5-5.0)

MERCEDES-BENZ TYPE W 3 A 040

450 SEL
450 SL
450 SLC

DESCRIPTION

Transmission is a fully automatic three speed unit consisting primarily of a three element welded torque converter and a compound planetary gear set. Two multiple-disc clutches, one overrunning clutch, and three brake bands provide the friction elements required to obtain the desired function of the planetary gear set. A hydraulic system, pressurized by a primary gear type pump and a secondary piston type pump provide the working pressure required to operate the friction elements and automatic controls.

NOTE — *An additional ball valve with compression spring is installed in shift valve housing; also, a new detent valve is installed in the transmission.*

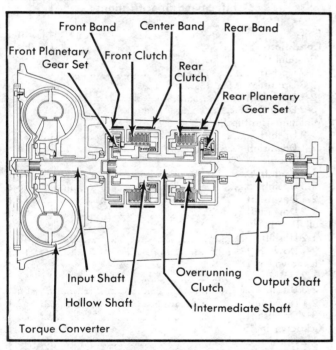

Fig. 1 Cutaway View of Mercedes-Benz 3-Speed Automatic Transmission Assembly

LUBRICATION & ADJUSTMENT

See AUTOMATIC TRANSMISSION SERVICING Section.

TROUBLE SHOOTING

SLIPS IN ALL SELECTOR POSITIONS

Incorrect modulating pressure. Modulating pressure control valve or pressure relief valve for modulating pressure dirty or sticking. Line to transmission vacuum unit clogged or leaking. Working pressure control valve dirty or sticking. Defective primary pump.

TRANSMISSION GRABS OR VEHICLE SHAKES WHEN STARTING OFF

Incorrect modulating pressure. Check transmission vacuum unit; if transmission fluid is found in vacuum unit, replace unit; if fuel is found in vacuum unit, check injection system and adjust.

TRANSMISSION SLIPS IN FIRST GEAR

Dirty or sticking valves in valve body. Defective center servo piston or piston sealing ring damaged. Defective center band or thrust body. Bleed valves for front clutch supporting flange sticking.

TRANSMISSION SLIPS ON UPSHIFTS

Incorrect modulating or working pressure. Faulty valve body assembly (replace sealing bushings on plug pipes). Defective front or rear clutch. Oil distribution sleeve damaged.

TRANSMISSION SLIPS IN THIRD GEAR

Valve body sealing bushings worn or damaged. Defective rear clutch assembly. Oil distributing sleeve damaged.

TRANSMISSION SLIPS IN FIRST AND SECOND GEARS

Rear band worn or damaged. Adjust brake band by installing a longer thrust pin.

TRANSMISSION SLIPS IN ALL GEARS

Incorrect modulating pressure. Defective modulating pressure relief valve or control valve.

TRANSMISSION WILL NOT ENGAGE PROPERLY

Torque converter not installed correctly. Driver not correctly engaging in drive gear of primary pump.

NO POSITIVE ENGAGEMENT IN REVERSE

Front band out of adjustment. Front servo piston sealing ring worn or damaged. Defective one-way clutch in gear unit assembly.

ROUGH JERK WHEN ENGAGING SELECTOR LEVER POSITION "D"

Adjust engine idle speed and emissions as specified. Incorrect modulating and/or working pressure. Vacuum leak. Defective pressure receiving piston in extension housing.

NOTE — *If a rough jerk results when shifting for short periods back and forth between "N" and "D", there is no reason for a complaint. The pressure receiver requires approximately 2 seconds to operate.*

ROUGH JERKS WHEN CHANGING GEAR

Check modulating pressure and working pressure and adjust modulating pressure if necessary. If working pressure is too high, replace valve body assembly. Vacuum lines or connections leaking. Control pressure linkage out of adjustment. Control valve converter adjustment incorrect.

Automatic Transmissions

MERCEDES-BENZ TYPE W 3 A 040 (Cont.)

ROUGH JERK ON 3-2 DOWNSHIFT

Rear servo piston sealing ring worn or damaged. Defective rear servo piston.

NO UPSHIFTS

Incorrect governor pressure. Defective governor assembly. Valve body dirty or valves sticking.

UPSHIFTS ONLY IN UPPER SPEED RANGE OF GEARS

Control pressure linkage out of adjustment. Defective governor assembly.

UPSHIFTS ONLY IN LOWER SPEED RANGE OF GEARS

Control pressure linkage damaged or out of adjustment. Accelerator linkage out of adjustment. Defective governor assembly.

POOR ACCERERATION AT START

Check stalling speed and if speed drops 400/700 RPM, replace torque converter.

NO KICKDOWN SHIFTS

Fuse for power supply to solenoid valve blown. Defective solenoid valve. Control pressure linkage damaged or out of adjustment. Kickdown control valve in valve body sticking.

TRANSMISSION NOT SHIFTING UP

Governor or command valve in shift valve housing require repair or replacement.

NO ENGINE BRAKING ON DOWNSHIFTS

Control pressure linkage out of adjustment. Defective servo piston(s). Defective valve body assembly.

TESTING

ROAD TEST

NOTE — *Before road testing, make sure fluid level and condition, and control linkage adjustments have been checked and corrected as necessary.*

1) During road test, transmission should upshift and downshift at approximately the speeds shown in Shift Speeds Chart. All shifts may vary somewhat due to production tolerances or tire size. The important factor to note is the quality of the shifts. All shifts should be smooth, responsive, and with no engine speed flare-up.

NOTE — *Shifts at full throttle and kickdown are somewhat firmer than part throttle shifts.*

2) Slipping or engine speed flare-up in any gear usually indicates clutch or band problems. The slipping clutch or band in a particular gear can usually be identified by noting transmission operation in all selector positions and comparing which internal units are applied in those positions. See *Clutch And Band Application Chart.*

3) Although this process of elimination can be used to detect any unit which slips, and to confirm proper operation of good units, the actual cause of the malfunction usually cannot be decided. Practically any condition can be caused by leaking hydraulic circuits or sticking valves. Therefore, unless an obvious condition exists, the transmission should never be disassembled until hydraulic pressure tests have been made.

Shift Speed Specifications	
Shift Condition	Shift Point (MPH)
Minimum Throttle In "D"	
1-2 Upshift	19
2-3 Upshift	28
2-1 Downshift	12
3-2 Downshift	22
Minimum Throttle In "S"	
1-2 Upshift	21
2-1 Downshift	14
Full Throttle In "D"	
1-2 Upshift	42
2-3 Upshift	86
2-1 Downshift	12
3-2 Downshift	37
Full Throttle In "S"	
1-2 Upshift	48
2-1 Downshift	17
Kickdown In "D"	
1-2 Upshift	42
2-3 Upshift	86
2-1 Downshift	32
3-2 Downshift	76
Kickdown In "S"	
1-2 Upshift	48
2-1 Downshift	39

CLUTCH AND BAND APPLICATION CHART
(ELEMENTS IN USE)

Gear Range	Front Clutch	Rear Clutch	Front Band	Center Band	Rear Band	Overrunning Clutch
FIRST GEAR				X	X	X
SECOND GEAR	X				X	
THIRD GEAR	X	X				
REVERSE			X			X
NEUTRAL OR PARK — All clutches and bands released and/or ineffective.						

MERCEDES-BENZ TYPE W 3 A 040 (Cont.)

HYDRAULIC PRESSURE TESTS

Preparation For Tests — Before making tests, be sure that fluid level and condition, manual and throttle linkages, EGR system, and neutral safety/back-up light switch have been checked and adjusted or corrected as necessary. Connect a suitable pressure gauge test set (116 589 15 21 00) to pressure take-off points on transmission (see illustration).

NOTE — *Make sure pressure gauge hoses do not drag on pavement or contact exhaust system.*

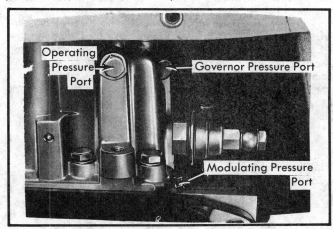

Fig. 2 Side View of Transmission Case Showing Pressure Test Take-Off Points

NOTE — *Modulating pressure must be measured (and corrected if necessary) before making working pressure and governor pressure tests.*

Modulating Pressure Test — Accelerate vehicle on the road or on a dynamometer to 53 MPH. Run engine at full throttle, and keep speed at 53 MPH by lightly applying service brakes. Read resulting pressure on the gauge attached to modulating pressure take-off point on transmission. Pressure should check as shown in chart; adjust as necessary.

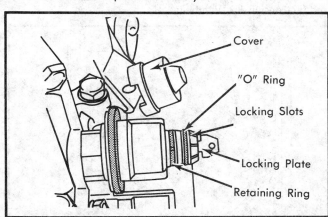

Fig. 3 Rear View of Transmission Showing Vacuum Modulator Assembly

Modulating Pressure Adjustment — 1) Compress circlip and remove vacuum modulator cover. Pull locking plate out of locking slots.

2) The adjusting screw in vacuum modulator can now be turned with the locking plate. One turn of adjusting screw changes modulating pressure approximately 3 psi (.2 kg/cm²).

3) After adjustment is completed, press locking plate into the next locking slot to lock adjusting screw in place. Reinstall vacuum modulator cover.

NOTE — *Working pressure is not adjustable. Pressure is automatically established with correctly adjusted modulating pressure.*

Working Pressure — To check pressure, drive vehicle in indicated range and speed shown in chart, and note pressure readings on gauge.

NOTE — *Governor pressure is a partial pressure of the working pressure and is controlled by centrifugal governor on output shaft.*

Governor Pressure — Drive vehicle on road or on a chassis dynamometer and compare pressures noted on gauge with pressures given on chart.

NOTE — *If values are not within specifications, disassemble and clean governor assembly.*

Hydraulic Pressure Specifications	
Application	**psi (kg/cm²)**
Modulating Pressure (In "D")	
At 53 MPH①	45 (3.2)
Stationary②	70 (4.9)
Working Pressure	
In "D" at 53 MPH	81-87 (5.7-6.1)
In "D" Stationary	175-187 (12.3-13.1)
In "R" Stationary	261 (18.4)
Governor Pressure	
At 12 MPH	7 (.5)
At 25 MPH	20 (1.4)
At 37 MPH	29 (2.0)
At 56 MPH	38 (2.7)
At 75 MPH③	49 (3.4)

① — With vacuum line connected, and at full throttle.
② — Pressures with vehicle stationary are reference values and are used only for orientation when making adjustments.
③ — Can be measured at full throttle only.

Control Pressure — Control pressure is a partial pressure of modulating pressure and is controlled by the position of accelerator pedal. If control pressure rod is correctly adjusted, control pressure will be arrived at automatically. No take-off point is provided for measuring control pressure.

STALL TEST

Testing Precautions — When making test, do not hold throttle open longer than five seconds or severe transmission damage may result from the heat generated. If engine speed exceeds maximum limits shown, release accelerator immediately as this is an indication of clutch or band slippage.

Testing Procedure — With engine at normal operating temperature, tachometer installed, and parking and service brakes applied firmly, stall test transmission by pushing accelerator to floor and noting engine speed on tachometer. Engine speed should be within limits in chart.

MERCEDES-BENZ TYPE W 3 A 040 (Cont.)

Stall Speed Specifications	
Application	Stall RPM
450 Series	2050-2250

Stall Test Results — If stall speed is higher than specified, general transmission problems are indicated and hydraulic pressure tests should be made to locate faulty units. If stall speed is lower than specified, torque converter roller clutch is faulty.

CAUTION — *Make sure engine performance is satisfactory before condeming converter assembly. Torque converter is a sealed unit and cannot be disassembled for service.*

SERVICE (IN VEHICLE)

NOTE — *The following units may be removed from transmission without removing transmission from vehicle: Oil Pan and Gasket, Shift Valve Body, Vacuum Modulator Unit, Speedometer Driven Gear Assembly, Secondary Pump Assembly, Extension Housing, Pressure receiving Piston, Modulating Pressure Housing and Bimetallic Spring, Speedometer Drive Gear, Secondary Pump Eccentric, Governor Assembly, Parking Pawl, and Parking Linkage. See procedures given in Transmission Disassembly and Transmission Reassembly.*

TRANSMISSION REMOVAL & INSTALLATION

1) Disconnect negative battery terminal and raise vehicle. Drain transmission fluid by disconnecting oil filler tube from pan and by removing torque converter drain plug. On 450 series models only, remove complete exhaust system. On all models, disconnect oil cooler lines at unions near converter housing-to-engine mating area, and cap lines to prevent entry of dirt.

NOTE — *When draining is completed, reinstall and tighten converter drain plug.*

2) Loosen, but do not remove the two center support bearing-to-body attaching bolts, then loosen the front section propeller shaft clamping nut. Remove two rear transmission mount-to-tunnel plate bolts, remove tunnel plate, then disconnect rear mount from transmsission. Disconnect front propeller shaft from transmission flange, leaving adapter plate attached to

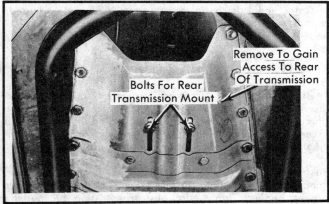

Fig. 4   Bottom View of Vehicle Showing Tunnel Plate and Rear Mount Attaching Bolts

propeller shaft. Slide propeller shaft rearward and place out of the way.

3) Disconnect neutral safety switch plug, then loosen clamping screw and pull control pressure lever from shaft of transmission. Disconnect electrical lead from kickdown solenoid, then disconnect shift rod from transmission and place manual lever in park position. Disconnect speedometer cable and modulator vacuum line.

4) Remove cover plug from front side of intermediate flange (between converter housing and engine) and remove six torque converter-to-drive plate attaching bolts. Slightly raise transmission with a transmission jack, then remove the transmission-to-intermediate flange bolts. Pull transmission rearward until converter clears intermediate flange, and remove from vehicle.

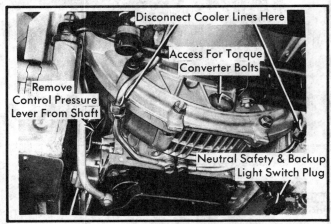

Fig. 5   View of Transmission Installed in Vehicle Showing Parts to be Removed

Installation — Reverse removal procedure and note the following: When installing torque converter into transmission, distance between front edge of converter ring gear and lip on front face of transmission case should be approximately .157" (4 mm). After installation, adjust transmission control linkage and fill transmission with fluid.

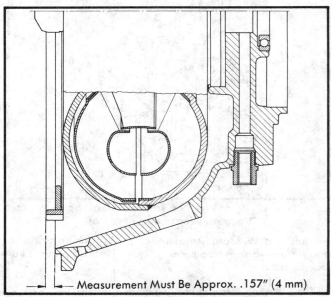

Fig. 6   Cutway View Showing Correct Torque Converter Installation

MERCEDES-BENZ TYPE W 3 A 040 (Cont.)

TORQUE CONVERTER

NOTE — *Torque converter is a sealed unit and cannot be disassembled for service. If hub of converter is scored, or if metallic particles are found in transmission fluid, replace converter assembly.*

TRANSMISSION DISASSEMBLY

1) Position transmission on a work bench with oil pan facing upward, then remove oil pan and gasket. Remove oil filter and bolts attaching valve body to transmission case, move selector lever between park and reverse positions, then lift valve body from case. Remove oil distributor pipes from case and withdraw the four sealing caps from the pipes.

2) Position transmission so extension housing faces upward. Remove vacuum modulator unit and thrust pin from extension housing. Using a screwdriver, remove secondary pump plug and spring from extension housing. Remove nut attaching output flange to output shaft and withdraw flange. Remove extension housing-to-case bolts, tap housing to break it loose, and remove extension housing.

3) Remove plate spring, speedometer drive gear, eccentric ring for secondary pump, and governor assembly from transmission output shaft. Remove parking pawl and pawl spring from rear face of case, then withdraw parking gear from output shaft. Rotate transmission so converter housing faces upward, remove converter housing-to-case attaching bolts, then remove housing from case, tapping with a soft mallet if necessary.

Governor
Secondary Pump Eccentric
Speedometer Drive Gear
Plate Spring
Parking Gear
Parking Pawl
Modulating Pressure Housing

Fig. 7 Rear View of Output Shaft Showing Components to be Removed

4) Rotate transmission to a horizontal position and remove downshift solenoid and control pressure lever (if not done during removal). Remove rear servo cover retaining ring, withdraw cover and piston assembly, then remove piston from cover. Mount a suitable compressor tool on transmission case over center servo assembly, compress servo cover, and remove retaining snap ring. Release tool and withdraw servo cover, servo piston, and compression spring.

5) Inside transmission case, remove the thrust pins for center and rear bands. On outside of case, loosen lock nut on front band adjusting screw, remove adjusting screw from case, then remove the two thrust pins from ends of front band. Withdraw front band through front of case. Grasp input shaft and pull from gear set. Using the rear servo cover retaining ring, clamp

center band ends together around gear set and remove entire gear set from case. Remove rear band and output shaft from case.

Center Band Held On Unit With Rear Servo Retaining Ring
Pull Gear Unit Out Front Of Case

Fig. 8 Gear Unit Removal

6) Remove bolts attaching modulating pressure housing to rear of case, then withdraw housing and extension housing gasket. Remove parking lock bracket and leaf spring, remove retaining screw, then withdraw range selector lever, detent plate, linkage arm, and needle bearing. On left side of case, remove attaching screws and withdraw neutral safety/backup light switch.

7) Unlock front servo cover clips from slots of case, remove cover retaining ring, and withdraw servo cover from case. Withdraw front servo piston and cone spring from servo bore. From front of case, remove retaining clip for front band lever bearing pin, knock out bearing pin in a downward direction, then withdraw lever from case. Inside case, remove retaining clip for center and rear band pressure bodies and remove both bodies from bores in case.

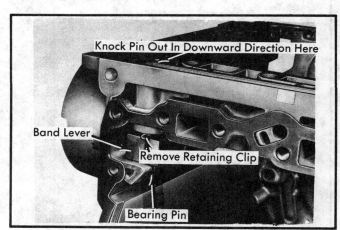

Knock Pin Out In Downward Direction Here
Band Lever
Remove Retaining Clip
Bearing Pin

Fig. 9 Front View of Transmission Case Showing Front Band Lever Removal

COMPONENT DISASSEMBLY & REASSEMBLY

VALVE BODY ASSEMBLY

Disassembly — 1) Loosen all valve body bolts and remove all except two, position assembly in a holding fixture with oil distributing plate downward, and remove two remaining through bolts. Hold upper body and separator plate together,

MERCEDES-BENZ TYPE W 3 A 040 (Cont.)

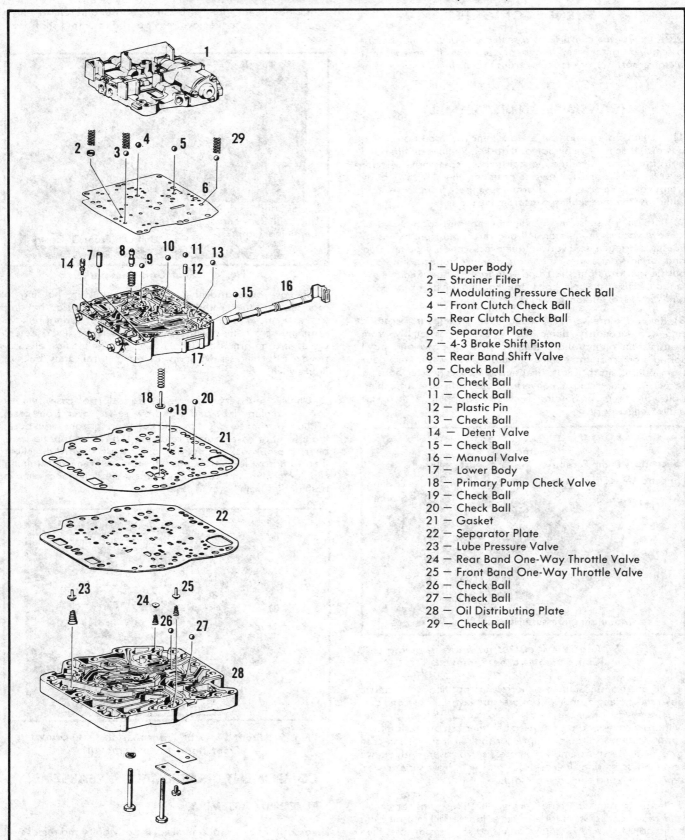

1 — Upper Body
2 — Strainer Filter
3 — Modulating Pressure Check Ball
4 — Front Clutch Check Ball
5 — Rear Clutch Check Ball
6 — Separator Plate
7 — 4-3 Brake Shift Piston
8 — Rear Band Shift Valve
9 — Check Ball
10 — Check Ball
11 — Check Ball
12 — Plastic Pin
13 — Check Ball
14 — Detent Valve
15 — Check Ball
16 — Manual Valve
17 — Lower Body
18 — Primary Pump Check Valve
19 — Check Ball
20 — Check Ball
21 — Gasket
22 — Separator Plate
23 — Lube Pressure Valve
24 — Rear Band One-Way Throttle Valve
25 — Front Band One-Way Throttle Valve
26 — Check Ball
27 — Check Ball
28 — Oil Distributing Plate
29 — Check Ball

Fig. 10   Exploded View of Valve Body Assembly

MERCEDES-BENZ TYPE W 3 A 040 (Cont.)

remove from assembly, and place on a bench with separator plate upward. Lift off separator plate and withdraw filter and spring, two 7 mm check balls, one 5.5 mm check ball with spring, and the modulating pressure relief valve with spring.

2) Lift lower body from assembly and remove the five 5.5 mm check balls from cored passages. Remove plastic pin, brake shift piston, primary pump check valve and spring, shift valve and spring, two 5.5 mm check balls, and the detent valve from surface of separator plate gasket. Remove gasket and separator plate from assembly, then withdraw lube pressure valve, front band one-way throttle valve, rear band one-way throttle valve, and two 5.5 mm check balls from oil distributing plate.

CAUTION — No further valve body disassembly information is available from manufacturer. If further disassembly of upper or lower bodies is anticipated, please note the following: As with any valve body assembly, valves and plugs are under considerable spring tension; therefore, exercise caution when removing end plates and retainers. In addition, tag all valves, plugs, and springs as they are removed to assure correct reassembly.

Reassembly — **1)** Install oil distributing plate onto a holding fixture with cored face upward. Install lube pressure valve, front band one-way throttle valve, and rear band one-way throttle valve into respective seats in distributing plate. Place the two 5.5 mm check balls into countersunk seats in plate, position separator plate and gasket over distributing plate, and temporarily hold in place using two clamps.

NOTE — After installing separator plate, push down on valves to check for free operation; valves must not be caught between oil distributing plate and separating plate. Diameter of rear band one-way valve is .059" (1.5 mm).

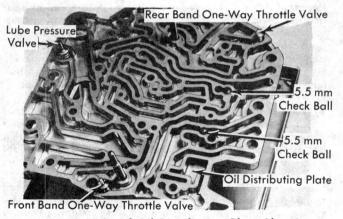

Fig. 11   View of Oil Distributing Plate Showing Check Ball and Valve Installation

2) Place two 5.5 mm check balls in position on top of separator plate gasket (see illustration). Install primary pump check valve and spring into lower body from underside, hold valve stem from upper side, then install lower body onto oil distributing plate and release valve stem.

NOTE — Valve should make an audible "click" against separator plate when valve stem is released.

3) Insert brake shift piston, shift valve and spring and plastic pin into passages in lower body. Install detent valve into valve body with small diameter in upward direction.

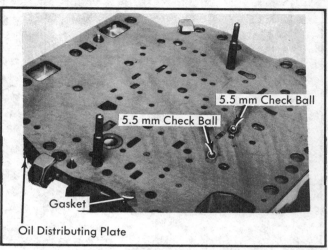

Fig. 12   Positioning Check Balls on Oil Distributor Gasket

4) Next, install five 5.5 mm check balls into countersunk seats in body (Fig. 14). With cored face of upper body facing upward, install screen filter with spring, two 7 mm check balls, and one 5.5 mm modulating pressure relief ball and spring (see Fig. 16).

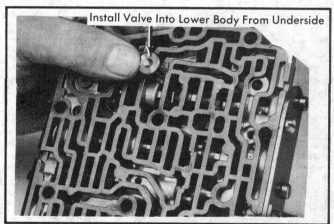

Fig. 13   Bottom View of Lower Valve Body Showing Installation of Primary Pump Check Valve

5) Position separator plate on top of upper body, making sure spring-loaded check ball and filter are not displaced. Hold

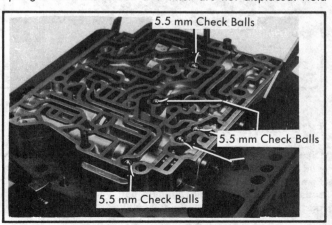

Fig. 14   View of Lower Valve Body Showing Locations of Check Balls

MERCEDES-BENZ TYPE W 3 A 040 (Cont.)

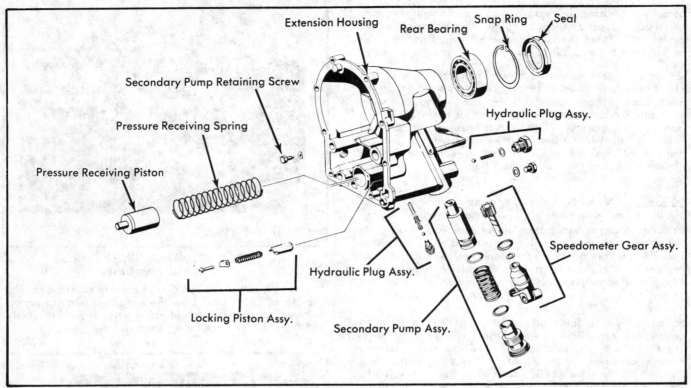

Fig. 15   Exploded View of Extension Housing Assembly

separator plate and upper body tightly together, invert, and position on lower valve body. Install two valve body through bolts into opposite sides of assembly and finger tighten, then remove valve body assembly from holding fixture and install and tighten remaining through bolts.

NOTE — *The two hex. head valve body bolts are used to screw down cover plate.*

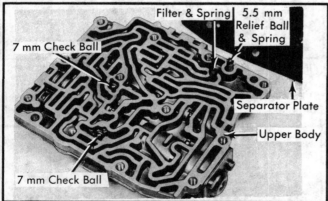

Fig. 16   View of Upper Valve Body Showing Positions of Check Balls and Valves

EXTENSION HOUSING

Disassembly — **1)** Inside housing, remove retaining screw and cover plate and withdraw locking piston and spring. Remove pressure receiving piston and spring. Remove speedometer driven gear retaining bolt, withdraw driven gear body from extension housing, then withdraw gear from body.

2) Remove secondary pump retaining bolt (located inside extension housing below bearing), then withdraw pump from housing. Using a screwdriver, remove rear seal from extension housing. Remove bearing retaining snap ring, and press rear bearing from housing. Unscrew hydraulic passage plugs, and withdraw check balls, springs, and thrust pins.

Reassembly — **1)** Using a suitable driver, install rear bearing, bearing snap ring, and rear seal into extension housing. Insert locking piston and spring into cavity in housing, position cover plate over spring and install retaining screw. Install a new "O" ring onto secondary pump, position pump in housing with retaining bolt hole in pump aligned with bolt hole in housing, then install and tighten pump retaining bolt.

2) Insert speedometer drive gear into gear body, install gear and body assembly into extension housing, then install and tighten retaining bolt. Install glass check ball, spring, and plug into bore on rear face of extension housing (bore at right angle to secondary pump bore). Install spring, plastic pin, steel check ball, and plug into bore on left side of extension housing (bore parallel to secondary pump bore). Install remaining hydraulic plug into bore of housing, using a new sealing washer. Position pressure receiving piston and spring into bore on the inside of housing.

GOVERNOR

Disassembly — Remove sealing rings from governor flange. Remove retaining bolts for shift housing and governor housing, then separate housings from governor flange. Remove lock washer, compression spring, and shift valve from shift valve housing. From governor housing, remove the spring plate, then withdraw centrifugal weight and thin compression spring from top of housing. Remove remaining spring, compensating washers, and control valve through bottom of housing.

MERCEDES-BENZ TYPE W 3 A 040 (Cont.)

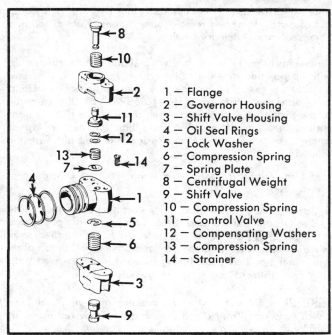

1 – Flange
2 – Governor Housing
3 – Shift Valve Housing
4 – Oil Seal Rings
5 – Lock Washer
6 – Compression Spring
7 – Spring Plate
8 – Centrifugal Weight
9 – Shift Valve
10 – Compression Spring
11 – Control Valve
12 – Compensating Washers
13 – Compression Spring
14 – Strainer

Fig. 17   Exploded View of Governor Assembly

ing onto flange so that oil slot of housing faces seal rings of flange. Install oil seal rings onto flange and hook ends to secure.

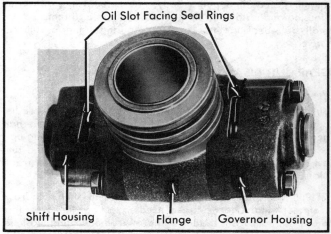

Fig. 18   View of Governor Showing Parts Alignment

Reassembly — 1) Clean all parts in solvent and air dry. Make sure valves slide easily in bores. Insert control valve into governor housing. Install centrifugal weight and thin compression spring into control valve, install compensating washers and remaining spring into assembly, then attach spring plate to centrifugal weight stem, making sure it is correctly seated.

2) Insert shift valve and spring into shift valve housing and retain with snap ring. **NOTE** — *Make sure spring is correctly seated on snap ring.* Position shift housing on governor flange so that oil slot of housing faces seal rings on flange, and oil passages are aligned in housing and flange. Position strainer into slot on opposite end of flange, then install governor hous-

CONVERTER HOUSING & PRIMARY PUMP ASSEMBLY

Disassembly — Loosen oil pump attaching bolts on rear side of converter housing, tap bolts lightly with a hammer to break pump loose, then remove bolts, pump assembly, and intermediate flange from housing. Withdraw "O" ring seal and pump lip seal from housing. If necessary, use a suitable puller (116 589 07 33 00) and remove ball bearing from rear side of converter housing.

Reassembly — 1) Install a new "O" ring seal on outside diameter of pump housing, and a new lip seal in front cavity of housing. Lubricate pump gears with transmission fluid and install into housing, matching marks made at disassembly.

NOTE — *The bevelled outer edge of driven gear should face into pump body.*

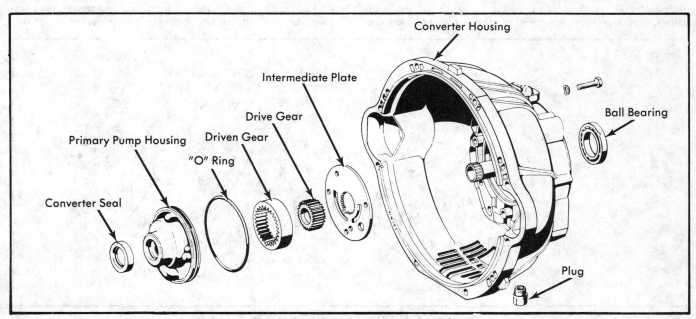

Fig. 19   Exploded View of Torque Converter Housing and Primary Pump Assembly

MERCEDES-BENZ TYPE W 3 A 040 (Cont.)

2) Install intermediate plate onto housing so oil passages and bolt holes are aligned in both plate and housing. Position an installation sleeve (116 589 19 61 00) onto stator shaft, screw aligning studs into pump body, insert pump into converter housing and install and tighten attaching bolts. If removed, install ball bearing into converter housing using a suitable driver.

GEAR UNIT DISASSEMBLY

1) Remove output shaft and rear planetary assembly by pulling straight out of gear unit, then withdraw caged needle bearing and needle thrust bearing from inside rear internal gear. Place gear unit on the bench with input shaft facing upward. Withdraw input shaft and front internal gear from assembly, then remove caged needle bearing from front planetary gear set.

2) Pull front planetary gear carrier from unit, then withdraw front sun gear and its caged needle bearing. Remove snap ring from hollow shaft, then withdraw compensating washers and front clutch assembly. Grasp oil distributing sleeve and pull sleeve and rear clutch support flange from rear clutch and hollow shaft. Remove hollow shaft and rear clutch assembly from intermediate shaft by pulling straight up, then withdraw caged needle bearing and thrust washer from intermediate shaft.

3) Remove hollow shaft and one-way clutch from rear clutch assembly by pulling out rear of clutch drum, then withdraw thrust washer from surface of roller clutch inner race (inside rear clutch drum). With rear clutch supporting flange on bench, compress snap ring retaining roller clutch outer race on flange and withdraw outer race. Using a puller, withdraw ball bearing from output shaft, then remove thrust washer, rear sun gear, two-piece caged needle bearing and roller thrust bearing.

FRONT CLUTCH

Disassembly — Using a screwdriver, pry clutch pack snap ring from clutch drum. Invert clutch drum and withdraw lined and steel clutch plates. Using a press, push down on piston spring retainer, remove retaining snap ring, then release press and withdraw spring retainer and return springs. Lift piston out of clutch drum and remove outer lip seal from piston and inner seal from clutch drum hub.

Reassembly — 1) Install a new lip seal on clutch drum hub, with lip pointing downward into drum. Install a new lip seal on piston, with seal lip facing away from spring pockets. Using a suitable seal protector tool (116 589 17 61 00), carefully rotate piston into position in clutch drum. Place piston return springs into pockets of piston, position retainer on top of springs, compress retainer and springs, and install retaining snap ring.

NOTE — *Make sure snap ring is fully seated in groove of clutch drum.*

2) Install clutch plates into drum, starting with a steel plate and alternating lined and steel plates until all plates are installed. **NOTE** — *If new lined plates are being installed, soak in transmission fluid before installation.* Next, install top plate with inner bevelled edge facing upward. Install waved snap ring into drum to secure clutch pack.

CAUTION — *Do not confuse front clutch snap ring with rear clutch snap ring; front clutch snap ring has 6 waved areas on surface.*

Front Clutch Plate Chart		
Application	Steel Plates	Lined Plates
450 Series	4	4

3) Measure clutch pack free play as follows: Using a depth gauge, measure distance from top of clutch drum to flat surface of top plate.

NOTE — *Make sure depth gauge touches top plate only lightly.*

4) Pull clutch pack up against snap ring and again check distance between top of clutch drum and surface of top plate.

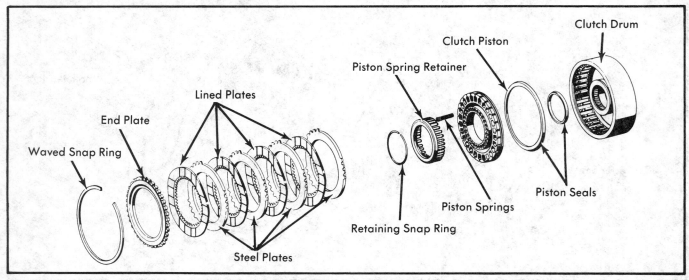

Fig. 20 Exploded View of Front Clutch Assembly

MERCEDES-BENZ TYPE W 3 A 040 (Cont.)

Clutch pack free play is determined by subtracting second measurement from first measurement. Resulting free play should be .032-.047" (.8-1.2 mm).

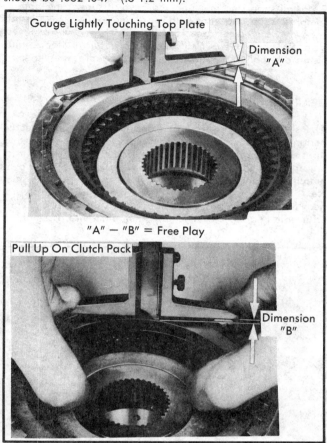

Gauge Lightly Touching Top Plate

Dimension "A"

"A" — "B" = Free Play

Pull Up On Clutch Pack

Dimension "B"

Fig. 21 Using a Depth Gauge to Measure Front Clutch Pack Clearance

5) If free play is not within specifications, install a thicker or thinner steel plate (as necessary) to bring clearance within specifications. Selective Steel plates are available in thicknesses of .177" (4.5 mm) and .197" (5.0 mm). After different selective plate has been installed, recheck clutch pack clearance to insure correct assembly.

REAR CLUTCH

Disassembly — With supporting flange end of rear clutch upward, remove flat snap ring from clutch drum and withdraw supporting flange and piston assembly. **CAUTION** — *Do not allow piston to separate from flange as damage may result.* Remove piston return springs and lined and steel clutch plates from clutch drum. Invert clutch drum and remove the waved snap ring from bottom of clutch drum. Withdraw steel plate with bevelled inside diameter and guide ring for piston return springs. Remove piston from supporting flange, then remove inner and outer piston lip seals.

Reassembly — **1)** Install waved snap ring into bottom groove of rear clutch drum, then install bottom plate (with bevel on inside diameter downward) and piston spring guide ring. Install clutch pack assembly into drum as follows: Install one lined plate, follow with thicker selective steel plate, then alternate one lined plate and one thinner steel plate until all plates are installed.

NOTE — *If new lined plates are being installed, soak in transmission fluid prior to assembly.*

2) Place clutch piston (without supporting flange) into clutch drum on top of clutch plates. Using a depth gauge, measure distance from top of clutch drum to flat surface of clutch piston. Next, remove piston from drum and measure distance from top of clutch drum to supporting flange contacting surface of clutch drum splines. Subtract second measurement from first measurement; resulting measurement is clutch piston release play.

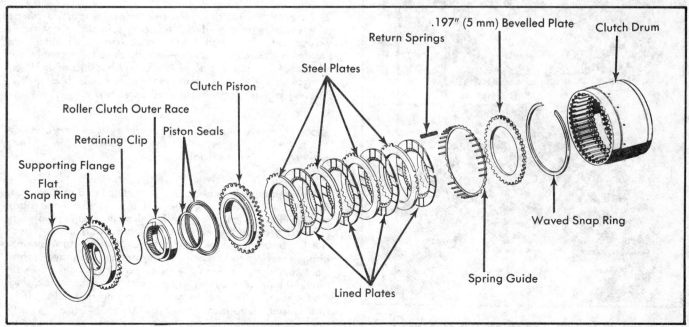

.197" (5 mm) Bevelled Plate

Return Springs

Clutch Drum

Steel Plates

Clutch Piston

Roller Clutch Outer Race

Retaining Clip

Piston Seals

Supporting Flange

Flat Snap Ring

Waved Snap Ring

Spring Guide

Lined Plates

Fig. 22 Exploded View of Rear Clutch Assembly

MERCEDES-BENZ TYPE W 3 A 040 (Cont.)

3) Clutch pack clearance should be .032-.047" (.8-1.2 mm). If not, selective thickness clutch plates are available to correct clearance. See Fig. 23 for selective clutch plate thicknesses. Install thicker or thinner plates as necessary to bring clutch pack clearance within specifications.

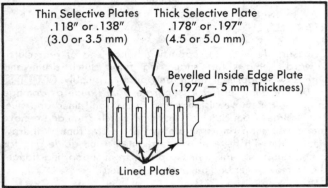

Fig. 23   Rear Clutch Pack Installation Diagram

4) Position all piston release springs on pegs of release spring guide. Install a new lip seal on center hub of supporting flange, with lip pointing downward into piston well. Also install a new sealing ring onto clutch piston, with lip facing away from splines. Lubricate seals with transmission fluid and install piston into supporting flange, using a pencil or ball point pen to start lip of seal into flange.

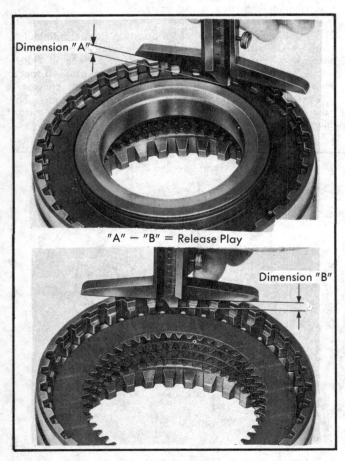

Fig. 24   Using a Depth Gauge to Measure Rear Clutch Pack Clearance

CAUTION — Do not use a sharp tool to start seal as damage to lip will result.

5) Install snap ring into upper groove of supporting flange, compress snap ring ends with needle nose pliers, then install one-way clutch outer race. **NOTE** — Outer race was removed from flange in Gear Unit Disassembly. Install flange and piston assembly into clutch drum, then install retaining snap ring.

GEAR UNIT REASSEMBLY

1) Install needle thrust bearing and two-piece caged needle bearing into gear cavity of output shaft. Position sun gear and thrust washer onto shaft, with offset side of thrust washer facing sun gear. Install ball bearing and parking lock gear over output shaft and press into place. Place assembly to the side. Next, position intermediate shaft on the bench with internal gear facing downward. Install tabbed thrust washer and caged needle bearing into assembly, then place this assembly to the side.

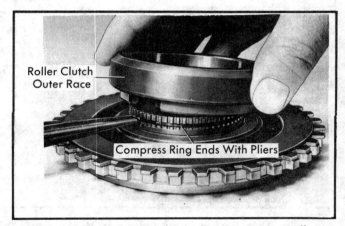

Fig. 25   View of Supporting Flange Showing Installation of Roller Clutch Outer Race

2) Position rear clutch on the bench with supporting flange downward (rear end of clutch facing upward). Coat thrust washer with grease and install into one-way clutch outer race (inside rear clutch). Install one-way clutch roller assembly into outer race, making sure edge with outer bead faces out of outer race. Install hollow shaft into one-way clutch assembly, rotating counterclockwise to ease assembly.

NOTE — When looking from bottom of rear clutch, hollow shaft should freewheel when rotated counterclockwise, and lock up when rotated clockwise.

3) Insert intermediate shaft into rear clutch and hollow shaft, rotating so assembly meshes with rear clutch lined plate splines. Place assembly on bench with shafts pointing upward. Install caged needle bearing over hollow shaft and into rear clutch supporting flange, then install oil distributing sleeve into flange, making sure sealing rings are fully engaged. Install front clutch onto assembly, making sure it engages fully with seal rings on distributing sleeve. Install retaining snap ring, then measure clearance between snap ring and hub of front clutch drum. Clearance should be .012-.016" (.3-.4 mm); if not, install compensating washers between snap ring and clutch drum hub.

MERCEDES-BENZ TYPE W 3 A 040 (Cont.)

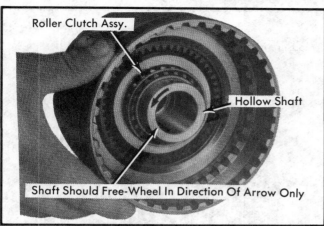

Roller Clutch Assy.

Hollow Shaft

Shaft Should Free-Wheel In Direction Of Arrow Only

Fig. 26 Bottom View of Rear Clutch Showing Correct Operation of One-Way Clutch

4) With front planetry gear carrier on the bench (clutch spline end upward), coat gear carrier-to-sun gear roller thrust bearing with grease and install into carrier. Using a depth gauge, measure distance from top of clutch splines on carrier to top of

one of the rollers on thrust bearing; this is dimension "A" (write down for future reference). Next, measure distance from top of carrier splines to shoulder of hub inside carrier; this is dimension "B". Now, measure distance from top of intermediate shaft to shoulder of the shaft (just below first set of splines); this is dimension "D".

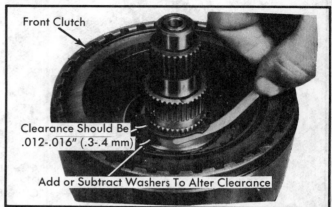

Front Clutch

Clearance Should Be .012-.016" (.3-.4 mm)

Add or Subtract Washers To Alter Clearance

Fig. 28 Using A Feeler Gauge to Measure Front Clutch Hub-to-Snap Ring Clearance

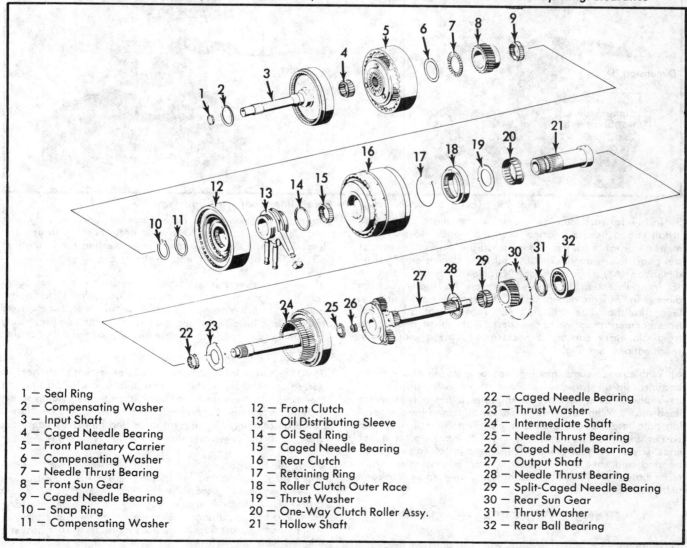

1 — Seal Ring	12 — Front Clutch	22 — Caged Needle Bearing
2 — Compensating Washer	13 — Oil Distributing Sleeve	23 — Thrust Washer
3 — Input Shaft	14 — Oil Seal Ring	24 — Intermediate Shaft
4 — Caged Needle Bearing	15 — Caged Needle Bearing	25 — Needle Thrust Bearing
5 — Front Planetary Carrier	16 — Rear Clutch	26 — Caged Needle Bearing
6 — Compensating Washer	17 — Retaining Ring	27 — Output Shaft
7 — Needle Thrust Bearing	18 — Roller Clutch Outer Race	28 — Needle Thrust Bearing
8 — Front Sun Gear	19 — Thrust Washer	29 — Split-Caged Needle Bearing
9 — Caged Needle Bearing	20 — One-Way Clutch Roller Assy.	30 — Rear Sun Gear
10 — Snap Ring	21 — Hollow Shaft	31 — Thrust Washer
11 — Compensating Washer		32 — Rear Ball Bearing

Fig. 27 Exploded View Showing Components of Gear Unit Assembly

MERCEDES-BENZ TYPE W 3 A 040 (Cont.)

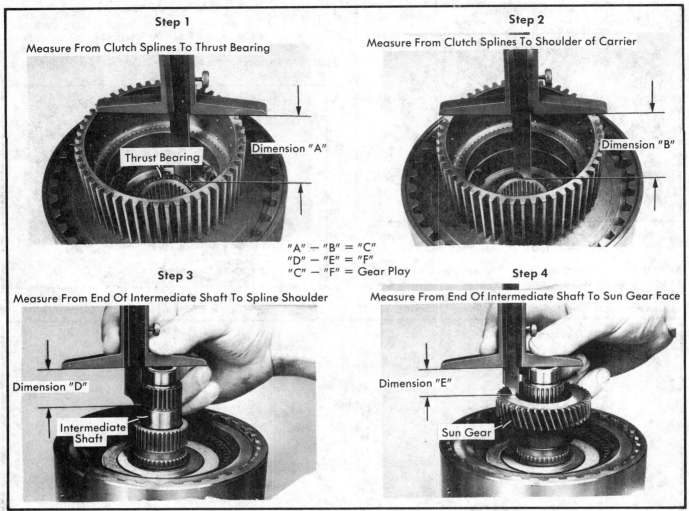

Step 1

Measure From Clutch Splines To Thrust Bearing

Thrust Bearing

Dimension "A"

Step 2

Measure From Clutch Splines To Shoulder of Carrier

Dimension "B"

"A" — "B" = "C"
"D" — "E" = "F"
"C" — "F" = Gear Play

Step 3

Measure From End Of Intermediate Shaft To Spline Shoulder

Dimension "D"

Intermediate Shaft

Step 4

Measure From End Of Intermediate Shaft To Sun Gear Face

Dimension "E"

Sun Gear

Fig. 29　Using a Depth Gauge to Determine Gear Unit End Play.

5) Install forward sun gear onto intermediate shaft, then install caged needle bearing over shaft and into sun gear. Measure distance from top of intermediate shaft to top face of sun gear; this is dimension "E". Subtract dimension "B" from dimension "A"; this is dimension "C". Next, subtract dimension "E" from dimension "D"; this is dimension "F". Finally, subtract dimension "F" from dimension "C"; the result is gear unit play. Gear play should be .008-.012" (.2-.3 mm); if not, add or subtract compensating washers under needle thrust bearing on front planetary carrier as necessary to bring play within specifications. See Fig. 29.

6) With proper compensating washer installed under thrust bearing, install forward planet carrier onto front clutch assembly, rotating carrier so it engages splines of front clutch lined plates. With carrier in place, install caged needle bearing onto intermediate shaft end, then install input shaft into carrier. Install a new metal seal ring onto input shaft and lock ends. Lay entire gear unit on its side and install caged needle bearing and needle thrust bearing into internal gear of intermediate shaft. Install output shaft into internal gear to complete assembly.

TRANSMISSION REASSEMBLY

1) Lubricate new "O" ring seals with transmission fluid and install into pressure body bores of case. Install center and rear band pressure bodies in bores, making sure the body with chamfered cap is installed in rear bore. Position front band lever in transmission case, drive lever bearing pin in through oil pan face of case, then install retining clip.

2) Install a new seal on front servo piston, position servo spring in case with large end against piston, then install piston into case. Install a new seal on front servo cover, mount cover to case, and install retaining snap ring. Position neutral safety and back-up light switch on case, install and tighten attaching screws.

3) At rear of transmission case, position detent plate next to bore of manual shaft, install manual lever and shaft through case and into teeth of detent plate, then tighten clamp screw to retain assembly. Loosen adjusting screw on manual lever, install an aligning pin through lever and into alignment hole of switch, then tighten adjusting screw and remove pin.

4) Install linkage arm with washer and roller onto rear of case. Install leaf spring, positioning end of spring on detent plate, then install needle bearing roller and parking lock bracket. Install parking pawl bearing pin on rear case face. Position a new extension housing gasket on rear case face, install modulating pressure valve housing (making sure gasket is aligned with bolt holes), then install and tighten housing attaching bolts.

MERCEDES-BENZ TYPE W 3 A 040 (Cont.)

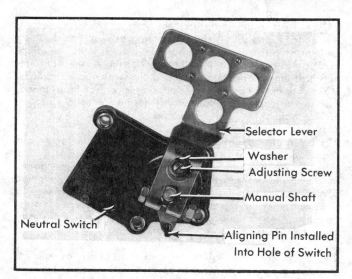

Fig. 30 *View of Neutral Safety Switch Showing Correct Method of Adjustment*

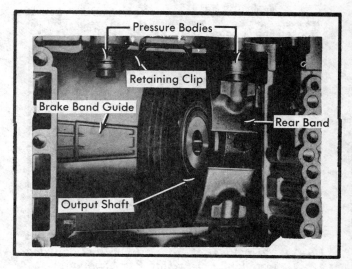

Fig. 32 *Bottom View of Transmission Showing Rear Band Installation*

5) Position transmission case on bench with oil pan face facing upward. Install brake band guide into case, positioning in slots machined in case. Temporarily remove output shaft and input shaft from gear unit, making sure thrust bearings remain attached to gear unit. Install output shaft assembly into case, tapping with a plastic hammer to seat fully. Position rear band in case, aligning it with servo and pressure body bores, and making sure it is engaged with brake band guide.

7) Insert front band into case and over gear unit, install pressure pins into band ends, then screw in band adjusting screw until band is secured in place. Install a fixture over front of transmission case to hold gear unit in place, then rotate transmission so rear of case is accessible. Install parking gear on output shaft, then position tensioning spring on pawl bearing pin and attach hooked end to case. Install pawl on bearing pin, engage spring with pawl, and check operation of parking lock.

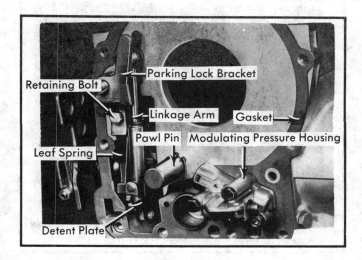

Fig. 31 *Rear View of Transmission Case Showing Installed Position of Linkage Components*

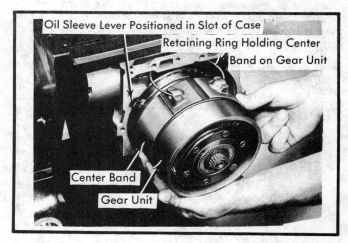

Fig. 33 *Front View of Transmission Case Showing Installation of Gear Unit*

6) Position center band over gear unit, and temporarily hold in place using the rear servo cover retaining ring. Make sure thrust bearings are still positioned in end of gear unit, then install gear unit into case, guiding supporting lever of oil distributing sleeve into groove of case. **NOTE** — *Make sure gear unit is fully engaged with output shaft. Make sure bearings are still in position on front of gear unit, then install input shaft into assembly*

8) Install centrifugal governor, eccentric ring for secondary pump, speedometer drive gear, and plate spring onto output shaft. Remove secondary pump plug and compression spring from extension housing (if installed) and push secondary pump delivery piston outwards. Make sure pressure receiving piston and spring are installed in extension housing, then install housing on transmission case. Install secondary pump compression spring and plug, and tighten.

MERCEDES-BENZ TYPE W 3 A 040 (Cont.)

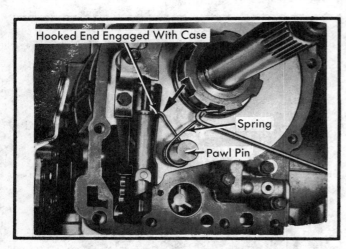

Fig. 34 Rear View of Transmission Case Showing Installation of Parking Pawl Spring

9) Screw modulator pressure pin measuring tool 115 589 11 21 00 into extension housing, insert pressure pin into tool, and push fully inward. End of pin should be flush with face of tool; if not, select a pin of proper length and install into modulator unit. Coat threads of vacuum modulator unit with sealer and install into extension housing. Place flange on output shaft, install and tighten retaining nut, then stake nut to secure in place.

10) Determine end play between gear unit and converter housing as follows: Place a suitable measuring bar (116 589 00 21 00) on transmission case and measure distance from top of bar to thrust surface of input shaft. **NOTE** — *After subtracting thickness of bar, resulting measurement is distance from face of transmission case to thrust surface of input shaft.* Next, install a new gasket on rear of converter housing, place measuring bar on housing, and measure distance from top of bar to inner bearing race.

NOTE — *After subtracting thickness of bar, resulting measurement is distance from gasket surface on housing to bearing race.*

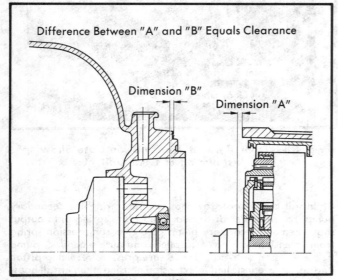

Fig. 35 Schematic of Gear Unit-to-Torque Converter Housing Clearance

11) Subtract smaller measurement from larger measurement; remainder is end play between bearing on converter housing and thrust surface of input shaft. End play should be .016-.020" (.4-.5 mm); if not, install compensating washers onto input shaft thrust surface to bring end play within specifications. Make sure gasket on converter housing is correctly positioned, then mount converter housing on transmission case. Coat attaching bolts with sealer, install and tighten.

12) If not already installed, insert thrust pins into center and rear band pressure bodies. Using a ring compressor, install rear servo piston into case, making sure piston stem engages bore of band. Install a new "O" ring on servo cover, position cover in case, and install retaining ring. Place new sealing rings on center servo piston and cover, position servo spring(s) on piston, then install assembly into case. Compress servo components into case and install retaining ring.

13) Check free play of center and rear bands as follows: Introduce air pressure into rear band release pressure passage in case (see illustration) and mark position of band end on drum. Next, introduce air pressure to rear band apply pressure passage in case and again mark position of band end on drum. Measure distance between two marks; measurement is rear band free play. For center band free play, first measure position of band end on drum in released position (spring pressure holds band in released position). Next, apply air pressure to center servo apply passage in case and again mark position of band end on drum. Distance between two marks is center band free play.

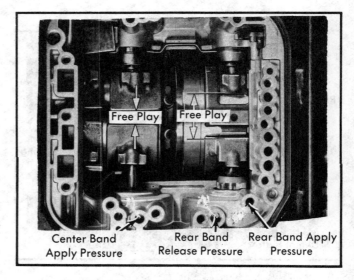

Fig. 36 Bottom View of Case Showing Measurement of Band Free Play

14) Free play for center and rear bands should be .118-.157" (3-4 mm), if not, install a pressure pin of correct length to bring free play within specifications.

NOTE — *Pressure pins for center and rear bands are available in the following lengths: .906" (23 mm), .945" (24 mm), .984" (25 mm), 1.024" (26 mm), 1.063" (27 mm) and 1.102" (28 mm).*

MERCEDES-BENZ TYPE W 3 A 040 (Cont.)

15) For front band, tighten band adjusting screw to 3.6 ft. lbs. (.5 mkg), then back off 1¾ turns. Tighten adjusting screw lock nut.

16) Install both oil feed pipes into oil distributing sleeve and place new valve body seals on pipes. Move selector in between park and reverse positions. Install locating pin for control pressure valve into valve body and guide bolt into transmission case. See *Fig. 37.*

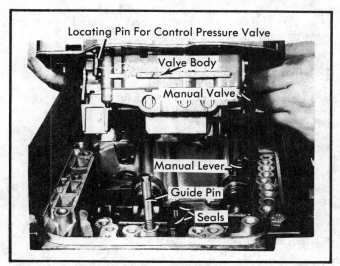

Fig. 37   Bottom View of Transmission Showing Installation of Valve Body

17) Install valve body into case making sure manual valve engages selector lever. Remove guide bolt from case, install valve body attaching bolts, and tighten in random sequence.

Remove locating pin for control pressure valve. Install oil filter, oil pan, and solenoid valve.

CAUTION — *Valve body bolts have varying lengths and must be installed in correct location.*

TIGHTENING SPECIFICATIONS

Application	Ft. Lbs. (mkg)
Valve Body-to-Case	9.4 (1.3)
Upper-to-Lower Valve Body	5.8 (.8)
Oil Filter-to-Valve Body	2.9 (.4)
Oil Pan-to-Case	5.1 (.7)
Neutral Safety Switch	3.6 (.5)
Kickdown Solenoid	14.5 (2.0)
Engine-to-Transmission	
M10 Bolts	39.8 (5.5)
M12 Bolts	47 (6.5)
Drive Plate-to-Torque Converter	30.4 (4.2)
Primary Pump-to-Case	14.5 (2.0)
Converter Housing-to-Case	9.4 (1.3)
Extension Housing-to-Case	9.4 (1.3)
Output Flange Nut	86.8 (12.0)
Selector Lever Detent Plate	7.2 (1.0)
Detent Leaf Spring	7.2 (1.0)
Governor Bolts	5.8 (.8)
Modulator Pressure Hsg.-to-Case	5.1 (.7)
Secondary Pump Retaining Screw	5.8 (.8)
Speedometer Driven Gear Bolt	5.8 (.8)

MERCEDES-BENZ TYPE W 4 B 025

240D
280 Series
300 Series

TRANSMISSION IDENTIFICATION

An identification tag is riveted to transmission case, near center servo cover. Top line of tag shows transmission assembly part number, and lower line is sequence built number.

DESCRIPTION

Transmission is a fully automatic four-speed unit consisting primarily of a three element welded torque converter and a compound planetary gear set. Two multiple disc clutches, one overrunning clutch, and three bands provide friction elements required to obtain desired function of the planetary gear set. A hydraulic system, pressurized by a primary gear type pump and secondary piston type pump provides working pressure required to operate friction elements and automatic controls.

LUBRICATION & ADJUSTMENT

See AUTOMATIC TRANSMISSION SERVICING Section.

TROUBLE SHOOTING

TRANSMISSION SLIPS IN ALL SELECTOR LEVER POSITIONS

Incorrect modulating pressure. Modulating pressure control valve sticking. Intake manifold-to-vacuum modulator vacuum line plugged. Working pressure control valve sticking. Defective primary pump.

TRANSMISSION GRABS OR VEHICLE SHAKES WHEN STARTING OFF

Incorrect modulating pressure. Check vacuum modulator for presence of fluid; if transmission fluid is found, replace modulator; if fuel is found, check and adjust carburetor or fuel injection system.

TRANSMISSION SLIPS IN 2nd GEAR OR SHIFTS FROM 1st TO 3rd GEAR

Center band control valve sticking or worn. Center band piston sealing ring worn or damaged. Center band worn or damaged. Bleed valves in front clutch supporting flange leaking.

TRANSMISSION SLIPS WHEN SHIFTING FROM 2nd TO 3rd OR FROM 3rd TO 4th GEAR

Modulating and/or working pressure incorrect. Valve body assembly worn or damaged. Defective front or rear clutch assembly.

TRANSMISSION SLIPS IN 4th GEAR, NO 1st GEAR ENGINE BRAKING

Sealing bushings on plug pipes of valve body worn or damaged. Rear clutch defective.

TRANSMISSION SLIPS IN 1st AND 2nd WHEN STARTING OFF

Rear band badly worn or damaged. Incorrect rear band pressure pin.

TRANSMISSION SLIPS IN ALL GEARS

Incorrect modulating pressure. Modulating pressure control valve worn or sticking. Modulating pressure relief valve worn, dirty or sticking.

NO POSITIVE ENGAGEMENT IN REVERSE

Front band out of adjustment. Sealing ring on rear band piston worn or damaged. One-way roller clutch in gear assembly worn or damaged.

ROUGH JERK WHEN ENGAGING "D"

Engine idle speed too high. Modulating and/or working pressure incorrect. Leak in vacuum modulator vacuum line. Pressure receiving piston in extension housing worn, damaged, or installed incorrectly. Feed bore in pressure receiving piston plugged.

NOTE — If a rough jerk results when shifting for short periods back and forth between "N" and "D", there is no reason for a complaint. The pressure receiver requires approximately 2 seconds to operate.

ROUGH JERKS WITH CHANGING GEARS

Incorrect modulating pressure. Incorrect working pressure. If working pressure is too high, replace valve body assembly. Vacuum line to vacuum modulator leaking. Control pressure linkage out of adjustment. Control valve converter adjustment incorrect.

NO UPSHIFTS

Worn or damaged governor assembly. Valve body assembly dirty and causing valves and springs to stick. Incorrect governor pressure.

UPSHIFTS ONLY IN UPPER SPEED RANGE

Control pressure linkage out of adjustment. Governor assembly worn or damaged. Control pressure control valve inoperable. Propeller shaft flange retaining nut loose.

UPSHIFTS ONLY IN LOWER SPEED RANGE

Clamping screw for control pressure lever on transmission loose. Control pressure linkage out of adjustment. Throttle valve out of adjustment. Defective governor causing high governor pressure.

MERCEDES-BENZ TYPE W 4 B 025 (Cont.)

NO KICKDOWN SHIFTS

Fuse for power supply to solenoid valve blown. Defective solenoid valve. Clamping screw for control pressure lever on transmission loose. Kickdown control valve in valve body worn or sticking.

NO BRAKE SHIFTS (4-3 AND 3-2)

Control pressure out of adjustment. Make brake shaft piston operable and exchange shift valve housing, if required.

DOWNSHIFT WITHOUT USING KICKDOWN SWITCH

Check kickdown solenoid valve and "O" ring. Check kickdown solenoid switch and replace if bad (stuck down or open). Check control pressure valve.

TESTING

ROAD TEST

NOTE — *Before road testing, be certain that fluid level and condition, and control linkage adjustments have been checked and corrected as necessary.*

1) During road test, transmission should upshift and downshift at approximately the speeds shown in Shift Speeds Charts. All shifts may vary somewhat due to production tolerances or tire size. The important factor to note is the quality of the shifts. All shifts should be smooth, responsive, and with no engine speed flare-up.

NOTE — *Shifts at full throttle and kickdown are somewhat firmer than part throttle shifts.*

Shift Speed Specifications (240D & 280 Models)		
Shift Condition	**Shift Point (MPH)**	
	240D Models	**280 Models**
Minimum Throttle		
In "D"		
2-3 Upshift	14	16
3-4 Upshift	24	27
3-2 Downshift	10	12
4-3 Downshift	18	22
In "S"		
2-3 Upshift	19	19
3-2 Downshift	13	17
In "L"		
1-2 Upshift	21	25
2-1 Downshift	5	5
Full Throttle		
In "D"		
2-3 Upshift	32	39
3-4 Upshift	58	81
3-2 Downshift	18	12
4-3 Downshift	34	43
In "S"		
2-3 Upshift	32	48
3-2 Downshift	14	20
In "L"		
1-2 Upshift	21	25
2-1 Downshift	11	14
Kickdown		
In "D"		
1-2 Upshift	16	22
2-3 Upshift	32	39
3-4 Upshift	58	81
2-1 Downshift	11	14
3-2 Downshift	30	29
4-3 Downshift	50	71
In "S"		
1-2 Upshift	20	22
2-3 Upshift	32	48
2-1 Downshift	12	14
3-2 Downshift	28	40
In "L"		
1-2 Upshift	21	25
2-1 Downshift	19	22

Shift Speed Specifications (300 Series)		
Shift Condition	**Shift Point (MPH)**	
	300SD	**All Others**
Minimum Throttle		
In "D"		
1-2 Upshift	8	7
2-3 Upshift	18	15
3-4 Upshift	30	25
3-2 Downshift	12	11
4-3 Downshift	23	21
In "S"		
1-2 Upshift	8	7
2-3 Upshift	18	15
3-2 Downshift	12	11
In "L"		
1-2 Upshift	27	22
2-1 Downshift	5	7
Full Throttle		
In "D"		
1-2 Upshift	21	17
2-3 Upshift	40	34
3-4 Upshift	70	62
3-2 Downshift	21	19
4-3 Downshift	40	36
In "S"		
1-2 Upshift	21	17
2-3 Upshift	40	34
3-2 Downshift	21	19
In "L"		
1-2 Upshift	27	22
2-1 Downshift	11	12
Kickdown		
In "D"		
1-2 Upshift	24	19
2-3 Upshift	40	34
3-4 Upshift	70	62
2-1 Downshift	12	12
3-2 Downshift	36	31
4-3 Downshift	60	52
In "S"		
1-2 Upshift	24	19
2-3 Upshift	40	34
2-1 Downshift	12	12
3-2 Downshift	36	31
In "L"		
1-2 Upshift	27	22
2-1 Downshift	22	18

AUTOMATIC TRANSMISSIONS

MERCEDES-BENZ TYPE W 4 B 025 (Cont.)

2) Slipping or engine speed flare-up in any gear usually indicates clutch or band problems. The slipping clutch or band in a particular gear can usually be identified by noting transmission operation in all selector positions and comparing which internal units are applied in those positions. *See Clutch And Band Application Chart.*

3) Although this process of elimination can be used to detect any unit which slips, and to confirm proper operation of good units, the actual cause of the malfunction usually cannot be decided. Practically any condition can be caused by leaking hydraulic circuits or sticking valves. Therefore, unless an obvious condition exists, the transmission should never be disassembled until hydraulic pressure tests have been made.

STALL TEST

Testing Precautions — When making test, do not hold throttle open longer than five seconds or severe transmission damage may result from the heat generated. If engine speed exceeds maximum limits shown, release accelerator immediately as this is an indication of clutch or band slippage.

NOTE — *In order to get an accurate RPM reading, a separate tachometer is to be used on all models except the 300SD. On this vehicle, only the vehicle tachometer is to be used since with the adapter screwed off the diagnosis socket on the engine the transmission overload protector is inoperative.*

Testing Procedure — With engine at normal operating temperature, tachometer installed, and parking and service brakes applied firmly, stall test transmission by pushing accelerator to floor and noting engine speed on tachometer. Engine speed should be within limits in chart.

Stall Speed Specifications	
Application	**Stall RPM**
240D	1500-1600
280 Series	1900-2000
300 Series	①1850-1950

① — 300SD has stall speed of 2000 RPM.

Stall Test Results — If stall speed is higher than specified, general transmission problems are indicated and hydraulic pressure test should be made to locate faulty units. If stall speed is lower than specified, torque converter roller clutch is faulty.

CAUTION — *Make sure engine performance is satisfactory before condemning converter assembly. Torque converter is a sealed unit and cannot be disassembled for service.*

HYDRAULIC PRESSURE TESTS

Preparation For Tests — Before making tests, be certain fluid level and condition, and control linkage adjustments have been checked and corrected as necessary. Connect a suitable pressure test gauge set (116 589 0421 00) to pressure takeoff points on transmission (see illustration).

CAUTION — *Make sure pressure hoses do not drag on pavement or contact exhaust system.*

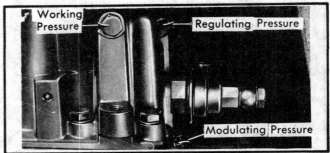

Fig. 1   View of Transmission Case Showing Hydraulic Pressure Test Points

NOTE — *Modulating pressure must be measured (and adjusted if necessary) before making working pressure and governor pressure tests.*

Modulating Pressure — Accelerate vehicle on the road or on a dynamometer to 40 MPH. Run engine at full throttle, and keep speed at 40 MPH by lightly applying service brakes. Read resulting pressure on gauge attached to modulating pressure test point on transmission. Pressure should check as shown in chart; adjust if necessary.

CLUTCH AND BAND APPLICATION CHART
(ELEMENTS IN USE)

Gear Range	Front Clutch	Rear Clutch	Front Band	Center Band	Rear Band	Overrunning Clutch
FIRST GEAR					X	X
SECOND GEAR				X	X	
THIRD GEAR	X				X	
FOURTH GEAR	X	X				
REVERSE			X			X
NEUTRAL OR PARK — All clutches and bands released and/or ineffective.						

MERCEDES-BENZ TYPE W 4 B 025 (Cont.)

NOTE — *On 300SD, actuate vacuum pump of the tester until 14.76 in. Hg is obtained. Move throttle slowly to full open position and vacuum must drop to "0" load stop.*

Modulating Pressure Adjustment — 1) Compress circlip and remove vacuum modulator cover. Pull locking plate out of locking slots.

2) The adjusting screw in vacuum modulator can now be turned with the locking plate. One complete turn of adjusting screw will change modulating pressure approximately 3 psi (.2 kg/cm²).

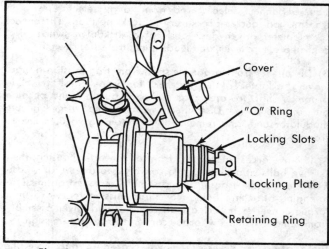

Fig. 2   Rear View of Transmission Showing Vacuum Modulator Assembly

3) After adjustment is completed, press locking plate into the next locking slot to lock adjusting screw in place. Reinstall vacuum modulator cover.

NOTE — *Working pressure is not adjustable. Pressure is automatically established with correctly adjusted modulating pressure.*

Working Pressure — To check pressure, drive vehicle in indicated range and speed, and note pressure reading on gauge.

NOTE — *Governor pressure is a partial pressure of working pressure and is controlled by centrifugal governor on output shaft.*

Governor Pressure — Drive vehicle on road or on chassis dynamometer and compare pressures noted on gauge with pressures given in chart.

NOTE — *If values are not within specifications, disassemble and clean governor assembly.*

SERVICE (IN VEHICLE)

NOTE — *The following units may be removed from transmission without removing transmission from vehicle: Oil Pan and Gasket, Shift Valve Body, Vacuum Modulator Unit, Speedometer Driven Gear Assembly, Secondary Pump Assembly, Extension Housing, Pressure Receiving Piston, Modulating Pressure Housing, Speedometer Drive Gear, Secondary Pump Eccentric, Governor Assembly, Parking Pawl, and Parking Linkage. See procedures given in Transmission Disassembly and Transmission Reassembly.*

TRANSMISSION REMOVAL & INSTALLATION

Removal — 1) Disconnect negative battery terminal and raise vehicle on a hoist. Disconnect fluid filler tube from oil pan and remove torque converter drain plug to drain fluid from transmission assembly. Disconnect fluid cooler lines from transmission case, then remove clips attaching lines to transmission and engine. Loosen bolts attaching center support bearing to body tunnel, but do not remove at this time.

2) Loosen clamping nut on front propeller shaft section, then remove mounting bracket for front exhaust pipe. Remove two bolts attaching transmission mount to rear crossmember, remove crossmember, then disconnect mount from transmis-

Hydraulic Pressure Specifications

Application	psi (kg/cm²)
Modulating Pressure (In "D")	
At 40 MPH①	
240D	55 (3.9)
280 Series, 300SD	55 (3.9)
300 Series②	
Federal	41 (2.9)
Calif.	44 (3.1)
Stationary③	
240D	61-67 (4.3-4.7)
280 Series	84-94 (5.9-6.6)
300 Series	59-65 (4.1-4.6)
300SD	70-73 (4.9-5.1)
Working Pressure (In "D")③	
At 40 MPH	
240D	73-78 (5.1-5.5)
280 Series, 300SD	90-96 (6.3-6.7)
300 Series②	78-84 (5.5-5.9)
Stationary	
240D, 300SD	149-161 (10.5-11.3)
Pressure in "R"	
All Models	261 (18.4)
Governor Pressure	
At 12 MPH	
300SD	9 (.6)
300 Series②	10 (.7)
All Other Models	7 (.5)
At 25 MPH	
300SD	17 (1.2)
300 Series②	19 (1.3)
All Other Models	20 (1.4)
At 37 MPH	
300SD	30 (2.1)
300 Series②	33 (2.3)
All Other Models	35 (2.5)
At 56 MPH④	
300SD	42 (3.0)
300 Series②	48 (3.4)
All Other Models	51 (3.6)
At 75 MPH④	
300SD	57 (4.0)
300 Series②	68 (4.8)
All Other Models	73 (5.1)

① — With vaccuum line connected and at full throttle.
② — Except 300SD models.
③ — Pressures with vehicle stationary are reference values and are used only for orientation when making adjustments.
④ — Can be measured at full throttle only.

Automatic Transmissions

MERCEDES-BENZ TYPE W 4 B 025 (Cont.)

sion. Disconnect selector rod from range selector lever on transmission and place lever in park position. Disconnect speedometer driven gear and cable, kickdown switch wire, control pressure lever, and leads to neutral safety switch.

3) Disconnect front propeller shaft from transmission flange, leaving adapter plate attached to propeller shaft. Slide propeller shaft towards rear as far as possible and position out of the way. Disconnect vacuum line from vacuum modulator unit, and remove clamp retaining vacuum line to transmission.

4) Remove access plate from front of converter housing, then remove bolts attaching torque converter to drive plate. Position a jack under transmission assembly, remove transmission-to-engine attaching bolts, move transmission rearward until torque converter hub clears drive plate, and lower assembly from vehicle. Withdraw torque converter from transmission.

Installation — Reverse removal procedure and note the following: When installing torque converter in transmission, lubricate torque converter tangs, turbine and stator shaft splines with molykote paste. When properly installed, distance between front face of transmission and converter mounting lugs should be more than .157" (4 mm). After installation, adjust transmission control linkage and fill transmission with fluid.

TORQUE CONVERTER

NOTE — *Torque converter is a sealed unit and cannot be disassembled for service. If hub or torque converter is scored, or if metallic particles are found in transmission fluid, replace converter assembly.*

TRANSMISSION DISASSEMBLY

1) Position transmission on a work bench with oil pan facing upward, then remove oil pan and gasket. Remove bolts attaching shift valve body to transmission case, move range selector lever between park and reverse positions, then lift shift valve body from case. Remove oil distributor pipes from transmission case, then withdraw sealing caps from pipes.

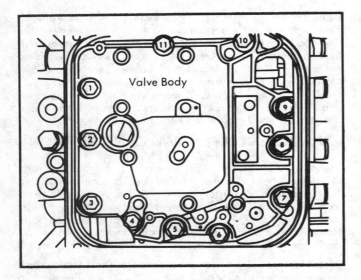

Fig. 3 Bottom View of Transmission Showing Location of Valve Body Attaching Bolts

2) Position transmission so extension housing faces upward. Remove vacuum modulator unit and thrust pin from extension housing. On diesel models, remove adjusting screw and compression spring from extension housing. Using a special socket (116 589 00 11 00), remove plug for secondary pump and withdraw compression spring from housing.

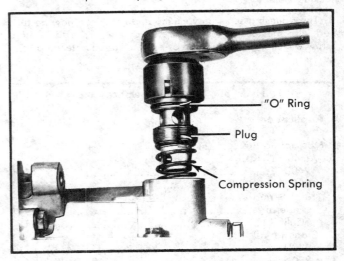

Fig. 4 Removing Secondary Pump Plug from Extension Housing

3) Remove nut attaching propeller shaft flange to transmission output shaft, then use a hammer to tap flange from shaft. Remove extension housing attaching bolts, and use a hammer to tap housing from transmission. Remove plate spring, speedometer drive gear, eccentric ring for secondary pump, and governor assembly from transmission output shaft. Remove parking pawl and pawl spring from rear of case, then pull parking gear off output shaft.

Fig. 5 Rear View of Transmission Case With Extension Housing Removed

4) Remove bolts attaching converter housing to front of case, then use a hammer to tap housing free. Place transmission in a horizontal position and remove solenoid valve and control pressure lever (if not done previously). Remove retaining ring for rear servo cover, remove cover from transmission, then withdraw rear servo piston from cover.

MERCEDES-BENZ TYPE W 4 B 025 (Cont.)

5) Mount a suitable compressor tool on transmission case over center servo assembly, compress servo cover, and remove retaining ring. Release tool and withdraw servo cover, servo piston, and both compression springs. Inside transmission case, remove thrust pins for center and rear bands. Loosen front band adjusting screw lock nut, screw out band adjusting screw, remove the two band thrust pins, then withdraw front band through front of transmission case.

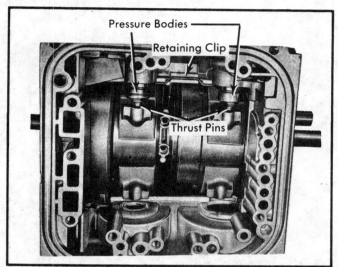

Fig. 6   Bottom View of Transmission Showing Position of Band Pressure Bodies and Thrust Pins

6) Using the rear servo cover retaining ring, clamp center band on gear unit, then withdraw gear unit from transmission case. Remove rear band from inside case. Remove bolts attaching modulating pressure sleeve housing to rear of case, then remove housing and extension housing gasket. Remove detent parking lock and leaf spring from rear of case, remove lock bolt on detent plate, then remove detent plate, linkage arm, and needle bearing.

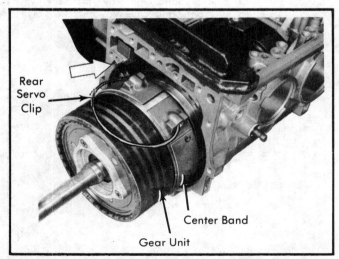

Fig. 7   Withdrawing Gear Unit Through Front of Transmission Case

7) On right side of case, remove retaining clip and plastic washer from control pressure shaft, and withdraw shaft from case. On left side of case, remove attaching screws and withdraw neutral safety and back-up light switch. Remove front servo retaining ring and withdraw servo cover, servo

piston, and spring. From front of case, remove retaining clip from front band lever, knock out lever pin, and withdraw lever from case. Finally, remove lock clip and withdraw center and rear band pressure bodies from bores inside case.

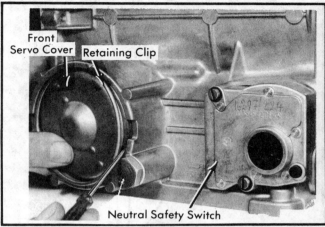

Fig. 8   Removing Front Servo Assembly From Left Side of Transmission Case

COMPONENT DISASSEMBLY & REASSEMBLY

SHIFT VALVE BODY

NOTE — *Two types of brake band guides are used. Early vehicles use an integral type which is a part of the upper valve body. Later vehicles use a non-integral type which is contoured to fit the valve body. See Fig. 9.*

Disassembly — 1) Remove brake band guide (if non-integral type). Loosen all valve body assembly through bolts and remove all except 2, position assembly in a holding fixture with oil distributing plate downward, then remove 2 remaining through bolts. Hold upper valve body and separator plate together, remove from assembly, and place on bench with separator plate. Remove strainer filter and spring, two 7 mm check balls, and one 5.5 mm check ball and spring from upper body.

2) Lift lower body off assembly, and remove the five check balls from cored passages. Remove the brake shift piston, primary pump check valve and spring, detent valve, 3-4 shift pin, and two 5.5 mm check balls from surface of separator plate gasket. Remove gasket and separator plate from oil distributing plate. On 280 series models only, remove detent valve. On all models, withdraw lubricating pressure valve, front band one-way throttle valve, and rear band releasing end one-way throttle valve from distributing plate. Finally, remove the two 5.5 mm check balls from the cored passages of the distributing plate.

CAUTION — *No further valve body disassembly information is available from manufacturer. If further disassembly of upper or lower valve bodies is anticipated, please note the following: As with any valve body assembly, valves and plugs are under considerable spring tension; therefore, excercise caution when removing end plates and retainers. In addition, tag all valves, plugs, and springs as they are removed to assure correct assembly.*

Inspection — Wash all parts in clean solvent and blow dry with compressed air. Check all valves for ease of movement in bores. If necessary, remove any minor damage on valves with crocus cloth, taking care not to round off the sharp self-cleaning edges of the valves.

MERCEDES-BENZ TYPE W 4 B 025 (Cont.)

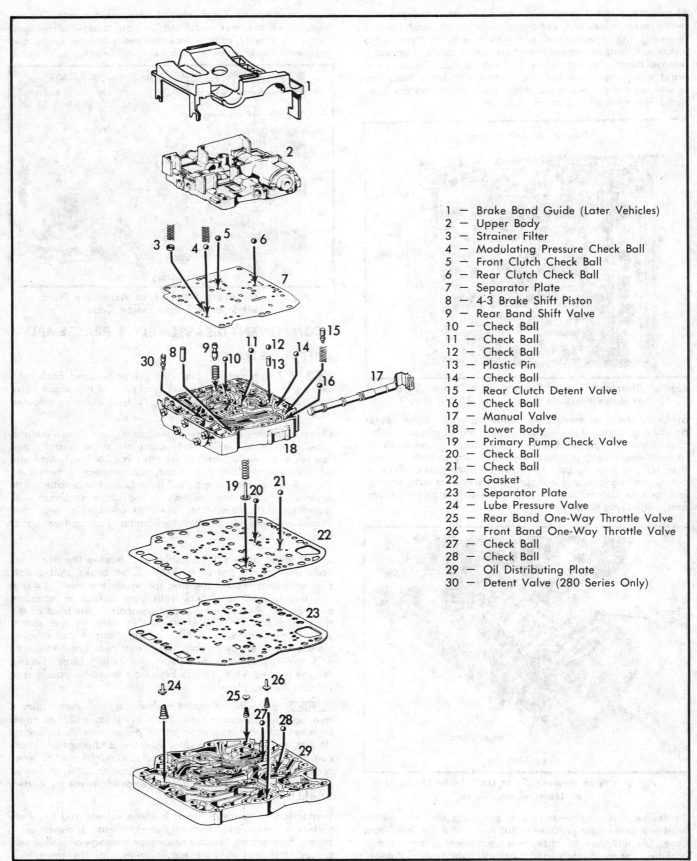

1 — Brake Band Guide (Later Vehicles)
2 — Upper Body
3 — Strainer Filter
4 — Modulating Pressure Check Ball
5 — Front Clutch Check Ball
6 — Rear Clutch Check Ball
7 — Separator Plate
8 — 4-3 Brake Shift Piston
9 — Rear Band Shift Valve
10 — Check Ball
11 — Check Ball
12 — Check Ball
13 — Plastic Pin
14 — Check Ball
15 — Rear Clutch Detent Valve
16 — Check Ball
17 — Manual Valve
18 — Lower Body
19 — Primary Pump Check Valve
20 — Check Ball
21 — Check Ball
22 — Gasket
23 — Separator Plate
24 — Lube Pressure Valve
25 — Rear Band One-Way Throttle Valve
26 — Front Band One-Way Throttle Valve
27 — Check Ball
28 — Check Ball
29 — Oil Distributing Plate
30 — Detent Valve (280 Series Only)

Fig. 9 Exploded View Showing Location of Valves and Check Balls In Valve Body Assembly

MERCEDES-BENZ TYPE W 4 B 025 (Cont.)

Reassembly — 1) Install oil distributing plate in a holding fixture with cored face upward. Install lubricating pressure valve, front band one-way throttle valve, and rear band releasing end one-way throttle valve into respective seats on plate. Place the two 5.5 mm check balls into countersunk seats in plate, place separator plate and gasket over oil distributing plate, and temporarily hold them in place using two clamps.

NOTE — *After installing separator plate, push down on valves and check for free operation; valve retainers must not be caught between oil disributing plate and separator plate.*

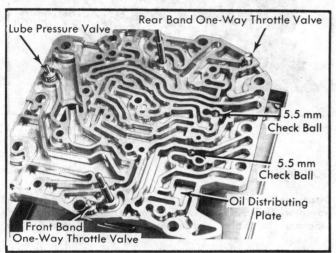

Fig. 10   Valve and Check Ball Positions In Distributing Plate

2) Place two 5.5 mm check balls on top of separator plate gasket *(see Fig. 11)*. Install the primary pump check valve and spring into lower body from underside, hold valve stem from upper side, then install lower body onto oil distributing plate assembly and release valve stem.

NOTE — *Valve should make an audible "click" against separator plate when released.*

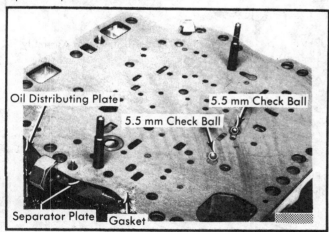

Fig. 11   Check Ball Positions on Separator Plate Gasket

3) Install the following into cored passages of lower body: Brake shift piston, rear clutch detent valve and spring, rear band releasing end valve and spring, plastic pin, and five 5.5 mm check balls. Install the two 7 mm check balls, one 5.5 mm check ball and spring, and strainer filter and spring into cored passages of upper body. Place remaining separator plate over upper body, making sure spring loaded check ball and

filter are correctly seated. Firmly hold separator plate and upper body together, turn assembly upside down, and place on lower body. Install 2 through bolts into assembly and tighten slightly. Remove valve body from holding fixture, install remaining bolts, and tighten from inside to outside. Position brake guide to valve body making sure contours are mated.

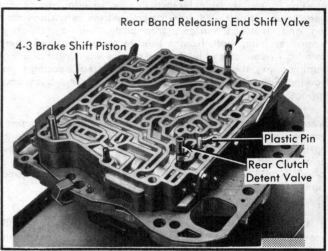

Fig. 12   Valve Locations In Lower Valve Body

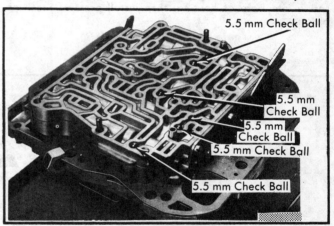

Fig. 13   Check Ball Positioning In Lower Valve Body Passages

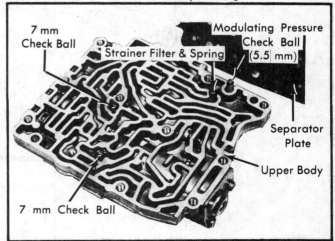

Fig. 14   Check Ball Positioning In Upper Valve Body Passages

MERCEDES-BENZ TYPE W 4 B 025 (Cont.)

EXTENSION HOUSING

Disassembly — Remove locking piston retaining bolt and cover plate, then withdraw locking piston and spring. Withdraw pressure receiving piston assembly, noting part position for reassembly reference. Remove speedometer driven gear retaining bolt, withdraw assembly from extension housing, and remove driven gear from body. Remove secondary pump retaining bolt from inside extension housing, then withdraw pump assembly. Remove rear seal and rear bearing retaining ring, then use a press and remove rear bearing from housing. Remove all hydraulic pressure plugs, check balls, and springs.

Reassembly — **1)** Install rear bearing into extension housing, then install snap ring and rear seal. Install locking piston and spring into housing, then install cover plate and retaining screw. Install secondary pump into housing, align locking hole of pump with retaining screw bore in housing, then install and tighten pump retaining screw.

2) Install new "O' rings into speedometer gear body, install speedometer gear into body, then install body into extension housing and install and tighten attaching bolt. Install and tighten all hydraulic plug assemblies. Install pressure receiving spring into bore of housing, then install pressure receiving piston.

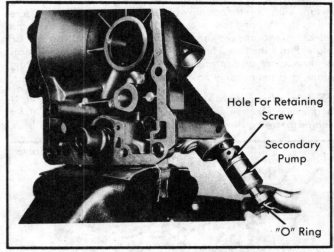

Hole For Retaining Screw

Secondary Pump

"O" Ring

Fig. 16   Installation of Secondary Pump Into Extension Housing

GOVERNOR

Disassembly — If necessary, remove oil seal rings from governor flange. Remove the four attaching bolts and separate shift valve housing and governor housing from

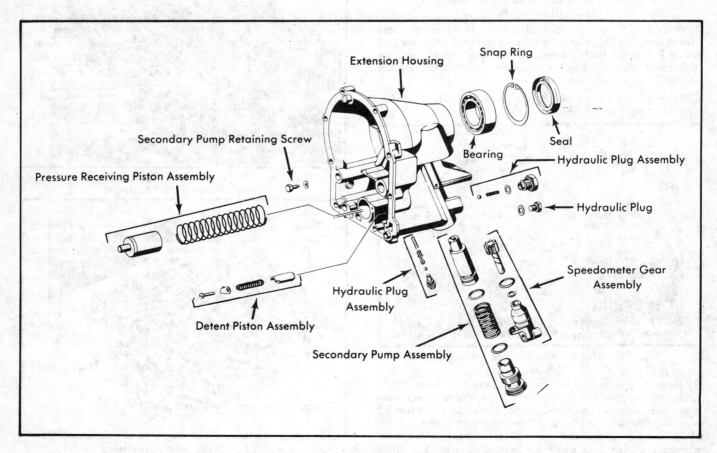

Secondary Pump Retaining Screw

Extension Housing

Snap Ring

Pressure Receiving Piston Assembly

Bearing

Seal

Hydraulic Plug Assembly

Hydraulic Plug

Detent Piston Assembly

Hydraulic Plug Assembly

Speedometer Gear Assembly

Secondary Pump Assembly

Fig. 15   Exploded View of Extension Housing Assembly

MERCEDES-BENZ TYPE W 4 B 025 (Cont.)

flange. Remove lock washer, then withdraw compression spring and shift valve from shift valve housing. Remove spring plate from governor housing assembly, then withdraw weight, compression spring, and spring guide from upper end of housing. From lower end of housing, withdraw heavier compression spring, compensating washers, and governor valve.

Inspection — Wash all parts in clean solvent and blow dry with compressed air. Check shift valve and governor valve for free movement in respective housings. Remove and clean oil strainer located in governor flange. If any part is found damaged, replace complete governor assembly.

Reassembly — 1) Insert governor valve into housing, then install light compression spring, spring guide, and weight into opposite end of housing. Push weight through governor valve, then install compensating washers and heavier compression spring over governor valve.

NOTE — *Do not alter number of compensating washers in assembly.*

2) Install spring retainer into assembly, making sure it is fully seated over spring. Install shift valve and compression spring into shift valve housing, then install lock washer, making sure the ends are not distorted in the valve groove. Position shift valve housing on governor flange, making sure oil slots of housing face oil sealing rings on flange, and that oil passages in both parts are aligned. Install attaching bolts and tighten.

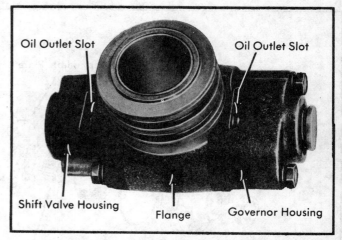

Fig. 18 Correct Positioning of Housings On Governor Flange

3) Install oil strainer into passage in governor housing end of governor flange, then position governor housing on assembly. Make sure oil slots of housing face oil seal rings on flange, and that oil passages in both parts are aligned. Install attaching bolts and tighten. If removed during disassembly, install oil seal rings on governor flange, and lock ends.

CONVERTER HOUSING & PRIMARY PUMP ASSEMBLY

Disassembly — Loosen oil pump attaching bolts on rear side of converter housing, tap heads of bolts lightly with a hammer to break pump loose, then remove bolts, pump assembly and intermediate plate from housing. Remove pump gears from pump housing, then remove "O" ring seal and lip seal from housing. Do not attempt to remove bronze bushing from pump housing. If necessary, remove ball bearing from rear side of converter housing.

NOTE — *If bronze bushing in pump housing is damaged, replace pump housing.*

Inspection — Wash all parts in clean solvent and blow dry with compressed air. Inspect all parts for wear or damage and replace as necessary.

Reassembly — 1) Install a new "O" ring and converter oil seal into pump housing. Lubricate gears with automatic transmission fluid, and install them into housing.

NOTE — *Make sure the bevelled outer edge of ring gear faces bronze bushing.*

2) Install intermediate plate into converter housing, aligning bolt and hydraulic passages. Install special installation sleeve (116 58 1 61 00) on stator shaft, then place two aligning studs into pump housing.

3) Install pump into converter housing, remove aligning studs, and install and tighten attaching bolts. If removed, install ball bearing onto converter housing.

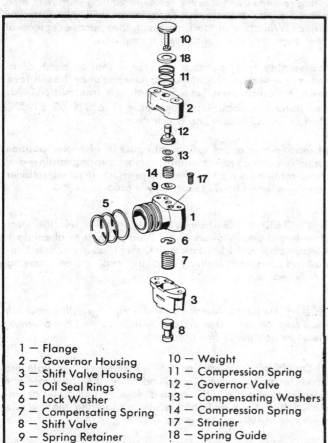

1 — Flange
2 — Governor Housing
3 — Shift Valve Housing
5 — Oil Seal Rings
6 — Lock Washer
7 — Compensating Spring
8 — Shift Valve
9 — Spring Retainer
10 — Weight
11 — Compression Spring
12 — Governor Valve
13 — Compensating Washers
14 — Compression Spring
17 — Strainer
18 — Spring Guide

Fig. 17 Exploded View of Governor Assembly

MERCEDES-BENZ TYPE W 4 B 025 (Cont.)

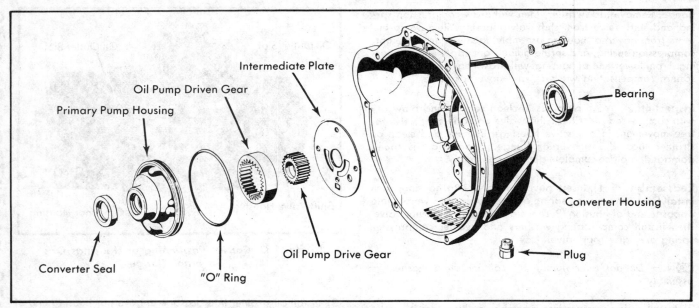

Primary Pump Housing

Oil Pump Driven Gear

Intermediate Plate

Bearing

Converter Housing

Plug

Oil Pump Drive Gear

Converter Seal

"O" Ring

Fig. 19   Exploded View of Converter Housing and Primary Pump Assembly

GEAR UNIT DISASSEMBLY

1) Remove output shaft with rear planetary gear set from assembly, then withdraw caged needle bearing and thrust bearing. Position gear unit in a holding fixture with input shaft upward, remove the three countersunk retaining screws from supporting flange, then withdraw flange and input shaft/sun gear from front planetary gear set.

2) Remove small snap ring retaining gear sets on intermediate shaft, and large snap ring retaining gear set. Lift drum for front band, and front and center gear sets off assembly. Withdraw center gear set sun gear from assembly, then withdraw front clutch assembly.

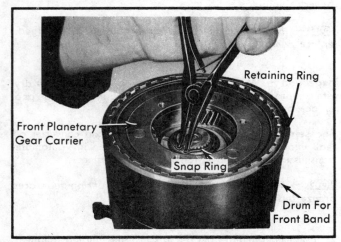

Retaining Ring

Front Planetary Gear Carrier

Snap Ring

Drum For Front Band

Fig. 20   Removing Snap Ring for Disassembly of Gear Unit

3) Remove oil distributor sleeve from assembly, then withdraw drum for rear band along with rear clutch. Remove hollow shaft, rear clutch hub, and overrunning clutch hub from intermediate shaft, then separate intermediate shaft from output shaft. Using a puller, remove bearing from output shaft, then withdraw sun gear from rear planetary set.

FRONT CLUTCH

Disassembly — Remove large snap ring retaining clutch pack in drum, then withdraw lined and steel clutch plates. Compress spring retainer using a press, remove retaining snap ring, then release press. Remove spring retainer and piston return springs. Withdraw piston from drum, then remove center seal from drum, and large piston seal from piston.

Reassembly — **1)** Install a new center seal on clutch drum and a new seal on piston, making sure lips of both seals face down into clutch drum. Lubricate seals with transmission fluid, then using a suitable installing sleeve (116 589 02 61 00), carefully install piston into clutch drum.

2) Insert piston return springs into pockets of piston, position spring retainer on top of springs, compress spring retainer and install retaining snap ring. Release pressure on spring retainer and make sure snap ring seats fully in groove.

3) On 240D and 300 series models, install 1 selective steel plate into drum, followed with 1 lined plate, then alternate 1 selective steel and 1 lined plate until all plates are installed. Install end plate and retaining snap ring, making sure snap ring is fully seated.

NOTE — *Do not confuse front clutch snap ring with rear clutch snap ring. On all except diesel models, snap ring has 6 waves; diesel models use a flat snap ring.*

4) On 280 series, install one .079" (2 mm) thick steel plate into clutch drum, follow with one lined plate, then alternate one selective steel plate and one lined plate until all plates are installed. Install end plate and retaining snap ring, making sure snap ring is fully seated in groove.

NOTE — *Do not confuse front clutch snap ring with rear clutch snap ring. Front clutch snap ring has 6 waves.*

MERCEDES-BENZ TYPE W 4 B 025 (Cont.)

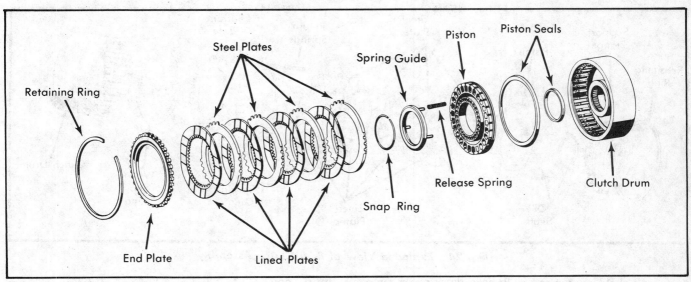

Fig. 21   *Exploded View of Front Clutch Assembly*

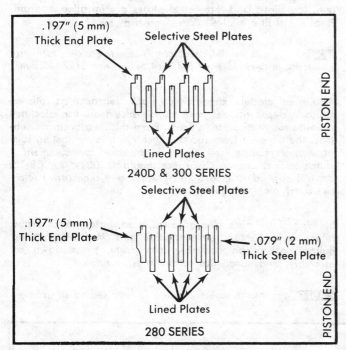

Fig. 22   *Clutch Plate Installation In Front Clutch Assembly*

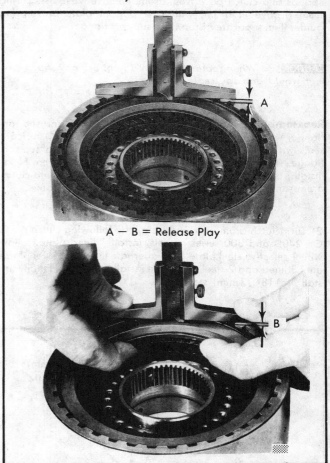

Fig. 23   *Measuring Front Clutch Release Play Using a Depth Gauge*

5) On all models, check release play of clutch pack as follows: Using a depth gauge, measure distance between top of clutch drum and end plate (press downward lightly on plate). Next, lift end plate up against ring and again measure distance from top of clutch drum to end plate. Subtract second measurement from first measurement; remainder is release play. On all models, play should be .031-.047" (.8-1.2 mm). If not, replace one or more selective steel plates in drum with correct thickness plate(s). On 240D, and 300 series models, selective steel plates are available in thicknesses of .177" (4.5 mm) and .197" (5 mm). On 280 series models, selective steel plates are available in thicknesses of .118" (3 mm) and .138" (3.5 mm).

REAR CLUTCH

Disassembly — Using a screwdriver, remove the flat snap ring retaining support flange and piston assembly in clutch drum. Withdraw piston and flange assembly from drum, tak-

MERCEDES-BENZ TYPE W 4 B 025 (Cont.)

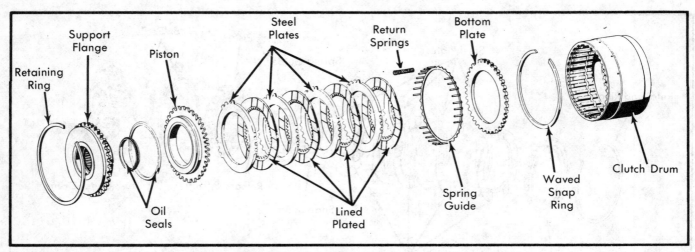

Fig. 24   Exploded View of Rear Clutch Assembly

ing care to hold parts together. Remove clutch piston return springs and clutch pack from drum. Remove waved snap ring from groove in drum, withdraw bottom plate and spring guide, then separate piston from support flange.

CAUTION — *When replacing seals, do not use any sharp tool that would damage seal lip.*

Reassembly — **1)** Install new oil seals on piston and support flange, with seal lips facing downward into flange. Lubricate seals with transmission fluid, then install piston into support flange, starting seal lip with a pencil or ball point pen. Next, install piston return spring guide and bottom plate into clutch drum, and position waved snap ring into drum groove.

2) Turn clutch drum over and install the following clutch pack: On 240D and 300 series models, install 1 lined plate, follow with 1 selective steel plate, then alternate lined and steel plates until 3 lined and 2 steel plates are installed in drum. Finally, install 1 .118" (3 mm) steel plate.

3) On 280 models, install one lined plate, follow with one selective steel plate, and then alternate lined and steel plates until four lined and three steel plates are installed in drum. Finally, install one .079" (2 mm) steel plate.

NOTE — *On all models, rear clutch selective steel plates are available in thicknesses of .177" (4.5 mm) and .197" (5 mm).*

4) On all models, check clutch pack clearance as follows: Using a depth gauge, measure distance from top of clutch drum to top steel plate in drum. From this measurement, subtract the distance from top of clutch drum to contacting face of support flange (see *Fig. 26*). Resulting measurement is clutch pack clearance. Clearance should be .031-.047" (.8-1.2 mm); if not, adjust clearance by varying thicknesses of selective clutch plates in drum.

5) With clutch pack clearance adjusted, install clutch piston return springs into drum on guide pins. Install supporting flange and piston assembly into drum, press down on assembly, and install flat retaining snap ring.

CAUTION — *Make sure snap ring is fully seated in groove.*

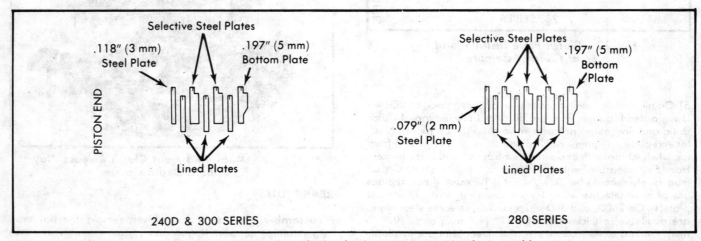

Fig. 25   Positioning of Clutch Plates In Rear Clutch Assembly

MERCEDES-BENZ TYPE W 4 B 025 (Cont.)

A — B = Clutch Pack Clearance

Fig. 26   Measuring Rear Clutch Pack Clearance Using a Depth Gauge

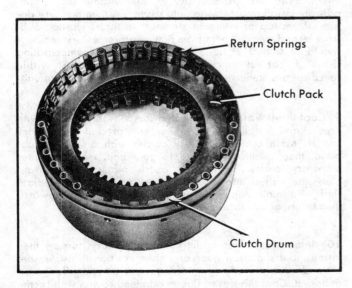

Fig. 27   Installation of Rear Clutch Assembly Return Springs

GEAR UNIT REASSEMBLY

NOTE — *When installing thrust washer, make sure stepped face of thrust washer is positioned against sun gear.*

1) Coat needle thrust bearing and split needle bearing with grease and install onto output shaft. Insert sun gear for rear gear set onto output shaft, then position thrust washer on top of gear. Position ball bearing and parking gear on shaft and press into place.

2) Position the two greased needle bearings into ring gear end of intermediate shaft, then mate output and intermediate shafts. Place assembly in a suitable holding fixture, then install needle bearing and thrust washer onto intermediate shaft.

3) Place hollow shaft into rear clutch assembly, making sure all clutch plates are engaged. Place rear clutch/hollow shaft assembly on intermediate shaft, then install needle bearing into overrunning clutch.

4) Check seal rings of oil distributor sleeve for correct position, then insert distributor sleeve into support flange of rear clutch assembly. Position front clutch on oil distributor sleeve, then install needle bearing over hollow shaft. Insert sun gear of center gear unit into front clutch.

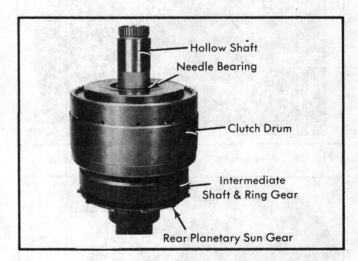

Hollow Shaft

Needle Bearing

Clutch Drum

Intermediate Shaft & Ring Gear

Rear Planetary Sun Gear

Fig. 28   View of Assembled Gear Unit

5) Place planetry gear carrier of center gear set on the bench with forward clutch splines upward. Temporarily install thrust washer (without compensating shim) inside assembly. Using a depth gauge, measure distance from top of clutch splines to surface of thrust washer. From this measurement, subtract the distance from the top of clutch splines to the shoulder of inner hub. Write down final measurement obtained.

6) Next, measure distance from thrust surface of center gear set sun gear to shoulder of hollow shaft. Subtract this measurement from the final measurement obtained in step 5). Resulting measurement is end play between inner shoulder of center planetary gear carrier and hollow shaft. End play should be .008-.012" (.2-.3 mm); if not, select a compensating shim of correct thickness to bring end play within specifications.

MERCEDES-BENZ TYPE W 4 B 025 (Cont.)

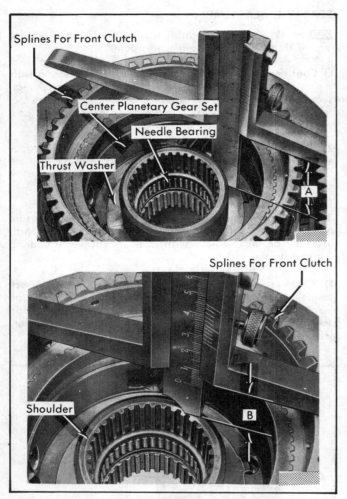

Splines For Front Clutch

Center Planetary Gear Set

Needle Bearing

Thrust Washer

A

Fig. 29 *Measuring Center Sun Gear Play (Step 1)*

Splines For Front Clutch

Shoulder

B

Shoulder
Of Hollow
Shaft

Fig. 30 *Measuring Center Sun Gear Play (Step 2)*

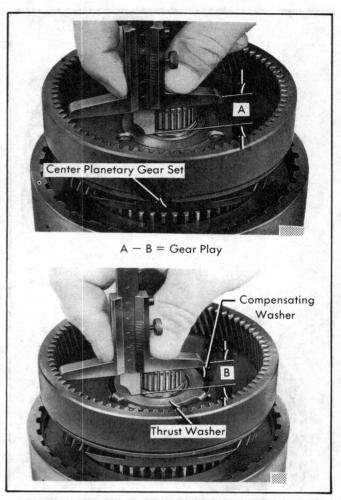

Center Planetary Gear Set

A

A − B = Gear Play

Compensating
Washer

B

Thrust Washer

Fig. 31 *Measuring Play of Front Gear Set*

8) Using a depth gauge, measure distance from top of intermediate shaft to shoulder of intermediate shaft. Temporarily install thrust washer into assembly, then measure distance from top of intermediate shaft to thrust washer. Subtract second measurement from first measurement; remeainder should be .008-.012" (.2-.3 mm). If not, select a compensating shim of correct thickness to bring end play within specifications. Remove center planetary carrier from gear unit.

9) Coat thrust washer and selected compensating washer with grease and install into ring gear end of center planetary carrier. Mesh center planetary carrier with drum for front band, then install assembly onto gear unit, meshing center planetary carrier with front clutch plates. Install front planetary carrier into assembly, then secure to intermediate shaft with small snap ring. Push drum for front band upward, then secure gear unit with large retaining ring.

7) Coat thrust washer and selected compensating shim with grease and position in front clutch spline end of center planetary carrier. Also, install the caged needle bearing into center bore of carrier. Temporarily install center planetary gear carrier into forward clutch (leaving off drum for front band), making sure parts are fully mated.

10) Insert thrust washer into front planetary carrier, then install input shaft/sun gear assembly. Position thrust washer on underside of supporting flange and position flange on gear unit. Coat threads of flange retaining screws with Loctite sealer, install and tighten. Install oil seal ring on input shaft, lock ends, and check for free movement of ring in groove.

MERCEDES-BENZ TYPE W 4 B 025 (Cont.)

Fig. 32 Installing Supporting Flange onto Gear Unit

- Supporting Flange
- Thrust Washer

TRANSMISSION REASSEMBLY

1) Position transmission case in a holding fixture with pan attaching face upward. Insert front band lever into case, install lever pin, and secure with retaining clip. Install new "O" rings into center and rear band pressure body bores, then install a new seal into selector lever bore. Position neutral safety and back-up light switch on transmission, install and tighten attaching screws.

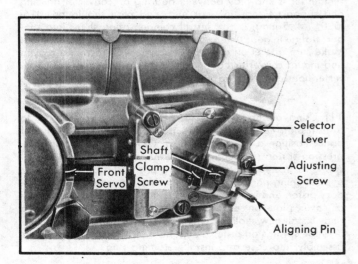

- Selector Lever
- Shaft Clamp Screw
- Front Servo
- Adjusting Screw
- Aligning Pin

Fig. 33 Adjusting Neutral Safety Switch

2) Install a new seal on front servo piston, position piston and return spring into case, then install servo cover and retaining ring. Position detent plate on rear of case, install selector lever and shaft through case and plate, then tighten clamp screw. Place selector lever in neutral position, loosen adjusting screw of neutral safety switch (*see Fig. 33*), install an alignment pin through link and into bore of housing, then tighten adjusting screw and remove pin.

3) Install control pressure shaft into case bore, insert plastic washer and secure with "E" clip. Install sealing ring into rear servo bore, making sure seal is flush with bore in housing. Install pressure bodies into center and rear band pressure body bores in case. Secure bodies in case with retaining clip.

CAUTION — *Center and rear band pressure bodies are not interchangeable. Center band body has identification grooves; rear band body has no grooves.*

4) On rear of case, install linkage arm, washer, and roller. Position leaf spring on case and over detent plate, then install needle bearing supported roller. Install parking lock bracket and retaining bolt. If removed, install parking pawl bearing pin. Position extension housing gasket on rear case face, and center over bores for fitted pins. Mount modulating pressure valve housing on rear of case, install and tighten attaching bolts, then check valve for free operation.

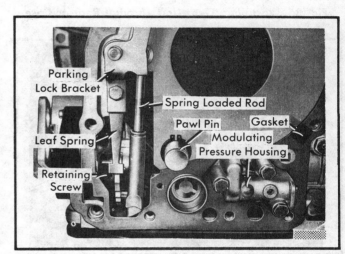

- Parking Lock Bracket
- Leaf Spring
- Retaining Screw
- Spring Loaded Rod
- Pawl Pin
- Modulating Pressure Housing
- Gasket

Fig. 34 Rear View of Transmission Case Showing Installation of Control Linkage

5) Remove output shaft from gear unit assembly, insert into transmission case, then seat into case using a plastic hammer. Position rear band into case over output carrier, making sure band end engages pressure pin. Position center band over gear unit, and temporarily hold in place with rear servo cover retaining ring (see illustration). Make sure bearings are still positioned in end of gear unit, then install gear unit into case, guiding supporting lever of oil distributor sleeve into groove of case.

NOTE — *Make sure gear unit is fully engaged with output shaft.*

6) Insert front band into case and over gear unit, install pressure pins into band ends, then screw in band adjusting screw until band is secured in place. Install a fixture over front of transmission case to retain gear unit in place. Install tensioning spring on parking pawl bearing pin and attach hooked end to case. Pull back spring, install parking pawl and release spring, then check operation of parking lock. Install governor, eccentric for secondary pump, speedometer drive gear, and plate spring on output shaft.

MERCEDES-BENZ TYPE W 4 B 025 (Cont.)

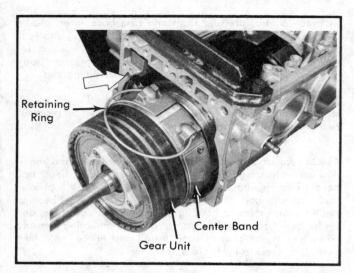

Fig. 35   *Installing Gear Unit Through Rear of Case*

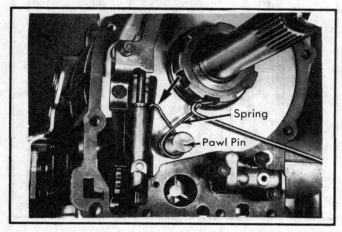

Fig. 36   *Rear View of Case Showing Installation of Parking Pawl Spring*

7) Make sure pressure receiving piston assembly is correctly positioned in extension housing, mount extension housing on transmission, and install and tighten attaching bolts. Install a new "O" ring seal on secondary pump plug, then install compression spring and plug into extension housing.

8) On all except diesel models, screw a suitable modulator pressure pin measuring tool (115 589 11 21 00) into extension housing, insert pressure pin into tool, and push in to stop. End of pin should be flush with face of tool; if not, select a pin of proper length and install into modulator unit. Coat threads of unit with sealer and install into extension housing. On diesel models, place a new sealing washer on adjusting screw, then install screw and compression spring into extension housing. On all models, install flange on output shaft, install and tighten retaining nut, then stake nut to secure in place.

9) Determine end play between gear unit and converter housing as follows: Place a suitable measuring bar (116 589 00 21 00) on transmission case, and measure distance from

top of bar to bearing surface of supporting flange in gear unit. **NOTE** — *After subtracting thickness of bar, resulting measurement is distance from face of transmission case to bearing surface of supporting flange.* Next, install a new gasket on rear of converter housing, place measuring bar on housing, and measure distance from top of bar to bearing race.

NOTE — *After subtracting thickness of bar, resulting measurement is distance from gasket surface to bearing race.*

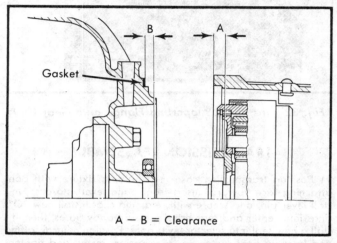

Fig. 37   *Gear Unit-to-Housing Clearance Diagram*

10) Subtract second measurement from first measurement; remainder is end play between bearing on converter housing and support flange in gear unit. End play should be .016-.020" (.4-.5 mm); if not, install compensating shims into support flange in gear unit to bring end play within specifications. Make sure gasket on converter housing is correctly positioned and mount converter housing on transmission case. Coat converter housing attaching bolts with sealer, install and tighten.

11) Using a ring compressor, install rear servo piston into transmission case making sure piston stem engages bore of band. Position a new "O" ring on servo cover, position compression spring (if used) over piston. Make sure small end of spring is positioned against servo piston. Install servo cover and retaining ring. Place new seal rings on center servo secondary piston and install into servo piston cover. Install new seals on cover, place on secondary piston and secure with retaining ring. Install new sealing "O" rings on assembly, position compression springs on piston stem and insert into case. Compress assembly into case and install retaining ring.

12) Check freeplay of center and rear bands as follows: Introduce air pressure into rear band release pressure passage in case (see illustration) and mark position of band end on drum. Next, introduce air pressure to rear band apply pressure passage in case and again mark position of band end on drum. Measure distance between two marks; measurement is rear band freeplay. For center band freeplay, first mark position of band end on drum in released position (spring pressure holds band in released position). Next, apply air pressure to center servo apply passage in case and again mark position of band end on drum. Distance between two marks is center band free play.

MERCEDES-BENZ TYPE W 4 B 025 (Cont.)

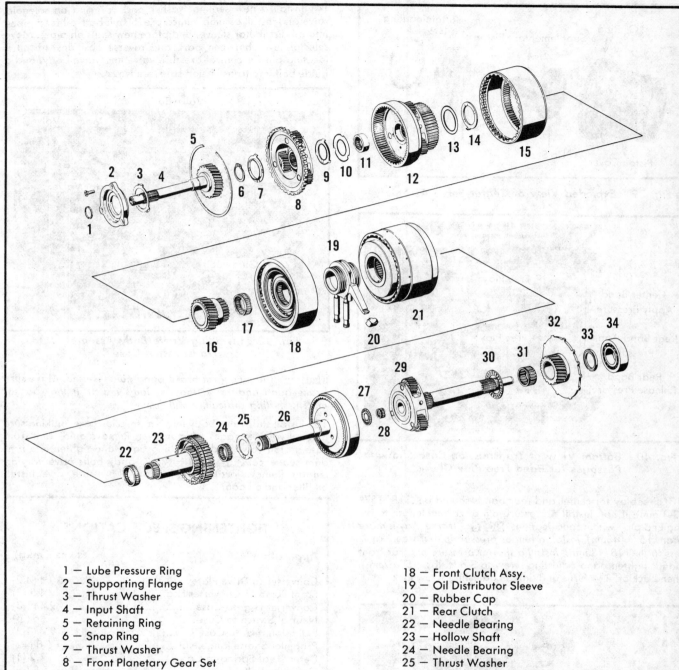

1 — Lube Pressure Ring
2 — Supporting Flange
3 — Thrust Washer
4 — Input Shaft
5 — Retaining Ring
6 — Snap Ring
7 — Thrust Washer
8 — Front Planetary Gear Set
9 — Thrust Washer
10 — Compensating Shim
11 — Needle Bearing
12 — Center Planetary Gear Set
13 — Compensating Washer
14 — Thrust Washer
15 — Drum For Front Band
16 — Sun Gear For Center Planetary
17 — Sun Gear Needle Bearing

18 — Front Clutch Assy.
19 — Oil Distributor Sleeve
20 — Rubber Cap
21 — Rear Clutch
22 — Needle Bearing
23 — Hollow Shaft
24 — Needle Bearing
25 — Thrust Washer
26 — Intermediate Shaft
27 — Thrust Bearing
28 — Roller Bearing
29 — Output Shaft & Rear Planetary Gear Set
30 — Thrust Bearing
31 — Split Needle Bearing
32 — Sun Gear For Rear Planetary
33 — Thrust Washer
34 — Rear Bearing

Fig. 38 Exploded View of Gear Unit Assembly

MERCEDES-BENZ TYPE W 4 B 025 (Cont.)

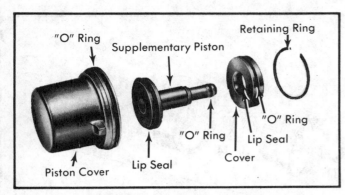

Fig. 39   Exploded View of Center Servo Assembly

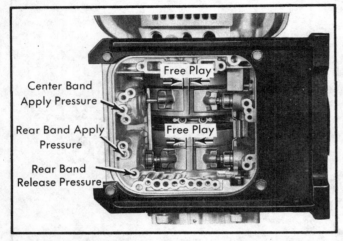

Fig. 40   Bottom View of Transmission Case Showing Passages for Band Free Play Check

13) Freeplay for center and rear bands should be .118-.157" (3-4 mm); if not, install a pressure pin of correct length to bring end play within specifications. **NOTE** — If free play is more than .157" (4 mm), install a longer pressure pin; if free play is less than .118" (3 mm), install a shorter pressure pin. For front band, tighten band adjusting screw to 3.6 ft. lbs. (.5 kg/cm²), then back off 1¾ turns and tighten adjusting screw lock nut.

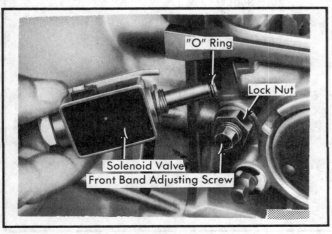

Fig. 41   Installing Solenoid Valve Into Transmission Case

14) Install a new sealing washer and "O" ring on solenoid valve and install assembly into case. Install both oil feed pipes into oil distributor sleeve, and place new seals on pipes. Move selector lever between park and reverse positions. Install a locating pin for control pressure valve into valve body, and a guide bolt into transmission case (see Fig. 42)

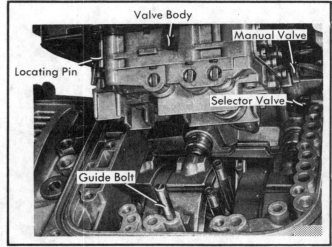

Fig. 42   Installing Valve Body Assembly Into Transmission Case

NOTE — If non-integral brake band guide is used. Make sure brake band and valve body contours match. If they do not match, shifting difficulties will result.

15) Install shift valve body into transmission case, making sure manual valve engages selector lever. Remove guide bolt from case, install valve body attaching bolts, and tighten in a random sequence. **CAUTION** — Valve body bolts have varying lengths. Remove locating pin for control pressure valve. Install oil filter and oil pan.

TIGHTENING SPECIFICATIONS

Application	Ft Lbs. (mkg)
Converter-to-Drive Plate	30.4 (4.2)
Front Pump-to-Converter Hsg.	14.5 (2)
Converter Hsg.-to-Case	9.4 (1.3)
Neutral Switch-to-Case	3.6 (.5)
Extension Hsg.-to-Case	9.4 (1.3)
Propeller Shaft Flange Nut	86.8 (12)
Detent Leaf Spring-to-Case	7.2 (1)
Governor Bolts	5.8 (.8)
Mod. Pressure Body-to-Case	5.0 (.7)
Secondary Pump Retaining Bolt	5.8 (.8)
Speedometer Drive Gear Bolt	5.8 (.8)
Interlock Piston Retaining Bolt	2.9 (.4)
Valve Body-to-Case	9.4 (1.3)
Oil Pan-to-Case	5.0 (.7)
Gear Set Support Flange Screws	5.0 (.7)
Upper Body-to-Lower Body	5.8 (.8)
Valve Body End Plates	2.9 (.4)
Selector Lever Clamp Bolt	5.8 (.8)
Selector Lever Adj. Screw	1.5 (.2)
Kickdown Solenoid-to-Case	21.7 (3)

TORQUEFLITE

Arrow
Arrow Pickup
Challenger

Colt Wagon
D50 Pickup
Sapporo

TRANSMISSION IDENTIFICATION

Three groups of numbers stamped on left side of case just above oil pan mating surface identify transmission. First group is a seven digit part number, center group is a four digit number code indicating date of manufacture, and last group of numbers are transmission serial number. Transmission is an MA-904A model and is used with 1600 cc, 2000 cc and 2600 cc engines.

DESCRIPTION

Transmission is a three speed unit combining a torque converter and a compound planetary gear system. Transmission case and converter housing are an integral aluminum casting. Transmission consists basically of two multiple-disc clutches, two bands and servos, an overrunning clutch, two planetary gear sets, and a hydraulic control system.

LUBRICATION & ADJUSTMENT

See AUTOMATIC TRANSMISSION SERVICING Section.

TROUBLE SHOOTING

**HARSH ENGAGEMENT FROM
NEUTRAL TO "D" OR "R"**

Engine idle speed too high. Valve body malfunction or leakage. Oil pressure too high. Worn or faulty rear clutch.

**DELAYED ENGAGEMENT FROM
NEUTRAL TO "D" OR "R"**

Oil pressure too low. Valve body malfunction or leakage. Low-reverse servo, band or linkage malfunction. Low fluid level. In-correct shift linkage adjustment. Oil filter clogged. Faulty oil pump. Worn or broken input shaft seal rings. Aerated fluid. Engine idle speed too low. Worn or broken reaction shaft support seal rings. Worn or faulty front clutch. Worn or faulty rear clutch.

RUNAWAY UPSHIFT

Oil pressure too low. Valve body malfunction or leakage. Low fluid level. Oil filter clogged. Aerated fluid. Incorrect throttle rod adjustment. Worn or broken reaction shaft support seal rings. Kickdown servo, band or linkage malfunction. Worn or faulty front clutch.

NO UPSHIFT

Oil pressure too low. Valve body leakage or malfunction. Low fluid level. Incorrect shift linkage adjustment. Incorrect throttle rod adjustment. Governor support seal rings broken or worn. Worn or broken reaction shaft support seal rings. Governor malfunction. Kickdown servo, band or linkage malfunction. Worn or faulty front clutch.

3-2 KICKDOWN RUNAWAY

Oil pressure too low. Valve body malfunction or leakage. Low fluid level. Aerated fluid. Incorrect throttle rod adjustment. Kickdown band out of adjustment. Worn or broken reaction shaft support seal rings. Kickdown servo, band or linkage malfunction. Worn or faulty front clutch.

**NO KICKDOWN OR
NORMAL DOWNSHIFT**

Valve body malfunction or leakage. Incorrect throttle rod adjustment. Governor malfunction. Kickdown servo, band or linkage malfunction.

SHIFTS ERRATIC

Oil pressure too low. Valve body malfunction or leakage. Low fluid level. Incorrect shift linkage adjustment. Oil filter clogged.

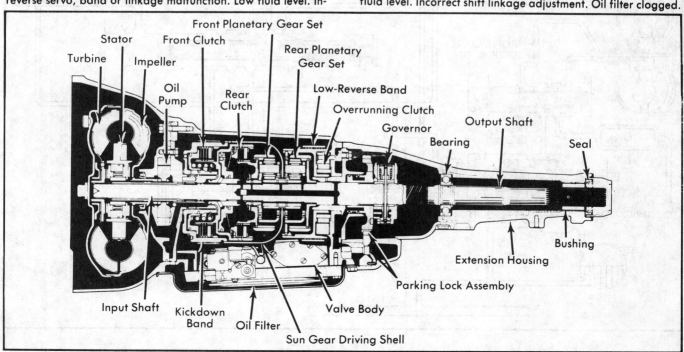

Fig. 1 Cutaway View of Torqueflite Transmission Showing Major Components

Automatic Transmissions

TORQUEFLITE (Cont.)

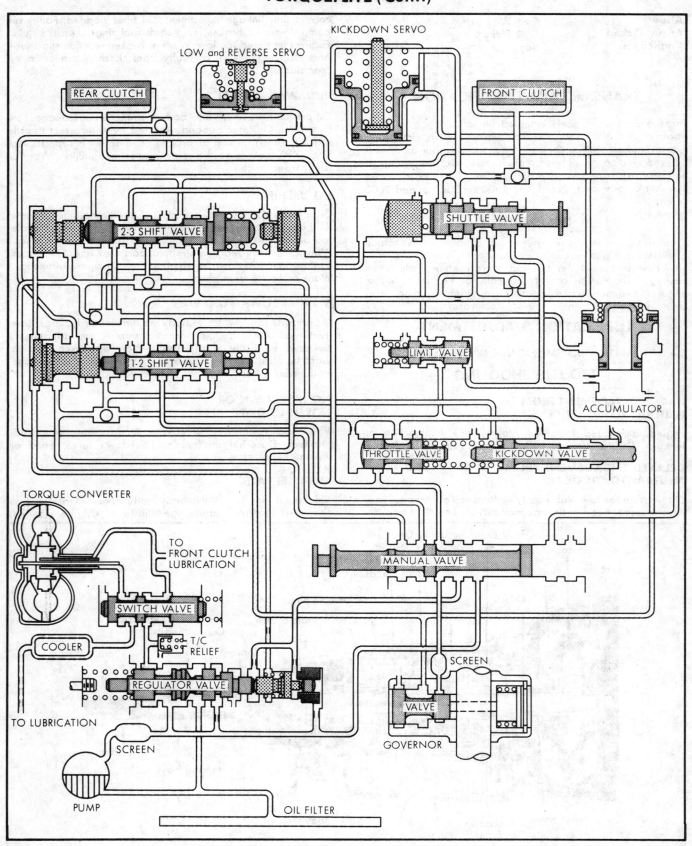

Fig. 2 Torqueflite Automatic Transmission Hydraulic Circuits Diagram

TORQUEFLITE (Cont.)

Faulty oil pump. Aerated fluid. Incorrect throttle rod adjustment. Governor support seal rings broken or worn. Worn or broken reaction shaft support seal rings. Governor malfunction. Kickdown servo, band or linkage malfunction. Worn or faulty front clutch.

SLIPS IN FORWARD DRIVE POSITIONS

Oil pressure too low. Valve body malfunction or leakage. Low fluid level. Incorrect shift linkage adjustment. Oil filter clogged. Faulty oil pump. Worn or broken input shaft seal rings. Aerated fluid. Incorrect throttle rod adjustment. Overrunning clutch not holding. Worn or faulty rear clutch. Overrunning clutch worn, broken or seized.

SLIPS IN REVERSE ONLY

Oil pressure too low. Low-reverse band out of adjustment. Valve body malfunction or leakage. Low-reverse servo, band or linkage malfunction. Low fluid level. Incorrect shift linkage adjustment. Faulty oil pump. Aerated fluid. Worn or broken reaction shaft support seal rings. Worn or faulty front clutch.

SLIPS IN ALL POSITIONS

Oil pressure too low. Valve body malfunction or leakage. Low fluid level. Oil filter clogged. Faulty oil pump. Worn or broken input shaft seal rings. Aerated fluid.

NO DRIVE IN ANY POSITION

Oil pressure too low. Valve body malfunction or leakage. Low fluid level. Oil filter clogged. Faulty oil pump. Planetary gear sets broken or seized.

NO DRIVE IN FORWARD DRIVE POSITIONS

Oil pressure too low. Valve body malfunction or leakage. Low fluid level. Worn or broken input shaft seals rings. Overrunning clutch not holding. Worn or faulty rear clutch. Planetary gear sets broken or seized. Overrunning clutch worn, broken or seized.

NO DRIVE IN REVERSE

Oil pressure too low. Low-reverse band out of adjustment. Valve body malfunction or leakage. Low-reverse servo, band or linkage malfunction. Incorrect shift linkage adjustment. Worn or broken reaction shaft support seal rings. Worn or faulty front clutch. Worn or faulty rear clutch. Planetary gear sets broken or seized.

DRIVES IN NEUTRAL

Valve body malfunction or leakage. Incorrect shift linkage adjustment. Insufficient clutch plate clearance. Worn or faulty rear clutch. Rear clutch dragging.

DRAGS OR LOCKS

Low-reverse band out of adjustment. Kickdown band adjustment too tight. Planetary gear sets broken or seized. Overrunning clutch worn, broken or seized.

HARSH UPSHIFT

Oil pressure too low. Incorrect throttle rod adjustment. Kickdown band out of adjustment. Oil pressure too high.

DELAYED UPSHIFT

Incorrect throttle rod adjustment. Kickdown band out of adjustment. Governor support seal rings broken or worn. Worn or broken reaction shaft support seal rings. Governor malfunction. Kickdown servo, band or linkage malfunction. Worn or faulty front clutch.

TRANSMISSION NOISE

Grating, Scraping, Or Growling — Low-reverse band out of adjustment. Kickdown band out of adjustment. Output shaft bearing and/or bushing damaged. Planetary gear sets broken or seized. Overrunning clutch worn, broken or seized.

Buzzing — Valve body malfunction or leakage. Low fluid level. Aerated fluid. Overrunning clutch inner race damaged.

HARD TO FILL, OIL BLOWS OUT FILLER TUBE

Oil filter clogged. Aerated fluid. High fluid level. Breather clogged.

TRANSMISSION OVERHEATS

Engine idle speed too high. Oil pressure too low. Low fluid level. Incorrect shift linkage adjustment. Faulty oil pump. Kickdown band adjustment too tight. Faulty cooling system. Insufficient clutch plate clearance.

TESTING

ROAD TEST

1) Before road testing, be certain that fluid level and condition, and control linkage adjustments have been checked and corrected if necessary. During test, transmission should upshift and downshift automatically at approximately the speeds shown in the Automatic Shift Speeds and Governor Pressure Chart. All shift speeds may vary somewhat due to production tolerances, rear axle ratio, or tire size. The important factor is the quality of the shifts. All shifts should be smooth, responsive, and with no slipping or engine speed flare-up.

2) Slipping or flare-up in any gear usually indicates clutch, band or overrunning clutch problems. The slipping clutch or band in a particular gear can usually be identified by noting transmission operation in other selector positions and comparing which internal units are applied in those positions.

3) For example, if transmission slips in "D" third gear, either the front or rear clutch is slipping. By selecting another gear which does not use one of those units (see Clutch and Band Application Chart), the unit which is slipping can be identified. If transmission slips in reverse, the front clutch is slipping. If transmission does not slip in reverse, the rear clutch is slipping.

4) Although this process of elimination can be used to detect any unit which slips and to confirm proper operating of good units, the actual cause of malfunction usually cannot be decided. Practically any condition can be caused by leaking hydraulic circuits or sticking valves. Therefore, unless an obvious condition exists, transmission should never be disassembled until hydraulic pressure tests have been made.

TORQUEFLITE (Cont.)
CLUTCH AND BAND APPLICATION CHART
(ELEMENTS IN USE)

Selector Lever Position	Front Clutch	Rear Clutch	Over-running Clutch	Front (Kickdown) Band	Rear (Low-Reverse) Band
D — DRIVE					
First		X	X		
Second		X		X	
Direct	X	X			
2 — SECOND					
First		X	X		
Second		X		X	
L — LOW (First)		X			X
R — REVERSE	X				X
NEUTRAL OR PARK — All clutches and bands released and/or ineffective.					

Automatic Shift Speeds & Governor Pressure Chart
(Approximate Miles Per Hour)①

Application	1600cc	2000cc & 2600cc
Wide Open Throttle		
1-2 Upshift	32-41	35-45
2-3 Upshift	59-68	65-75
Kickdown Limit		
3-2 WOT Downshift	47-61	52-68
3-1 WOT Downshift	21-30	24-34
Governor Pressure		
15 psi	18-19	20-21
40 psi	32-36	35-40
60 psi	47-52	52-57

① — Figures given are typical. Changes in tire size or axle ratio will cause shift points to occur at correspondingly higher or lower vehicle speeds.

moved forward to 90-96 psi (6.3-6.8 kg/cm²). Rear servo pressure should read the same as line pressure within 3 psi (.2 kg/cm²). This tests pump output, pressure regulation, and condition of rear clutch and rear servo hydraulic circuits.

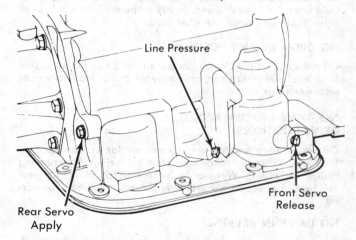

Fig. 3   View of Right Side of Transmission Case Showing Pressure Test Ports

HYDRAULIC PRESSURE TESTS

Before making pressure tests, be certain that fluid level and condition, and control linkage adjustments have been checked and corrected if necessary. Install an engine tachometer, raise vehicle on hoist which allows rear wheels to turn, and position tachometer so it can be read under vehicle. Disconnect throttle rod and shift rod from transmission levers so they can be controlled under vehicle. Make sure transmission fluid is at normal operating temperature (150-200°F).

Pressure Test (Selector in "L") — 1) Attach 0-100 psi gauges to line and rear servo ports. Operate engine at 1000 RPM for test. Move selector lever on transmission all the way forward ("L" position). Read pressures on both gauges as throttle lever on transmission is moved from full rearward position to full forward position.

2) Line pressure should read 54-60 psi (3.8-4.2 kg/cm²) with throttle lever rearward and gradually increase, as lever is

Pressure Test (Selector in "2") — 1) Install a "T" connection at rear cooler line fitting. Attach 0-100 psi gauges to "T" connection and line pressure port. Operate engine at 1000 RPM for test. Move selector lever on transmission 1 detent rearward from full forward position (into selector "2" position).

2) Read pressures on both gauges as throttle lever on transmission is moved from full rearward position to full forward position. Line pressure should read 54-60 psi (3.8-4.2 kg/cm²) with throttle lever rearward and gradually increase, as lever is moved forward to 90-96 psi (6.3-6.8 kg/cm²).

3) Lubrication pressure should be 5-15 psi (.4-1.1 kg/cm²) with lever rearward, and 10-30 psi (.7-2.1 kg/cm²) with lever forward. This tests pump output, pressure regulation, and condition of rear clutch and lubrication hydraulic circuits.

Pressure Test (Selector in "D") — 1) Attach 0-100 psi gauges to line and front servo release ports. Operate engine

TORQUEFLITE (Cont.)

at 1600 RPM for test. Move selector lever on transmission 2 detents rearward from full forward position (selector in "D" position).

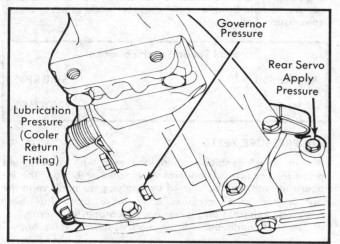

Fig. 4   Rear View of Transmission Case Showing Pressure Test Ports

2) Read pressure on both gauges as throttle lever on transmission is moved from full rearward position to full forward position. Line pressure should read 54-60 psi (3.8-4.2 kg/cm²) with throttle lever rearward and gradually increase, as lever is moved forward.

3) Front servo release is pressurized only in direct drive and should be same as line pressure within 3 psi (.2 kg/cm²), up to downshift point. This tests pump output, pressure regulation, and condition of rear clutch and front clutch hydraulic circuits.

NOTE — *A 0-300 psi gauge is required for the following test.*

Pressure Test (Selector in Reverse) — **1)** Attach gauge to rear servo apply port. Operate engine at 1600 RPM for test. Move selector lever on transmission 4 detents rearward from full forward position (into selector "R" position).

2) Rear servo pressure should read 230-260 psi (16.2-18.3 kg/cm²). This tests pump output, pressure regulation, and condition of front clutch and rear servo hydraulic circuits.

3) Move selector lever on transmission to "D" position to check that rear servo pressure drops to zero. This tests for leakage into rear servo, due to case porosity, which can cause reverse band to burn out.

Pressure Test Indication — **1)** If proper line pressure, minimum to maximum, is found in any one test, the pump and pressure regulator are working properly. Low pressure in "D", "L" and "2" but correct pressure in "R", indicates rear clutch circuit leakage.

2) Low pressure in "D" and "R", but correct pressure in "L", indicates front clutch circuit leakage. Low pressure in "R" and "L", but correct pressure in "2", indicates rear servo circuit leakage, low line pressure in all positions indicates a defective pump, clogged filter, or stuck pressure regulator valve.

NOTE — *Test only if transmission shifts at wrong vehicle speeds when throttle rod is correctly adjusted.*

Governor Pressure — Connect a 0-100 psi (0-7.0 kg/cm²) gauge to governor pressure port. Operate transmission in third

gear to read pressures and compare speeds shown in Automatic Shift Speeds and Governor Pressure Chart. If governor pressures are incorrect at the given vehicle speeds, governor valve and/or weights are probably sticking. Governor pressure should respond smoothly to changes in MPH and should return to 0-1.5 psi (0-.1 kg/cm²) when vehicle is stopped.

NOTE — *High governor pressure at stand still (above 2 psi) will prevent transmission from downshifting.*

Throttle Pressure — No gauge port is provided for testing throttle pressure. Incorrect throttle pressure should only be suspected if part throttle upshift speeds are either delayed or occur too early in relation to vehicle speeds. Engine runaway on either upshifts or downshifts can also be an indicator of incorrect (low) throttle pressure setting.

CAUTION — *In no case should throttle pressure be adjusted until transmission throttle rod adjustment has been checked, and corrected if necessary.*

HYDRAULIC PRESSURE ADJUSTMENTS

NOTE — *An incorrect throttle pressure setting will cause incorrect line pressure readings even though line pressure adjustment is correct. Always inspect and correct throttle pressure adjustment before adjusting line pressure.*

Throttle Pressure — **1)** Remove valve body from transmission. Insert gauge C-3763 between throttle lever cam and kickdown valve.

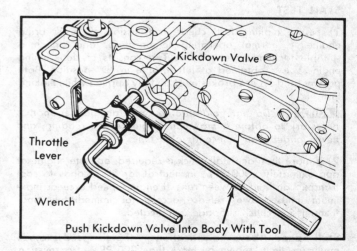

Fig. 5   View of Valve Body Showing Throttle Pressure Adjustment

2) By pushing in on tool, compress kickdown valve against spring so valve is completely bottomed inside the valve body. As force is being exerted to compress spring, turn throttle lever stop screw with an Allen wrench until head of screw touches throttle lever tang with throttle lever cam touching tool and throttle valve bottomed.

CAUTION — *Be sure adjustment is made with spring fully compressed and valve bottomed in valve body.*

Line Pressure — **1)** Turn Allen screw in end of pressure regulator spring bracket so measurement between valve body and inner edge of adjusting nut is 1⁵⁄₁₆". See Fig. 6.

TORQUEFLITE (Cont.)

NOTE — *Due to manufacturing tolerances, adjustment can be varied to obtain specified line pressure.*

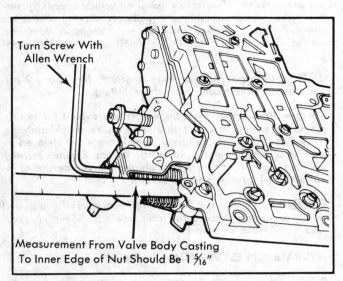

Turn Screw With Allen Wrench

Measurement From Valve Body Casting To Inner Edge of Nut Should Be 1 5/16"

Fig. 6   View of Valve Body Showing Line Pressure Adjustment

2) One complete turn of adjusting screw changes closed throttle line pressure approximately 1⅔ psi (.12 kg/cm²). Turning adjusting screw counterclockwise increases pressure; clockwise decreases pressure.

STALL TEST

1) Before making test, check transmission oil level, bring engine to normal operating temperature, and attach a suitable tachometer to engine. Test consists of determining engine speed obtained at full throttle in "D" position. Both parking and service brakes must be fully applied while making test.

CAUTION — *Do not hold throttle open any longer than is necessary to obtain a maximum engine speed reading, and never longer than 5 seconds at a time.*

2) If more than one stall check is required, operate engine at approximately 1000 RPM in neutral for 20 seconds to cool transmission fluid between runs. If engine speed exceeds maximum limits shown, release accelerator immediately since transmission clutch slippage is indicated.

Stall Speed Above Specification — If stall speed exceeds maximum limits shown by more than 200 RPM, transmission clutch slippage is indicated. Make hydraulic pressure and air pressure checks to determine cause of slippage.

Stall Speed Below Specification — Low stall speeds (with a properly tuned engine) indicate torque converter stator clutch problems. A road test will be necessary to identify the exact problem. If stall speeds are 250-350 RPM below specifications, and vehicle operates properly at highway speeds, but has poor through-gear acceleration, stator overrunning clutch is slipping. If stall speed and acceleration are normal, but abnormally high throttle opening is required to maintain highway speeds, stator clutch has seized. Both of these stator defects require replacement of torque converter.

Noise — A whining or siren-like noise due to fluid flow is normal during stall operation with some converters; however, loud metallic noises from loose parts or interference within the assembly indicate a defective converter. To be sure noise originates within the converter, raise vehicle on hoist and operate at light throttle in "D" and "N" while listening under transmission bell housing.

Stall Speed Specifications	
Application	**Stall RPM**
All Models	2200-2650

AIR PRESSURE TESTS

A "No Drive" condition could exist even with correct fluid pressure, because of inoperative clutches or bands. The inoperative units can be located by applying air pressure to the appropriate case passages after valve body has been removed. If clutches and servos operate properly, no upshift or erratic shift conditions indicate malfunctions in valve body.

CAUTION — *The compressed air supply must be free of dirt and moisture. Use a pressure of 30-100 psi (2.1-7.0 kg/cm²).*

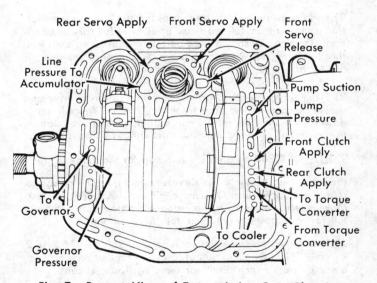

Rear Servo Apply   Front Servo Apply   Front Servo Release

Line Pressure To Accumulator

Pump Suction
Pump Pressure
Front Clutch Apply
Rear Clutch Apply
To Torque Converter
From Torque Converter

To Governor

To Cooler

Governor Pressure

Fig. 7   Bottom View of Transmission Case Showing Air Pressure Test Ports

Front Clutch — Direct air pressure into front clutch apply passage. Operation of clutch is indicated by a dull thud which may be heard, or felt. Hold air pressure on for a few seconds and check system for excessive oil leaks.

Rear Clutch — Direct air pressure into rear clutch apply passage. Operation of clutch is indicated by a dull thud which may be heard, or felt. Also check for excessive oil leaks.

Kickdown Servo (Front) — Direct air pressure into front servo apply passage. Operation of servo is indicated by a tightening of front band. Spring tension on servo piston should release the band.

Low-Reverse Servo (Rear) — Direct air pressure into rear servo apply passage. Operation of servo is indicated by a tightening of rear band. Spring tension of servo piston should release the band.

TORQUEFLITE (Cont.)

SERVICE (IN VEHICLE)

SPEEDOMETER PINION GEAR

Removal — Remove bolt and retainer securing speedometer pinion adapter in extension housing. With cable housing connected, carefully work adapter and pinion out of extension housing.

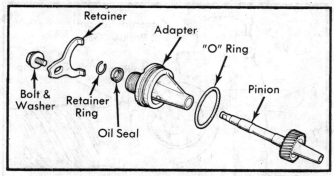

Fig. 8   Disassembled View of Speedometer Drive

Seal Replacement — If transmission fluid is found in cable housing, replace seal in adapter. Start seal and retainer ring in adapter, then push into adapter using suitable tool (C-4004) until tool bottoms.

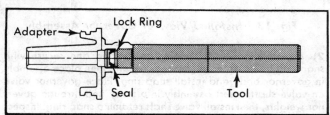

Fig. 9   Speedometer Pinion Seal Installation

CAUTION — *To avoid misalignment, make sure adapter flange and its mating area on extension housing are clean.*

Installation — Note number of gear teeth and install speedometer pinion gear into adapter. Rotate pinion gear and adapter assembly so that number on adapter, corresponding with number of teeth on gear, is in 6 o'clock position as assembly is installed. Install retainer and bolt, with tangs in adapter positioning slots. Tap adapter firmly into extension housing, then tighten retainer bolt.

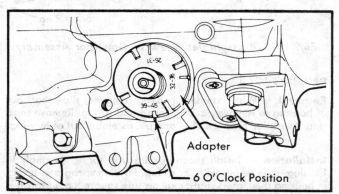

Fig. 10   View of Extension Housing Showing Speedometer Pinion and Adapter Installation

NEUTRAL SAFETY SWITCH

See Automatic Transmission Servicing.

EXTENSION HOUSING YOKE SEAL

CAUTION — *Use care not to damage yoke and splines.*

Removal — Marking parts for reassembly reference, remove propeller shaft. Cut boot end of extension housing yoke seal, then use a puller to remove seal from extension housing.

Installation — Using a suitable tool, drive new seal into extension housing. Install propeller shaft, aligning marks made at removal.

EXTENSION HOUSING

Removal — 1) Marking parts for reassembly reference, remove propeller shaft, then remove extension housing seal. Remove speedometer pinion adapter assembly, then drain approximately two quarts of transmission fluid. Remove extension housing-to-crossmember bolts, raise transmission slightly with suitable service jack, then remove center crossmember and support assembly. Remove extension housing-to-transmission bolts.

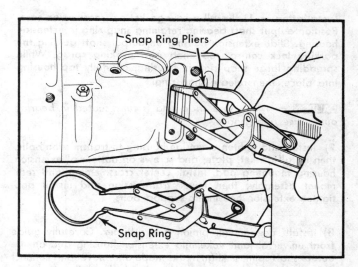

Fig. 11   Bottom View of Extension Housing Showing Removal of Retaining Snap Ring

NOTE — *When removing or installing extension housing, gearshift lever must be in "L" position, placing parking lock control rod rearward so it can be disengaged or engaged with parking lock sprag.*

2) Remove 2 screws, plate and gasket from bottom of housing mounting pad. With large snap ring on output shaft bearing spread as far as possible, tap extension housing off output shaft bearing, then pull carefully rearward to remove parking lock control rod knob past parking sprag and remove housing.

Bearing Replacement — Using heavy duty snap ring pliers, remove output shaft bearing rear snap ring, then remove bearing from shaft. Install new bearing on shaft with outer race ring groove toward front, then install rear snap ring.

TORQUEFLITE (Cont.)

Bushing Replacement — Using suitable driver, remove bushing from extension housing. Align hole in new bushing with oil slot in extension housing, drive or press bushing into housing, then install new seal.

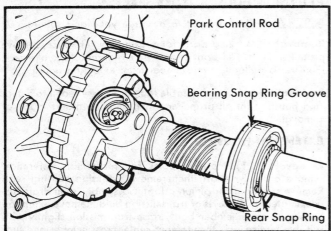

Fig. 12   Rear View of Transmission Showing Output Shaft Bearing Installation

Installation — 1) Install a new gasket on transmission case. Position output shaft bearing retaining snap ring in extension housing. Slide extension housing on output shaft guiding the parking lock control rod knob past parking sprag. While spreading large snap ring in housing, carefully tap housing into place, then release snap ring.

CAUTION — *Make sure snap ring is fully seated in bearing outer race ring groove.*

2) Install and tighten extension housing-to-transmission bolts, then install gasket, plate, and screws on bottom of extension housing mounting pad. Install center crossmember and rear mount assembly, then lower transmission and install and tighten extension housing-to-support bolts.

3) Install speedometer pinion and adapter. Carefully guide front universal joint yoke into extension housing and on the output shaft splines. Align marks made at removal and connect propeller shaft to rear axle pinion shaft yoke. Adjust transmission fluid level as necessary.

GOVERNOR & PARKING GEAR

Removal — Remove extension housing and output shaft bearings as outlined above, carefully pry snap ring from weight end of governor valve shaft, then slide valve and shaft assembly out of governor body. Remove large snap ring from weight end of governor body, then lift out governor weight assembly. Remove snap ring from inside governor weight, then remove inner weight and spring from outer weight. Remove snap ring from behind governor body, then slide governor and support assembly off output shaft. Remove bolts and separate governor body and screen from parking gear.

Inspection — Inspect all parts for wear or damage, and spring for distortion. Weights and valve should fall freely in bores when clean and dry. Remove any roughness with crocus cloth.

Installation — 1) Assemble governor body and screen to support and tighten bolts finger tight, making sure oil passage of governor body aligns with passage in support. Position support and governor assembly on output shaft, aligning so valve shaft hole in body mates with hole in output shaft. Slide assembly into place, install snap ring behind governor body, then tighten body-to-support bolts and bend ends of lock straps over bolt heads.

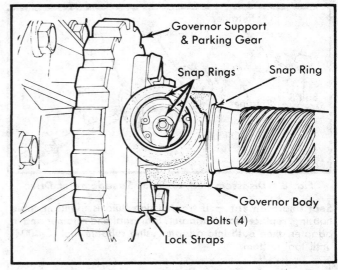

Fig. 13   Installed View of Governor Assembly

2) Assemble governor weights and spring and secure with snap ring inside of large governor weight, then place assembly in governor body and install snap ring. Place governor valve on valve shaft, insert assembly into body and through governor weights, then install valve shaft retaining snap ring. Inspect valve and weight assembly for free movement, then install output shaft bearing and extension housing.

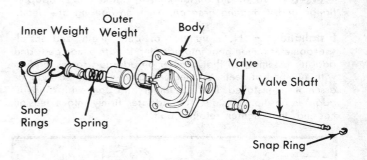

Fig. 14   Disassembled View of Governor Assembly

PARKING LOCK

Removal — With extension housing removed, slide shaft out of housing to remove parking sprag and spring. Remove snap ring, then slide reaction plug and pin assembly out of housing.

Installation — Install reaction plug and spring assembly in housing, then secure with snap ring. Position sprag and spring in housing then insert shaft, making sure square lug on sprag is toward parking gear, and spring is positioned so it moves sprag away from gear. Install extension housing.

TORQUEFLITE (Cont.)

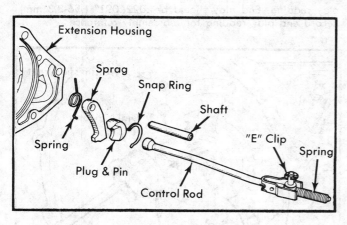

Fig. 15 Disassembled View Showing Components of Parking Lock Assembly

VALVE BODY ASSEMBLY & ACCUMULATOR PISTON

Removal — 1) Loosen oil pan bolts, tap pan to break it loose allowing fluid to drain, then remove pan. Loosen clamp bolts, then remove throttle and shift levers from transmission. Remove neutral safety switch, then remove valve body-to-transmission case bolts and lower valve body down and forward out of case. If necessary, rotate propeller shaft to align parking gear and sprag to permit knob on end of parking control rod to pass sprag.

2) Remove accumulator piston and spring from transmission case, then inspect for damage. If valve body manual lever shaft seal requires replacement, drive out of case with punch. Drive new seal into case with a 15/16" socket and hammer.

NOTE — *Seal may be replaced without removing valve body from case by using a small screwdriver to pry seal out of case. Take care not to damage shaft or seal bore in case.*

Installation — 1) With neutral safety switch removed from case, place valve body manual lever in low position to move parking rod to rear position. Use screwdriver to push sprag into engagement with parking gear, turning output shaft to ensure engagement. This will allow knob on end of parking rod to move past sprag as valve body is installed. Install accumulator piston in case. Position accumulator spring between piston and valve body.

2) Place valve body in position, working park rod through opening and past sprag, then install retaining bolts finger tight. Install neutral safety switch, then place manual lever in neutral position, shifting valve body if necessary to center neutral finger over switch plunger. Install and tighten valve body-to-case bolts evenly. Install gearshift lever and tighten clamp bolt. Move lever through all detent positions to ensure shaft does not bind in case. If binding exists, loosen valve body bolts and realign. Be sure throttle shaft seal is in place, then install flat washer and throttle lever and tighten clamp bolt. Connect throttle and gearshift linkage, adjust as required. Install oil pan with new gasket, then adjust transmission fluid level.

TRANSMISSION REMOVAL & INSTALLATION

REMOVAL

NOTE — *Transmission and converter must be removed as an assembly to prevent damage to drive plate, pump bushing, and oil seal. Do not allow weight of transmission to rest on drive plate at any time during removal or installation.*

1) Disconnect battery ground cable for safety. Remove oil cooler lines at transmission. Remove starter motor and cooler line bracket. Loosen pan to drain transmission.

2) Mark converter and drive plate for reassembly reference. Using socket wrench on crankshaft vibration damper bolt, rotate engine clockwise to position converter attaching bolts for removal, then remove bolts. Remove propeller shaft.

3) Disconnect electrical leads. Disconnect gearshift rod and torque shaft assembly, throttle rod lever from left side of transmission, and linkage bellcrank (if so equipped) from transmission.

4) Remove oil filler tube and speedometer cable. Support rear of engine with suitable fixture. With a transmission support on a service jack, support transmission. Raise transmission slightly to relieve load on supports. Remove bolts securing transmission mount to crossmember and crossmember to frame, then remove crossmember.

5) Remove all converter housing bolts, then carefully work transmission and converter assembly rearward off engine block dowels and disengage converter hub from end of crankshaft. **NOTE** — *Attach a small "C" clamp to edge of converter housing to hold converter in place during transmission removal.* Lower transmission and remove from under vehicle. To remove converter assembly, remove "C" clamp from edge of converter housing then carefully slide assembly from transmission.

INSTALLATION

1) Reverse removal procedures and note the following: To install converter, rotate pump rotors with suitable tool (C3756) until two small holes in handle are vertical. Carefully slide converter over input shaft and reaction shaft. Make sure converter hub slots are also vertical and fully engage pump inner rotor lugs. Test for full engagement by placing straight edge on face of converter housing. Surface of converter front cover lug

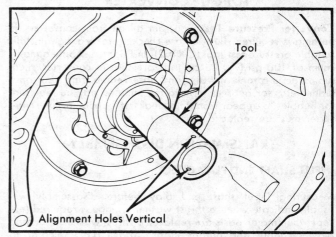

Fig. 16 Using Special Tool to Align Pump Rotors for Torque Converter Installation

TORQUEFLITE (Cont.)

should be at least ½" (12.7 mm) to rear of straightedge when converter is pushed all the way into transmission. Attach a small "C" clamp to converter housing to hold converter in place during transmission installation.

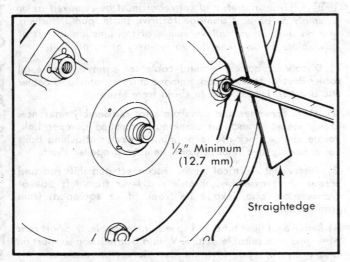

Fig. 17   Measuring for Full Converter Engagement

2) Inspect converter drive plate for distortion or cracks and replace if necessary. **NOTE** — *When drive plate replacement has been necessary, make sure both transmission dowel pins are in engine block and they are protruding far enough to hold transmission in alignment.* Coat converter hub hole in crankshaft with muti-purpose grease.

3) Place transmission and converter assembly on a suitable jack and position under vehicle for installation. Raise or tilt as necessary to align transmission to engine. Rotate converter so that mark on converter (made during removal) will align with mark on drive plate. Carefully work transmission assembly forward over engine block dowels with converter hub entering crankshaft opening.

4) After transmission is in position on engine, install and tighten all bolts. Adjust shift and throttle linkage, then refill transmission with DEXRON type automatic transmission fluid.

TORQUE CONVERTER

Converter Pressure Test — Drain all oil from converter. If flushing is required, flush before checking for leakage. Install suitable pressure test tool (C-4102) and tighten. Apply a maximum of 100 psi (7.0 kg/cm²) air pressure to converter, then submerge in a tank of water and observe hub, ring gear and seam welds for bubbles. Five to ten minutes may be required for bubbles to appear from small leaks. If leakage occurs, converter must be replaced.

TRANSMISSION DISASSEMBLY

INPUT SHAFT END PLAY CHECK

Measuring input shaft end play before disassembly will usually indicate when a thrust washer change is required (except when major parts are replaced). Thrust washer is located between input and output shafts. Attach dial indicator to transmission converter housing with plunger seated against end of input shaft. Move input shaft in and out to obtain end

play reading. End play should be .022-.091" (.56-2.3 mm). Record end play reading for reassembly reference.

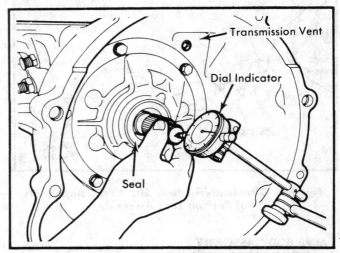

Fig. 18   Using a Dial Indicator to Measure Input Shaft End Play

VALVE BODY ASSEMBLY & ACCUMULATOR PISTON

See Service (In Vehicle)

EXTENSION HOUSING

See Service (In Vehicle)

GOVERNOR

See Service (In Vehicle)

OIL PUMP & REACTION SHAFT SUPPORT

Tighten front band adjusting screw until band is tight on front clutch retainer, preventing retainer from coming out with pump, damaging clutches. Remove oil pump housing retaining bolts, then install suitable slide hammers in threaded holes in pump housing flange. Operating both hammers evenly, withdraw pump and reaction shaft support assembly from case.

FRONT BAND & FRONT CLUTCH

Loosen front band adjuster, remove band strut then slide band out of case. Slide front clutch assembly out of case.

INPUT SHAFT & REAR CLUTCH

Grasp input shaft, then slide input shaft and rear clutch assembly out of case.

CAUTION — *Do not lose thrust washer located between rear end of input shaft and forward end of output shaft.*

PLANETARY GEAR ASSEMBLIES, SUN GEAR & DRIVING SHELL

While supporting output shaft and driving shell, carefully slide assembly forward and out through case.

CAUTION — *Do not damage ground surfaces on output shaft during removal.*

REAR BAND & LOW-REVERSE DRUM

Remove low-reverse drum, loosen rear band adjuster and remove band strut and link, then remove band from case.

TORQUEFLITE (Cont.)

OVERRUNNING CLUTCH

Note position of overrunning clutch rollers and springs before disassembly to aid in reassembly. Carefully slide out clutch hub, then remove rollers and springs.

KICKDOWN SERVO (FRONT)

Using suitable tool, compress kickdown servo spring, then remove snap ring. Remove rod guide, springs, and piston rod from case, taking care not to damage piston rod or guide during removal. Withdraw piston from transmission case.

LOW-REVERSE SERVO (REAR)

Compress low-reverse servo piston spring using suitable tool, then remove snap ring, spring retainer, spring, and servo piston and plug assembly from case.

COMPONENT DISASSEMBLY & REASSEMBLY

VALVE BODY DISASSEMBLY

NOTE — *Tag all springs for reassembly reference as they are removed.*

Filter, Transfer Plate & Pressure Regulators — 1) With valve body assembly on suitable repair stand, remove screws from fluid filter, then lift off filter. Remove top and bottom screws from spring retainer and adjustment screw bracket. **CAUTION** — *Hold spring retainer firmly against spring pressure while removing last retaining screw from side of valve body.* Remove spring retainer with line and throttle pressure adjusting screws (do not disturb settings), then remove line pressure and torque converter regulator springs.

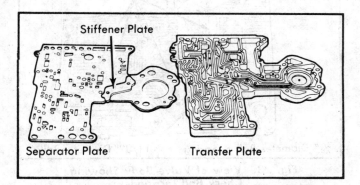

Stiffener Plate

Separator Plate   Transfer Plate

Fig. 19   Valve Body Transfer and Separator Plates

2) Slide line pressure and torque converter valves from bores. Remove transfer plate retaining screws, then lift off transfer plate and separator plate assembly. Remove screws from stiffener and separator plate, then separate parts for cleaning. Remove rear clutch ball check valve from transfer plate, and regulator valve screen from separator plate for cleaning. Remove seven balls and spring from valve body.

Shuttle Valve & Governor Plugs — Turn valve body over, then remove shuttle valve cover plate. Remove governor plug end plate, then slide out shuttle valve throttle plug and spring, 1-2 shift valve governor plug, and 2-3 shift valve governor plug. Remove shuttle valve "E" clip and slide shuttle valve from bore. Remove "E" clip and park control rod from manual lever.

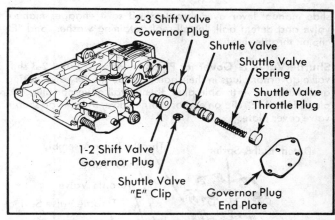

2-3 Shift Valve
Governor Plug

Shuttle Valve

Shuttle Valve
Spring

Shuttle Valve
Throttle Plug

1-2 Shift Valve
Governor Plug

Shuttle Valve
"E" Clip

Governor Plug
End Plate

Fig. 20   Exploded View of Valve Body Showing Shuttle Valve and Governor Plugs

Manual Lever & Throttle Lever — Remove "E" clip and washer from throttle lever shaft. Remove any burrs from shaft, then while holding manual lever detent ball and spring in bore, slide manual lever off throttle shaft. Remove detent ball and spring, then slide manual valve from bore. Slide out kickdown detent, kickdown valve, throttle valve spring, and throttle valve.

Shift Valves & Regulator Valve Pressure Sensing Plugs — Remove line pressure regulator valve end plate, then slide out regulator valve sleeve, line pressure plug, and throttle pressure plug. Remove downshift housing and slide throttle plug out of it, then remove limit valve and spring end plate. Remove shift valve springs and slide both shift valves from their bores.

Inspection — Wash all parts in a suitable solvent, then blow dry with compressed air. Inspect all parts for nicks, burrs, scratches, or distortion. Small nicks and burrs may be removed with crocus cloth, taking care not to round off any machined sharp edges. Make sure all passages are clean and free from obstructions, and all metering holes in steel plate and valve body are open. Inspect all valve springs for distortion and collapsed coils. Inspect manual and throttle valve operating levers and shafts for being bent, worn or loose. If a lever is loose on its shaft, it may be **silver soldered only**, or lever and shaft assembly should be replaced. DO NOT attempt to straighten bent levers. When bores, valves and plugs are clean and dry, valves and plugs should fall freely in their bores.

VALVE BODY REASSEMBLY

Shift Valves & Regulator Valve Pressure Sensing Plugs — Slide shift valves and springs into proper valve body bores, then sub-assemble downshift housing as follows: Insert limit valve and spring into housing, then slide spring retainer into groove in housing. Insert throttle plug in housing bore, position assembly against shift valve springs, then install end plate and tighten to 35 INCH lbs. (40 cmkg). Install throttle pressure plug, line pressure plug and sleeve, then fasten end plate to valve body.

Manual Lever & Throttle Lever — Install throttle valve, throttle valve spring, kickdown valve, and kickdown detent, then slide manual valve into bore. Install throttle lever and shaft on valve body, then insert detent ball and spring in bore in valve body. Depress ball and spring with suitable tool, then

TORQUEFLITE (Cont.)

slide manual lever over throttle shaft so it engages manual valve and detent ball. Install seal, retaining washer, and "E" clip on throttle shaft.

Shuttle Valve & Governor Plugs — Place 1-2 and 2-3 shift valve governor plugs in their bores, install shuttle valve, spring and shuttle valve throttle plug, then install governor plug end plate. Install "E" clip on end of shuttle valve, then install shuttle valve cover plate.

assembly on springs and fasten with screw which goes into side of valve body. This screw is to be tightened first, after starting top and bottom screws. Install oil filter and tighten. After valve body has been completely assembled, measure throttle and line pressure adjustment. If pressures were satisfactory prior to disassembly, use original settings. Install parking lock rod and "E" clip retainer to manual lever.

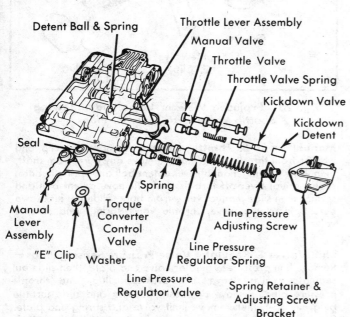

Fig. 21 *Exploded View of Valve Body Showing Pressure Regulators and Manual Control*

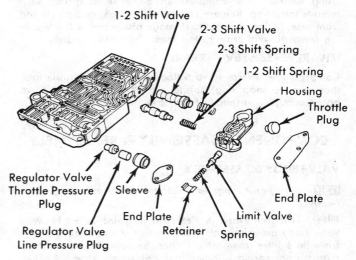

Fig. 22 *Exploded View of Valve Body Showing Shift Valves and Pressure Regulator Valve Plugs*

Filter, Transfer Plate, & Pressure Regulators — 1) Install seven balls and spring in valve body, then install rear clutch ball check valve in transfer plate, and regulator valve screen in separator plate. Install screws in stiffener and separator plate, then place transfer plate assembly on valve body. Be careful to align filter screen and spring loaded ball as the 17 shorter screws are installed (3 longer screws are for oil filter). Tighten screws starting at center and working outward.

2) Slide torque converter and line pressure valves and springs into bores, then install pressure adjusting screw and bracket

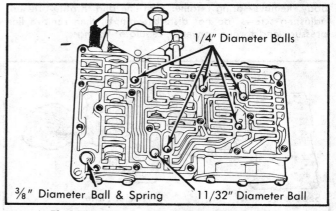

Fig. 23 *View of Valve Body Showing Check Ball Locations*

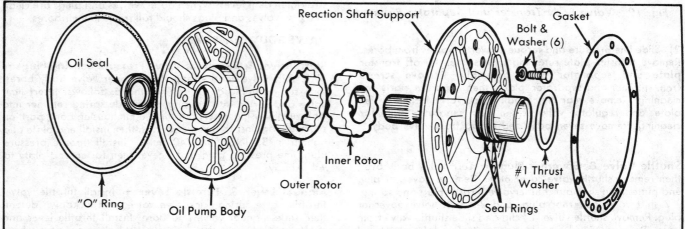

Fig. 24 *Exploded View of Oil Pump and Reaction Shaft Support*

TORQUEFLITE (Cont.)

OIL PUMP & REACTION SHAFT SUPPORT

Disassembly — Remove bolts from rear side of reaction shaft support, then lift support off pump. Remove rubber seal ring from pump body flange, then drive out oil seal with blunt punch.

Inspection — 1) Inspect all parts for wear or damage. Be sure interlocking seal rings turn freely in groves. Inspect front clutch piston retainer to reaction shaft support thrust washer for wear; thickness should be .061-.063" (1.55-1.60 mm), replace if necessary.

NOTE — *Seal rings must be removed to allow clearance for thrust washer removal or installation.*

2) With rotors installed in pump body, place a straightedge across faces of rotors and pump body. Using a feeler gauge, measure clearance between straightedge and pump rotors. Clearance should be .001-.003" (.03-.08 mm). Rotor tip clearance between inner and outer rotor teeth should be .005-.010" (.13-.25 mm). Clearance between outer rotor and rotor bore in pump body should be .004-.008" (.10-.20 mm).

Pump Bushing Replacement — Place pump housing (rotor cavity down) on a clean smooth surface. Using suitable tool, drive bushing straight down and out of bore, being careful not to cock tool in bore. Drive new bushing into place in pump cavity using suitable installing tool. Stake bushing in place using a blunt punch or other suitable tool. Using a narrow bladed knife or similar tool, remove high points or burrs around staked area. Do not use a file or any tool that would remove more metal than necessary.

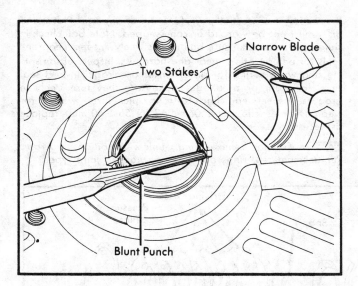

Fig. 25   Rear View of Oil Pump Housing Showing Staking Positions in Bushing

Reaction Shaft Bushing Replacement — Thread a bushing remover tool into bushing. Withdraw bushing from reaction shaft. Support reaction shaft upright then using a driving tool, drive new busing into place in reaction shaft.

NOTE — *If bushing failed in service, inspect support for wear from input shaft seal ring lands. If worn or grooved, replace support assembly.*

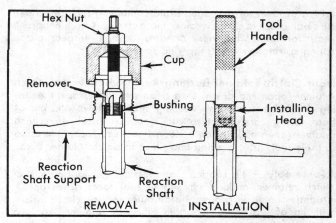

Fig. 26   Tool Set-Up for Reaction Shaft Bushing Replacement

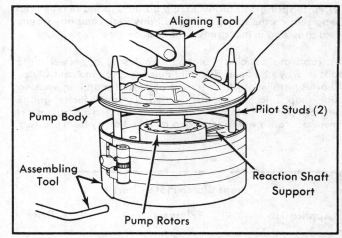

Fig. 27   Tool Set-Up for Assembling Oil Pump and Reaction Shaft Support

Reassembly — Place reaction shaft support in a suitable assembling tool with hub of support and tool on a smooth, flat surface, then install two pilot studs in threaded holes in support flange. Assemble rotors in center of support, then lower pump body over pilot studs. Using suitable tool, center rotors in pump body, then with pump body firmly against reaction shaft support, tighten assembling tool securely. Invert pump and tool assembly, then install support to pump bolts and tighten evenly. Remove assembling tool, pilot studs, and aligning tool. Using suitable tool, install new pump oil seal.

FRONT CLUTCH

Disassembly — Remove large waved snap ring that secures pressure plate in clutch piston retainer, then lift pressure plate and clutch plates from retainer. Install suitable tool over piston spring retainer, then compress spring(s). Invert clutch retainer assembly and bump on wood block to remove piston, then remove seals from piston and clutch retainer hub.

Inspection — Inspect plates and discs for flatness; they must not be warped or cone-shaped. Inspect facing material on all driving discs, replace if damaged. Inspect discs and plates for wear on splines or lugs, then check clutch retainer for damag-

TORQUEFLITE (Cont.)

ed lug grooves, or damaged band contacting surfaces. Make sure ball check in clutch retainer moves freely. Check neoprene seals for wear, hardness or deterioration. Inspect piston spring(s), retainer and snap ring for distortion.

Front Clutch Retainer Bushing Replacement — Lay clutch retainer (open end down) on a clean smooth surface, then using a suitable tool, drive bushing straight down and out of bore, being careful not to cock tool. To install, lay clutch retainer (open end up) on a clean smooth surface, then using suitable tool, drive bushing into place in clutch retainer bore.

Reassembly — 1) Lubricate and install inner seal on hub of clutch retainer, making sure lip of seal faces down and is properly seated in groove. Install outer seal on clutch piston, with lip of seal toward bottom of clutch retainer. Apply a coating of wax type lubricant to outer edge of seal, then place piston assembly in retainer and carefully seat piston in bottom of retainer.

2) Place spring on piston hub and position spring retainer and snap ring on the spring. Using suitable tool, compress spring, seat snap ring in hub groove, then remove tool.

3) Lubricate all clutch plates, then install one steel plate followed by one lined disc until number given in Front Clutch Chart is installed. Install pressure plate and snap ring, making sure snap ring is properly seated. Insert a feeler gauge between pressure plate and waved snap ring to measure maximum clearance where snap ring is waved away from pressure plate.

Front Clutch Plate Chart

Application	Plates	Discs
All Models	3	3

4) With clutch assembly completed, insert a feeler gauge between pressure plate and waved snap ring to measure maximum clearance where snap ring is waved away from pressure plate. Clearance should be .077-.122" (1.96-3.1 mm).

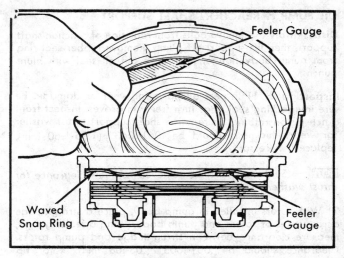

Fig. 29   Using a Feeler Gauge to Measure Front Clutch Clearance

REAR CLUTCH

Disassembly — Remove large selective snap ring securing pressure plate in clutch piston retainer, then lift pressure plate, clutch plates, and inner pressure plate out of retainer. Carefully pry one end of wave spring out of groove in clutch retainer, then remove wave spring, and clutch piston spring. Invert clutch piston retainer assembly and bump it on a wood block to remove piston, then remove seals from piston. If necessary, remove snap ring and press input shaft from piston retainer.

Inspection — Inspect all parts for wear or damage. Plates and discs must not be warped or cone-shaped. Note ball check in clutch retainer, make sure ball moves freely. Inspect neoprene seals for deterioration, wear and hardness. Inspect piston spring and wave spring for distortion or breakage. Inspect seal rings for wear or breakage, make sure they turn freely in grooves. Inspect rear clutch-to-front clutch thrust washer for wear. Thickness should be .061-.063" (1.55-1.60 mm), replace as necessary.

NOTE — Do not remove rings unless conditions warrant. Replacement seal rings are cast iron hooked joint type.

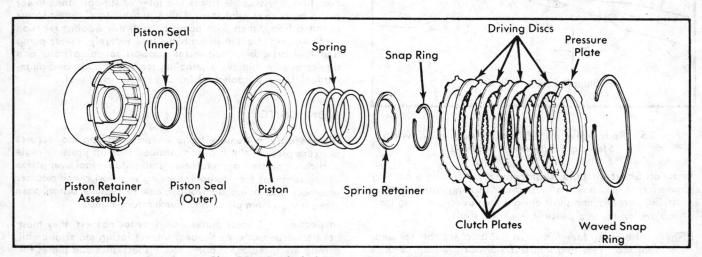

Fig. 28   Exploded View of Front Clutch Assembly

TORQUEFLITE (Cont.)

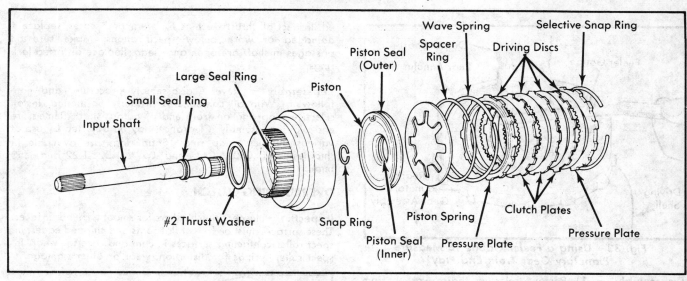

Fig. 30   Exploded View of Rear Clutch Assembly

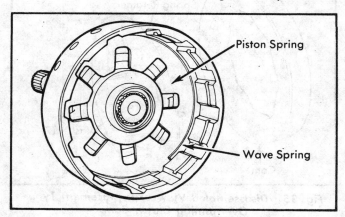

Fig. 31   Installing Piston Spring and Wave Spring in Rear Clutch Drum

Reassembly — 1) If removed, press input shaft into piston retainer and install snap ring. Lubricate and install inner and outer seals on clutch piston, making sure lips of seals face toward head of clutch retainer and are properly seated in grooves. Place piston assembly in retainer and, with a twisting motion, seat piston in bottom of retainer.

2) Place clutch piston spring on top of piston in clutch retainer. Start one end of wave spring in retainer groove, then progressively push or tap spring into place making sure it is fully seated in groove.

3) Install inner pressure plate in clutch retainer with raised portion of plate resting on spring. Lubricate all clutch plates, then install one lined disc followed by one steel plate until all plates are installed. Install outer pressure plate and selective snap ring.

Rear Clutch Plate Chart		
Application	**Plates**	**Discs**
All Models	2	3

4) Measure rear clutch clearance by pressing down firmly on outer pressure plate, then inserting a feeler gauge between plate and snap ring. Clearance should be .032-.055" (.82-1.39 mm), with low limit clearance desirable. Install new snap ring of proper thickness to obtain specified clearance. Snap rings are available in thicknesses of .060", .068" and .076" (1.52, 1.73, and 1.93 mm).

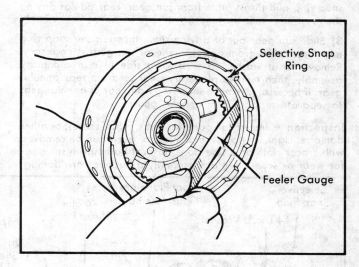

Fig. 32   Using a Feeler Gauge to Measure Rear Clutch Clearance

PLANETARY GEAR TRAIN

End Play — Measure end play of planetary gear assemblies, sun gear and driving shell before removing from output shaft. Stand assembly upright with forward end of output shaft on a wood block so that all parts will move forward against snap ring at front of shaft. Insert a feeler gauge between rear annulus gear support hub and shoulder on output shaft. Clearance should be .006-.033" (.16-.83 mm). If clearance exceeds specifications, replace thrust washers and/or necessary parts.

Automatic Transmissions

TORQUEFLITE (Cont.)

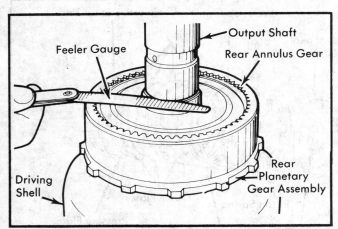

Fig. 33 Using a Feeler Gauge to Measure Planetary Gear Train End Play

Disassembly — 1) Remove selective thrust washer from forward end of output shaft, then remove selective snap ring and thrust washer from forward hub of front planetary gear assembly, then slide front annulus gear and support off planetary gear set.

2) If necessary, remove snap ring from front of annulus gear to separate support from annulus gear. Slide sun gear, driving shell and rear planetary assembly off output shaft, then lift sun gear and driving shell off rear planetary assembly. Remove snap ring and thrust plate from sun gear (rear side of driving shell).

3) Slide sun gear out of driving shell, then remove snap ring and thrust plate from opposite end of sun gear if necessary. Remove thrust washer from forward side of rear planetary assembly, then remove planetary gear set from rear annulus gear. If necessary, remove snap ring from rear of annulus gear to separate support from annulus gear.

Inspection — Inspect all parts for nicks, burrs, scores, or other damage. Light scratches, small nicks or burrs can be removed with crocus cloth or a fine stone. Inspect bushings in sun gear for wear or scores, replace assembly if bushings are damag-

ed. Inspect all thrust washers for wear and scores, replace if damaged or worn below specifications. Make sure oil passages in shaft are open and clean. Replace distorted lock rings.

Reassembly — Reverse disassembly procedure and note following: With all components properly positioned, install selective snap ring on front end of output shaft. Remeasure end play of assembly. Clearance may be adjusted by use of various thickness snap rings. Snap rings are available in thicknesses of .040", .048" and .059" (1.02, 1.22 and 1.50 mm).

OVERRUNNING CLUTCH

Inspection — Inspect clutch rollers for smooth, round surfaces. These surfaces must be free of flat spots and chipped edges. Inspect roller contacting surfaces in cam and race for wear. Inspect roller springs for distortion, wear or other damage.

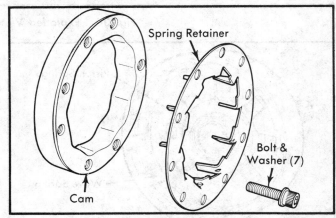

Fig. 35 Disassembled View of Replacement Type Overrunning Clutch Cam

Overruning Clutch Cam Replacement — 1) Remove bolts securing output shaft support to rear of transmission case, then tap support rearward and out of case with soft faced hammer. Center punch rivets exactly in center of each rivet head.

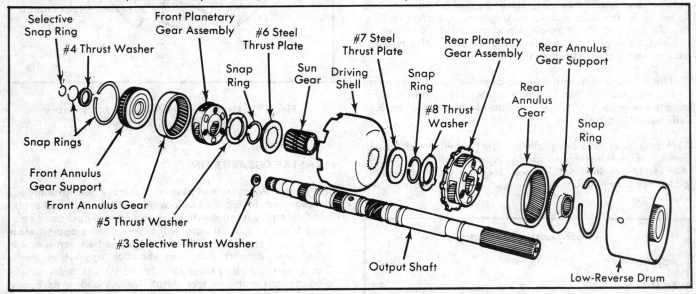

Fig. 34 Exploded View of Planetary Gear Train and Output Shaft

TORQUEFLITE (Cont.)

2) Drill through each rivet head with a ⅜" drill, taking care not to drill into transmission case. Chip off rivet heads with small chisel, then drive rivets and cam from case using a blunt punch. Enlarge rivet holes in case using a ¹⁷/₆₄" drill. Remove all chips and foreign material from case.

3) To install, position cam and roller spring retainer in case, align cam bolt holes with holes in case, then thread all 7 retaining bolt and washer assemblies into cam a few turns. Cone washers must be installed so inner diameter is coned toward bolt head.

4) Tap cam firmly into case if necessary, then tighten bolts evenly. Screw 2 pilot studs into case, then position support over studs and tap firmly onto place using a soft faced hammer. Remove pilot studs, then install and tighten bolts evenly.

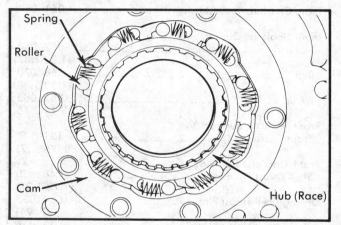

Fig. 36   Installed View of Overrunning Clutch Assembly

KICKDOWN SERVO & BAND

Disassembly — Disassemble servo piston by removing small snap ring from servo piston, then remove washer, spring and piston rod from servo piston.

Inspection — Inspect all parts for nicks, burrs, wear or damage. Be sure piston and guide seal rings turn freely in grooves. Do not remove seal rings unless conditions warrant. Inspect piston bore in case for scores or other damage. Inspect fit of guide on piston rod, and piston spring for distortion. Inspect band lining for wear or damage. If lining is worn so grooves are not visible at ends or any portion of band, replace band.

Reassembly — Carefully push servo piston into transmission case bore then install piston rod, springs and guide. Compress kickdown servo springs with suitable spring compressor and install snap ring.

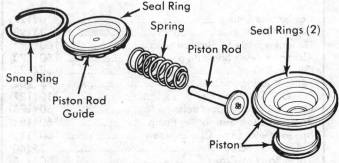

Fig. 37   Exploded View of Kickdown Servo

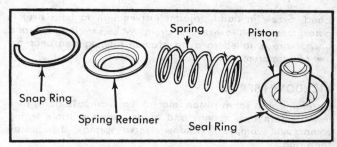

Fig. 38   Exploded View of Low-Reverse Servo

LOW-REVERSE SERVO & BAND

Disassembly — Remove snap ring, then remove piston, plug retainer and spring.

Inspection — Inspect seal for deterioration, wear and hardness. Inspect piston for cracks, burrs, scores and wear. Inspect piston bore for scores or damage. Check springs for distortion. Inspect band lining for wear and bond of lining to band. If lining is worn so grooves are not visible at ends or any portion of band, replace band.

Reassembly — Low-Reverse Servo & Band are reassembled when reassembling transmission. See *LOW-REVERSE SERVO & BAND under TRANSMISSION REASSEMBLY* in this article.

TRANSMISSION REASSEMBLY

NOTE — *Use only Dexron type Automatic Transmission Fluid to lubricate transmission parts during reassembly.*

OVERRUNNING CLUTCH

With transmission case in upright position, insert clutch hub inside cam, then install overrunning clutch rollers exactly as shown in *Fig. 36*.

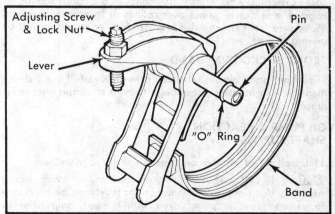

Fig. 39   Assembled View of Low-Reverse Band and Linkage Assembly

LOW-REVERSE SERVO & BAND

Low-Reverse Servo — Carefully work servo piston into transmission case with a twisting motion, then place spring, retainer and snap ring over piston. Using a suitable spring compressor, compress low-reverse servo piston, then install snap ring.

Low-Reverse Band — Position rear band in transmission case, install short strut, then connect long link and anchor to

TORQUEFLITE (Cont.)

band. Screw in band adjuster just enough to hold strut in place, then install low-reverse drum. Make sure long link and anchor are installed so as to provide running clearance for low-reverse drum.

KICKDOWN SERVO

Carefully push servo piston into transmission case bore, then install piston rod, springs and guide. Using suitable spring compressor, compress kickdown servo springs, then install snap ring.

PLANETARY GEAR, SUN GEAR & DRIVING SHELL

While supporting assembly in case, insert output shaft through rear support. Carefully work assembly rearward, engaging rear planetary carrier lugs into low-reverse drum slots.

CAUTION — *Do not damage ground surfaces on output shaft during installation.*

FRONT & REAR CLUTCH ASSEMBLIES

NOTE — *Front and rear clutches, front band, oil pump and reaction shaft support are more easily installed with transmission in upright position.*

1) Apply a coat of grease to selective thrust washer and install on front end of output shaft. If input shaft end play was not within specifications (.022-.091" or .56-2.3 mm) when tested prior to disassembly, replace thrust washer with one of proper thickness. *See Thrust Washer Chart for avaiable thrust washers.*

2) Align front clutch plate inner splines, then place assembly in position on rear clutch, making sure front clutch plate splines are fully engaged on rear clutch splines. Align rear clutch plate splines, grasp input shaft, then lower assemblies into case. Carefully work clutch assemblies in a circular motion to engage rear clutch splines over splines of front annulus gear. Make sure front clutch drive lugs are fully engaged in slots of driving shell.

FRONT (KICKDOWN) BAND

Slide front band over front clutch assembly. Install band strut, then screw in adjuster just enough to hold strut and anchor in place.

OIL PUMP & REACTION SHAFT SUPPORT

1) Install thrust washer on reaction shaft support hub.

NOTE — *If difficulty was encountered in removing pump assembly due to an exceptionally tight fit, it may be necessary to expand case in pump area with a heat lamp prior to installation.*

2) Screw two pilot studs into pump opening in case, then install a new gasket over studs. Place a new rubber seal ring in groove on outer flange of pump housing, making sure seal is not twisted. Coat seal ring with grease, then install pump assembly into case, tapping lightly with a soft mallet, if necessary. Remove pilot studs, install bolts and snug down evenly. Rotate input and output shafts to see that no binding exists, then tighten bolts. Check shafts again for free rotation, then adjust both bands.

GOVERNOR

See Service (In Vehicle).

EXTENSION HOUSING

See Service (In Vehicle).

TORQUE CONVERTER

See Transmission Removal & Installation

THRUST WASHER CHART

Application	Thickness In. (mm)
Reaction Shaft Support to Front Clutch Retainer (#1)	.061-.063 (1.55-1.60)
Front Clutch to Rear Clutch (#2)	.061-.063 (1.55-1.60)
Input Shaft to Output Shaft (#3) Natural	.052-.054 (1.32-1.37)
Red	.068-.070 (1.73-1.77)
Black	.083-.085 (2.11-2.15)
Front Annulus Support to Front Carrier (#4)	.121-.125 (3.08-3.17)
Front Carrier to Driving Shell Thrust Plate (#5)	.048-.050 (1.22-1.27)
Driving Shell Thrust Plate (#6)	.034-.036 (.87-.91)
Driving Shell Thrust Plate (#7)	.034-.036 (.87-.91)
Rear Carrier to Driving Shell (#8)	.048-.050 (1.22-1.27)

TIGHTENING SPECIFICATIONS

Application	Ft. Lbs. (mkg)
Drive Plate-to-Crankshaft	83-90 (11-12)
Converter-to-Drive Plate	25-30 (3-4)
Extension Housing-to-Case	24 (3.3)
Extension Housing-to-Mount	50 (6.9)
Band Adjusting Screw Lock Nut	
Kickdown Band	35 (4.8)
Reverse Band	30 (4.2)
Transmission-to-Engine	28 (3.9)

Application	INCH Lbs. (cmkg)
Cooler Line Fitting	110 (127)
Cooler Line Nut	85 (98)
Governor Body-to-Support	100 (115)
Kickdown Lever Shaft Plug	150 (173)
Oil Pan Bolt	150 (173)
Pump Housing-to-Case	175 (202)
Pressure Test Port Plug	110 (127)
Output Shaft Support Bolt	150 (173)
Reaction Shaft Support-to-Pump	160 (184)
Speedometer Drive Clamp Screw	100 (115)
Valve Body Screw	35 (40)
Valve Body-to-Case	100 (115)

TOYOTA A-40 & A-40D

A-40 3-Speed
  Corolla
  Celica
  Corona
  Pickup
A-40D 4-Speed (Overdrive)
  Cressida
  Supra

TRANSMISSION IDENTIFICATION

Transmission can be identified by the lack of external adjustment levers or bolts on the transmission case. The oil pan is long and deep.

DESCRIPTION

The A-40 and A-40D automatic transmissions have no bands, eliminating any internal adjustments. The only external adjustments are for throttle cable position and shift linkage adjustment. The A-40 transmission has 3 forward speeds and reverse. The A-40D transmission has 4 forward speeds (overdrive) and reverse. Control of these shift sequences can be exercised in low or second lever position. The torque converter is a three-element type. Planetary gears are actuated by three multi-disc brakes and two clutches. Engine load and speed determine gear changes by use of throttle valve position and output shaft speed. Tests, specifications and repair procedures are the same except where noted.

LUBRICATION & ADJUSTMENT

See AUTOMATIC TRANSMISSION SERVICING Section.

TROUBLE SHOOTING

NO MOVEMENT IN ANY FORWARD RANGE

Check fluid level, line pressure. Adjust manual linkage. Faulty valve body and/or primary regulator, front clutch piston, No. 2 one-way clutch, or valve body.

NO MOVEMENT IN REVERSE RANGE

Check fluid level, adjust manual linkage. Check line pressure. Faulty valve body and/or primary regulator, oil pump, rear clutch piston, or Brake No. 3 pistons.

NO MOVEMENT IN ANY RANGE

Check fluid level, adjust manual linkage, check line pressure. Faulty park lock pawl, torque converter, valve body, multiple element damage, valve body primary regulator, oil pump or internal leakage.

NO FORWARD DRIVE OR SLIPS IN FORWARD RANGES (REVERSE OK)

Check line pressure, adjust manual linkage. Faulty valve body and primary regulator, Brake No. 3, rear clutch, oil pump, or oil seal rings.

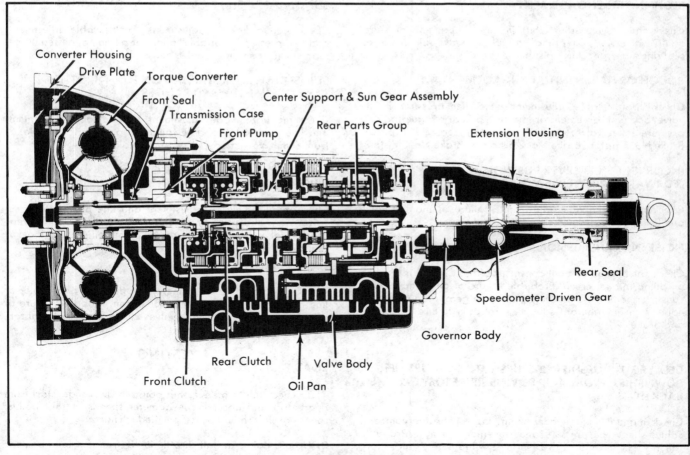

Fig. 1 Cutaway View of Toyota A-40 Automatic Transmission Assembly

TOYOTA A-40 & A-40D (Cont.)

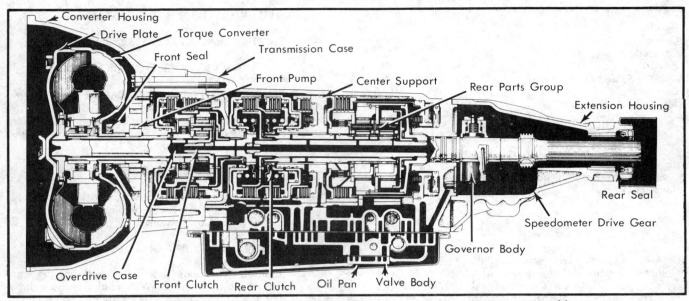

Fig. 2 Cutaway View of Toyota A-40D Automatic Transmission Assembly

DELAYED OR NO INITIAL ENGAGEMENT

Check fluid level, adjust shift linkage, check line pressure. Faulty valve body and primary regulator, Brake No. 3, rear clutch, oil pump, or oil seal rings.

SLOW INITIAL ENGAGEMENT

Check fluid level, adjust shift linkage, check line pressure. Faulty valve body or primary regulator valve, oil pump, oil seal rings, or front clutch piston.

ROUGH OR HARSH INITIAL ENGAGEMENT

Check throttle cable adjustment, check line pressure. Faulty valve body or accumulator pistons, primary regulator and pressure relief valve, front clutch piston, rear clutch piston, Brake No. 1 piston, Brake No. 2 piston, or Brake No. 3 piston.

INCORRECT SHIFT LEVER POSITION (FORWARD OR REVERSE MOVEMENT IN "N")

Check manual linkage adjustment. Failure of manual valve and lever, or front clutch.

NOISE IN TRANSMISSION WITH ENGINE RUNNING

Check for broken or bent converter plate. Check for blocked oil pump intake screen. Probable failure of oil pump, torque converter, one-way clutches, planetary gear or bushings. If noise is an intermittant squawk, probable failure is clutches and Brakes.

DELAYED 1-2 UPSHIFT, 2-3 UPSHIFT, 3-OD UPSHIFT, DOWNSHIFT FROM 4-3, DOWNSHIFT FROM 3-2 THEN BACK TO 3

Check manual linkage adjustment, inspect throttle cam and cable, check line pressure and governor pressure. Probable failure of throttle valve, primary regulator, secondary regulator, or oil seal rings.

SLIP ON 1-2 UPSHIFT

Check manual linkage adjustment, throttle cable adjustment, and line pressure. Probable failure of throttle valve, primary regulator, secondary regulator, or oil seal rings.

SLIP ON 2-3 UPSHIFT

Check manual linkage adjustment, throttle cable adjustment, and line pressure. Probable failure of oil pump, oil seal rings, rear clutch assembly, or valve body.

SLIP, SQUAWK, OR SHUDDER ON FULL THROTTLE TAKE-OFF IN FORWARD RANGES

Check manual linkage adjustment, throttle cable adjustment, and line pressure. Probable failure of one-way clutch No. 2, front clutch, valve body, or oil pump leakage.

SLIP, SQUAWK, OR SHUDDER ON TAKE-OFF IN "R"

Check manual linkage adjustment and line pressure, inspect valve body and primary regulator. Probable failure of rear clutch, Brake No. 3, valve body, oil pump, oil sealing rings, or rear clutch leakage.

HARSH DOWNSHIFT

Check throttle cable adjustment, throttle cam and cable, or line pressure, inspect accumulator piston. Probable failure of primary regulator, throttle valve, clutch and brake piston, valve body, or sequence valve.

TESTING

ROAD TEST

1) To check full throttle upshift points in "D" range, start from dead stop and observe speedometer speeds at shift points, speeds at shift should be as specified in chart.

2) Upshift points at half throttle in "D" range should be near speeds given in chart.

TOYOTA A-40 & A-40D (Cont.)

Shift Speed Specifications

Shift Condition	Shift Point (MPH)
Corolla	
1-2 Upshift In "D"	29-39
2-3 Upshift In "D"	56-66
3-2 Downshift In "D"	53-63
2-1 Downshift In "D"	23-31
2-1 Downshift In "L"	①25-34
Celica	
1-2 Upshift In "D"	34-43
2-3 Upshift In "D"	63-73
3-2 Downshift In "D"	59-69
2-1 Downshift In "D"	27-34
2-1 Downshift In "L"	①29-39
Corona	
1-2 Upshift In "D"	34-43
2-3 Upshift In "D"	63-73
3-2 Downshift In "D"	59-69
2-1 Downshift In "D"	26-34
2-1 Downshift In "L"	①29-39
Pickup	
1-2 Upshift In "D"	32-42
2-3 Upshift In "D"	61-70
3-2 Downshift In "D"	57-66
2-1 Downshift In "D"	25-33
2-1 Downshift In "L"	①27-36
Cressida & Supra	
1-2 Upshift In "D"	32-41
2-3 Upshift In "D"	61-70
3-OD Upshift In "D"	①19-26
3-2 Downshift In "D"	55-65
2-1 Downshift In "D"	23-31
2-1 Downshift In "L"	①28-38

① — With throttle closed.

3) To check coast downshift speed, let off accelerator and allow vehicle to slow, engine speed should fall off in direct relation to vehicle speed. Downshift should occur from third speed to first as indicated on chart.

4) Allow vehicle to decelerate from a high speed in 3rd gear, then try to make transmission kickdown at 5 MPH intervals, record highest speed when kickdown occured from 3rd to 2nd, then repeat for 2nd to 1st gear. Kickdown speeds should be as specified on chart.

5) Drive vehicle at road speed in "D" or "Overdrive" range, manually downshift into 2nd gear, vehicle should shift immediately and engine speed should decelerate vehicle. Downshift from 2nd into "L" range; 2-1 downshift should occur when vehicle has decelerated to speed specified on chart, engine should continue to brake vehicle.

6) Check "2" range full throttle upshift and kickdown by driving vehicle at full throttle from standing start. Note road speed at upshift, take foot off accelerator and attempt kickdown, check highest speed at which kickdown occurs. Both upshift and kickdown should happen at speeds given on chart.

7) With gear shift lever in "2" position, drive vehicle at half throttle, observe road speed at 1-2 upshift. Shift should happen near speed given on chart.

8) Start vehicle under way in "L" range, accelerate to about 40 MPH, transmission should remain in "L" until lever is moved to next position.

HYDRAULIC PRESSURE TESTS

With transmission fluid at normal operating temperature, raise and support rear of vehicle so that rear wheels are free to turn.

CLUTCH & BRAKE APPLICATION CHART
(ELEMENTS IN USE — A40 ONLY)

Selector Lever Position	Front Clutch	Rear Clutch	Brake No. 1	Brake No. 2	Brake No. 3
D — DRIVE					
First	X ①				
Second	X ②			X	
Third	X	X ③		X	
2 — SECOND	X		X⑤	X②	
L — LOW	X				X①④
R — REVERSE		X			X
NEUTRAL OR PARK — All clutches and brakes released and/or ineffective.					

① — 1-way clutch No. 2 applied.   ② — 1-way clutch No. 1 applied.
③ — Inner piston applied.   ④ — Outer piston applied.
⑤ — Applied when engine is braking.

TOYOTA A-40 & A-40D (Cont.)

Connect pressure gauges to line pressure and governor pressure test ports on transmission as shown in *Fig. 3*. Check hydraulic pressures as follows:

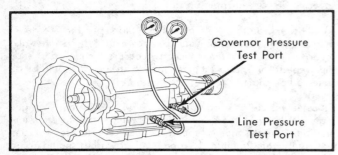

Fig. 3   View of Transmission Case Showing Hydraulic Pressure Test Ports

Governor Pressure — 1) Start engine and release parking brake. Slowly accelerate engine with transmission in "D" and check governor pressure at speeds specified in "Governor Pressures" table.

2) If governor pressures are not as specified, check for the following: Incorrect line pressure; Fluid leakage in governor pressure circuit; Governor valve operation defective.

Governor Pressure Specifications		
Vehicle Speed (MPH)	Output Shaft (RPM)	Pressure psi (kg/cm^2)
18-19	1000	12.8-21.3 (0.9-1.5)
31-33	1800	22.8-31.3 (1.6-2.2)
60-64	3500	58.3-75.4 (4.1-5.3)

Line Pressure — 1) Fully apply parking brake and block all 4 wheels. Start engine and shift transmission into "D". Apply firm pressure to brake pedal and accelerate engine to 1000 RPM. Line pressure should be as shown in "Line Pressures" table.

2) Increase engine to Stall Speed and again check line pressure. If specified line pressures are not obtained, check throttle cable adjustment and repeat test.

3) Repeat line pressure tests with transmission in "R". Line pressure should be as shown in "Line Pressures" table.

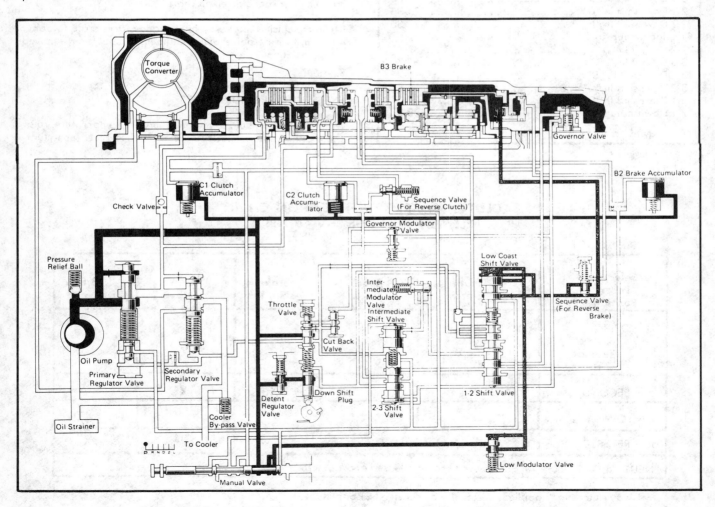

Fig. 4   Toyota A40 Automatic Transmission Hydraulic Circuits Diagram

TOYOTA A-40 & A-40D (Cont.)

Line Pressure Specifications

Engine Speed	Pressure psi (kg/cm²)
At 1000 RPM	
"D"	
Cressida, Supra	64-70 (4.5-4.8)
All Other Models	57-64 (4.0-4.5)
"R"	82-97 (5.8-6.8)
At Stall Speed	
"D"	
Cressida, Supra	139-175 (9.8-12.3)
All Other Models	135-171 (9.5-12.0)
"R"	
Cressida, Supra	171-213 (13.0-15.0)
All Other Models	200-242 (14.0-17.0)

Line Pressure Test Results — 1) If line pressure in all ranges is higher than specified, check for the following:
- Defective regulator valve
- Defective throttle valve
- Throttle cable out of adjustment

2) If line pressure is low in all ranges, check for the following:
- Defective oil pump
- Defective regulator valve
- Defective throttle valve
- Throttle cable out of adjustment
- Defective OD clutch (A-40D only)

3) If line pressure is low in "D" range only, check for the following:
- Defective front clutch
- Fluid leak in "D" range circuit
- Defective OD clutch (A-40D only)

4) If line pressure is low in "R" range only, check for the following:
- Defective rear clutch
- Defective No. 3 brake
- Fluid leak in "R" range circuit
- Defective OD clutch (A-40D only)

STALL TEST

1) With engine and transmission at normal operating temperature, connect a tachometer to engine. Fully apply parking brake and block front wheels.

CAUTION — *DO NOT maintain stall RPM for more than 5 seconds.*

2) Start engine, apply brake pedal and place transmission in "D". Accelerate engine to full throttle and check maximum speed obtained. Repeat test in "R".

Stall Test Specifications

Application	Stall RPM
Corolla (A-40)	
Calif.	2000-2300
Federal	2100-2400
Cressida, Supra (A-40D)	1800-2100
Celica, Corona, Pickup (A-40)	1750-2050

Stall Test Results — 1) If stall speed is the same for both ranges but lower than specified in table, engine output may be insufficient, or stator one-way clutch may not be operating properly.

NOTE — *If stall RPM is more than 600 RPM lower than specifications, torque converter could be at fault.*

2) If stall speed is higher than specified in table in "L" range, front clutch may be slipping, one-way No. 2 clutch may not be operating, or line pressure may be low.

3) If stall speed is higher than specified in table, rear clutch may be slipping, brake No. 3 may be slipping, or line pressure may be low.

SERVICE (IN VEHICLE)

The following components can be removed from transmission with transmission installed in vehicle: Oil Pan; Valve Body Assembly; Throttle Cable; Parking Pawl Assembly; Manual Valve Shaft Oil Seal; Speedometer Drive Gear; Rear Oil Seal; Extension Housing; Speedometer Driven Gear; Governor Assembly.

NOTE — *For above components, procedures given in Transmission Disassembly, Component Disassembly and Reassembly, and Transmission Reassembly will apply.*

TRANSMISSION REMOVAL & INSTALLATION

Removal — 1) Disconnect negative battery cable and remove air cleaner. Remove upper starter mounting nut and disconnect throttle cable and bracket. Raise vehicle and drain transmission. Check outside of transmission case for oil leaks or cracks which may necessitate repair while unit is out of vehicle. Unbolt and remove starter.

2) Remove parking brake equalizer support bracket. Scribe locator marks on propeller shaft and companion flange to ensure correct position at reassembly. Remove propeller shaft from vehicle, use suitable plug or sleeve to prevent fluid leakage from transmission housing.

3) Disconnect manual selector linkage, exhaust pipe clamp at converter housing, oil cooler lines (at transmission) and oil cooler line bracket from converter housing, speedometer cable, and right and left stiffener braces from converter housing. Jack transmission up slightly and remove rear crossmember.

4) Remove six torque converter mounting bolts using service holes at rear of engine, radiator splash pan can be removed to rotate engine for access to bolts. Use suitable guide pin(s) to ease removal of converter with transmission. Remove all converter housing bolts, then push on guide pin(s) to start transmission and converter moving out of engine, using suitable transmission jack, pull assembly out of vehicle, remove and drain torque converter. Proceed with necessary repairs.

Installation — 1) Replace all pieces removed from transmission case while out of vehicle. Apply small amount of lubricant to center hub of torque converter and pilot hole in drive plate. Place converter in transmission and check housing distance from center hub of converter to front surface of converter housing. Correct distance is 0.689" (17.5 mm) for Corolla, 1.02" (26 mm) for Cressida and Supra with A-40D, and .0453" (11.5 mm) for all other models.

2) Position transmission into vehicle, install two bolts into converter housing and tighten six converter-to-drive plate bolts. Reinstall radiator splash pan (if removed). With transmission raised, reinstall rear crossmember. Lower

TOYOTA A-40 & A-40D (Cont.)

transmission and remove transmission jack, install and tighten four other converter housing bolts, right and left stiffener braces, and starter motor.

3) Replace all lines, cables, clamps, and linkage in reverse of removal procedure. Install and align propeller shaft, tighten bolts. Lower vehicle, reconnect battery negative cable, and fill transmission with specified amount of automatic transmission fluid. Road test vehicle for proper operation of all functions.

TORQUE CONVERTER

Converter Flushing — If transmission appears contaminated, thoroughly flush converter before reassembly. Use suitable transmission cleaner to flush converter. Clean outside of converter and case.

One-Way Clutch Test — **1)** With converter placed on suitable work surface, insert special tool SST 09350-20010. Kit consists of two pieces; a turning tool and a stopper. Insert turning tool in inner race of one-way clutch, insert stopper to fit in notch of converter hub and other race of one-way clutch.

2) Clutch should lock when turned counterclockwise, but should turn freely when rotated clockwise. Torque required to turn clutch clockwise should be less than 22 INCH lbs. (25 cm kg). If necessary, clean converter and retest clutch, replace converter if clutch still fails test.

Stator End Play Test — Using snap ring pliers, move stator spline up and down. Measure free play with suitable vernier caliper measure. If free play is in excess of .012" (.30 mm) replace torque converter.

TRANSMISSION DISASSEMBLY

1) With torque converter removed, remove attaching bolts and pull oil pump assembly from transmission case using a suitable puller. Remove attaching bolts and separate converter housing from transmission case.

2) Remove neutral safety switch and overdrive (OD) indicator lamp switch (A-40D only) from transmission case. Remove speedometer driven gear from extension housing, then remove extension housing from case using care not to damage rear oil seal.

3) Remove snap ring and slide speedometer drive gear and key off output shaft. Pry up on governor retainer spring with a screwdriver and pull off governor assembly. Remove extension housing gasket.

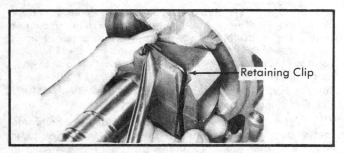

Fig. 5   Governor Assembly Removal

4) Remove oil pan. On A-40D transmission only, note installation position of the three valve body oil pipes for reassembly reference, then remove pipes from valve body.

5) On all transmissions, remove oil strainer, then remove valve body attaching bolts. Carefully lift up valve body and disconnect throttle cable from throttle cam, then remove valve body assembly from case. Hold throttle cable retainer with a 10 mm socket and pull cable from case. See *Fig. 6*.

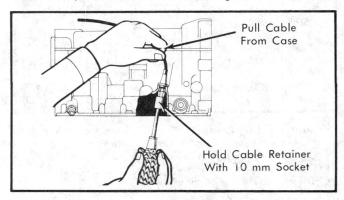

Fig. 6   Removing Throttle Cable

6) Remove attaching bolts and lift off parking pawl bracket. Unhook spring from parking pawl, pull out pivot pin and remove parking pawl and spring from case.

7) Drive slotted spring pin from manual valve shaft. Remove manual valve shaft, lever and parking lock rod from transmission case.

8) Remove accumulator pistons and springs from case by blowing compressed air through holes in case indicated in *Fig. 7*. Identify each accumulator piston and spring for reassembly reference.

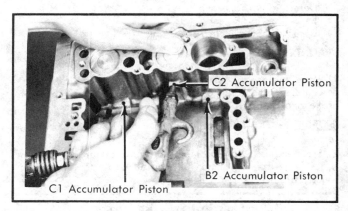

Fig. 7   Using Compressed Air to Remove Accumulator Pistons and Springs

9) On A-40D transmission only, pull overdrive input shaft and case assembly from case. On all transmissions, pull front multiple disc clutch assembly from case.

10) Pull rear multiple disc clutch assembly from case. Remove the two center support mounting bolts at valve body side of case, then pull center support and sun gear assembly from case.

TOYOTA A-40 & A-40D (Cont.)

11) Using a screwdriver, remove large snap ring from case groove, then pull rear parts group from transmission case using intermediate shaft.

12) If brake apply tube did not come out with rear parts group, remove it from case. Remove output shaft thrust bearing and race from inside case.

Pull Rear Parts Group from Case Using Intermediate Shaft

Fig. 8   Removing Rear Parts Group

COMPONENT DISASSEMBLY & REASSEMBLY

BUSHING SERVICE

Inspection — Using the following tables, check bushings for excessive wear. If a bushing requires replacement, the component containing the bushing must also be replaced.

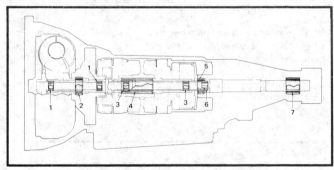

Fig. 9   View of A-40 Transmission Showing Bushing Locations

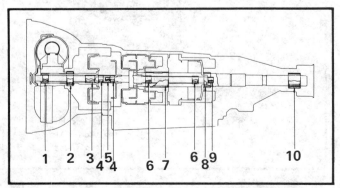

Fig. 10   View of A-40D Transmission Showing Bushing Locations

A-40 Transmission Bushing Specifications		
Bushing	Finish Bore In. (mm)	Bore Limit In. (mm)
1 - Stator Shaft	.8465-.8475 (21.501-21.527)	.8495 (21.577)
2 - Oil Pump	1.5005-1.5015 (38.113-38.138)	1.5035 (38.188)
3 - Sun Gear	.8465-.8475 (21.501-21.527)	.8495 (21.577)
4 - Center Support	1.4325-1.4335 (36.386-36.411)	1.4355 (36.461)
5 - Case	1.5005-1.5015 (38.113-38.138)	1.5035 (38.188)
6 - Output Shaft	.7087-.7096 (18.001-18.025)	.7117 (18.076)
7 - Extension Hsg.	1.4961-1.4970 (38.000-38.025)	1.4990 (38.075)

NOTE — See Fig. 9 for bushing location.

A-40D Transmission Bushing Specifications		
Bushing	Finished Bore In. (mm)	Bore Limit In. (mm)
1 - Stator Support	.8465-.8475 (21.501-21.527)	.8495 (21.577)
2 - Oil Pump	1.5005-1.5015 (38.113-38.138)	1.5035 (28.188)
3 - Stator Support	.8465-.8475 (21.501-21.527)	.8495 (21.577)
4 - OD Sun Gear Front	.8465-.8475 (21.501-21.527)	.8495 (21.577)
Rear	.8480-.8490 (21.538-21.564)	.8509 (21.614)
5 - OD Input Shaft	.4409-.4418 (11.200-11.221)	.4437 (11.271)
6 - Sun Gear	.8465-.8475 (21.501-21.527)	.8495 (21.577)
7 - Center Support	1.4325-1.4335 (36.386-36.411)	1.4355 (36.461)
8 - Case	1.5005-1.5015 (38.113-38.138)	1.5035 (38.188)
9 - Output Shaft	.7087-.7097 (18.001-18.026)	.7117 (18.076)
10 - Extension Hsg.	1.4972-1.4970 (38.000-38.025)	1.5256 (38.075)

NOTE — See Fig. 10 for bushing location.

OIL PUMP & STATOR SHAFT

Disassembly — Remove large "O" ring from oil pump body diameter. Remove attaching bolts and separate pump body from stator shaft. Mark drive and driven gears for reassembly in the same position, then remove gears from pump body.

TOYOTA A-40 & A-40D (Cont.)

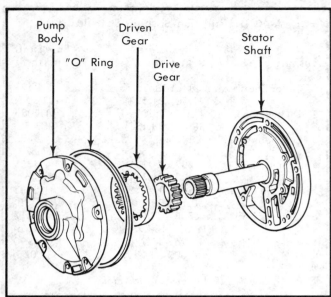

**Fig. 11   Exploded View of Oil Pump and
Stator Shaft Assembly**

Inspection — 1) Wash disassembled parts and blow dry with compressed air. Inspect pump oil seal and transmission seal ring for damage.

2) Inspect contacting surfaces between body and driven gear for ridged wear. Check gears for wear and body crescent for damage. Check pump gear contacting surface on stator shaft for damage and wear.

3) With a feeler gauge, measure clearance between driven gear and oil pump body with gear pushed over fully to the other side. Clearance should be .003-.006″ (.07-.15 mm). If clearance exceeds .012″ (.3 mm), replace pump assembly.

4) Measure clearance between crescent and driven gear. Clearance should be .004-.006″ (.11-.14 mm). If clearance exceeds .012″ (.3 mm) replace oil pump assembly.

5) Measure clearance between crescent and drive gear. Clearance should be .010-.013″ (.25-.33 mm). If clearance exceeds specifications, replace oil pump assembly.

6) Using a feeler gauge and straightedge, measure clearance between pump body face and top of gears. Clearance should be .001-.002″ (.02-.05 mm). If clearance exceeds .004″ (.1 mm) replace oil pump assembly.

7) Inspect stator shaft splines by inserting stator shaft into torque converter. Shaft should slide in smoothly and there should be no excessive looseness. Replace stator shaft if defective.

Reassembly — 1) Coat drive and driven gears with automatic transmission fluid, then install them into pump body, aligning marks made at disassembly.

2) Assemble stator shaft to pump body, then install, but do not tighten attaching bolts. Using oil pump aligning tool SST 09350-20010 for A-40 transmission or SST 09363-20010 for A-40D transmission, align centers of stator shaft and oil pump body and tighten attaching bolts to specifications.

3) With pump body and stator shaft assembled, check drive gear with a screwdriver to ensure that it rotates freely. Lubricate and install "O" ring on pump body diameter.

OVERDRIVE CASE & BRAKE (BO) (A-40D ONLY)

Disassembly — 1) Compress clutch pack and remove retaining snap ring, then lift out flange, clutch plates, clutch discs and cushion plate.

2) Remove ring gear and bearing from overdrive case. Compress piston return springs and remove snap ring, then lift out piston return springs and seat.

3) Using compressed air, force overdrive clutch piston from case as shown in *Fig. 13*. Remove oil seals from piston and from case.

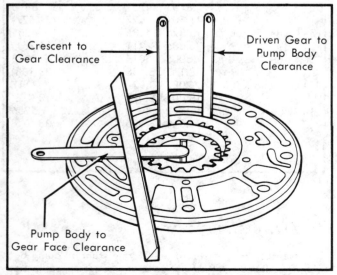

**Fig. 12   View of Oil Pump Body Showing
Clearance Measurements**

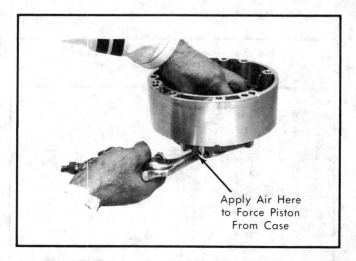

**Fig. 13   Using Compressed Air to Remove Piston
from Overdrive Clutch Case**

TOYOTA A-40 & A-40D (Cont.)

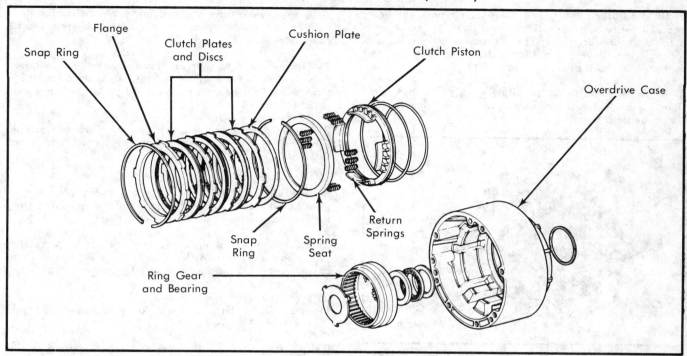

Fig. 14 Exploded View of Overdrive Case and Brake BO
(A-40D Transmissions Only)

Inspection — 1) Wash all parts (except discs) thoroughly in clean solvent. Air dry all parts with compressed air.

2) Inspect all parts for wear or damage and replace as necessary. Inspect clutch plates, discs and flange for signs of burning.

NOTE — *New clutch disc must be soaked in automatic transmission fluid for at least 2 hours prior to installation.*

3) Check piston return springs for wear, damage and collapsed coils. Measure free length of springs. Free length of springs should be .6346" (16.12 mm). Replace return springs if length is less than .618" (15.7 mm).

Reassembly — 1) Coat all surfaces with transmission fluid for assembly. Lubricate and install oil seals on piston and clutch case. Carefully install piston into case.

2) Position return springs into pockets of clutch piston, then install spring seat over springs. Compress return springs and install retaining snap ring.

3) Install bearing and races on ring gear as shown in *Fig. 15*, then install ring gear assembly into clutch case.

4) Install cushion plate into clutch case with beveled side down. Install clutch pack into case starting with an externally splined plate and alternating plates and discs. *See Fig. 14.*

5) Install flange into clutch case with raised portion of flange facing up. Install clutch pack retaining snap ring into groove in case and ensure that it is fully seated.

6) Using a feeler gauge, measure clutch pack clearance between flange and snap ring. Clearance should be .014-.063" (.35-1.6 mm), with a maximum clearance of .083" (2.1 mm) allowed.

OVERDRIVE INPUT SHAFT & CLUTCH (C0) (A-40D ONLY)

Disassembly — 1) Remove thrust washer from rear of overdrive planetary gear. Remove large retaining snap ring, then lift out brake hub, input shaft and planetary gear assembly.

2) From inside planetary gear assembly, remove snap ring, thrust washer, one-way clutch, one-way clutch outer race and tanged thrust washer.

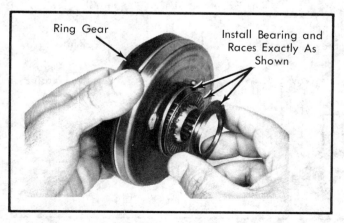

Fig. 15 View of Ring Gear Showing Correct Installation of Bearing and Races

TOYOTA A-40 & A-40D (Cont.)

3) Lift clutch disc out of clutch drum, then remove snap ring and pull out remaining clutch disc and clutch plates. Using a suitable compressor tool, compress piston return springs and remove retaining snap ring. Lift piston return spring seat and springs from clutch drum.

4) Assemble clutch drum onto oil pump as shown in *Fig. 16*. Using compressed air, force clutch piston from drum. Remove "O" rings from piston and clutch drum.

Apply Air to Oil Hole
In Oil Pump to
Force Out Piston

Fig. 16 Removing Overdrive Direct Clutch Piston
(A-40D Transmission Only)

Inspection — 1) Thoroughly clean all parts and inspect them for wear and damage. Check clutch plates for signs of burning. Replace parts as necessary.

NOTE — *If new clutch plates and discs are to be installed, they must be soaked in automatic transmission fluid for at least 2 hours prior to installation.*

2) Inspect piston return springs for wear, damage or collapsed coils. Measure free length of springs, which should be .625" (15.9 mm). Replace return springs if free length is less than .618" (15.7 mm)

3) Inspect clutch piston and "O" rings for wear or damage. Check clutch piston to ensure that piston check ball is not sticking.

Reassembly — 1) Lubricate all parts with transmission fluid prior to installation. Lubricate and install "O" rings on piston, then carefully install piston into clutch drum.

2) Position return springs into pockets of piston, then install spring seat over springs. Using a suitable compressor tool, compress springs and seat and install retaining snap ring.

3) Install clutch plates and discs into clutch drum in the following order: Disc (internal splines), plate (external splines), disc, and plate.

NOTE — *DO NOT install clutch pack retaining snap ring at this time. Piston travel must be checked as follows:*

4) Temporarily install brake hub and the snap ring which retains it into clutch drum. Install clutch drum onto oil pump, then mount a dial indicator so that indicator tip touches top of clutch piston. See *Fig. 18*.

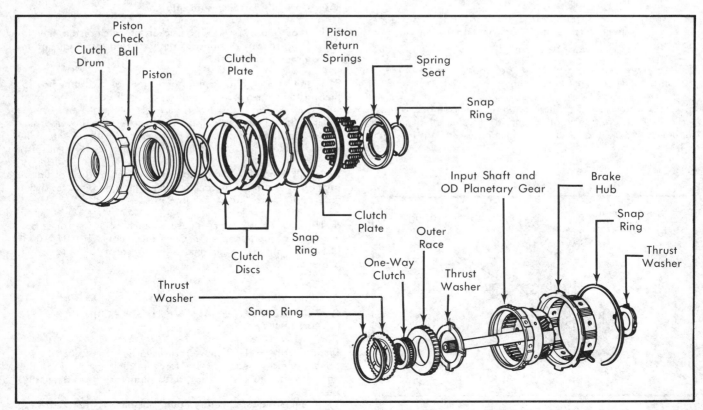

Fig. 17 Exploded View of Overdrive Input Shaft and Clutch C0
(A-40D Transmission)

TOYOTA A-40 & A-40D (Cont.)

5) Apply pressure to oil hole in oil pump as shown in *Fig. 18* and read piston travel on dial indicator. Piston travel with 57-114 psi (4-8 kg/cm²) air pressure applied should be .052-.084" (1.31-2.13 mm), with a maximum travel of .0925" (2.35 mm) allowed.

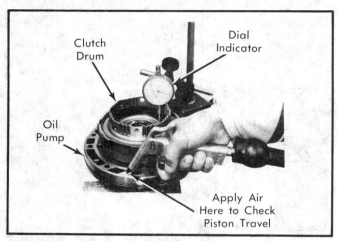

Fig. 18   Checking Clutch C0 Piston Travel (A-40D Transmission Only)

6) Remove dial indicator. Separate clutch drum from oil pump and remove brake hub snap ring, hub and top clutch plate from clutch drum. Install clutch pack retaining snap ring, then reinstall top clutch plate into drum.

7) Assemble one-way clutch assembly using *Fig. 17* as a guide, then install one-way clutch assembly into planetary gear and make sure it is installed as shown in *Fig. 19*.

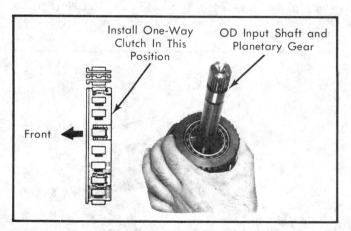

Fig. 19   View Showing Correct Installation of One-Way Clutch Assembly

8) Install OD input shaft and planetary gear assembly into clutch drum. Install brake hub and retaining snap ring. Install thrust washer onto back of planetary gear.

9) With reassembly completed, check operation by holding clutch drum and turning input shaft. Shaft should turn freely when rotated clockwise and lock when rotated counter-clockwise.

FRONT CLUTCH

Disasembly — 1) Remove snap ring and pull rear clutch hub and front clutch hub (with thrust bearing and races attached) from clutch drum.

2) Remove clutch plate and clutch disc, then remove snap ring and pull out remaining clutch plates and discs. Using a suitable compressor tool, compress piston return spring and remove snap ring. Take out spring seat and return spring.

3) On A-40 transmissions, assemble clutch drum onto oil pump, then remove clutch piston from drum by applying compressed air to oil pump oil hole indicated in *Fig. 20*. Remove "O" rings from piston.

4) On A-40D transmissions, assemble clutch drum onto over-drive clutch case, then remove piston by applying compressed air to case oil hole as indicated in *Fig. 20*. Remove "O" rings from clutch piston.

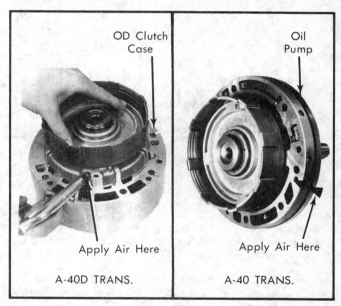

Fig. 20   Removing Front Clutch Piston Using Compressed Air

Inspection — 1) Thoroughly clean all parts and inspect them for wear and damage. Check clutch plates and discs for signs of burning and replace as necessary.

NOTE — *If new clutch plates are to be installed they must be soaked in automatic transmission fluid for at least 2 hours prior to installation.*

2) Check input shaft bearing and bushing contacting surfaces for damage, excessive wear and burning. Insert input shaft into torque converter and ensure that it slides in smoothly and that there is no excessive looseness.

3) Inspect toothed parts of clutch drum and clutch hubs for wear and damage. Inspect piston and clutch drum sliding surfaces for burning.

TOYOTA A-40 & A-40D (Cont.)

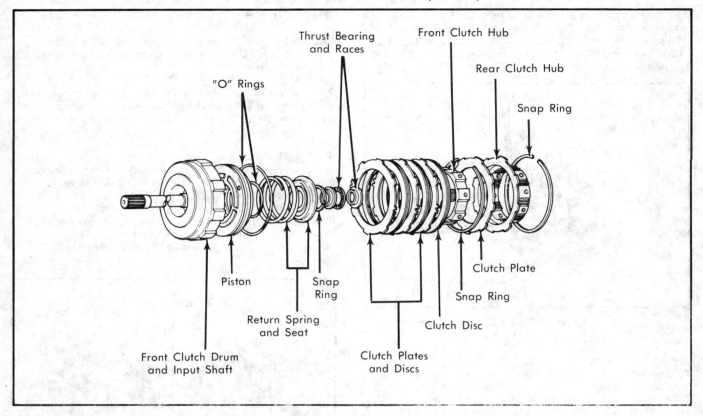

Fig. 21   Exploded View of Front Clutch Assembly

4) Check return spring for wear, damage or collapsed coils. Check free length of return spring which should be 1.311" (33.3 mm). If spring length is less than 1.268" (32.2 mm), it should be replaced.

5) Inspect check ball in clutch piston for sticking by shaking piston. Also, apply compressed air from inner side of piston and inspect check ball for air leaks.

Reassembly — 1) Lubricate and install new "O" ring onto clutch piston. Carefully install piston into clutch drum. Position piston return spring and seat on piston, then compress spring and install snap ring.

2) Place thrust bearing and races into position in clutch drum then install front clutch hub. Install clutch plates into drum starting with a clutch plate (external splines) and alternating discs and plates until all are installed. Do not install clutch pack retaining snap ring at this time. Check clutch clearance as follows:

3) Temporarily install rear clutch hub and snap ring into clutch drum. On A-40 transmission, check clearance between rear clutch hub and snap ring using a feeler gauge. Clearance should be .016-.051" (.4-1.3 mm), with a maximum allowable clearance of .075" (1.9 mm).

4) On A-40D transmission, check clutch clearance by installing front clutch drum onto overdrive case. Assemble a dial indicator with indicator tip touching clutch piston. Apply air pressure of 57-114 psi (4-8 kg/cm²) to oil hole in OD case and

check piston travel on indicator. See *Fig. 22*. Piston travel should be .056-.092" (1.42-2.33 mm), with a maximum allowable travel of .106" (2.7 mm).

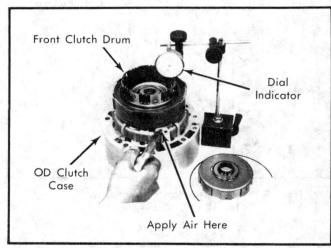

Fig. 22   Checking Front Clutch Piston Travel (A-40D Transmission Only)

5) On all transmissions, remove snap ring and lift out rear clutch hub and one clutch plate and one clutch disc. Install clutch pack snap ring, then reinstall clutch plate, disc, rear clutch hub and retaining snap ring.

TOYOTA A-40 & A-40D (Cont.)

REAR CLUTCH

Disassembly — 1) Remove snap ring and lift clutch flange, clutch discs and clutch plates from rear clutch drum. Using a suitable compressor tool, compress piston return spring and remove snap ring, then lift out spring and spring seat.

2) Assemble clutch drum on center support. Apply compressed air to oil hole in center support and remove inner and outer pistons from clutch drum. See Fig. 23. Remove "O" rings from pistons.

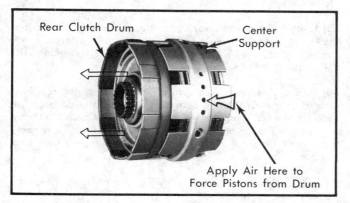

Fig. 23   Using Compressed Air to Remove Rear Clutch Inner and Outer Pistons

Inspection — 1) Thoroughly clean all parts and inspect them for wear and damage. Inspect toothed parts and piston sliding surfaces of clutch drum for wear or damage.

2) Inspect clutch plates and discs for signs of burning. Also check plate and disc splines (teeth) for wear and damage.

3) Inspect clutch pistons for wear and damage. Shake pistons and make sure that check balls are not stuck. Also, apply air pressure to the check balls to see that they do not leak. Check free length of piston return spring as outlined under *Front Clutch Inspection*.

Reassembly — 1) Install "O" rings on inner and outer pistons. Apply a thin coat of automatic transmission fluid to "O" rings, then insert pistons carefully into clutch drum, making sure not to damage "O" rings.

2) Place piston return spring and spring seat on piston, then compress spring and install snap ring. Install clutch plates, clutch discs and clutch flange into drum in sequence shown in Fig. 24. Install clutch pack snap ring.

NOTE — *Make sure that clutch flange is installed with raised portion facing forward.*

3) On A-40 transmission, check clutch pack clearance by measuring the clearance between clutch flange and snap ring using a feeler gauge. Clearance should be .016-.047" (.4-1.2 mm), with a maximum allowable clearance of .063" (1.6 mm).

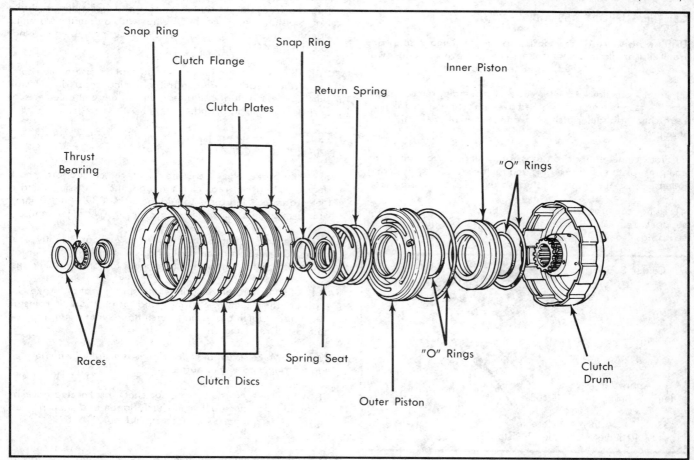

Fig. 24   Exploded View of Rear Clutch Assembly

TOYOTA A-40 & A-40D (Cont.)

4) On A-40D transmission, install rear clutch drum on center support and measure piston travel using a dial indicator and compressed air as shown in *Fig. 25*. With an air pressure of 57-114 psi (4-8 kg/cm²) applied, piston travel should be .043-.051" (1.1-1.3 mm), with a maximum allowable travel of .059" (1.5 mm).

NOTE — *If clutch clearance (A-40) or piston travel (A-40D) exceeds specifications, correct by installing a different thickness flange.*

Fig. 25   Checking Rear Clutch Piston Travel (A-40D Transmission)

CENTER SUPPORT ASSEMBLY

Disassembly (A-40 Transmission) — 1) Remove snap ring from end of planetary sun gear, then remove sun gear (with one-way clutch attached) from center support.

2) From front side of center support assembly, remove Brake No. 1 assembly as follows: Remove snap ring then take out rear clutch flange, clutch disc and clutch plate from center support.

3) Place center support on press and using suitable adapters, compress piston return springs and remove retaining snap ring. Release press, then remove return springs (12) and spring seat.

4) Using compressed air, remove brake piston from center support. *See Fig. 26.* Remove "O" rings from piston and oil seal rings from center support.

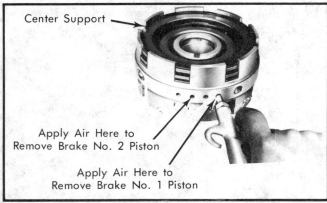

Fig. 26   Removing Brake Pistons from Center Support (A-40 Transmission Only)

5) From rear side of center support, remove Brake No. 2 assembly, following the same disassembly procedures as was used for Brake No. 1.

Inspection (A-40 Transmission) — 1) Thoroughly clean parts and dry with compressed air. Inspect center support for wear and damage to oil seal rings, seal ring grooves, bushing, clutch plate slots and snap ring groove.

2) Check brake pistons for wear and damage to sliding surfaces. Inspect clutch plates and discs for signs of burning, and for damage to splines.

3) Inspect piston return springs for wear, damage and collapsed coils. Measure free length of return springs. Free length should be .625" (16.12 mm). If free length is less than .618" (15.7 mm), springs must be replaced.

4) Inspect one-way clutch sprags and ribbon spring for wear and damage. Check end bearings for wear and damage. Inspect brake No. 2 hub for wear and damage. Check planetary sun gear for wear and damage to one-way clutch inner race, sun gear bushings, sun gear seal rings and sun gear teeth and splines.

CAUTION — *Use care when blowing dry one-way clutch as sprags tend to come out.*

Reassembly (A-40 Transmission) — 1) Assemble oil seal rings on front side of center support and "O" rings on Brake No. 1 piston. Lightly coat "O" rings with automatic transmission fluid, then install piston into center support using care not to damage "O" rings.

2) Position return springs and spring seat on piston, then compress return springs and install retaining snap ring. Install clutch plate, clutch disc and rear clutch flange into center support and install snap ring.

NOTE — *Make sure rear clutch flange is installed with beveled edge facing into the center support.*

3) With Brake No. 1 assembled in center support, check clearance between rear clutch flange and snap ring using a feeler gauge. Clearance should be .016-.039" (.4-1.0 mm), with a maximum allowable clearance of .047" (1.2 mm).

4) Assemble "O" rings on Brake No. 2 piston. Lightly coat piston "O" rings with automatic transmission fluid, then install piston into center support using care not to damage "O" rings.

5) Position piston return springs and spring seat on Brake No. 2 piston, then compress springs and install snap ring. Install clutch discs, clutch plates and clutch flange into center support and install retaining snap ring.

NOTE — *Make sure that clutch flange is installed with beveled edge facing into center support.*

6) With Brake No. 2 assembled, check brake clearance by measuring clearance between clutch flange and snap ring using a feeler gauge. Clearance should be .016-.047" (.4-1.2 mm).

7) Assemble one-way clutch into Brake No. 2 hub, making sure that the 2 end bearings are positioned correctly. Assemble

TOYOTA A-40 & A-40D (Cont.)

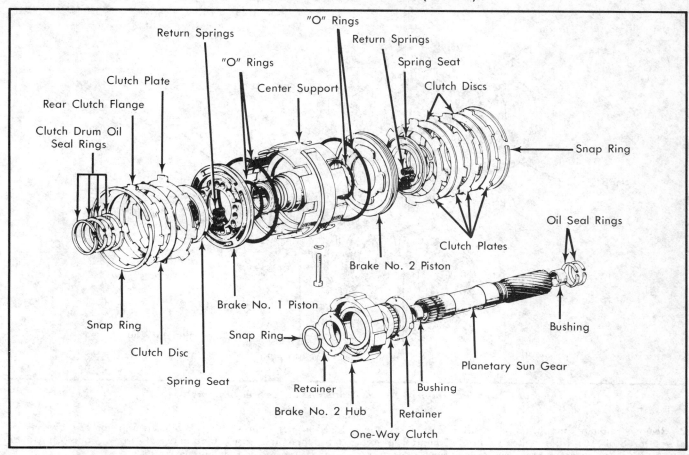

Fig. 27   Exploded View of A-40 Transmission Center Support Assembly

one-way clutch retainer plates in the following order and using *Fig. 28* as a guide:

- Use new retainer plates. First, bend down the 4 lips using pliers.
- Push retainer plate into Brake No. 2 hub with fingers.
- Finally, hold brake hub in a vise and bend down the plate lips with a chisel.

NOTE – *Make sure that retainer plates have been correctly secured to brake hub and that the center of retainer plates are in align with center of hub.*

8) Install one-way clutch assembly on planetary sun gear. Check one-way clutch operation by holding brake hub (outer race) and turning sun gear (inner race). Sun gear should rotate smoothly when turned clockwise and lock when turned counter-clockwise.

9) Insert planetary sun gear, with one-way clutch attached, into center support and lock in place with snap ring.

Disassembly (A-40D Transmission) – 1) Remove snap ring from end of planetary sun gear, then pull sun gear from center support.

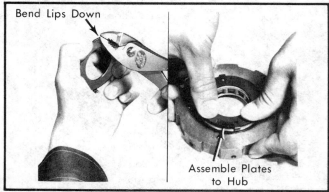

Fig. 28   Assembling One-Way Clutch Retainer Plates to Brake No. 2 Hub (A-40 Only)

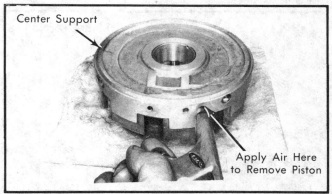

Fig. 29   Removing Brake B1 Piston from Center Support (A-40D)

TOYOTA A-40 & A-40D (Cont.)

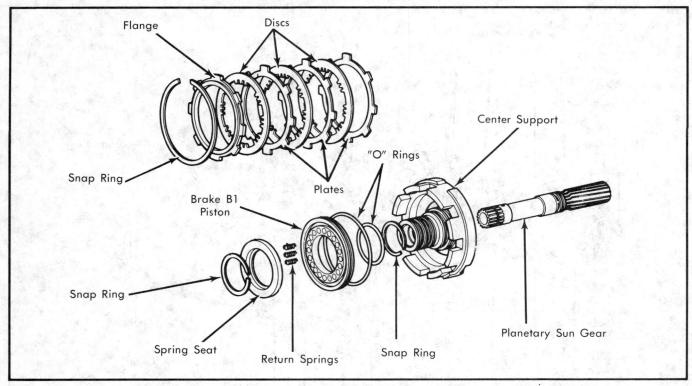

Flange — Discs — Center Support — "O" Rings — Plates — Brake B1 Piston — Snap Ring — Spring Seat — Return Springs — Snap Ring — Planetary Sun Gear — Snap Ring

Fig. 30 Exploded View of A-40D Transmission Center Support Assembly

2) Remove retaining snap ring, then lift flange, discs and plates for Brake B1 from center support. Compress piston return springs and remove snap ring, then remove return springs and spring seat from center support.

3) Using compressed air, remove Brake B1 piston from center support as shown in *Fig. 29*. Remove "O" rings from piston.

Inspection (A-40D Transmission) — Inspect all parts for wear or damage. Check plates and discs for signs of burning. Check free length of return springs. Spring free length should be .6346" (16.12 mm); if less than .618" (15.7 mm), springs should be replaced.

Reassembly (A-40D Transmission) — **1)** Assemble "O" rings on Brake B1 piston. Lightly coat "O" rings with automatic transmission fluid, then install piston into center support using care not to damage "O" rings.

2) Position returns springs in pockets of piston as shown in *Fig. 31*, then place spring seat on top of springs. Compress springs and seat and install snap ring.

3) Install plates and discs into center support in sequence shown in *Fig. 30*. Install flange on top of plates and discs with raised portion facing up.

4) Using a dial indicator and compressed air as shown in *Fig. 32*, check Brake B1 piston travel. Piston travel with 57-114 psi (4-8 kg/cm²) air pressure applied should be .040-.047" (1.0-1.2 mm), with a mximum allowable travel of .052" (1.3 mm).

5) If piston travel is not within specifications, correct by installing new plates or discs. Install clutch pack retaining snap ring.

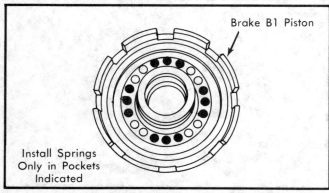

Brake B1 Piston

Install Springs Only in Pockets Indicated

Fig. 31 Correct Installation of Return Springs in Brake B1 Piston (A-40D Only)

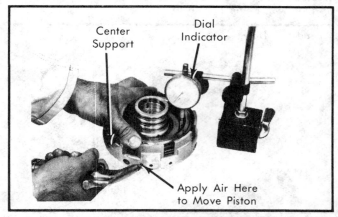

Center Support — Dial Indicator — Apply Air Here to Move Piston

Fig. 32 Checking Brake B1 Piston Travel (A-40D Transmission)

TOYOTA A-40 & A-40D (Cont.)

FRONT PLANETARY GEAR

Disassembly — Separate brake reaction plate from front planetary carrier. Remove snap ring from carrier and lift one-way clutch, and thrust washer from carrier.

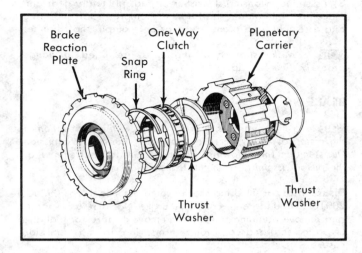

Fig. 33 *Exploded View of Front Planetary Gear*

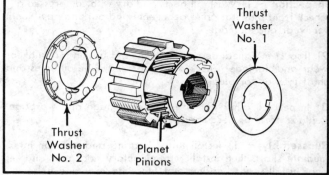

Fig. 34 *View of Front Planetary Pinions and Thrust Washers*

Reassembly — 1) Assemble thrust washer No. 2 (nylon) and thrust washer No. 1 to planetary carrier as shown in *Fig. 34*.

2) Assemble one-way clutch into carrier, using care to see that the 2 end bearings are positioned correctly. Install snap ring, then assemble brake reaction plate to front of planetary gear.

3) With reassembly complete, check operation of one-way clutch. Hold reaction plate and turn planetary gear. Planetary gear should rotate smoothly when turned counterclockwise and lock when turned clockwise.

Inspection — 1) Wash disassembled parts and blow dry with compressed air. Inspect thrust washers for wear, warpage and burning.

2) Inspect carrier thrust surfaces for warpage and wear. Check planetary pinions for wear and damage. Inspect one-way clutch outer race surface in carrier for wear.

3) Check reaction plate toothed part and sliding surface for wear and damage. Check one-way clutch sliding surface of reaction plate for wear and damage.

REAR PLANETARY GEAR & OUTPUT SHAFT

Disassembly — 1) Compress intermediate shaft snap ring and remove shaft, with front planetary ring gear attached, from output shaft flange.

2) Remove front planetary ring gear, thrust washer, and rear planary gear from intermediate shaft. Remove thrust bearing and race from inside rear planetary gear. Remove set ring with a screwdriver and take planetary ring gear and thrust bearing race from intermediate shaft.

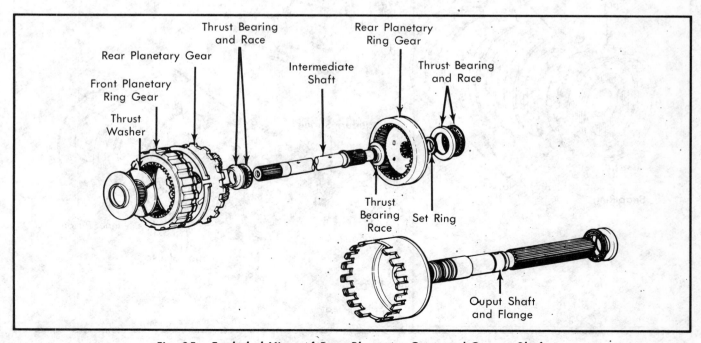

Fig. 35 *Exploded View of Rear Planetary Gear and Output Shaft*

TOYOTA A-40 & A-40D (Cont.)

Inspection — 1) Wash all parts and dry with compressed air. Check front planetary ring gear teeth and parking pawl teeth for wear and damage.

2) Inspect intermediate shaft splines and bushing journal for wear and damage. Check shaft cup plug, lube oil holes and shaft interior for plugging.

3) Inspect all other parts for wear, damage and warpage. Replace parts as necessary.

Reassembly — 1) Install thrust bearing and race on intermediate shaft, then install rear planetary ring gear and set ring. Install thrust bearing and race into rear ring gear.

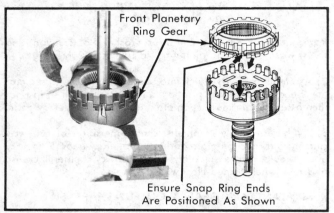

Fig. 36   View Showing Correct Positioning of Snap Ring Ends in Output Shaft Flange

2) Place output shaft in a vise with output flange up. Position thrust bearing and race in flange, then insert intermediate shaft, with rear planetary ring gear attached, into output shaft flange.

3) Assemble nylon thrust washer on rear planetary gear and place them into output shaft flange. Compress shaft snap ring and assemble front planetary gear onto output shaft flange.

NOTE — *Make sure snap ring ends are fitted in flange properly. See Fig. 36.*

BRAKE NO. 3

NOTE — *All components of Brake No. 3, with the exception of the piston assembly, were disassembled during Transmission Disassembly. The following procedures are for the removal of the piston assembly from the transmission case.*

Disassembly — 1) Using special compressor tool (SST 09350-20010 and adapters), compress Brake No. 3 return springs and remove retaining snap ring. Remove compressor tool and lift spring seat and 16 piston return springs from transmission case.

2) Position transmission with front opening facing down. Using two air guns, blow in SIMULTANEOUSLY through the brake cylinder holes indicated in *Fig. 38* and remove inner piston, outer piston and brake reaction sleeve as a unit.

NOTE — *Place shop towels under transmission case to protect pistons.*

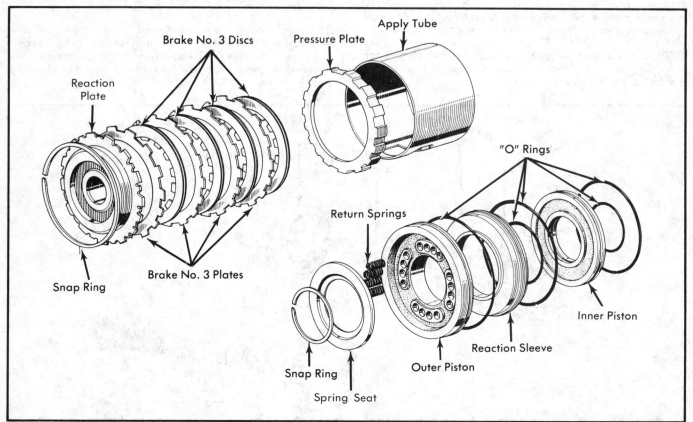

Fig. 37   Exploded View of Brake No. 3 Components

TOYOTA A-40 & A-40D (Cont.)

3) Remove inner and outer piston from reaction sleeve. Remove "O" rings from pistons and reaction sleeves.

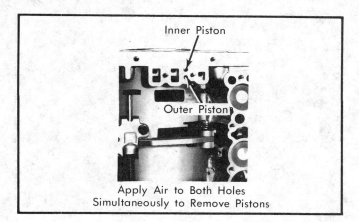

Apply Air to Both Holes
Simultaneously to Remove Pistons

Fig. 38 View of Rear End of Transmission Case Showing Brake No. 3 Piston Removal

Inspection — Wash all parts and blow dry with compressed air. Inspect all parts for wear, damage, warpage and signs of burning.

NOTE — *For inspection of piston return springs, follow inspection procedures for Brake No. 1 and Brake No. 2 under Center Support Assembly.*

Reassembly — 1) Install new "O" rings on pistons and on reaction sleeve. Lightly coat "O" rings with automatic transmission fluid, then carefully install inner and outer pistons into reaction sleeve.

2) Insert piston and reaction sleeve assembly into transmission case using care not to damage "O" rings. Apply grease on piston return springs and assemble them along with spring seat into outer piston. Using same tools as were used at disassembly, compress springs and install snap ring.

NOTE — *Remaining Brake No. 3 components will be assembled during Transmission Reassembly*

VALVE BODY

Disassembly (A-40 Transmission) — 1) Disassemble valve body using *Fig. 39* as a guide and note the following:

2) As valve trains are removed from each valve body bore, place individual parts in correct order in relative position to valve body to simplify reassembly.

3) When disassembling, use care not to damage valve surfaces or form burrs around the valve body bores.

4) When separating upper valve bodies (front and rear) from lower valve body, be very careful not to lose check balls and springs.

Inspection (A-40 Transmission) — 1) Wash all disassembled parts and blow dry with compressed air. Inspect all valves for wear and damage, then insert them into the valve body and check to ensure that they operate smoothly while being turned.

2) Inspect valve body bore sliding surfaces for damage and wear. Check all oil holes and oil passages for clogging.

3) Inspect all valve springs for wear, damage, excessive weakness and collapsed coils. Check free length of all springs and replace if not as specified. *See "A-40 Valve Body Spring Table".*

4) Inspect valve body cover plates and check balls for wear and damage. Check pressure relief valve for wear and damage. Inspect oil strainer for clogging and replace if necessary.

Valve Body Spring Specifications (A-40 Transmission)

Spring	Free Length In. (mm)	No. Of Coils
Front Upper Body		
Throttle Valve	.757 (19.24)	8
Downshift Plug	①1.693 (43)	15.5
Sec. Reg. Valve	2.946 (74.83)	15
Rear Upper Body		
Int. Reg. Valve	1.395 (35.43)	14
Sequence Valve	1.450 (36.83)	15
Gov. Mod. Valve	1.420 (36.07)	12
Low Mod. Valve	1.667 (42.35)	15
2-3 Shift Valve	1.382 (35.10)	12.5
Detent Reg. Valve	1.263 (32.08)	13.5
Lower Body		
Sequence Valve	1.478 (37.55)	14.5
1-2 Shift Valve	1.363 (34.62)	13
Pres. Relief Ball	1.265 (32.14)	9
Check Valve	1.207 (30.65)	7
Pri. Reg. Valve	2.887 (73.32)	15

① — Corolla downshift spring free length should be 1.563" (39.7 mm).

Reassembly (A-40 Transmission) — 1) Prior to reassembly wash all components in fresh transmission fluid and blow them dry with compressed air.

CAUTION — *Never use waste or shop towels for drying valve body components.*

2) To reassemble lower valve body, install primary regulator valve train into lower body and secure with seat. Install 1-2 shift valve and valve plug into its bore and secure with seat.

3) Assemble shift spring, low coast valve, sequence valve and spring into valve body, then install cover plate and tighten attaching bolts.

4) Install pressure relief valve ball, spring and seat into body. Insert spring and check balls (rubber) into valve body passages shown in *Fig. 40*. Install check valve spring and check valve into position in valve body.

TOYOTA A-40 & A-40D (Cont.)

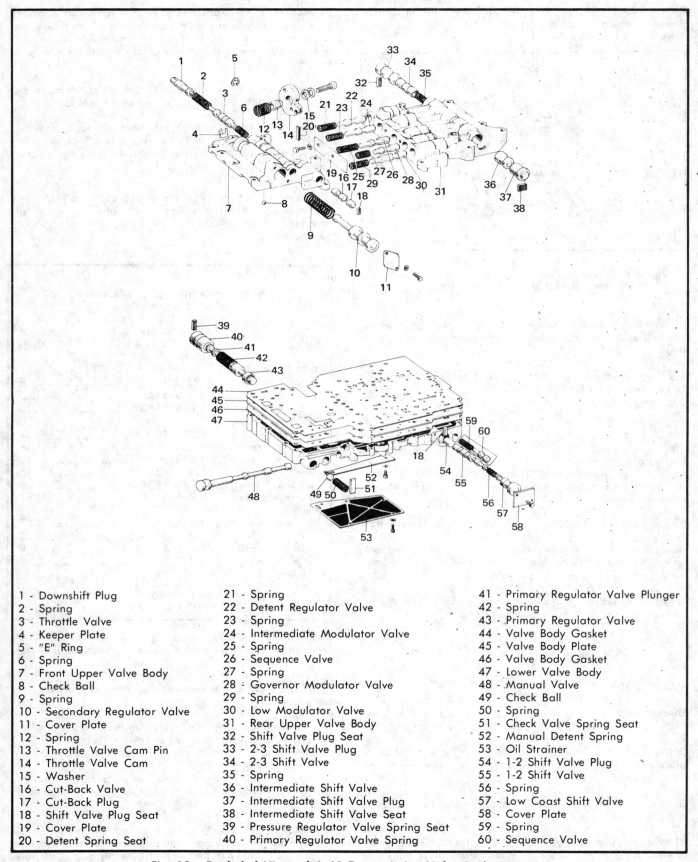

1 - Downshift Plug
2 - Spring
3 - Throttle Valve
4 - Keeper Plate
5 - "E" Ring
6 - Spring
7 - Front Upper Valve Body
8 - Check Ball
9 - Spring
10 - Secondary Regulator Valve
11 - Cover Plate
12 - Spring
13 - Throttle Valve Cam Pin
14 - Throttle Valve Cam
15 - Washer
16 - Cut-Back Valve
17 - Cut-Back Plug
18 - Shift Valve Plug Seat
19 - Cover Plate
20 - Detent Spring Seat

21 - Spring
22 - Detent Regulator Valve
23 - Spring
24 - Intermediate Modulator Valve
25 - Spring
26 - Sequence Valve
27 - Spring
28 - Governor Modulator Valve
29 - Spring
30 - Low Modulator Valve
31 - Rear Upper Valve Body
32 - Shift Valve Plug Seat
33 - 2-3 Shift Valve Plug
34 - 2-3 Shift Valve
35 - Spring
36 - Intermediate Shift Valve
37 - Intermediate Shift Valve Plug
38 - Intermediate Shift Valve Seat
39 - Pressure Regulator Valve Spring Seat
40 - Primary Regulator Valve Spring

41 - Primary Regulator Valve Plunger
42 - Spring
43 - Primary Regulator Valve
44 - Valve Body Gasket
45 - Valve Body Plate
46 - Valve Body Gasket
47 - Lower Valve Body
48 - Manual Valve
49 - Check Ball
50 - Spring
51 - Check Valve Spring Seat
52 - Manual Detent Spring
53 - Oil Strainer
54 - 1-2 Shift Valve Plug
55 - 1-2 Shift Valve
56 - Spring
57 - Low Coast Shift Valve
58 - Cover Plate
59 - Spring
60 - Sequence Valve

Fig. 39   Exploded View of A-40 Transmission Valve Body Assembly

TOYOTA A-40 & A-40D (Cont.)

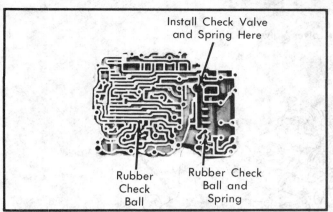

Fig. 40 Installing Check Balls and Check Valve (A-40 Transmission Only)

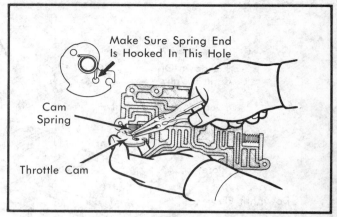

Fig. 42 Installing Throttle Cam and Spring

5) Assemble spring, 2-3 shift valve, plug and seat into rear upper valve body. Install intermediate shift valve, plug and seat. Install detent regulator valve, spring and seat.

6) Assemble low modulator valve, governor modulator valve, sequence valve and intermediate modulator valve into valve body, then install springs and cover plate.

7) Install damping springs and check balls into rear upper valve body as shown in *Fig. 41*.

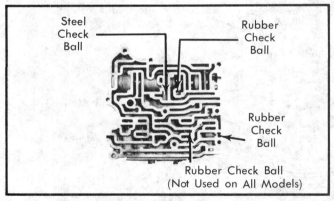

Fig. 41 Install Check Balls in Rear Upper Body (A-40 Transmission Only)

8) To reassemble front upper body, install secondary regulator valve spring and valve into valve body, then install cover plate and tighten attaching bolts.

9) Install throttle valve, throttle valve secondary spring, retainer and "E" rings into valve body. Assemble throttle valve primary spring and downshift plug.

CAUTION — *Install the same number of "E" rings as were removed as they are used to adjust the throttle valve.*

10) Install throttle cam and spring on front upper body, then install retaining bolt finger tight. Make sure throttle cam spring is properly positioned on the body, then hook spring end into cam. *See Fig. 42.* Tighten throttle cam bolt to 52-78 INCH lbs. (60-90 cmkg). After throttle cam is installed, pull it to make sure that it turns smoothly without sticking and that it turns full stroke.

11) Install cut-back valve (small diameter land first), valve plug and seat into valve body. Install rubber check ball into position in front upper body (See *Fig. 43*).

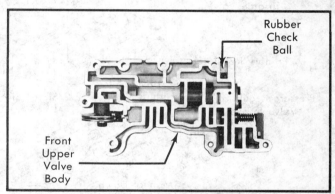

Fig. 43 Installing Front Upper Body Check Ball (A-40 Transmission Only)

12) Position lower valve body gasket on lower valve body, then place separator plate on top of gasket and temporarily install 2 bolts to secure it as shown in *Fig. 44*

NOTE — *Do not confuse lower valve body gasket with upper valve body gasket. See Fig 46 for gasket identification.*

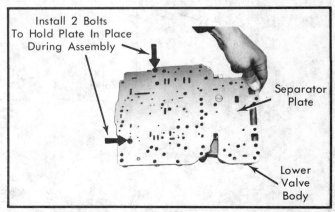

Fig. 44 View of Lower Body Showing Separator Plate Installation (A-40)

Automatic Transmissions

TOYOTA A-40 & A-40D (Cont.)

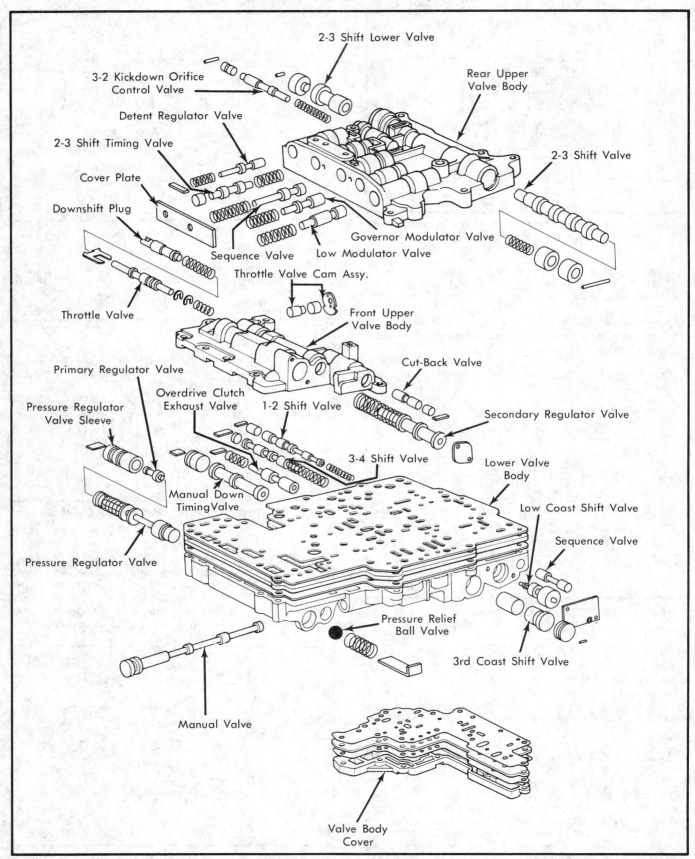

2-3 Shift Lower Valve

3-2 Kickdown Orifice Control Valve

Rear Upper Valve Body

Detent Regulator Valve

2-3 Shift Timing Valve

2-3 Shift Valve

Cover Plate

Downshift Plug

Governor Modulator Valve

Sequence Valve

Low Modulator Valve

Throttle Valve

Throttle Valve Cam Assy.

Front Upper Valve Body

Primary Regulator Valve

Cut-Back Valve

Overdrive Clutch Exhaust Valve

1-2 Shift Valve

Pressure Regulator Valve Sleeve

Secondary Regulator Valve

3-4 Shift Valve

Lower Valve Body

Manual Down Timing Valve

Low Coast Shift Valve

Sequence Valve

Pressure Regulator Valve

Pressure Relief Ball Valve

3rd Coast Shift Valve

Manual Valve

Valve Body Cover

Fig. 45 Exploded View of A-40D Transmission Valve Body Assembly

TOYOTA A-40 & A-40D (Cont.)

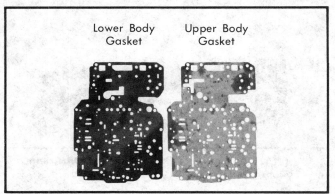

Fig. 46 Valve Body Gasket Identification (A-40 Transmission)

13) Place front upper valve body on work stand with cored face up, then position lower valve body onto front upper body and tighten attaching bolts finger tight. Remove the 2 bolts installed to hold separator plate in place.

14) Place rear upper valve body on work stand with cored face up, then position lower valve body onto rear upper body and install attaching bolts finger tight.

15) Turn valve body assembly over and install remaining valve body attaching bolts and tighten them to specifications. Turn valve body over and tighten front and rear upper body attaching bolts to specifications. Install manual valve into valve body.

Disassembly (A-40D Transmission) — **1)** Disassemble valve body using *Fig. 45* as a guide and note the following:

2) As valve trains are removed from each valve body bore, place individual parts in correct order in relative position to valve body to simplify reassembly.

3) When disassembling, use care not to damage valve surfaces or form burrs around valve body bores.

4) When separating upper valve bodies (front and rear) from lower valve body, be very careful not to lose check balls and springs.

Inspection (A-40D Transmission) — See *Inspection* procedures for A-40 Transmission

NOTE — See the following table for valve body spring specifications for the A-40D transmission.

Valve Body Spring Specifications (A-40D Transmission)

Spring	Free Length In.(mm)	No. Of Coils
Front Upper Body		
Throttle Valve	.8638 (21.94)	8
Downshift Plug	1.5634 (39.71)	11.5
Sec. Reg. Valve	2.8059 (71.27)	15.8

Valve Body Spring Specifications (Cont.) (A-40D Transmission)

Spring	Free Length In, (mm)	No Of Coils
Rear Upper Body		
2-3 Shift Valve	1.1740 (29.82)	9
Sequence Valve	1.4783 (37.55)	14.5
Gov. Mod. Valve	1.4201 (36.07)	12
Low Mod. Valve	1.6673 (42.35)	15
2-3 Shift Valve	1.3421 (34.09)	10.5
Detent Reg. Valve	1.1980 (30.43)	13
3-2 Kickdown	1.2976 (32.96)	11.5
Lower Body		
1-2 Shift Valve	1.3630 (34.62)	13
Pres. Relief Ball	1.2654 (32.14)	9
Check Valve	1.2067 (30.65)	7
Pri. Reg. Valve	2.3677 (60.14)	13
3-4 Shift Valve	1.3248 (33.65)	14.5
OD Clutch Exh.	1.2240 (31.09)	12.5
Check Valve	1.3118 (33.32)	7

Reassembly (A-40D Transmission) — **1)** To reassemble valve body use *Fig. 45* and note the following:

2) When installing throttle valve, install the same number of "E" rings as were removed, as they are used for throttle valve adjustment. Install throttle valve retainer as shown in *Fig. 47*.

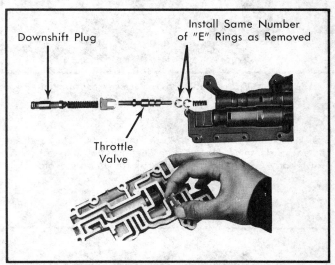

Fig. 47 Installing Throttle Valve and Downshift Plug Valve Train (A-40D Transmission)

3) When assembling throttle valve cam and spring, make sure that spring end is hooked in cam hole shown in *Fig. 42*. After cam and spring are installed, check operation.

4) Install cut-back valve with small diameter land end installed first.

5) To install check balls in lower valve body: Place lower body on work stand with valve body cover side up. Install 4 rubber check balls into passages shown in *Fig. 48*, then position cover gaskets on lower body and install attaching bolts finger tight.

NOTE — Make sure cover gaskets are installed correctly. See *Fig. 49* for identification.

TOYOTA A-40 & A-40D (Cont.)

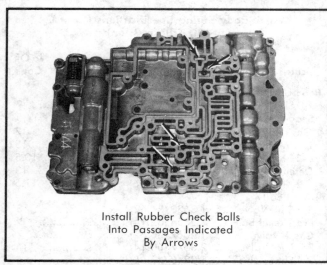

Install Rubber Check Balls
Into Passages Indicated
By Arrows

**Fig. 48   Installing Check Balls In Lower Valve Body
(A-40D Transmission Only)**

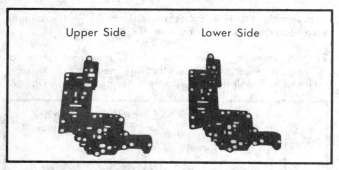

Upper Side   Lower Side

**Fig. 49   Valve Body Cover Gasket Identification
(A-40D Transmission Only)**

6) Turn lower valve body over and install check balls and check valve into passages as shown in *Fig. 50*. Install a gasket on each side on separator plate, then position plate on lower valve body. Temporarily install 2 bolts to keep separator plate in place during assembly.

NOTE — *Make sure separator plate gaskets are installed correctly. See Fig. 51 for gasket identification.*

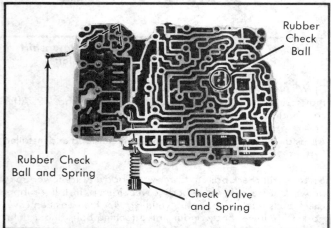

Rubber
Check
Ball

Rubber Check
Ball and Spring

Check Valve
and Spring

**Fig. 50   Installing Lower Valve Body Check Balls
(A-40D Transmission Only)**

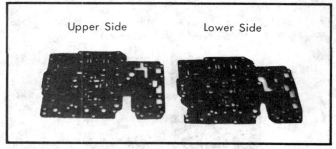

Upper Side   Lower Side

**Fig. 51   Separator Plate Gasket Identification
(A-40D Transmission Only)**

7) Before assembling upper valve bodies to lower body, install check balls into rear upper body as shown in *Fig. 52*, then install check ball into front upper body as shown in *Fig. 53*.

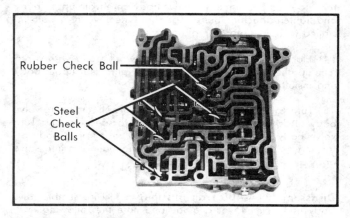

Rubber Check Ball

Steel
Check
Balls

**Fig. 52   Installing Check Balls Into Rear Upper
Valve Body (A-40D Transmission)**

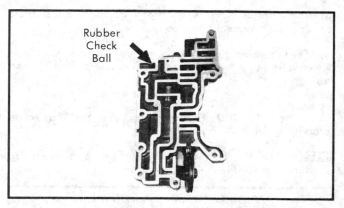

Rubber
Check
Ball

**Fig. 53   Installing Check Ball Into Front Upper
Valve Body (A-40D Transmission)**

8) Assemble upper valve bodies to lower valve body and tighten all bolts finger tight. Make sure valve bodies are correctly aligned, then tighten all valve body attaching bolts to specifications.

TOYOTA A-40 & A-40D (Cont.)

GOVERNOR VALVE ASSEMBLY

Disassembly — Remove "E" ring and lift off governor weight. Remove governor valve shaft, spring and governor valve from governor body.

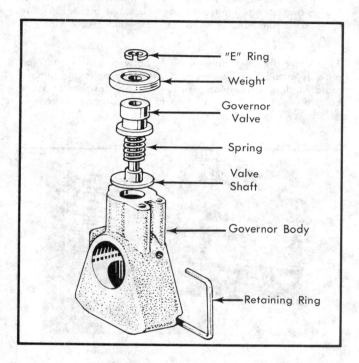

Fig. 54   Exploded View of Governor Assembly

"E" Ring
Weight
Governor Valve
Spring
Valve Shaft
Governor Body
Retaining Ring

Inspection — Inspect all parts for wear and damage. Insert valve shaft into body and make sure that it slides smoothly. Check oil passage for clogging. Check that governor spring free length is .812" (20.63 mm) and has 7.5 coils.

Reassembly — Reverse disassembly procedure.

TRANSMISSION REASSEMBLY

NOTE — *During transmission reassembly note the following:*
- *Dry all parts with compressed air. Never use waste or shop towels.*
- *Soak new clutch discs in automatic transmission fluid for at least 2 hours prior to installation.*
- *Apply automatic transmission fluid on all sliding and rotating surfaces before assembly.*
- *Do not use adhesive cements on gaskets and similar parts.*
- *Use all new "O" rings and gaskets.*

1) Place transmission case on a cylinder with front facing up. Install output shaft thrust bearing and race into case with lip on race facing down over bearing. Install brake apply tube into case.

CAUTION — *Install apply tube so that its lip ("A") fits into transmission case at "B". Also, make sure that lip at apply tube end is fitted inside the piston. See Fig. 55.*

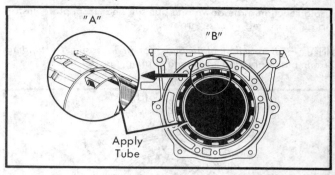

"A"   "B"

Apply Tube

Fig. 55   View Showing Correct Installation of Brake Apply Tube

2) Place thrust washer on planetary carrier and ensure that tang of washer fits in groove of carrier. Install planetary carrier assembly into transmission case, using care not to damage or misplace bearings.

3) Install Brake No. 3 pressure plate into transmission case and push it in until it meshes with brake apply tube. Apply grease to rear side of thrust washer for rear side of front carrier, then place washer in position on carrier. Install front carrier assembly into case.

4) Install Brake No. 3 plates and discs into case, starting with a disc and alternating plates and discs until all are intalled. Measure Brake No. 3 clearance as follows:

5) Measure clearance between the top clutch disc and point "A" of transmission case as shown in *Fig. 56*. Clearance should be .032-.071" (.8-1.8 mm), with a clearance limit of .016-.087" (.4-2.2 mm).

NOTE — *If brake clearance is larger than specified, recheck wear on the parts. If smaller than specified, parts are installed incorrectly.*

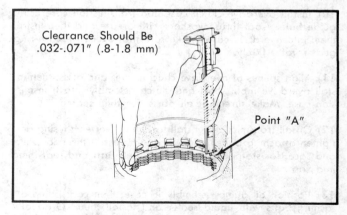

Clearance Should Be .032-.071" (.8-1.8 mm)

Point "A"

Fig. 56   Measuring Brake No. 3 Clearance

6) Remove sun gear from center support assembly. Place transmission case on work bench. Insert sun gear into reaction plate, then install them into case and make sure that reaction plate lug with notch is installed in case as shown in *Fig. 57.*

Automatic Transmissions

TOYOTA A-40 & A-40D (Cont.)

Hold reaction plate down and pull sun gear from plate. Install large snap ring in case groove.

NOTE — *If reaction plate does not fit in easily, try holding front planetary ring gear and turning the sun gear.*

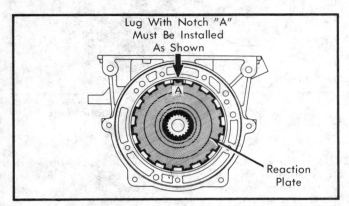

Fig. 57   View Showing Correct Installation of Brake Reaction Plate

7) Assemble sun gear on center support, then insert center support assembly into case. Push center support assembly fully into case until seated, then install and tighten center support attaching bolts.

NOTE — *Center support cannot be fully seated in case unless one-way clutch is fully seated in center support.*

8) Install rear clutch assembly into case. Assemble thrust bearing and races on front clutch assembly using grease to hold them in place. Install front clutch assembly into case.

9) On A-40D transmission only, install suitable guide rods (SST 09362-30011 or equivalent) into 2 oil pump mounting holes (opposite each other). Install needle roller bearing onto front clutch drum. Coat needle bearing race with grease to retain it in place.

10) Install overdrive clutch case into transmission case using guide bolts. Coat thrust washers with grease and then install them into overdrive case. Make sure that overdrive case ring gear rotates freely.

11) Align splines of overdrive clutch plates and discs, then install overdrive input shaft and clutch assembly into transmission case. Make sure that all parts are fully seated.

12) On all transmissions, install torque converter housing and tighten attaching bolts to specifications. Install thrust bearing and race (for stator shaft rear) on input shaft and seat them into case.

13) Position oil pump assembly in case, then coat pump attaching bolts with liquid sealer and install them. Gradually tighten attaching bolts in 2 or 3 stages in diagonal order.

14) With oil pump installed, check input shaft has play in axial direction and that it turns smoothly. Also, make sure output shaft thrust play is .012-.035" (.3-.9 mm).

15) Assemble parking lock rod on manual valve lever. Insert manual valve shaft into case and drive in NEW throttle spring

pin. Install lock pawl in case, then install lock pawl shaft and spring. Install lock pawl bracket, then push it forward and tighten attaching bolts.

16) Lubricate throttle cable "O" ring, then install cable into case using care not to damage "O" ring. Install accumulator pistons and springs into transmission case. Use a suitable plate to hold accumulator pistons in case until valve body is installed.

17) Attach throttle cable to valve body throttle cam. Temporarily install 2 or 3 valve body attaching bolts and remove plate holding accumulator pistons. Align position of valve body manual valve against that of manual valve lever pin.

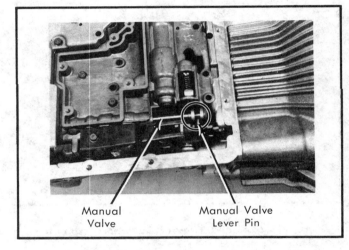

Fig. 58   View Showing Correct Positioning of Valve Body Manual Valve

18) Install remaining valve body attaching bolts and gradually tighten them to specifications in 2 or 3 stages. On A-40D transmission, install oil pipes on valve body as shown in *Fig. 59* On all transmissions, install oil strainer.

Fig. 59   View Showing Correct Installation of Oil Pipes (A-40D Transmission Only)

TOYOTA A-40 & A-40D (Cont.)

19) Shift transmission to "L" and "P" ranges and check detent spring roller to make sure it fits properly against the various detent lever parts. Place a clean magnet in bottom of oil pan, then install oil pan and new gasket and tighten attaching bolts.

20) Install a flat tip screwdriver under governor retaining ring and install governor on output shaft. Remove screwdriver and make sure retaining ring seats in output shaft hole.

21) Install speedometer drive gear on output shaft, then install retaining snap ring. Install extension housing on transmission case using a new gasket, then install and tighten attaching bolts. Install speedometer driven gear assembly in extension housing. Install neutral safety switch and control lever.

NOTE — *Make sure slit in neutral safety switch aligns with neutral base line on case.*

TIGHTENING SPECIFICATIONS

Application	Ft. Lbs. (mkg)
Transmission-to-Engine	①37-57 (5.1-7.9)
Converter Housing-to-Case	
Short Bolts	20-30 (2/8-4.2)
Long Bolts	35-49 (4.8-6.8)
Extension Hsg.-to-Case	20-30 (2.8-4.2)
Oil Pump-to-Case	14-18 (1.9-2.5)
Center Support-to-Case	18-20 (2.5-2.8)
Oil Pan Drain Plug	11-15 (1.5-2.1)
Converter-to-Drive Plate	11-15 (1.5-2.1)

Application	INCH Lbs. (cmkg)
Oil Pan-to-Case	38-43 (43.8-49.6)
Strainer-to-Valve Body	43-52 (49.6-59.9)
Valve Body-to-Case	69-104 (79.5-119.9
Lock Pawl Bracket-to-Case	52-78 (59.9-89.9)
Test Plugs-to-Case	52-78 (59.9-89.9)

① — Cressida and Supra should be 22-32 Ft. Lbs. (3.0-4.5 mkg).

TURBO HYDRA-MATIC 200

LUV

DESCRIPTION

Transmission is a fully automatic three speed unit consisting primarily of a three-element hydraulic torque converter and a compound planetary gear set. Three multiple-disc clutches, a roller clutch, and one brake band provide the friction elements required to obtain the desired function of the planetary gear set. A hydraulic system pressurized by a gear-type pump provides the working pressure required to operate the friction elements and automatic controls.

LUBRICATION & ADJUSTMENT

See AUTOMATIC TRANSMISSION SERVICING Section.

TROUBLE SHOOTING

NO DRIVE IN DRIVE RANGE

Incorrect fluid level, fluid leakage. Manual linkage out of adjustment. Low oil pressure: Plugged or restricted oil screen, screen gasket out of position, pump assembly or pressure regulator faulty, pump drive gear tangs damaged by converter, case porosity in intake bore area. Valve body manual valve disconnected from lever pin. Forward clutch: Piston cracked, seals missing or damaged, clutch plates burned, or snap ring out of groove; forward clutch seal rings missing or

damaged on turbine shaft, leak in feed circuits, pump-to-case gasket out of position, ball check stuck or missing in clutch housing. Cup plug leaking or missing in rear of turbine shaft in clutch apply passage, wrong piston or number of clutch plates in forward clutch housing, or feed orifice plugged in turbine shaft. Roller clutch assembly: Springs missing in roller clutch, or rollers galled or missing.

1-2 AND 2-3 SHIFTS, FULL THROTTLE ONLY

Throttle valve cable binding, unhooked, broken, or misadjusted. Throttle valve lever and bracket assembly binding or unhooked. T.V. exhaust ball lifter or No. 5 ball binding, out of position, or unhooked. **NOTE** — Allowing No. 5 ball to seat causes full T.V. pressure regardless of throttle valve position. Throttle valve and plunger binding. Control valve body gaskets leaking, damaged, or incorrectly installed. Case porosity.

FIRST SPEED ONLY, NO 1-2 SHIFT

Plugged governor oil feed orifice in spacer plate. Plugged orifice in spacer plate that feeds governor oil to shift valves. Governor ball(s) missing in governor assembly. Inner governor cover rubber "O" ring seal missing or leaking. **NOTE** — If outer seal leaks, an external leak will be present along with no upshifts. Governor shaft seal missing or damaged. Governor driven gear stripped. Governor weights binding on pin. Governor assembly missing. Valve body 1-2 shift valve or 1-2 throttle valve stuck in downshift position. Porosity in case channels or undrilled second speed feed holes. Leakage between case and band apply ring. Band anchor pin missing or unhooked from band. Broken or missing band.

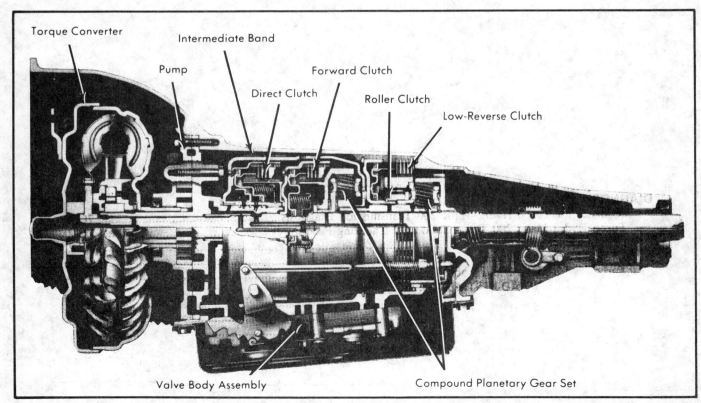

Fig. 1   Cutaway View of Turbo Hydra-Matic 200 Automatic Transmission Assembly

TURBO HYDRA-MATIC 200 (Cont.)

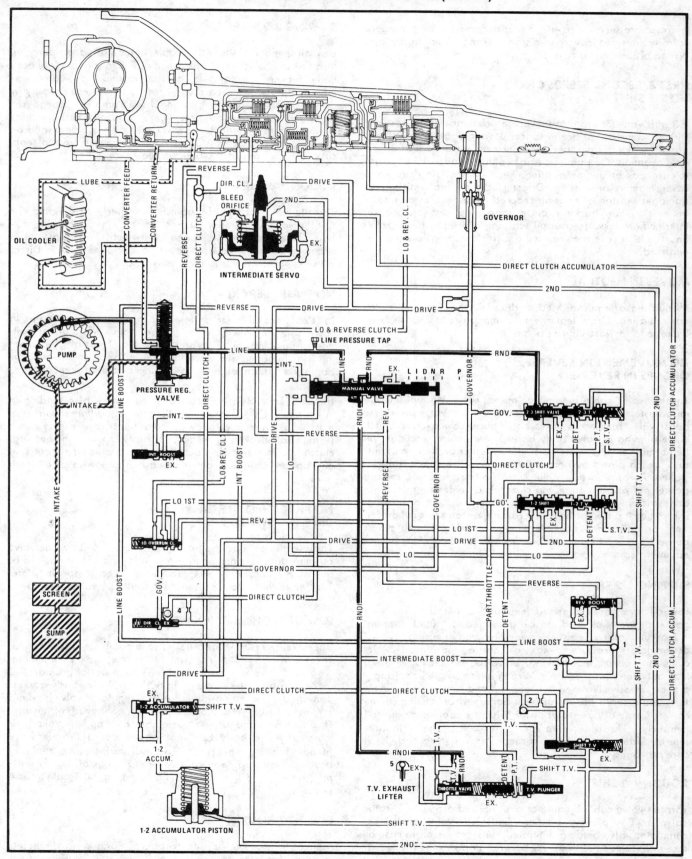

Fig. 2 Turbo Hydra-Matic 200 Hydraulic Circuits Diagram

TURBO HYDRA-MATIC 200 (Cont.)

Intermediate servo-to-cover oil seal ring missing or damaged. Porosity in servo cover or piston. Wrong band apply pin. Wrong piston and/or cover.

FIRST & SECOND SPEEDS ONLY, NO 2-3 SHIFT

2-3 shift valve or 2-3 throttle valve stuck in downshift position. Direct clutch feed orifice in spacer plate plugged. Valve body gaskets leaking, damaged, or incorrectly installed. Porosity in case channels. Oil pump passages plugged or leaking. Pump-to-case gasket out of position. Rear oil seal ring on pump cover leaking or missing. Direct clutch oil seals missing or damaged, piston or housing cracked, clutch plates damaged or missing, or backing plate snap ring out of groove. Intermediate servo-to-case oil seal ring broken or missing. Exhaust hole in case between servo piston seal rings plugged or undrilled.

MOVES IN NEUTRAL

Manual linkage misadjusted or disconnected. Forward clutch not releasing. Cross leakage in pump passages. Case cross leakage to forward clutch passages.

NO MOVEMENT IN REVERSE, OR SLIPS IN REVERSE

Throttle valve cable binding or misadjusted. Manual linkage misadjusted. Throttle valve binding. Shift T.V. valve or reverse boost valve binding in valve body bore. Low overrun clutch valve binding in valve body bore (line pressure readings will be normal). Reverse clutch piston cracked or broken, seals missing, clutch plates burned, or wrong selective spacer ring installed. Porosity in direct clutch case passages. Pump-to-case gasket out of position. Pump channels cross-feeding, leaking, or restricted. Pump cover oil seal rings damaged or missing. Direct clutch piston or housing cracked, piston seals cut or missing, or ball check stuck, leaking or missing. Clutch plates burned. Incorrect clutch piston. Orifices in spacer plate plugged. Intermediate servo-to-case oil seal ring cut or missing.

SLIPPING 1-2 SHIFT

Low oil level. Second speed feed orifice in spacer plate or gasket partially blocked, gasket damaged, or out of position. 1-2 accumulator valve sticking in valve body causing low 1-2 accumulator pressure; weak or missing spring. 1-2 accumulator piston seal leaking, or spring broken or missing; leak between piston and pin. Wrong intermediate band apply pin, or excessive leakage between pin and case. Porosity in intermediate servo piston, oil seal damaged or missing, or incorrect usage of cover and piston. Throttle cable not adjusted properly. Throttle valve or shift T.V. valve binding. Intermediate band worn or burned. Porosity in second clutch case passages.

ROUGH 1-2 SHIFT

Throttle valve cable binding or not adjusted properly. Throttle valve or T.V. plunger binding. Shift T.V. valve or 1-2 accumulator valve binding. Intermediate servo piston-to-case oil seal ring damaged or missing, or wrong apply pin installed. 1-2 accumulator oil ring damaged, piston stuck, spring missing or broken, or bore damaged.

SLIPPING 2-3 SHIFT

Low oil level. Throttle valve cable not adjusted properly or throttle valve binding. Direct clutch orifice in spacer plate partially blocked, or gasket out of position or damaged. Intermediate servo-to-case oil seal ring damaged. Porosity in direct clutch feed channels in case. Pump-to-case gasket damaged or out of position. Pump channels cross feeding, leaking, or restricted. Pump cover oil seal rings damaged or missing. Direct clutch piston or housing cracked, piston seals cut or missing, or clutch plates burned.

ROUGH 2-3 SHIFT

Throttle valve cable not adjusted properly or binding, or throttle valve or plunger binding. Shift T.V. valve binding. Exhaust hole undrilled or plugged between intermediate servo piston seals, not allowing piston to complete stroke. Direct clutch exhaust valve ball check missing or out of position.

NO ENGINE BRAKING

In "L2" (Second Gear) — Intermediate boost valve binding in valve body. Intermediate-Reverse ball check No. 3 out of position or missing. Shift T.V. ball check No. 1 out of position or missing. Intermediate servo-to-cover oil seal ring missing or damaged. Intermediate band off anchor pin, broken, or burned.

In "L1" (Low Gear) — Low overrun clutch valve binding in valve body. **NOTE** — *A "No Reverse" condition should also exist with any of the following conditions:* Low-reverse clutch piston seals broken or missing, porosity in piston or housing, clutch housing snap ring out of case, cup plug or rubber seal missing or damaged between case and low-reverse clutch housing.

NO PART THROTTLE OR DETENT DOWNSHIFTS

Throttle plunger bushing passages not open. 2-3 throttle valve bushing passages not open. Valve body gaskets damaged or out of position. Hole plugged or undrilled in spacer plate. Throttle valve cable improperly set. Shift T.V. valve binding.

LOW OR HIGH SHIFT POINTS

Check oil pressures. Throttle valve binding or disconnected. Throttle valve, shift T.V. valve, or throttle valve plunger binding. Shift T.V. ball check No. 1 missing or out of position. 1-2 or 2-3 throttle valves binding in bushings. Valve body gaskets damaged or out of position. Pressure regulator valve binding. T.V. exhaust ball No. 5 out of position, unhooked, or missing. Throttle lever and bracket assembly binding, unhooked, or loose at valve body bolt; not positioned at throttle valve plunger bushing pin locator. Governor shaft-to-cover seal ring broken or missing. Governor cover "O" rings broken or missing (outer ring will leak externally, inner ring internally). Case porosity.

WILL NOT HOLD IN "P"

Manual linkage not adjusted properly. Parking pawl binding in case. Actuator rod or plunger damaged. Parking pawl broken. Parking bracket loose or damaged. Inside detent lever

TURBO HYDRA-MATIC 200 (Cont.)

and pin assembly nut loose, or hole in lever worn or damaged. Manual detent roller and spring assembly retaining bolt loose, pin or roller damaged, out of position, or missing.

TRANSMISSION NOISY

Pump Noise — Oil level setting low. Cavitation due to plugged screen, porosity in intake circuit, or water in fluid. Pump gears damaged.

Gear Noise — Transmission grounded to body. Roller bearings worn or damaged.

THUMPING SOUND AT 1-5 MPH IN DRIVE OR INTERMEDIATE RANGES

Governor assembly spring(s) damaged, out of position, or tilted.

TESTING

ROAD TEST

"D" Range — With selector lever in drive range, accelerate vehicle from a standstill. A 1-2 and 2-3 shift should occur at all throttle openings. **NOTE** — *Shift points will vary with throttle openings.* As vehicle speed decreases to zero MPH, 3-2 and 2-1 downshifts should occur.

"L2" or "S" Range — With selector lever in intermediate range, accelerate vehicle from a standstill. A 1-2 shift should occur at all throttle openings. The 1-2 shift point will vary with throttle opening. As vehicle speed decreases to 0 MPH, a 2-1 downshift should occur.

NOTE — *No 2-3 upshift or 3-2 downshift can be obtained in this range.*

"L1" or "L" Range — Place selector lever in low range and accelerate vehicle from a standstill. No upshift should occur in this range.

2nd Gear ("L2" or "S") Overrun Braking — With selector lever in drive range, lift foot off accelerator and move selector lever to intermediate range ("L2" or "S"). An increase in engine RPM and an engine braking effect should be noted.

1st Gear ("L1" or "L") Overrun Braking — With selector lever in intermediate range, and vehicle speed approximately 30 MPH at constant throttle, move selector lever to low range ("L1" or "L"). An increase in engine RPM and an engine braking effect should be noted.

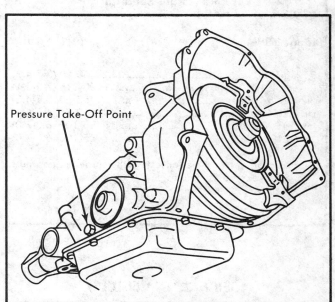

Pressure Take-Off Point

Fig. 3   View of Transmission Showing Location of Line Pressure Take-Off Point

CONTROL PRESSURE CHECK

Connect a tachometer to engine, and a suitable pressure gauge to line pressure take-off point in transmission. With transmission fluid at correct level and at operating

CLUTCH & BRAKE APPLICATION CHART
(ELEMENTS IN USE)

Selector Lever Position	Direct Clutch	Forward Clutch	Low & Reverse Clutch	Inter-mediate Band	Low Roller Clutch
D — DRIVE First Gear		X			X
Second Gear		X		X	
Third Gear	X	X			
S or L2 — INTERMEDIATE First Gear		X			X
Second Gear		X		X	
L or L1 — LOW		X	X		X
R — REVERSE	X		X		
NEUTRAL OR PARK — Band and clutches released and/or ineffective.					

TURBO HYDRA-MATIC 200 (Cont.)

temperature, pressure in each range can be checked by running engine at indicated RPM. Pressures should be within limits of table.

Control Pressure Specifications

Range@RPM	psi (kg/cm²)
Park@1000	50-60 (3.5-4.2)
Reverse@1000①	100-115 (7.0-8.1)
Neutral@1000	55-60 (3.9-4.2)
Drive@1200①	60-75 (4.2-5.3)
Int.@1000①	85-100 (6.0-7.0)
Low@1000①	85-100 (6.0-7.0)

① — Total running time for tests with vehicle in gear must not exceed 2 minutes.

SERVICE (IN VEHICLE)

NOTE — *Following units may be removed from transmission without removing transmission from vehicle: Oil Pan and Gasket, Fluid Screen, Pressure Regulator Valve, Governor Assembly, Valve Body, Intermediate Servo, Speedometer Drive Gear, Rear Oil Seal, Inside Detent Lever, and Parking Actuator Rod, Throttle Lever and Bracket Assembly, Detent Roller and Spring Assembly, Manual Shaft and Seal, and Parking Pawl. See procedures given in Transmission Disassembly and Transmission Reassembly.*

TRANSMISSION REMOVAL & INSTALLATION

Removal — 1) Disconnect negative battery cable, and detach detent cable, from bracket and carburetor. Remove air cleaner and transmission dipstick. Remove dipstick tube upper mounting bolt.

2) Raise vehicle on a hoist. Remove dust cover from lower side of converter housing. Mark propeller shaft for reassembly reference and remove. Disconnect speedometer cable, and oil cooler lines from transmission. Disconnect shift control linkage.

3) Support transmission with suitable jack and remove rear transmission support bolt and mount. Remove exhaust pipe bracket.

NOTE — *Mark converter and flywheel for reassembly in the same position.*

4) Remove torque converter bolts under pan. Lower transmission until jack barely supports it and remove transmission-to-engine attaching bolts. Raise transmission to normal position. Support engine with a jack. Slide transmission rearward from engine and lower it away from vehicle.

NOTE — *Use a suitable converter holding tool to prevent converter from sliding out of transmission during removal.*

Installation — 1) Reverse removal procedure and note the following: Before installing drive plate-to-converter bolts, make sure welded brackets on converter are flush with drive plate, and that converter rotates freely by hand in this position.

2) Hand start all 3 bolts and finger tighten before final tightening to ensure correct converter alignment. After installation, adjust shift linkage, downshift cable, and fill transmission with fluid.

TORQUE CONVERTER

NOTE — *Torque converter is a sealed unit and cannot be disassembled for service.*

LEAKAGE CHECK

1) Install suitable pressure test plug tool (J-21369) into torque converter hub. Tighten hex nut to expand tool. Install safety strap to prevent tool from blowing out when air pressure is applied.

2) Apply 80 psi (5.6 kg/cm²) air pressure to air valve in tool. Submerge converter in water and check for leaks.

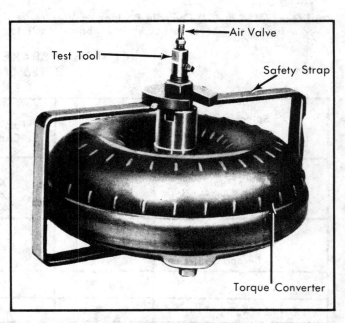

Fig. 4   Installation of Special Tool for Torque Converter Leakage Check

TURBO HYDRA-MATIC 200 (Cont.)

END CLEARANCE CHECK

1) Install suitable end clearance checking tool (J-25020) into converter hub until collet end of tool bottoms. Tighten tool cap nut to 5 ft. lbs. (.7 mkg). Install support collar (J-21371-3) and tighten hex nut to 3 ft. lbs. (.4 mkg). See *Fig. 5*.

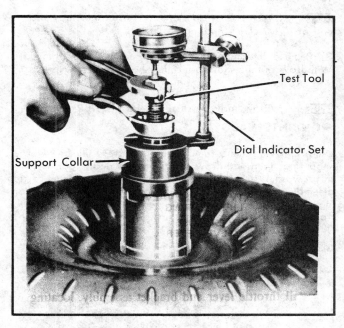

Fig. 5   Installation of Torque Converter End Clearance Checking Tools

2) Install a dial indicator and set it at zero while its plunger rests on cap nut of checking tool. Loosen hex nut while holding cap nut stationary. When hex nut is fully loosened, the indicator reading obtained will be torque converter end clearance.

3) Torque converter end clearance should be .050" (1.27 mm) or less. If clearance exceeds specifications, torque converter must be replaced.

TRANSMISSION DISASSEMBLY

GOVERNOR, OIL PAN & SCREEN

1) Using a screwdriver, remove governor cover retaining ring. Remove governor cover using pliers. Discard governor cover seal rings.

NOTE — *Governor cover seal rings may remain in transmission case.*

2) Remove governor assembly from case, rotating output shaft counterclockwise to ease removal. Remove oil pan and gasket. Remove oil screen and gasket.

NOTE — *Screen attaching bolts are approximately ⅜" (9.5 mm) longer than valve body bolts and are not interchangeable.*

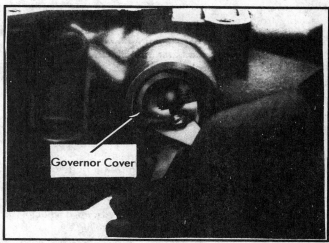

Fig. 6   Using Pliers to Remove Governor Cover

VALVE BODY & LINKAGE

1) Remove throttle lever and bracket assembly, do not bend throttle lever link.

NOTE — *T.V. exhaust valve lifter and spring may separate from throttle lever and bracket assembly.*

2) Remove manual detent roller and spring assembly. Remove remaining control valve assembly attaching bolts. Holding manual valve with finger, remove control valve assembly, spacer plate, and gasket together.

3) To prevent dropping of 4 check valves, lay control valve assembly down with spacer plate side up and discard gasket. Remove 1-2 accumulator spring. Remove 5th check ball located in case.

SPEEDOMETER DRIVEN GEAR & INTERMEDIATE SERVO

1) Remove speedometer driven gear bolt, washer and retainer. Withdraw gear from extension housing. Using a small screwdriver, remove intermediate servo cover retaining ring. Using pliers, remove servo cover from case. Discard seal rings

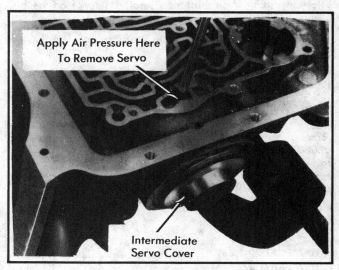

Fig. 7   Using Air Pressure to Remove Intermediate Servo Assembly

TURBO HYDRA-MATIC 200 (Cont.)

from cover, then withdraw servo piston and apply pin assembly from case.

NOTE — *If servo assembly cannot be removed easily, place shop towels and hand over cover and case before applying air pressure.*

2) Apply air pressure into direct clutch accumulator port and force servo assembly from case *(see Fig. 7 for location to apply air pressure).* Make a band apply pin selection check at this time to determine correct pin for use at reassembly.

Band Apply Pin Selection Check — 1) Install special band apply pin gauge (J-25014-2) in intermediate servo bore and retain with servo cover retaining ring. Align ring with gap at case slot. Install gauge pin (J-25014-1) into gauge.

NOTE — *Make sure tapered pin end is properly located against band apply lug. Also, make sure band anchor pin is properly located in case and band anchor lug.*

2) Install dial indicator as shown in *Fig. 8* and position indicator plunger on top of gauge post. Set dial indicator to zero. Seat gauge pin squarely against servo retaining ring.

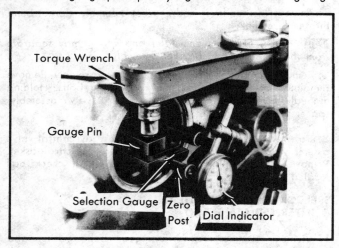

Fig. 8   Intermediate Band Apply Pin Selection

3) Align stepped side of gauge pin with torquing arm of selection gauge. Arm must stop against step of gauge pin.

NOTE — *If band selection pin does not register between high and low limits, look for possible problem with intermediate band, direct clutch or case.*

4) Apply 100 INCH lbs. (1.2 mkg) torque to hex nut on selection gauge. Slide indicator over gauge pin. Read indicator and select correct band apply pin from following chart.

NOTE — *Dial indicator travel is reversed, making the indicator readings backwards. On an indicator that ranges from 0-100, a .020" (5 mm) travel will read .080" (2 mm), a .060" (1.5 mm) travel will read .040" (1 mm).*

Intermediate Band Apply Pin Selection Chart	
Indicator Reading In. (mm)	**Apply Pin** Identification
.0-.029 (.0-.72)	1 Ring
.029-.057 (.72-1.44)	2 Rings
.057-.086 (1.44-2.16)	3 Rings
.086-.114 (2.16-2.88)	Wide Band

OIL PUMP & FRONT UNIT COMPONENTS

1) Turn transmission so oil pump faces upward. Remove oil pump-to-case bolts and washers, then withdraw oil pump and gasket. Grasp turbine shaft and remove direct and forward clutch assemblies from case. Lift direct clutch assembly off forward clutch assembly.

NOTE — *Direct-to-forward clutch thrust washer may stick to end of direct clutch housing.*

2) Remove intermediate band and anchor pin from case. Withdraw output shaft-to-turbine shaft front selective thrust washer.

NOTE — *Washer may be stuck to end of turbine shaft.*

FRONT INTERNAL GEAR

Using snap ring pliers, remove output shaft-to-selective washer snap ring, then withdraw front internal gear, rear selective thrust washer, and tanged thrust washer. Remove front carrier assembly and front internal gear-to-front carrier roller bearing assembly. Remove front sun gear, and front sun gear-to-front carrier roller thrust bearing and thrust race.

NOTE — *Bearing may have come out with front carrier.*

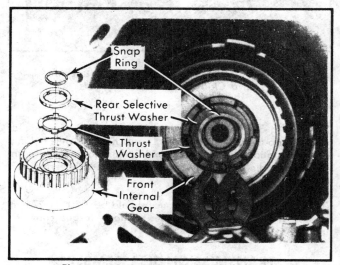

Fig. 9   Removing Front Internal Gear

INPUT DRUM, REAR SUN GEAR & LOW-REVERSE CLUTCH HOUSING

Remove input drum and rear sun gear from case, then withdraw input drum-to-low and reverse clutch housing thrust washer from rear of input drum or from clutch housing. Using a No. 14 sheet metal screw, remove housing-to-case cup plug and seal by turning screw in 2 or 3 turns and pulling straight out; discard cup plug and seal. Remove low and reverse clutch housing-to-case beveled snap ring. Using a suitable remover tool (J-25012), withdraw low and reverse clutch housing from case. Remove low and reverse clutch housing-to-case spacer ring. See *Fig. 10*.

NOTE — *Flat side of snap ring is positioned against clutch housing with beveled side up.*

TURBO HYDRA-MATIC 200 (Cont.)

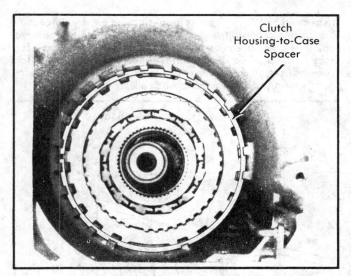

Fig. 10   Removing Low and Reverse Clutch Spacer

REAR GEAR COMPONENTS

Grasp output shaft, lift out remaining rear unit parts, and place on bench in a horizontal position. Remove low and reverse clutch selective spacer, roller clutch, and rear carrier from output shaft. Remove rear carrier-to-rear internal gear thrust washer from end of rear carrier or from inside internal gear. Remove low and reverse clutch plates off output shaft, then withdraw rear internal gear-to-rear sun gear roller thrust bearing off rear internal gear. Finally, remove rear internal gear from output shaft.

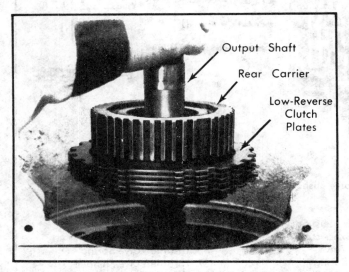

Fig. 11   Removing Rear Internal Gear Components

MANUAL SHAFT & PARKING LINKAGE

Remove nut retaining inside detent lever to manual shaft, then remove parking brake actuator rod and inside detent lever assembly. Remove manual shaft retaining pin from case and slide out manual shaft. If necessary, pry out manual shaft seal with a screwdriver. Remove parking brake bracket, then

remove parking pawl shaft retaining pin. Using a No. 4 Easy-out, withdraw parking pawl cup plug and discard. Then, with a sheet metal screw or No. 3 Easy-out, remove parking pawl shaft. To complete disassembly, withdraw parking pawl and return spring.

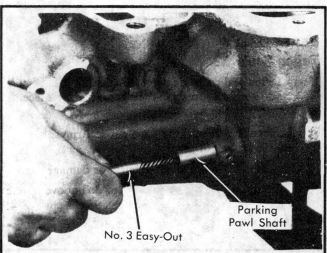

Fig. 12   Removing Parking Pawl Shaft

COMPONENT DISASSEMBLY & REASSEMBLY

VALVE BODY

NOTE — *As valve trains are removed from each valve body bore, place individual parts in correct order in relative position to valve body to simplify reassembly. Valves and springs are not interchangeable, and all parts must be installed in correct order in proper valve body bore. See Fig. 15. Remove all coiled pins except the 2 pins which retain throttle valve train by pushing through from rough case surface side of body.*

Disassembly — 1) Position valve body with cored face upward and 1-2 accumulator pocket at lower left (see illustration). Remove four check balls from cored passages of valve body (fifth ball is in case), then remove 1-2 accumulator piston. From upper bore, remove manual valve.

2) From upper right side bore, remove the 2-3 valve train. From next bore down, remove the 1-2 valve train. From next bore down, remove the reverse boost valve train.

3) If necessary to remove shift T.V. valve train, remove coiled pin and place valve body with rough casting surface up. Use needle nose pliers and push in on valve then hold in place with a small screwdriver. Position a 1/4″ (6.3 mm) diameter rod, 3/8″ (9.5 mm) long against end of valve, pry on rod with a screwdriver, remove small screwdriver, and remove plug, spring and valve.

4) From lower right side bore, remove outer coiled pin and withdraw bushing, plunger, spring, and detent pin. Using a 1/16″ (1.5 mm) Allen wrench with ground sides to fit inside pin, remove inner coiled pin and throttle valve.

TURBO HYDRA-MATIC 200 (Cont.)

5) From upper left side bore, remove intermediate boost valve train. From next bore down, remove low overrun clutch valve train. From next bore down, remove direct clutch exhaust valve train. From lower left side bore, remove 1-2 accumulator valve train.

Inspection — Wash all parts in solvent and air dry. Inspect 1-2 accumulator piston and seal for damage; do not remove seal unless replacement is required. Check valve body for cracks, damage, or scored bores, and valves and plugs for scores, cracks, and free movement in valve body bores. Inspect springs for distortion and collapsed coils.

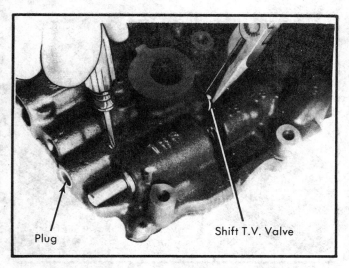

Fig. 13 Removing Shift T.V. Valve Train

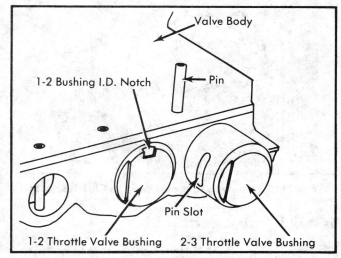

Fig. 14 Installing Throttle Valve Bushings

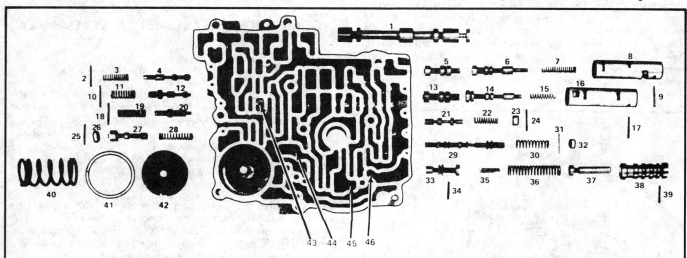

Fig. 15 Exploded View of Valve Body Assembly

1. Manual Valve
2. Coiled Pin
3. Intermediate Boost Spring
4. Intermediate Boost Valve
5. 2-3 Shift Valve
6. 2-3 Throttle Valve
7. 2-3 Throttle Valve Spring
8. 2-3 Throttle Valve Bushing
9. Coiled Pin
10. Coiled Pin
11. Low Overrun Clutch Spring
12. Low Overrun Clutch Valve
13. 1-2 Shift Valve
14. 1-2 Throttle Valve
15. 1-2 Throttle Valve Spring

16. 1-2 Throttle Valve Bushing
17. Coiled Pin
18. Coiled Pin
19. Direct Clutch Exhaust Spring
20. Direct Clutch Exhaust Valve
21. Reverse Boost Valve
22. Reverse Boost Spring
23. Reverse Boost Bore Plug
24. Coiled Pin
25. Coiled Pin
26. 1-2 Accumulator Bore Plug
27. 1-2 Accumulator Valve
28. 1-2 Accumulator Valve Spring
29. Shift T.V. Valve
30. Shift T.V. Spring

31. Coiled Pin
32. Shift T.V. Bore Plug
33. Throttle Valve
34. Coiled Pin
35. Detent Pin
36. Throttle Valve Spring
37. Throttle Valve Plunger
38. Throttle Valve Plunger Bushing
39. Coiled Pin
40. 1-2 Accumulator Spring
41. 1-2 Accumulator Piston Seal
42. 1-2 Accumulator Piston
43. Check Ball #4
44. Check Ball #3
45. Check Ball #2
46. Check Ball #1

TURBO HYDRA-MATIC 200 (Cont.)

Reassembly — Reverse disassembly procedure and note the following: Install all coiled pins from machined face side except pin retaining throttle valve bushing, plunger, spring, and detent pin; install this coiled pin from rough casting side. **NOTE** — *Coiled pins do not fit flush on rough casting side.* When installing 1-2 throttle bushing and 2-3 throttle bushing, align in bores of valve body so that retaining pin can be installed in pin slot *(see Fig. 14).*

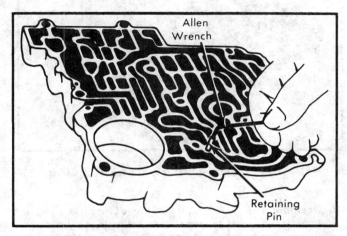

Fig. 16   Removing Throttle Valve Inner Roll Pin

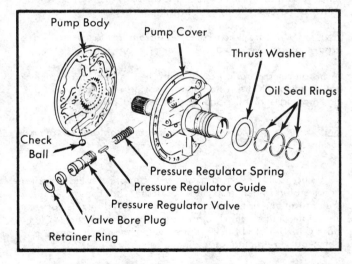

Fig. 17   Exploded View of Oil Pump Assembly

OIL PUMP

Disassembly — Remove pump-to-case seal, then position pump on bench with cover side upward. Remove pump-to-direct clutch thrust washer, and three teflon oil seal rings if replacement is required. Using a small screwdriver, push in on pressure regulator bore plug, remove retaining ring, and withdraw bore plug, pressure regulator valve, guide and spring. Remove pump body-to-cover bolts. Separate cover from body. Remove pump gears, marking for reassembly reference in same position.

Inspection — Check drive and driven gears for scoring, galling, or other damage. Inspect gear pocket and crescent in body for scoring or damage. Check pump cover and body for

nicks, open oil passages, and overall flatness. Using a feeler gauge, measure pump body face-to-gear face clearance; clearance should be .0007-.0021" (.020-.055 mm). Inspect pressure regulator valve bore in pump cover and pressure regulator valve assembly for wear or damage, and make sure parts operate freely in bore. Inspect the seven cup plugs in pump cover for damage or leaks; if damaged, replace as follows:

Pump Cover Cup Plug Replacement — **1)** Using a $\frac{9}{32}$" (7.14 mm) drill for small plugs or a $\frac{5}{16}$" (7.92 mm) drill for larger plugs, carefully remove staking marks around cup plugs.

CAUTION — *Do not damage pump cover.*

2) Use a No. 4 screw extractor for small plugs or a No. 5 extractor for larger plugs and withdraw plugs from cover. Install plugs into cover $\frac{1}{32}$" (.79 mm) below machined surface, then stake in 2 places using a $\frac{9}{32}$" (7.14 mm) rod on small plugs or a $\frac{5}{16}$" rod on larger plugs.

Reassembly — **1)** Install driven gear into pump body with production identification mark facing downward against gear pocket. Install drive gear into body with production identification marks on converter drive tangs facing upward. **NOTE** — *Make sure gears are installed in same position as removed.* Assemble pump cover to pump body. Align parts with a suitable aligning strap (J-25015), then tighten attaching bolts evenly.

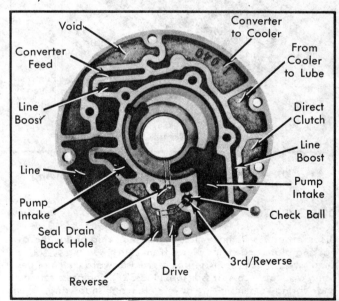

Fig. 18   View of Oil Pump Body Showing Oil Passages and Check Ball Location

2) Install pressure regulator spring, spring guide, regulator valve (stem end out), and bore plug into pump cover bore. Compress assembly in bore by pushing in on bore plug with a screwdriver, then install retaining ring. If removed, install three new oil seal rings making sure ends are correctly mated; retain with petrolatum. Install pump-to-case seal ring with chamfered side out, taking care not to twist ring in groove. Install pump-to-direct clutch thrust washer and retain with petrolatum.

TURBO HYDRA-MATIC 200 (Cont.)

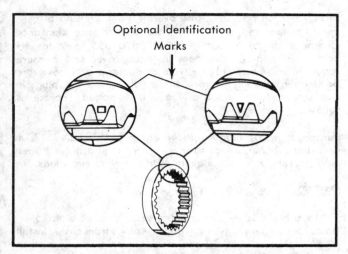

Fig. 19   View of Oil Pump Driven Gear Showing Identification Marks

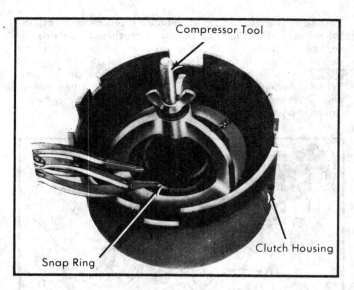

Fig. 21   Removing Direct Clutch Snap Ring

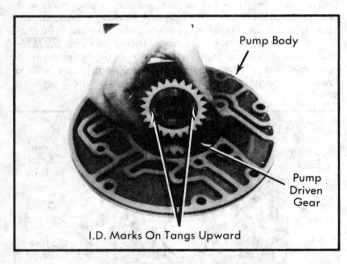

Fig. 20   View of Oil Pump Drive Gear Showing Identification Marks

DIRECT CLUTCH

Disassembly — Remove clutch pack snap ring and withdraw backing plate and clutch plates from clutch housing. **NOTE** — Keep direct clutch plates separate from forward clutch plates. Using a suitable compressor tool (J-23327), compress retainer and spring assembly, remove retaining snap ring, then withdraw retainer and spring assembly. Withdraw release spring guide, clutch piston, and apply ring from housing. Remove inner and outer seals from piston, and center seal from clutch housing.

Inspection — Inspect composition plates, steel plates, and backing plate for wear, burning, or scoring. Check release springs and retainer for damage or a collapsed condition. Inspect clutch piston assembly for distortion, cracks, and other damage. Check direct clutch housing for cracks, wear, and open passages, and make sure ball check operates freely. Inspect snap ring grooves and bushings in housing for wear or damage.

Reassembly — **1)** Install apply ring on clutch piston, then install new inner and outer seals on piston, with seal lips facing away from clutch apply ring side. Install a new center seal into direct clutch housing, with seal lip facing upward. Install a suitable seal protector (J-25010) over oil seals, lubricate seals with transmission fluid, and install clutch piston.

NOTE — Use care when installing piston past larger snap ring groove as groove could cut outer seal on piston.

2) Install release spring guide with the omitted rib over check ball in piston. Install retainer and spring assembly into housing, making sure all parts are positioned properly.

NOTE — Retainer and spring assembly contain 16 release springs.

3) Using tool used at disassembly, compress release springs and install retainer snap ring. Lubricate with transmission fluid then install one flat steel clutch plate followed by one composition plate until all clutch plates are installed (see Direct Clutch Plate Chart). Install backing plate with chamfered side up and clutch pack retaining snap ring.

NOTE — Make sure composition plates turn freely with clutch assembled.

Direct Clutch Plate Chart		
Application	**Flat Steel**①	**Composition**
LUV 5		 5
① — Plate thickness is .091" (2.3 mm).		

FORWARD CLUTCH

Disassembly — Remove forward clutch-to-direct clutch thrust washer, then inspect teflon oil seals on turbine shaft for

TURBO HYDRA-MATIC 200 (Cont.)

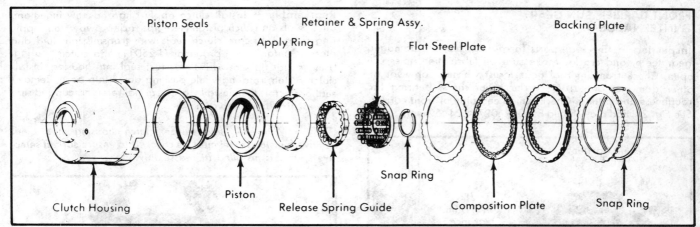

Fig. 22 *Exploded View Showing Components of Direct Clutch Assembly*

damage and remove if replacement is required. Remove clutch pack snap ring and withdraw backing plate and clutch plates from housing. **NOTE** — *Keep forward clutch plates separate from direct clutch plates.* Using an arbor press, compress retainer and spring assembly, remove retaining snap ring, then withdraw retainer and springs from housing. Remove clutch piston from housing, then remove inner and outer seals from piston. **NOTE** — *Do not remove clutch apply ring from piston unless piston or apply ring requires replacement.*

Inspection — Inspect composition plates, steel plates, and backing plate for wear, scores, or other damage. Check spring retainer and release springs for distortion or collapse. Inspect piston and housing for cracks, distortion, open oil passages, or other damage. Inspect snap ring grooves for wear or damage, and make sure ball check in housing operates freely. Check turbine shaft for open passages on both ends of shaft, and check journals for damage. Inspect clutch housing cup plug and if damaged, remove using a No. 4 easy-out (grind to fit). Install new cup plug to .039" (1 mm) below surface.

Reassembly — **1)** Install clutch apply ring on piston, then install new inner and outer seals on piston, with seal lips facing away from apply ring side. Lubricate seals with transmis-

sion fluid, then install piston into housing. **CAUTION** — *Use care when installing piston past large snap ring groove as groove could cut outer piston seal.* Install retainer and return spring assembly into housing, compress retainer and springs, and install retaining snap ring.

2) Lubricate with transmission fluid then install one waved steel plate (plate with three missing teeth) into housing, and alternate one composition plate followed by one steel plate until all plates are installed (see Clutch Plate Chart). Install backing plate (chamfered side up) and clutch pack snap ring. **NOTE** — *Make sure composition plates turn freely with clutch assembled.* If removed, install new turbine shaft seal rings and forward clutch-to-direct clutch thrust washer.

Forward Clutch Plate Chart		
Application	**Flat Steel①②**	**Composition**
LUV	3	4

① — Plus one waved steel plate installed into housing first.
② — Plate thickness is .077" (1.97 mm).

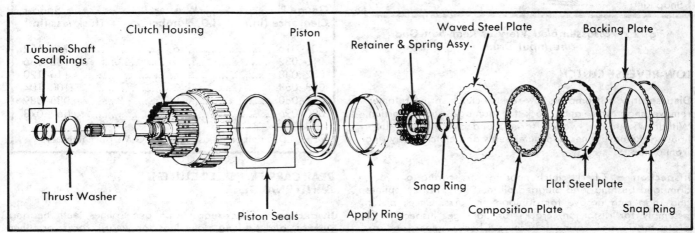

Fig. 23 *Exploded View Showing Components of Forward Clutch Assembly*

TURBO HYDRA-MATIC 200 (Cont.)

FRONT CARRIER, SUN GEAR & INTERNAL GEAR

Inspection — Check all parts for pitting, scoring, damaged gear teeth, and cracks. Make sure all lubrication holes are open. Check front internal gear thrust washers for wear or other damage, and front carrier roller thrust bearing for roughness and pitting. Check pinion end play of front carrier. *See Fig. 24.* End play should be .009-.027" (.24-.69 mm).

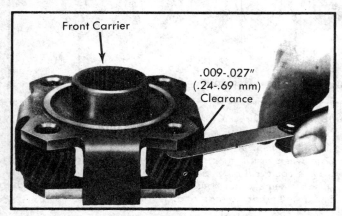

Fig. 24   Using a Feeler Gauge to Measure Front Carrier Pinion End Play

REAR SUN GEAR & INPUT DRUM

Inspection — Check rear sun gear for cracks, splits, spline damage, gear or journal wear, and for plugged lubrication holes. If necessary, remove snap ring and separate sun gear from input drum and inspect drum splines for damage. Check input drum-to-low-reverse clutch housing thrust washer for scoring or distorted tangs.

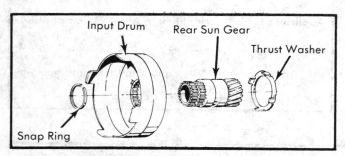

Fig. 25   Disassembled View of Rear Sun Gear and Input Drum

LOW-REVERSE CLUTCH

Disassembly — Compress low-reverse clutch spring retainer, remove snap ring, and check for damage and distortion. Withdraw retainer, waved spring, and clutch piston from housing. Remove inner and outer seals and clutch apply ring from piston.

Inspection — Check clutch housing for scoring or wear, damaged bushing, and plugged oil feed hole. Inspect splines and snap ring groove for damage or burrs. Check piston assembly for distortion, cracks, or damage. Inspect clutch plates for signs of scoring or burning. Check retainers and spring for damage or distortion.

Reassembly — Install clutch apply ring and new inner and outer seals on clutch piston (seal lips facing away from apply ring side). Lubricate clutch seals with transmission fluid and place a suitable seal protector (J-25011) into clutch housing. Using a flat tip screwdriver to start seal into housing, install clutch piston, rotating while pushing down into bore. Remove seal protector, then install waved spring, retainer (cupped side downward), and snap ring.

NOTE — *Whenever low-reverse clutch housing has been removed, piston travel must be checked to ensure correct selective spacer is installed at reassembly.*

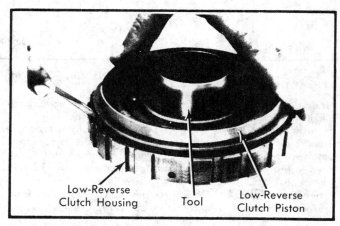

Fig. 26   Installing Low-Reverse Clutch Piston

NOTE — *Use of a suitable spacer gauge (J-25023) is required for this adjustment.*

Low-Reverse Clutch Piston Travel Adjustment — Center clutch housing and piston assembly on gauge plate, position clutch pack to be used at reassembly on top of apply ring, then place gauge pin fixture over clutch plates with pin facing housing. Install tool spring, washer and nut onto assembly and tighten nut until washer bottoms. Using a feeler gauge, measure distance between end of gauge pin and top of housing. With clearance determined, refer to Low-Reverse Clutch Spacer Chart for proper thickness spacer to use at reassembly of transmission.

Low-Reverse Clutch Spacer Chart		
Gauge Pin Clearance (In.)	**Washer I.D. Number**①	**Spacer Thickness (In.)**
.001-.016	6	.148-.152
.016-.032	5	.132-.136
.032-.048	4	.116-.120
.048-.064	3	.100-.104
.064-.080	2	.085-.089
.080-.096	1	.069-.073

① — I.D. number is last digit of G.M. part number.

REAR CARRIER, ROLLER CLUTCH & INTERNAL GEAR

Inspection — Check rear internal gear splines, teeth, bearing surface, and parking pawl lugs for wear, cracks, or other damage. Inspect roller clutch race and spline for scoring or

TURBO HYDRA-MATIC 200 (Cont.)

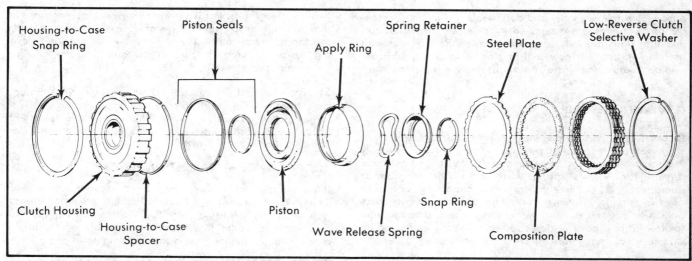

Fig. 27   Exploded View Showing Components of Low-Reverse Clutch Assembly

wear, and roller bearings, cage and springs for wear, scoring, distortion, or collapse. Inspect thrust washers for excessive wear or damaged tangs. Check rear carrier roller clutch cam ramps and bushing for scoring or other damage. Inspect planet pinions for damage, rough bearings, tilt, and correct end play. End play should be .009-.027" (.24-.69 mm).

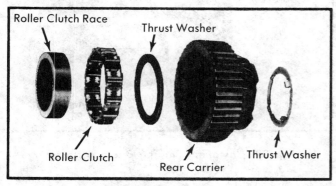

Fig. 28   Disassembled View of Rear Carrier and Roller Clutch

OUTPUT SHAFT

Inspection — Inspect journals and snap ring grooves for wear or damage. Check lubrication holes for being plugged or damaged. Inspect shaft splines and governor drive gear for rough or damaged surfaces. Check speedometer drive gear and retaining clip for wear or damage.

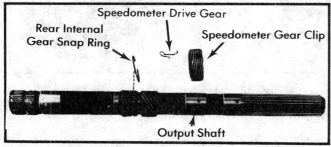

Fig. 29   Output Shaft and Speedometer Drive Gear Assembly

Speedometer Drive Gear Replacement — 1) Depress speedometer drive gear retaining clip. Remove gear and clip, tapping gear lightly with a plastic hammer.

2) To install, place speedometer drive clip with tanged end in hole in output shaft. Align slot of gear with clip and install gear.

INTERMEDIATE SERVO

Disassembly — Using a suitable "C" clamp-type compressor tool (J-22269-01), compress servo piston spring, remove servo pin-to-piston retaining ring, remove tool and separate parts.

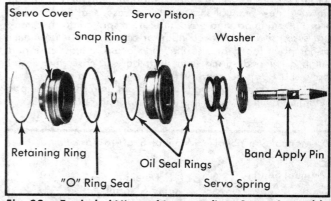

Fig. 30   Exploded View of Intermediate Servo Assembly

Inspection — 1) Check intermediate servo pin for wear or damage, and for proper fit in case bore. Inspect inner and outer seal rings for damage, and for proper fit in seal ring grooves of piston.

CAUTION — Do not remove seal rings from piston unless replacement is required.

2) Check servo piston and cover for cracks or other damage. Inspect servo spring for collapsed coils or distortion.

Reassembly — Install washer on snap ring end of servo pin, position spring on top of washer, then install assembly into servo piston, spring end first. Using compressor tool, compress servo spring and install servo pin-to-piston retaining ring. If

TURBO HYDRA-MATIC 200 (Cont.)

removed, install new inner and outer seal rings on piston, making sure cut ends are assembled in same relationship as cut, and that rings are fully seated in grooves. Retain rings with petrolatum. Install a new seal ring on servo cover, lubricate with petrolatum, then install piston assembly into piston cover.

GOVERNOR ASSEMBLY

Inspection — Inspect governor cover for damage, scored or worn bore, or plugged oil passage. Wash governor assembly in cleaning solvent and blow out oil passage. Inspect governor driven gear, weights, spring, shaft, and washer for wear or damage. **NOTE** — *Some governors use one spring, and some use two springs.* Inspect governor for presence of two check balls. Check governor shaft seal rings for cuts, damage, and for free fit in groove. If damaged, cut ring off shaft, and install new seal rings. Lubricate seals with petrolatum.

TRANSMISSION CASE

Inspection — Check case assembly for cracks, porosity, and interconnected oil passages. Inspect reverse clutch lugs, governor bore, intermediate servo bore, speedometer bore, and snap ring grooves for wear or other damage. Make sure all vents and passages are open and clear. Inspect vent assembly in case for damage; do not remove unless replacement is required. Check cooler line connectors for damage; do not remove unless replacement is required.

TRANSMISSION REASSEMBLY

MANUAL SHAFT & PARKING LINKAGE

1) Place transmission in a horizontal position, oil pan side up. Install a new manual shaft seal into case, seal lip facing inward. Position parking pawl and return spring into case, making sure pawl tooth faces inside of case, spring is positioned under pawl tooth, and spring ends locate against case pad. Align pawl and spring with shaft bore in case, then install pawl shaft (tapered end first). Using a ⅜" diameter rod, install a new shaft cup plug (open end out) into shaft bore, past retaining pin hole. Install parking pawl shaft retaining pin.

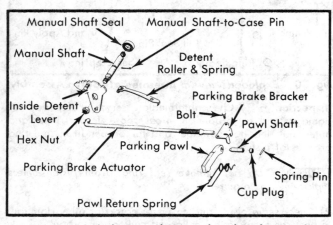

Fig. 31   Exploded View of Manual and Parking Linkage

2) Install parking brake bracket into case with parking pawl positioned between guides of bracket, then install and tighten

two attaching bolts. Install parking brake actuator rod into inside detent lever (on pin side), locating lever between actuator rod tangs. Install rod and lever assembly into case, with lever pin toward center of transmission and actuator plunger between parking pawl and parking brake bracket.

3) Install manual shaft (small I.D. ring groove first) through case. Install manual shaft-to-case retaining pin, indexing with larger groove on manual shaft. Align inside detent lever with flats on manual shaft, position lever on shaft, then install and tighten nut on manual shaft.

OUTPUT SHAFT & REAR INTERNAL GEAR

If removed, install a new rear internal gear-to-output shaft snap ring into groove on output shaft, then install rear internal gear (hub end first) onto shaft. Position rear internal gear-to-rear sun gear roller thrust bearing assembly over shaft by placing small diameter race against rear internal gear.

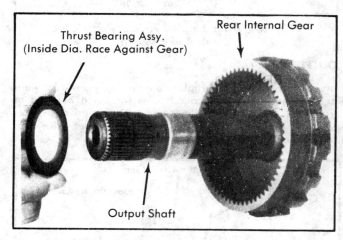

Fig. 32   Installing Parking Brake Actuator

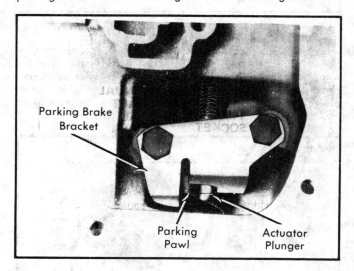

Fig. 33   Installing Rear Internal Gear

ROLLER CLUTCH & REAR CARRIER

1) Install roller clutch-to-rear carrier thrust washer into rear carrier, then install roller and spring assembly. **NOTE** — *Install rollers that may have come out of cage by compressing*

TURBO HYDRA-MATIC 200 (Cont.)

energizing spring with forefinger, and inserting roller from outer edge. Install roller clutch race (spline end out), and rotate counterclockwise into position. Install rear carrier-to-rear internal gear thrust washer (four tangs) onto carrier and retain with petrolatum. Position roller clutch and rear carrier assembly over output shaft and install into rear internal gear.

2) Install a suitable output shaft support tool (J-25013) on rear of transmission as follows: Place sleeve (J-25013-1) into rear of case, open end first. Then bolt bracket and screw assembly (J-25013-5) into rear mount bolt holes on extension housing. Turn case to a vertical position, pump end upward. Install rear unit parts (output shaft, rear internal gear, and rear carrier previously assembled) into transmission case and into support sleeve (J-25013-1).

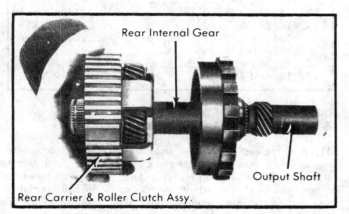

Fig. 34 Installing Roller Clutch and Rear Carrier

3) Using adjusting screw on tool bracket (J-25013-5) and looking through parking pawl case slot, adjust height of the rear internal gear parking pawl lugs to align flush with the parking pawl tooth.

CAUTION — Make sure speedometer drive gear is visible through speedometer gear bore of case. If drive gear is not visible, it may be located on wrong journal of shaft.

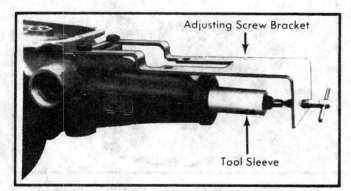

Fig. 35 Installing Output Shaft Support Tools

LOW-REVERSE CLUTCH

1) Install proper low-reverse clutch selective spacer (determined in Component Disassembly & Reassembly) into case. Lubricate with transmission fluid then install low-reverse clutch plates, starting with a flat steel plate, and alternating composition and flat steel plates until all plates are installed (see Low-Reverse Clutch Plate Chart).

Low-Reverse Clutch Plate Chart		
Application	Flat Steel	Composition
LUV	6	4

2) Install low-reverse clutch housing-to-case spacer ring into case, then install low-reverse clutch housing assembly, aligning housing oil feed hole with case oil feed passage. If housing does not seat past snap ring groove, proceed as follows: Install input drum and rear sun gear assembly into case and rotate back and forth to align roller clutch race and low-reverse clutch hub splines, then remove input drum and sun gear.

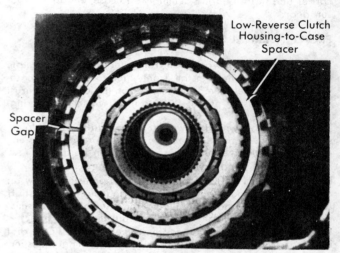

Fig. 36 Installing Housing-to-Case Spacer

3) Repeat above procedure if low-reverse clutch housing still is not fully seated past case snap ring groove.

NOTE — It may be necessary to loosen adjusting screw on output shaft support tool to install snap ring.

4) With parts properly seated, install low-reverse clutch housing-to-case snap ring, with flat side of ring against housing (beveled side upward). Locate snap ring gap opposite parking brake rod.

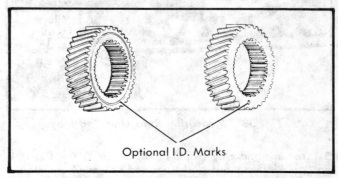

Fig. 37 Front Sun Gear Identification Marks

TURBO HYDRA-MATIC 200 (Cont.)

REAR SUN GEAR, INPUT DRUM & FRONT SUN GEAR

Position thrust washer (four tangs) on input drum over sun gear end, align washer tangs with slots in drum, and retain with petrolatum. Install rear sun gear and input drum assembly into case. Install front sun gear, with drill spot or groove on face against input drum. Install front sun gear-to-front carrier thrust bearing and race on front sun gear, with bearing roller side against gear.

FRONT CARRIER

Position front carrier-to-front internal gear thrust bearing assembly on front carrier, with smaller diameter race against carrier and retain in place with petrolatum. Install front carrier and thrust bearing assembly into case, engaging front sun gear.

FRONT INTERNAL GEAR

Install tanged thrust washer on front internal gear and retain with petrolatum, then install front internal gear into case. Install rear unit selective thrust washer on top of tanged thrust washer, then install output shaft-to-thrust washer snap ring.

NOTE — *It may be necessary to lift output shaft upward to install snap ring. At this time, measure rear unit end play to ensure correct selective thrust washer has been installed.*

Rear Unit End Play Check — **1)** Loosen adjusting screw on output shaft support tool (J-25013-5) and push output shaft fully downward. Install a dial indicator assembly on transmission so button of indicator rests on output shaft. **CAUTION** — *Do not clamp indicator to any machined surface.* Zero dial indicator. Move output shaft upward by turning adjusting screw on output shaft support tool, until white or scribbed line on tool sleeve begins to disappear. At this time, read resulting end play on gauge.

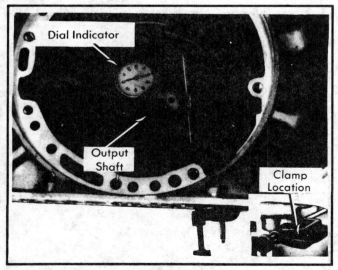

Fig. 38   Measuring Rear Unit End Play

2) Rear unit end play should be .004-.025" (.10-.64 mm); if not, the selective thrust washer located between front internal gear thrust washer and output shaft snap ring must be

changed. *See Rear Unit Thrust Washer Chart for thicknesses.* Install correct thrust washer (with I.D. number toward front of case), then reinstall output shaft snap ring, making sure it is fully seated in groove.

Rear Unit Thrust Washer Chart	
Washer Thickness In. (mm)	Identification Number Or Color
.114-.119 (2.9-3.0)	1 Orange
.121-.126 (3.1-3.2)	2 White
.128-.133 (3.3-3.4)	3 Yellow
.135-.140 (3.5-3.6)	4 Blue
.143-.147 (3.6-3.7)	5 Red
.150-.154 (3.8-3.9)	6 Brown
.157-.161 (4.0-4.1)	7 Green
.164-.168 (4.2-4.3)	8 Black
.171-.175 (4.4-4.5)	9 Purple

DIRECT CLUTCH, FORWARD CLUTCH & INTERMEDIATE BAND

1) Position direct clutch over hole in bench with clutch plate end upward. Make sure forward clutch-to-direct clutch thrust washer is still in place on forward clutch, then install forward clutch (turbine shaft first) into direct clutch. Hold direct clutch housing and rotate forward clutch until forward clutch is seated.

NOTE — *When properly seated, end of forward clutch drum will be about ⅝" (15.8 mm) from tang end of direct clutch housing.*

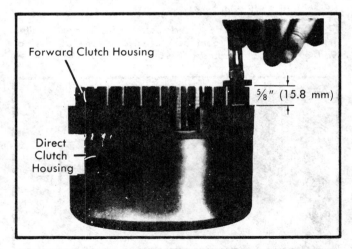

Fig. 39   Measuring Forward Clutch Engagement

2) Position intermediate band into case, locating band apply lug and anchor pin lug in case slots. Install front unit selective thrust washer into end of output shaft (retain with petrolatum), then install direct and forward clutch assemblies into transmission case as a unit, rotating into position.

NOTE — *When properly seated, direct clutch housing will be approximately 1⁵⁄₁₆" (33.3 mm) from pump face in case.*

TURBO HYDRA-MATIC 200 (Cont.)

Fig. 40   Checking Clutch Assembly Installation

OIL PUMP

1) Install new pump-to-case gasket on rear of pump assembly and retain with petrolatum. Install 2 guide pins into pump attaching bolt holes in case, 180° opposite each other. Install pump assembly into case, then install attaching bolts finger tight. Then, gradually tighten bolts, rotating turbine shaft in the process.

NOTE — *Before installing oil pump, make sure intermediate band anchor pin lug is aligned with band anchor pin hole in case.*

2) NOTE — *If turbine shaft cannot be rotated as pump is being pulled into place, the forward or direct clutch housings have not been installed properly to index with all the clutch plates. This condition must be corrected before pump is pulled fully into place. Remove alignment pins, and install remaining bolts and tighten.* **NOTE** — *Make sure turbine shaft still rotates freely.* At this time, make a front unit end play check to ensure correct front unit selective thrust washer has been installed.

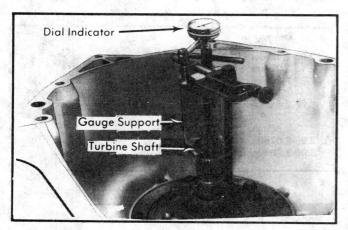

Fig. 41   Measuring Front Unit End Play

Front Unit End Play Check — **1)** With transmission in a vertical position (pump side upward), remove one pump-to-case attaching bolt and install a bolt approximately 11" long

to support a dial indicator assembly. Push turbine shaft fully downward.

NOTE — *Output shaft support tool should still be attached to rear of transmission; if not, reinstall using procedure given in Roller Clutch & Rear Carrier section of Component Disassembly & Reassembly.*

Front Unit Thrust Washer Chart	
Washer Thickness In. (mm)	**Identification Number And/Or Color**
.065-.070 (1.66-1.77)	1
.070-.075 (1.79-1.90)	2
.076-.080 (1.92-2.03)	3 Black
.081-.085 (2.05-2.16)	4 Lt. Green
.086-.090 (2.18-2.29)	5 Scarlet
.091-.095 (2.31-2.42)	6 Purple
.096-.100 (2.44-2.55)	7 Cocoa Brown
.101-.106 (2.57-2.68)	8 Orange
.106-.111 (2.70-2.81)	9 Yellow
.111-.116 (2.83-2.94)	10 Lt. Blue
.117-.121 (2.96-3.07)	11
.122-.126 (3.09-3.20)	12
.127-.131 (3.22-3.33)	13 Pink
.132-.136 (3.35-3.46)	14 Green
.137-.141 (3.48-3.59)	15 Gray

2) Mount a dial indicator assembly on bolt installed in oil pump, so button of indicator contacts turbine shaft. Move output shaft upward by turning adjusting screw in output shaft support tool until white or scribed line on tool sleeve begins to disappear. Zero dial indicator. Pull turbine shaft upward and read resulting end play on gauge; end play should be .022-.051" (.56-1.3 mm)

3) Selective thrust washer controlling front unit end play is located between output shaft and turbine shaft. If more or less washer thickness is required to bring end play within specifications, remove oil pump and forward and direct clutch assemblies, and install correct thickness washer on end of output shaft. *See Front Unit Thrust Washer Chart for washer thickness and identification.*

GOVERNOR

1) Lubricate with petrolatum and install 2 new seal rings on governor cover, then install governor assembly (seal ring end first) into cover. Install governor-to-case washer against governor driven gear and retain with petrolatum. Install governor and cover assembly into case, rotating governor and output shaft slightly.

NOTE — *Governor cover fits tight in bore the last 1/16" (1.5 mm) of travel.*

2) Install governor retaining ring, aligning ring gap with an end showing in case slot.

NOTE — *If retaining ring cannot be installed, governor shaft is not aligned with case hole.*

BAND ANCHOR PIN & INTERMEDIATE SERVO

Inspect anchor pin for damage, then install pin (stem end first) into its bore in case valve body attaching face (see illustration). **NOTE** — *Make sure anchor pin stem locates in*

TURBO HYDRA-MATIC 200 (Cont.)

hole of intermediate band lug. Lubricate seals of intermediate servo assembly with petrolatum and install assembly into case, tapping with a rubber hammer if necessary. Install servo retaining ring, locating ring gap with an end showing in case slot.

Fig. 42 Installing Intermediate Band Anchor Pin

VALVE BODY

1) Before installing valve body assembly, install low-reverse clutch housing-to-case seal and cup plug as follows: Position seal in case passage, then install cup plug (smaller hole end first). *See illustration.* Using a ⅜" (9.5 mm) diameter rod, drive plug into passage until flush with top of plug hole in case.

Fig. 43 Installing Cup Plug and Seal

2) Install 5th check ball onto case. T.V. exhaust passage. See Fig. 44. Install accumulator spring into case accumulator bore. Install 2 guide pins into case to align valve body parts, then install 4 check balls into ball seat pockets in control valve assembly and retain with patrolatum. See Fig. 15 in Component Disassembly and Reassembly for ball locations.

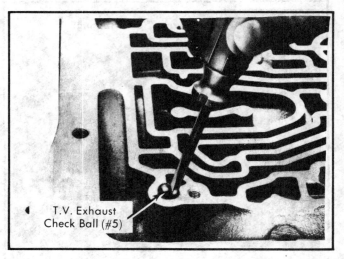

Fig. 44 Installing Fifth Check Ball in Case

3) Place control valve assembly to spacer plate marked "VB" on control valve assembly. Place valve body spacer plate on gasket marked "VB". Place spacer plate to case gasket marked "C" on spacer plate. Insert 2 control valve assembly-to-case attaching bolts through control valve assembly, gaskets and spacer plate and install these parts, aligning manual valve with detent lever pin.

CAUTION — *Make sure check balls, 1-2 accumulator piston and manual valve do not fall out.*

4) Start control valve assembly-to-case attaching bolts, except throttle lever, bracket assembly and oil screen attaching bolts.

NOTE — *The 2 oil screen bolts are approximately ⅜" (9.5 mm) longer than valve body attaching bolts and are not interchangeable.*

5) To install throttle lever and bracket assembly, install spring on top of lifter (if removed), and place lifter (spring first) into bracket. Install parts into case, locating slot in bracket with coiled pin. Align lifter through valve body hole, and link through T.V. linkage case bore, retain with nut. Tighten all valve body retaining bolts to specifications.

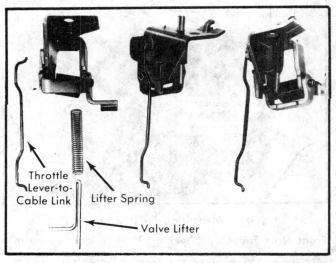

Fig. 45 Throttle Lever and Bracket Assembly

TURBO HYDRA-MATIC 200 (Cont.)

OIL SCREEN, OIL PAN & SPEEDOMETER DRIVEN GEAR

Install a new screen gasket on oil screen, retain with petrolatum, then install screen on valve body and install and tighten attaching bolts. Position a new pan gasket on case, install oil pan and attaching bolts, and tighten. If necessary, install a new "O" ring seal on speedometer driven gear housing, install housing into case, then install retainer and attaching bolt, aligning slot in housing with retainer.

TORQUE CONVERTER

Install torque converter into pump assembly, making sure converter hub drive slots are fully engaged with pump drive gear tangs, and that converter is fully installed towards rear of transmission

NOTE — When properly installed, the distance between engine mounting face of case and front face of converter cover drive lugs will be at least 1" (25.4 mm) minimum. Retain converter in case with suitable converter holding tool.

TIGHTENING SPECIFICATIONS

Application	Ft. Lbs. (mkg)
Pump Cover Bolts	15-20 (2.1-2.8)
Pump-to-Case Bolts	15-20 (2.1-2.8)
Parking Pawl Bracket Bolts	15-20 (2.1-2.8)
Valve Body-to-Case Bolts	9-12 (1.2-1.7)
Oil Screen Bolts	9-12 (1.2-1.7)
Oil Pan-to-Case Bolts	10-13 (1.4-1.8)
Manual Shaft Nut	20-25 (2.8-3.5)
Speedometer Retainer Bolt	6-10 (.8-1.4)
Cooler Line Connector	15-20 (2.1-2.8)

ZF 3 HP - 22

BMW	Peugeot
320i	504
528i	505
633CSi	
733i	

TRANSMISSION IDENTIFICATION

Transmission identification is stamped on a metal tag fastened to the lower left of the center housing.

DESCRIPTION

Transmission is a fully automatic three-speed unit. The transmission is equipped with a torque converter and simpson planetary gear set.

LUBRICATION & ADJUSTMENT

See AUTOMATIC TRANSMISSION SERVICING Section.

TROUBLE SHOOTING

NO FORWARD OR REVERSE MOVEMENT

Oil level to low. Pump drive defective. Drive plate broken. Parking lock pawl stuck or clutches A and B defective.

NO REVERSE

Selector linkage incorrectly adjusted. Clutches B or D defective. Clutch valve and damper B malfunction. Oil level too low.

MOVES IN ONE GEAR ONLY

First Gear Only — 1st-2nd shift valve stuck. Governor bushing seized.

Second Gear Only — 1st-2nd and 2nd-3rd shift valve stuck.

First and Second Gears Only — 2nd-3rd shift valve stuck.

Third Gear Only — 1st-2nd and 2nd-3rd shift valve stuck. Governor bushing seized.

TRANSMISSION SLIPPAGE

In Third Gear — Clutch B slips. Accelerator cable disengaged or misadjusted. Oil level too low. Throttle pressure valve stuck.

In Reverse — Clutch B or D damaged. Loss of oil in supply line to clutch B or D.

NO BRAKING EFFECT

In First Gear In "2" and "1" — Clutch valve/damper D defective. Clutch D defective.

In Second Gear In "2" and "1" — Clutch C' defective

SHIFT POINTS INCORRECT

Too High — Throttle cable adjustment incorrect. Governor bushing jammed, or seal rings leaking. Valve body faulty.

Too Low — Throttle cable adjustment incorrect. Governor bushing jammed. Valve body faulty.

NO KICKDOWN

In 1-2 & 2-3 — Throttle pressure too low. Accelerator cable not adjusted properly. Throttle pressure valve seized. Balls in valve body worn.

NO UPSHIFT

To 2nd Gear — Governor seized. 1-2 shift valve seized.

To 3rd Gear — Governor seized. Throttle pressure too high. Throttle pressure valve stuck. Clutch B damaged.

TRANSMISSION NOISES

In All Positions When Cold — Suction noise at oil pump due to loose valve body bolts. Defective valve body.

Noise In 1st Gear On Acceleration and Deceleration — Worn planetary gears.

Light Grinding Noise Which Is Speed Sensitive — Needle bearing in transmission extension housing defective.

TESTING

ROAD TEST

1) Before testing, make sure fluid level is correct and all linkage adjustments are correct. Transmission should upshift and down shift at approximately speeds shown in Shift Speeds chart. Speeds may vary due to tire size and axle ratio. The important factor is that all shifts should be smooth and with no slipping or engine racing.

2) Slipping or engine racing during shifts usually indicates clutch or brake slipping problems. Unless an obvious condition exists, transmission should never be disassembled until hydraulic pressure tests have been performed.

STALL TEST

1) With engine and transmission at normal operating temperature, connect a tachometer to engine, apply service and parking brakes and place selector lever in "D".

CAUTION — DO NOT maintain stall speed more than 10 seconds.

2) Accelerate engine to full throttle and note engine speed. Repeat test in selector lever position "R".

Stall Test Results — If stall speeds are below specifications, check engine output for being below specifications. If stall speeds are above specifications, refer to Clutch and Band Application Chart for clutches or brakes that could be slipping.

Stall Speed Specifications	
Application	**Stall RPM**
BMW	
320i	2050
528i	2050-2150
633CSi, 733i	1870-1970
Peugeot	
504, 505	.....

ZF 3 HP - 22 (Cont.)

CLUTCH AND BAND APPLICATION CHART
(ELEMENTS IN USE)

Gear Range	(A) Clutch	(B) Clutch	(C') Brake	(C) Brake	(D) Brake	Front Overrunning Clutch	Rear Overrunning Clutch
FIRST GEAR	X				X①		X
SECOND GEAR	X		X	X		X	
THIRD GEAR	X	X		X			
REVERSE		X			X		

PARK OR NEUTRAL — All bands and clutches released and/or ineffective.

① — Applied in "1" and "2" selector position only.

BMW Shift Speeds

Shift Conditions	MPH

320i

Full Throttle
- 1-2 Upshift 25-30
- 2-3 Upshift 57-63
- 3-2 Downshift 43-50

Kickdown
- 1-2 Upshift 36-42
- 2-3 Upshift 64-70
- 3-2 Downshift 61-67
- 2-1 Downshift 33-38

Manual Downshift (Max.)
- 3-2 65-72
- 2-1 35-42

528i

Full Throttle
- 1-2 Upshift 30-38
- 2-3 Upshift 68-74
- 3-2 Downshift 52-60

Kickdown
- 1-2 Upshift 43-50
- 2-3 Upshift 77-83
- 3-2 Downshift 73-79
- 2-1 Downshift 40-46

Manual Downshift
- 3-2 77-85
- 2-1 43-51

633CSi

Full Throttle
- 1-2 Upshift 30-37
- 2-3 Upshift 68-74
- 3-2 Downshift 53-60

Kickdown
- 1-2 Upshift 45-50
- 2-3 Upshift 76-83
- 3-2 Downshift 73-80
- 2-1 Downshift 40-47

Manual Downshift
- 3-2 77-85
- 2-1 43-50

BMW Shift Speeds (Cont.)

Shift Conditions	MPH

733i

Full Throttle
- 1-2 Upshift 30-36
- 2-3 Upshift 66-74
- 3-2 Downshift 78-84
- 2-1 Downshift 45-51

Kickdown
- 1-2 Upshift 44-50
- 2-3 Upshift 76-82
- 3-2 Downshift 78-84
- 2-1 Downshift 45-51

Peugeot Shift Speeds

Shift Conditions	MPH

504 & 505

Full Throttle
Gasoline Models
- 1-2 Upshift 25
- 2-3 Upshift 57
- 3-2 Downshift 45
- 2-1 Downshift 15

Diesel Models
- 1-2 Upshift 22
- 2-3 Upshift 43
- 3-2 Downshift 35
- 2-1 Downshift 19

Kickdown
Gasoline Models
- 1-2 Upshift 39
- 2-3 Upshift 64
- 3-2 Downshift 62
- 2-1 Downshift 32

Diesel Models
- 1-2 Upshift 29
- 2-3 Upshift 50
- 3-2 Downshift 48
- 2-1 Downshift 28

ZF 3 HP - 22 (Cont.)

Peugeot Shift Speeds (Cont.)

Shift Conditions	MPH
Minimum Throttle	
Gasoline Models	
1-2 Upshift	9
2-3 Upshift	20
3-2 Downshift	14
2-1 Downshift	4
Diesel Models	
1-2 Upshift	12
2-3 Upshift	20
3-2 Downshift	17
2-1 Downshift	6

HYDRAULIC PRESSURE

1) Connect pressure gauge hose to main pressure and clutch A pressure. *See Fig. 1.* Disconnect transmission kickdown cable from throttle linkage and set engine idle speed to 1200-1500 RPM.

NOTE — *To check kickdown pressures, pull on kickdown cable.*

2) With transmission in "N" position, check main pressure. First check pressure in idle, then check pressure in kickdown position. With transmission in "R", check main pressure. With transmission in "D", check (A) clutch pressure in idle and kickdown positions. Pressure obtained should be within limits of hydraulic pressure chart.

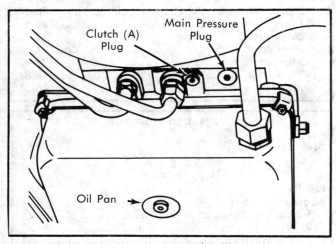

Fig. 1   Checking Hydraulic Pressure

BMW Hydraulic Pressures

Pressure Test & Cable Position	psi (kg/cm²)
320i & 528i	
Main pressure (In "R")	
Idle	178-206 (12.5-14.5)
Kickdown	243-270 (17.1-19.0)
Clutch A Pressure (In "D")	
Idle	78-91 (5.5-6.4)
Kickdown	105-118 (7.4-8.3)

BMW Hydraulic Pressures (Cont.)

Pressure Test & Cable Position	psi (kg/cm²)
633CSi	
Main Pressure (In "R")	
Idle	178-206 (12.5-14.5)
Kickdown	246-276 (17.3-19.4)
Clutch A Pressure (In "D")	
Idle	78-91 (5.5-6.4)
Kickdown	108-121 (7.6-8.5)
733i	
Main Pressure (In "R")	
Idle	188-206 (13.2-14.5)
Kickdown	250-276 (17.6-19.4)
Clutch A Pressure (In "D")	
Idle	82-91 (5.8-6.4)
Kickdown	109-121 (7.7-8.5)

Peugeot Hydraulic Pressures

Pressure Test & Cable Positions	psi (kg/cm²)
Gasoline Models	
Main Pressure	
@Idle	
P-R-N	184-223 (12.9-15.7)
3-2-1	83-99 (5.8-7.0)
@Kickdown	
P-R-N	238-276 (16.7-19.4)
3-2-1	106-122 (7.5-8.6)
(A) Clutch Pressure	
@Idle	
3-2-1	83-99 (5.8-7.0)
@Kickdown	
3-2-1	106-122 (7.5-8.6)
Diesel Models	
Main Pressure	
@Idle	
P-R-N	184-223 (12.9-15.7)
3-2-1	83-99 (5.8-7.0)
@Kickdown	
P-R-N	225-261 (15.8-18.4)
3-2-1	102-115 (7.2-8.1)
(A) Clutch Pressure	
@Idle	
3-2-1	83-99 (5.8-7.0)
@Kickdown	
3-2-1	102-115 (7.2-8.1)

TRANSMISSION REMOVAL & INSTALLATION

Removal (BMW) — **1)** Disconnect negative battery cable, and detach transmission throttle cable from accelerator cross shaft and bracket. Remove oil filler tube from transmission and plug hole in transmission. Remove all transmission-to-engine attaching bolts that can be removed from above, then drain transmission fluid.

ZF 3 HP - 22 (Cont.)

2) Detach exhaust system bracket from transmission extension housing, disconnect exhaust pipe from exhaust manifold, then turn steering wheel to full left lock to provide removal clearance. Disconnect propeller shaft from transmission output flange by removing the three bolts and nuts, remove center support-to-body bolts, and position propeller shaft out of the way.

3) Remove retaining bolt and withdraw speedometer cable from transmission extension housing, and disconnect transmission shift lever from selector lever rod. Disconnect electrical leads from neutral safety switch. Remove thrust bracket (if equipped) and converter cover plate, rotate engine, and remove the four converter-to-drive plate bolts. Disconnect oil cooler lines from transmission. Position a jack under transmission, disconnect crossmember, remove remaining transmission-to-engine attaching bolts, and remove transmission.

Installation — Reverse removal procedure and note the following: Check for correct engagement of torque converter in transmission by measuring distance from front of transmission case to torque converter-to-drive plate lugs. Distance should be approximately $\frac{1}{2}''$ (12 mm). When installing oil cooler lines, check condition of line-to-case gaskets and replace if necessary. Fill transmission with fluid and adjust transmission control linkage.

Removal (Peugeot) — 1) Disconnect negative battery terminal from battery. Remove air duct between metering unit and butterfly housing. Remove 2 bolts from the control pressure regulator.

2) Remove upper and lower radiator mounts. Place a piece of cardboard between radiator and fan to protect radiator from damage during transmission removal. Disconnect kickdown control cable at throttle linkage.

3) Remove exhaust-to-manifold nuts and disconnect all exhaust system hangers. Remove heat shield from above muffler. Remove front seat stiffener located above muffler.

4) Remove the vibration damper from the drive shaft tube. Disconnect differential from its mount. Mark position of lower steering column flange coupling and remove bolts.

5) Remove front crossmember-to-front mount bolts and replace with 2" (50 mm) long bolts. Then, remove remaining crossmember bolts. Lower crossmember approximately 2" by unscrewing the 2 front bolts in crossmember.

6) Drain transmission fluid and disconnect cooler lines from transmission. Remove starter motor bolts and disconnect filler tube from transmission. Remove torque converter cover plate from bell housing. Remove torque converter-to-flywheel bolts. Using a suitable tool, secure torque converter in housing so it will not fall out of housing during transmission removal.

7) Place suitable transmission jack under transmission and remove 4 bolts securing drive shaft tube to transmission. Separate transmission from tube and install special tool 8.0403SZ between the 2 units and install 2 bolts to hold tool in place.

8) Pull differential and drive shaft assembly to the rear of vehicle and allow front of tube to rest on rear crossmember. Disconnect gear shift linkage, speedometer and electrical connections from transmission. Lower and tilt transmission as far as possible.

9) Install suitable engine lift equipment to front of engine. Lift engine far enough to gain access to upper transmission-to-engine bolts. Remove bolts and remove transmission from vehicle.

Installation — Reverse removal procedure and note the following: Apply grease to torque converter pilot bushing. Adjust shift and throttle linkage as necessary. Fill transmission with fluid and check for leaks.

TRANSMISSION DISASSEMBLY

1) Place transmission in a suitable holding fixture and remove oil pan and gasket. Remove bolts retaining valve body, remove valve body. Remove retaining circlips from oil supply bores in transmission case and withdraw compression springs. Remove sealing sleeves from oil bores, using the type of puller that threads into the sleeve. Screw tool into sleeve and pull out sharply.

2) Lock transmission output shaft by engaging parking gear, hold output flange, remove retaining nut and remove flange. Remove extension housing. Loosen nut and unscrew stud, (about 3 turns) and pull governor off shaft.

3) Remove torque converter housing with intermediate plate, thrust washer, needle bearing and angled disc. Remove input shaft and clutch A. Remove clutch A carrier plate, plastic thrust washer and metal thrust washer. Remove clutch B snap ring.

4) When removing clutch B, two hooks will have to be used. See Fig. 2. Remove snap ring and pull complete assembly, (Clutches C', C, D and planetary gears with output shaft). See Fig. 3. Remove thrust washer, needle bearing and angled disc from output shaft. Remove planetary gears and sungear shaft. Noting needle bearing and thrust washer. See Fig. 4.

Fig. 2   Removing Clutch B

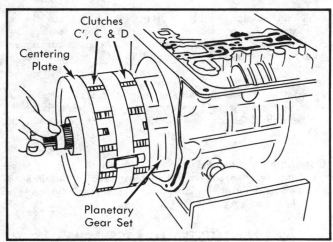

Fig. 3 Removing Output Shaft Assembly

Fig. 4 Removing Planetary Gears and Sun Gear Shaft

COMPONENT DISASSEMBLY & REASSEMBLY

CONVERTER HOUSING & OIL PUMP ASSEMBLY

Disassembly — Remove torque converter. Remove converter bell housing with intermediate plate. Remove intermediate plate from converter housing by loosening the two bolts (do not remove bolts). See *Fig. 5*. Separate primary pump from converter housing by tapping lightly on bolts.

Inspection (BMW) — Clean all parts and check for signs of scoring or other wear. Check clearance between pump driven gear (large gear) and pump housing; clearance must be .003-.006″ (.072-.161 mm). Next, check pump housing-to-gear face clearance; clearance must be .0012-.0019″ (.03-.05 mm). If any measurement is not within specifications, replace oil pump assembly.

Inspection (Peugeot) — Clean all parts and check for signs of scoring and other wear. Check clearance between pump driven gear (large gear) and pump housing; clearance must be .0034-.006″ (.087-.161 mm). Next, check pump housing to gear face clearance; clearance must be .0008-.0015″ (.02-.04 mm). Finally, check clearance between gear and crescent; clearance must be .010-.015″ (.250-.386 mm). If any measurement is not within specifications, replace oil pump assembly.

Reassembly — Reassemble in reverse of disassembly procedure noting the following: Replace all gaskets and seals. Install angled disc, with collar facing needle bearing on input shaft. Hold thrust washer on converter housing with grease.

NOTE — *If any part of oil pump assembly is defective complete pump must be replaced.*

Fig. 5 Removing Intermediate Plate from Converter Housing

Torque Converter Identification		
Application	**Color/Letter**	**F & S No.**
BMW		
320i	...../G	005
528i	...../J	031 001
633CSi	Yellow/L	031 003
733i	Yellow/.....	031 003
Peugeot		
504, 505	.....	.....

CLUTCHES

Disassembly — 1) To disassemble Clutch A, press clutch assembly together and remove large snap ring. See *Fig. 7*. Remove carrier plate and remove clutch plates and diaphragm. Remove snap ring from Clutch B, then remove plates.

2) Clutch C′, insert clutch assembly into a pipe with an inside diameter of 1.142″ (29 mm) and clamp assembly in a vise. Remove centering plate, outer plates, lined plates and one-way clutch for 2nd gear.

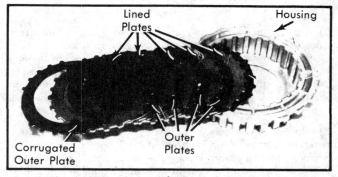

Fig. 6 Housing and Plates for Clutch A

ZF 3 HP - 22 (Cont.)

3) Clutch C, remove snap ring and plates. Clutch D, lift clutch body and clutch plates off planetary gears. Remove snap ring and plates.

Reassembly — 1) Clutch A, Place diaphragm in input shaft housing (concave side down). Install set of plates with plate carrier, press clutch assembly together and install snap ring.

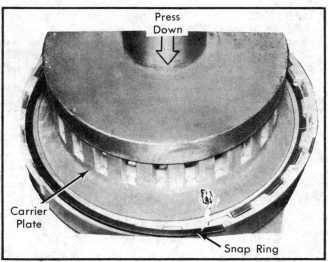

Fig. 7   Removing Snap Ring from Clutch A

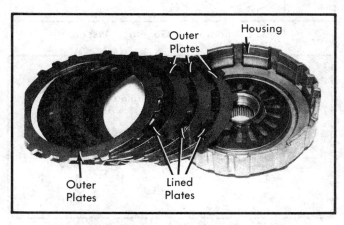

Fig. 8   Housing and Plates for Clutch B

2) Clutch B, install clutch plates into carrier, then install snap ring. *See Fig. 8.* Clutch C', install one-way clutch so that bent tabs of the retaining plate are visible from above. Install clutch plates and centering plate. *See Fig. 9.*

3) Clutch C and D, install plates and snap rings. *See Fig. 10.*

NOTE — *With ATF at a temperature of 160°F (70°C), soak new liner plates for about 20 minutes.*

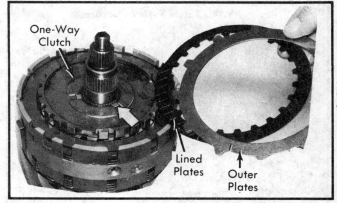

Fig. 9   One-Way Clutch and Plates for Clutch C'

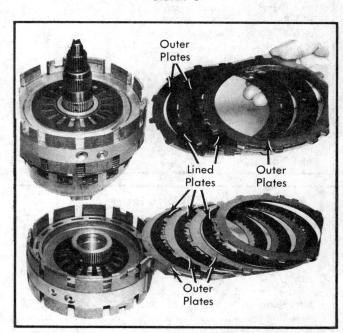

Fig. 10   Housing and Plates for Clutches C & D

BMW Clutch Plates	
Application	**No. of Plates**
320i	
Clutch "A"	
Spring Plates	2
Outer Plates	5
Lined Plates	4
Clutch "B"	
Outer Plates	3
Lined Plates	3
Thick Plate	1
Clutch "C'"	
Outer Plate	1
Lined Plate	1
Clutch "C"	
Outer Plates	2
Lined Plates	2
Thick Plate	1

ZF 3 HP - 22 (Cont.)

BMW Clutch Plates (Cont.)
320i

Application	No. of Plates
Clutch "D"	
Outer Plates	3
Lined Plates	3
Thick Plate	1

528i, 633CSi & 733i

Application	No. of Plates
Clutch "A"	
Spring Plates	2
Outer Plates	6
Lined Plates	5
Clutch "B"	
Outer Plates	4
Lined Plates	4
Thick Plate	1
Clutch "C"	
Outer Plates	2
Lined Plates	2
Thick Plate	1
Clutch "C'"	
Outer Plate	2
Lined Plate	2
Clutch "D"	
Outer Plates	4
Lined Plates	4
Thick Plate	1

Peugeot Clutch Plates

Application	No. of Plates
504 & 505	
Clutch "A"	
Spring Plates	2
Outer Plates	5
Lined Plates	4
Clutch "B"	
Outer Plates	3
Lined Plates	3
Thick Plate	1
Clutch "C'"	
Outer Plate	1
Lined Plate	1
Clutch "C"	
Outer Plate	2
Lined Plate	2
Thick Plate	1
Clutch "D"	
Outer Plates	3
Lined Plates	3
Thick Plate	1

PLANETARY GEAR UNIT

Disassembly — Remove large snap ring retaining clutches C and D. Remove clutch pack C, then remove clutch pack D with housing. Lift one-way clutch with planetary gears. Remove sun gear, then remove large snap ring securing output ring gear. Remove ring gear, then rear planetary gears. Remove roller bearing and washer, then mainshaft and input gear assembly.

Remove large snap ring holding input ring gear to mainshaft, and separate. Remove washers and bearing. Remove other large snap ring.

Reassembly — To reassemble planetary gear unit, reverse disassembly procedure and note the following: Make sure a large snap ring is on both sides of input ring gear when assembled to mainshaft. After installation of mainshaft to output shaft, make sure that a washer is placed onto output shaft first, then the roller bearing. Make sure all snap rings are properly installed and fully seated.

GOVERNOR

Disassembly — Remove transmission cover, loosen nut and unscrew stud, (by about 3 turns) pull governor off shaft. *See Fig. 11.* Remove governor cover from housing, remove circlip, washer, piston, spring and bushing. *See Fig. 12.*

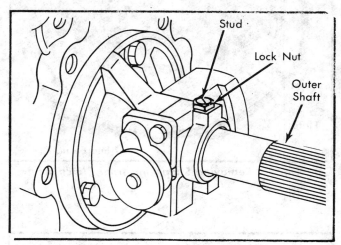

Fig. 11   Removing Governor Assembly

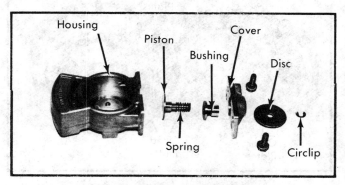

Fig. 12   Exploded View of Governor

Reassembly — Assemble governor in reverse of disassembly procedure, ensuring that the piston slides into the bushing without restriction. Press piston rings together while sliding the governor onto the flange. Remove stud to help find the depression in the output shaft. Secure the governor by aligning the stud with the depression. Lock governor by counterpunching the stud.

VALVE BODY

NOTE — *Valve body disassembly is not recommended. If a valve body malfunction is determined, replace valve body.*

ZF 3 HP - 22 (Cont.)

TRANSMISSION REASSEMBLY

1) Install needle bearing and thrust washer on output shaft. Guide entire output assembly into transmission case, ensuring that the keys are in the center of cylinder groove and the 4 oil bores in the output assembly are aligned with the bores in the case. See Fig. 13.

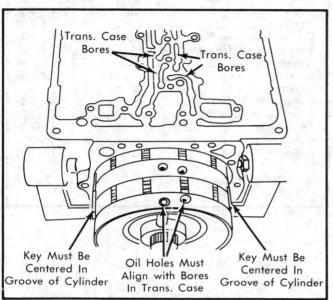

Fig. 13   Aligning Output Shaft Keys and
Oil Holes in Transmission Case

2) Install snap ring, clutch B and press in seal with support disc. Install snap ring and lubricate plastic thrust washer, ensuring that the tabs engage in openings of cylinder A. See Fig. 14. Install metal thrust washer in plate carrier, install plate carrier into clutch A, (by turning back and forth slightly). Install clutch A into transmission case.

3) Install angled disc on input shaft, with collar facing needle bearing. Install thrust washer and gasket on coverter housing, slide converter housing onto input shaft and secure.

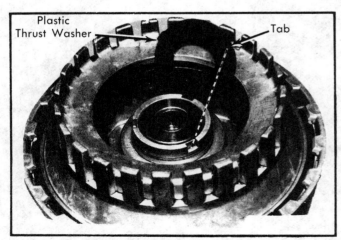

Fig. 14   Installing Plastic Thrust Washer
in Clutch A

4) Check input shaft axial play of .012-.059" (.3-1.5 mm). See Fig. 15. Install governor to output shaft. Install seal and transmission output flange, securing with lockplate and nut.

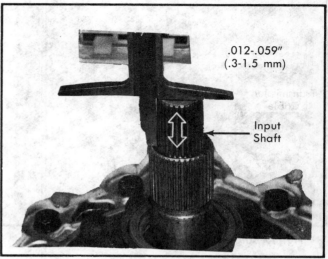

Fig. 15   Checking Input Shaft Axial Play

5) Using a suitable punch, drive in the 4 sealing sleeves, up to the stop. Install and secure springs (both short springs are installed on the selector lever side .See Fig. 16.

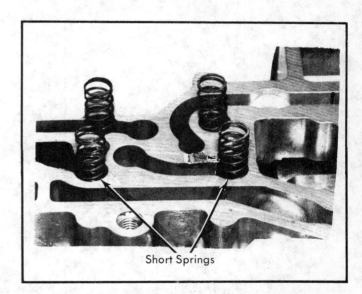

Fig. 16   Installing Springs in Valve Body

6) Install the valve body so that the clamp on the selector sliding valve can be engaged in the opening arm of the pawl, by tightening the transmission cable slightly. See Fig. 17.

7) Align valve body with pin in the throttle pressure piston. Clearance must be .453" (11.5 mm). Tighten valve body screws. Install oil pan gasket and magnetic disc, (next to oil filter screen). Install oil pan on to transmission case, (short arm of retaining bracket presses down on oil pan).

ZF 3 HP - 22 (Cont.)

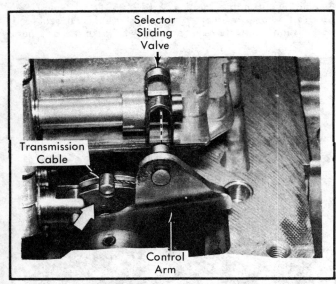

Fig. 17 Aligning Sliding Valve and Control Arm

TIGHTENING SPECIFICATIONS

Application	Ft. Lbs. (mkg)
BMW	
Transmission-to-Engine	35-38 (4.8-5.3)
10 mm	35-38 (4.8-5.3)
8 mm	18-20 (2.5-2.8)
Converter-to-Drive Plate	①35-38 (4.8-5.3)
Bell Housing-to-Transmission Case	17-19 (2.4-2.6)
Governor Studs	2.2-2.6 (.3-.4)
Extension Housing	17-19 (2.4-2.6)
Peugeot	
Transmission-to-Engine	40 (5.5)
Converter-to-Drive Plate	22 (3.0)
Bell Housing-to-Transmission Case	17 (2.4)
Governor Set Screw	1.8-2.5 (.25-.35)
Extension Housing	17 (2.4)

① — BMW 320i models should be 18-20 ft. lbs. (2.5-2.8 mkg).

CONTENTS Page

**AUTOMATIC
TRANSAXLES**
Section 3

Section 3

AUTOMATIC TRANSAXLES

NOTE — ALSO SEE GENERAL INDEX.

AUDI 4000 & 5000, PORSCHE 924 & VOLKSWAGEN DASHER

TRANSAXLE IDENTIFICATION

Transmission type may be identified by a group of letters cast into top of case. Audi and Porsche use a type 087 transmission while the Dasher uses a type 089 transmission. The main difference between the two transmissions is turbine shaft length. The type 087 uses a 16.713" (424.5 mm) shaft while the type 089 uses a 15.815" (401.7 mm) shaft. Testing, disassembly and reassembly procedures are the same for both types of transmissions. Transaxle model may be identified by a group of figures stamped into torque converter housing. These figures consist of a model code and a build date code. Model codes are as follows:

Transaxle Model Codes

Application	Code
Audi	
4000	RR
5000	RM, RY
5000 Turbo	RP
Porsche	
924	RL
Volkswagen	
Dasher	ET

DESCRIPTION

Transaxle assembly consists of two main units: Automatic Transmission and final drive assembly. The transmission housing contains two planetary gear sets, two multiple-disc clutches, one brake band and servo, one multiple-disc brake, a one-way clutch, and a hydraulic control system. The final drive housing contains torque converter, governor for transmission, ring gear, Pinion gear and differential carrier with pinion and side gears.

LUBRICATION & ADJUSTMENT

See *AUTOMATIC TRANSMISSION SERVICING* Section.

TROUBLE SHOOTING

NO MOVEMENT

In Any Gear — Low fluid level. Manual lever not connected to manual valve. Torque converter disconnected from drive plate. Main pressure valve sticking. Oil pump drive plate and/or shaft defective.

In Forward Gears — Forward clutch internal damage (worn plates, broken diaphragm spring, seals leaking, etc.). Forward planetary gears damaged.

In First Gear in "D" or "2" — One-way clutch not holding. Forward clutch internal damage.

In First Gear in "1" — First-reverse brake plates worn or burnt. One-way clutch slipping.

In Second Gear — Second gear brake band out of adjustment or burnt, or servo defective.

In Third Gear — Direct-Reverse clutch plates burnt or worn.

In Reverse — First-Reverse brake plates worn or burnt. Direct-Reverse clutch internal damage. Forward clutch seized in applied position.

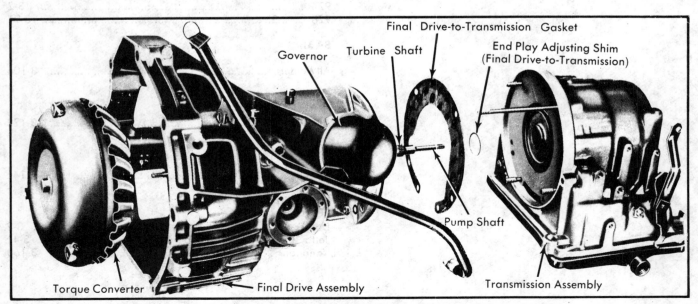

**Fig. 1 Audi, Porsche and Volkswagen Automatic Transaxle Assembly
(Dasher Model Shown — 924, 4000 and 5000 Models Similar)**

AUDI 4000 & 5000, PORSCHE 924 & VOLKSWAGEN DASHER (Cont.)

NO DOWNSHIFT

Into Third Gear — Governor or valve body dirty. 2-3 shift valve sticking. Transfer plate check balls missing. Oil pump bolts loose.

Into First Gear — Governor dirty. 1-2 shift valve sticking.

Into Second Gear — Governor dirty. 2-3 shift valve sticking.

DELAYED ENGAGEMENT ON UPSHIFTS

1-2 Upshift — Low fluid level. Dirty valve body. Second gear brake band worn, burnt or out of adjustment. Second gear servo defective, possible wrong piston.

2-3 Upshift — Low fluid level. Dirty valve body. Second gear brake band worn, burnt or out of adjustment. Second gear servo defective. Direct-Reverse clutch plates worn or burnt. Wrong Direct-Reverse clutch installed.

ERRATIC DRIVE

Low fluid level. Bushing in one-way clutch support and turbine shaft worn. Oil filter dirty.

INCORRECT SHIFT SPEEDS

Governor dirty. Valve body dirty. Planetary gears or separation plate gasket damaged.

TESTING

ROAD TESTING

1) Before road testing, be certain that fluid level and condition, and control linkage adjustments have been checked and corrected as necessary. During the test, transmission should upshift and downshift at approximately the speeds shown in Shift Speeds Chart. All shifts may vary somewhat due to production tolerances or tire size. The important factor

Shift Speeds		
Application	**Shift Points (MPH)**	
	Full Throttle	**Kickdown**
1-2 Upshift		
Dasher	19-24	35-39
924	22-26	39-42
4000	22-27	40-43
5000	20-26	39-42
2-3 Upshift		
Dasher	49-53	64-66
924	54-57	71-72
4000	58-61	73-74
5000	54-57	68-70
3-2 Downshift		
Dasher	30-36	61-63
924	34-39	67-68
4000	33-38	68-70
5000	32-38	65-67
2-1 Downshift		
Dasher	14-17	31-35
924	16-17	35-37
4000	16-17	36-38
5000	15-17	34-38

is the quality of the shifts. All shifts should be smooth, responsive, and with no slippage or engine speed runaway.

2) Slippage or engine runaway in any gear usually indicates clutch, band, or brake problems. The slipping unit in a particular gear can usually be identified by noting transmission operation in other selector positions and comparing which internal units are applied in those positions. See *Clutch and Band Application Chart.*

3) This process of elimination can be used to detect any unit which slips, and to confirm proper operation of good units, however, the actual cause of the malfunction usually cannot be easily decided. Practically any condition can be caused by leaking hydraulic circuits or sticking valves. Therefore, unless an obvious condition exists, do not disassemble transmission until a hydraulic pressure test has been made.

HYDRAULIC PRESSURE TEST

1) Connect a pressure gauge to main pressure test point on case (adjacent to servo cover). With transmission at normal operating temperature, place selector lever in "D", run engine at idle speed and note pressure reading on gauge.

Arrow Indicates Pressure Connection

Fig. 2 View of Transmission Case Showing Pressure Test Connection Point

2) Next, run engine at full throttle with vehicle speed above 25 MPH, and again note pressure reading in "D".

3) Next, with vehicle at a standstill, place selector lever in "R" position, and note reading on pressure gauge.

4) Finally, on 924 models, keep selector lever in "R" and measure pressure at full throttle with vehicle at stall speed.

5) Pressures obtained in each phase of test should be approximately as shown in Main Pressures chart. If not, check for the following: Defective oil pump; Oil leaks; Sticking valves in valve body assembly.

AUDI 4000 & 5000, PORSCHE 924 & VOLKSWAGEN DASHER (Cont.)

CLUTCH AND BAND APPLICATION CHART (ELEMENTS IN USE)

Selector Lever Position	Forward Clutch	Direct-Reverse Clutch	First-Reverse Brake	Second Gear Band	One Way Clutch
D — DRIVE					
First Gear	X				X
Second Gear	X			X	
Third Gear	X	X			
2 — INTERMEDIATE					
First Gear	X				X
Second Gear	X			X	
1 — LOW (First)	X		X		
R — REVERSE		X	X		

NEUTRAL OR PARK — All Clutches, brake, and band released and/or ineffective.

Main Pressures

Application	psi (kg/cm²)
"D" at Idle①	41-43 (2.9-3.0)
"D" at Full Throttle②③④	83-85 (5.8-6.0)
"R" at Idle①⑤	108-117 (7.6-8.2)
"R" at Full Throttle⑥	Min. 256 (18.0)

① — Vehicle Stationary.
② — Road speed above 25 MPH. Test should be performed on a dynamometer whenever possible.
③ — 4000 pressure is 81-82 psi (5.7-5.8 kg/cm²).
④ — 5000 pressure is 104-105 psi (7.3-7.4 kg/cm²).
⑤ — 4000 and 924 pressure is 101-110 (7.1-7.7 kg/cm²).
⑥ — 924 only. Perform test at stall speed.

STALL SPEED

Testing Precautions — When making test, do not hold throttle open any longer than the time it takes to read tachometer. Maximum stall speed test time is 20 seconds. If engine speed exceeds limits shown in Stall Speeds table, release accelerator immediately as clutch or band slippage is indicated.

Testing Procedure — With engine at normal operating temperature, connect a tachometer. Start engine and set parking and service brakes. Place selector lever in "D". Depress accelerator briefly to full throttle and note maximum RPM obtained. Engine speed should be within the limits shown in Stall Speeds table.

NOTE — Normal stall speed will drop approximately 125 RPM per 3200 feet altitude. Also, stall speed will drop slightly with high ambient air temperature.

Stall Test Results — 1) If stall speed is higher than specified, forward clutch or one-way clutch for first gear is slipping. If stall speed in "D" range is too high, repeat stall test in "1". If RPM is within specifications, one-way clutch for first gear is defective.

Stall Speeds

Application	Stall RPM
Dasher	1950-2550
924	2250-2650
4000	2250-2550
5000	2250-2500
5000 Turbo	3000-3400

2) If stall speed is approximately 200 RPM below specification, engine performance may be unsatisfactory. If stall speed is approximately 400 RPM below specifications, torque converter stator one-way clutch is faulty and complete converter should be replaced.

REMOVAL & INSTALLATION

NOTE — For Axle Drive Shaft, Constant Velocity (CV) Joint, and Axle Shaft replacement procedures, see appropriate manual transaxle article in MANUAL TRANSAXLES Section.

TRANSAXLE ASSEMBLY

NOTE — Transaxle is removed from below vehicle.

Removal (Audi 4000) — 1) Disconnect battery ground and disconnect accelerator linkage rod. Disconnect speedometer cable then remove upper engine-to-transaxle bolts.

2) Install an engine support. Disconnect automatic transaxle cooler hoses. Disconnect exhaust pipe from manifold, exhaust pipe bracket at transaxle and unbolt exhaust pipe from catalytic converter. Remove axle shaft guard plate, then disconnect axle shafts from transaxle flanges. Wire axle shafts back out-of-way.

3) Remove starter. Remove the 3 bolts securing torque converter to drive plate. Remove subframe rear mounting bolts and loosen front (do not remove). Disconnect linkage rod from

AUDI 4000 & 5000, PORSCHE 924 & VOLKSWAGEN DASHER (Cont.)

transaxle. Remove selector cable holder and circlip, then disconnect selector cable and "O" ring.

4) Place transaxle jack under transaxle and raise slightly. Remove accelerator cable holder, then disconnect accelerator cable. Remove lower engine-to-transaxle bolts. Remove transaxle rubber mount bolts. Separate transaxle from engine, then lower transaxle out of vehicle.

NOTE — *Secure torque converter to transaxle to prevent converter from falling when removing transaxle.*

Installation — To install transaxle, reverse removal procedures. Make sure torque converter is fully seated to transaxle and all linkage is properly installed and adjusted.

Removal (Audi 5000) — **1)** Disconnect battery ground cable. Disconnect hoses from transaxle cooler. Disconnect accelerator linkage and speedometer cable. Install suitable engine support and remove upper engine-to-transaxle bolts. Remove guard plate from subframe and remove front exhaust pipe.

2) Remove right guard plate at right axle drive shaft and remove drive shaft bolts. Remove starter, selector lever cable holder and selector lever cable at transaxle lever.

3) Disconnect lower accelerator linkage rod and accelerator cable from transaxle lever. Remove right side guard plate from subframe. Remove both transaxle mounts from subframe. Remove torque converter-to-drive plate bolts.

4) Support transaxle with suitable jack and raise slightly. Remove lower engine-to-transaxle bolts and rear subframe bolts. Position driveshafts to rear of vehicle. Separate transaxle from engine and lower from vehicle.

NOTE — *When removing transaxle assembly, secure torque converter in place.*

Installation — Reverse removal procedure and note the following: When attaching torque converter to drive plate use new bolts and lock washers. After transaxle installation, check and adjust (if necessary) accelerator cable and throttle linkage.

Removal (Porsche 924) — **1)** Remove heat shield and rear muffler bracket. Disconnect axle drive shafts at transaxle and support them in a horizontal position to prevent damage to dust covers.

2) Remove oil filler protective shield. Detach selector lever and transmission lever cables. Working through inspection hole in rear bell housing, remove converter-to-drive plate attaching bolts.

3) Using a transmission jack, lift transaxle assembly slightly. Remove transaxle-to-bell housing attaching bolts and transaxle mounts. Lower transaxle assembly slightly and move it back far enough so that converter holding tool can be installed to prevent converter from falling during removal. Lower transaxle toward rear and remove.

Installation — Reverse removal procedure.

Removal (Volkswagen Dasher) — **1)** Remove battery ground cable. Disconnect speedometer cable. Remove engine-to-transaxle mounting bolts. Disconnect exhaust pipe from manifold.

2) Remove bolts holding starter to engine. Take out bolts securing converter cover plate to transaxle. Disconnect converter drive plate bolts.

3) Detach circlip holding selector lever cable to lever on transaxle and push cable to one side.

4) Remove bolts securing axle drive shafts and secure shafts out of way. Mark position of ball joint on left track control arm and remove. Disconnect exhaust pipe bracket/transaxle support.

5) Support transaxle using a suitable transmission jack. Remove transaxle filler pipe. Remove transaxle/engine mounting bolts. Lower transaxle from vehicle.

NOTE — *When removing transaxle assembly, secure torque converter in place.*

Installation — Reverse removal procedure and note the following: Ensure that track control arm ball joints are aligned with marks made at removal for proper positioning. Tighten all nuts and bolts to specifications. After installation, check and adjust (if necessary) accelerator cable and throttle cable.

TORQUE CONVERTER

NOTE — *The torque converter is a sealed unit and cannot be disassembled for service.*

BUSHING REPLACEMENT

1) Check bushing wear using an inside micrometer. Wear limit is 1.343" (34.12 mm) on 4000 or 1.348" (34.25 mm) on all other models. Maximum allowable out-of-round is .001" (.03 mm).

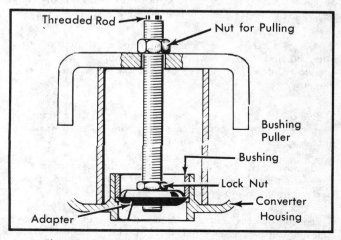

Fig. 3 Removing Torque Converter Bushing

AUDI 4000 & 5000, PORSCHE 924 & VOLKSWAGEN DASHER (Cont.)

2) To replace bushing, use a suitable bushing puller (US 691 and adapter US 4452) to withdraw bushing from converter hub. Press new bushing into place using a suitable bushing driver.

TRANSMISSION DISASSEMBLY

NOTE — *To separate transaxle units, withdraw torque converter from final drive housing and remove impeller shaft from center of turbine shaft. Disconnect filler pipe from oil pan. Remove attaching nuts from transmission studs that attach final drive to transmission, then separate final drive unit from transmission case. Withdraw turbine shaft from final drive. For final drive disassembly and reassembly, see Final Drive information at rear of this article.*

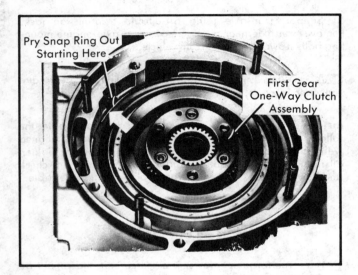

Fig. 4   Installed View of One-Way Clutch Assembly Showing Location of Retaining Snap Ring

1) Mount transmission assembly in a suitable holding fixture. Remove separation plate attaching screws and lift plate and gasket from transmission case. Remove reverse planetary ring gear, needle bearing and thrust washer.

2) Using a screwdriver, carefully remove large snap ring retaining first gear one-way clutch assembly in case. Lift out one-way clutch, first/reverse gear brake discs, and reverse planetary gear set as a unit.

3) Remove thrust washers, then lift the following components from case as an assembly: Sun gear, driving shell, forward planetary gear set, and forward clutch.

4) Remove second gear brake band servo cover snap ring. Then using a rubber mallet, tap cover until cover and piston pop out under spring pressure.

5) Loosen second gear brake band lock nut and remove adjusting screw and lock nut, then withdraw pushrod for adjusting screw.

6) Lift out remaining planetary gear system components that are housed in first/reverse gear brake shell. Remove bolts from first/reverse brake spring plate, withdraw spring plate and springs, then pull driving shell, brake piston, and oil pump from case.

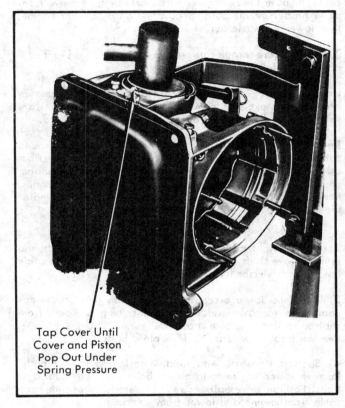

Fig. 5   Using a Rubber Mallet to Remove Brake Band Servo Cover

7) Invert transmission so that oil pan is facing up. Remove attaching bolts and lift off oil pan and gasket. Remove screws from oil strainer and separate strainer from valve body.

8) Remove the 11 valve body attaching bolts and lift valve body assembly from case using care not to drop manual valve. Remove attaching screws for accumulator cover plate, then remove the cover, spring and accumulator piston. If necessary for parts replacement, disassemble kickdown and selector linkage using *Fig. 7* as a disassembly guide.

COMPONENT DISASSEMBLY & REASSEMBLY

OIL PUMP ASSEMBLY

CAUTION — *Pump cover is under spring tension.*

Disassembly — 1) Remove pump cover attaching screws and separate cover from pump housing. Remove check ball and spring, then lift out inner and outer pump gears and drive plate.

2) Using needlenose pliers, unhook oil seal ring ends and carefully remove seal rings from pump housing. Remove thrust washer from pump housing.

AUDI 4000 & 5000, PORSCHE 924 & VOLKSWAGEN DASHER (Cont.)

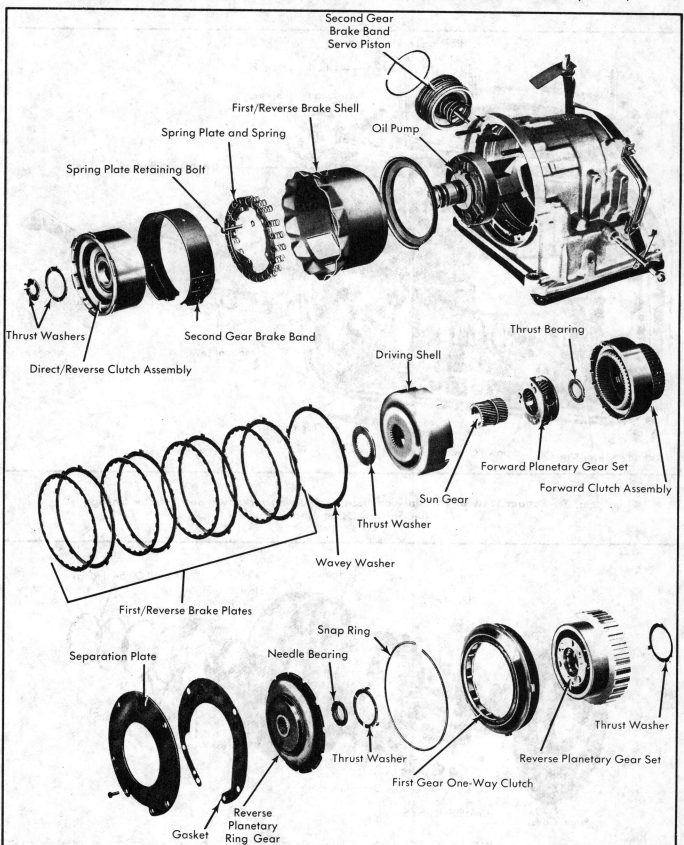

Fig. 6 *Exploded View of Transmission Case and Main Components*

Automatic Transaxles

AUDI 4000 & 5000, PORSCHE 924 & VOLKSWAGEN DASHER (Cont.)

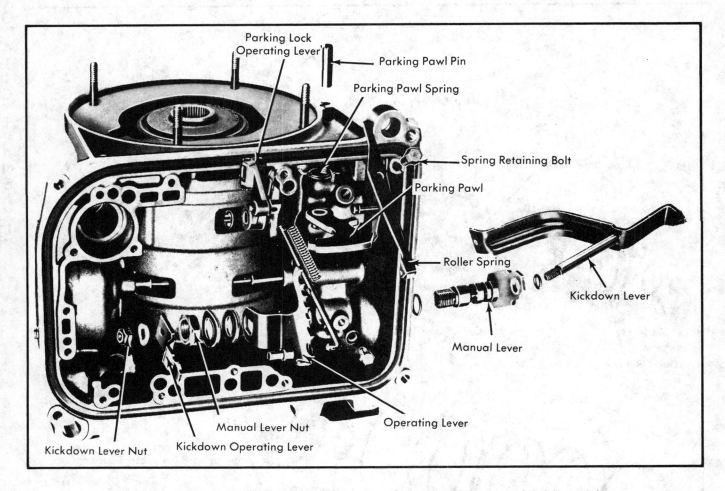

Fig. 7 Bottom View of Transmission Housing Showing Kickdown and Selector Linkage (Dasher Shown; Other Models Similar)

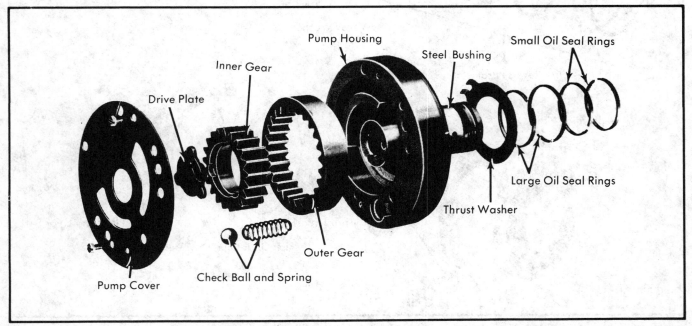

Fig. 8 Exploded View Showing Components of Oil Pump Assembly

AUDI 4000 & 5000, PORSCHE 924 & VOLKSWAGEN DASHER (Cont.)

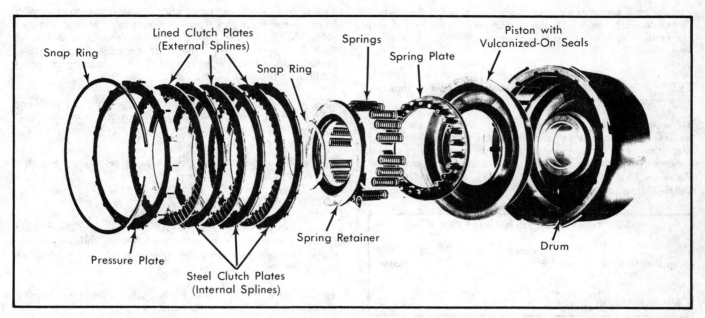

Snap Ring

Lined Clutch Plates (External Splines)

Snap Ring

Springs

Spring Plate

Piston with Vulcanized-On Seals

Spring Retainer

Drum

Pressure Plate

Steel Clutch Plates (Internal Splines)

Fig. 9 Exploded View Showing Components of Direct/Reverse Clutch Assembly

Inspection — Wash all parts in kerosene and blow out oil passages with compressed air. Inspect all parts for wear, scoring, chipped teeth and any other damage. Replace parts as necessary.

NOTE — If either of the pump gears, the pump housing or cover are damaged, the entire oil pump assembly must be replaced. The drive plate, oil seal rings and thrust washer can be replaced individually.

Reassembly — 1) Install thrust washer on pump housing so that tangs on washer engage lug on housing. Carefully install first the large oil seal rings and then the small seal rings on pump housing, ensuring that ring ends hook correctly.

2) Lubricate all parts with automatic transmission fluid. Install inner and outer gears into housing, then install drive plate with extended hub inserted into pump housing shaft opening. Install check ball spring and ball into housing. Align cover with housing, then install and tighten attaching screws.

NOTE — After reassembly, insert pump shaft into oil pump and ensure that gears rotate freely. Gear rotation should also be rechecked after pump is installed in transmission case.

DIRECT/REVERSE CLUTCH

Disassembly — 1) Using a screwdriver, pry clutch pack retaining snap ring from clutch drum. Withdraw clutch pressure plate, lined clutch plates and steel clutch plates from drum.

2) Place clutch drum in a press, apply downward pressure to piston spring retainer and remove retaining snap ring. Release press and remove spring retainer. Using a twisting motion, remove piston with return springs from drum. Remove piston seals and springs from piston.

3) If necessary for replacement, place clutch drum in a press and drive bushing out of drum using a suitable bushing driver.

Inspection — 1) Inspect friction surfaces of piston and drum for wear or damage. Check clutch drum ball valve for free movement. Inspect piston springs for wear or collapsed coils and replace as necessary.

2) Inspect steel (externally splined) clutch plates. If plates are scored or have radial grooves, they must be replaced. Plates that are only discolored can be reused.

3) Inspect lined (internally splined) clutch plates. Replace any plate that is worn, damaged, or burned.

NOTE — New lined clutch plates must be soaked in automatic transmission fluid for at least 15 minutes prior to installation.

Reassembly — 1) If removed, press new bushing into clutch drum until it is .067" (1.7 mm) below lip of drum hub on all models except Porsche 924 models. On 924 models, press bushing in until it is flush with hub of drum.

Only Install Lined Plates with Grooves as Shown

Fig. 10 View of Direct/Reverse Clutch Lined Plate Showing Identification Grooves

AUDI 4000 & 5000, PORSCHE 924 & VOLKSWAGEN DASHER (Cont.)

2) Lubricate piston seals with transmission fluid, then install them into clutch drum with lips facing into drum. Using a stiff plastic sheet to protect piston seals, install piston into drum using a twisting motion.

NOTE — *Only install direct/reverse clutch lined plates that are grooved as shown in Fig. 10.*

3) Position piston return springs on piston. Place spring retainer on springs, then compress retainer and install snap ring. Install clutch plates into clutch drum starting with a steel (externally splined) plate and alternating lined and steel plates until all clutch plates are installed. See *Direct/Reverse Clutch Plate chart.*

Direct/Reverse Clutch Plates Chart

Application	Steel Plates	Lined Plates
Dasher	3	3
All Other Models	4	4

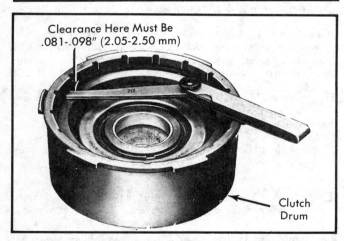

Fig. 11   Using a Feeler Gauge to Measure Direct/Reverse Clutch Clearance

4) Install pressure plate and clutch pack retaining snap ring. Using a feeler gauge measure clearance between pressure plate and retaining snap ring. Clearance should be .081-.098" (2.05-2.50 mm); if not, remove clutch pack snap ring and replace with a snap ring of correct thickness to bring clearance within specifications.

NOTE — *Direct/Reverse clutch assembly clutch pack retaining snap rings are available in various thicknesses from .059" (1.5 mm) to .098" (2.5 mm).*

5) Install correct thickness clutch pack retaining snap ring. Recheck clutch pack clearance.

FORWARD CLUTCH

Disassembly — **1)** Using a screwdriver, pry clutch pack retaining snap ring from clutch drum. Then withdraw pressure plate, forward planetary ring gear, lined and steel clutch plates, and thrust plate.

2) Carefully pry out diaphragm spring snap ring. Remove diaphragm spring. Lift out clutch piston.

NOTE — *It may be necessary to force clutch piston from drum using compressed air.*

Inspection — **1)** Inspect clutch drum for scoring, wear, or other damage. Check clutch drum ball valve for free movement and ensure that drilling is clear.

2) Inspect diaphragm spring and piston for damage. Also, place diaphragm spring onto piston and ensure that top of spring reaches to at least the lower edge of snap ring groove; if not replace spring.

NOTE — *The forward clutch piston sealing lips are vulcanized to the piston. Replace the entire piston if there is damage to the sealing lip or if there is leakage past the sealing lips.*

3) Use direct-reverse clutch inspection procedures to inspect the lined and steel clutch plates.

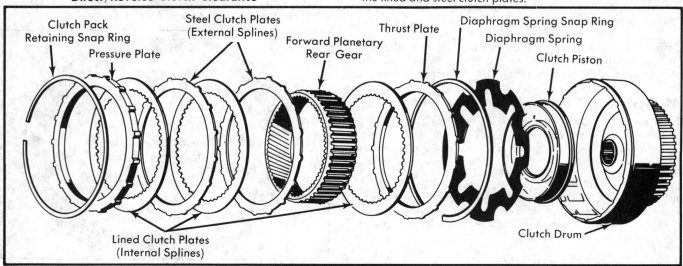

Fig. 12   Exploded View of Forward Clutch Assembly

AUDI 4000 & 5000, PORSCHE 924 & VOLKSWAGEN DASHER (Cont.)

NOTE — *If new lined (internally splined) clutch plates are to be installed, they must be soaked in automatic transmission fluid for at least 15 minutes prior to installation.*

Reassembly — 1) Lubricate piston sealing lips with automatic transmission fluid, then install piston into drum using a twisting motion. Install diaphragm spring, with convex side toward piston, into clutch drum. Install retaining snap ring.

NOTE — *With snap ring installed, diaphragm spring should be lightly tensioned; if not, replace spring.*

2) Install thrust plate into drum. If one side of thrust plate is chamfered, install chamfered side toward diaphragm spring.

NOTE — *Only install forward clutch lined plates that are grooved as shown in Fig. 13.*

Only Install Lined Plates
with Grooves as Shown

**Fig. 13   View of Forward Clutch Lined Plate
Showing Identification Grooves**

3) Install one lined (internally splined) clutch plate, then install forward planetary ring gear so that short splines beneath its retaining ridge are engaged in the lined clutch plates. Install the remaining clutch plates starting with a steel (externally splined) clutch plate and alternating lined and steel plates until all clutch plates are installed. *See Forward Clutch Plate Chart.*

Forward Clutch Plate Chart		
Application	**Steel Plates**	**Lined Plates**
Dasher	2	3
924 & 4000	3	4
5000	4	5

4) Install pressure plate and retaining snap ring into clutch drum. Next, position a dial indicator on clutch assembly so that indicator pointer contacts pressure plate, then zero dial face.

5) Measure forward clutch end play by moving forward planetary ring gear up and down so that dial indicator will show play between pressure plate and snap ring.

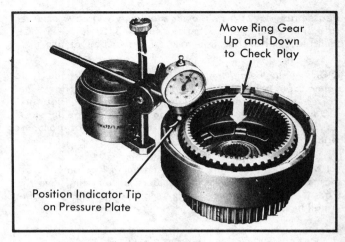

Move Ring Gear
Up and Down
to Check Play

Position Indicator Tip
on Pressure Plate

**Fig. 14   Using a Dial Indicator to Measure
Forward Clutch End Play**

6) Forward clutch end play should be .020-.035" (.50-.90 mm); if not, replace pressure plate with one of correct thickness to bring play within specifications. After correct pressure plate has been installed, recheck end play.

NOTE — *Forward clutch pressure plates are available in thicknesses of .091" (2.3 mm) to .154" (3.9 mm) on 4000 models, or .236" (6.0 mm) to .299" (7.6 mm) on all other models, all in .016" (.4 mm) increments.*

FIRST GEAR ONE-WAY CLUTCH

Disassembly — Remove one-way clutch rollers and spring. Remove snap rings. Using a plastic hammer, carefully drive roller cage out of outer race.

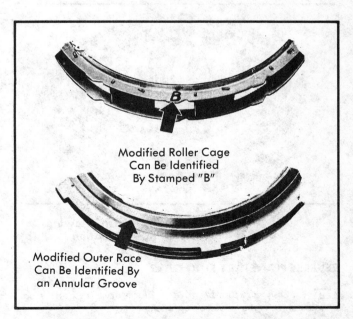

Modified Roller Cage
Can Be Identified
By Stamped "B"

Modified Outer Race
Can Be Identified By
an Annular Groove

**Fig. 15   Modified Roller Cage and Outer Race
Identification (Dasher Models Only)**

Inspection — Inspect all parts for wear, scoring, or other damage and replace parts as necessary.

AUDI 4000 & 5000, PORSCHE 924 & VOLKSWAGEN DASHER (Cont.)

Reassembly — 1) Install lower snap ring in groove of outer race. If necessary, heat outer race to 300-375°F (150-190°C), then place roller cage into race using two pair of pliers.

NOTE — *The heat from outer race will transfer quickly to roller cage, causing cage to stick inside race. If cage is not correctly positioned against lower snap ring and inside race, DO NOT attempt to press it into position after cage has stuck. Carefully knock cage out of outer race and repeat procedure again after race has cooled down.*

2) Make sure that short sides of retaining lugs on cage are positioned correctly against shoulders in outer ring. See *Fig. 16.* If necessary, turn cage slightly immediately after installation.

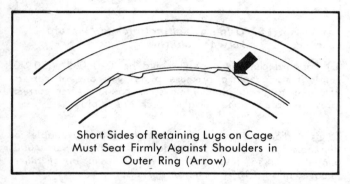

Short Sides of Retaining Lugs on Cage Must Seat Firmly Against Shoulders in Outer Ring (Arrow)

Fig. 16   View of Outer Race and Cage Showing Correct Installation

3) Install upper snap ring. Install rollers and springs into cage as shown in *Fig. 17.*

Rollers and Springs Must Be Installed as Shown

Fig. 17   View of One-Way Clutch Showing Correct Roller & Spring Installation

REVERSE PLANETARY RING GEAR

NOTE — *Only disassemble reverse planetary ring gear if one of the components require replacement.*

Disassembly & Reassembly — Remove snap ring and lift ring gear hub from ring gear. Inspect parking lock notches on ring gear for wear and replace if worn. To reassemble, reverse disassembly procedure.

VALVE BODY ASSEMBLY

NOTE — *As valve body components are removed from each valve body bore, place individual parts in correct order in relative position to valve body to simplify reassembly.*

Disassembly — 1) Remove transfer plate-to-main valve body attaching screws. Lift transfer plate and separator plate from main valve body. Withdraw the four main valve body check balls from passages in valve body.

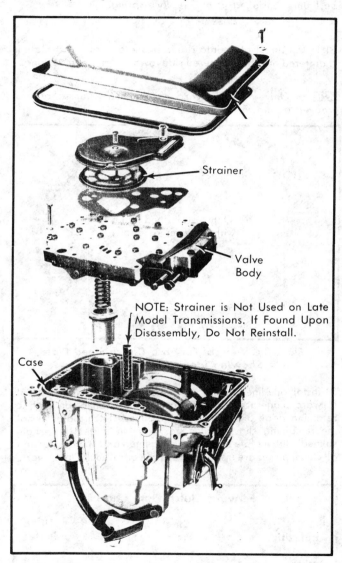

Strainer

Valve Body

NOTE: Strainer is Not Used on Late Model Transmissions. If Found Upon Disassembly, Do Not Reinstall.

Case

Fig. 18   Exploded View Showing Removal of Strainers and Valve Body Assembly

CAUTION — *DO NOT alter settings of adjusting screws.*

2) Remove rear end cover plate and withdraw valves, springs, and adjusting screws. Remove remaining end plates one at a time and withdraw all valves, plugs, springs and adjusting screws. Tag all parts for reassembly reference.

AUDI 4000 & 5000, PORSCHE 924 & VOLKSWAGEN DASHER (Cont.)

VALVE BODY SPRING IDENTIFICATION				
Valve Spring	Length In. (mm)	Diameter In. (mm)①	Number Of Coils	Wire Thickness In. (mm)
Throt. Pres. Limiting Valve	1.390 (35.3)	.303 (7.7)	14.5	.043 (1.1)
Main Pres. Limiting Valve	1.276 (32.4)	.303 (7.7)	11.0	.047 (1.2)
Main Pres. Valve	2.819 (71.6)②	.469 (11.9)	16.5	.059 (1.5)
Throt. Pres. Valve	1.705 (43.3)	.305 (7.75)	16.0	.049 (1.25)
Modulator Valve				
4000	1.126 (28.6)	.305 (7.75)	11.5	.031 (0.8)
All Other Models	.736 (18.7)	.209 (5.3)	12.0	.028 (0.7)
1-2 Shift Valve	.783 (19.9)	.319 (8.1)	6.5	.035 (0.9)
2-3 Shift Valve	.783 (19.9)	.319 (8.1)	6.5	.035 (0.9)
3-2 Control Valve	1.276 (32.4)	.303 (7.7)	12.5	.040 (1.0)
Converter Pres. Valve				
4000	.874 (22.2)	.303 (7.7)	8.5	.049 (1.25)
All Other Models	1.276 (32.4)	.303 (7.7)	12.5	.040 (1.0)
3-2 Kickdown Valve	1.118 (28.4)	.319 (8.1)	11.5	.035 (0.9)

① — Inner diameter of coils; within a tolerance of ±.012" (0.3 mm).
② — 4000 should be 3.031" (77.0 mm).

Inspection — 1) Wash all parts in clean kerosene and dry them with compressed air only (do not use fluffy rags, etc.). Check all parts for burrs and scores; replace assembly if damage is found.

NOTE — *Valves which are slightly scored may be reused. This will not affect operation of transmission.*

2) When valves are clean and lubricated with fluid, they should fall of their own weight in respective bore; if not, check for valve or bore damage.

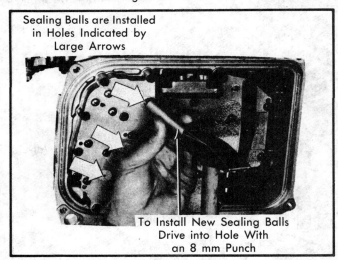

Sealing Balls are Installed in Holes Indicated by Large Arrows

To Install New Sealing Balls Drive into Hole With an 8 mm Punch

Fig. 19 *View of Valve Body Installed in Vehicle Showing Location of Sealing Balls in Transfer Plate*

3) Check all valve body springs for damage and collapsed coils.

CAUTION — *Several springs have similar dimensions; however, they must not be interchanged as they have different tolerances. See Valve Body Spring Identification table.*

4) Take care not to disturb settings of adjusting screws; pressures affected by these screws can only be measured and adjusted accurately on a test stand.

5) Some transfer plates are equipped with three sealing balls. See Fig. 19. If transmission does not shift into 3rd gear, trouble may be caused by a missing sealing ball. To install new sealing balls, stick .118" (3 mm) diameter sealing ball on an 8 mm diameter punch with a small amount of grease and drive ball flush into hole of transfer plate.

Reassembly — 1) Lubricate all parts with automatic transmission fluid and install into proper valve body bores, in reverse order of disassembly. When tightening end plate attaching screws, be careful not to overtighten them as this could easily strip the threads or distort the valve body enough to cause a valve to stick.

2) Ensure all check balls are installed in proper valve body passages. Install transfer plate-to-main valve body screws and tighten from center outward, taking care not to overtighten.

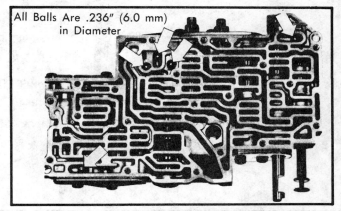

All Balls Are .236" (6.0 mm) in Diameter

Fig. 20 *View of Main Body Showing Location of Check Balls*

Automatic Transaxles

AUDI 4000 & 5000, PORSCHE 924 & VOLKSWAGEN DASHER (Cont.)

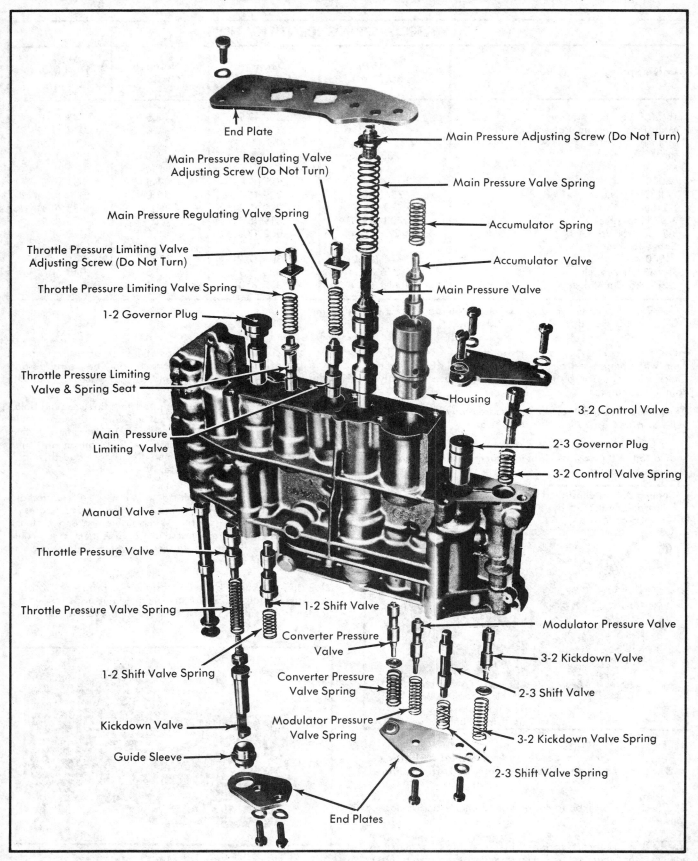

End Plate

Main Pressure Adjusting Screw (Do Not Turn)

Main Pressure Regulating Valve Adjusting Screw (Do Not Turn)

Main Pressure Valve Spring

Main Pressure Regulating Valve Spring

Accumulator Spring

Throttle Pressure Limiting Valve Adjusting Screw (Do Not Turn)

Accumulator Valve

Throttle Pressure Limiting Valve Spring

Main Pressure Valve

1-2 Governor Plug

Throttle Pressure Limiting Valve & Spring Seat

Housing

3-2 Control Valve

Main Pressure Limiting Valve

2-3 Governor Plug

3-2 Control Valve Spring

Manual Valve

Throttle Pressure Valve

Modulator Pressure Valve

Throttle Pressure Valve Spring

1-2 Shift Valve

3-2 Kickdown Valve

Converter Pressure Valve

2-3 Shift Valve

1-2 Shift Valve Spring

Converter Pressure Valve Spring

Kickdown Valve

Modulator Pressure Valve Spring

3-2 Kickdown Valve Spring

Guide Sleeve

2-3 Shift Valve Spring

End Plates

Fig. 21 *Exploded View of Main Body Showing Valve Trains*

AUDI 4000 & 5000, PORSCHE 924 & VOLKSWAGEN DASHER (Cont.)

Install Check Ball Here

Fig. 22 *View of Transfer Plate Showing Location of Check Ball*

GOVERNOR ASSEMBLY

NOTE — *Governor is mounted in final drive housing.*

Removal — Remove attaching bolts and washers and remove governor cover and "O" ring from final drive housing. Withdraw governor from housing using a clockwise twisting motion that will allow governor drive gear to disengage drive pinion gear.

Disassembly — Remove two attaching screws and withdraw thrust plate and governor housing. Remove transfer plate, balance weight and oil strainer. Remove "E" clips and withdraw centrifugal weight, valve, spring and dished washer from pin.

Reassembly — Reverse disassembly procedure and note the following: Lubricate all parts with transmission fluid when assembling. Install oil strainer as shown in *Fig. 23*. Make sure angle in thrust plate is in center of housing so cover will bear against it.

Installation — Reverse removal procedure and note the following: Prior to installation, check governor oil seal and needle bearing located in final drive housing for damage and wear, and replace as necessary. After installation, rotate governor to engage drive gear.

BAND SERVO

Disassembly — Pull servo piston assembly out of cover, then remove "O" ring seals from outside diameter of cover. Remove retaining "E" clip and separate piston pin, accumulator spring, spring seat, and adjusting shim from servo piston. Withdraw two lip seals from servo piston.

Inspection — Clean all parts and check for wear, scoring, or other damage. If replacement of piston is necessary, pin, spring, spring seat, accumulator spring, and shim must also be replaced as this is serviced as an assembly only.

Reassembly — 1) Position spring seat, accumulator spring, and shim on piston pin, install assembly into servo piston, and install retaining "E" clip onto pin.

2) Install lip seals onto piston as follows: Smaller (upper) seal is installed onto piston with lip facing upward, or into servo cover. Larger seal is installed on piston with lip pointed downward, or out of servo cover. Lubricate assembly thoroughly and install piston into cover. Install "O" rings onto outer diameter of servo cover.

NOTE — *Dasher servo cover uses 3 "O" rings, all other models have a servo cover that uses 2 "O" rings.*

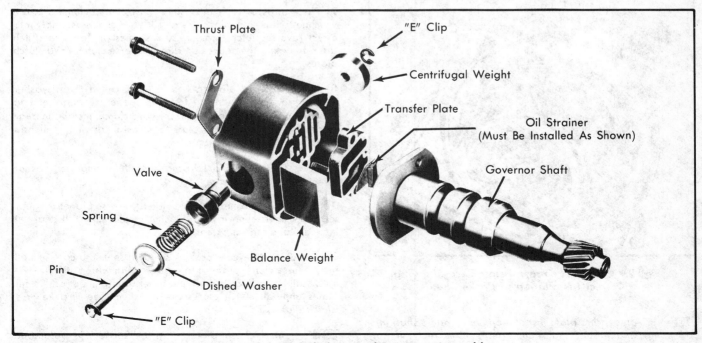

Fig. 23 *Exploded View of Governor Assembly*

AUDI 4000 & 5000, PORSCHE 924 & VOLKSWAGEN DASHER (Cont.)

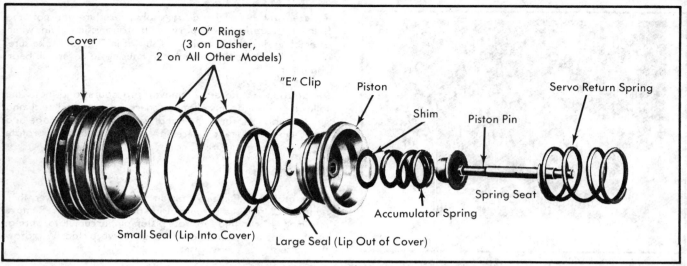

Fig. 24   Exploded View of Band Servo Assembly

TRANSMISSION REASSEMBLY

1) Lubricate first/reverse gear brake piston with automatic transmission fluid. Install brake piston on oil pump. Install oil pump and piston assembly into case, and position pump so that thin rib on pump face is toward top of case. Install thrust washer on pump with thrust washer slot engaging pump rib.

2) Install first/reverse gear brake shell into transmission case so that lug engages in groove at top of case. Position low/reverse brake piston return springs on spring plate, insert assembly into case with springs downward, then install attaching bolts and tighten to specified torque using a diagonal pattern.

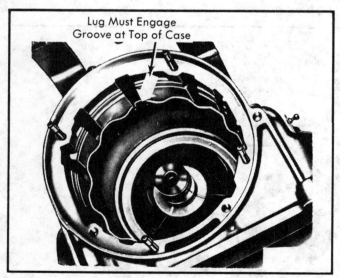

Fig. 25   View of Transmission Case Showing Correct Installation of Brake Shell

NOTE — *After spring plate installation, insert pump shaft into oil pump and ensure that pump gears turn freely; if not, remove oil pump and ensure that it is assembled properly.*

3) Lubricate servo cover "O" rings, then install servo assembly into case and install retaining snap ring. Rotate transmission on work stand so that servo cover points down.

4) Position second gear brake band in case and ensure that it engages servo piston. Loosely install pushrod for adjusting screw, then install adjusting screw and lock nut.

5) Lubricate direct/reverse clutch assembly, then install it into case, sliding it onto oil pump neck and into second gear brake band.

6) Tighten brake band adjusting screw just enough to prevent band from shifting its position on direct/reverse clutch drum. Rotate transmission case so that open end is facing up.

7) Place thrust washer in position on forward clutch and use vaseline to hold it in place. Install forward clutch assembly into direct/reverse clutch, making sure splines on forward clutch drum fully engage splines on direct/reverse clutch lined clutch plates.

8) Install forward planetary-to-forward clutch thrust washer into forward clutch. Install forward planetary gear set into forward planetary ring gear in forward clutch. Install sun gear (short end first) into gear set, then install driving shell and thrust washer over sun gear.

NOTE — *Ensure lugs of driving shell fully engage tabs of direct/reverse clutch drum.*

9) Install thrust washer on underside of reverse planetary gear set and use vaseline to hold washer in place. Install gear set into case and onto sun gear.

10) Install first/reverse brake waved washer into case. Install first/reverse clutch plates into case starting with a steel (externally splined) clutch plate and alternating lined and steel plates until all clutch plates are installed. See *First/Reverse Clutch Plate Chart.*

NOTE — *Lined clutch plates must be soaked in automatic transmission fluid for at least 15 minutes prior to installation.*

AUDI 4000 & 5000, PORSCHE 924 & VOLKSWAGEN DASHER (Cont.)

First/Reverse Clutch Plate Chart

Application	Steel Plates	Lined Plates
Dasher	4	4
All Other Models	5	5

11) Install first gear one-way clutch assembly into transmission case, then push clutch downward while rotating reverse planetary gear set to fully engage parts.

NOTE — *With one-way clutch installed, it should not be possible to rotate reverse planetary gear set counterclockwise due to the locking of the one-way clutch.*

Parts are Installed Correctly if Groove for One-Way Clutch Snap Ring is Exposed

Fig. 26 Installing One-Way Clutch Snap Ring

12) Install one-way clutch-to-case snap ring. If all parts are correctly installed, then one-way clutch snap ring groove will be exposed. Do not attempt to force snap ring into groove on an incorrectly assembled transmission.

13) Position both thrust washers on rear side of reverse planetary ring gear, then install ring gear into case so that it fully engages reverse planetary gear set.

14) Install separation plate gasket over case studs, place separation plate on top of gasket, then install and tighten retaining screws.

NOTE — *At this time, second gear brake band must be adjusted. To adjust brake band, the transmission case must be horizontal to prevent band from jamming. Adjust band as follows:*

15) Tighten brake band adjusting screw to 7 ft. lbs. (1 mkg), loosen screw, then tighten again to 4 ft. lbs. (.5 mkg). Finally, back adjusting screw off exactly 2 turns for 4000 models or exactly 2½ turns for all other models. Tighten adjusting screw lock nut.

16) If case linkage was disassembled, reinstall in case using *Fig. 7* as an assembly guide.

17) Install a new seal on accumulator piston (lip pointing toward case), and install piston and spring into case. Install valve body assembly into case, making sure manual valve engages manual lever, and kickdown valve engages kickdown lever. Install valve body-to-case bolts and tighten from center outward.

18) Position a new pan gasket on transmission case. Install oil pan, then install and tighten oil pan attaching bolts.

NOTE — *This completes assembly of transmission. Installation of impeller shaft, pump shaft, and measurement of play between transmission and final drive will be made in Final Assembly, located near end of this article.*

FINAL DRIVE

DISASSEMBLY

NOTE — *Prior to final disassembly, it is recommended that backlash and turning torque be measured and recorded. See Pinion Depth and Bearing Preload adjusting procedure for measuring procedure.*

1) Place final drive housing in a suitable holding fixture. Remove speedometer driven gear assembly (except 924) and governor assembly from final drive housing.

2) Remove final drive housing front cover attaching bolts, then lift off cover. It may be necessary to use a puller to remove front cover. Remove rear cover attaching bolts and pull off cover.

3) Remove retaining bolt from center of each axle drive flange, then using care not to damage oil seals, pull flanged shafts out of final drive housing.

4) If the same differential side bearings are to be reinstalled, use a depth micrometer and measure the depths to which each side bearing adjusting ring is installed into final drive housing. Note each measurement for reassembly and adjusting reference, then carefully mark the position of each adjusting ring in housing using a scribe or gear paint.

5) Remove bolts and lock plates from adjusting rings. Remove adjusting rings. Tilt differential assembly to one side and lift pinion shaft out of housing. Lift out differential assembly.

NOTE — *If necessary for bearing replacement, press bearing outer races out of adjusting rings.*

6) To disassemble differential assembly, proceed as follows: If necessary for replacement, pull differential side bearings from differential case using puller. On 4000 and 5000 models, use same puller to pull speedometer drive gear from differential case.

NOTE — *On 4000 and 5000 models, the speedometer drive gear will be destroyed when pulled from differential case. Do not remove the gear unless it is worn or damaged and requires replacement.*

7) Place differential assembly in a soft jaw vise with ring gear attaching bolts up. Loosen attaching bolts and remove ring gear by tapping lightly on bolt heads.

AUDI 4000 & 5000, PORSCHE 924 & VOLKSWAGEN DASHER (Cont.)

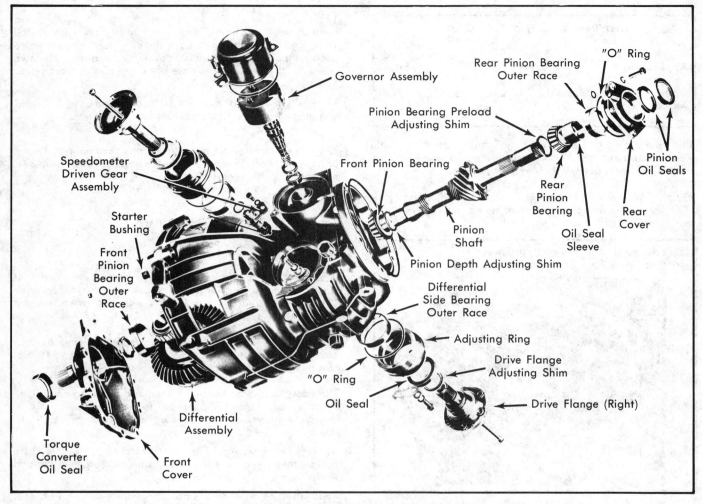

Fig. 27 *Exploded View of Dasher Final Drive Assembly*

8) On all models, separate differential housing cover from housing using a screwdriver. Using a drift, drive out differential pinion gear shaft. Withdraw pinion gears, side gears, thrust washers, and nuts for axle drive flange shaft retaining bolts.

9) If pinion bearings on pinion shaft require replacement, proceed as follows: Place pinion shaft in a press and using press plates positioned under bearings, drive pinion shaft out of bearings and oil seal race.

NOTE — *If original parts are to be reinstalled, note number and thickness of pinion adjusting shims on pinion shaft for reassembly reference.*

10) Pinion bearing outer races and oil seals will also have to be replaced if pinion bearings are replaced. Remove front cover torque converter seal by driving it out of cover using a cold chisel. Remove front cover pinion seal(s). Press pinion bearing outer race from front cover.

NOTE — *If pinion bearing outer race is being removed from both the front and rear cover, use care to keep them separated.*

11) Drive both pinion oil seals from rear cover using a driver. Press pinion bearing outer race from rear cover using a driver.

REASSEMBLY & ADJUSTMENTS

Differential Assembly — **1)** Inspect all thrust surfaces on differential housing, cover, ring gear, pinion gear shaft and thrust washers. Replace all worn parts. Inspect gear teeth for burrs or excessive wear and replace as necessary.

NOTE — *If pinion shaft or ring gear requires replacement, both components must be replaced as they are a matched set.*

2) Position differential side gears, large thrust washers, dished thrust washers, and pinion gear into differential housing. Align pinion gear holes with holes in housing. Drive pinion gear shaft through pinion gears.

NOTE — *If pinion gear shaft does not fit tightly, replace it with a new shaft.*

3) Place differential cover on differential case. Install two centering pins in two opposite ring gear attaching bolt holes to

AUDI 4000 & 5000, PORSCHE 924 & VOLKSWAGEN DASHER (Cont.)

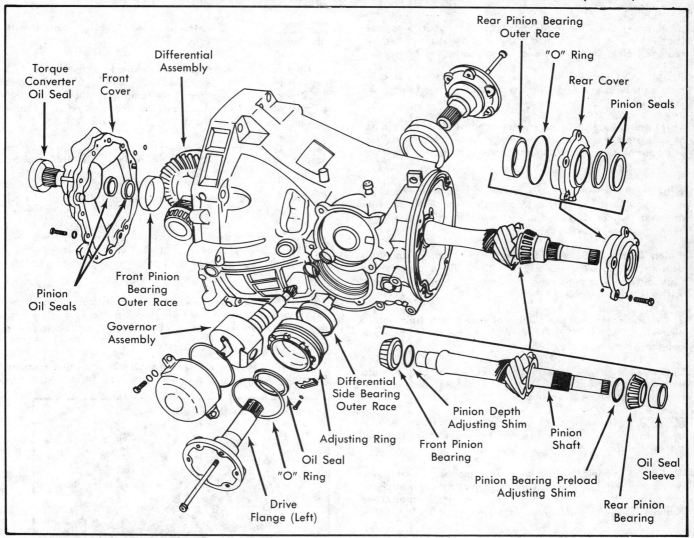

Fig. 28 Exploded View of 924, 4000 and 5000 Final Drive Assembly

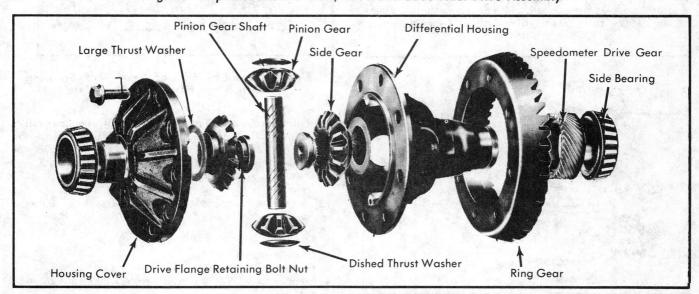

**Fig. 29 Exploded View of Differential Assembly
(4000 and 5000 Shown, All Others Similar)**

AUDI 4000 & 5000, PORSCHE 924 & VOLKSWAGEN DASHER (Cont.)

align ring gear during installation. Heat ring gear to approximately 212°F (100°C), then position it on housing. Remove centering pins, then install and tighten attaching bolts.

NOTE — *On Audi 5000 models, a new speedometer drive gear must be pressed onto differential case prior to side bearing installation.*

4) If differential side bearing were removed, heat them in hot oil and press them onto differential housing and cover. Press side bearing outer races into position in side bearing adjusting rings.

NOTE — *If original parts are reused, use same thickness pinion depth and bearing preload adjusting shims as were removed during disassembly. For replacement gear sets or bearing, proceed as follows:*

Pinion Depth & Bearing Preload — 1) Heat pinion shaft bearings to approximately 212°F (100°C). Press larger of the 2 pinion bearings onto rear end (gear end) of pinion shaft **without** adjusting shim.

2) On Dasher models, press smaller bearing onto front end of pinion shaft with a .059" (1.5 mm) test shim installed between bearing and pinion shaft flange.

3) On 924, 4000 and 5000 models, press smaller bearing onto pinion shaft with a .043" (1.1 mm) test shim installed between bearing and pinion shaft flange.

CAUTION — *If pinion shaft is installed into housing without this test shim installed, it will contact housing and cause an incorrect reading.*

4) On all models, install final drive housing front cover (without oil seals), then install and tighten attaching bolts. Position pinion shaft in place in housing, then install rear cover (without oil seals) and tighten attaching bolts.

5) Install magnetic plate (VW 385/17) onto rear end of pinion shaft. Attach a dial indicator to final drive housing so that indicator tip is touching magnetic plate on pinion shaft. Zero indicator. Move pinion shaft up and down (without turning shaft) and note indicator reading.

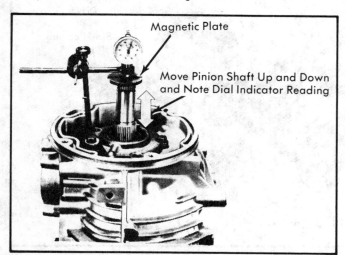

Magnetic Plate

Move Pinion Shaft Up and Down and Note Dial Indicator Reading

Fig. 30   Measuring Pinion Shaft Play to Determine Total Pinion Adjusting Shim Thickness

CAUTION — *If pinion shaft is turned during measurement, reading will be incorrect.*

6) Next, add the thickness of the installed test shim, .059" (1.5 mm) on Dasher models or .043" (1.1 mm) on 924, 4000 and 5000 models; .006" (.15 mm) for bearing preload, and .004" (.1 mm) allowance for setting of bearing to the dial indicator reading obtained in step 5).

7) The resulting sum is total thickness of adjusting shims necessary to obtain correct pinion depth and bearing preload settings. Record shim thickness.

8) On all models, remove front cover and pinion shaft from final drive housing.

9) On Dasher models, subtract thickness of installed shim (.059" or 1.5 mm) from total obtained in step 6), then install a shim of this thickness between bearing and gear on gear end of pinion shaft.

10) On 924, 4000 and 5000 models, press front pinion bearing from shaft, remove test shim, then install a shim of the total thickness determined in step 6). Press bearing back onto pinion shaft.

11) On all models, install pinion shaft into final drive housing. Reinstall front cover and tighten attaching bolts.

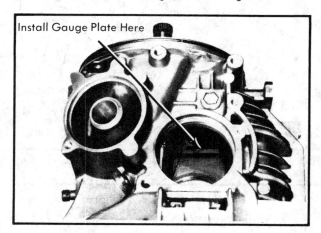

Install Gauge Plate Here

Fig. 31   Installed View of Pinion Shaft Showing Positioning of Special Gauge Plate

12) Install special gauge plate (VW 385/28) on pinion shaft as shown in *Fig. 31*. Next, adjust clamp ring on universal measuring bar (VW 385/1) until distance "A" in *Fig. 32* is 2.28" (58 mm) on Dasher models or 3.23" (82 mm) on 924, 4000 and 5000 models.

13) Assemble the following measuring tools to universal measuring bar as shown in *Fig. 32*:

- Dial Indicator
- Centering Discs VW 385/2
- Measuring Pin VW 385/13
- Extension VW 385/20 (Dasher) or VW 385/15 (924, 4000 and 5000)
- Setting Gauge VW 385/5 (Dasher) or VW 385/26 (924, 4000 and 5000)

AUDI 4000 & 5000, PORSCHE 924 & VOLKSWAGEN DASHER (Cont.)

With all tools assembled, zero dial indicator with a .118" (3.0 mm) preload.

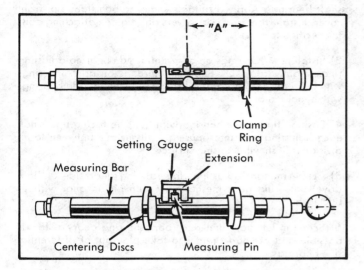

Fig. 32   Assembling Measuring Tools for Pinion Depth Shim Selection

14) Place an "O" ring on left side differential side bearing adjusting ring. Lightly lubricate "O" ring and adjusting ring threads with multi-purpose grease. Install adjusting ring (with side bearing outer race installed) into final drive housing until outer surface of adjusting ring is flush with surface of housing.

15) Insert measuring bar assembly into housing. Place an "O" ring on right adjusting ring. Lubricate "O" ring and adjusting ring threads. Install adjusting ring into final drive housing.

CAUTION — *Do not let measuring pin touch measuring plate.*

16) Turn knob on end of measuring bar to move setting ring and centering disc outward, until bar can just barely be turned by hand. Hand turn pinion shaft back and forth to settle pinion bearings.

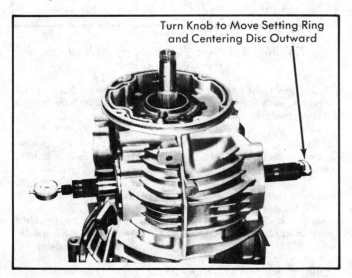

Fig. 33   Installed View of Universal Measuring Bar

17) Rotate measuring bar until pin extension rests squarely against gauge plate. Then rotate bar back and forth over center. Read and record maximum dial indicator reading.

18) To determine thickness of correct pinion depth adjusting shim to install on Dasher models, first subtract the dial indicator reading obtained in step **17)** from the thickness of the installed test shim (.059" or 1.5 mm), then to the difference add the deviation number stamped on ring gear. See *Fig. 34.* The resulting sum is the thickness of correct pinion depth adjusting shim to install.

NOTE — *The deviation number stamped on ring gear is in hundredth-millimeters.*

19) To determine thickness of correct pinion depth adjusting shim to install on 924, 4000 and 5000 models, subtract the ring gear deviation number from the dial indicator reading obtained in step **17)**. The remainder is thickness of pinion depth adjusting shim to install.

NOTE — *As with Dasher models, the ring gear deviation number is in hundredth-millimeters.*

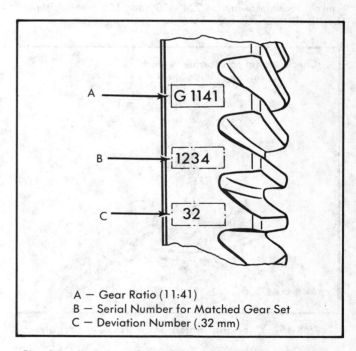

A — Gear Ratio (11:41)
B — Serial Number for Matched Gear Set
C — Deviation Number (.32 mm)

Fig. 34   Location of Deviation Number on Ring Gear (924, 4000 and 5000 Shown — Dasher Similar)

20) To determine thickness of correct pinion bearing preload adjusting shim to install on all models, subtract thickness of pinion depth adjusting shim that was just determined, from the total thickness of bearing preload and pinion depth adjusting shims that was determined in step **6)**.

NOTE — *Pinion depth and bearing preload adjusting shims are available in thicknesses of .043" (1.1 mm) to .075" (1.9 mm) in increments of .001" (.025 mm). Also, always check thickness of adjusting shims at several points using a micrometer.*

AUDI 4000 & 5000, PORSCHE 924 & VOLKSWAGEN DASHER (Cont.)

21) Remove measuring bar assembly from final drive housing. Take off final drive housing front cover and remove pinion shaft. Press both bearings from shaft and remove test shim.

22) Install selected pinion bearing preload shim on gear end of shaft. Install selected pinion depth shim on opposite end of shaft. Heat bearings to approximately 212°F (100°C) and press them into position on pinion shaft. Press pinion oil seal sleeve onto rear end of shaft.

23) Lubricate bearings with hypoid gear oil, then reinstall pinion shaft and front cover. Reinstall measuring bar assembly, then zero dial indicator with .040" (1.0 mm) preload for Dasher models or .118" (3.0 mm) preload for 924, 4000 and 5000 models.

24) Repeat procedure outlined in step **17)**. If correct depth and preload shims are installed, dial indicator reading should be the ring gear deviation number with a tolerance of ±.0016" (.04 mm).

25) After installing correct pinion adjusting shims, use a torque wrench and check turning torque of pinion shaft. Turning torque for Dasher models should be 22-56 INCH Lbs. (25-65 cmkg). Turning torque for 924, 4000 and 5000 models should be 22-48 INCH Lbs. (25-55 cmkg).

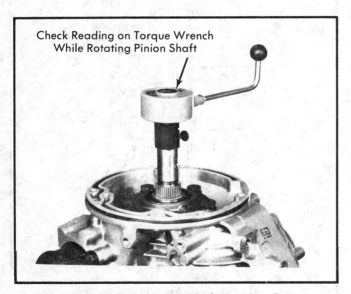

Check Reading on Torque Wrench While Rotating Pinion Shaft

Fig. 35　Checking Pinion Shaft Turning Torque

NOTE — *Turning torque values given are for new bearings only. If used bearings are reinstalled, the turning torque should be measured prior to final drive disassembly. When correctly assembled, turning torque with used bearings should be approximately 1.7-3.5 INCH Lbs. (2-4 cmkg) greater than it was prior to disassembly.*

26) If turning torque is not within specified value, sufficient shim thickness for bearing preload and bearing settling have not been allowed.

Side Bearing Preload & Ring Gear Backlash — 1) After adjusting pinion shaft, remove front and rear covers from final drive housing. Withdraw pinion shaft.

2) Install differential assembly and pinion shaft into final drive housing. Install new oil seals into front and rear covers. Install new "O" ring on rear cover. Lubricate "O" ring and pinion shaft bearings. Apply a suitable sealer to bolt flange of front cover. Install front and rear covers and tighten attaching bolts to specified torque.

3) Install new "O" rings on differential side bearing adjusting rings. Lightly coat "O" rings and threads on adjusting rings with multi-purpose grease. Lubricate differential side bearings with hypoid gear oil.

4) Position final drive housing with left side facing up. Install each adjusting ring into housing until surface between tooth division is flush with housing surface.

5) Screw in right adjusting ring (at ring gear side of final drive) until ring gear meshes fully with pinion gear without backlash.

6) Screw in left adjusting ring (opposite ring gear) as far as possible and preload slightly to take play out of differential side bearings.

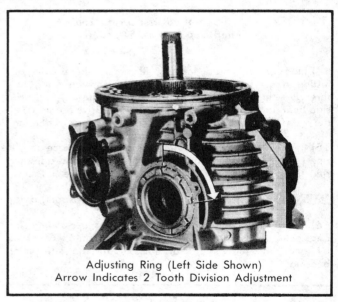

Adjusting Ring (Left Side Shown)
Arrow Indicates 2 Tooth Division Adjustment

Fig. 36　Adjusting Side Bearing Preload and Ring Gear Backlash

7) Unscrew right adjusting ring ½ tooth division. Screw in left adjusting ring 2 tooth divisions. This should correctly set side bearing preload and ring gear backlash.

8) To check ring gear backlash, turn pinion shaft several times in both directions to settle bearings. Using a suitable holding tool (VW 386), lock pinion shaft so that it cannot turn.

9) Insert clamping sleeve (VW 521/4) with slotted sleeve (VW 521/7 Dasher or VW 521/8 924, 4000 and 5000) into differential and secure with nut. Adjust length of backlash measuring bar (VW 388) to 2.441" (62 mm) on Dasher models or to 2.677" (68 mm) on 924, 4000 and 5000 models.

NOTE — *See Figures 37 and 38 for assembly and positioning of ring gear backlash measuring tools.*

AUDI 4000 & 5000, PORSCHE 924 & VOLKSWAGEN DASHER (Cont.)

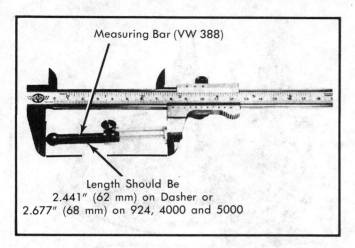

Measuring Bar (VW 388)

Length Should Be
2.441" (62 mm) on Dasher or
2.677" (68 mm) on 924, 4000 and 5000

Fig. 37 Adjusting Measuring Bar Length for Ring Gear Backlash Check

10) Attach measuring bar to clamping sleeve. Install dial indicator with square end extension (VW 382/10) in holder (VW 387) and bolt holder to final drive housing.

NOTE — *Dial indicator must be located at a right angle to backlash measuring tool.*

11) Turn ring gear to take up backlash. Zero dial indicator and clamp in holder. Turn ring gear in opposite direction until it is stopped by pinion gear and note indicator reading. This reading is ring gear backlash.

12) Check ring gear backlash at four locations (90° apart) around circumference of ring gear. Add the four

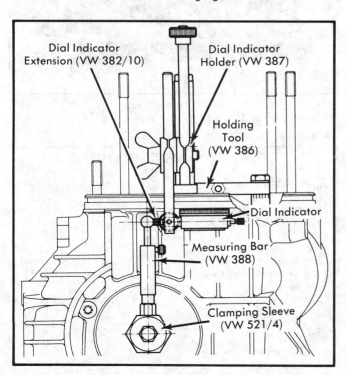

Dial Indicator
Extension (VW 382/10)

Dial Indicator
Holder (VW 387)

Holding
Tool
(VW 386)

Dial Indicator

Measuring Bar
(VW 388)

Clamping Sleeve
(VW 521/4)

Fig. 38 Positioning of Ring Gear Backlash Measuring Tools

measurements together, then divide this by four. Resulting sum is average ring gear backlash. Ring gear backlash should be .006-.010" (.15-.25 mm).

NOTE — *Difference between the four backlash measurements must not exceed .002" (.05mm). If measurements differ more than this, ring gear or pinion shaft is incorrectly installed.*

13) If backlash is not within specifications, correct by turning both side bearing adjusting rings by equal amounts in opposite directions.

NOTE — *If new differential side bearings have been installed as well as new pinion shaft bearings, recheck pinion shaft turning torque. With differential installed, pinion shaft turning torque should be approximately 3.5-4.4 INCH Lbs. (4.5 cmkg) more than it was when only the pinion shaft was installed.*

14) Install side bearing adjusting ring lock plates. Recheck total bearing preload to ensure no alterations were made during backlash adjustment.

Final Assembly of Transaxle — 1) To measure play between final drive housing and transmission, place a straight edge on transmission attaching face of final drive housing, and using a depth gauge, measure distance from top surface of straight edge down to edge of pinion shaft oil seal sleeve (measurement "A" in *Fig. 39*). Next, measure distance from top surface of straight edge to face of final drive housing (measurement "B" in *Fig. 39*). Subtract measurement "B" from measurement "A" and note answer for future reference.

2) Place a new gasket on transmission separation plate, position straight edge on transmission case and measure distance from top surface of striaght edge down to gasket surface (measurement "D" in *Fig. 39*). Next, measure distance from top surface of striaght edge down to shim surface on shoulder of reverse planetary gear set ring gear (measurement "E" in *Fig. 39*). Subtract measurement "E" from measurement "D" and note answer for future reference.

3) Subtract the last measurement obtained in step **2)** from last measurement obtained in step **1)**. Remainder is end play (without shims) between final drive and transmission. Select proper end play shim(s) to use by finding applicable end play reading in first column of End Play Shim Chart, and obtaining shim thickness noted in second column.

4) Install selected end play adjusting shim(s) into final drive case, on top of pinion shaft oil seal sleeve. Next, install sealing "O" ring and final drive housing-to-transmission oil seal into pinion cavity of final drive housing.

NOTE — *Transmission-to-final drive end play adjusting shims are available in thicknesses of .016" (.4 mm) and .047" (1.2 mm). Combine shim thicknesses to obtain total thickness required.*

5) Install impeller shaft and pump shaft fully into transmission, position "O" ring seal on final drive case, then mate final drive and transmission cases. Install final drive-to-transmission case nuts and tighten to specified torque.

AUDI 4000 & 5000, PORSCHE 924 & VOLKSWAGEN DASHER (Cont.)

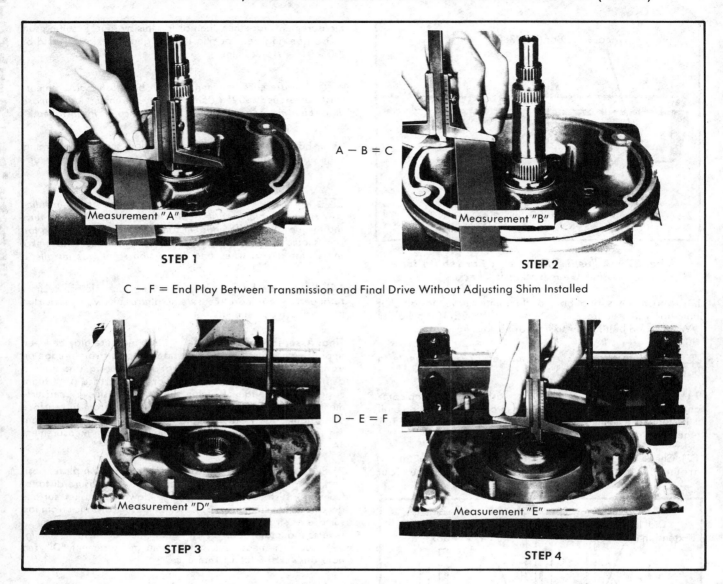

Measurement "A"

STEP 1

$A - B = C$

Measurement "B"

STEP 2

C — F = End Play Between Transmission and Final Drive Without Adjusting Shim Installed

Measurement "D"

STEP 3

$D - E = F$

Measurement "E"

STEP 4

Fig. 39   Using a Depth Gauge to Determine Transmission-to-Final Drive End Play Adjusting Shim

6) Place new "O" ring seals onto governor, governor cover, and speedometer driven gear assembly, and install into case. Finally, install torque converter onto stator support to complete assembly.

End Play Shim Selection Chart

If End Play Is In. (mm)	Install This Shim In. (mm)
.009-.033 (.23-.84)	None
.033-.049 (.85-1.24)	.016 (.4)
.049-.065 (1.25-1.64)	.032 (.8)
.065-.080 (1.65-2.04)	.048 (1.2)
.081-.096 (2.05-2.44)	.064 (1.6)
.096-.112 (2.45-2.84)	.080 (2.0)
.112-.128 (2.85-3.24)	.096 (2.4)
.128-.143 (3.25-3.64)	.112 (2.8)
.144-.153 (3.65-3.88)	.128 (3.2)

TIGHTENING SPECIFICATIONS

Application	Ft. Lbs. (mkg)
Transmission-to-Final Drive	
924 Models	18 (2.5)
All Other Models	22 (3.0)
Torque Converter-to-Drive Plate	22 (3.0)
Drive Flange-to-Differential	18 (2.5)
Front or Rear Cover-to-Housing	18 (2.5)
Ring Gear-to-Differential Case	
924 Models	58-69 (8.0-9.5)
All Other Models	50 (7.0)
Band Adjusting Screw Lock Nut	14 (2.0)
Rear Mount-to-Case	40 (5.5)
Transmission-to-Engine	
All Models (Exc. 924)	40 (5.5)
Manual Valve Lever Nut	14 (2.0)
Kickdown Lever Nut	11 (1.5)

Automatic Transaxles

CHAMP & COLT

DESCRIPTION

The Champ and Colt model KM170 automatic transaxle assembly consists of the following: Automatic transmission; transfer assembly; and the differential. The complete transaxle assembly is contained in a single housing. Both units use a common oil sump and oil supply. The automatic transmission consists of a front and rear clutch, kickdown band, low-reverse brake, one-way clutch and a planetary gearset. Transfer assembly consists of a drive gear, idler gear, driven gear and a transfer shaft. The differential consists of a differential case, ring gear, pinion shaft and gears, and 2 side gears.

LUBRICATION & ADJUSTMENT

See AUTOMATIC TRANSMISSION SERVICING Section.

SERVICE (IN VEHICLE)

AXLE SHAFTS

Removal — 1) Remove front wheel dust cap and loosen lock nut. Raise vehicle and remove tires and undercover panel. Remove lower ball joint and strut from lower control arm. Drain transaxle fluid.

2) Use suitable tool and insert between transaxle case and Double Offset Joint (D.O.J.). Apply pressure to the tool handle and force axle shaft from transaxle.

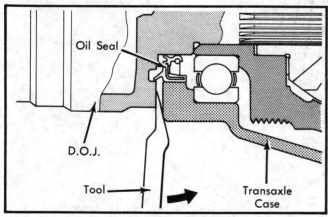

Fig. 1   Drive Axle Shaft Removal

NOTE — Replace D.O.J. side retainer ring each time the drive shaft is removed from transaxle case.

3) Force drive shaft out of hub with axle puller (CT-1003). When the drive shaft is forced out, do not let spacer fall out of hub (inner side).

Disassembly — Remove inner joint boot. Remove circlip from joint and remove outer race. Remove snap ring and inner race. Remove cage and balls as an assembly.

NOTE — Do not disassemble inner bearing assembly as they are mated parts and should not be disturbed.

Reassembly — To assemble, reverse disassembly procedure and note the following: Apply grease to inner and outer races. Install CV joint assembly on shaft with chamfered edge of inner race facing outer edge of shaft. Install new boots and place boot clamps 3.5" (90 mm) apart.

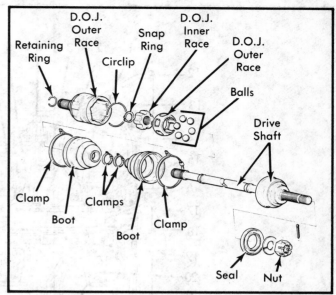

Fig. 2   Exploded View of Drive Shaft

Installation — To install, reverse removal procedure and note the following: Install a new D.O.J. side retainer ring.

WHEEL BEARINGS

Removal — 1) Remove drive shaft and brake assembly from hub. Remove tie rod end from knuckle. Disconnect knuckle from upper strut and lower control arm. Remove hub and knuckle as an assembly.

2) Mount hub and knuckle assembly in a vise and drive hub from knuckle with soft hammer. Remove brake disc. Using a hammer and drift, drive out inner and outer bearing races.

Installation — 1) Drive outer races of inner and outer bearings into knuckle. Apply grease to knuckle, oil seals and bearings. Mount brake disc to hub and tighten bolts evenly. Install outer wheel bearing, then press in outer oil seal. Hold·inner race of outer bearing with bearing holder (MB990776-A), then press hub into knuckle.

NOTE — Wheel bearing preload adjustment MUST be performed without inner oil seal installed.

2) Install inner wheel bearing and install spacer selection gauge (MB990768) into hub assembly. Tighten nut to approximately 14 ft. lbs. (2.8 mkg). Rotate hub and gauge assembly several times to seat bearings. Install dial indicator and load indicator by .19" (5 mm). Zero indicator, hold threaded stud of gauge and back off axle nut until travel no longer registers on indicator.

3) Note indicator reading and repeat procedure. Average both readings and select proper spacer. Remove gauge, install inner oil seal and complete installation by reversing removal procedure. Spacer MUST be installed on end of hub with chamfered side facing knuckle.

NOTE — Spacers are available in 5 thicknesses from .139" (3.55 mm) to .159" (4.03 mm) in .012" (.12 mm) increments.

CHAMP & COLT (Cont.)

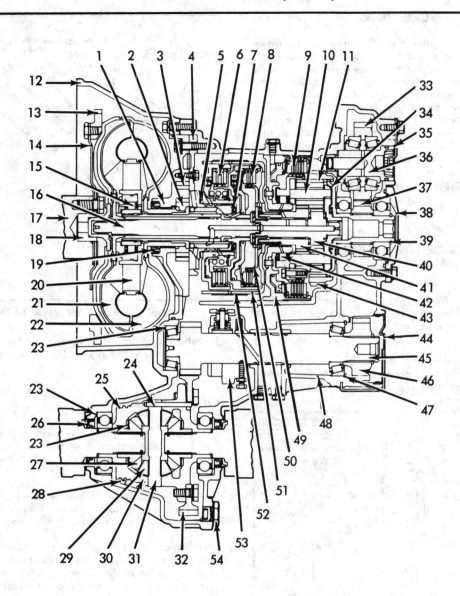

1. Oil Pump Housing
2. Oil Pump Drive Gear
3. Oil Pump Driven Gear
4. Reaction Shaft Support
5. Selective Thrust Washer
6. Front Clutch
7. Selective Thrust Race
8. Rear Clutch
9. Low-Reverse Brake
10. Planetary Gear Set
11. Annulus Gear
12. Converter Housing
13. Starter Ring Gear
14. Flexible Plate
15. One-way Clutch
16. Input Shaft
17. Crankshaft
18. Bushing
19. Oil Seal
20. Stator
21. Turbine
22. Impeller
23. Selective Spacer
24. Pinion Shaft Lock Pin
25. Speedometer Drive Gear
26. Oil Seal
27. Side Gear
28. Speedometer Driven Gear
29. Pinion Gear
30. Differential Case
31. Pinion Shaft
32. Differential Ring Gear
33. Transfer Idle Gear
34. Output Flange
35. Lock Plate
36. Transfer Idle Shaft
37. Transfer Drive Gear
38. Bearing Retainer
39. Selective Snap Ring
40. Foward Sun Gear
41. Reverse Sun Gear
42. One-way Clutch
43. Parking Sprag
44. Cover
45. Transfer Shaft
46. Transfer Driven Gear
47. Snap Ring
48. Transaxle Case
49. Center Support
50. Clutch Hub
51. Kickdown Drum
52. Kickdown Band
53. Governor
54. Drain Plug

Fig. 3 Cross-Sectional View of Champ and Colt Model KM170 Automatic Transaxle Assembly

CHAMP & COLT (Cont.)

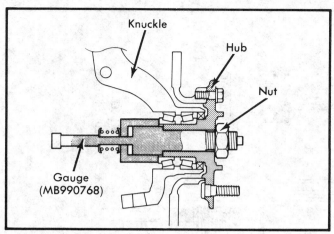

Fig. 4 Installing Gauge to Measure Bearing Preload

TROUBLE SHOOTING

NO STARTER OPERATION IN "P" OR "N"

Faulty or misadjusted inhibitor switch. Manual linkage out of adjustment.

NO DRIVE IN "D"

Throttle control cable out of adjustment. Low fluid level. Manual linkage out of adjustment. Line pressure too low. Faulty rear clutch and piston. Faulty overrunning clutch. Valve body malfunction. Defective oil pump.

NO DRIVE IN "R"

Throttle control cable out of adjustment. Low fluid level. Manual linkage out of adjustment. Line pressure too low. Valve body malfunction. Faulty front clutch and piston. Faulty low-reverse brake and piston. Missing "O" ring in front clutch circuit between valve and body case. Defective oil pump.

HARSH ENGAGEMENT

From "N" to "D", "2", "L" or "R" — Idle speed too high. Throttle control cable out of adjustment. Line pressure too high.

3-2 Kickdown — Throttle control cable out of adjustment. Low fluid level. Line pressure too low. Valve body malfunction. Kickdown band out of adjustment.

POOR PERFORMANCE OR OVERHEATING IN "D"

Faulty torque converter.

TRANSMISSION SLIPS IN "D"

Throttle control cable out of adjustment. Low fluid level. Manual linkage out of adjustment. Line pressure too low. Faulty rear clutch and piston. Faulty overrunning clutch. Valve body malfunction.

TRANSMISSION SLIPS IN "R"

Throttle control cable out of adjustment. Low fluid level. Manual linkage out of adjustment. Line pressure too low. Valve body malfunction. Faulty front clutch and piston. Faulty low-reverse brake and piston. Missing "O" ring in front clutch circuit between valve body and case.

TRANSMISSION SLIPS ON 1-2 UPSHIFT

Throttle control cable out of adjustment. Low fluid level. Line pressure too low. Valve body malfunction. Faulty kickdown band or servo. Kickdown band out of adjustment.

TRANSMISSION SLIPS ON 2-3 UPSHIFT

Throttle control cable out of adjustment. Low fluid level. Line pressure too low. Valve body malfunction. Faulty front clutch and piston.

TRANSMISSION SLIPS OR SHUDDERS ON STARTS IN "L"

Throttle control cable out of adjustment. Low fluid level. Manual linkage out of adjustment. Valve body malfunction.

NO DOWNSHIFT IN "D" TO "L" SHIFT

Manual shift linkage out of adjustment. Valve body malfunction. Faulty kickdown band or servo. Kickdown band out of adjustment.

NO 1-2 UPSHIFT OR WRONG SPEED 1-2 UPSHIFT

Throttle control cable out of adjustment. Low fluid level. Line pressure too low. Valve body malfunction. Governor valve malfunction. Faulty kickdown band or servo. Kickdown band out of adjustment.

NO 2-3 UPSHIFT OR WRONG SPEED 2-3 UPSHIFT

Throttle control cable out of adjustment. Low fluid level. Line pressure too low. Valve body malfunction. Faulty front clutch or piston. Governor valve malfunction.

UPSHIFT IN "L"

Manual linkage out of adjustment.

"P" WILL NOT ENGAGE

Manual linkage out of adjustment. Faulty parking mechanism.

CONVERTER NOISE

Defective oil pump. Interference of oil pump gear teeth, and wear of bushing.

TESTING

ROAD TEST

1) Before road testing, be certain that fluid level and condition, and control linkage adjustments have been checked and corrected as necessary. During test, transmission should upshift and downshift at approximately the same speeds as shown in Shift Speeds chart. All shifts may vary slightly due to production tolerances or tire size. The important factor is the quality of the shifts. All shifts should be smooth, responsive, and with no slippage or engine speed runaway.

2) Slippage or engine runaway in any gear usually indicates clutch or band problems. The slipping clutch or band in a par-

CHAMP & COLT (Cont.)

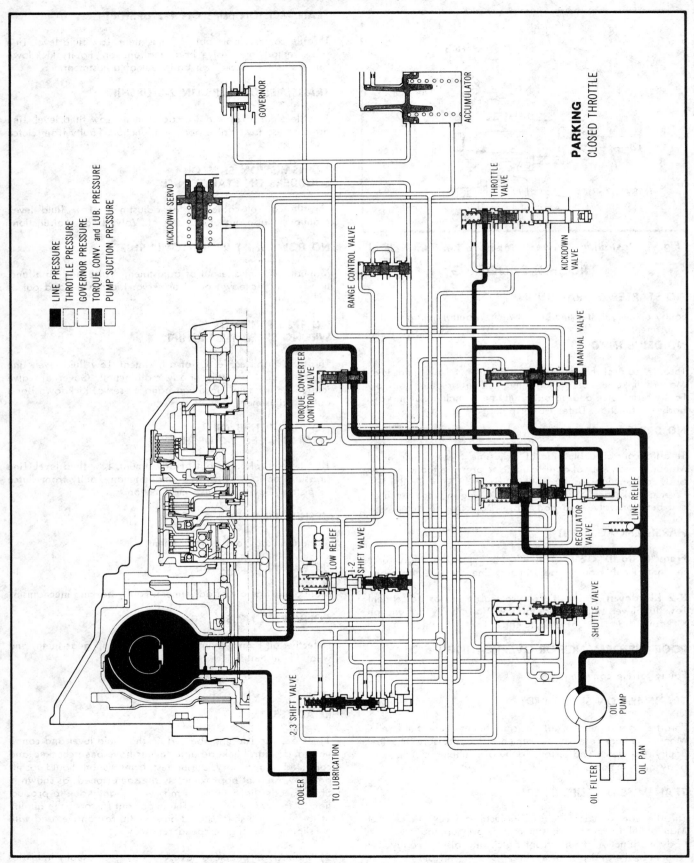

Fig. 5 Champ and Colt Model KM170 Hydraulic Circuits Diagram

CHAMP & COLT (Cont.)

CLUTCH AND BAND APPLICATION CHART
(ELEMENTS IN USE)

Selector Lever Position	Forward Clutch	Direct-Reverse Clutch	First-Reverse Brake	Second Gear Band	One Way Clutch
D — Drive First Gear Second Gear Third Gear	X	X X X		X	X X
2 — INTERMEDIATE First Gear Second Gear		X X		X	X
1 — LOW (First)		X	X		
R — REVERSE	X		X		

NEUTRAL OR PARK — All clutches, brake and band release and/or ineffective.

ticular gear can usually be identified by noting transmission operation in other selector positions and comparing internal units which are applied in these positions. See Clutch and Band Application chart.

3) The process of elimination given can be used to detect any unit which slips and to confirm proper operation of good units, but actual cause of a malfunction cannot be easily decided. Practically any condition can be caused by leaking hydraulic circuits or sticking valves. Unless an obvious condition exists, transmission should never be disassembled until hydraulic pressure tests have been made.

Shift Speeds Chart

Application	Shift Points (MPH)
Minimum Throttle	
1-2 Upshift	7-12
2-3 Upshift	11-16
3-1 Downshift	5-9
Full Throttle	
1-2 Upshift	30-37
2-3 Upshift	58-64
Kickdown	
3-2 Full Throttle	52-58
3-1 Full Throttle	24-29
3-2 Half Throttle	32-40

STALL TEST

Testing Precautions — When making stall test, do not hold throttle open any longer than 10 seconds to obtain steady gauge reading. After each stall test, move selector lever to "N" and run engine at 1000 RPM for at least 1 minute to cool down engine and transmission. If engine speed exceeds limits shown in Stall Speed table, release accelerator immediately as clutch or band slippage is indicated.

Testing Procedure — With engine at normal operating temperature, tachometer installed, and parking and service brakes applied, make transmission stall test in "D" and "R" ranges at full throttle and note maximum RPM obtained. Engine speed should be within limits shown in Stall Speed table.

Stall Speeds

Application	Stall RPM
All Models	1650-2050

Stall Speed Too High — In all ranges: general transmission problems are indicated and a control pressure test should be made to locate faulty unit(s). In "D"; Stator overrunning clutch is defective, rear clutch is slipping, line pressure is low or overrunning clutch in planetary gear is defective. In "R"; front clutch or low-reverse brake is slipping, line pressure is low or stator overrunning clutch is defective.

Stall Speed Too Low — Torque converter is faulty, engine output is not sufficient.

NOTE — Make sure engine performance is satisfactory before condemning converter assembly. Converter cannot be overhauled and must be replaced if defective.

HYDRAULIC PRESSURE TESTS

NOTE — Make sure transmission fluid level is to specifications, control cable is adjusted correctly and transmission is at normal operating temperature. Connect a tachometer, disconnect throttle control cable from carburetor and raise vehicle so front wheels are off ground.

Line Pressures — 1) Connect oil pressure gauge(s) to each of the following: line pressure port, low-reverse brake pressure port, front clutch pressure port, and "tee" into transmission "To Cooler" line. See Fig. 6 for pressure port locations. See Hydraulic Pressure chart for pressure specifications.

2) Place manual control lever to "L" position (all the way reward). Take pressure reading at idle, half throttle then with full throttle (engine speed should be at stall speed). Also note low-reverse brake pressure.

3) Place manual control lever to "2" position (1 detent forward). Note pressures at idle, half and full throttle. Also note lubrication (from "to Cooler" line) pressure.

CHAMP & COLT (Cont.)

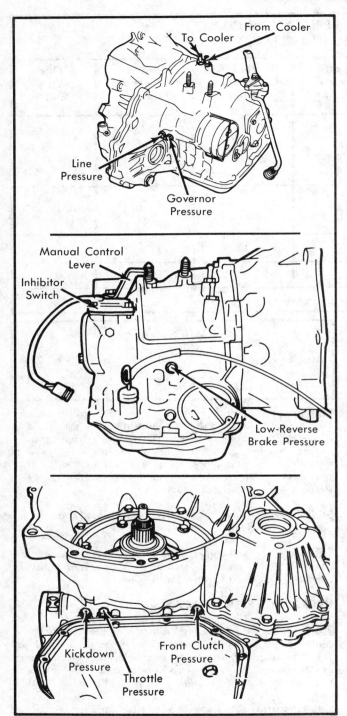

Fig. 6 Pressure Test Hookup Locations

4) Place manual control lever in "D" position (2 detents forward). Note pressures at idle, half and full throttle.

5) Place manual control lever in "R" position (4 detents forward). With pressure gauge attached to low-reverse pressure port, note pressures at idle, half and full throttle.

Line Pressure Test Results — 1) If line pressure was to specifications in any one test, pump and pressure regulator are working properly.

Hydraulic Pressures

Application	psi (kg/cm²)
Line Pressure in All Ranges	
Idle	58-67 (4.1-4.7)
Half Throttle	96 (6.7)
Full Throttle①	98-100 (6.9-7.0)
Low-Reverse Brake Pressure	
In "L"	24-33 (1.7-2.3)
In "R"	199-284 (14.0-20.0)
Lubrication Pressure	
In "2"	7-21 (.5-1.5)

① — Full throttle should be at stall speed specification.

2) A low pressure reading in "L", "2" and "D" but correct pressure in "R" indicates rear clutch circuit leakage.

3) A low pressure reading in "D" and "R" but correct pressure in "L" indicates front clutch circuit leakage.

4) A low pressure reading in "L" and "R" but correct pressure in "2" indicates low-reverse brake circuit leakage.

5) Low pressure readings in all positions indicates a defective pump, clogged filter or a stuck pressure regulator valve.

Governor Pressure Test — 1) Make this test only if vehicle shifts at wrong speeds with throttle cable properly adjusted. Connect pressure gauge to governor pressure port. *See Fig. 6.*

2) Place manual control lever in "D" position and increase vehicle speed and note pressures at which transmission shifts. Transmission should shift at indicated speeds and governor pressure should be as indicated in Governor Pressure chart. If not, governor valve is sticking, or filter in governor body is clogged.

Governor Pressure

Speed (MPH)	psi (kg/cm²)
Vehicle Stopped	0-2.8 (0-.2)
16-19	14 (1.0)
32-35	43 (3.0)
53-57	71 (5.0)

Throttle Pressure Test — Connect pressure gauge to throttle port. *See Fig. 6.* Note pressure readings at idle, half throttle and at full throttle (stall speed). Pressure readings should be as indicated in Throttle Pressure chart.

Throttle Pressure

Application	psi (kg/cm²)
Idle	0-1.4 (0-.1)
Half Throttle	41-51 (2.9-3.6)
Full Throttle	98-100 (6.9-7.0)

CHAMP & COLT (Cont.)

TRANSAXLE REMOVAL & INSTALLATION

Removal — 1) Disconnect battery ground cable. Disconnect throttle cable at carburetor and at transaxle. Remove inhibitor switch connector, cooler hoses and the 4 top engine-to-transaxle mounting bolts.

2) Raise vehicle and remove front wheels. Remove under cover and drain transaxle fluid. Remove steering knuckle ball joints from lower arms. Remove both drive shafts from transaxle case.

3) Remove starter and disconnect speedometer cable from transaxle. Remove attaching bolts at each end of stabilizer bar.

4) Remove converter housing then remove the 3 special bolts attaching converter to drive plate. Make sure torque converter is loose from engine and will come out with transmission.

5) Install an engine support. Place transmission jacks under transaxle assembly and remove remaining bolts holding engine-to-transaxle assembly. Remove transaxle mounting bolts and lower transaxle assembly (with torque converter) out of vehicle.

Installation — To install transaxle assembly, reverse removal procedure, noting the following: Install torque converter to transaxle, not to engine. Make sure transaxle assembly is filled with fluid and all cables are properly connected and adjusted.

TORQUE CONVERTER

NOTE — *Torque converter is a sealed unit and cannot be disassembled for service. Replace if found to be defective.*

TRANSAXLE DISASSEMBLY

1) Remove torque converter, speedometer pinion adapter, manual control lever and inhibitor switch. Attach dial indicator to measure input shaft end play. See Fig. 7. Record end play measurement.

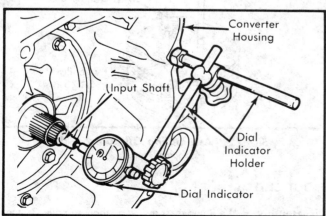

Fig. 7   Measuring Input Shaft End Play

2) Remove oil pan and filter. Disconnect throttle cable. Remove valve body, being careful that manual shift valve does not fall out of valve body.

NOTE — *Low-reverse brake clutch "O" ring is attached to valve body by petroleum jelly, be careful not to dislodge or misposition seal when removing or installing valve body.*

3) Remove throttle cable, accumulator and spring, being careful not to damage cable or retainer end. Rotate transaxle assembly so it sets on converter housing. Remove idler shaft lock plate, idler shaft and idler gear. Remove 2 bearing inner races and spacer from inside transaxle case.

NOTE — *For reassembly reference, note that machined groove in gear faces away from torque converter.*

4) Remove transfer shaft cover then attach dial indicator to measure transfer shaft end play. See Fig. 8. Record measurement. Rotate transaxle assembly so converter housing is up and remove converter housing.

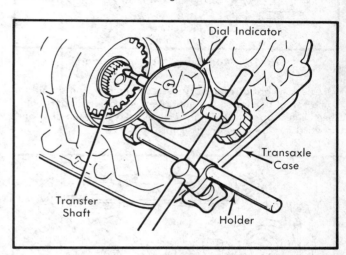

Fig. 8   Measuring Transfer Shaft End Play

5) Remove oil pump bolts and install pump remover tools (MD998333) into pump removing holes (located in pump housing). See Fig. 9. Pump may tilt up (side B) when removing, if so, tap on pump (side A) with a mallet. Refer to Fig. 9.

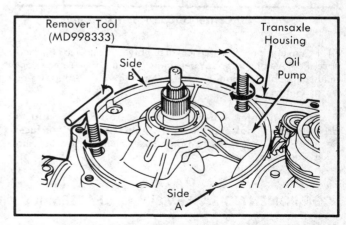

Fig. 9   Removing Oil Pump from Transaxle Housing

6) Remove differential assembly, then remove fiber thrust washer from front clutch assembly. Remove front clutch assembly and remove fiber thrust washer, 2 metal thrust races and 1 needle bearing. Remove rear clutch assembly, thrust washer and needle bearing. Remove clutch hub, 2 thrust washers and needle bearing. Remove kickdown drum and band. See Fig. 10.

CHAMP & COLT (Con.t)

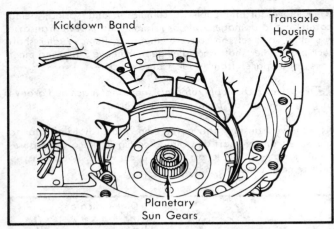

Fig. 10   Removing Kickdown Band

7) Check height of planetary gear set, long pinion should be same height as reverse sun gear. Remove center support bolts, then center support. See *Fig. 11*. Remove reverse sun gear and forward sun gear as an assembly.

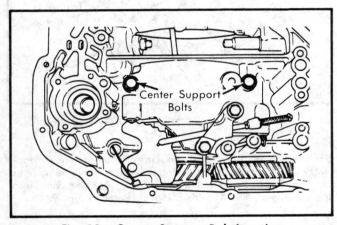

Fig. 11   Center Support Bolt Location

8) Remove planetary carrier assembly, thrust bearing and race. Remove annulus gear bearing snap ring, then remove annulus gear, output flange, transfer drive gear and bearing as an assembly.

9) Remove transfer rear end snap ring. Use a brass drift to drive transfer shaft out toward engine mounting surface. Remove snap ring from transaxle case, then remove bearing inner and outer races.

COMPONENT DISASSEMBLY & REASSEMBLY

OIL PUMP

Disassembly — 1) Remove bolts to separate pump housing from reaction shaft support. If pump gears are to be reused, mark gears (with felt pen, do not scribe) so they can be reinstalled in original position.

2) Remove drive and driven gears from pump housing. Remove steel ball from pump housing then remove 2 steel rings from reaction shaft support. Pry out pump housing oil seal.

Reassembly— 1) Apply ATF fluid to oil seal and install oil seal to pump housing. Lubricate pump gears with ATF fluid, then install to pump housing. If original gears are being reinstalled, install them in original positions using marks made upon disassembly as a guide.

2) Make the following measurements of pump gears to pump housing: driven gear-to-pump housing clearance, driven gear-to-crescent clearance, driven gear side clearance, drive gear-to-cresent clearance and drive gear side clearance. If clearances are not to specifications (refer to Oil Pump Clearance chart), replace components as necessary.

Oil Pump Clearances	
Application	**Clearance In. (mm)**
Driven Gear-to-Housing	.003-.006 (.08-.15)
Driven Gear-to-Crescent	.004-.009 (.11-.24)
Driven Gear Side Clerance	.001-.002 (.025-.05)
Drive Gear-to-Crescent	.009-.013 (.24-.34)
Drive Gear Side Clearance	.001-.002 (.025-.05)

3) Install steel ball in pump housing, then install 2 seal rings (coated with ATF fluid) to reaction shaft support. Place reaction shaft support to pump housing, then tighten bolts finger tight.

4) Install guide pin (MD998336) and pump band (C-3759) to assembled pump, then fully tighten pump bolts. See *Fig. 12*. After tightening bolts, make sure pump gear turns freely. If not, disassemble and recheck reassembly procedures and clearances. Install a new large "O" ring to outside circumference of pump and lubricate with petrolatum.

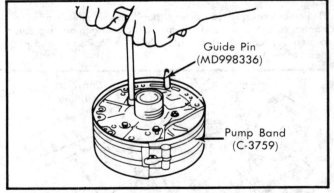

Fig. 12   Assembling Oil Pump with Special Tools

FRONT CLUTCH

Disassembly — 1) Remove snap ring, then remove 3 steel plates and 2 lined plates. If plates are to be reused, keep them in order and direction (as removed) for reassembly. See *Fig. 13*.

2) Compress return spring (use tool C-3575-A). Remove snap ring, spring retainer and return spring. Remove piston from front clutch. Remove "D" section rings from outside of piston and front clutch retainer.

CHAMP & COLT (Cont.)

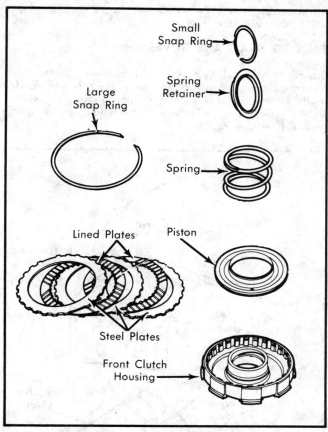

Fig. 13   Front Clutch Components

Reassembly — 1) Install "D" section rings to piston and front clutch retainer (round side of ring facing out), then lubricate rings with ATF fluid. Push piston into front clutch retainer by hand, being careful not to damage rings.

2) Using a spring compressor (C-3575-A) install spring and spring retainer to clutch retainer. Install small snap ring to hold spring to clutch retainer. Install 3 steel plates and 2 lined plates, starting with steel plate and alternating with a lined plate. If old plates are reinstalled, install them in same order and direction as removed.

NOTE — *Soak new lined plates in ATF fluid for at least 2 hours before installation.*

3) Install large snap ring to clutch retainer and measure clearance between snap ring and steel plate. Clearance should be .016-.024" (.4-.6 mm). If clearance is not to specifications, install a selective snap ring to give correct clearance. Snap rings are available in thicknesses from .063" (1.6 mm) to .118" (3.0 mm) in .008" (.2 mm) increments.

REAR CLUTCH

Disassembly — 1) Remove large snap ring, reaction plate, 2 lined plates, clutch plate and pressure plate from rear clutch retainer. If plates are to be reused, keep them in order and direction (as removed) for reassembly.

2) Remove seal ring, small snap ring and thrust race. Use a press to compress piston, then remove waved snap ring.

Release press pressure and remove waved snap ring, return spring and piston. Remove the 2 "D" section rings from piston.

Reassembly — 1) Install "D" section rings to piston with round side facing out. Lubricate rings with ATF fluid and install piston in rear clutch retainer by hand. Be careful not to damage rings.

2) Install return spring with waved snap ring to clutch retainer. Use a press to compress return spring until waved snap ring seats in groove of clutch retainer. Install pressure plate, lined plate, clutch plate, lined plate and finally the reaction plate. See Fig. 14.

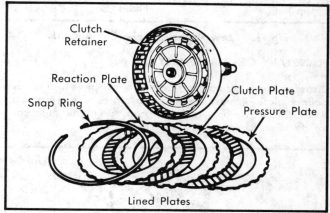

Fig. 14   Rear Clutch Components

NOTE — *Soak new lined plates in ATF fluid for at least 2 hours before installation.*

3) Install large snap ring to clutch retainer and measure clearance between reaction plate and snap ring. Clearance should be .012-.020" (.3-.5 mm). If clearance is not to specifications, selective snap ring are available from .063" (1.6 mm) to .118" (3.0 mm) in .008" (.2 mm) increments.

4) Install thrust race, small snap ring and new seal ring.

LOW-REVERSE BRAKE

Disassembly — 1) Remove snap ring. Remove reaction plate, 4 lined plates, 3 steel plates and the pressure plates. If plates are to be reused, keep them in order and direction (as removed) for reassembly.

2) Compress piston and remove piston snap ring, then remove return spring and waved spring. Remove piston, then remove "D" section rings from piston.

Reassembly — 1) Install "D" section rings to piston with round side of ring out. Lubricate rings with ATF fluid and install piston by hand, being careful not to damage rings. Install waved spring and return spring. Compress springs and install snap ring. Install pressure plate, then install plates starting with a lined plate and alternating with steel plates, ending with reaction plate. See Fig. 15.

2) Install large snap ring and measure clearance between reaction plate and snap ring. Clearance should be .031-.040" (.8-1.0 mm). If clearance is not to specifications, selective snap rings are available from .063" (1.6 mm) to .118" (3.0 mm) in .008" (.2 mm) increments.

CHAMP & COLT (Cont.)

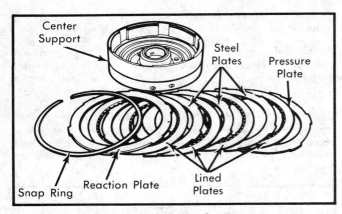

Fig. 15 Low-Reverse Brake Components

PLANETARY GEAR ASSEMBLY

Disassembly — Straighten tabs of stopper plate and remove stopper plate. Remove bearing end plates and overrunning clutch. Check overrunning clutch sprag, spring and outer race for damage. See *Fig. 16.*

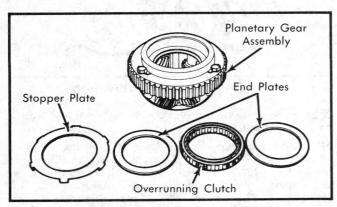

Fig. 16 Planetary Gear and Overrunning Clutch Assembly

Reassembly — Install end plate to overrunning clutch. Install overrunning clutch to planetary gear assembly with arrow (stamped on outside of overrunning clutch) pointing toward planetary gears. Install end plate then stopper plate. Bend tabs of stopper plate to secure stopper plate to planetary gear assembly.

ANNULUS GEAR, OUTPUT FLANGE AND TRANSFER DRIVE GEAR

Disassembly — Remove snap ring from rear of output flange. Using a bearing puller, remove bearing, transfer drive gear and bearing. Remove snap ring and separate annulus gear from output flange.

NOTE — *Annulus gear and output flange are a matched set. If one is damaged, replace both components.*

Reassembly — Install annulus gear to output flange and install snap ring. Using a bearing installer, install bearing, transfer drive gear and bearing. Select snap ring of largest size that will fit in groove and install snap ring. Snap ring-to-bearing clearance should be 0-.002" (0-.06 mm). Snap rings

are available from .074" (1.88 mm) to .081" (2.06 mm) in .002" (.06 mm) increments.

TRANSFER SHAFT AND GOVERNOR

Disassembly — **1)** Remove seal rings from transfer shaft. Loosen governor set screws and slide governor off transfer shaft. Remove "E" clip from governor body, then remove weight, valve, spring and retainer. From inside governor body, remove filter. See *Fig. 17.*

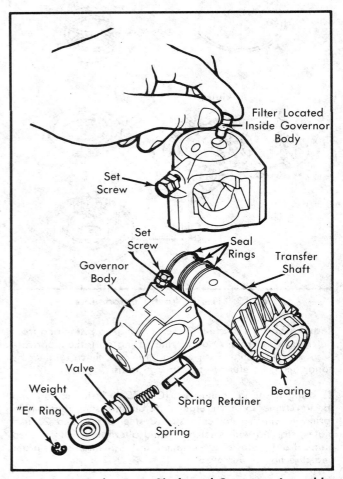

Fig. 17 Transfer Gear Shaft and Governor Assembly

2) Using bearing puller and adapter (adapter with thin fingers), remove bearing from transfer shaft.

NOTE — *If replacing transfer shaft bearing, always replace inner and outer races as a set.*

Reassembly — **1)** Install transfer shaft bearing outer race into converter housing. Install transfer shaft bearing inner race to transfer shaft.

2) Install spring retainer, spring, governor valve and weight to governor body, then install "E" clip to retain components in governor. Install governor filter (new filter if old filter is dirty).

3) Slide governor body onto transfer shaft in same direction as removed, then tighten set screws. Install seal rings to transfer shaft.

CHAMP & COLT (Cont.)

VALVE BODY

NOTE — *When disassembling valve body, place each component in order and relation to removal sequence for reassembly reference.*

Disassembly — 1) Remove bolts securing throttle cam to valve body and remove throttle cam assembly. Remove the 19 bolts (1 shorter than others) attaching separating plate to transfer plate, separate plates.

2) Remove stiffener plate, then separating plate. Remove line relief and low relief steel balls with their springs. See *Fig. 18*. Remove manual valve, kickdown valve, throttle valve and 2 springs. Remove the 2 regulator plugs.

3) Remove rear end cover and gasket. Remove 1-2 shift valve and 2-3 shift plug. Remove front end cover. Remove all valves, springs and plugs (lay components out in order). Remove snap ring, then remove shuttle valve.

Reassembly — 1) Install 2-3 shift valve then spring to valve body. Install shuttle valve, spring and plug, then install snap ring to retain shuttle valve components.

2) Install 1-2 shift plug and spring. Install regulator valve, spring and adjusting screw. Install torque converter valve and spring, then the range control valve and spring. See *Fig. 19*.

NOTE — *For spring identification, see Valve Body Spring Identification table.*

3) Install 2-3 Shift plug, then 1-2 shift valve to valve body. Install rear end cover and gasket. Install 2 regulator plugs (small one first), then install manual valve to valve body.

4) Install kickdown spring, throttle valve, throttle spring and kickdown valve into valve body. Install stopper plate to valve body, then install 4 steel balls to valve body. See *Fig. 19*.

5) Install line relief and low relief steel balls, with their springs, to transfer plate. See *Fig. 18*. Install guide pins to transfer plate and install separating plate to transfer plate. Install stiffener plate and bolts.

6) Remove guide pins from transfer plate and install them in the valve body. Using guide pins as a guide, install transfer/separating plates to valve body and install the 19 retaining bolts (1 short and 18 long). Install throttle cam assembly.

NOTE — *Make sure short valve body bolt is installed in its proper location. Long bolts will not tighten down properly.*

Valve Body Spring Identification		
Location of Spring	**Diameter In. (mm)**	**Length In. (mm)**
Throttle Spring	.374 (9.5)	1.276 (32.4)
Kickdown Spring	.252 (6.4)	1.028 (26.1)
Converter Control Spring	.331 (8.4)	.949 (24.1)
Range Control Spring	.331 (8.4)	.949 (24.1)
Regulator Spring	.606 (15.4)	2.024 (51.4)
1-2 Shift Spring	.299 (7.6)	1.535 (39.0)
Shuttle Spring	.260 (6.6)	2.343 (59.5)
2-3 Shift Spring	.268 (6.8)	1.189 (30.2)
Low Relief Spring	.260 (6.6)	.661 (16.8)
Line Relief Spring	.276 (7.0)	.961 (24.4)

DIFFERENTIAL

Disassembly — 1) Straighten ring gear lock washers and remove ring gear bolts, then remove ring gear. Remove pinion shaft lock pin, pinion shaft, pinion gears and washers.

2) Remove side gears and spacers. Keep right side gear and spacer separate from left side gear and spacer. Remove differential carrier side bearings if necessary.

Reassembly — 1) Install differential carrier side bearings if removed. Install side gears and spacers. If original side gears are reused, make sure they are installed in their original positions. If new side gears are used, use new spacers of .040" (1.0 mm) thickness.

2) Place washers to back of pinion gears, then install pinion gears at same time. Rotate pinion gears to mesh them with side gears. Install pinion shaft.

3) Measure backlash between side gears and pinion gears (measure both right and left side gear backlash). See *Fig. 20*. Backlash should be 0-.003" (0-.08 mm) on both sides. If backlash is not to specifications, remove pinion and side gears and install thicker or thinner spacers behind side gears to achieve correct backlash. See Side Gear Spacers chart for spacers available.

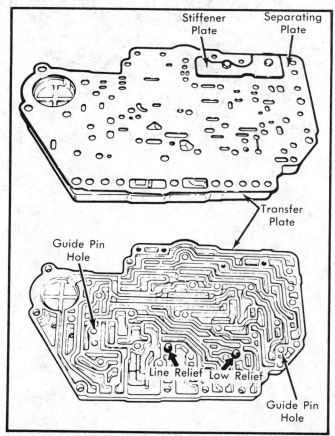

Fig. 18   Transfer Plate, Separating Plate and Stiffener Plate with Line and Low Relief Ball Locations

Automatic Transaxles

CHAMP & COLT (Cont.)

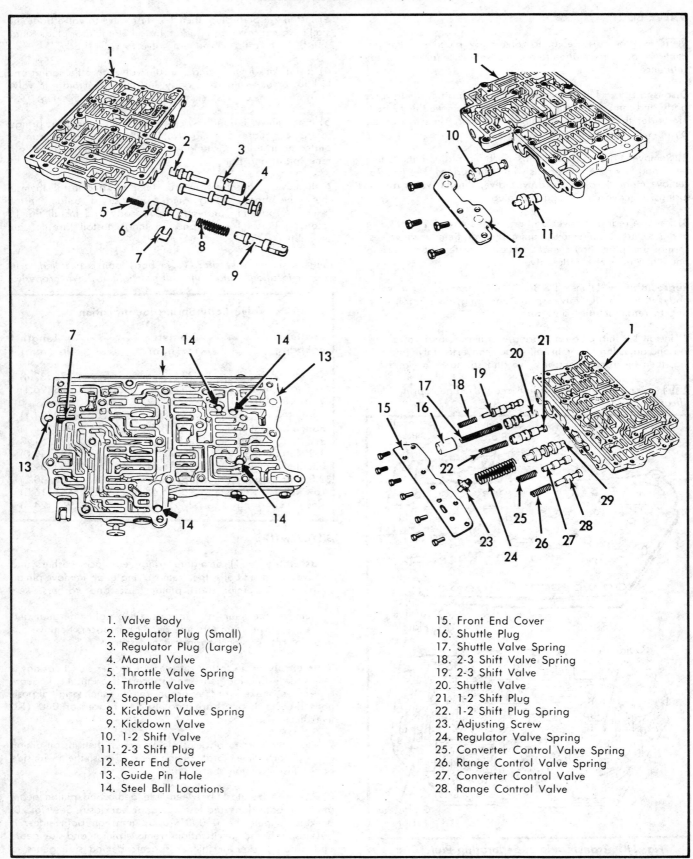

1. Valve Body	15. Front End Cover
2. Regulator Plug (Small)	16. Shuttle Plug
3. Regulator Plug (Large)	17. Shuttle Valve Spring
4. Manual Valve	18. 2-3 Shift Valve Spring
5. Throttle Valve Spring	19. 2-3 Shift Valve
6. Throttle Valve	20. Shuttle Valve
7. Stopper Plate	21. 1-2 Shift Plug
8. Kickdown Valve Spring	22. 1-2 Shift Plug Spring
9. Kickdown Valve	23. Adjusting Screw
10. 1-2 Shift Valve	24. Regulator Valve Spring
11. 2-3 Shift Plug	25. Converter Control Valve Spring
12. Rear End Cover	26. Range Control Valve Spring
13. Guide Pin Hole	27. Converter Control Valve
14. Steel Ball Locations	28. Range Control Valve

Fig. 19 Exploded View of Throttly Body and Components

CHAMP & COLT (Cont.)

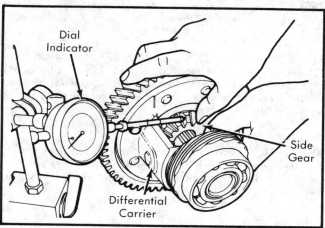

Fig. 20 *Measuring Side Gear-to-Pinion Gear Backlash*

Side Gear Spacers

Shim Part No.	Thickness In. (mm)
MA180862	.030-.033 (.75-.82)
MA180861	.033-.037 (.82-.92)
MA180860	.037-.040 (.92-1.0)
MA180875	.040-.043 (1.0-1.08)
MA180876	.043-.046 (1.08-1.16)

4) Install ring gear. Install pinion shaft lock pin, then install new lock washers and ring gear bolts. Make sure one of the lock washers retains the pinion shaft lock pin. See *Fig. 21*.

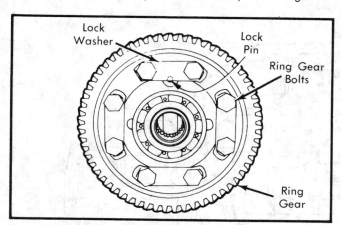

Fig. 21 *Installation of Ring Gear Bolts and Lock Washer That Retains Pinion Shaft Lock Pin*

5) Tighten ring gear bolts and bend lock washers along a flat of ring gear bolts. Make sure lock washers are not cracked along bend.

TRANSAXLE REASSEMBLY

NOTE — *Handle all parts carefully to avoid damaging bearing and mating surfaces. Lubricate all components with ATF fluid prior to reassembly. Gaskets and thrust washers may be held in place with petrolatum.*

1) Place transaxle case on bench with oil pan mounting surface up. Install annulus gear and output flange assembly (with bearings and transfer drive gear attached) to inside of transaxle case. Install snap ring to bearing.

2) Install bearing outer races, inner races and spacer (in correct direction) to transfer idle gear. See *Fig. 22*.

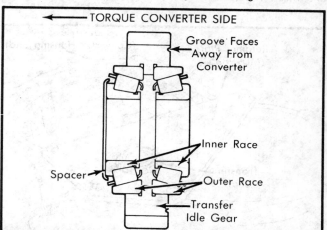

Fig. 22 *Installation of Transfer Gear, Bearings and Spacer*

3) Install transfer idle gear assembly to transaxle case. Insert idler shaft from outside case, then screw in and tighten idler shaft to transaxle case. Install new "O" ring to idler shaft.

4) Using a torque wrench and socket, measure output flange turning torque (preload). See *Fig. 23*. Preload should be 12 INCH lbs. (13.8 cmkg). If preload is not to specification, tighten or loosen transfer idler shaft until correct specification is obtained.

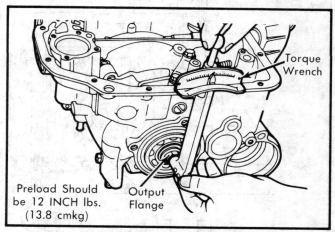

Fig. 23 *Measuring Output Flange Preload*

5) With preload adjusted correctly, install idler shaft lock plate and tighten bolt. Install new "O" ring to groove around output flange, then install bearing retainer. Install transfer shaft, with governor, into case. Install a transfer shaft retainer plate (MD998351) to converter housing mating surface (to retain transfer shaft). See *Fig. 24*.

6) Install transfer shaft bearing, inner race, outer race and snap ring, to transfer shaft (end opposite retainer plate). In-

CHAMP & COLT (Cont.)

stall transfer driven gear onto transfer shaft. Install snap ring to end of transfer shaft. Turn transaxle case so engine mating side is up.

NOTE — *Refer to Fig. 25 for location of thrust bearings, thrust races and thrust washers. Refer to Thrust Bearing, Thrust Race and Thrust Washer chart for components available.*

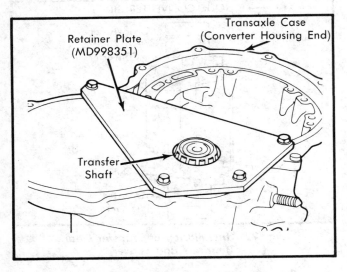

Fig. 24   *Transfer Shaft Retainer Plate*

NOTE — *Coat thrust races, thrust bearings and thrust washers with petrolatum to hold them in place during installation.*

7) Install thrust race "E" to output flange. Attach thrust races "D" and "J" with thrust bearings "A" and "B" to front and rear of planetary gear carrier. *Refer to Fig. 25 for locations of thrust races and bearings.* Install planetary gear carrier to transaxle case.

8) Assemble forward sun gear with reverse sun gear and install into planetary gear carrier. Make sure reverse sun gear toothed area is approximately same height as planetary gear long pinion.

9) Lubricate overrunning clutch area of low-reverse brake (center support) with ATF, then install low-reverse brake to case. Install the 2 low-reverse brake (center support) lock bolts.

CAUTION — *Do not turn transaxle case upside down or thrust washers will fall out of place.*

10) Insert manual control shaft to case, pushing it fully toward manual control lever. After shaft is installed, install a new "O" ring to manual control shaft. *See Fig. 26.*

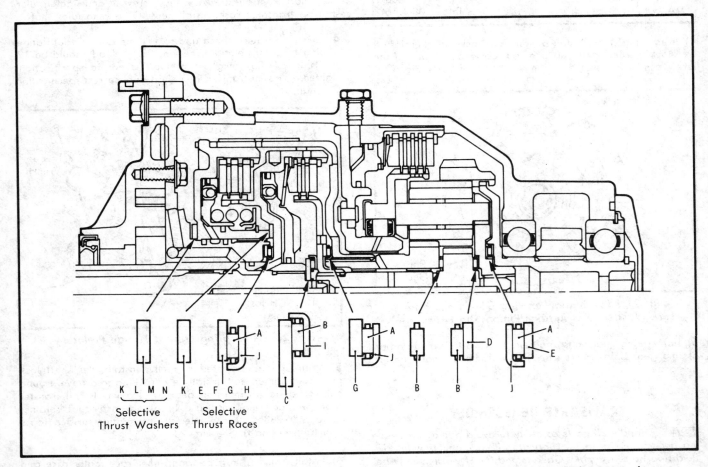

Fig. 25   *Cross-Sectional View Showing Locations of Thrust Bearings, Thrust Races and Thrust Washers*

CHAMP & COLT (Cont.)

Component I.D. Mark	Outside Diameter In. (mm)	Inside Diameter In. (mm)	Thickness In. (mm)
Thrust Bearing			
A	1.894 (48.1)	1.417 (36.0)	.....
B	1.437 (36.5)	.874 (22.2)	.....
Thrust Race			
C	1.378 (35.0)	.496 (12.6)	.094 (2.4)
D	1.457 (35.0)	.925 (23.5)	.031 (0.8)
E	1.925 (48.9)	1.457 (37.0)	.031 (0.8)
F	1.925 (48.9)	1.457 (37.0)	.047 (1.2)
G	1.925 (48.9)	1.457 (37.0)	.063 (1.6)
H	1.925 (48.9)	1.457 (37.0)	.080 (2.0)
I	1.496 (38.0)	.925 (23.5)	.....
J	1.482 (47.0)	1.354 (34.4)	.....
Thrust Washer			
K	2.756 (70.0)	2.193 (55.7)	.071 (1.8)
L	2.756 (70.0)	2.193 (55.7)	.087 (2.2)
M	2.756 (70.0)	2.193 (55.7)	.102 (2.6)
N	2.756 (70.0)	2.193 (55.7)	.118 (3.0)

THRUST BEARING, THRUST RACE AND THRUST WASHER DIMENSIONS

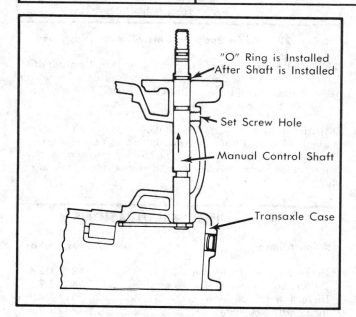

"O" Ring is Installed After Shaft is Installed

Set Screw Hole

Manual Control Shaft

Transaxle Case

Fig. 26 Installation of Manual Control Shaft

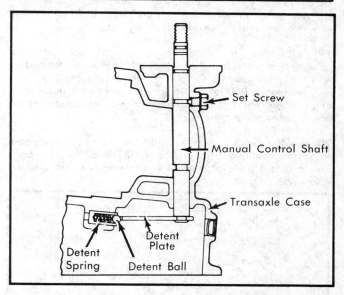

Set Screw

Manual Control Shaft

Transaxle Case

Detent Plate

Detent Ball

Detent Spring

Fig. 27 Installation of Set Screw, Detent Ball and Spring to Manual Control Shaft

NOTE — If "O" ring is installed before shaft is pushed into case, "O" ring will be damaged by the set screw hole.

11) Pull manual control shaft back into case until set screw groove is aligned with set screw hole and install set screw with gasket. Install detent ball and spring at same time as shaft is pulled back to install set screw. See Fig. 27.

12) Install kickdown servo spring, piston and sleeve into case. Install large and small "D" section rings to piston and a new "O" ring to sleeve before installation of piston. Using spring compressor, compress piston spring and install snap ring.

13) Install kickdown band; attach band ends to end of anchor rod and servo piston adjusting screw. Install kickdown drum, meshing splines with reverse sun gear. Place kickdown band on kickdown drum and tighten kickdown servo adjusting screw to hold band in place.

14) Install thrust race "J" and a thrust bearing "A" to kickdown drum. Refer to Fig. 25. Install thrust races "I" and "G" to both ends of clutch hub. Attach thrust bearing "B" to engine side of thrust race and install clutch hub to forward sun gear splines.

15) Install rear clutch assembly. Install thrust washer "K" to rear clutch retainer. Install thrust race "J" and a thrust bearing "A" to rear clutch retainer. Install front clutch assembly and differential assembly. Install a new oil pump gasket and install thrust washer to rear end of oil pump assembly.

CHAMP & COLT (Cont.)

16) If end play, measured at disassembly, is out of specification of .020-.055" (.5-1.4 mm), install selective thrust race (E, F, G or H) to obtain correct end play. Refer to Thrust Bearing, Thrust Race and Thrust Washer chart for thrust race thicknesses.

NOTE — *If thrust race was replaced with one of a different thickness, also replace the thrust washer located between oil pump and front clutch. Replacement thrust washer should be .040" (1.0 mm) thicker than thrust race. Refer to Thrust Bearing, Thrust Race and Thrust Washer chart for correct thrust washer identification.*

17) Install new selected thrust washer, determined in preceding step, to front clutch. Install new "O" ring to oil pump groove and lubricate it with ATF. Install oil pump assembly by tightening the 6 oil pump bolts evenly. Be careful that thrust washer does not drop out of place.

18) Recheck input shaft end play for correct specification, also make sure transfer shaft end play (measured upon disassembly) is to specifications. End play should be between a loose .001" (.025 mm) and a tight .001" (.025 mm). If not to specifications, install selective spacer. Spacers are available from .072" (1.84 mm) to .106" (2.68 mm) in .001" (.025 mm) increments. If selective spacer is to be installed, remove bearing outer race from transaxle case and replace old spacer with new selected spacer. Reinstall bearing outer race.

19) Place spacer (removed upon disassembly) on differential bearing outer race. Install new gasket to transaxle case and install converter housing. Check differential case end play. End play should be 0-.006" (0-.15 mm). Also recheck input shaft and transfer shaft end play. If any end play measurements are not to specifications, readjust.

20) Install transfer shaft cover and holder. Turn transaxle case so oil pan mounting surface is facing Up. Install parking sprag rod to detent plate of manual control shaft. Install parking sprag rod support. *See Fig. 28.*

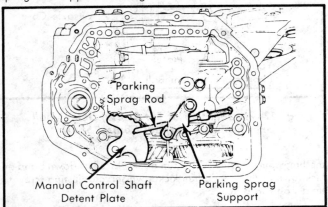

Fig. 28   Parking Sprag Rod and Support Installation

21) Install accumulator piston and spring. Install "O" ring at center of top of valve body assembly (brake oil pressure passage). Install valve body to transaxle case, fitting detent plate pin (for manual control shaft) in slot of manual valve. Install and tighten valve body bolts noting that 1 bolt (A) is shorter than the others (B). *See Fig. 29.*

22) Insert throttle cable into transaxle case and connect throttle cable inner cable to throttle cam. Install oil filter, oil pan gasket and oil pan. Install drive shaft oil seals to transaxle case.

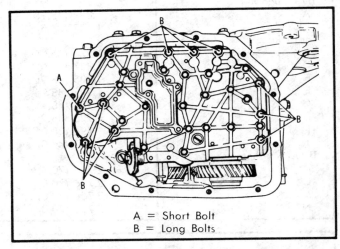

A = Short Bolt
B = Long Bolts

Fig. 29   Valve Body Bolt Installation Locations

23) Install inhibitor switch and manual lever, then adjust inhibitor switch. Lubricate torque converter surface (where converter slides into oil pump) with ATF fluid and carefully install converter to oil pump.

24) After torque converter installation, measure distance from mating surface of converter housing to torque converter. If measurement is not more than .6" (.15 mm), torque converter is not installed completely. Remove converter and install correctly.

TIGHTENING SPECIFICATIONS

Application	Ft. Lbs. (mkg)
Center Support (Low-Reverse Brake)	15-19 (2.1-2.6)
Differential Carrier-to-Ring Gear	47-54 (6.5-7.5)
Drive Plate-to-Converter	26-30 (3.6-4.1)
Idler Shaft Lock Plate	15-19 (2.1-2.6)
Oil Pump Bolts	11-15 (1.5-2.1)
Rear Cover	14-17 (1.9-2.4)
Sprag Rod Support Bolts	15-19 (2.1-2.6)
Sway Bar Coupling Bolts	22-30 (3.0-4.1)
Transaxle-to-Engine	
M8 Bolts	21-25 (2.9-3.5)
M10 Bolts	31-40 (4.3-5.5)
Transaxle-to-Mount Bracket	36-43 (5.0-5.9)
Valve Body Bolts	3-4 (0.4-0.6)
Valve Body-to-Case	7.5-8.5 (1.0-1.2)

FIAT STRADA, VOLKSWAGON JETTA, PICKUP, RABBIT & SCIROCCO

TRANSMISSION IDENTIFICATION

Transmission type may be identified by a group of numbers cast into top of case, behind case rib. One of the numbers is "010", and this denotes the VW "two planetary" type transmission. Transmission model maybe identified by a group of figures stamped into converter housing near governor. Figures consist of a model code (EQ) and a build date code.

NOTE — *All references to "Rabbit" include Pickup.*

DESCRIPTION

Transaxle assembly consists of two main units: Automatic transmission and final drive assembly. The transmission housing contains two planetary gear sets, two multiple-disc clutches, one brake band and servo, one multiple-disc brake, a one-way clutch, and a hydraulic control system. The final drive housing contains torque converter, governor for transmission, three-gear type ring and pinion assembly, and differential unit.

LUBRICATION & ADJUSTMENT

See AUTOMATIC TRANSMISSION SERVICING Section.

TROUBLE SHOOTING

NO MOVEMENT

In Any Gear — Low fluid level. Manual lever disconnected from manual valve. Torque converter disconnected from drive plate. Main pressure valve sticking. Oil pump drive plate or shaft defective.

In Forward Gears — Forward clutch internal damage (worn plates, spring broken, seals leaking, etc.)

In First Gear in "D" or "2" — One-way clutch not holding. Forward clutch internal damage.

In First Gear in "1" — First-reverse brake plates worn or burnt.

In Second Gear — Second gear brake band out of adjustment or burnt, or servo defective.

In Third Gear — Direct-reverse clutch internal damage (worn plates, seals leaking, etc.).

In Reverse — First-reverse brake plates worn or burnt. Direct-reverse clutch internal damage. Forward clutch seized in applied position.

NO UPSHIFT

Into Second Gear — Governor drive defective. Governor dirty or improperly assembled. Accumulator cover plate loose. Valve body dirty. 1-2 shift valve sticking.

Into Third Gear — Governor dirty. Valve body dirty. 2-3 shift valve sticking. Sealing balls missing from transfer plate.

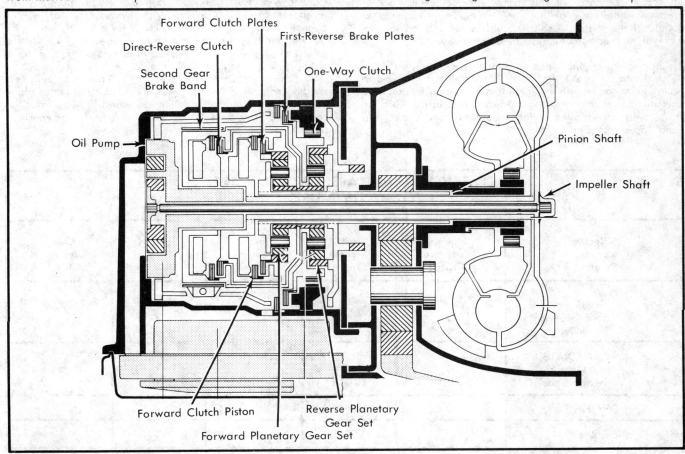

Fig. 1   Cross-Sectional View of Volkswagen Type 010 Automatic Transmission Assembly

FIAT STRADA, VOLKSWAGON JETTA, PICKUP, RABBIT & SCIROCCO (Cont.)

NO DOWNSHIFTS

Governor or valve body dirty, shift valves sticking.

DELAYED ENGAGEMENT ON UPSHIFTS

1-2 — Fluid level too low. Valve body dirty. Second gear brake band out of adjustment or burnt. Second gear servo faulty.

2-3 — Fluid level too low. Valve body dirty. Second gear brake band out of adjustment or burnt. Second gear servo faulty. Gears damaged. Direct-reverse clutch plates worn or burnt. Direct-reverse clutch improperly assembled.

SHIFT SPEEDS FAULTY

Governor or valve body dirty, damaged, or improperly installed. Gasket or "O" ring between transmission and final drive leaking.

TESTING

ROAD TEST

1) Before road testing, be certain that fluid level and condition, and control linkage adjustments have been checked and corrected as necessary. During test, transmission should upshift and downshift at approximately the speeds shown in Shift Speeds chart. All shifts may vary somewhat due to production tolerances or tire size. The important factor is the quality of the shifts. All shifts should be smooth, responsive, and with no slippage or engine speed runaway.

2) Slippage or engine runaway in any gear usually indicates clutch, band, or brake problems. The slipping unit in a particular gear can usually be identified by noting transmission operation in other selector positions and comparing which internal units are applied in those positions. See Clutch and Band Application Chart

3) This process of elimination can be used to detect any unit which slips, and to confirm proper operation of good units; however, the actual cause of the malfunction usually cannot be easily decided. Practically any condition can be caused by leaking hydraulic circuits or sticking valves. Therefore, unless an obvious condition exists, do not disassemble transmission until hydraulic pressure tests have been made.

Shift Speeds		
Application	Shift Points (MPH)	
	Full Throttle	Kickdown
Strada		
1-2 Upshift	22	38
2-3 Upshift	52	67
3-2 Downshift	32	64
2-1 Downshift	16	31
All Others		
1-2 Upshift	20-23	36-39
2-3 Upshift	51-54	68-69
3-2 Downshift	31-36	64-65
2-1 Downshift	15-17	32-35

HYDRAULIC PRESSURE TEST

Connect a pressure gauge to main pressure test point on case (adjacent to servo cover). With transmission at normal operating temperature, place selector lever in "D", run engine at idle speed, and note pressure on gauge. Next, run engine at full throttle with vehicle speed above 25 MPH, and again note pressure with transmission in "D". Finally, with vehicle at a standstill, place selector lever in "R" position, and note reading on pressure gauge. Pressures obtained in each phase of test should be approximately as shown in Main Pressures chart. If not, disassemble and clean valve body and check especially for sticking valves.

CLUTCH AND BAND APPLICATION CHART
(ELEMENTS IN USE)

Selector Lever Position	Forward Clutch	Direct-Reverse Clutch	First-Reverse Brake	Second Gear Band	One Way Clutch
D — DRIVE					
First Gear	X				X
Second Gear	X			X	
Third Gear	X	X			
2 — INTERMEDIATE					
First Gear	X				X
Second Gear	X			X	
1 — LOW (First)	X		X		
R — REVERSE		X	X		
NEUTRAL OR PARK — All clutches, brake, and band released and/or ineffective.					

FIAT STRADA, VOLKSWAGON JETTA, PICKUP, RABBIT & SCIROCCO (Cont.)

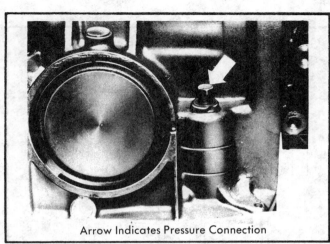

Arrow Indicates Pressure Connection

Fig. 2   View of Transmission Case Showing Pressure Test Connection

Main Pressures

Application	Psi (kg/cm²)
Strada	
"D" @ Idle①	56-58 (3.9-4.0)
"D" @ Full Throttle②	91-92 (6.3-6.4)
"R" @ Idle	105-107 (7.3-7.4)
All Others	
"D" @ Idle①	41-42 (2.9-3.0)
"D" @ Full Throttle②	83-84 (5.8-5.9)
"R" @ Idle	102-107 (7.1-7.7)

① — Vehicle Stationary.
② — Road speed above 25 MPH. Test should be performed on a dynamometer whenever possible.

STALL SPEED TEST

Testing Precautions — When making test, do not hold throttle open any longer than the time it takes to read tachometer. Maximum stall speed test time is 20 seconds. If engine speed exceeds limits shown in Stall Speeds table, release accelerator immediately as clutch or band slippage is indicated.

Testing Procedure — With engine at normal operating temperature, connect a tachometer to engine. Start engine and set parking and service brakes. Place selector lever in "D". Depress accelerator briefly to full throttle and note maximum RPM obtained. Engine speed should be within limits shown in Stall Speeds table.

NOTE — *Normal stall speed will drop approximately 125 RPM per 3200 feet altitude. Also, stall speed will drop slightly at high ambient temperature.*

Stall Speeds

Application	Stall RPM
Jetta & Rabbit	2250-2500
Scirocco	2100-2350
Strada	2260

REMOVAL & INSTALLATION

NOTE — *For Axle Drive Shaft, Constant Velocity (CV) Joint, and Axle Shaft replacement procedures, see Volkswagen Transverse Transaxle article in MANUAL TRANSAXLE Section.*

TRANSAXLE ASSEMBLY

Removal (Jetta, Rabbit and Scirocco) — 1) Disconnect battery ground strap and starter cable at battery. Disconnect speedometer cable from transmission. Remove 2 upper engine-to-transmission attaching bolts, install a support fixture (10-222) and raise assembly slightly.

2) Under vehicle, disconnect transmission side carrier from body. Disconnect rear transmission carrier from case and body, and remove. Mark axle drive shafts for reassembly reference, and disconnect from final drive flanges. Remove starter bolts and position starter out of the way.

3) Remove transmission protection plate and converter cover plate, then remove drive plate-to-torque converter bolts. Place selector lever in "P" position and disconnect selector cable from transmission lever. Remove cable bracket from transmission, then disconnect accelerator and pedal cables from bracket.

4) Detach side carrier and mount from transmission. Remove lower transmission-to-engine bolt, lift assembly and swing left axle upward. Remove remaining transmission-to-engine bolts, pull transmission forward and, taking care not to allow torque converter to drop, remove from vehicle.

Installation — Reverse removal procedure and note the following: Make sure rear carrier on transmission is installed in a centered position in body bracket (equal space between carrier and bracket on both sides). Adjust selector cable (in "P" position), accelerator cable and pedal cable.

Removal (Strada) — 1) Position vehicle on hydraulic lift, remove engine compartment hood. Disconnect battery negative terminal. Drain cooling system and disconnect hoses to engine. Remove air cleaner and disconnect all linkage and electrical connections necessary for engine removal.

2) Disconnect speedometer cable from transaxle. Remove engine-to-motor mount nuts. Raise vehicle, remove engine and transaxle shields. Disconnect stabilizer bar and axle shafts. Disconnect all linkage from transmission. Connect suitable engine lift to engine. Remove engine crossmember, lower engine and transaxle assembly through bottom of vehicle and place on engine stand.

Installation — To install, reverse removal procedure and adjust selector and throttle linkage as necessary. Fill cooling system and check for leaks.

TORQUE CONVERTER

NOTE — *Torque converter is a sealed unit and cannot be disassembled for service.*

BUSHING REPLACEMENT

1) Check bushing for wear using an inside micrometer. Wear limit of bushing is 1.348" (34.25 mm), and maximum allowable out-of-round is .001" (.03 mm).

FIAT STRADA, VOLKSWAGON JETTA, PICKUP, RABBIT & SCIROCCO (Cont.)

2) To replace bushing, use a bushing puller (US 691 and adapter US 4452 for Jetta, Rabbit and Scirocco, and A 40206 and adapter 40207/816 for Strada) to withdraw bushing from converter hub. Press new bushing into place using a bushing driver.

TRANSMISSION DISASSEMBLY

NOTE — *To separate transmission and final drive assembly, withdraw torque converter from final drive housing. Remove governor cover and gasket, then pull governor from final drive housing using a clockwise twisting motion to disengage governor drive gear from gear on transmission annulus gear. Remove nuts from the transmission-to-final drive studs and separate transmission from final drive. Withdraw pump shaft and impeller shaft from transmission. For final drive disassembly and reassembly procedures, see Final Drive information at rear of this article.*

1) Remove screws retaining separation plate in transmission case, then withdraw plate and gasket. Remove governor drive gear/ring gear assembly from case, then withdraw needle bearing and thrust washer from top of reverse (front) planetary gear set. Remove large snap ring retaining one-way clutch assembly in case, then using 2 hooks fabricated from ³⁄₁₆" welding rod, lift one-way clutch assembly from case.

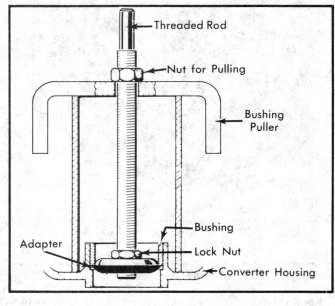

Fig. 3   Removing Torque Converter Bushing (Jetta, Rabbit & Scirocco Shown)

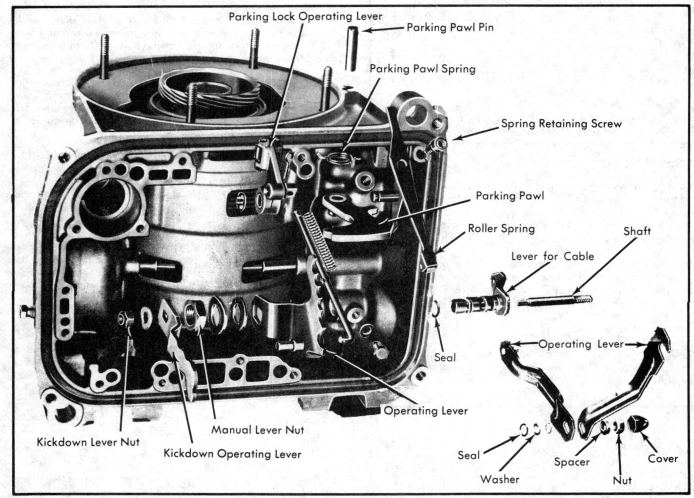

Fig. 4   Bottom View of Transmission Case Showing Kickdown and Selector Linkage

FIAT STRADA, VOLKSWAGON JETTA, PICKUP, RABBIT & SCIROCCO (Cont.)

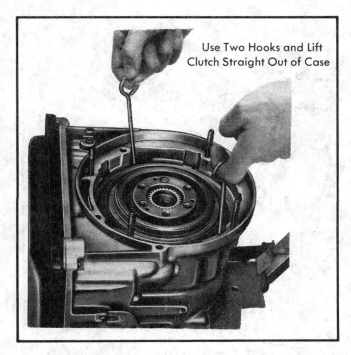

Fig. 5   Removing One-Way Clutch from Case

Use Two Hooks and Lift Clutch Straight Out of Case

2) Grasp reverse (front) planetary gear set and pull from case along with its thrust washer. Remove first-reverse brake plates and wave washer from assembly, then withdraw sun gear and driving shell (with thrust washer) and forward (rear) planetary gear set. Slide forward clutch out of assembly, remove the two forward clutch-to-direct-reverse clutch thrust washers, then withdraw direct-reverse clutch from case.

3) Push second gear servo assembly down into transmission case, remove retaining snap ring, then withdraw servo assembly (cover, piston, and spring) from case. On opposite side of case, loosen second gear band adjusting screw, then from inside case, withdraw second gear band. Remove bolts from first-reverse brake spring plate, withdraw spring plate and springs, then pull driving shell, brake piston, and oil pump from case.

4) Position transmission case on bench with oil pan upward. Remove pan bolts and withdraw pan and gasket. Remove screws from oil strainer and separate strainer from valve body. Remove 11 hex-head bolts from valve body, lift valve body from case taking care not to lose manual valve, then withdraw accumulator spring and piston from case. If necessary for parts replacement, disassemble kickdown and selector linkage using *Fig. 4* as a guide.

COMPONENT DISASSEMBLY & REASSEMBLY

OIL PUMP ASSEMBLY

Disassembly — Remove metal sealing rings and thrust washer from front of pump housing. On rear of housing, hold cover plate tight against housing, remove cover plate screws, then withdraw cover plate, check ball and spring **CAUTION** — *Plate is under spring tension.* Withdraw pump drive plate, mark pump gears for reassembly reference, then remove gears from housing.

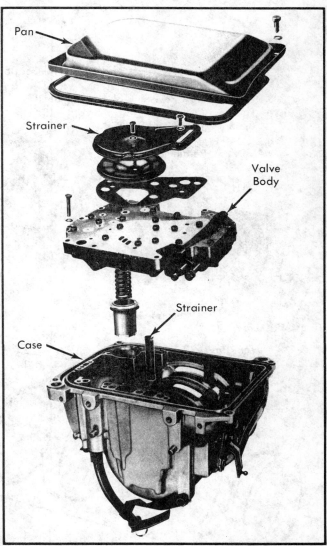

Fig. 6   Exploded View Showing Removal of Strainer and Valve Body Assembly

Pan

Strainer

Valve Body

Strainer

Case

Inspection — Wash all parts in solvent and air dry. Check parts for wear, scoring, chipped teeth, and any other damage. Replace parts as necessary.

Reassembly — Coat pump gears with transmission fluid and install into pump housing, aligning marks made at disassembly. Position drive plate on top of inner gear and check ball and spring in housing. Place cover plate over rear of assembly, compress spring and check ball taking care not to displace them, then install and tighten cover-to-housing screws. Install thrust washer and metal sealing rings (locking ends) on front of pump housing. Insert pump shaft into oil pump, rotate gears, and check for free operation.

VALVE BODY ASSEMBLY

Disassembly — Remove screws attaching oil strainer to body and remove strainer. Remove 19 transfer plate-to-main valve body screws, withdraw transfer and separator plates off main body, then withdraw 5 check balls from passages of main

Automatic Transaxles

FIAT STRADA, VOLKSWAGON JETTA, PICKUP, RABBIT & SCIROCCO (Cont.)

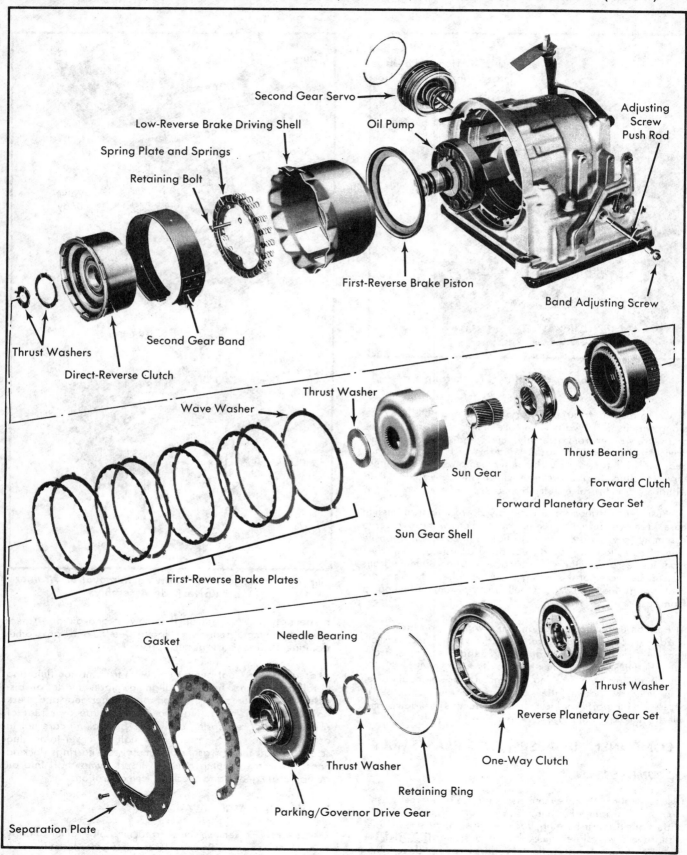

Fig. 7 Exploded View of Automatic Transmission Assembly

FIAT STRADA, VOLKSWAGON JETTA, PICKUP, RABBIT & SCIROCCO (Cont.)

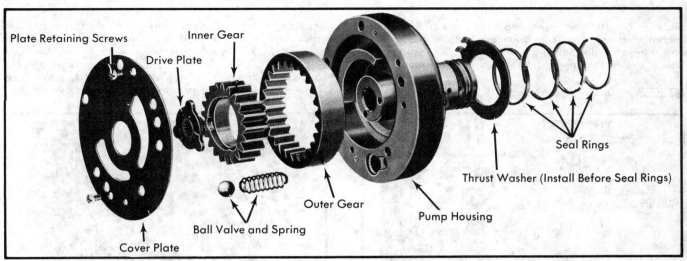

Fig. 8 Exploded View of Oil Pump Assembly

VALVE BODY SPRING IDENTIFICATION JETTA, RABBIT & SCIROCCO

Valve Spring	Length In. (mm)	Diameter In. (mm)①	Number Of Coils	Wire Thickness In. (mm)
Throttle Pressure Limiting Valve	1.388 (35.2)	.303 (7.7)	14.5	.043 (1.1)
Main Pressure Valve	3.031 (77.0)	.468 (11.9)	16.5	.059 (1.5)
Main Pressure Limiting Valve	1.274 (32.6)	.303 (7.7)	11	.047 (1.2)
Control Valve	1.274 (32.4)	.303 (7.7)	12.5	.039 (1.0)
Throttle Pressure Valve	1.703 (43.3)	.304 (7.75)	16	.048 (1.25)
1-2 Shift Valve	.783 (19.9)	.319 (8.1)	6.5	.035 (.9)
Converter Pressure Valve	1.276 (32.4)	.303 (7.7)	12.5	.039 (1.0)
Modulator Pressure Valve	1.125 (28.6)	.305 (7.7)	11.5	.031 (.8)
2-3 Shift Valve	.783 (19.9)	.319 (8.1)	6.5	.035 (.9)
3-2 Kickdown Valve	1.118 (28.4)	.319 (8.1)	11.5	.035 (.9)
Apply Valve	1.118 (28.4)	.319 (8.1)	11.5	.035 (.9)

① — Inner diameter of coils, within tolerance of ± .012″ (.3 mm)

VALVE BODY SPRING IDENTIFICATION STRADA

Valve Spring	Length In. (mm)	Diameter In. (mm)①	Number Of Coils	Wire Thickness In. (mm)
Throttle Pressure Limiting Valve	1.358 (34.5)	.303 (7.7)	13.5	.043 (1.1)
Main Pressure Valve	2.748 (69.8)	.468 (11.9)	15.5	.059 (1.5)
Main Pressure Limiting Valve	1.248 (31.7)	.303 (7.7)	11	.043 (1.1)
Control Valve	1.256 (31.9)	.303 (7.7)	11.5	.039 (1.0)
Throttle Pressure Valve	1.709 (43.4)	.304 (7.75)	16	.048 (1.25)
1-2 Shift Valve	.783 (19.9)	.319 (8.1)	6.5	.035 (.9)
Converter Pressure Valve	1.244 (31.6)	.303 (7.7)	11	.039 (1.0)
Modulator Pressure Valve	.740 (18.8)	.209 (5.3)	5	.028 (.7)
2-3 Shift Valve	.783 (19.9)	.319 (8.1)	6.5	.035 (.9)
3-2 Kickdown Valve	1.118 (28.4)	.319 (8.1)	10	.035 (.9)
Apply Valve	1.118 (28.4)	.319 (8.1)	11.5	.035 (.9)

① — Inner diameter of coils, within tolerance of ±.2″ (.3 mm).

FIAT STRADA, VOLKSWAGON JETTA, PICKUP, RABBIT & SCIROCCO (Cont.)

body. See *Fig. 10*. Remove rear end plate and withdraw valves, springs, and adjusting screws. Remove remaining end plates one at a time and withdraw all valves, plugs, springs, and adjusting screws, tagging all parts for reassembly reference.

CAUTION — *Do not alter settings of adjusting screws.*

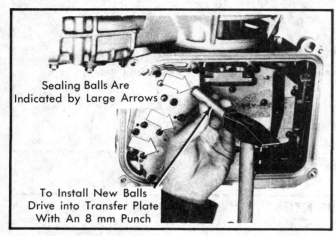

**Fig. 9   View of Valve Body Showing
Location of Transfer Plate Sealing Balls**

Inspection — Wash all parts in solvent and air dry only (do not use fluffy rags, etc.). Check all parts for burrs and scores; replace assembly if damage is found. When valves are clean and lubricated with fluid, they should fall of their own weight in respective bore; if not, check for valve or bore damage. Check all springs for damage and collapsed coils. **CAUTION** — *Several springs have similar dimensions; however, they must not be interchanged as they have different tolerances. Take care not to disturb settings of adjusting screws; pressures affected by these screws can only be measured and adjusted accurately on a test stand.*

NOTE — *If transmission does not shift into 3d gear, trouble may be caused by a missing sealing ball in the transfer plate. See Fig. 9. To install a new sealing ball, stick the .118" (3 mm) diameter sealing ball on an 8 mm punch with a small amount of grease, then drive ball flush into hole of transfer plate.*

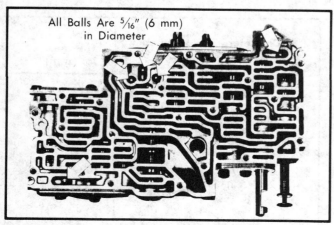

**Fig. 10   View of Main Valve Body Showing
Location of Check Balls**

Reassembly — Lubricate all parts with transmission fluid and install into proper valve body bores, in reverse order as removed. Make sure all parts slide freely in bores. Make sure check balls are installed in proper body passages (see *Fig. 10 and 11*). Install transfer plate-to-main body screws and tighten from center outward, using care not to overtighten.

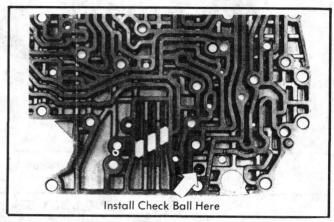

**Fig. 11   View of Transfer Plate Showing
Location of Check Ball**

GOVERNOR

Disassembly — Remove two attaching screws and withdraw thrust plate and housing. Remove transfer plate, balance weight and if equipped, oil strainer. Remove "E" clips and withdraw centrifugal weight, valve, spring, and dished washer from pin.

Reassembly — Reverse disassembly procedure and note the following: Lubricate all parts with transmission fluid when assembling. Make sure angle in thrust plate is in center of housing so cover will bear against it.

NOTE — *If equipped, ensure that oil strainer is installed as shown in Fig. 13.*

BAND SERVO

Disassembly — Pull servo piston assembly out of cover, then remove "O" ring seals from outside diameter of cover. Remove retaining clip and separate piston pin, accumulator spring, spring seat, and adjusting shim(s) from servo piston. Withdraw two lip seals from servo piston.

Inspection — Clean all parts and check for wear, scoring, or other damage. If replacement of piston is required, pin, spring retainer, accumulator spring, and shim(s) must also be replaced as this unit is serviced as an assembly only.

Reassembly — Position spring retainer, accumulator spring, and shim(s) on piston pin, install assembly into servo piston, and install retaining "E" clip onto pin. Install lip seals onto piston as follows: Smaller (upper) seal is installed onto piston with lip facing upward, or into servo cover. Larger seal is installed on piston with lip pointed downward, or out of servo cover. Lubricate assembly thoroughly and install piston into cover. Install "O" rings onto outer diameter of servo cover.

FIAT STRADA, VOLKSWAGON JETTA, PICKUP, RABBIT & SCIROCCO (Cont.)

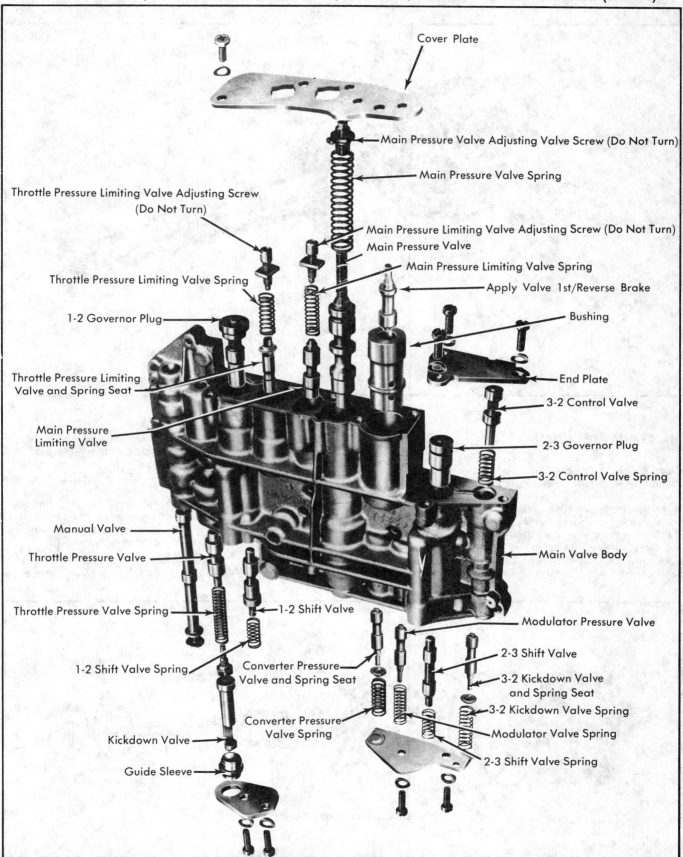

Cover Plate

Main Pressure Valve Adjusting Valve Screw (Do Not Turn)

Main Pressure Valve Spring

Throttle Pressure Limiting Valve Adjusting Screw (Do Not Turn)

Main Pressure Limiting Valve Adjusting Screw (Do Not Turn)

Main Pressure Valve

Throttle Pressure Limiting Valve Spring

Main Pressure Limiting Valve Spring

Apply Valve 1st/Reverse Brake

1-2 Governor Plug

Bushing

Throttle Pressure Limiting Valve and Spring Seat

End Plate

3-2 Control Valve

Main Pressure Limiting Valve

2-3 Governor Plug

3-2 Control Valve Spring

Manual Valve

Throttle Pressure Valve

Main Valve Body

Throttle Pressure Valve Spring

1-2 Shift Valve

Modulator Pressure Valve

1-2 Shift Valve Spring

Converter Pressure Valve and Spring Seat

2-3 Shift Valve

3-2 Kickdown Valve and Spring Seat

3-2 Kickdown Valve Spring

Converter Pressure Valve Spring

Modulator Valve Spring

Kickdown Valve

Guide Sleeve

2-3 Shift Valve Spring

Fig. 12 Exploded View of Main Valve Body Showing Valves and Springs

FIAT STRADA, VOLKSWAGON JETTA, PICKUP, RABBIT & SCIROCCO (Cont.)

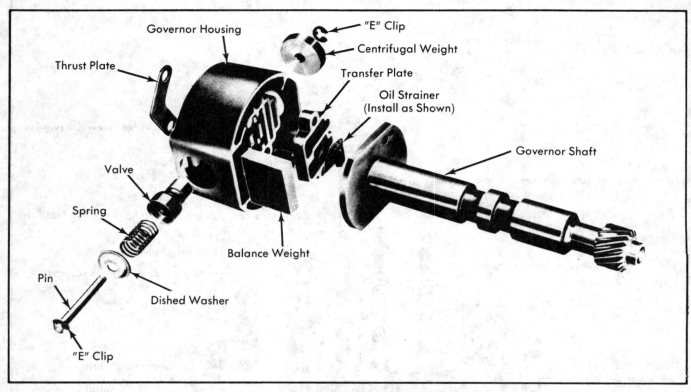

Fig. 13   Exploded View of Governor Assembly

DIRECT-REVERSE CLUTCH

Disassembly — Remove clutch pack retaining snap ring from drum, then withdraw pressure plate and lined and steel clutch plates. Place clutch drum in a press, apply downward pressure to piston spring retainer, remove retaining snap ring and release press. Withdraw spring retainer, piston springs, and clutch piston. Remove seals from clutch piston and drum. If necessary, place clutch drum in a press and drive bushing out of clutch drum using a driver (US 1099 for Jetta, Rabbit and Scirocco, and A45052 for Strada).

Inspection — Clean all parts in solvent and air dry. Check piston and drum for scoring or other damage. Inspect steel plates for wear and burn marks, and replace if worn (or blue). Check lined plates for wear, cracking, or chipping, and replace if unsuitable. **NOTE** — *If new plates are to be used, soak in transmission fluid 15 minutes prior to installation.* Inspect check ball in clutch drum for freedom of operation and proper sealing. Check piston return springs for distortion or collapsed coils. Replace any part found damaged.

Reassembly — 1) If removed, use a press and suitable bushing driver (VW 433) and install bushing into clutch drum

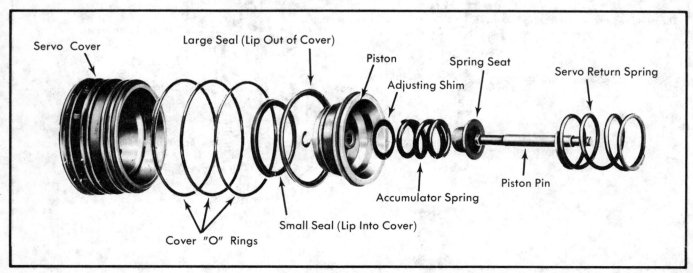

Fig. 14   Exploded View of Second Gear Servo

FIAT STRADA, VOLKSWAGON JETTA, PICKUP, RABBIT & SCIROCCO (Cont.)

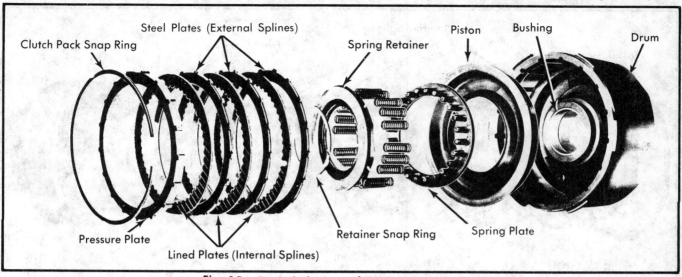

Clutch Pack Snap Ring

Steel Plates (External Splines)

Spring Retainer

Piston

Bushing

Drum

Pressure Plate

Lined Plates (Internal Splines)

Retainer Snap Ring

Spring Plate

Fig. 15   Exploded View of Direct-Reverse Clutch

hub until it is .067" (1.7 mm) below hub lip. Install a new seal on clutch drum and a new seal on piston, making sure that seal lips face downward into drum. Completely lubricate piston assembly with automatic transmission fluid and install into drum.

2) Position piston return springs on top of piston, place retainer on top of springs, compress assembly and install retaining snap ring. Lubricate all clutch plates with automatic transmission fluid and install into clutch drum, starting with a steel (external splines) plate and alternating lined (internal splines) and steel plates until all clutch plates are installed. Install pressure plate and clutch pack retaining snap ring.

Direct-Reverse Clutch Plate Chart

Application	Steel Plates	Lined Plates
All Models	3	3

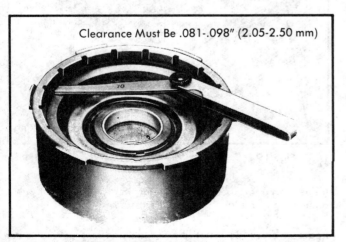

Clearance Must Be .081-.098" (2.05-2.50 mm)

Fig. 16   Using a Feeler Gauge to Measure Direct-Reverse Clutch Clearance

3) Using a feeler gauge, measure clearance between clutch pack retaining snap ring and pressure plate. Clearance should be .081-.098" (2.05-2.50 mm); if not, remove clutch pack snap ring and replace with a snap ring of correct thickness to bring clearance within specifications. Snap rings are available in various thicknesses from .059" (1.5 mm) to .098" (2.5 mm). Recheck clearance after installing replacement snap ring.

FORWARD CLUTCH

Disassembly — Remove waved snap ring from clutch drum and withdraw pressure plate, lined and steel clutch plates, planetary ring gear, and thrust plate. Remove flat snap ring from drum and withdraw diaphragm spring and clutch piston.

Inspection — Use inspection procedures given for direct-reverse clutch, and add the following: Check planetary ring gear inner and outer splines for wear, scoring or other damage and replace if necessary.

Reassembly — **1)** Coat clutch piston with transmission fluid and install into drum. Position diaphragm spring in drum with convex side facing towards bottom of drum, then install flat retaining snap ring.

NOTE — *With snap ring installed, diaphragm spring should be lightly tensioned; if not, replace spring.*

2) Lubricate with transmission fluid and install thrust plate and one lined plate into clutch drum. Next, install planetary ring gear into assembly, engaging inner splines of lined plate. When installed, lined plate should be under retaining edge on outer splines of ring gear. Install remaining clutch plates , starting with a steel plate and alternating with lined plates until all plates are installed. Install pressure plate and waved snap ring.

Forward Clutch Plate Chart

Application	Steel Plates	Lined Plates
All Models	2	3

FIAT STRADA, VOLKSWAGON JETTA, PICKUP, RABBIT & SCIROCCO (Cont.)

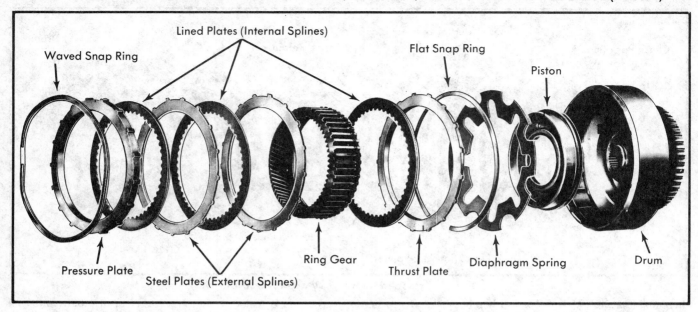

Fig. 17   Exploded View of Forward Clutch

3) Position a dial indicator on assembly so indicator pointer contacts pressure plate, then zero dial face. Pull up on planetary ring gear and note reading on dial gauge. End play of assembly should be .020-.035" (.5-.9 mm); if not, replace pressure plate with one of sufficient thickness to bring play within specifications.

NOTE — *Forward clutch assembly pressure plates are available in thicknesses of .236" (6.0 mm) to .299" (7.6 mm) in increments of .016" (.40 mm).*

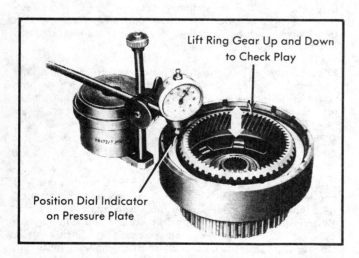

Fig. 18   Using a Dial Indicator to Measure Forward Clutch End Play

ONE-WAY CLUTCH

Disassembly — Remove upper retaining ring from assembly and withdraw roller cage, rollers and springs. Remove lower retaining ring from outer race. Inspect all parts for wear, scoring, or other damage and replace as necessary.

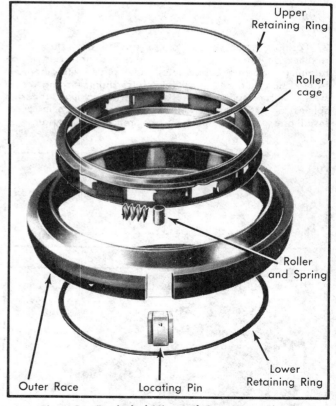

Fig. 19   Exploded View of One-Way Clutch

Inspection — Inspect all parts for wear, scoring, or other damage and replace parts as necessary.

Reassembly — 1) Install lower snap ring in groove of outer race. If necessary, heat outer race to 300° F (150° C), then place roller cage into race using two pair of pliers.

FIAT STRADA, VOLKSWAGON JETTA, PICKUP, RABBIT & SCIROCCO (Cont.)

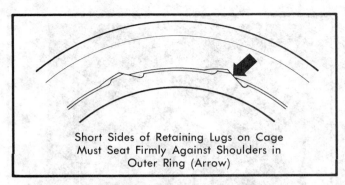

Short Sides of Retaining Lugs on Cage Must Seat Firmly Against Shoulders in Outer Ring (Arrow)

Fig. 20 View of Outer Race and Cage Showing Correct Installation

NOTE — *The heat from outer race will transfer quickly to roller cage, causing cage to stick inside race. If cage is not correctly positioned against lower snap ring inside race, DO NOT attempt to press it into position after cage has stuck. Carefully knock cage out of race and repeat procedure again after race has cooled down.*

2) Install upper snap ring. Install rollers and springs into cage making sure to point guide lug on spring (if so equipped) toward roller. See Fig. 21.

Guide Lug

Rollers and Springs Must Be Assembled as Shown

Fig. 21 View of One-Way Clutch Showing Roller and Spring Installation

TRANSMISSION REASSEMBLY

1) Coat first-reverse brake piston with transmission fluid and install onto oil pump housing, then insert pump housing into transmission case (thin rib of pump pointing upward). Install first-reverse driving shell into case so that tab of shell engages upper groove in transmission case *(Fig. 22)*. Position low-reverse brake piston return springs on spring plate, insert assembly into case with springs downward, then install and tighten retaining bolts.

2) Position second gear band in transmission case. Install second gear servo into case making sure piston pin engages band end inside case, then install servo-to-case snap ring. On opposite side of case, install band adjusting screw push rod making sure it engages band end inside case, then install adjusting screw only enough to hold band in place.

Engage Shell Tab with Case Groove

Fig. 22 First-Reverse Driving Shell Installation

3) Coat forward clutch-to-direct-reverse clutch thrust washers with petroleum jelly and position on rear end of forward clutch. Install forward clutch into direct-reverse clutch, making sure splines on forward clutch drum fully engage splines on direct-reverse clutch lined plates. With transmission case opening angled downwards, install assembled clutch units into case and over neck of oil pump, taking care not to damage pump seal rings. Rotate transmission case so opening faces upward.

4) Install forward planetary-to-forward clutch thrust bearing into forward clutch, then install forward planetary gear set into ring gear in forward clutch. Install sun gear (short end first) into gear set, then install driving shell and thrust washer over sun gear. **NOTE** — *Make sure lugs of driving shell fully engage tabs on direct-reverse clutch drum.* Position thrust washer on underside of reverse planetary gear set, then install gear set into case and onto sun gear.

First-Reverse Brake Plate Chart		
Application	**Steel Plates**	**Lined Plates**
All Models 4		 4

5) Install first-reverse brake wave washer into case, then follow with brake lined and steel plates, starting with a steel plate. **NOTE** — *Soak new lined plates in transmission fluid for 15 minutes prior to installation.* Install one-way clutch assembly into transmission case, and push clutch downward while rotating reverse planetary gear set to fully engage parts. **NOTE** — *With one-way clutch installed, it should not be possible to rotate reverse planetary gear set counterclockwise.* With all parts properly engaged, install one-way clutch-to-case retaining snap ring.

FIAT STRADA, VOLKSWAGON JETTA, PICKUP, RABBIT & SCIROCCO (Cont.)

Fig. 23   Installing One-Way Clutch Snap Ring

6) Position needle bearing and thrust washer on rear side of governor drive gear/ring gear assembly, then install unit into transmission case, fully engaging reverse planetary gear set. Install separation plate gasket over case studs, place separation plate on top of gasket, then install and tighten plate retaining screws. At this time, adjust second gear brake band as follows: Tighten band adjusting screw to 7 ft. lbs. (1 mkg), loosen screw, tighten again to 4 ft. lbs. (.5 mkg), then back screw off 1¾ to 2 turns and tighten lock nut.

NOTE — *When adjusting brake band, the transmission must be horizontal in order to keep band from slipping or jamming.*

7) If case linkage was disassembled, reinstall in case using *Fig. 4* as an assembly guide. Install a new seal on accumulator piston (lip pointing toward case), and install piston and spring into case. Install valve body assembly into case, making sure manual valve engages manual lever, and kickdown valve engages kickdown lever. Install valve body-to-case bolts and tighten from center outward. Position a new pan gasket on transmission case, install oil pan, then install and tighten pan bolts.

NOTE — *This completes assembly of transmission. Installation of impeller shaft, pump shaft, and measurement of play between transmission and final drive will be made in Final Assembly, located near the end of this article.*

FINAL DRIVE

DISASSEMBLY

1) Place final drive assembly in a suitable holding fixture and remove oil pan and gasket. Rotate differential assembly in case until differential pinion gear opening appears, then using two screwdrivers, remove two clips retaining axle drive flanges in differential. Pull axle drive flanges out of assembly, turning slightly to prevent catching on differential side gear thrust washers. At this time, remove retaining bolt and withdraw speedometer driven gear assembly straight out of case.

Fig. 24   View of Differential Assembly Showing Location of Drive Flange Retaining Clips

2) Using a scribe or gear paint, mark relationship of differential side bearing adjusting ring and case. **NOTE** — *If bearings are not replaced, ring will be reset to this position at reassembly.* Remove lock clip from adjusting ring and screw ring out of case. On opposite side of case, remove nuts and withdraw the other differential side bearing retainer (cover). Grasp differential and ring gear assembly and remove from final drive case.

Fig. 25   Removing Differential Side Bearing Adjusting Ring

3) Inside converter housing area of final drive case, mark relationship of intermediate gear shaft and case with a scribe or gear paint. **NOTE** — *If bearings are not replaced, shaft will be reset to this position at reassembly.* Remove lock clip from intermediate gear shaft and screw shaft out of case. From inside case, withdraw intermediate gear along with bearings. Remove bolts retaining stator support to converter housing area of case, then withdraw support and pinion shaft assembly from case.

4) To disassemble differential assembly, first remove two differential pinion shaft retaining rings and remove shaft from differential case using a drift. Move differential pinion gears around to case openings, withdraw from case along with thrust washers, then remove differential side gears and their thrust washers. Remove ring gear attaching bolts and

FIAT STRADA, VOLKSWAGON JETTA, PICKUP, RABBIT & SCIROCCO (Cont.)

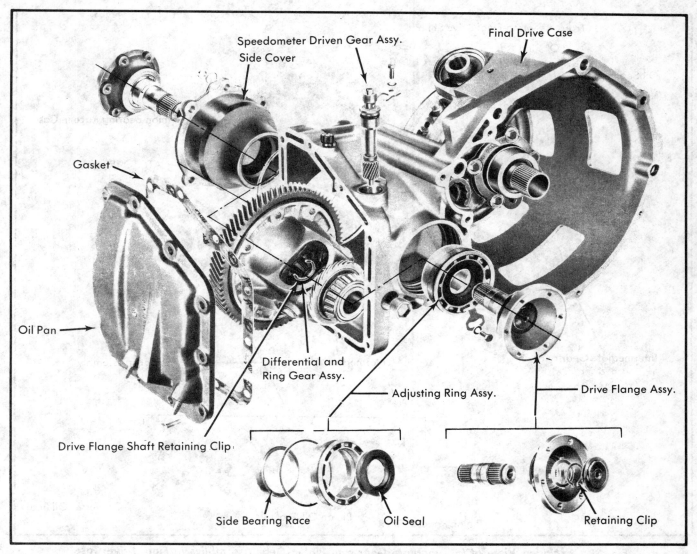

Fig. 26 *Exploded View of Differential and Related Parts in Final Drive Case*

Mark Shaft and Case Before Unscrewing

Fig. 27 *Removing Intermediate Gear Shaft*

separate ring gear from case using a press. If required, withdraw differential side bearings and speedometer drive gear from case using a press, then withdraw bearing races from adjusting ring and side cover.

5) If replacement of pinion bearings or pinion shaft is required, proceed as follows: Place pinion assembly in a press, and using press plates positioned under bearings, drive bearings from pinion shaft. In addition, place stator support in press and drive out pinion bearing race along with preload shim and pinion oil seal. From opposite end of support, use a chisel and remove converter oil seal. Finally, use a hammer and drift and drive remaining pinion bearing race out of final drive case.

REASSEMBLY & ADJUSTMENT

Pinion Reassembly & Preload Adjustment — 1) If pinion gear and/or pinion bearings were replaced, lubricate bearings with final drive lubricant and press onto pinion shaft. Using a drift, install pinion bearing race into final drive hous-

FIAT STRADA, VOLKSWAGON JETTA, PICKUP, RABBIT & SCIROCCO (Cont.)

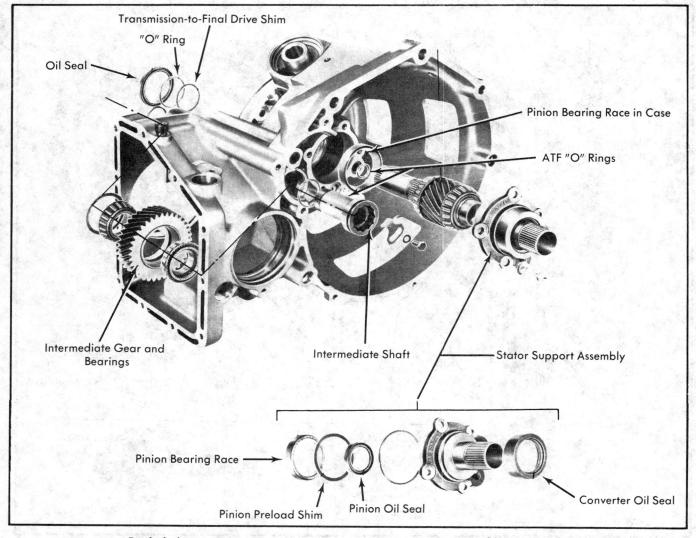

Transmission-to-Final Drive Shim

"O" Ring

Oil Seal

Pinion Bearing Race in Case

ATF "O" Rings

Intermediate Gear and Bearings

Intermediate Shaft

Stator Support Assembly

Pinion Bearing Race

Pinion Preload Shim

Pinion Oil Seal

Converter Oil Seal

Fig. 28   Exploded View of Intermediate Gear and Pinion Gear Assemblies in Final Drive Case

ing. Temporarily install remaining pinion bearing race (without adjusting shim) into stator support, then install pinion assembly into final drive case, tightening stator support bolts securely.

2) With transmission attaching face of final drive housing facing upward, position a dial indicator on housing with button of indicator contacting pinion shaft. Zero dial face, then move pinion shaft up and down (without turning) and note maximum play reading on dial indicator. To this figure, add .008" (.2 mm); resulting figure is thickness of pinion preload shim to be installed under bearing race in stator support.

NOTE — *Pinion preload shims are available in thicknesses of .039" (1.0 mm) to .087" (2.2 mm) in increments of .002" (.05 mm).*

3) Remove pinion assembly from final drive case and press bearing race out of stator support. Install pinion oil seal into support, follow with preload shim just selected, then position bearing race in support and press into place. Install converter oil seal on front side of support and sealing "O" ring on rear

Move Pinion Up and Down For Reading Then Add .008" (.2 mm) For Proper Bearing Preload

Fig. 29   Using Dial Indicator to Determine Pinion Preload Shim Thickness

FIAT STRADA, VOLKSWAGON JETTA, PICKUP, RABBIT & SCIROCCO (Cont.)

side. Also install new automatic transmission fluid passage "O" rings into final drive case, at stator support attaching face.

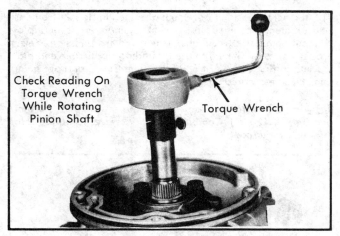

Fig. 30   Checking Pinion Bearing Preload

4) Thoroughly coat pinion bearings with final drive lubricant, position pinion assembly in final drive case, then install stator support and tighten retaining bolts. Attach a torque wrench to pinion shaft, and while turning shaft with wrench, note torque reading and record for future reference.

NOTE — *This reading is the basis for intermediate shaft and differential assembly preload adjustments, and must be noted before any further assembly steps are taken.*

Intermediate Gear Reassembly & Preload Adjustment —
If intermediate gear and bearings were replaced, coat bearings with final drive lubricant and install into intermediate gear. Position gear assembly into final drive case, insert intermediate shaft, and tighten shaft slightly. With torque wrench attached to pinion shaft, rotate pinion shaft and note preload reading on dial face. While continuing to rotate pinion shaft, turn intermediate shaft left or right until preload reading on gauge is approximately 13 INCH lbs. (15 cmkg) higher than reading obtained in step 4) of Pinion Reassembly and Preload Adjustment. With proper preload obtained, install and tighten shaft lock plate bolt.

Differential Reassembly & Preload Adjustment — 1)
Lubricate differential side gears and thrust washers with final drive lubricant and position in differential case. Coat differential pinion gears and thrust washers with lubricant, place gears and washers onto side gears through opening in differential case, then rotate into alignment with differential pinion shaft bores in case.

NOTE — *Pinion gears must be exactly opposite one another in order to install shaft.*

2) Install differential pinion shaft into differential case and through pinion gears, then install pinion shaft retaining clips. If removed, install differential side bearings and speedometer drive gear onto differential case using a press. If ring gear is being replaced, install guide pins into differential case bolt holes, heat ring gear in hot oil to approximately 212° F (100° C), and install over guide pins and onto case. Install and tighten attaching bolts.

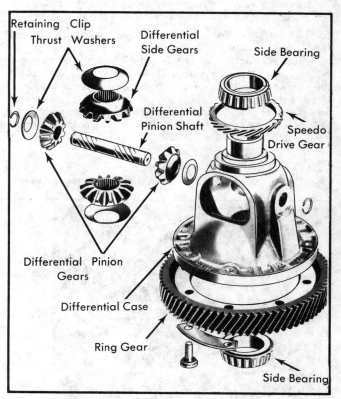

Fig. 31   Exploded View of Differential and Ring Gear Assembly

NOTE — *If differential case, pinion gears, side gears, thrust washers, or axle drive flange shafts are being replaced, selection of drive flange shaft retaining rings must be made at this time.*

3) Install each flange shaft into differential case and bottom against differential pinion shaft. While holding side gear against differential case, attempt to install the thicker of two snap rings which are available. If thicker ring jams at sides and cannot be installed, select thinner retaining ring for use when drive flanges are installed.

4) If side bearing races were removed from adjusting ring and side cover, install at this time along with new oil seals. Install new sealing "O" rings on ring and cover. Thoroughly coat ring gear and side bearings with final drive lubricant, position differential assembly in final drive case, and engage with intermediate gear. Install side cover to engage with side bearing, then install and tighten cover retaining nuts. Screw side bearing adjusting ring into case and over side bearing so differential is firmly supported.

5) With torque wrench attached to pinion shaft, rotate pinion shaft and note reading on gauge. While continuing to rotate pinion shaft, rotate side bearing adjuster left or right until preload reading on gauge is approximately 6 INCH lbs. (7 cmkg) greater than last reading obtained in Intermediate Gear Reassembly and Preload Adjustment. With proper preload obtained, install and tighten adjusting ring lock.

6) If disassembled, install drive flanges onto flange shafts, and secure with spring rings and lock clips. Install end caps into flange shafts, then install shafts into final drive case,

FIAT STRADA, VOLKSWAGON JETTA, PICKUP, RABBIT & SCIROCCO (Cont.)

securing with retaining clips previously selected. Position a new pan gasket on case and install oil pan.

Final Assembly of Transaxle — 1) To measure play between final drive and transmission, place a straight edge on transmission attaching face of final drive housing, and using a depth gauge, measure distance from top surface of straight edge down to surface of pinion bearing inner race. Next, measure distance from top surface of straight edge to face of final drive housing; subtract this second measurement from first measurement obtained in this step and note for future reference.

2) Place a new gasket on transmission separation plate, position straight edge on transmission case, and measure distance from top surface of straight edge down to gasket sur-

face. Next, measure distance from top surface of straight edge down to inner shoulder of governor drive gear; subtract this measurement from first measurement obtained in this step and write down for future reference.

3) Subtract the last measurement obtained in step **2)** from last measurement obtained in step **1)**. Remainder is end play (without shims) between final drive and transmission. Select proper end play shim(s) to use by finding applicable end play reading in first column of End Play Shim Chart, and obtaining shim thickness noted in second column.

NOTE — *Shims are available in thicknesses of .016" (.4 mm) and .047" (1.2 mm). Combine shim thicknesses to obtain total thickness required.*

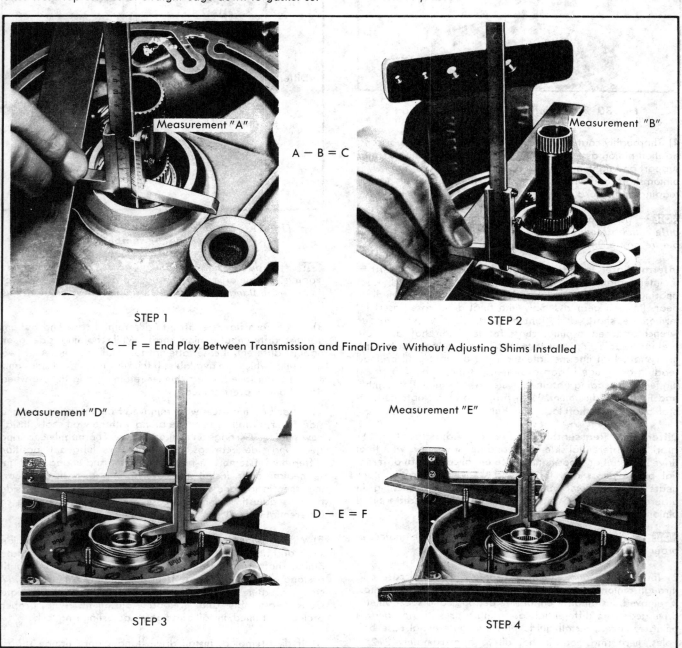

Measurement "A"

A − B = C

Measurement "B"

STEP 1　　　　STEP 2

C − F = End Play Between Transmission and Final Drive Without Adjusting Shims Installed

Measurement "D"

D − E = F

Measurement "E"

STEP 3　　　　STEP 4

Fig. 32　Using a Depth Guage to Determine Transmission-to-Final Drive End Play Shim

FIAT STRADA, VOLKSWAGON JETTA, PICKUP, RABBIT & SCIROCCO (Cont.)

4) Install selected shim(s) into final drive case, on top of pinion bearing inner race. Next, install sealing "O" ring and final drive-to-transmission oil seal into pinion cavity of final drive housing. Install impeller shaft and pump shaft fully into transmission, position a new "O" ring seal on final drive case, then mate final drive and transmission cases. Install final drive-to-transmission case nuts and tighten. Place new "O" ring seals onto governor, governor cover, and speedometer driven gear assembly, and install into case. Finally, install torque converter onto stator support to complete assembly.

End Play Shim Chart

If End Play Is In (mm)	Install This Shim In. (mm)
.900-.033 (.23-.84)	None
.034-.049 (.85-1.24)	.016 (.4)
.050-.065 (1.25-1.64)	.032 (.8)
.066-.080 (1.65-2.04	.048 (1.2)
.081-.096 (2.05-2.44)	.064 (1.6)
.097-.112 (2.45-2.84)	.080 (2.0)
.113-.128 (2.85-3.24)	.096 (2.4)
.129-.143 (3.25-3.64)	.112 (2.8)
.144-.153 (3.65-3.88)	.128 (3.2)

TIGHTENING SPECIFICATIONS

Application	Ft. Lbs. (mkg)
Transmission	
Locknut on 2nd gear brake band adjusting screw	14 (2)
Pan-to-Transmission Case	14 (2)
Transaxle-to-Engine	40 (5.5)
Converter-to-Drive Plate	22 (3)
Converter Cover Plate-to-Bell Housing	11 (1.5)
Starter-to-Bell Housing	22 (3)
Constant Velocity Joint-to-Drive Flange	32 (4.5)
Transmission Case-to-Final Drive Housing	22 (3)
Manual Valve-to-Shaft Nut	14 (2)
Kickdown Valve-to-Shaft Nut	11 (1.5)

	INCH lbs. (cmkg)
Valve Body-to-Case	35 (40)
Strainer-to-Valve Body	26 (30)
Pump-to-Case	35 (40)

Final Drive	Ft. Lbs. (mkg)
Side Bearing Cover	22 (3)
Cover-to-Final Drive Housing	36 (5)
Ring Gear	50 (7)

HONDAMATIC

Civic

DESCRIPTION

Transaxle assembly is a two-speed unit, consisting basically of a torque converter, a mainshaft-countershaft type gear system, two disc clutches and one servo to control this gear system, and a differential-type final drive assembly. The two clutches are used to select the two forward gear ratios, while the servo is used to engage reverse gear. A gear type pump (internal in valve body) is used to develop fluid pressure for the hydraulic control system. The final drive assembly is driven off the transmission countershaft.

LUBRICATION & ADJUSTMENT

See *AUTOMATIC TRANSMISSION SERVICING* Section.

TROUBLE SHOOTING

NO DRIVE IN ANY POSITION

Incorrect fluid level. Manual linkage out of adjustment. Incorrect oil pressure. Defective servo valve piston. Defective reverse gear selector spline. Converter pump inner hub slipping. Damaged pump drive gear spline. Axles not engaged in differential assembly.

TRANSMISSION SLIPS IN ALL GEARS

Incorrect fluid level. Manual linkage out of adjustment. Incorrect oil pressure. Defective torque converter pump. Clogged pump strainer. Defective or sticking regulator valve in valve body assembly.

NO DRIVE IN "D" OR "R"

Incorrect fluid level. Manual linkage out of adjustment. Incorrect stall RPM. Throttle control cable not properly adjusted. Sticking or defective reverse idler gear. Defective torque converter one-way clutch.

TRANSMISSION SLIPS IN "D" OR "R"

Incorrect fluid level. Manual linkage out of adjustment. Incorrect oil pressure. Defective high clutch.

NO DRIVE OR SLIPS IN "L"

Incorrect fluid level. Manual linkage out of adjustment. Incorrect oil pressure. Defective low clutch.

TRANSMISSION SLIPS IN "R"

Incorrect fluid level. Manual linkage out of adjustment. Incorrect oil pressure. Defective servo valve piston. Defective reverse gear selector spline. Defective high clutch.

POOR ACCELERATION

Incorrect fluid level. Manual linkage out of adjustment. Defective low or high clutch. Defective torque converter one-way clutch.

TRANSMISSION GRINDS IN "R"

Incorrect fluid level. Manual linkage out of adjustment. Defective servo valve piston. Sticking or defective reverse idler gear. Servo piston sticking in transmission housing recess.

BUZZING NOISE IN "L" OR "D"

Torque converter pump defective. Loose countershaft lock nut.

TESTING

HYDRAULIC PRESSURE TEST

1) Before performing pressure tests, be sure that fluid level and condition have been checked and corrected as necessary. With engine at normal operating temperature, connect a tachometer.

NOTE — *See Fig. 1 for location of the various pressure test take-off points on transmission.*

2) Connect an oil pressure gauge to line pressure take-off point on transmission case. Start engine and run at 1000 RPM. Read transmission line pressure with transmission in "P" or "N". Pressure should be approximately as shown in Pressure Test Specifications chart. If not, check for a defective torque converter, oil pump pressure regulator, or torque converter check valve.

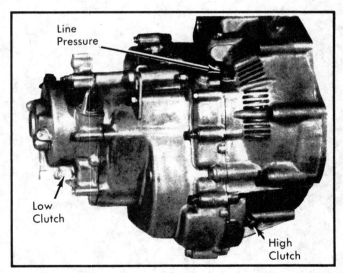

Fig. 1   View of Transmission Case Showing Pressure Test Take-Off Points

3) Connect pressure gauge to high clutch take-off point, start engine and run at 1000 RPM. Place transmission in "D" and read gauge. Pressure should be approximately as shown in Pressure Test Specifications chart. If not, check for a defective high clutch.

4) With gauge connected to high clutch take-off point, place transmission in "R" and read pressure on gauge. Pressure should be approximately as shown in Pressure Test Specifications chart. If not, check for a defective servo piston and/or high clutch.

HONDAMATIC (Cont.)

5) Connect pressure gauge to low clutch take-off point, start engine and run at 1000 RPM. Place transmission in "L" and read pressure gauge. Pressure should be approximately as shown in Pressure Test Specifications chart. If not, check for a defective low clutch.

Pressure Test Specifications		
Application	Standard psi (kg/cm²)	Service Limit psi (kg/cm²)
Line Pressure	71-114 (5.0-8.0)	57 (4.0)
High Clutch Pressure		
In "D"	71-114 (5.0-8.0)	57 (4.0)
In "R"	71-114 (5.0-8.0)	57 (4.0)
Low Clutch		
Pressure	71-114 (5.0-8.0)	57 (4.0)

STALL TEST

Testing Precautions — When making test, do not hold throttle open longer than 10 seconds at a time, or damage to converter may occur. If engine speed exceeds maximum limit, release accelerator immediately as this is an indication of clutch slippage. Also, allow two minutes between tests to allow transmission to cool.

Testing Procedure — With engine at normal operating temperature, tachometer installed, and parking and service brakes applied, stall test transmission in each driving range by depressing accelerator to floor. Read maximum RPM obtained.

Stall Speed Specifications	
Application	Stall RPM
Civic	2500-3200

Test Results — If stall speed is high in all ranges, check for incorrect fluid level, defective oil pump, clogged oil strainer, or defective pressure regulator valve. If high in "D" and "R" positions, check for a slipping high clutch. If high in "L" position, check for a slipping low clutch. If stall speed is low in all positions, check for low engine power output, a faulty torque converter one-way clutch, or throttle control cable out of adjustment.

REMOVAL & INSTALLATION

NOTE — *For Axle Drive Shaft, Drive Shaft "U" Joint, and Front Wheel Bearing replacement procedures, see appropriate Honda manual transaxle article in MANUAL TRANSAXLE Section.*

TRANSAXLE ASSEMBLY

Removal — 1) Disconnect battery ground and ground strap at transmission. Release steering lock and place selector lever in "N". Disconnect battery cable from starter and wires from starter solenoid. Disconnect wire from water temperature sender and wire from ignition timing thermosensor.

2) Disconnect cooler hoses and wire them up out of way so they will not drain. Remove starter mounting bolt on transmission side and top transmission mounting bolt. Remove forward bolt for rear torque arm bracket. Remove speedometer cable from transmission.

3) Remove center console and control cable from center console shift lever. Raise and support vehicle, then remove front wheels. Remove control cable retainer plate bolts then pull cable out of center console. Drain transmission and reinstall plug.

4) Disconnect lower control arm pivot bolts on right and left sides of vehicle. Turn right steering knuckle outward as far as it will go then pry axle shaft out of transmission case about ½" (12 mm). This will compress spring clip on axle shaft inside transmission. Pull axle shaft out of transmission. Repeat procedure for left axle shaft.

5) Remove nuts from each end of stabilizar bar, then remove brackets and stabilizar bar. Raise engine just enough to take weight off mounts. Remove front and rear torque rods then remove rear torque rod brackets. Remove rear engine mount and bracket.

6) Place block of wood under oil pan and on crossmember, lower engine until it rests on block of wood. Remove engine damper bracket and converter cover plate from transmission. Remove converter-to-drive plate bolts.

7) Remove starter. Place jack under transmission, then remove remaining 2 transmission-to-engine bolts. Move transmission away from engine and lower out of vehicle.

Installation — To install transmission, reverse removal procedure. Make sure engine-to-transmission dowel pins are aligned, converter is fully seated and attached to drive plate. When installing axle shafts into transmission, use new spring clips on axle shafts. After installation, refill transmission with fluid and adjust shift control linkage.

TRANSAXLE DISASSEMBLY

1) Remove oil filler tube, then remove end cover. Shift transmission to "P". Using special mainshaft holder (07923-6890201), lock mainshaft from turning. Bend tabs of mainshaft lock washer down and remove mainshaft lock nut. See Fig. 2.

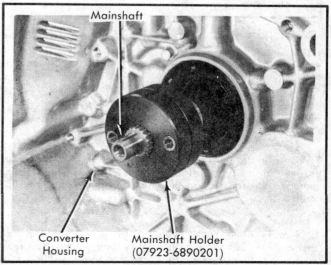

Fig. 2 Installation of Special Holder Tool to Mainshaft for Removing Mainshaft Lock Nut

HONDAMATIC (Cont.)

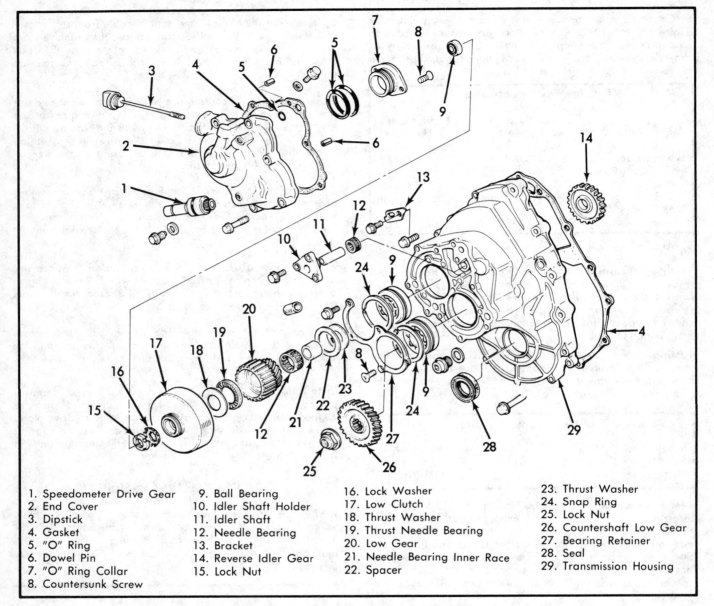

1. Speedometer Drive Gear	9. Ball Bearing	16. Lock Washer	23. Thrust Washer
2. End Cover	10. Idler Shaft Holder	17. Low Clutch	24. Snap Ring
3. Dipstick	11. Idler Shaft	18. Thrust Washer	25. Lock Nut
4. Gasket	12. Needle Bearing	19. Thrust Needle Bearing	26. Countershaft Low Gear
5. "O" Ring	13. Bracket	20. Low Gear	27. Bearing Retainer
6. Dowel Pin	14. Reverse Idler Gear	21. Needle Bearing Inner Race	28. Seal
7. "O" Ring Collar	15. Lock Nut	22. Spacer	29. Transmission Housing
8. Countersunk Screw			

Fig. 3 Exploded View of Transmission and End Housing Assemblies

2) Remove low clutch, thrust washer, thrust needle bearing and low gear as a unit. Remove needle bearing inner race, spacer and thrust washer. Pry staked portion of staked lock nut up on countershaft. Remove countershaft lock nut, then remove countershaft low gear.

3) Remove transmission-to-converter housing bolts. Loosen transmission housing by tapping with a mallet. Screw a slide hammer into transmission housing, then remove transmission housing from converter housing. *See Fig. 5.*

4) Remove inner race, needle bearing and countershaft reverse gear. Bend tab on lock plate and remove bolt from reverse shift fork. Remove shift fork and selector sleeve as a unit. Lift mainshaft and countershaft out of converter housing as an assembly.

5) Remove oil pump pickup, then remove servo assembly (6 bolts). Remove lubrication pipe and sealing ring seat. Remove stator shaft stop pin and tap stator shaft out of converter side of housing.

6) Remove clip, pin and spacers from manual valve. Remove manual valve body (4 bolts). Be careful not to drop converter check valve and spring. *See Fig. 6.* Remove oil pump gears and oil pump shaft, then remove separator plate from converter housing.

7) Remove control cable retainer from converter housing. Disconnect control cable from shift arm, then bend down tab on shift arm bolt lock plate. Remove bolt and shift arm. Lift out shift tram and parking pawl shaft together.

HONDAMATIC (Cont.)

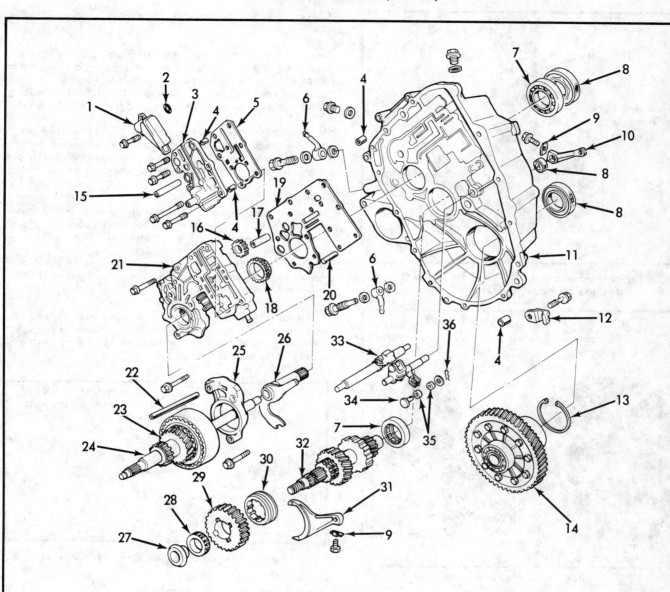

Fig. 4 Exploded View of Converter Housing Assembly

1. Oil Pump Pickup
2. "O" Ring
3. Servo Assembly
4. Dowel Pin
5. Gasket
6. Cooler Hose Connection
7. Roller Bearing
8. Seal
9. Lock Plate
10. Shift Arm
11. Converter Housing
12. Cable Retainer
13. Snap Ring
14. Differential
15. Line Pressure Pipe
16. Oil Pump Driven Gear
17. Oil Pump Shaft
18. Oil Pump Drive Gear
19. Separator Plate
20. Stop Pin
21. Valve Body
22. Feed Pipe
23. Mainshaft Assembly
24. High Clutch
25. Sealing Ring Assembly
26. Stator Shaft
27. Bearing Inner Race
28. Needle Bearing
29. Countershaft Reverse Gear
30. Reverse Selector Sleeve
31. Reverse Shift Fork
32. Countershaft Assembly
33. Shift Arm & Parking Pawl Shafts
34. Pin
35. Spacer
36. Clip

HONDAMATIC (Cont.)

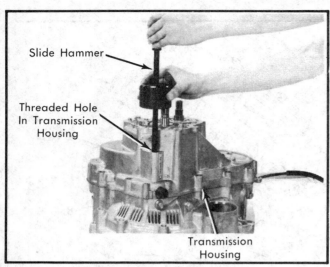

Fig. 5 Installation of Slide Hammer to Transmission Housing Threaded Hole

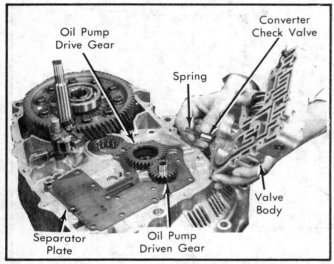

Fig. 6 Removing Manual Valve Body

COMPONENT DISASSEMBLY & REASSEMBLY

TORQUE CONVERTER

NOTE — *Before torque converter disassembly, ensure that alignment marks on converter cover and impeller are visible. If necessary, scribe new alignment marks. Converter impeller and cover MUST be reassembled in the same position.*

Disassembly — Remove bolts attaching torque converter cover to impeller and ring gear, withdraw cover, then remove cover-to-turbine thrust washer. Withdraw turbine, turbine-to-stator thrust washer, stator assembly, stator-to-impeller thrust washer, and "O" ring seal from impeller. Remove one-way clutch retaining snap rings from stator, then withdraw side plates, stator cam, stator ring, and stator rollers and springs.

Inspection — Check thickness of thrust washers. Minimum allowable thickness for cover-to-turbine thrust washer is .098" (2.5 mm), and minimum allowable thickness for turbine-to-stator and stator-to-impeller thrust washers is .079" (2.0 mm). Replace any washer with a thickness less than specifications.

Check all other components for scores, cracks, or other damage.

Reassembly — 1) Install stator side plate (grooved side out) and snap ring into stator. Install stator ring and cam into stator with widest shoulder of cam towards converter impeller. Install rollers and springs into stator cam. Install remaining stator side plate (grooved side out) and snap ring into stator.

2) With stator assembly reassembled, insert converter stator shaft into stator assembly from impeller side. Check operation of stator one-way clutch by rotating stator shaft. Stator should rotate when turned counterclockwise and lock-up when turned clockwise.

3) Install thrust washer in converter impeller. Install stator assembly into impeller with thicker vane side out. Install serrated thrust washer flush with stator surface.

4) Clean "O" ring grooves in impeller body, then install new "O" rings into grooves. Install turbine onto impeller, then install thrust washer on turbine.

5) Install torque converter cover on impeller body, ensuring that marks are aligned as shown in *Fig. 7*. Install ring gear with flat side towards converter cover. Install converter-to-impeller attaching bolts and tighten.

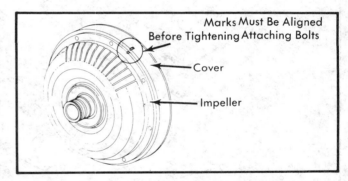

Fig. 7 Aligning Torque Converter Marks

HIGH & LOW CLUTCH ASSEMBLIES

Disassembly — Remove clutch pack retaining snap ring and withdraw end plate, lined clutch discs, and steel clutch plates. Compress clutch piston return spring, remove retaining snap ring, then withdraw spring retainer, piston return spring, and cushion spring. Apply compressed air to oil passage hole in clutch drum and remove clutch piston. Remove inner and outer seals from piston. Remove oil seal rings from clutch drum (if necessary).

Inspection — Check oil seal rings for wear or damage and replace as necessary. Inspect clutch piston return spring for wear or distortion and replace if damaged. Check steel clutch plates for burning and flaking, and lined clutch discs for glazing and wear. Replace any lined plate if worn to a point where oil grooves are no longer evident. Check splines of plates and discs, and splines of clutch drum; replace any parts found damaged. Inspect check valve in clutch piston for free operation.

HONDAMATIC (Cont.)

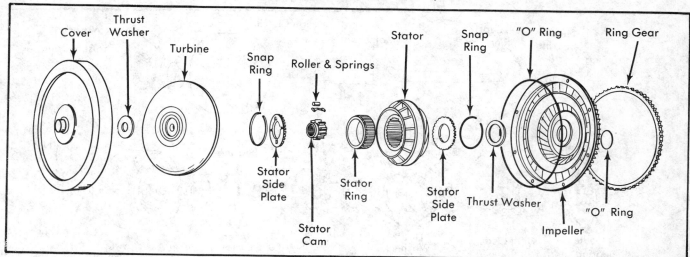

Fig. 8   Exploded View of Torque Converter Assembly

Reassembly — 1) Install two oil seal rings on clutch drum with ring gaps 180° apart. Install new "O" ring on piston, then position cushion spring on piston with bevel facing away from piston.

2) Install new "O" ring on clutch drum hub. Lubricate all "O" rings with automatic transmission fluid. Install piston into drum using a twisting motion.

3) Install clutch return spring and spring retainer. Compress return spring until retainer is below snap ring groove in clutch drum hub, then install snap ring in groove. Remove compressor tool and ensure snap ring is fully seated in groove.

4) Soak clutch plates in transmission fluid. Install clutch plates into drum starting with a steel plate, and alternating lined and steel plates until all plates are installed. Install end plate with flat side towards clutch plates. Install clutch pack retaining snap ring.

5) Using a feeler gauge, measure clearance between top clutch plate and end plate as shown in *Fig. 9*. Clearance should be .020-.032" (.5-.8 mm). If not within specifications, install an end plate of sufficient thickness to bring clearance within limits. *See Clutch End Plate Selection chart.*

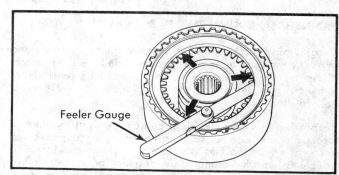

Fig. 9   Using a Feeler Gauge to Measure Clutch Plate Clearance

Clutch End Plate Selection

Identification Number	Thickness In. (mm)
1	.071 (1.8)
2	.083 (2.1)
3	.095 (2.4)
4	.106 (2.7)
No Mark	.118 (3.0)
6	.130 (3.3)

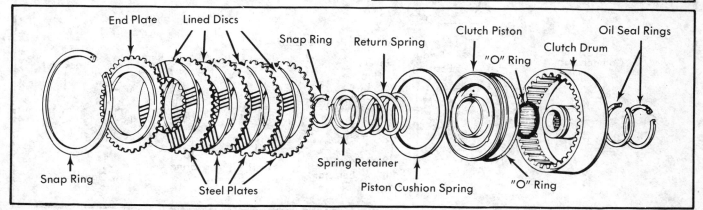

Fig. 10   Exploded View of Hondamatic Disc Clutch Assembly

Automatic Transaxles

HONDAMATIC (Cont.)

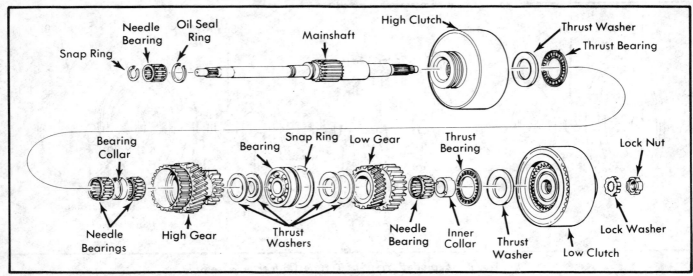

Fig. 11 Exploded View of Mainshaft Assembly

MAINSHAFT, COUNTERSHAFT & GEARS

Disassembly — On mainshaft, remove 2 thrust washers and high gear. Remove needle bearings and bearing collar. Remove thrust bearing, thrust washer and high clutch. From other end of mainshaft, remove snap ring, needle bearing and oil seal ring.

Inspection — Check mainshaft and countershaft for worn or broken splines, damaged bearing races, or out-of-round. Inspect all thrust washers and needle thrust bearings for wear, roughness, or other damage. Check gears for worn or broken teeth, damaged splines, or damaged needle bearing bores. Replace any part found damaged.

Reassembly — Install new oil seal ring, then install needle bearing and snap ring. On other end of mainshaft, slide high clutch on, making sure clutch is fully seated on mainshaft. Install thrust washer, thrust bearing, needle bearings and bearing collar. Install high gear and 2 thrust washers.

END COVER

Disassembly — Remove screws attaching low clutch oil seal ring guide to end cover, then remove seal ring guide and "O"

ring seals. Remove bolt retaining speedometer gear assembly in end cover and remove driven gear assembly. Withdraw retaining pin and separate driven gear, collar and oil seal from driven gear housing. See Fig. 3.

Inspection — Check oil seal ring guide or scratches or other damage. Inspect speedometer driven gear for broken teeth and for proper fit in collar and housing. Using compressed air, blow through hydraulic passages to check for restricted lines; clean as necessary. Replace any parts found damaged.

Reassembly — Reverse disassembly procedure and note the following: Use a new speedometer driven gear seal and new seal ring guide "O" ring seals when assembling.

TRANSMISSION HOUSING

Disassembly — From outer side of transmission housing, remove reverse idler shaft and needle bearing. From inside housing, lift out reverse idler gear. Using a driver, remove differential assembly oil seal, then drive out mainshaft bearing and countershaft bearing.

Reassembly — Reverse disassembly procedure and note the following: Install snap rings onto mainshaft and countershaft

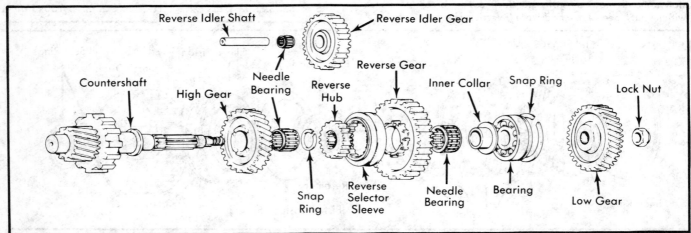

Fig. 12 Exploded View of Countershaft Assembly

HONDAMATIC (Cont.)

bearing before driving bearings into case. Both the mainshaft and countershaft bearings should be installed with bearing face slightly below case surface. Lubricate differential oil seal prior to installation.

TORQUE CONVERTER HOUSING

Disassembly — Using a puller, withdraw converter oil seal and remove mainshaft ball bearing. Using a punch, remove shift shaft oil seal from housing. Using a slide hammer, remove countershaft roller bearing from housing. Remove snap ring and drive differential side bearing oil seal from converter housing.

NOTE — *Mainshaft and countershaft bearings MUST be replaced if they are removed from housing.*

Inspection — Check bearings for roughness and wear and replace as necessary. Inspect housing attaching surface and valve body attaching surface for burrs or nicks and repair or replace as necessary. Using compressed air, blow out all oil passages and check for restrictions. Clean out hydraulic lines as necessary.

Reassembly — Reverse disassembly procedure and note the following: Press countershaft bearing in until it is flush with housing surface. Drive mainshaft bearing in until it bottoms in housing, then install oil seal flush with housing.

VALVE BODY & OIL PUMP ASSEMBLY

Disassembly — Withdraw oil pump drive and driven gears from valve body bore. **NOTE** — *Pump driven gear must be installed with the same side facing the housing as removed.* Remove detent rollers and spring and withdraw manual valve. Remove pressure regulator valve retainer bolt, then remove retainer spring, spring seat and retainer. Withdraw pressure regulator valve along with inner and outer valve springs.

NOTE — *Valve body and oil pump gears are serviced as an assembly. If the following clearances are not within specifications, replace complete assembly.*

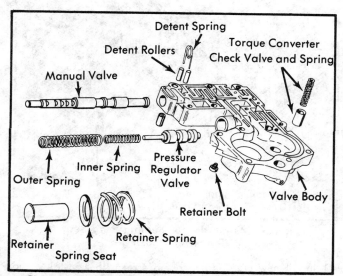

Fig. 13 Exploded View of Valve Body Assembly

Inspection — Check oil pump driven gear side clearance using a feeler gauge. Clearance should be .001-.002" (.03-.06 mm). Check drive gear to housing clearance, which should be .004-.006 (.10-.15 mm). Check driven gear to housing clearance, which should be .002-.0035" (.06-.09). If clearances are not to specifications, replace valve body and pump gears. Using compressed air, blow out all oil passages and check for restrictions. Clean hydraulic lines as necessary.

Reassembly — Reverse disassembly procedure and note the following: Ensure all parts are thoroughly cleaned and dried with compressed air prior to reassembly. Coat all valves and springs with automatic transmission fluid before installation.

DIFFERENTIAL ASSEMBLY

NOTE — *Prior to disassembly, pinion gear-to-side gear backlash should be checked as follows:*

Pinion Gear Backlash — 1) Mount differential assembly on "V" blocks and install a dial indicator as shown in *Fig. 14*. Install both drive axles into differential assembly.

2) Check backlash of each pinion gear and record measurement for reassembly reference. Pinion gear backlash should be .002-.010" (.05-.25 mm). If backlash is not to specifications, pinion thrust washers will have to be replaced with washers of the correct thickness which will provide the specified backlash.

NOTE — *Pinion thrust washers are available in the following thickness: .028" (.7 mm), .032" (.8 mm), .035" (.9 mm), and .039" (1 mm). Thrust washers must be of equal thickness on each side.*

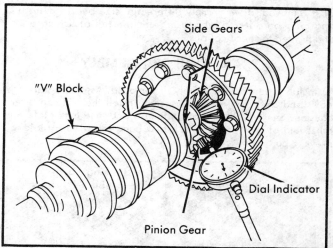

Fig. 14 Using a Dial Indicator to Measure Differential Pinion Gear Backlash

Disassembly — 1) If replacement is necessary, remove differential side bearings using a suitable puller. Place differential assembly in a vise. Remove ring gear attaching bolts, then lift off ring gear.

NOTE — *Ring gear attaching bolts have left-hand threads.*

2) Using a punch, drive lock pin out of pinion shaft. Slide pinion shaft out of pinion gears, then withdraw differential

HONDAMATIC (Cont.)

side gears, pinion gears and thrust washers. Inspect all parts for wear, scoring, or other damage and replace as necessary.

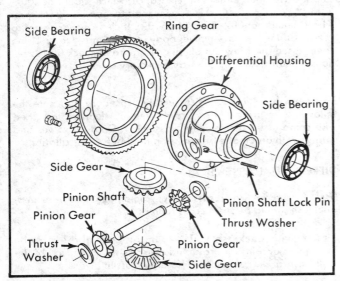

Fig. 15   Exploded View of Differential Assembly

Reassembly — 1) Coat all parts with Molykote (or equivalent) prior to reassembly. Install both side gears into differential housing. Mesh pinion gears with side gears, exactly opposite each other. Rotate pinion gears clockwise and align pinion gear holes with pinion shaft holes.

2) Install a pinion thrust washer of correct thickness (selected during backlash check) behind each pinion gear. Insert pinion shaft into gears and housing and lock in place with lock pin.

3) If removed, drive on new differential side bearings. Install ring gear on differential housing, then install attaching bolts and tighten to specifications.

TRANSAXLE REASSEMBLY

1) Install differential assembly, if removed. Assemble parking pawl and shift arm assemblies, then install them in converter housing. See Fig. 16. Install shift arm and new lock plate on other end of shaft, tighten bolt and bend tab of lock plate to prevent bolt from loosening.

Fig. 16   Installation of Parking Pawl, Shift Arm Shafts and Springs to Converter Housing

2) Install separator plate, dowel pin, pump gears and shaft to converter housing. Make sure chamfered side of oil pump driven gear is facing down. Install torque converter check valve and spring to valve body and install valve body to converter housing. See Fig. 17.

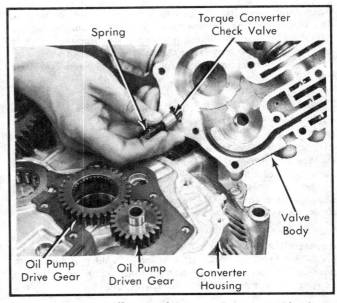

Fig. 17   Installation of Torque Converter Check Valve and Spring Into Valve Body

3) Install stator shaft, then install sealing ring seat, stator arm pin and lubrication pipe. See Fig. 18. Install servo line pressure pipe, gasket and dowel pins. Install servo assembly to converter housing. Install bolts of lengths shown in Fig. 19 to servo assembly.

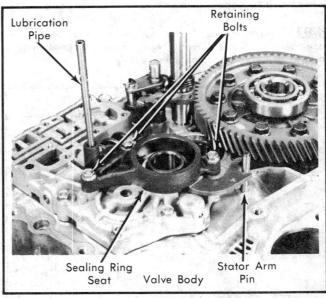

Fig. 18   Installation of Sealing Ring Seat to Converter Housing

4) Install new "O" ring to pump screen, then install pump screen to servo assembly. Place a spacer on each side of manual valve stem, then attach valve to lever with pin. Secure

HONDAMATIC (Cont.)

with clip. Make sure clip is installed in line with manual lever. See Fig. 20.

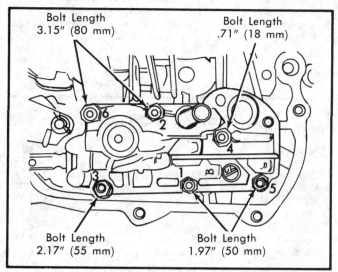

Fig. 19   Installation of Correct Bolt Lengths to Servo Assembly

5) Install countershaft and mainshaft to converter housing together as an assembly. Assemble reverse shift fork and selector sleeve, then install them as an assembly on the countershaft. Make sure groove in selector sleeve is facing down.

6) Install reverse shift fork over servo valve stem, aligning hole in stem with hole in reverse shift fork. Install bolt and new lock plate to reverse shift fork, then bend tab on lock plate so bolt will not turn.

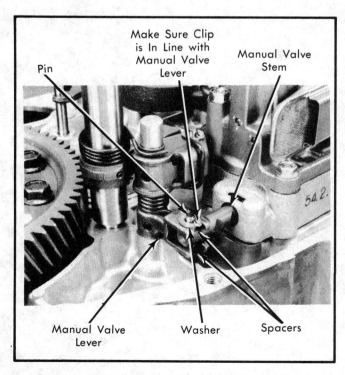

Fig. 20   Installation of Manual Valve Lever to Manual Valve Stem

7) Install countershaft reverse gear, needle bearing and inner race on countershaft. Install new converter housing-to-transmission housing gasket. Install 2 dowel pins in converter housing. Install transmission bearings in transmission housing, if removed.

8) Install converter housing-to-transmission housing bolts in sequence shown in Fig. 21. Make sure parking pawl shaft lines up with hole in housing and reverse idler gear meshes with mainshaft gear or transmission housing will not go on converter housing.

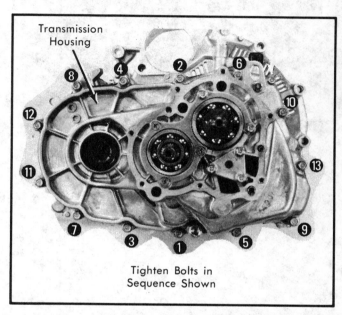

Fig. 21   Installation of Transmission Housing to Converter Housing

9) Install countershaft low gear with raised shoulder side towards bearing retainer. Shift transmission to "P" and install mainshaft holder. Install a new countershaft lock nut. Stake base of lock nut to slot in countershaft low gear.

10) Install a .079" (2.0 mm) thrust washer, a .472" (12.0 mm) spacer, the inner race and needle bearing on mainshaft. Install a thrust needle bearing and a .118" (3.0 mm) thrust washer into low gear. Install low gear into low clutch, rotating gear until fully seated.

11) Coat a .047" (1.2 mm) spacer with ATF fluid, then place it over mainshaft and into low gear recess. Install low gear and clutch on mainshaft as an assembly. Attach mainshaft holder from underside of converter housing. See Fig. 2. Install new lock washer and lock nut on mainshaft. Tighten nut and bend tabs on lock washer into slots of lock nut.

NOTE — Install lock nut with recessed side down. Install lock washer with tabs facing up.

12) Install dowel pins and new gasket to transmission housing. Install new "O" ring to line pressure pipe. Coat sealing rings on clutch hub with ATF, then install end cover to transmission housing. Install hoist bracket and dipstick.

HONDAMATIC (Cont.)

13) Using a bearing driver, tap differential side bearing on transmission housing to firmly seat snap ring in converter housing. Then, tap differential from opposite side so side bearing butts up against transmission housing side. Using a feeler gauge, check clearance between snap ring in converter housing and side bearing outer race.

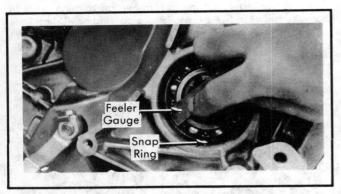

Fig. 22   Using a Feeler Gauge to Measure Differential Bearing Clearance

14) Clearance should be .004-.008" (.1-.2 mm); if not, install a snap ring of correct thickness to obtain proper clearance. Snap rings are available in thicknesses of .096" (2.45 mm) to .116" (2.95 mm) in .004" (.1 mm) increments. With proper clearance set, install both differential side oil seals.

TIGHTENING SPECIFICATIONS

Application	Ft. Lbs. (mkg)
Countershaft Lock Nut	69 (9.5)
Mainshaft Lock Nut	36 (5.0)
Stabilizer Bar	31 (4.3)
Starter Bolts	33 (4.5)
Transmission-to-Converter Hsg.	20 (2.7)
Transmission-to-Engine	33 (4.5)
Torque Rod Bolts	54 (7.5)

HONDA 3-SPEED

Accord
Prelude

TRANSAXLE IDENTIFICATION

Transaxle may be identified by a group of letters and numbers stamped on a pad on top of transaxle. First 2 letters are transaxle type. Next 7 numbers are transaxle serial number.

Transaxle Model Code	
Application	Code
Accord & Prelude	AK

DESCRIPTION

The Honda 3-speed automatic transaxle is a combination of a 3-phase torque converter, dual shift transmission and a differential-type final drive assembly. The transmission consists of a mainshaft and a countershaft. Transmission is controlled by the main valve body, regulator valve body and the servo valve. Countershaft is in constant mesh with the differential ring gear.

LUBRICATION & ADJUSTMENT

See *AUTOMATIC TRANSMISSION SERVICING* Section.

SERVICE (IN VEHICLE)

AXLE SHAFTS

Removal — 1) Drain transmission, then bend tabs on spindle nut washer and loosen nut. Raise and support vehicle. Remove nut and wheel.

2) On Accord models, remove pivot bolt and radius arm bolts on lower control arm. On Prelude models, remove ball joint nut and separate steering knuckle from ball joint. Pull steering knuckle outward until axle shaft is clear of front hub.

3) Pry constant velocity (CV) joint out of transaxle case approximately ½" (12 mm), this will collapse spring clip (on axle shaft inside transaxle case) and allow axle shaft to be withdrawn from case.

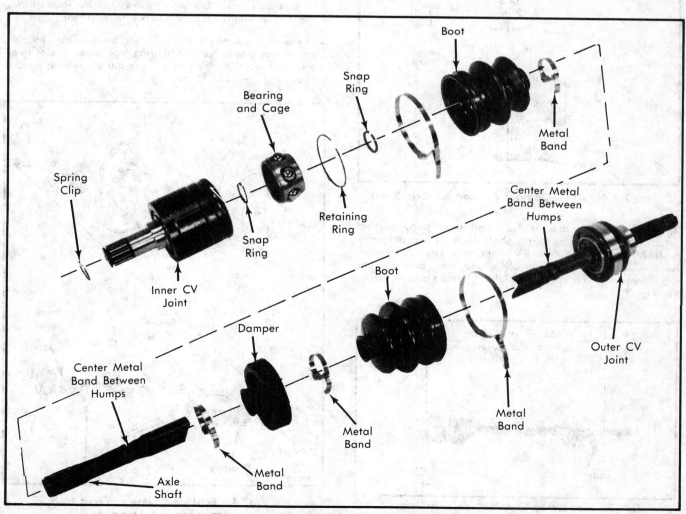

Fig. 1 Exploded View of Axle Shaft Assembly

HONDA 3-SPEED (Cont.)

4) Pull axle shaft out of transaxle case and out of front hub assembly (Accord models only). Repeat procedures for other axle shaft.

Disassembly — 1) Remove metal bands securing rubber boot to axle shaft and inner constant velocity joint. Slide boot back onto axle shaft and remove snap rings. Pull axle shaft from inner constant velocity joint. See *Fig. 1.*

NOTE — *Outer constant velocity joint is not removable.*

2) Remove retaining ring, then ball bearing cage with bearing race and balls. Remove balls from bearing race by prying out with a screwdriver. Remove band from damper and remove damper toward inside of axle shaft. Remove outer rubber boot. Inspect all parts for wear, pitting or other damage. Replace parts as necessary.

Reassembly — 1) Install outer rubber boot and metal bands. Slide damper onto axle shaft and secure damper so that face is .008" (2 mm) from beginning of taper. See *Fig. 2.* Assemble constant velocity joint bearing with cage and insert balls, packed with grease.

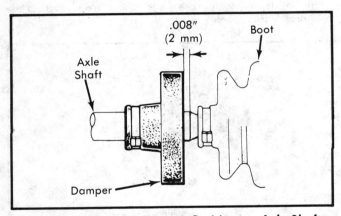

Fig. 2 Adjusting Damper Position on Axle Shaft

2) Install boot to axle shaft. Install snap ring, bearing assembly, then snap ring to axle shaft. Slide CV joint onto axle shaft. Attach rubber boot to CV joint and to axle shaft. Adjust length of axle shaft to specifications and install a new spring clip in inner end of axle shaft (end that fits into transaxle case). See *Fig. 3.*

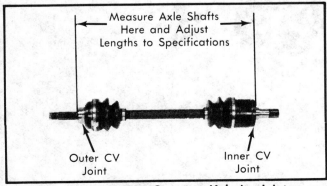

Fig. 3 Measuring Constant Velocity Joint Separating Distances

Axle Shaft Length	
Application	**Length In. (mm)**
Accord	
Right Axle Shaft	18.6-19.0 (472-483)
Left Axle Shaft	29.5-29.9 (749-759)
Prelude	
Right Axle Shaft	18.5-18.9 (469-479)
Left Axle Shaft	29.8-30.2 (757-767)

NOTE — *Pack CV joints with grease before installation of protective rubber boots.*

Installation — To install axle shafts, reverse removal procedures.

WHEEL BEARINGS

Removal — 1) Remove wheel and spindle nut. Remove caliper bolts and hang caliper out of way. Using a slide hammer, remove brake rotor.

2) Disconnect tie rod ball joint and lower control arm ball joint from steering knuckle. Disconnect shock absorber from steering knuckle and remove steering knuckle from vehicle.

3) Remove splash guard and snap ring from steering knuckle. Remove seal, inner race and bearing from inner side of steering knuckle. Press bearing outer race out of steering knuckle (toward outside). See *Fig. 4.*

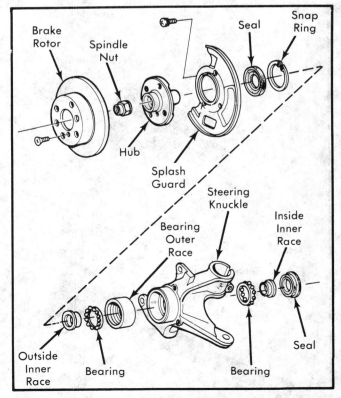

Fig. 4 Exploded View of Front Hub and Bearing Assembly

HONDA 3-SPEED (Cont.)

4) Using a puller, remove steering knuckle inside inner race from hub, then pry seal from hub.

NOTE — *Pack both wheel bearings with grease before installing. Also, apply grease to lips of seals.*

Installation — 1) Press bearing outer race into steering knuckle. Install bearing, outside inner race and snap ring to steering knuckle.

2) Install seal to outside of steering knuckle. Install inner bearing and race to inside of steering knuckle. Install splash guard. Slide hub into steering knuckle, install seal.

3) Place steering knuckle in position on vehicle and attach shock absorber. Attach lower control arm ball joint and tie rod ball joint to steering knuckle. Install rotor, caliper and axle shafts to steering knuckle. Install spindle nut, then wheel.

TROUBLE SHOOTING

NO MOVEMENT

In Any Gear — Low fluid level. Faulty pump. Regulator valve stuck or damaged spring. Servo shaft stuck. Reverse hub splines stuck. Mainshaft damaged. Manual shift cable out of adjustment or broken.

In "D1"; OK in Other Gears — Low fluid level. Manual shift cable out of adjustment. Worn or damaged one-way clutch. Low gear damaged. 1st clutch piston stuck, damaged "O" ring, damaged feed pipe or "O" rings, check valve stuck, worn or burnt clutch discs.

In "2"; OK in Other Gears — Low fluid level. Manual shift cable out of adjustment. 2nd gear damaged. Faulty 2nd clutch.

In "R"; OK in Other Gears — Low fluid level. Servo shaft stuck. Faulty 2nd clutch. Damaged reverse gear.

ENGINE RACES IN "D"

Stall RPM High in "D" and "2" — Low fluid level. Faulty pump. Regulator valve stuck or spring damaged. Manual shift cable out of adjustment.

Stall RPM High in "D" Only — Low fluid level. Faulty pump. Manual shift cable out of adjustment. 1st clutch piston stuck, damaged clutch "O" ring, clutch feed pipe or "O" ring damaged, check valve stuck, worn or burnt clutch discs.

Stall RPM High in "2" — Manual shift cable out of adjustment.

Stall RPM OK — 1-2 shift valve faulty. Faulty governor valve. Fluid level too high. Faulty torque converter one-way clutch.

Stall RPM Low — Throttle cable at carburetor out of adjustment. Throttle control cable at automatic transmission out of adjustment. Engine performance not to specifications.

NO "D1-D2" UPSHIFT

"D2-D3" OK — Damaged 2nd gear.

Engine Races in "2" — 2nd clutch faulty.

UPSHIFT SPEED TOO HIGH

Governor valve faulty. Throttle cable at carburetor out of adjustment. Defective throttle valve.

JUMPS FROM "D1" TO "D2"

Defective 2-3 shift valve.

UPSHIFT TOO EARLY

"D1-D2" and "D2-D3" — Faulty governor valve. Throttle cable at carburetor out of adjustment. Defective throttle valve.

"D1-D2" — 1-2 shift valve faulty.

"D2-D3" — 2-3 shift valve faulty.

KICKDOWN TOO LOW

Faulty 1-2 shift valve or 2-3 shift valve.

ENGINE RACES IN "D2-D3" SHIFT

Throttle valve "B" defective. 2nd accumulator, 3rd accumulator or orifice control valve faulty. Main orifice plugged.

ENGINE VIBRATES IN "D2-D3" SHIFT

Orifice control valve faulty or second orifice plugged.

VEHICLE CREEPS IN "N"

Manual shift cable out of adjustment. Faulty 1st or 2nd clutch. Throttle cable at carburetor out of adjustment. Damaged needle bearing or thrust washer.

DELAYED ENGAGEMENT

From "N" to "D" — Manual shift cable out of adjustment. Faulty 1st clutch. Low orifice plugged.

From "N" to "R" — Servo shaft stuck. Manual shift cable out of adjustment. Faulty 2nd clutch.

PROBLEMS AFTER REASSEMBLY

Loud Noise in All Selector Positions — Oil pump gear installed backwards.

Vehicle Will Not Move in Any Gear — Splined washer on mainshaft assembled incorrectly. Splined washer or thrust washer assembled incorrectly.

No Movement in Forward Gears; Movement in Reverse — Reverse gear hub installed backwards.

Acceleration to 30 MPH Only — Stator assembled backwards in torque converter.

Vibration in All Gears — Torque converter not fully seated.

TESTING

ROAD TEST

1) Before road testing, be certain that fluid level and condition, and control linkage adjustments have been checked and

HONDA 3-SPEED (Cont.)

Selector Lever Position	Low Clutch	Second Clutch	Third Clutch	Sprag Clutch
CLUTCH AND BAND APPLICATION CHART (ELEMENTS IN USE)				
D — DRIVE First Second Third	 X X X	 X 	 X	 X
2 — MANUAL		X		
REVERSE		X		
NEUTRAL OR PARK — All Clutch and sprag clutch released and/or ineffective.				

corrected as necessary. During test, transmission should upshift and downshift at approximately the speeds shown in Shift Speeds chart. All shifts may vary somewhat due to production tolerances or tire size. The important factor is the quality of the shifts. All shifts should be smooth, responsive and with no slippage or engine speed runaway.

2) Slippage or engine runaway in any gear usually indicates clutch or sprag problems. The slipping unit in a particular gear can usually be identified by noting transmission operation in other selector positions and comparing which internal units are applied in those positions. See Clutch and Sprag Application chart.

3) This process of elimination can be used to detect any unit which slips, and to confirm proper operation of good units; however, the actual cause of the malfunction usually cannot be easily decided. Practically any condition can be caused by leaking hydraulic circuits or sticking valves. Therefore, unless an obvious condition exists, do not disassemble transmission until hydraulic pressure tests have been made.

Shift Speed Specifications

Application	Shift Speed (MPH)
Upshift	
Full Throttle	
1-2 Shift	35-40
2-3 Shift	60-65
Half Throttle	
1-2 Shift	17-22
2-3 Shift	25-35
Closed Throttle	
1-2 Shift	10-15
2-3 Shift	22-27
Downshift	
Full Throttle	
3-2 Shift	50-60
2-1 Shift	30-35
Closed Throttle	
3-2 Shift	15-20
2-1 Shift	5-10

HYDRAULIC PRESSURE TESTS

1) Before performing pressure tests, be sure that fluid level and condition have been checked and corrected as necessary. With engine at normal operating temperature, connect a tachometer to engine.

2) Connect pressure gauges to the following pressure test points: line pressure port, 1st clutch pressure port, 2nd clutch pressure port and 3rd clutch pressure port. See Fig. 5.

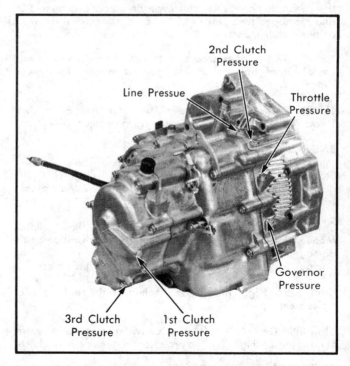

Fig. 5 Pressure Test Point Locations

3) Raise front of vehicle so front wheels are off ground and support with safety stands. Start and run engine at 1000 RPM. Place selector lever in the following positions: "P", "N", "D", "D1" and "R". Note pressure readings at each selector lever position and compare readings to Pressure Test Specifications chart.

HONDA 3-SPEED (Cont.)

4) If reading in "P" or "N" is not to specifications, check torque converter, oil pump pressure regulator or torque converter check valve. If reading in "D" (high gear) is not to specifications, check 3rd clutch. If reading in "D1" is not to specifications, check 1st clutch. If reading in "2" (manual), check 2nd clutch. If reading in "R" is not to specifications, check servo valve.

NOTE — *Allow engine to return to idle before changing selector positions.*

5) Stop engine and remove pressure gauge connections from transmission. Connect pressure gauge to throttle pressure port and disconnect throttle cable at carburetor. Start engine, place selector lever in "D" and run engine at 1000 RPM. Depress accelerator pedal so throttle control lever is in full throttle position and note pressure reading. Compare reading with Pressure Test Specifications chart.

6) If throttle pressure reading in "D" is not to specifications, check throttle valve "A" or throttle modulator valve.

7) Stop engine and remove pressure gauge from throttle pressure port and reconnect throttle cable at carburetor. Place vehicle on a chassis dynamomator or raise and support front of vehicle on safety stands. Connect pressure gauge to governor pressure port. Start engine, place selector lever in "D" and increase engine speed to 38 MPH. Note pressure reading and compare it to Pressure Test Specifications chart.

8) If governor pressure reading was not to specifications, check governor valve.

Main Pressures	
Application	**psi (kg/cm²)**
Line	
"P", "N", "2", "R"	92-97 (6.5-6.8)
"D1", "D2", "D3"	92-97 (6.5-6.8)
Throttle (In "D")	90-92 (6.3-6.5)
Governor (In "D")	44-46 (3.2-3.3)

STALL SPEED TEST

Testing Precautions — When making test, do not hold throttle open any longer than the time it takes to read tachometer. Maximum stall speed test time is 10 seconds. Allow engine to run at idle for at least 2 minutes in "N" to cool transmission between tests. If engine speed exceeds limits shown in Stall Speeds chart, release accelerator immediately as clutch slippage is indicated.

Testing Procedure — With engine at normal operating temperature, connect a tachometer to engine. Start engine and set parking brake and service brakes. Place selector lever in "D". Depress accelerator briefly (6 to 8 seconds) to full throttle and note maximum RPM obtained. Allow 2 minutes for cooling and repeat test in "2" and "R". Engine speed should be within limits shown in Stall Speeds chart.

Stall Speeds	
Application	**Stall RPM**
Accord, Prelude	2300-2900

REMOVAL & INSTALLATION

TRANSAXLE ASSEMBLY

Removal — 1) Disconnect battery ground and ground strap at transmission. Release steering lock and place selector lever in "N". Disconnect battery cable from starter and wires from starter solenoid. Disconnect wire from water temperature sender and wire from ignition timing thermosensor.

2) Disconnect cooler hoses and wire them up out of way, so they won't drain. Remove stater mounting bolt, on transmission side, and top transmission mounting bolt. Raise and support front of vehicle. Remove wheels. Remove fender well shield from right front wheel well on Accord models only.

3) Drain transmission and reinstall plug. Remove throttle control cable from transmission. Remove speedometer cable from transmission.

CAUTION — *Do not remove speedometer cable holder or speedometer gear may fall into transmission housing.*

4) On Accord models only, remove starter side mounting bolt and remove 2 upper transmission mounting bolts. Place a jack under transmission and attach an engine support to engine. Remove crossbeam. Disconnect radius rods, then disconnect axle shafts from transmission. See *Axle Shaft removal in this article.*

5) Remove remaining starter bolt and remove starter. Remove transmission damper bracket, located in front of torque converter cover plate, then remove cover plate. Remove center console and shift indicator. Place selector lever in "R" and remove shift cable from shift lever. Loosen nuts and pull shift cable out of transmission housing.

6) Remove torque converter-to-drive plate bolts. Remove 3 engine-to-transmission mounting bolts and lower transmission mounting bolt. Pull transmission rearwards, then lower transmission out of vehicle.

7) On Prelude models only, remove splash shields, stabilizer bar nuts, mounting brackets and then remove stabilizer bar. Remove axle shafts from transmission. See *Axle Shaft Removal in this article.* Remove engine torque rods and brackets. Remove engine side starter mounting bolt, then remove starter.

8) Attach engine support to engine and place a jack under transmission. Remove nuts from front and rear engine mounts. Remove crossbeam bolts and crossbeam. Remove torque converter cover plate and center damper bracket.

9) Remove center console and shift indicator. Place selector lever in "R" and remove shift cable from selector lever. Loosen "U" bolt nuts and pull shift cable out of transmission housing. Remove torque converter-to-drive plate bolts. Remove remaining transmission mounting bolts and pull transmission rearward. Lower transmission out of vehicle.

Installation — 1) Attach shift cable to shift lever and place cable out of way. Install torque converter to transmission. Place transmission on jack and raise to installation height. Make sure dowel pins are installed in transmission, then push transmission up to engine, aligning dowel pins with holes in engine block.

HONDA 3-SPEED (Cont.)

2) Attach transmission to engine with 2 lower mounting bolts. Install 2 engine-to-rear mount bolts and 1 transmission housing-to-rear mount bolt. Remove transmission jack. Install torque converter-to-drive plate bolts. Install torque converter cover plate and damper bracket.

3) Install crossbeam and remove engine support. Install starter using engine side mount bolt. Install front and rear torque rods and brackets on Prelude models. On all models, install axle shafts to transmission housing. Refer to Axle Shaft installation in this article. Install torque rods on Accord models only. Install stabilizer bar and brackets on Prelude models only.

4) Install speedometer cable to transmission. Install splash shields on Prelude models only. Install transmission side starter mounting bolt and transmission top mounting bolt. Connect cooling hoses. Install and adjust throttle cable.

5) Reconnect ignition timing thermosensor wire, water temperature sending wire, starter solenoid wire and battery cable to starter. Connect battery ground. Install and connect shift cable to selector lever. Install shift indicator and center console. Fill transmission with fluid.

TORQUE CONVERTER

Disassembly — 1) With transmission removed and torque converter pulled off stator shaft, remove washer then all torque converter cover-to-pump bolts. Remove torque converter washer and turbine. See *Fig. 6*.

2) From stator, remove snap ring. Remove side plate then one-way clutch. Turn stator over and remove other snap ring and side plate. Remove large "O" ring from pump, then remove starter ring gear from pump.

Inspection — Clean all parts in solvent and dry with compressed air. Blow out all passages with compressed air. Inspect all thrust surfaces for scoring and wear. Always replace "O" rings.

Reassembly — 1) On stator, install a side plate (grooved side facing out) and snap ring. Turn stator over and install one-way clutch ring. Then install cam, rollers and springs. Install second side plate (grooved side facing out) and snap ring.

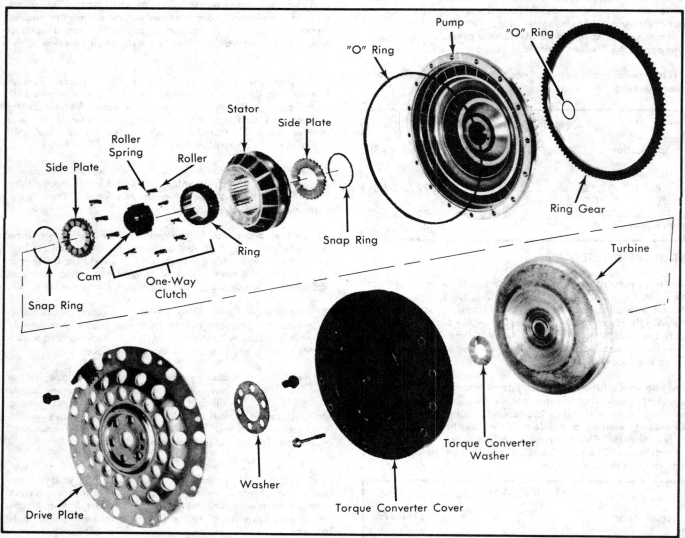

Fig. 6 Exploded View of Honda 3-Speed Automatic Transaxle Torque Converter

HONDA 3-SPEED (Cont.)

2) Using a stator shaft, check that one-way clutch will only turn in a counterclockwise direction. If one-way clutch turns clockwise or in both directions, check stator cam and rollers for proper installation. If installed properly, replace one-way clutch.

3) Install new "O" rings into grooves (both sides of pump) of pump. Install stator with thin vanes facing pump, then place turbine on top of pump. Place torque converter washer on turbine.

4) Install torque converter cover on pump, make sure alignment marks (made upon disassembly) are aligned. Install ring gear with flat side towards torque converter, and tighten bolts. See *Fig. 7*.

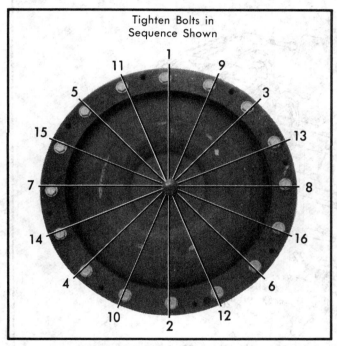

Fig. 7   Tightening Sequence of Ring Gear To Torque Coverter Bolts

TRANSAXLE DISASSEMBLY

1) Remove dipstick. Remove bolts from end cover, then remove cover. Shift transmission to "P". Lock mainshaft using holding tool (07923-6890200) as shown in *Fig. 8*.

2) Remove endcover gasket, dowel pins and "O" rings. Pry staked edge of lock nut flange out of notch in 1st clutch. Remove mainshaft lock nut, then remove 1st clutch. Remove 1st clutch thrust washer, needle bearing and 1st gear. Remove bearing and thrust washer from mainshaft.

3) Pry staked edge of lock nut out of notch in parking gear. Remove countershaft lock nut and parking pawl stop pin. Remove parking pawl, shaft and spring. Remove parking gear and countershaft 1st gear as a unit. Remove bearing and 1st gear collar from countershaft. Remove "O" ring and 1st gear collar from mainshaft.

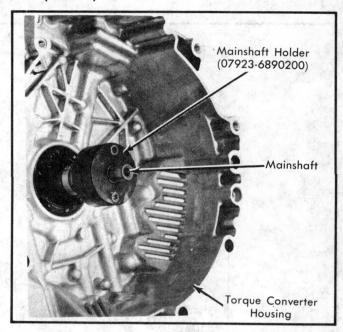

Fig. 8   Locking Mainshaft Using Special Holding Tool

4) Remove reverse idler bearing holder. Bend down tab on lock plate under parking shift arm bolt. Remove bolt then parking shift arm. Lift out parking shift arm, then remove shift arm spring.

5) Bend down tab on throttle control lever bolt lock plate and remove bolt. Remove throttle control lever and spring from shaft. Remove torque converter housing-to-transmission housing bolts. See *Fig. 9*.

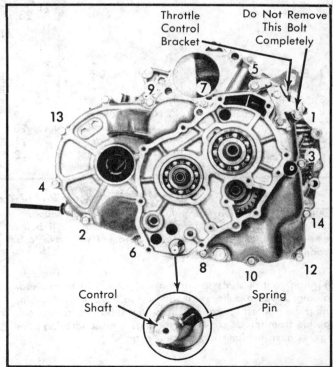

Fig. 9   Location of Converter Housing To Transmission Housing Bolts

HONDA 3-SPEED (Cont.)

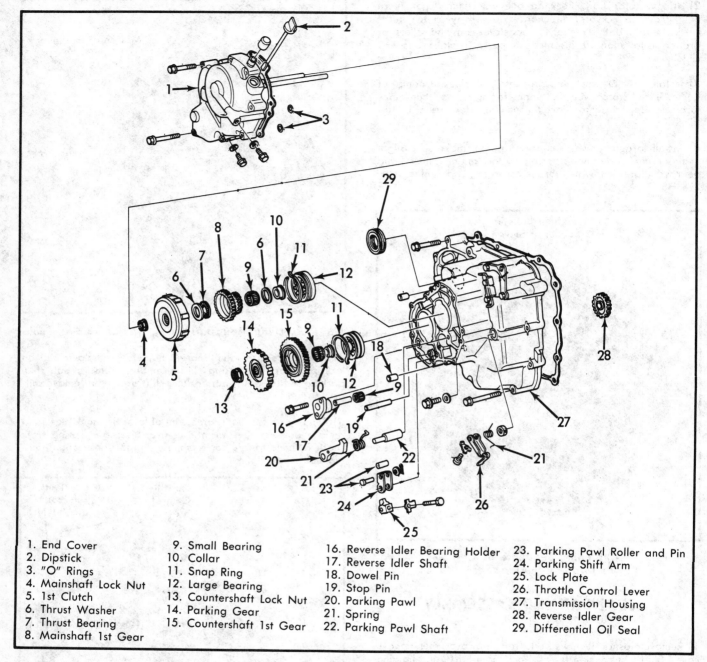

1. End Cover	9. Small Bearing	16. Reverse Idler Bearing Holder	23. Parking Pawl Roller and Pin
2. Dipstick	10. Collar	17. Reverse Idler Shaft	24. Parking Shift Arm
3. "O" Rings	11. Snap Ring	18. Dowel Pin	25. Lock Plate
4. Mainshaft Lock Nut	12. Large Bearing	19. Stop Pin	26. Throttle Control Lever
5. 1st Clutch	13. Countershaft Lock Nut	20. Parking Pawl	27. Transmission Housing
6. Thrust Washer	14. Parking Gear	21. Spring	28. Reverse Idler Gear
7. Thrust Bearing	15. Countershaft 1st Gear	22. Parking Pawl Shaft	29. Differential Oil Seal
8. Mainshaft 1st Gear			

Fig. 10   Exploded View of Transmission Housing and Components

NOTE — *Do not remove bolt number 1, just loosen enough so bolt threads are free of torque converter housing. If bolt is removed completely, throttle control bracket will have to be readjusted.*

6) Align control shaft spring pin with cutout in transmission housing. Install a puller (that will bolt to transmission housing and press against the countershaft) and separate transmission housing from torque converter housing. After separating housings, remove transmission housing completely.

7) On gear side of torque converter housing, remove gasket, dowel pins and 1st and 3rd oil feed pipes. Remove reverse

gear collar, needle bearing and countershaft reverse gear. Bend down tab on lock plate and remove bolt from reverse shift fork. Remove reverse shift fork and selector sleeve as a unit.

8) Remove countershaft 2nd gear. Remove mainshaft and countershaft together. To clear governor, pull shafts up at a slight angle. Bend governor tabs down and remove bolts holding governor to torque converter housing.

CAUTION — *Accumulator cover is spring loaded, hold cover down while removing bolts in a criss cross pattern.*

HONDA 3-SPEED (Cont.)

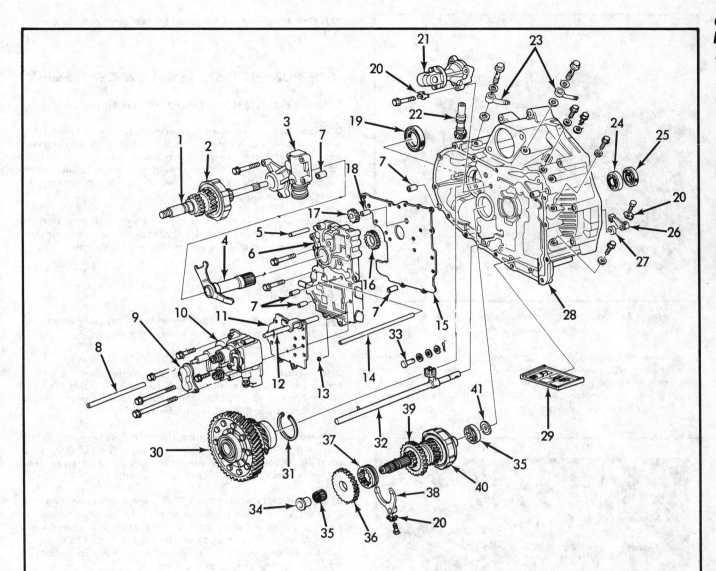

1. Mainshaft Assembly
2. 2nd Clutch
3. Regulator Assembly
4. Stator Shaft
5. Stop Pin
6. Valve Body Assembly
7. Dowel Pin
8. Feed Pipe for 1st Gear
9. Accumulator Cover
10. Servo Valve Assembly
11. Servo Separator Plate
12. Throttle Control Shaft
13. Steel Ball
14. Feed Pipe for 3rd Gear

15. Valve Body Separator Plate
16. Pump Drive Gear
17. Pump Driven Gear
18. Pump Shaft
19. Differential Oil Seal
20. Lock Plate
21. Governor Assembly
22. Speedometer Drive Gear
23. Transmission Cooler Lines
24. Mainshaft Bearing
25. Mainshaft Oil Seal
26. Shift Lever
27. Oil Seal
28. Torque Converter Housing

29. Filter Screen
30. Differential
31. Snap Ring
32. Shift Shaft
33. Manual Valve Pin
34. Reverse Gear Collar
35. Bearing
36. Countershaft Reverse Gear
37. Selector Hub
38. Reverse Shift Fork
39. Countershaft Assembly
40. 3rd Clutch
41. Oil Guide Plate

Fig. 11 *Exploded View of Torque Converter Housing and Components*

HONDA 3-SPEED (Cont.)

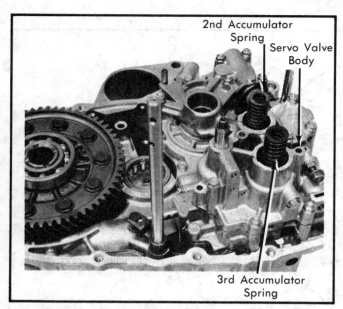

Fig. 12   Removing Accumulator Springs from Servo Valve Body

9) Remove accumulator cover, 2nd and 3rd accumulator springs. See *Fig. 12.* Remove "E" clip from throttle control shaft and remove shaft. Remove servo body bolts (7) and servo body. Remove separator plate and dowel pins. Remove steel ball from valve body oil passage. See *Fig. 13.*

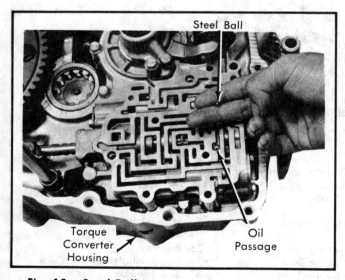

Fig. 13   Steel Ball Location in Servo Valve Body

10) Remove regulator valve body bolts (6). Remove stator shift arm, dowel pins stop pin and bolts (4) holding valve body to torque converter housing. Remove cotter pin, washer, rollers and pin from manual valve. Remove valve body, being careful not to lose the torque converter check valve and spring.

11) Remove pump gears and shaft. Remove separator plate, dowel pins, check valve and spring. Remove filter screen. Remove control lever cable holder, then remove cotter pin, control pin, and control lever roller from control lever. Bend tab down on control lever bolt and remove bolt and control lever.

12) Turn torque converter housing over and remove control shaft.

COMPONENT DISASSEMBLY & REASSEMBLY

ONE-WAY CLUTCH AND PARKING GEAR

Disassembly — Separate countershaft 1st gear from parking gear by gripping 1st gear in left hand and turning parking gear counterclockwise. Remove one-way clutch from counter 1st gear by prying out with a screw driver. Inspect countershaft 1st gear and parking gear for wear, damage or scoring. Inspect one-way clutch for damage.

Reassembly — To reassemble one-way clutch and parking gear, reverse disassembly procedures. When reassembled, check one-way clutch for movement in one direction only.

VALVE BODY

NOTE — *When disassembling valve body, lay out components in order of removal for reassembly reference.*

Disassembly — 1) Remove torque converter check valve and spring. Remove relief valve cap, spring and valve. Remove orifice control valve plate, spring and valve. Remove detent spring and rollers. Remove manual valve.

2) Remove 1-2 shift valve plate, then carefully remove 1-2 shift valve with sleeve. Remove 1-2 shift spring. On 1-2 shift valve, carefully slide sleeve off valve, being careful to catch steel balls (2) and spring as sleeve is removed.

3) Remove and disassemble 2-3 shift valve in same manner as 1-2 shift valve. Check all components for wear or damage. Replace springs if not to specifications, replace complete valve body assembly if valve body or any valve is worn or damaged. *See Governor Regulator, Servo and Valve Body Identification table for spring specifications. See Fig. 14.*

NOTE — *Coat all parts in ATF fluid before reassembly.*

Reassembly — 1) Slide 1-2 shift valve spring into hole in 1-2 shift valve. Press steel balls (1 on each side of spring) into hole of shift valve and slide sleeve over shift valve and balls. Place 1-2 shift spring in valve body, then install shift valve (with sleeve) into valve body. Install 1-2 shift valve plate and bolts to valve body.

2) Assemble 2-3 shift valve in same manner as 1-2 shift valve and install it to valve body. Place relief spring in relief valve and install in valve body. Compress spring with a screwdriver and insert valve spring cap (with cutout aligned with screwdriver).

3) Install manual valve into valve body, then install detent rollers and spring. Install oil pump driven gear shaft and driven gear (make sure chamfered side of gear faces away from tralve body). Install oil pump drive gear.

HONDA 3-SPEED (Cont.)

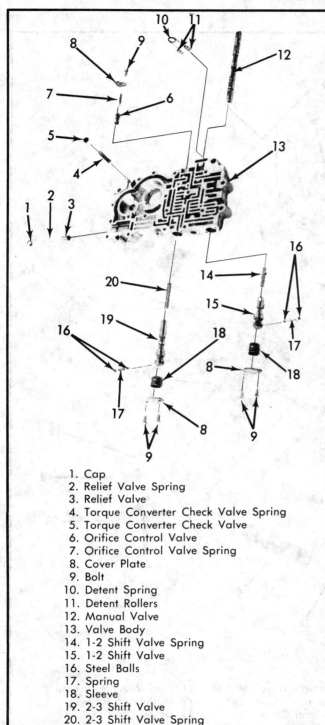

1. Cap
2. Relief Valve Spring
3. Relief Valve
4. Torque Converter Check Valve Spring
5. Torque Converter Check Valve
6. Orifice Control Valve
7. Orifice Control Valve Spring
8. Cover Plate
9. Bolt
10. Detent Spring
11. Detent Rollers
12. Manual Valve
13. Valve Body
14. 1-2 Shift Valve Spring
15. 1-2 Shift Valve
16. Steel Balls
17. Spring
18. Sleeve
19. 2-3 Shift Valve
20. 2-3 Shift Valve Spring

Fig. 14 Exploded View of Valve Body and Components

4) Measure driven gear-to-valve body thrust clearance. Clearance should be .001-.003" (.03-.08 mm). Measure side clearance of driven and drive gears. Driven gear side clearance should be .002-.004" (.05-.10 mm), drive gear side clearance should be .004-.005" (.10-.12 mm). See Fig. 15. If clearance is not to specifications, check valve body for excessive wear, if wear exists, replace valve body assembly.

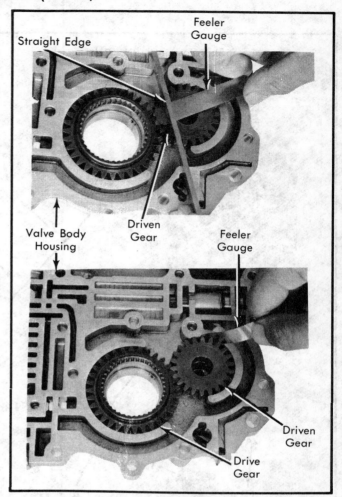

Fig. 15 Measuring Oil Pump-to-Valve Body Gear Clearance

SERVO VALVE ASSEMBLY

NOTE — Clean all parts in solvent and blow dry with air. Replace servo valve as an assembly if any parts are worn or damaged.

Disassembly — 1) Push out 2nd and 3rd accumulator pistons, then remove "O" rings. Remove servo valve and spring, then remove "O" ring from valve. Remove throttle control valve "B", then separate control valve "B" from inner and outer springs and plug. See Fig. 16.

2) Remove retainer bolt and retainer of throttle control valve "A". Remove plug, outside spring, throttle control valve "A" and inside spring. Remove throttle control cover then separator plate. Remove oil passage pipe from valve body.

3) Remove plug and washer from servo valve body. Remove modulator valve retainer plate, spring and modulator valve. Inspect all components for wear or damage. Check springs against specifications in Governor, Regulator, Servo and Valve Body Identification table. Replace springs that are not to specifications or complete servo assembly if any part is worn or damaged.

Automatic Transaxles

HONDA 3-SPEED (Cont.)

Shift Point Adjusting Bolt is Factory Adjusted. Do Not Remove or Loosen or Shift Points Will be Affected

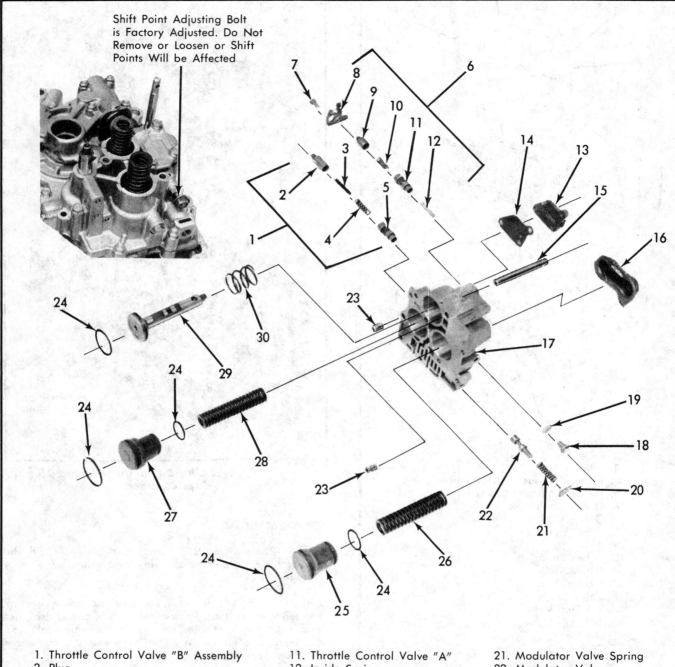

1. Throttle Control Valve "B" Assembly	11. Throttle Control Valve "A"	21. Modulator Valve Spring
2. Plug	12. Inside Spring	22. Modulator Valve
3. Inner Spring	13. Throttle Control Cover	23. Dowel Pin
4. Outer Spring	14. Separator Plate	24. "O" Ring
5. Throttle Control Valve "B"	15. Oil Passage Pipe	25. 2nd Accumulator Piston
6. Throttle Control Valve "A" Assembly	16. Accumulator Cover	26. 2nd Accumulator Spring
7. Bolt	17. Servo Valve Body	27. 3rd Accumulator Piston
8. Retainer Plate	18. Plug	28. 3rd Accumulator Spring
9. Plug	19. Washer	29. Servo Valve
10. Outside Spring	20. Spring Retainer Plate	30. Servo Valve Return Spring

Fig. 16 Exploded View of Servo Valve Assembly

HONDA 3-SPEED (Cont.)

GOVERNOR, REGULATOR, SERVO AND VALVE BODY SPRING IDENTIFICATION CHART

Valve Spring	Length In. (mm)	Diameter In. (mm)①	Number Of Coils	Wire Thickness In. (mm)
Regulator Valve Springs				
Spring "A"	3.303 (83.9)	.579 (14.7)	17	.071 (1.8)
Spring "B"	1.732 (44.0)	.378 (9.6)	9	.071 (1.8)
Stator Reaction Spring	1.193 (1.512)	1.512 (38.4)	2	.236 (6.0)
Torque Converter Check Valve Spring	1.559 (39.6)	.331 (8.4)	15	.035 (.9)
Throttle Modulator Spring	1.138 (28.9)	.370 (9.4)	8	.047 (1.2)
Relief Valve Spring	1.878 (47.7)	.331 (8.4)	15	.031 (.8)
Governor Spring	1.122 (28.5)	.740 (18.8)	3.5	.047 (1.2)
Orifice Control Spring	1.157 (29.4)	.268 (6.8)	16	.035 (.9)
Throttle Control Valve A Spring				
Inner	1.181 (30.0)	.244 (6.2)	8	.031 (.8)
Outer	.850 (21.6)	.335 (8.5)	6	.040 (1.0)
Throttle Control Valve B Spring				
Inner	1.476 (37.5)	.193 (4.9)	22	.031 (.8)
Outer	1.181 (30.0)	.335 (8.5)	6.5	.047 (1.2)
1-2 Shift Spring	1.575 (40.0)	.280 (7.1)	17	.028 (.7)
1-2 Shift Ball Spring	.677 (17.2)	.177 (4.5)	11	.018 (.45)
2-3 Shift Spring	2.071 (52.6)	.299 (7.6)	25	.040 (1.0)
2-3 Shift Ball Spring	.567 (14.4)	.177 (4.5)	10	.020 (.5)
2nd Accumulator Spring	3.693 (93.8)	.854 (21.7)	17.5	②
3rd Accumulator Spring	3.815 (96.9)	.811 (20.6)	19.25	②
Servo Return Spring	1.201 (30.5)	1.165 (29.6)	4	.102 (2.6)

① — Outside diameter of spring coil.
② — Wire shape is oval, dimensions are as follows: .154" x .098" (3.9 x 2.5 mm).

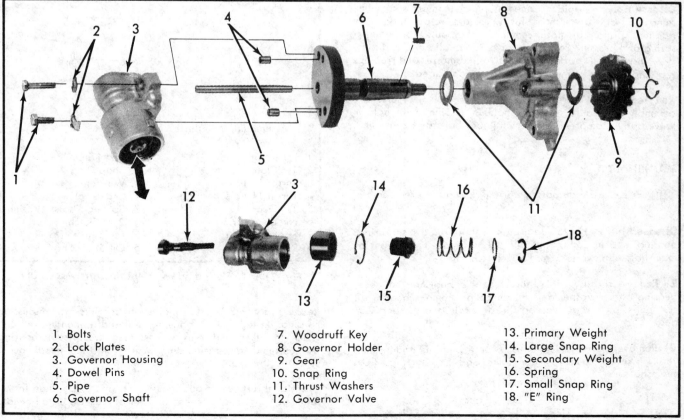

1. Bolts	7. Woodruff Key	13. Primary Weight
2. Lock Plates	8. Governor Holder	14. Large Snap Ring
3. Governor Housing	9. Gear	15. Secondary Weight
4. Dowel Pins	10. Snap Ring	16. Spring
5. Pipe	11. Thrust Washers	17. Small Snap Ring
6. Governor Shaft	12. Governor Valve	18. "E" Ring

Fig. 17 Exploded View of Governor Assembly

HONDA 3-SPEED (Cont.)

Reassembly — To reassemble servo valve, reverse disassembly procedure and note the following. Always replace "O" rings with new ones.

NOTE — *Do not remove or adjust shift adjustment bolt. Adjustment bolt is factory set and should not be changed or shift points will be changed.*

GOVERNOR ASSEMBLY

NOTE — *Replace governor assembly if any part is worn or damaged, or if governor does not operate smoothly.*

Disassembly — 1) Remove governor housing lock plate bolts and remove governor housing. Remove "E" ring from governor housing, then remove small snap ring, spring and secondary weight. Remove larger snap ring and primary weight. Remove governor valve. See Fig. 17.

2) On governor holder, remove snap ring, gear and thrust washer. From governor shaft, remove pipe. Pull governor shaft out of governor holder and remove Woodruff key and thrust washer. Inspect all parts for wear or damage. Check for smooth operation of all parts.

Reassembly — To reassemble governor, reverse disassembly procedure, replace lock plates with new ones and check for smooth operation after reassembly.

REGULATOR VALVE BODY

Disassembly — Hold retainer in place (compressed) while removing lock bolt, then slowly release retainer. Remove retainer, spring seat, stator reaction spring, outer spring, inner spring and pressure regulator valve. Clean all parts and blow dry. Inspect all parts for wear or damage and replace regulator valve if any part is worn or damaged.

Reassembly — To reassemble regulator valve, reverse disassembly procedure, aligning hole in retainer with hole in valve body. Compress retainer until lock bolt can be installed.

MAINSHAFT

NOTE — *Lubricate all parts with ATF fluid during reassembly.*

Disassembly — 1) From rear of mainshaft, remove snap ring, bearing, spacer collar and oil seal rings (2). From front of mainshaft, remove lock nut and 1st clutch.

2) Remove thrust washer, thrust needle bearing, 1st gear, bearing, thrust washer and spacer collar. Remove bearing, 2 "O" rings, snap ring, washer, thrust needle bearing and 2nd gear.

3) Remove bearings (2), thrust needle bearing and splined thrust washer. Remove 2nd clutch and 2 "O" rings from mainshaft.

NOTE — *When installing thrust needle bearings, install unrolled edge of bearing cage facing thrust washer.*

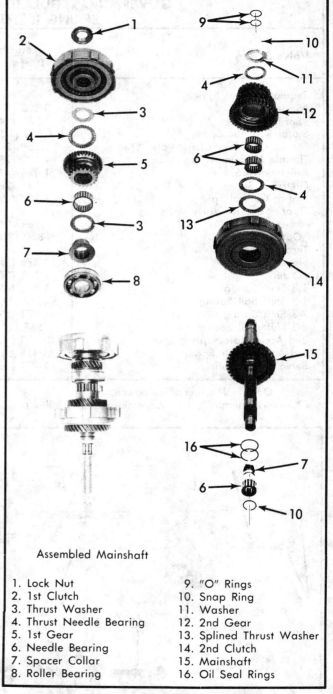

Assembled Mainshaft

1. Lock Nut	9. "O" Rings
2. 1st Clutch	10. Snap Ring
3. Thrust Washer	11. Washer
4. Thrust Needle Bearing	12. 2nd Gear
5. 1st Gear	13. Splined Thrust Washer
6. Needle Bearing	14. 2nd Clutch
7. Spacer Collar	15. Mainshaft
8. Roller Bearing	16. Oil Seal Rings

Fig. 18 Exploded View of Mainshaft Assembly

Reassembly — 1) Install mainshaft bearing to transmission housing. Install 2 "O" rings to mainshaft, then install 2nd clutch. Install splined thrust washer then thrust needle bearing with unrolled edge facing thrust washer. Install 2 needle bearings and 2nd gear.

2) Install thrust needle bearing, washer and 2 "O" rings. Install roller bearing, spacer collar and thrust washer. Install needle bearing and 1st gear. Install thrust needle bearing, thrust washer, 1st clutch and lock nut.

HONDA 3-SPEED (Cont.)

3) With mainshaft assembled, measure clearance between thrust needle bearing and shoulder on washer. See *Fig. 19*. Clearance should be .004-.008" (.1-.2 mm), if not, select splined thrust washer of proper thickness to obtain clearance specification. *See Splined Thrust Washer Thickness chart.*

Splined Thrust Washer Thicknesses	
Thrust Washer	Thickness In. (mm)
A	.116-.120 (2.95-3.05)
B	.120-.123 (3.05-3.15)
C	.123-.128 (3.15-3.25)
D	.128-.131 (3.25-3.35)
E	.131-.136 (3.35-3.45)

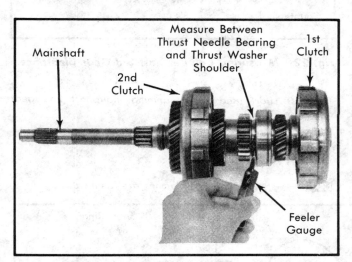

Fig. 19 Measuring Mainshaft Gear Clearance

COUNTERSHAFT

NOTE — *Lubricate all parts with ATF fluid during reassembly.*

Disassembly — 1) Remove lock nut, parking gear, 1st gear and roller bearing. Remove reverse gear collar, needle bearing and reverse gear. Remove reverse selector gear, selector hub and 2nd gear with needle bearing.

2) Remove spacer collar, thrust washer, 3rd gear and needle bearing. Remove thrust needle bearing, splined thrust washer and 3rd clutch. Remove 2 "O" rings from countershaft. Remove countershaft bearing from transmission housing.

NOTE — *When installing thrust needle bearing, install unrolled edge of bearing cage facing thrust washer.*

Reassembly — 1) Install countershaft bearing to transmission housing. Install 2 new "O" rings to countershaft. Install splined thrust washer, thrust needle bearing and 3rd gear with needle bearing. Install thrust washer, spacer collar and 2nd gear with needle bearing.

2) Install selector hub, reverse selector gear and reverse gear with needle bearing. Install reverse gear collar, roller bearing, 1st gear, parking gear and lock nut. See *Fig. 20.*

3) With countershaft assembled, measure clearance between selector hub and shoulder on 2nd gear. See *Fig. 21*. Clearance should be .004-.008" (.1-.2 mm). If clearance is more than specifications, install a thrust washer of proper thickness to achieve correct clearance. *See Thrust Washer Thickness chart.*

Thrust Washer Thicknesses	
Thrust Washer	Thickness In. (mm)
A	.092-.096 (2.35-2.45)
B	.096-.100 (2.45-2.55)
C	.100-.104 (2.55-2.65)

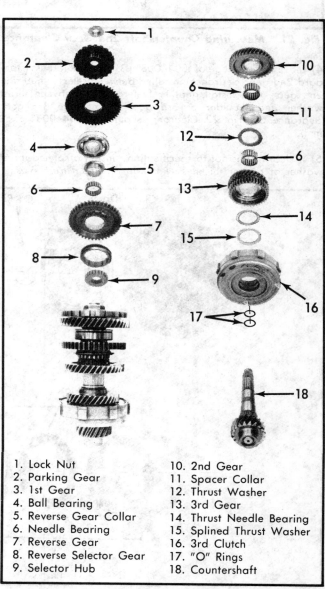

1. Lock Nut
2. Parking Gear
3. 1st Gear
4. Ball Bearing
5. Reverse Gear Collar
6. Needle Bearing
7. Reverse Gear
8. Reverse Selector Gear
9. Selector Hub
10. 2nd Gear
11. Spacer Collar
12. Thrust Washer
13. 3rd Gear
14. Thrust Needle Bearing
15. Splined Thrust Washer
16. 3rd Clutch
17. "O" Rings
18. Countershaft

Fig. 20 Exploded View of Countershaft Assembly

HONDA 3-SPEED (Cont.)

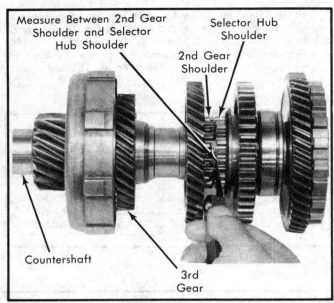

Fig. 21 Measuring Countershaft 2nd Gear Clearance

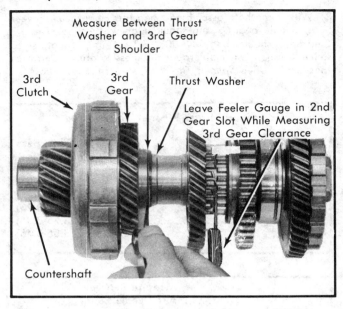

Fig. 22 Measuring Countershaft 3rd Gear Clearance

4) Leave feeler gauge of .004-.008" (.1-.2 mm) thickness (standard 2nd gear clearance) installed between selector hub and 2nd gear, then install another feeler gauge between thrust washer and shoulder of 3rd gear to measure 3rd gear clearance. See Fig. 22. Clearance should be .004-.008" (.1-.2 mm).

5) If clearance is not to specifications, install a splined thrust washer of proper thickness. Refer to Splined Thrust Washer

Thickness chart used in determining mainshaft 2nd gear clearance.

CLUTCH ASSEMBLIES

NOTE — 1st, 2nd and 3rd clutches are identical.

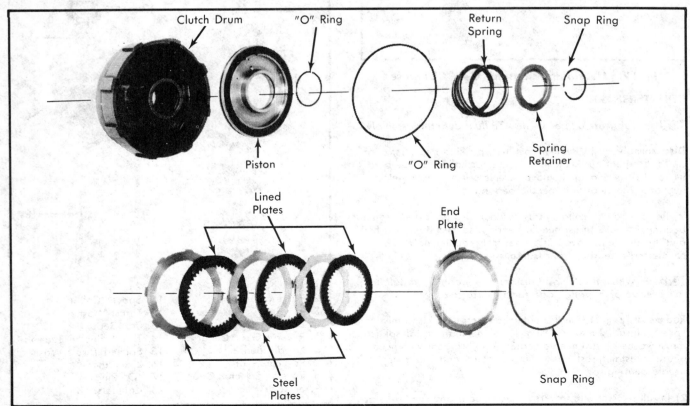

Fig. 23 Exploded View of 1st, 2nd and 3rd Clutch Assemblies

HONDA 3-SPEED (Cont.)

Disassembly — 1) Remove large snap ring retaining end plate and clutches. Remove end plate and clutch pack, keep steel plates and lined plates in order removed. See *Fig. 23*.

2) Install a spring compressor that seats against clutch drum and against spring retainer. Compress spring and remove small snap ring. Slowly release spring compressor, then remove spring retainer, return spring, large "O" ring, small "O" ring and piston.

3) Check condition of piston and check valve. Check for excessive wear or scoring on steel plates and lined plates. Replace steel or lined plates if necessary. Replace clutch assembly if piston is damaged.

NOTE — *If new lined plates are installed, soak in ATF fluid before installation.*

Reassembly — 1) Lubricate all parts with ATF fluid before assembling. Install new "O" ring on piston. Make sure clutch piston spring washer is installed with high side facing away from clutch drum. Install piston (lubricate "O" ring with ATF fluid) to clutch drum. Apply pressure to piston (by hand) and rotate piston to ensure proper seating.

2) Install return spring and spring retainer. Position a new snap ring on spring retainer, then install a spring compressor to clutch drum and spring retainer. Compress spring and fit snap ring to groove. Slowly release spring compressor and make sure snap ring seats properly. Install large "O" ring to clutch drum.

End Plate Thicknesses

End Plate Number	Thickness In. (mm)
1	.091 (2.3)
2	.102 (2.6)
3	.114 (2.9)
4	.126 (3.2)
5	.138 (3.5)

3) Install clutch pack, starting with a steel plate and alternating with lined plates, ending with the end plate. Install large snap ring to clutch drum. Measure clearance between end plate and lined plate. Clearance should be .016-.028" (.4-.7 mm).

4) If clearance is not to specifications, select an end plate to obtain correct clearance. See *End Plate Thickness chart*. With correct end plate installed, check operation of clutch by blowing compressed air into oil passage in clutch drum. Clutch should apply. Remove air pressure and clutch should release.

TRANSMISSION HOUSING, END HOUSING AND TORQUE CONVERTER HOUSING

Disassembly — 1) If seals are to be replaced or if differential needs repair, lift differential out of torque converter housing. Remove differential seal snap ring and drive seal out.

2) On end cover, remove snap rings to feed pipes "A" and "B". Remove feed pipes with collars, then remove pins and collars from feed pipes. See *Fig. 24*.

3) On torque converter housing, drive in oil seals and bearings for mainshaft and countershaft. On transmission housing, expand snap rings (do not remove) and push bearings out by hand. Push out idler gear shaft and bearing from inside transmission housing then remove idler gear.

Reassembly — 1) Install idler gear, then idler gear shaft and bearing to transmission housing. Expand mainshaft and countershaft bearing snap rings and install bearings to transmission housing. On torque converter housing, drive mainshaft and countershaft bearings and seals into housing.

2) On end housing, install feed pipe "O" rings, collars and washers to feed pipes. Install pins to feed pipes and install feed pipes to end cover. Install snap rings retaining feed pipes.

NOTE — *Make sure lugs on feed pipe collars are aligned with slots in end cover housing.*

3) To determine side clearance of differential to transmission, temporarily install snap ring to converter housing (do not install oil seal at this time). Install differential to converter housing.

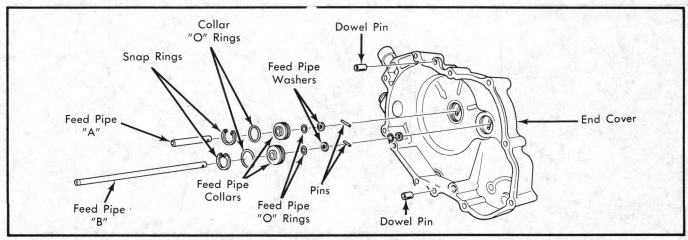

Fig. 24 Exploded View of End Housing Assembly

HONDA 3-SPEED (Cont.)

4) Install mainshaft and countershaft to converter housing. Install new gasket to converter housing, install dowel pins and install transmission housing to converter housing. Install and tighten converter housing-to-transmission bolts.

5) Make sure differential is bottomed in transmission housing, then use a feeler gauge to check clearance between snap ring and outer race of bearing in converter housing. Clearance should be .006" (.15 mm) maximum. If clearance is not to specifications, select snap ring to give proper clearance. See *Side Clearance Snap Ring Thickness* chart.

Side Clearance Snap Ring Thicknesses	
Snap Ring	Thickness In. (mm)
1	.096 (2.45)
2	.100 (2.55)
3	.104 (2.65)
4	.108 (2.75)
5	.112 (2.85)
6	.116 (2.95)

6) Disassemble temporarily assembled transmission and install oil seal and correct snap ring to converter housing. Install differential and snap ring to converter housing.

DIFFERENTIAL

Disassembly — 1) With differential removed from torque converter housing, place differential in "V" blocks. Check backlash of both pinion gears. Backlash should be .002-.010" (.05-.25 mm). *See Fig. 25.* If backlash is not to specifications disassemble differential and install new thrust washers to obtain correct backlash.

l) Using a bearing puller, remove bearings from both sides of differential. Remove speedometer gear snap ring and speedometer gear. Remove bolts retaining ring gear to carrier and remove ring gear.

CAUTION — *Ring gear bolts have left hand threads.*

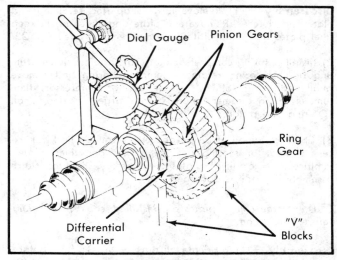

Fig. 25 Checking Backlash of Differential

3) Drive out spring pin that retains pinion shaft and remove pinion shaft, pinion gears, side gears and thrust washers. Wash all components and check for excessive wear or damage.

Reassembly — 1) Install side gears in differential carrier. Install pinion gears and mesh with side gears. Install thrust washers of equal and proper thickness to obtain correct backlash. *See Thrust Washer Thickness chart.* Install pinion shaft while rotating gears to align holes in gears with hole in carrier. Align hole in pinion shaft with hole in carrier and install spring pin. *See Fig. 26.*

Thrust Washer Thicknesses	
Thrust Washer	Thickness In. (mm)
1	.028 (.7)
2	.031 (.8)
3	.035 (.9)
4	.040 (1.0)

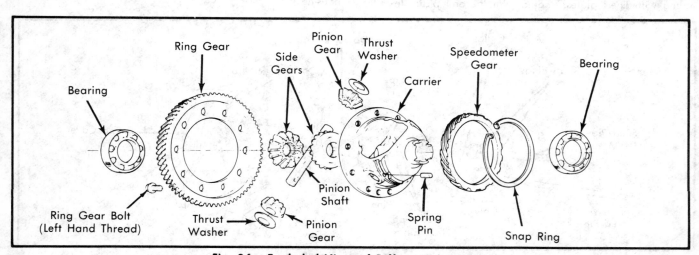

Fig. 26 Exploded View of Differential Assembly

HONDA 3-SPEED (Cont.)

2) With differential assembled with new thrust washers, again measure backlash. If backlash is still not to specifications, replace both pinion gears and recheck backlash. If still not to specifications, replace both side gears and recheck backlash. If still out of specifications, replace complete carrier assembly.

3) Install bearings to carrier. Install speedometer gear (with chamfer facing carrier) and install snap ring. Make sure snap ring ends do not align with carrier bearing support. *See Fig. 27.*

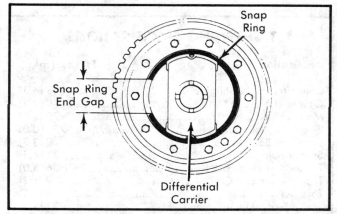

Fig. 27   Installation of Snap Ring on Differential Carrier

4) Install ring gear to carrier with chamfer on inside diameter of ring gear facing carrier. Install ring gear bolts (left hand threads) and tighten.

TRANSAXLE REASSEMBLY

NOTE — *Lubricate all parts with ATF fluid during reassembly.*

1) Assemble manual valve lever on control shaft, then install torque converter housing. Install control lever and new lock plate on other end of control shaft, install and tighten bolt. Bend tab of lock plate up to prevent bolt from turning.

2) Install new filter screen in converter housing. Install separator plate, dowel pin, oil pump gears and shaft. Make sure chamfered side of driven gear and shouldered side of drive gear is facing down. Install check valve and spring, then install valve body on converter housing.

3) Install and tighten valve body bolts. Install stator shaft arm, stop pin and dowel pins. Install regulator valve. Install steel ball in valve body oil passage. *Refer to Fig. 13.* Install separator plate, throttle control shaft and dowel pins.

4) Install servo. Make sure the correct length of bolt is installed or servo will not seal to housing. *See Fig. 28.* Place a roller on each side of manual valve stem, then attach valve to lever with pin. Secure with cotter pin.

5) Install 2nd and 3rd accumulator spring in servo body. *Refer to Governor, Regulator, Servo and Valve Body Spring Identification chart for accumulator spring diameters and lengths.* Install accumulator cover; compress accumulator springs before tightening bolts.

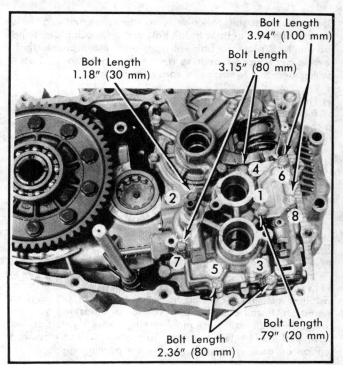

Fig. 28   Installation of Servo-to-Converter Housing Showing Attaching Bolt Lengths

6) Install governor valve, using new lock plates, then bend lock plate tabs over so bolts will not turn. Install mainshaft and countershaft in converter housing, as an assembly.

NOTE — *Do not tap on shaft ends to force shafts to seat.*

7) Remove lock nuts from mainshaft and countershaft, if installed, then install countershaft 2nd gear and reverse selector sleeve with reverse shift fork (assembled before installation). Groove on selector sleeve faces down.

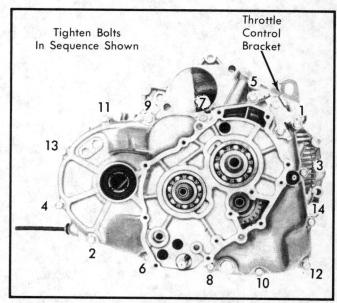

Fig. 29   Transmission Housing-to-Converter Housing Bolt Tightening Sequence

HONDA 3-SPEED (Cont.)

8) Install reverse shift fork over servo valve stem and align hole in stem with hole in fork. Install bolt and new lock plate. Bend tab on lock plate so bolt will not turn. Install countershaft reverse gear, needle bearing and reverse gear collar. Install gasket and 2 dowel pins in converter housing.

9) Place transmission housing on converter housing and install oil feed pipes. Make sure throttle control shaft aligns with hole in converter housing. Tighten bolts in 2 steps in order shown in Fig. 29.

10) Install control lever and spring on control shaft, then install bolt and new lock plate. Bend tab against bolt. Install parking shift arm and spring on shift shaft, use new lock tab and bend tab against bolt.

NOTE — Parking shift arm spring should put clockwise tension on shift arm, forcing it against stop pin.

11) Install 1st gear collar and needle bearing on countershaft. Install reverse idler bearing holder then install "O" rings to mainshaft. Install countershaft 1st gear and parking gear on countershaft. Install stop pin, parking pawl shaft, parking pawl and pawl release spring. Spring should put clockwise tension on pawl, forcing it away from parking gear.

12) Shift lever to "P" and install mainshaft holder. Install new countershaft lock nut. Stake lock nut flange into gear groove.

Install needle bearing and thrust washer on mainshaft. Install 1st gear, needle bearing and thrust washer on mainshaft.

13) Install 1st clutch on the mainshaft. Attach mainshaft holder from underside of converter housing, then install new mainshaft lock nut. Stake lock nut to groove in 1st clutch.

14) Install gasket, dowel pins and "O" rings on transmission housing. Install end cover and bolts. Install dipstick, cooler fittings. Do not tighten cooler fittings until transmission is installed in vehicle.

TIGHTENING SPECIFICATIONS

Application	Ft. Lbs. (mkg)
Converter Hsg.-to-Engine	33 (4.5)
Countershaft Lock Nut	70 (9.5)
Mainshaft Lock Nut	70 (9.5)
Ring Gear Bolts	72 (10.0)
Stabilizer Bar	28 (3.9)
Starter Bolts	33 (4.5)
Torque Converter Bolts	36 (5.0)
Transmission End Cover	9 (1.2)
Torque Rods	54 (7.5)
Transmission Mounting Bolts	33 (4.5)
Transmission-to-Converter Hsg.	20 (2.7)

PORSCHE 928

DESCRIPTION

The transaxle assembly consists of 3 main units: Automatic transmission, torque converter and final drive assembly. The automatic transmission is an A22.02 fully automatic 3 speed, planetary gear type and consists of 2 planetary gear sets, 3 brake bands, 2 multiple-disc clutches, oil pump, valve body and input and output shafts. The torque converter is located on the front of the transmission and is housed in a 2 piece bell housing. The final drive is attached to the rear of the transmission case and contains a ring and pinion gear, side gears and pinion gears. The operation of the final drive is the same as conventional differentials.

LUBRICATION & ADJUSTMENT

See *AUTOMATIC TRANSMISSION SERVICING* Section

TROUBLE SHOOTING

SLIPS IN ALL SELECTOR POSITIONS

Incorrect modulating pressure. Modulating pressure control valve or pressure relief valve for modulating pressure dirty or sticking. Line to transmission vacuum unit clogged or leaking. Working pressure control valve dirty or sticking. Defective pump.

TRANSMISSION GRABS OR VEHICLE SHAKES WHEN STARTING OFF

Incorrect modulating pressure. Check transmission vacuum unit; if transmission fluid is found in vacuum unit, replace unit. If fuel is found in vacuum unit, check injection system and adjust.

TRANSMISSION SLIPS IN FIRST GEAR

Dirty or sticking valves in valve body. Defective center servo piston or piston sealing ring damaged. Defective center band or thrust body.

TRANSMISSION SLIPS ON UPSHIFT

Incorrect modulating pressure. Faulty valve body assembly (replace sealing bushings on plug pipes). Defective front or rear clutch. Oil distribution sleeve damaged.

TRANSMISSION SLIPS IN THIRD GEAR

Valve body sealing bushings worn or damaged. Defective rear clutch assembly. Oil distributing sleeve damaged.

TRANSMISSION SLIPS IN FIRST AND SECOND GEARS

Rear band worn or damaged. Adjust brake band by installing a longer thrust pin.

TRANSMISSION SLIPS IN ALL GEARS

Incorrect modulating pressure. Defective modulating pressure relief valve or control valve.

TRANSMISSION WILL NOT ENGAGE PROPERLY

Torque converter not installed correctly. Driver not correctly engaging in drive gear.

NO POSITIVE ENGAGEMENT IN REVERSE

Front band out of adjustment. Front servo piston sealing ring worn or damaged. Defective one-way clutch in gear unit assembly.

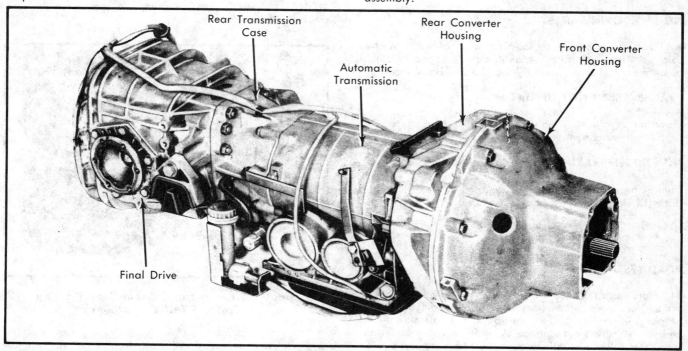

Rear Transmission Case

Rear Converter Housing

Front Converter Housing

Automatic Transmission

Final Drive

Fig. 1   928 Automatic Transaxle Assembly

PORSCHE 928 (Cont.)

ROUGH JERK WHEN ENGAGING SELECTOR LEVER POSITION "D"

Adjust engine idle speed and emissions as specified. Incorrect modulating and/or working pressure. Vacuum leak. Defective pressure receiving piston in extension housing.

ROUGH JERK WHEN CHANGING GEAR

Check modulating pressure and working pressure and adjust modulating pressure of necessary. If working pressure is too high, replace valve body assembly. Vacuum lines or connections leaking. Control pressure linkage out of adjustment

ROUGH JERK ON 3-2 DOWNSHIFT

Rear servo piston sealing ring worn or damaged. Defective rear servo piston.

NO UPSHIFTS

Incorrect governor pressure. Defective governor assembly.

UPSHIFTS ONLY IN UPPER SPEED RANGE OF GEARS

Control pressure linkage out of adjustment. Defective governor assembly.

UPSHIFTS ONLY IN LOWER SPEED RANGE OF GEARS

Control pressure linkage damaged or out of adjustment. Accelerator linkage out of adjustment. Defective governor assembly.

POOR ACCELERATION AT START

Check stalling speed, if speed drops 400/700 RPM, replace torque converter.

NO KICKDOWN SHIFTS

Fuse for power supply to soleniod valve blown. Defective solenoid valve. Control pressure linkage damaged or out of adjustment. Kickdown control valve in valve body sticking.

TRANSMISSION NOT UPSHIFTING

Governor or command valve in shift valve housing requires repair or replacement.

NO ENGINE BRAKING ON DOWNSHIFTS.

Control pressure linkage out of adjustment. Defective servo piston(s). Defective valve body assembly.

TESTING

ROAD TESTING

1) Before road testing, be certain that the fluid level is at its proper level. Also make certain the control linkage is set properly. During the road test the upshift and downshift should be smooth and without slippage. All shifts may vary somewhat from the following shift speed chart due to production tolerances or tire size.

2) Slippage or engine runaway in any gear usually indicates clutch or band problems. The slipping unit in a particular gear can usually be identified by noting transmission operation in other selector positions and comparing which internal units are applied in those positions. *See Clutch and Band Application Chart.*

3) This process of elimination can be used to detect any unit which slips, and to confirm proper operation of good units. The actual cause of the malfunction usually cannot be determined. Practically any condition can be caused by leaking hydraulic circuits or sticking valves. Therefore, unless an obvious condition exists, do not disassemble transmission until a hydraulic pressure check has been completed.

Shift Speeds		
Application	**Shift Points (MPH)**	
	Upshift	**Downshift**
Part Throttle		
1-2-1	16-21	10-14
2-3-2	26-30	20-23
Full Throttle		
1-2-1	60-65	28-32
2-3-2	93-98	35-53
Kickdown		
3-2	....	76-83
2-1	....	36-48

HYDRAULIC PRESSURE TEST

1) Connect 0-350 psi (0-24.1 kg/cm²) pressure gauge to main pressure check point. Connect 0-140 psi (0-9.6 kg/cm²) pressure gauge to governor pressure check point. Connect 0-140 (0-9.6 kg/cm²) pressure gauge to modulator pressure check point. *See Fig. 2.*

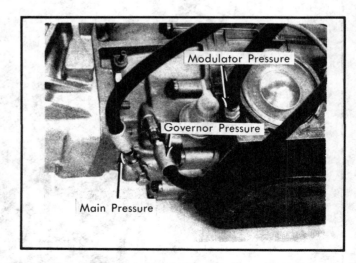

Fig. 2   View of Transmission Case Showing Pressure Test Connections

2) Route pressure gauges through front passenger window and place in a position for easy observation.

PORSCHE 928 (Cont.)

NOTE — *Modulator pressure must be checked and adjusted before main pressure or governor pressure can be checked, because modulator pressure affects main and governor pressures.*

3) At full throttle in "D" at approximately 55 MPH, with vacuum line disconnected, read modulator pressure. Next, remove vacuum line and check modulator pressure at stall speed (2200-2600 RPM). To adjust, remove modulator pressure cover. Slightly pull adjusting key out, to increase pressure turn key to the right, to decrease pressure turn key to the left. After adjustment is made, push key into the nearest slot and install modulator cover.

4) Check main pressure as follows: With vacuum line disconnected, gear selector in "D" and vehicle at stall speed (2200-2600), read main line pressure. Next, repeat above in "R" and read main line pressure. Final main line pressure check is performed at full throttle in "D" at approximately 55 MPH and vacuum line connected.

5) Governor pressure is checked at desiganted speeds with vacuum line disconnected. See *Pressure Chart Below.*

Transmission Operating Pressures	
Application	**Psi (kg/cm²)**
Modulating Pressure	
"D" @ 55 MPH	44-45 (3.0-3.1)
At Stall Speed in "D" ①	65-70 (4.5-4.8)
Main Pressure	
At Stall Speed in "D" ①	149-159 (10.3-10.9)
At Stall Speed in "R" ①	263-279 (18.1-19.2)
At Full Throttle in "D" 55 MPH ②	74-80 (5.1-5.5)
Governor Pressure	
At 12 MPH	7-9 (.4-.6)
At 31 MPH	21-24 (1.4-1.6)
At 47 MPH	30-31 (2.0-2.1)
At 62 MPH	36-37 (2.4-2.5)
At 81 MPH	44-47 (3.0-3.2)
At 99 MPH	55-58 (3.7-3.9)

① — Vavuum line disconnected.
② — Vacuum line connected.

STALL SPEED

Testing Precautions — Set parking brake, block wheels, and apply foot brake. Maximum stall speed test time is 5 seconds. If engine speed exceeds limits shown in Stall Speed Table, release accelerator immediately as clutch or band slippage is indicated.

Testing Procedure — Connect tachometer to engine and place in a position for easy observation, run engine at 2000 RPM for 2 minutes in neutral before testing. Place selector lever in "D" and floor accelerator pedal. Read stall speed on tachometer.

Test Result — If stall speed is higher than specified by 300 RPM, slippage in transmission is indicated. If stall speed drops by approximately 400 to 700 RPM, one-way clutch in torque converter is slipping. If stall speed is correct and top speed is not reached one-way clutch is locking up.

NOTE — *Stall speed will drop approximately 125 RPM for every 3900 feet of altitude above sea level. Also high outside temperatures could cause stall speed to drop slightly.*

Stall Speeds	
Application	**Stall RPM**
All Models	2200-2600

SERVICE (IN VEHICLE)

AXLE DRIVE SHAFTS

Removal & Installation — Raise vehicle on suitable hoist. Remove bolts from constant velocity joint-to-mating flang and remove drive axle from vehicle. To install, reverse removal procedure and tighten to specifications.

CLUTCH AND BAND APPLICATION CHART
(ELEMENTS IN USE)

Gear Range	Front Clutch	Rear Clutch	Front Band	Center Band	Rear Band	Overrunning Clutch
FIRST GEAR				X	X	X
SECOND GEAR	X				X	
THIRD GEAR	X	X				
REVERSE			X			X

NEUTRAL OR PARK — All clutches and bands released and/or ineffective.

PORSCHE 928 (Cont.)

CONSTANT VELOCITY JOINTS

NOTE — *Axle shafts must be removed from vehicle before servicing.*

Removal - Clamp axle shaft in a vise with soft jaws. Remove boot clamp and push boot to center of axle. Remove circlip from axle shaft, press joint from axle shaft using special tools VW 401 and VW 408.

Disassembly — Swing ball and ball cage from joint and press out in direction of arrow. *See Fig. 3.* Tilt ball hub out of ball cage via ball groove. *See Fig.4.* Clean all parts in a cleaning solvent and blow dry. Inspect for wear and damage.

NOTE — *Ball hub and joint are paired. Do not mix parts. The 6 balls are also mated together and cannot be mixed with others.*

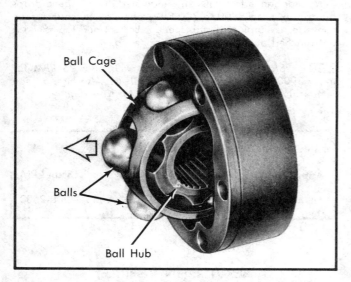

Fig. 3   Ball Hub and Ball Cage Removal

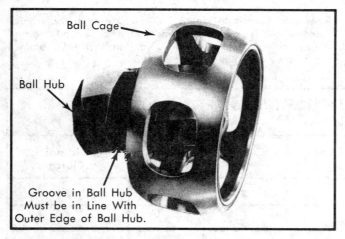

Fig. 4   Removal of Ball Hub From Cage

Reassembly — Place ball hub in ball cage. Press balls into cage. Install hub with cage and balls into joint and swing into assembled position. Check for smooth operation.

Installation — Reverse removal procedure and note the following: Install a new gasket on flange cover. Pack joint with molybdenum grease.

FLANGE SHAFT SEAL

Removal — Remove axle drive shaft, remove inner flange bolt while holding flange with suitable tool. Remove flange and seal using suitable tools.

Installation — Fill cavity between sealing and dust lips with multi-purpose grease and drive seal in place with suitable tool. Replace flange and axle drive shaft and tighten to specifications.

TRANSAXLE REMOVAL & INSTALLATION

Removal — **1)** Disconnect and remove battery. Remove self-locking nuts from spring struts in trunk. Disconnect multiple plug in spare wheel well and pull toward rear. Disconnect parking brake cable and lock. Remove rear wheels and splash shield. Drain torque converter and transmission oil sump. Remove oil filler tube. Disconnect transmission oil cooler lines.

2) Remove lower body brace. Disconnect exhaust pipe from catalytic converter. Remove exhaust pipe heat shields. Remove battery box. Remove rubber cap from inspection hole in front converter housing and turn crankshaft to position coupling so that socket head screw can be removed. Disconnect brake calipers and suspend with wire. Disconnect axle shafts and swing out of the way. Remove rear reinforcement plate. Disconnect stabilizer bar from lower control arm.

3) Support transaxle with suitable tool (9164) and remove 2 bolts from transaxle mounts. Remove 2 bolts holding rear axle crossmember to frame. Mark position of eccentric bolts and remove bolts. Mark position of rear axle crossmember for reinstallation. Place jack under transaxle crossmember and remove mounting bolts from crossmember.

4) Lower rear axle carefully and take care that spring struts, crossmember and bearing brackets do not tilt. Mount special tool 9163 on adjustable floor jack. Lift transaxle and remove special tool 9164. Lower transaxle slightly and remove selector lever. Disconnect modulator vacuum line. Remove 6 bolts from central tube. Pull transaxle out of coupling splines and lower carefully.

NOTE — *Transaxle has to be lowered as far as possible to gain access to all tube bolts.*

Installation — To install, reverse removal procedure and check rear end alignment.

TORQUE CONVERTER

NOTE — *The torque converter is a sealed unit and cannot be disassembled for service.*

TRANSMISSION DISASSEMBLY

NOTE — *Transmission has to be separated from final drive before it can be disassembled.*

PORSCHE 928 (Cont.)

1) Detach final drive assembly and remove bearing and pinion assembly. Remove final drive housing, centrifugal governor and modulating pressure housing.

NOTE — *Vacuum modulator must be removed before removing final drive housing.*

2) Pull parking lock gear off output shaft. Remove front torque converter housing and torque converter. Remove oil pan, valve body and kickdown solenoid. Remove snap ring for number 2 brake band piston and remove cover. Install special tool 9305 and press out piston. Attach special tool 9304 for number 1 brake band piston, preload piston and remove snap ring. Release special tool and remove cover, piston and springs.

3) Mark pins for brake bands 1 and 2, then remove pins. Position transmission in horizontal position. Remove number 3 brake band adjusting screw and take out both pins. Pull number 3 brake band forward slightly. Remove input shaft from gear assembly by using the snap ring from number 2 piston cover. See *Fig. 5*.

4) Remove gear assembly from case by pulling forward. Output shaft is removed from case by driving it forward with a plastic hammer.

Fig. 5   Gear Assembly Removal

COMPONENT DISASSEMBLY & REASSEMBLY

VALVE BODY

NOTE — *Manufacturer does not supply information on valve body disassembly. If transmission fluid smells burnt or there are metal particles or sludge in oil pan, manufacturer suggests that entire torque converter and transmission should be replaced. Also oil cooler and lines will have to be cleaned.*

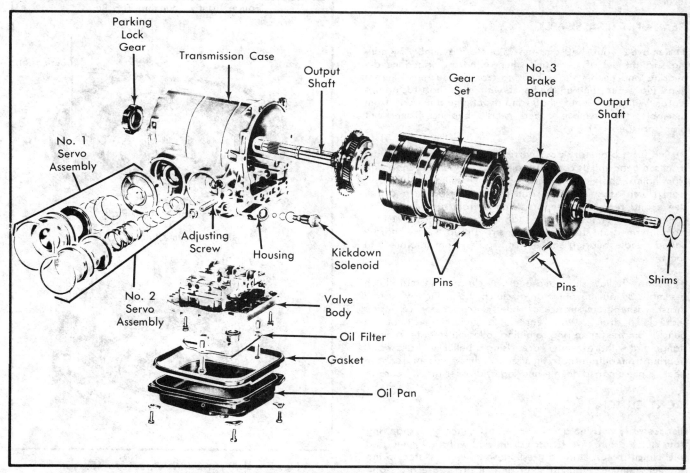

Fig. 6   Exploded View of Transmission Case and Main Components.

PORSCHE 928 (Cont.)

GOVERNOR

Disassembly — 1) Remove sealing rings from governor flange. Remove retaining bolts for shift housing and governor housing, then separate housing from governor flange.

2) Remove lock washer, compression spring, and shift valve from shift valve housing.

3) From governor housing, remove the spring plate, then withdraw centrifugal weight and thin compression spring from top of housing. Remove remaining spring, compensating shims, and control valve through bottom of housing.

Reassembly — 1) Clean all parts in solvent and air dry. Make sure valves slide easily in bores. Insert control valve into governor housing. Install centrifugal weight and thin compression spring into control valve, install compensating washers and remaining spring into assembly, then attach spring plate to centrifugal weight stem, making sure it is correctly seated.

2) Insert shift valve and spring into shift valve housing and retain with snap ring. Position shift housing on governor flange so that oil slot of housing faces seal rings on flange, and oil passages are aligned in housing and flange. Position strainer into slot on opposite end of flange, then install governor housing into flange so that slot of housing faces seal rings of flange. Install oil seal rings onto flange and hook ends to secure.

GEAR UNIT DISASSEMBLY

1) Remove output shaft and rear planetary assembly by pulling straight out of gear unit, then withdraw caged needle bearing and needle thrust bearing from inside rear internal gear. Place gear unit on the bench with input shaft facing upward. Withdraw input shaft and front internal gear from assembly, then remove caged needle bearing from front planetary gear set.

2) Pull front planetary gear carrier from unit, then withdraw front sun gear and its caged needle bearing. Remove snap ring from hollow shaft, then withdraw compensating washers and front clutch assembly. Grasp oil distributing sleeve and pull sleeve and rear clutch support flange from rear clutch and hollow shaft. Remove hollow shaft and rear clutch assembly from intermediate shaft by pulling straight up, then withdraw caged needle bearing and thrust washer from intermediate shaft.

3) Remove hollow shaft and one-way clutch from rear clutch assembly by pulling out rear of clutch drum, then withdraw thrust washer from surface of roller clutch inner race (inside rear clutch drum). With rear clutch supporting flange on bench, compress snap ring retaining roller clutch outer race on flange and withdraw outer race. Using a puller, withdraw ball bearing from output shaft, then remove thrust washer, rear sun gear, 2-piece caged needle bearing and roller thrust bearing.

FRONT CLUTCH

Disassembly — Using a screwdriver, pry clutch pack snap ring from clutch drum. Invert clutch drum and withdraw lined and steel clutch plates. Using a press, push down on piston spring retainer, remove retaining snap ring, then release press and withdraw spring retainer and return springs. Lift piston out of clutch drum and remove outer lip seal from piston and inner seal from clutch drum hub.

Reassembly — 1) Install new lip seal on clutch drum hub, with lip pointing downward into drum. Install new lip seal on piston, with seal lip facing away from spring pockets. Using a suitable seal protector tool (9308), carefully rotate piston into position in clutch drum. Place piston return springs into pockets of piston, position retainer on top of springs, compress retainer and springs, and install retaining snap ring.

2) Install clutch plates into drum, starting with a steel plate and alternating lined and steel plates until all plates are installed. Next, install top plate with inner bevelled edge facing upward. Install snap ring into drum to secure clutch pack.

NOTE — *If new lined plates are used, soak them in transmission fluid before installation.*

3) Measure clutch pack free play as follows: Using a depth gauge, measure distance from top of clutch drum to flat surface of top plate. Next, pull clutch up against snap ring and again check distance between top of clutch drum and surface of top plate. Clutch pack free play is determined by subtracting second measurement from first measurement. Resulting free play should be .032-.047" (.8-1.2 mm).

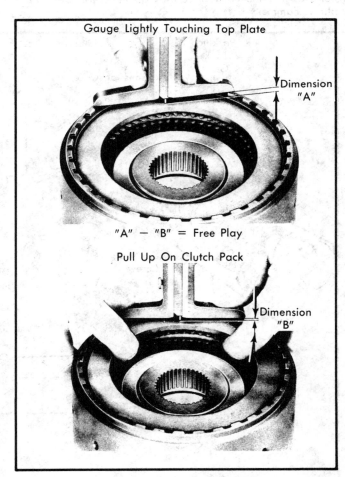

Fig. 7 Using a Depth Gauge to Measure Front Clutch Pack Clearance

PORSCHE 928 (Cont.)

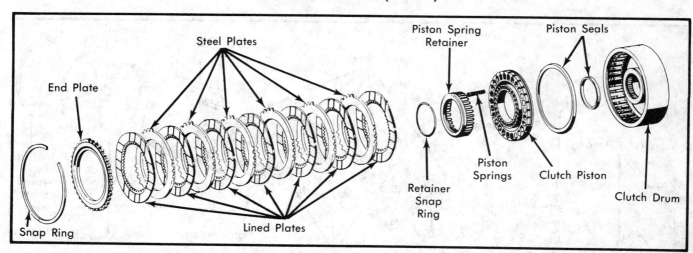

Fig. 8 Exploded View of Front Clutch Assembly

4) If free play is not within specifications, install a thicker or thinner steel plate (as necessary) to bring clearance within specifications. Selective steel plates are available in thicknesses of .118" (3.0 mm) and .138" (3.5 mm).

REAR CLUTCH

Disassembly — 1) With supporting flange end of rear clutch upward, remove flat snap ring from clutch drum and withdraw supporting flange and piston assembly.

CAUTION — *Do not allow piston to separate from flange as damage may result.*

2) Remove piston return springs and lined and steel clutch plates from clutch drum. Invert clutch drum and remove the waved snap ring from bottom of clutch drum. Withdraw steel plate with bevelled inside diameter and guide ring for piston return springs. Remove piston from supporting flange, then remove inner and outer piston lip seals.

Reassembly — 1) Install waved snap ring into bottom groove of rear clutch drum, then install bottom plate (with bevel on inside diameter downward) and piston spring guide ring.

2) Install clutch pack assembly into drum as follows: Install 1 lined plate, follow with thicker selective steel plate, then alternate 1 lined plate and 1 thinner steel plate until all plates are installed.

NOTE — *If new lined plates are being installed, soak in transmission fluid prior to assembly.*

3) Place clutch piston into clutch drum on top of clutch plates. Using a depth gauge, measure distance from top of clutch drum to flat surface of clutch piston. Next, remove piston from drum and measure distance from top of clutch drum supporting flange contacting surface of clutch drum splines. Subtract second measurement from first measurement; resulting measurement is clutch piston release play.

4) Clutch pack clearance should be .032-.047" (.8-1.2 mm). If not, selective thickness clutch plates are available to correct clearance. Install thicker or thinner plates as necessary to bring clutch pack clearance within specifications. Position all piston

release springs on pegs of release spring guide. Install a new lip seal on center hub of supporting flange, with lip pointing downward into piston well. Also install a new sealing ring onto clutch piston, with lip facing away from splines. Lubricate seals with transmission fluid and install piston into supporting flange, using a pencil or ball point pen to start lip of seal into flange.

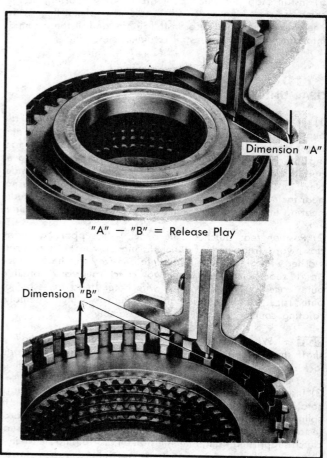

Fig. 9 Using a Depth Gauge to Measure Rear Clutch Pack Clearance

PORSCHE 928 (Cont.)

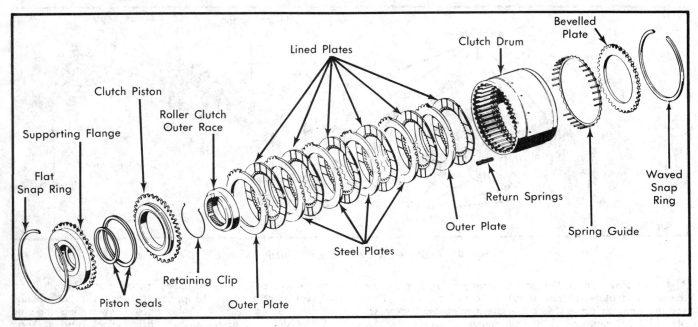

Fig. 10   Exploded View of Rear Clutch Assembly

5) Install snap ring into upper groove of supporting flange, compress snap ring ends with needle nose pliers, then install one-way clutch outer race. Install flange and piston assembly into clutch drum, then install retaining snap ring.

GEAR UNIT REASSEMBLY

1) Install needle thrust bearing and 2 piece caged needle bearing into gear cavity of output shaft. Position sun gear and thrust washer onto shaft, with offset side of thrust washer facing sun gear. Install ball bearing and parking lock gear over output shaft and press into place. Place assembly to the side. Next, position intermediate shaft on the bench with internal gear facing downward. Install thrust washer and caged needle bearing into assembly, then place this assembly to the side.

2) Position rear clutch on the bench with supporting flange downward (rear end of clutch facing upward). Coat thrust washer with grease and install into one-way clutch outer race (inside rear clutch). Install one-way clutch roller assembly into outer race, making sure edge with outer bead faces out of outer race. Install hollow shaft into one-way clutch assembly, rotating counterclockwise to ease assembly.

NOTE — *When looking from bottom of rear clutch, hollow shaft should freewheel when rotated counterclockwise, and lock up when rotated clockwise.*

3) Insert intermediate shaft into rear clutch and hollow shaft, rotating so assembly meshes with rear clutch lined plate splines. Place assembly on bench with shafts pointing upward. Install caged needle bearing over hollow shaft and into rear clutch supporting flange, then install oil distributing sleeve into flange, making sure sealing rings are fully engaged. Install front clutch onto assembly, making sure it engages fully with seal rings on distributing sleeve. Install retaining snap ring,

then measure clearance between snap ring and hub of front clutch drum. Clearance should be .012-.016" (.3-.4 mm); if not, install compensating washers between snap ring and clutch drum hub.

4) With front planetary gear carrier on the bench (clutch spline end upward), coat gear carrier-to-sun gear roller thrust bearing with grease and install into carrier. Using a depth gauge, measure distance from top of clutch splines on carrier to top of one of the rollers on thrust bearing; this is dimension "A" (write down for future reference). Next, measure distance from top of carrier splines to shoulder of hub inside carrier; this is dimension "B". Now measure distance from top of intermediate shaft to shoulder of the shaft (just below first set of splines); this is dimension "D".

5) Install forward sun gear into intermediate shaft, then install caged needle bearing over shaft and into sun gear. Measure distance from top of intermediate shaft to top face of sun gear; this is dimension "E". Subtract dimension "B" from "A"; this is dimension "C". Next, subtract dimension "E" from dimension "D"; this is dimension "F". Finally, subtract dimension "F" from dimension "C"; the result is gear unit end play. Gear play should be 008-.012" (.2-.3 mm); if not, add or subtract compensating washers under needle thrust bearing on front planetary carrier as necessary to bring play within specifications.

6) With proper compensating washer installed under thrust bearing, install forward planet carrier onto front clutch assembly, rotating carrier so it engages splines of front clutch lines plates. With carrier in place, install caged needle bearing onto intermediate shaft end, then install input shaft into carrier. Install a new metal seal onto input shaft and lock ends. Lay entire gear unit on its side and install caged needle bearing and needle thrust bearing into internal gear of intermediate shaft. Install output shaft into internal gear to complete assembly.

PORSCHE 928 (Cont.)

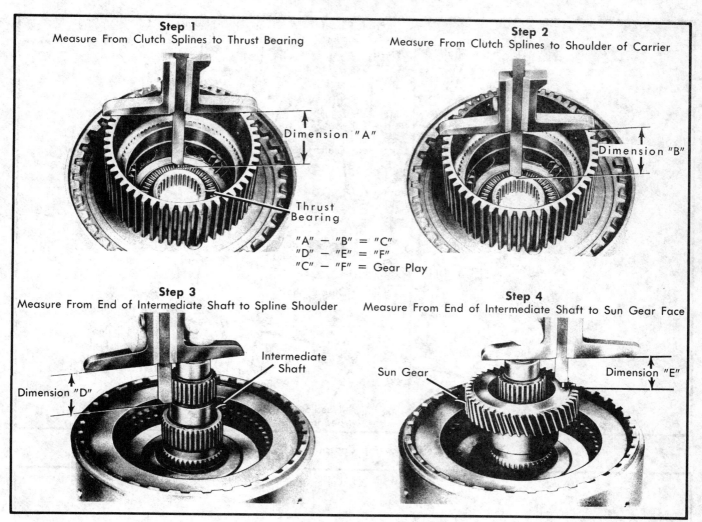

Step 1
Measure From Clutch Splines to Thrust Bearing

Dimension "A"

Thrust Bearing

"A" — "B" = "C"
"D" — "E" = "F"
"C" — "F" = Gear Play

Step 2
Measure From Clutch Splines to Shoulder of Carrier

Dimension "B"

Step 3
Measure From End of Intermediate Shaft to Spline Shoulder

Intermediate Shaft

Dimension "D"

Step 4
Measure From End of Intermediate Shaft to Sun Gear Face

Sun Gear

Dimension "E"

Fig. 11 Using a Depth Gauge to Determine Gear Unit End Play

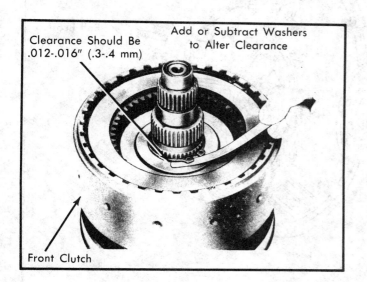

Clearance Should Be
.012-.016" (.3-.4 mm)

Add or Subtract Washers
to Alter Clearance

Front Clutch

Fig. 12 Using a Feeler Gauge to Measure Front Clutch Hub-to-Snap Ring Clearance

CONVERTER HOUSING & OIL PUMP ASSEMBLY

Disassembly — Remove oil pump attaching bolts at rear of pump. Install 2 bolts, 2" (50 mm) long, in oil pump bolt holes and tap lightly to remove oil pump. Withdraw "O" ring seal and pump lip seal from housing. If necessary, use a suitable puller and remove ball bearing from rear side of converter housing.

Reassembly — 1) Install a new "O" ring seal on outside diameter of pump housing, and a new lip seal in front cavity of housing. Lubricate pump gears with transmission fluid and install into housing.

2) Install intermediate plate onto housing so that bolt holes are aligned in both plate and housing. Install 2 guide bolts in oil pump body, insert oil pump into converter housing, install and tighten bolts to specifications.

Automatic Transaxles

PORSCHE 928 (Cont.)

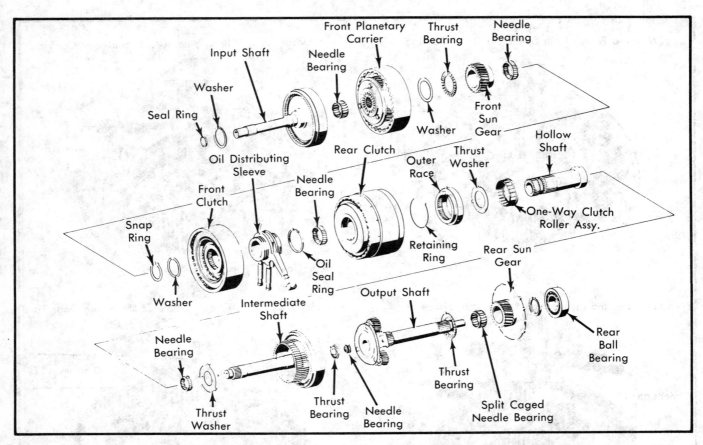

Fig. 13 Exploded View Showing Components of Gear Unit Assembly

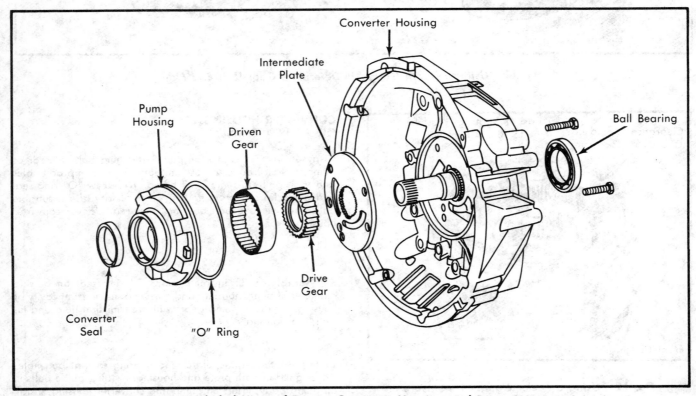

Fig. 14 Exploded View of Torque Converter Housing and Pump Housing

PORSCHE 928 (Cont.)

FINAL DRIVE HOUSING

Disassembly — Drive out seals with suitable tool. Remove engagement accumulator and spring. Remove piston retainer, spring and piston.

Reassembly — To install, reverse removal procedure and note the following: Install inner seal with lip facing transmission. Install outer seal with lip facing final drive.

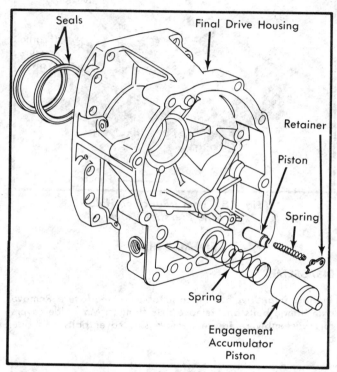

Fig. 15   Exploded View of Final Drive Housing

TRANSMISSION REASSEMBLY

NOTE — *Use automatic transmission fluid on bearings and all moving parts when assembling transmission.*

1) Install output shaft with ball bearing into transmission case and drive in with a plastic hammer. Install parking lock gear onto output shaft. Install governor onto output shaft, then install "O" ring. Install modulating pressure valve housing and check regulating valve for easy movement after tightening mounting bolts.

2) Install a new final drive-to-transmission gasket, then install final drive housing and tighten bolts to specifications. Check length of pin to be used for vacuum modulator with special tool 9303 and install modulator.

NOTE — *The pinion assembly has to be checked for proper end play adjustment any time it is removed.*

3) Use a depth gauge to measure the distance from the tapered roller bearing surface to bearing flange surface. The proper end play is 1.38" ± .020" (35 ±.5 mm). See Fig. 16.

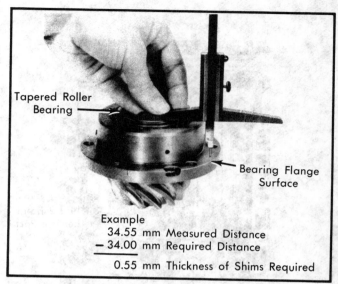

Example
34.55 mm Measured Distance
− 34.00 mm Required Distance

0.55 mm Thickness of Shims Required

Fig. 16   Measuring Pinion Bearing End Play

4) Install pinion assembly on final drive case and tighten bolts to specifications. Install number 2 brake band guide and band in transmission case. Position number 1 brake band over gear unit, and temporarily hold in place with rear servo retaining ring. Make sure thrust bearings are still positioned in end of gear unit, then install gear unit into case, guiding supporting lever of oil distributing sleeve into groove of case.

NOTE — *Make sure gear unit is seated in output shaft.*

5) Make sure bearings are still in position on front of gear unit, then install input shaft into assembly. Insert number 3 brake band into case and over gear unit, install pressure pins into band ends, then screw in band adjusting screw until band is secured in place. Turn transmission until input shaft faces up.

6) Determine end play between gear unit and converter housing as follows: Measure the distance from upper edge of input shaft-to-upper edge of stator shaft with a depth gauge. This distance is "A". Pull up on input shaft and repeat measurement. This measurement is "B". End play is the difference between "A, and "B". Install compensating washers onto input shaft thrust surface to bring end play within specifications.

7) Install pins from number 1 and 2 brake bands. Install number 2 brake band piston into transmission case with special tool 9305. Install new "O" ring on number 2 brake band cover, and place in case and secure with snap ring. Install piston and cover for number 1 brake band into transmission case with special tool 9304 and secure with snap ring. Check free play of number 1 and 2 brake band as follows: Apply air pressure into number 1 brake band release port in case (see illustration) and mark position of band on drum. Next, introduce air pressure to number 1 brake apply port and again mark position of band position on drum. Measure distance between 2 marks; measurement is number 1 band free play.

8) For number 2 band adjustment, first measure position of band end on drum in released position (spring pressure holds band in released position). Next, apply air pressure to number 2 apply port in case and again mark position of band end on drum. Distance between 2 marks is band free play. Free play for number 1 and 2 bands is .118-.157" (3-4 mm).

Automatic Transaxles

PORSCHE 928 (Cont.)

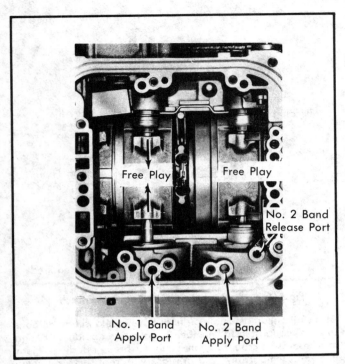

Fig. 17 Bottom View of Case Showing
Measurement of Band Free Play

9) For number 3 band adjustment, tighten band adjusting screw to 4 ft. lbs. (.5 mkg), then check gap, unscrew adjusting screw 1 ¾ turns, recheck gap, difference between both measurements is free play, which should be .118″ (3 mm). Tighten locknut to specification.

10) Install both oil feed pipes into oil distributing sleeve and place new valve body seals on pipes. Screw 2 centering pins into transmission case. Install centering pin (suitable punch) for throttle pressure valve into valve body (see illustration). Guide valve body in place, making sure manual valve engages correctly in plate. Install valve body-to-case bolts and tighten to specifications. Install valve body, oil filter and oil pan.

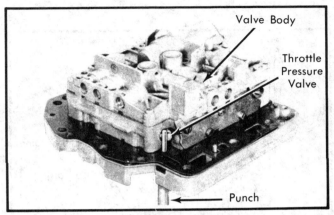

Fig. 18 Using Punch to Hold
Throttle Pressure Valve

FINAL DRIVE

DISASSEMBLY

1) Place final drive housing in suitable holding fixture. Remove axle flange bolts and remove axle flanges. Mark side covers for reassembly reference, remove side cover bolts and side covers.

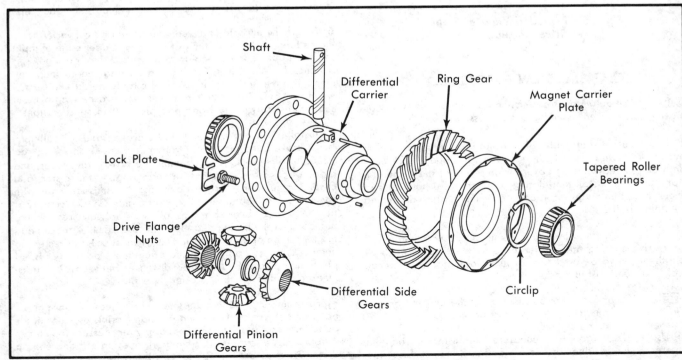

Fig. 19 Exploded View of Differential Assembly

PORSCHE 928 (Cont.)

NOTE — *Record number and thickness of shims for reassembly reference on each side.*

2) Remove oil seals from side covers with suitable tool. Remove rear cover and pull differential assembly from case. Place differential assembly in vise fitted with jaw protectors. Remove ring gear bolts and drive ring gear from housing. Remove bearings (if required) using suitable puller.

3) Drive differential shaft lock pin out, then remove differential shaft with a plastic mallet.

REASSEMBLY & ADJUSTMENTS

Differential Assembly — 1) Heat ring gear to about 212°F (100°C) and place on case using centering pins to align bolt holes. Install new bolts and tighten crosswise to specifications. Bend lock plate ends over side of bolt heads.

2) Coat large gears with grease and install in differential carrier. Install small gears and align with bore, then insert shaft, position correctly and install locking pin. Drive tapered roller bearings on carrier with suitable tool.

Pinion Gear Adjustment — 1) When adjusting pinion and ring gear, the following sequence should be used:

- Determine the total shim thickness ("S1" + "S2") for the specified preload of the tapered roller bearing/differential.
- Determine shim thickness ("S3").
- Divide total shim thickness in "S1" and "S2" to provide correct backlash between the pinion and ring gear.

2) The adjustment distance "E" is calculated from known design distance "R" = 2.86" (72.20 mm) + deviation "r" which is located on face of pinion.

3) With pinion bearing adjusted and pinion nut tightened to proper specifications, install final drive housing (without shims) to transmission and tighten all nuts to specifications. Install 1 side cover (without "O" ring) and secure with 2 bolts.

4) Set adjusting ring of master gauge (VW 385/1) at 1.61" (41 mm) See *Fig. 21*. Install centering discs (VW 385/4) on master gauge and attach plunger (VW 385/14) with dial indicator extension See *Fig. 22*.

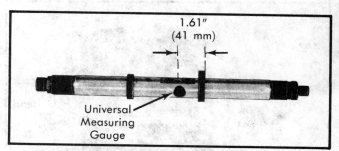

Fig. 21 Universal Master Measuring Gauge

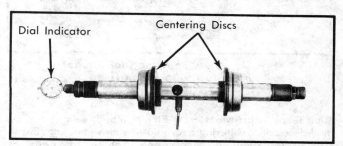

Fig. 22 Universal Master Measuring Gauge with Dial Indicator and Centering Discs Attached

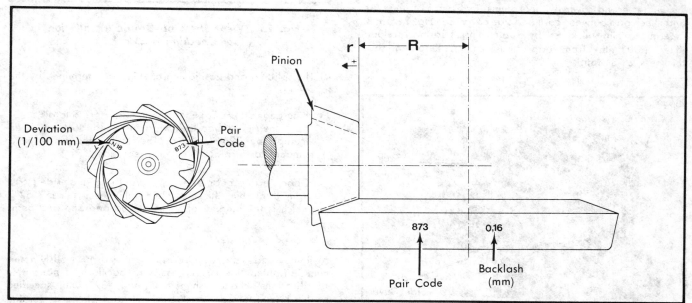

Fig. 20 Manufacture's Codes Stamped in Pinion and Ring Gears

PORSCHE 928 (Cont.)

5) Install measuring gauge in case, install second side cover (without "O" ring) and secure with 2 bolts. Set dial indicator to distance "E" + .20" (5 mm). Install measuring bar (VW385/1) and set at "O" with .004" (1 mm) preload.

6) Turn measuring bar until dial gauge extension is vertical to face of pinion head See Fig. 23. At this moment, dial gauge needle will reach its point of reversal (highest point) and dial gauge should be read. Install determined shim thickness ("S3") between the transmission case and final drive housing. Recheck distance after installation of shims. A deviation of ±.0012" (.03 mm) is permissible.

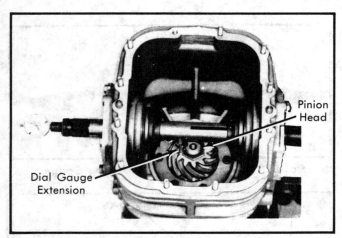

Fig. 23   View Showing Dial Gauge in Contact with Pinion Head

Ring Gear Adjustment — 1) Clamp final drive in a vise. Install differential with ring gear into final drive housing. Install side cover (without shims) and tighten all bolts to specifications.

2) Guide second cover (without shims) into place on the case and check gap between case and side cover. See Fig. 24. Then, determine shim thickness by subtracting bearing preload .012" (.30 mm) from gap measurement. Resulting shim thickness is "S" total.

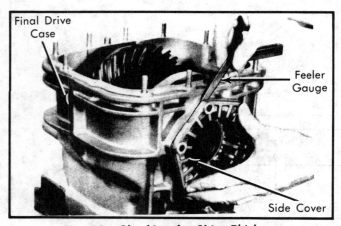

Fig. 24   Checking for Shim Thickness Between Final Drive Case and Side Cover

Ring Gear Backlash Adjustment — 1) Place shims determined for pinion adjustment between transmission case and final drive case. Install final drive to transmission and tighten all mounting bolts to specifications. Install differential assembly into case, install side covers with shims on ring gear side and tighten all bolts to specifications.

2) Turn differential in both directions several times to settle bearings. Install dial indicator (VW388) and set to 3.1" (mm). See Fig. 25. Engage parking lock, turn ring gear by hand against stop and set dial indicator to zero.

3) Hold pinion with locally made tool and turn back ring gear and read amount of backlash. The measured backlash must be within specified tolerance:

- Getrag Pinion — .006-.008" (.15-.20 mm).

- Hurth Pinion — .008-.010" (.20-.25 mm).

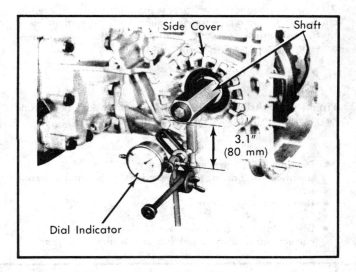

Fig. 25   View Showing Gauge Installation for Checking Backlash

4) The splitting and positioning of shims is determined by the following:

- Ring gear side — Take total shim thickness ("S total"), subtract measured backlash, add inscribed backlash, then multiply by .026" (.66 mm). The result is the proper shim amount to be placed on ring gear side ("S1").

- Opposite ring gear side — Subtract ring gear side ("S1) from total shim thickness ("S total") the result is ("S2") which is the amount of shims placed opposite ring gear side.

5) Remove side covers and position shims as previously determined. Tighten side covers. Measure backlash, if not within specifications, change shim "S1" and "S2" until specified backlash is obtained. Check backlash at 4 places by turning ring gear 90° each time. The 4 measurements must not deviate from each other by more than .002" (.05 mm).

PORSCHE 928 (Cont.)

TIGHTENING SPECIFICATIONS

Application	Ft. Lbs. (mkg)
Transmission	
Rear Converter Housing-to-Transmission	20-23 (2.7-3.2)
Front-to-Rear Converter Housing	14-17 (1.9-2.3)
Drive Plate-to-Torque Converter	23-28 (3.2-3.9)
Transmission Case-to-Final Drive	20-23 (3.2-3.9)
Oil Pan	5 (.7)
Oil Filter	3 (.4)
Valve Body-to-Transmission	9.5 (1.3)
Kickdown Solenoid-to-Case	14 (2.0)
Modulator-to-Case	5 (.7)
No. 3 Brake Lock Nut	18-22 (2.5-3)
Pinion Nut	146-175 (20-24)
Pinion Bearing Assembly-to-Transmission	20-23 (2.7-3.2)
Final Drive	
Final Drive-to-Transmission	28-33 (3.9-4.6)
Side Covers	14-17 (1.9-2.3)
Rear Cover	14-17 (1.9-2.3)
Ring Gear	110-131 (15-18)

SAAB — BORG-WARNER MODEL 35

900

TRANSAXLE IDENTIFICATION

The transaxle identification number is stamped on a plate attached to torque converter housing near throttle cable.

DESCRIPTION

The transaxle assembly is a three-speed unit mounted beneath the engine. Transaxle assembly consists basically of a three-element torque converter, planetary gear set, two multi-disc clutches, a one-way clutch, two servos and brake bands, an oil pump, a hydraulic control system and a differential-type final drive assembly. Power is transmitted from the turbine shaft of torque converter to the input shaft of transmission via a chain.

LUBRICATION & ADJUSTMENT

See AUTOMATIC TRANSMISSION SERVICING Section.

TROUBLE SHOOTING

NO DRIVE IN ANY LEVER POSITION

Incorrect fluid level. Manual linkage incorrectly adjusted or assembled. Oil tubes missing or incorrectly installed. Sealing rings missing or broken. Valve body screws missing or improperly tightened. Primary regulator valve sticking. Input shaft broken. Pump drive tangs on converter hub broken. Defective oil pump. Defective converter or one-way clutch. Stator support broken.

NO DRIVE IN FORWARD RANGES

Manual linkage incorrectly adjusted or assembled. Sealing rings missing or broken. Valve body screw missing or improperly tightened. Defective front clutch. One-way clutch slipping or incorrectly installed.

NO DRIVE IN REVERSE RANGE

Manual linkage incorrectly adjusted or assembled. Incorrect rear band adjustment. Oil tubes missing or installed incorrectly. Sealing rings missing or broken. Valve body screws missing or improperly tightened. 1-2 shift valve or 2-3 shift valve sticking. Defective rear clutch or rear band.

HARSH ENGAGEMENT

Downshift valve cable incorrectly assembled or adjusted. Incorrect engine idle speed. Valve body screws missing or improperly tightened. Primary regulator valve sticking. Throttle valve sticking. Defective front clutch. Defective rear clutch.

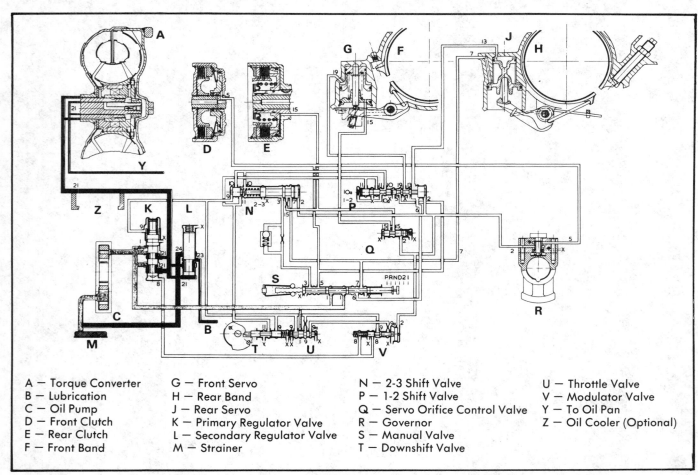

A — Torque Converter	G — Front Servo	N — 2-3 Shift Valve	U — Throttle Valve
B — Lubrication	H — Rear Band	P — 1-2 Shift Valve	V — Modulator Valve
C — Oil Pump	J — Rear Servo	Q — Servo Orifice Control Valve	Y — To Oil Pan
D — Front Clutch	K — Primary Regulator Valve	R — Governor	Z — Oil Cooler (Optional)
E — Rear Clutch	L — Secondary Regulator Valve	S — Manual Valve	
F — Front Band	M — Strainer	T — Downshift Valve	

Fig. 1 Saab (Borg-Warner Model 35) Hydraulic Circuits Diagram

SAAB — BORG-WARNER MODEL 35 (Cont.)

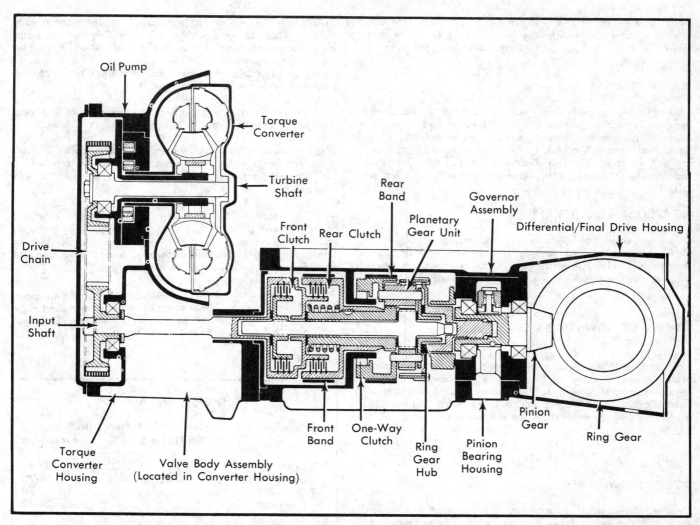

Fig. 2   Cutaway View of Saab (Borg-Warner Model 35) Automatic Transaxle Assembly

DELAYED ENGAGEMENT

Incorrect fluid level. Manual linkage incorrectly adjusted or assembled. Incorrect engine idle speed. Oil tubes missing or incorrectly installed. Sealing rings missing or broken. Valve body screws missing or improperly tightened. Primary regulator valve sticking. Converter out check valve missing or sticking. Defective front clutch. Defective rear clutch. Rear band slipping due to defective servo, worn or broken band. Worn oil pump.

NO 1-2 OR 2-3 UPSHIFT

Manual linkage incorrectly adjusted or assembled. Incorrect front band adjustment (1-2 upshift only). Oil tubes missing or incorrectly installed. Sealing rings missing or broken. Valve body screws missing or improperly tightened. Throttle or modulator valves sticking. Governor valve sticking, leaking or incorrectly installed. 1-2 shift valve sticking (1-2 upshift only). 2-3 shift valve sticking. 2-3 shift valve plunger sticking. Defective rear clutch (2-3 upshift only). Front band slipping due to defective servo, worn or broken band (1-2 upshift only).

SHIFT POINTS INCORRECT

Upshifts — Downshift valve cable incorrectly assembled or adjusted. Sealing rings missing or broken. Valve body screws missing or improperly tightened. Primary regulator valve sticking. Throttle or modulator valves sticking. Governor valve sticking, leaking or incorrectly installed. 1-2 or 2-3 shift valve sticking. 2-3 shift valve plunger sticking.

Downshifts — Downshift valve cable incorrectly assembled or adjusted. Sealing rings broken or missing. Valve body screws missing or improperly tightened. Throttle valve sticking. Governor valve sticking, leaking or installed incorrectly. 1-2 or 2-3 shift valves sticking. 2-3 shift valve plunger sticking.

SLIPPING ON UPSHIFTS

Incorrect fluid level. Downshift valve cable incorrectly assembled or adjusted. Manual linkage incorrectly assembled or adjusted. Incorrect front band adjustment. Oil tubes missing or incorrectly installed. Sealing rings missing or broken. Valve

SAAB — BORG-WARNER MODEL 35 (Cont.)

body screws missing or improperly tightened. Primary regulator valve sticking. Throttle valve sticking. Defective rear clutch. Front band slipping due to defective servo, or worn or broken band.

ROUGH UPSHIFTS

Downshift valve cable incorrectly assembled or adjusted. Incorrect front band adjustment. Valve body screws missing or improperly tightened. Primary regulator valve sticking. Throttle or modulator valves sticking. Governor valve sticking, leaking or incorrectly installed. Defective front clutch. Defective rear clutch. One-way clutch slipping, incorrectly installed or seized.

NO 2-1 OR 3-2 DOWNSHIFT

Downshift valve cable incorrectly assembled or adjusted. Governor valve sticking, leaking or incorrectly installed. 1-2 shift valve sticking. Defective rear clutch. Front or rear band slipping due to defective servo, or worn or broken band.

SLIPPING ON DOWNSHIFTS

Incorrect front band adjustment. Oil tubes missing or incorrectly installed. Sealing rings missing or broken. Valve body screws missing or improperly tightened. Primary regulator valve sticking. Throttle valve sticking. Orifice control valve sticking. Defective rear clutch. Front clutch slipping due to defective servo, or worn or broken band. One-way clutch slipping.

ROUGH DOWNSHIFTS

Incorrect front band adjustment. Sealing rings missing or broken. Valve body screws missing or improperly tightened. Primary regulator valve sticking. Throttle valve sticking. Orifice control valve sticking. Defective front clutch. Defective rear clutch. Front band slipping due to defective servo, or worn or broken band. One-way clutch slipping or incorrectly installed.

TRANSMISSION OVERHEATING

Incorrect fluid level. Incorrect front or rear band adjustment. Defective converter or one-way clutch. Broken stator support.

TESTING

ROAD TEST

1) Before road test, ensure that fluid level and condition, and control linkage adjustments have been checked and corrected as necessary. During test, transmission should upshift and downshift at approximately same speed as shown in Shift Speeds Chart. All shifts may vary slightly due to production tolerances or tire size. The important factor is the quality of the shifts. All shifts should be smooth, responsive, and with no slippage or engine speed runaway.

2) Slippage or engine speed runaway in any gear usually indicates clutch or band problems. The slipping clutch or band in a particular gear can usually be identified by noting transmission operation in other selector positions and comparing internal units which are applied in these positions. See *Clutch and Band Application Chart.*

3) With vehicle at a standstill, accelerate both at minimum and full throttle and ensure a 1-2 and 2-3 shift occurs.

NOTE — *At minimum throttle opening, shifts may be difficult to detect. Confirmation that transmission is in third gear may be obtained by shifting to "2" when a 3-2 downshift should occur.*

4) With vehicle at 25 MPH in third gear, depress accelerator to full throttle position (not through detent). Vehicle should accelerate without a downshift. With vehicle at 30 MPH in third gear, depress accelerator through detent. Vehicle should downshift to second gear before accelerating.

5) With vehicle at 40 MPH, release accelerator and move selector lever to "2". Vehicle should downshift to second gear and engine braking should be noticed. Finally, check reverse operation by accelerating at full throttle and check for slipping.

Shift Speeds Chart

Application	Shift Points (MPH)	
	Full Throttle	Kickdown
1-2 Upshift	23-37	37-48
2-3 Upshift	48-60	67-78
3-2 Downshift		57-70
2-1 Downshift		29-42

STALL TEST

Testing Precautions — When making test, do not hold throttle open any longer than ten seconds. If engine speed exceeds limits shown in Stall Speeds table, release accelerator immediately as clutch or band slippage is indicated.

Testing Procedure — With engine at normal operating temperature, tachometer installed and parking and service brakes applied, make transmission stall test in "D", "1" and "R" ranges at full throttle and note maximum RPM obtained. Engine speed should be within limits shown in Stall Speeds table.

Stall Speed Specifications

Application	Stall RPM
All Models	1900-2300

SAAB — BORG-WARNER MODEL 35 (Cont.)

Stall Test Results — If stall speed is approximately 300 RPM below specifications, engine performance may be unsatisfactory. If stall speed is approximately 800 RPM below specifications, Stator one-way clutch in torque converter is defective and complete converter must be replaced. If stall speed is above specifications in "D" range, either front clutch or one-way clutch is defective; if above specifications in "1", either front clutch or rear band is defective; if above specifications in "R" range, either rear clutch or rear band is defective.

TRANSAXLE REMOVAL & INSTALLATION

NOTE — *Engine and transaxle must be removed as an assembly.*

Removal — 1) Disconnect negative battery terminal from battery. Remove engine compartment hood and disconnect the following: Starter cable, and all other electrical connections necessary for engine removal. Drain radiator and disconnect hoses from engine. Disconnect hydraulic line to slave cylinder. Remove air cleaner, preheater hose and crankcase ventilation hose.

2) Disconnect fuel line and plug. Disconnect choke, throttle cable, hose to expansion tank and brake servo vacuum hose. Remove clamps from drivers side inner universal joint. Place special tool 83 93 209 between the upper control arm underside and frame (insert tool from engine compartment side) then, raise vehicle and place it on jack stands.

3) Remove lower control arm-to-ball joint bolts. Pull control arm assembly from control arm and support with jack stand. Remove gear selector cable screw at transmission. Pull cable out of transmission and slide back spring loaded sleeve, then disconnect from control lever. Disconnect speedometer cable from transmission. Remove rear engine mounting bolts.

4) Loosen front engine mounting nut so mounting can be lifted from bracket. Attach engine lifting device on 2 engine lifting lugs and raise engine slightly. Move engine assembly side to

side and free universal joints, then lift engine assembly from vehicle and place on engine stand.

Installation — To install, reverse removal procedure and note the following: Pack inner universal joints with grease, adjust shift cable if necessary and check cooling system for leaks.

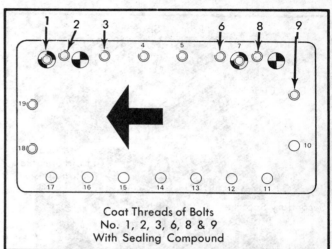

Coat Threads of Bolts
No. 1, 2, 3, 6, 8 & 9
With Sealing Compound

Fig. 3 *Engine-to-Transaxle Mating Surface Bolt Pattern*

TORQUE CONVERTER

NOTE — *Torque converter is a sealed unit and cannot be disassembled for service; therefore it must be replaced as a unit if found defective. Ventilation holes in torque converter housing must be kept free from dirt.*

TRANSAXLE DISASSEMBLY

1) Remove drain plugs and drain fluid from transaxle assembly, then invert transaxle and remove front and rear oil pans. Remove torque converter housing front cover. Hold drive

CLUTCH AND BAND APPLICATION CHART
(ELEMENTS IN USE)

Selector Lever Position	Rear Band	Front Band	Front Clutch	One-Way Clutch	Rear Clutch
D — DRIVE First Gear Second Gear Third Gear		X	X X X	X	X
2 — INTERMEDIATE First Gear Second Gear		X	X X	X	
1 — LOW (First)	X		X		
R — REVERSE	X				X
NEUTRAL OR PARK — All clutches and bands released and/or ineffective.					

SAAB — BORG-WARNER MODEL 35 (Cont.)

chain sprockets stationary and remove sprocket attaching bolts, then remove drive chain along with sprockets. Remove cover from right side of transaxle and disconnect throttle valve control cable. Remove oil tubes from valve body assembly. Remove attaching screws, then lift valve body assembly straight up and remove the two large oil pipes from oil pump.

Fig. 4   Removing Drive Chain and Sprockets

2) Turn transaxle right side up. Loosen attaching bolts and remove oil pump, then lift out torque converter. If necessary, disconnect throttle cable from transaxle housing. Remove torque converter housing-to-transaxle housing attaching bolts. **NOTE** — *There are ten attaching bolts, five inside and five outside.* Pull gear selector rod as far forward as possible, then remove the three remaining oil pipes and at the same time remove torque converter housing and gasket.

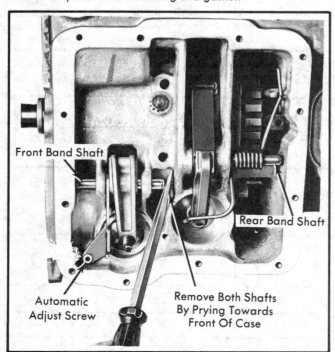

Fig. 5   Bottom View of Transaxle Case Showing Band Lever Shafts Removal

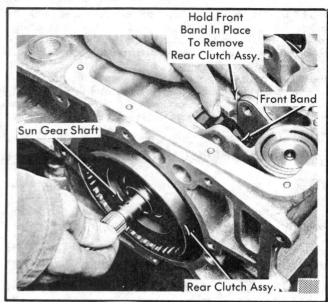

Fig. 6   Pulling Rear Clutch Assembly from Case

3) Loosen front band automatic adjusting screw, then push out front band lever shaft. Unhook rear band spring, then push out rear band lever shaft, removing spring at the same time. Remove the three bolts securing center support to transaxle housing, then pull out front clutch assembly noting position of thrust washer. Hold front band in place and remove rear clutch assembly, then remove front band. Compress rear band to hold planetary gear assembly in place, then remove center support. Remove planetary gear assembly noting position of thrust bearing and washer, then remove rear band.

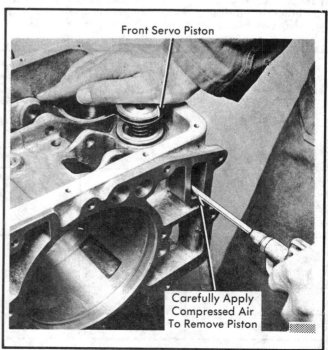

Fig. 7   Using Compressed Air to Remove Front Servo Piston

SAAB — BORG-WARNER MODEL 35 (Cont.)

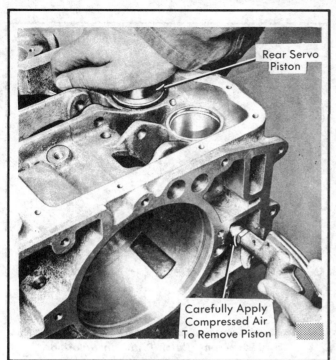

Fig. 8   *Using Compressed Air to Remove Rear Servo Piston*

4) Remove snap ring and then using compressed air, remove front servo piston. Remove rear servo by forcing compressed air to servo apply passage. Pry out parking pawl shaft and remove parking pawl and spring.

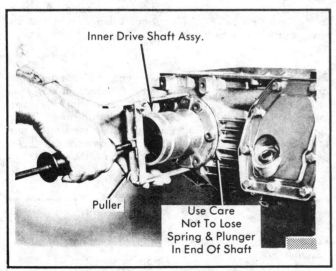

Fig. 9   *Removing Inner Drive Shaft Assembly*

5) From both sides of transaxle, remove inner drive shaft assembly housing retaining bolts. Using a suitable puller and slide hammer, separate housings from transaxle.

NOTE — *Use care not to lose adjusting shims and spring and plunger from end of drive shafts when removing differential assembly from case.*

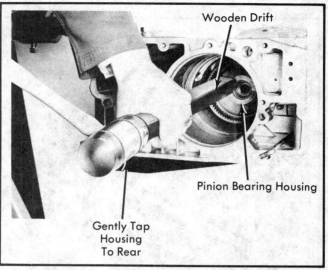

Fig. 10   *Driving Pinion Housing from Transaxle Case*

6) Remove bolts securing pinion bearing housing to transaxle case then using a wooden drift, drive pinion housing from case. Place pinion bearing housing in a press and separate ring gear hub from pinion bearing housing.

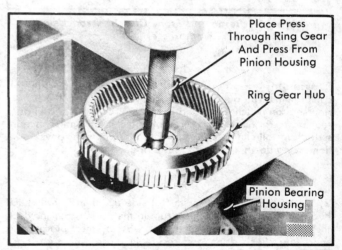

Fig. 11   *Pressing Ring Gear Hub from Pinion Housing*

COMPONENT DISASSEMBLY & REASSEMBLY

FRONT CLUTCH ASSEMBLY

Disassembly — 1) Slide clutch sealing plate from input shaft. Remove snap ring and lift input shaft and thrust washer from clutch drum. Lift out clutch hub and clutch plates from drum.

NOTE — *Take notice of the number of clutch plates used and the order in which they are installed for reassembly reference.*

2) Remove pressure plate from clutch drum. Remove piston return spring snap ring and remove spring from clutch drum. Remove clutch piston from drum with the aid of compressed air. Inspect all seals and clutch plates for wear or damage and replace if necessary. Check movement of spring loaded valve in rear of clutch piston; valve movement should be .020-.039" (.5-1.0 mm).

SAAB — BORG-WARNER MODEL 35 (Cont.)

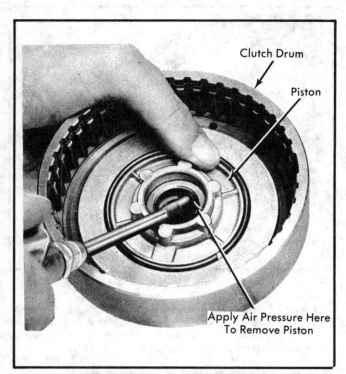

Clutch Drum

Piston

Apply Air Pressure Here
To Remove Piston

*Fig. 12   Removing Front Clutch Piston Using
Compressed Air*

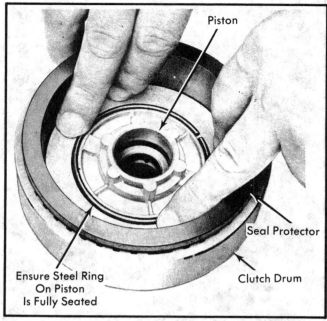

Piston

Ensure Steel Ring
On Piston
Is Fully Seated

Seal Protector

Clutch Drum

Fig. 14   Front Clutch Piston Installation

Reassembly — 1) Prior to reassembly, lubricate all components with automatic transmission fluid. Install new "O" ring seal on clutch drum and in piston groove. Using suitable seal protector, install piston into clutch drum until it is fully seated. Install clutch return spring into drum with convex portion facing down, then install snap ring.

2) Install pressure plate with flat side up, then install clutch hub. Place clutch plates into drum in the same order in which they were removed. Install thrust washer, then place input shaft into clutch drum and secure in place with snap ring. **NOTE** — *Ensure seal rings on input shaft rotate freely in their grooves.*

REAR CLUTCH ASSEMBLY

Disassembly — Pull forward sun gear shaft from rear clutch assembly noting thrust bearings on each side of sun gear. Remove clutch drum snap ring, then remove clutch plates and pressure plate. **NOTE** — *Take notice of number of clutch plates used and the order in which they are installed for reassembly reference.* Install a suitable clutch spring compressor tool and remove clutch return spring snap ring, spring seat and return (coil) spring. Using compressed air, remove piston from clutch drum.

Reassembly — Install all new "O" rings on piston and clutch drum. Lubricate seals with automatic transmission fluid, then using a suitable seal protector, install piston (flat side down) into clutch drum until it is fully seated. Install return spring, spring seat and snap ring using suitable compressor tool. Install clutch plates in reverse order of disassembly. **NOTE** — *Outer clutch plates are cambered, and the cambers must face*

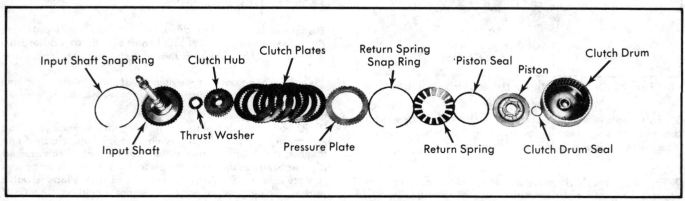

Input Shaft Snap Ring   Clutch Hub   Clutch Plates   Return Spring
Snap Ring   Piston Seal   Piston   Clutch Drum

Input Shaft   Thrust Washer   Pressure Plate   Return Spring   Clutch Drum Seal

Fig. 13   Exploded View of Front Clutch Assembly and Input Shaft

SAAB — BORG-WARNER MODEL 35 (Cont.)

the same way. Install pressure plate and snap ring. **NOTE** — Forward sun gear shaft is installed in rear clutch at Transaxle Reassembly.

NOTE — There are 2 versions of the sun gear wheel, planet gear carrier and planet gear. The sun wheel of one version cannot be used with the planet carrier and planet gear of the other version. Identification grooves are used on the later version to enable the 2 designs to be distinguished. The rear sun wheel has a groove cut into the tops of the cogs while the planet gear carrier has a groove around its perimeter.

Fig. 15   Removing Rear Clutch Return Spring Snap Ring

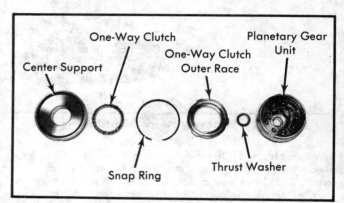

Fig. 18   Exploded View of Planetary Gear Unit and Center Support

Reassembly — Install one-way clutch outer race and secure in place with snap ring. Install one-way clutch, with flange on inner roller retainer facing outwards, into outer race. Install center support. After reassembly, one-way clutch should rotate in a clockwise direction only.

PINION BEARING HOUSING

Disassembly — Remove pinion bearing housing seal cover, then fit housing to suitable holding fixture (8790636 and retaining ring 8790651). Remove pinion bearing housing "O" ring, then place housing in a vise with jaws of vise pressed against holding fixture. Remove pinion nut, front pinion bearing and adjusting shim(s), then withdraw pinion shaft and governor assembly from housing. **NOTE** — Use care not to lose drive ball when removing pinion shaft and governor assembly. Press rear pinion bearing from shaft. Remove both pinion shaft seals from housing. If new pinion bearings are to be installed, gently tap bearing outer races from housing.

NOTE — Before reassembling pinion bearing housing, governor assembly should be disassembled and inspected for wear or damage. See Governor Assembly Disassembly and Reassembly.

Fig. 16   Using Compressed Air to Remove Rear Clutch Piston

PLANETARY GEAR ASSEMBLY

Disassembly — Remove center support from planetary gear assembly. Remove one-way clutch from outer race. Remove snap ring for one-way clutch outer race and remove race from planet carrier.

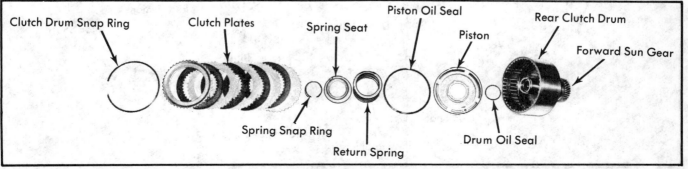

Fig. 17   Exploded View Showing Components of Rear Clutch Assembly

SAAB — BORG-WARNER MODEL 35 (Cont.)

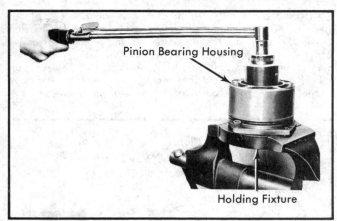

Fig. 19 Removing Pinion Shaft Lock Nut

Reassembly — 1) If removed, install new front and rear pinion bearing outer races into housing until they are fully seated. Install two new pinion shaft seals (back-to-back) into housing. Press rear pinion bearing onto shaft. Fit governor assembly in housing with cover plate facing forward. Hold pinion shaft horizonal with drive ball in socket on shaft, then install shaft into housing so that drive ball engages track in governor assembly.

2) Install adjusting shim(s) and front pinion bearing onto pinion shaft, then install pinion nut and tighten to specified torque. Using a spring pull gauge, check pinion bearing preload; preload should be 5.9-10.1 lbs. (2.7-4.6 kg) with new bearings or 3.3-5.3 lbs. (1.5-2.4 kg) with used bearings (any bearing with over 1200 miles). Adjustment of pinion bearing preload is made by varying thickness of adjusting shim(s) located between front pinion bearing and governor assembly. Install a new pinion bearing housing "O" ring, then install housing seal cover and retain with cover screws.

GOVERNOR ASSEMBLY

Disassembly — Remove screws attaching governor housing halves, then remove cover washer from housing. Remove circlip and weight from end of governor shaft. Separate governor housing and withdraw governor shaft along with governor valve and spring. Inspect all parts for wear or damage. Scratches on governor valve may be cleaned with fine emery cloth.

Reassembly — Before reassembly, lubricate all parts with automatic transmission fluid. To reassemble, reverse disassembly procedure. After reassembly, shake governor assembly and ensure governor valve moves freely.

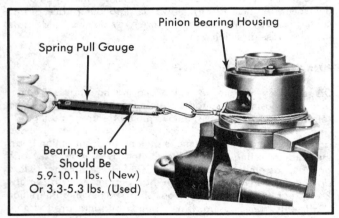

Fig. 20 Using Spring Pull Gauge to Check Pinion Bearing Preload

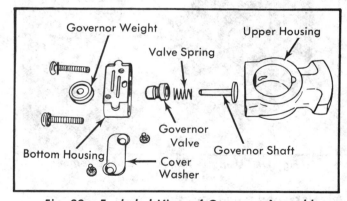

Fig. 22 Exploded View of Governor Assembly

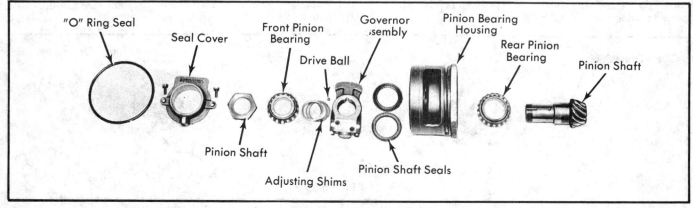

Fig. 21 Exploded View of Pinion Bearing Housing Assembly

SAAB — BORG-WARNER MODEL 35 (Cont.)

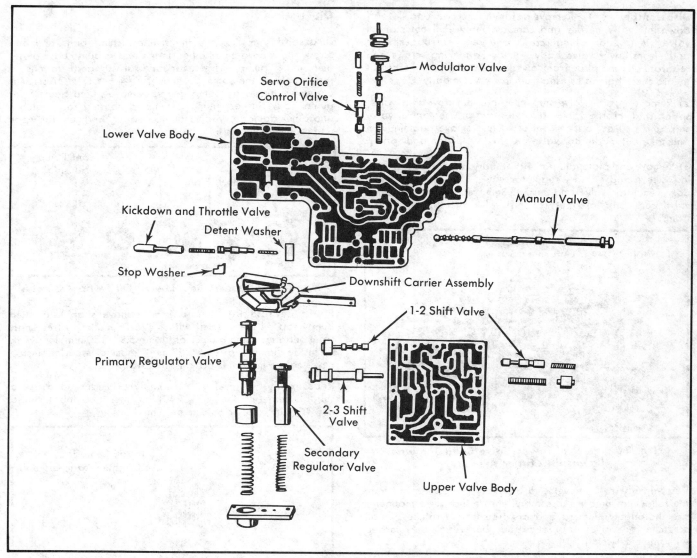

Fig. 23 Exploded View of Upper and Lower Valve Body Assembly

VALVE BODY ASSEMBLY

NOTE — As valve trains are removed from each valve body bore, place individual parts in correct order and in relative position to valve body to simplify reassembly.

CAUTION — Valves and springs are not interchangeable; all parts must be installed in correct order in proper valve body bore. See Illustration.

VALVE BODY SPRING IDENTIFICATION				
Valve Spring	Length In. (mm)	Diameter In. (mm)	Number Of Coils	Color
1-2 Shift Valve	1.094 (27.8)	.235 (5.97)	13.5	.....
2-3 Shift Valve	1.590 (40.4)	.352 (8.94)	22.5	.....
Primary Regulator Valve	2.850 (72.4)	.600 (15.24)	14.25	.....
Secondary Regulator Valve	2.593 (65.9)	.485 (12.32)	21.5	.....
Orifice Control Valve	1.005 (25.53)	.203 (5.16)	17	.....
Modulator Valve	1.069 (27.15)	.211 (5.36)	19	.....
Throttle Valve (Inner)	.807 (20.5)	.141 (3.58)	28	.....
Throttle Valve (Outer)	1.185 (30.1)	.236 (5.97)	18	.....

SAAB – BORG-WARNER MODEL 35 (Cont.)

Disassembly – 1) Remove retaining screws and lift off downshift valve carrier and cam assembly. Pull out manual valve. Remove attaching screws and separate upper valve body from lower valve body. Remove attaching screws and separate oil tube plate from lower valve body, taking care not to lose check ball and spring from lower valve body.

2) Remove throttle valve stop, then pull out downshift valve, spring and throttle valve. Remove servo orifice control valve stop and pull out orifice control valve. Remove retaining pin and take out modulator valve plug, valve, piston and spring.

3) Remove end plate and pull out primary regulator valve spring, sleeve and primary regulator valve, then remove secondary regulator valve and spring. Remove cover from upper valve body and take out 1-2 shift valve and 2-3 shift valve trains.

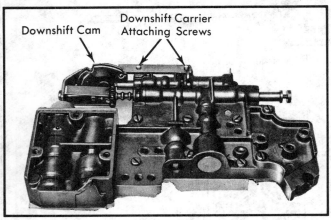

Fig. 24　View of Lower Valve Body Showing Downshift Carrier Assembly

Reassembly – 1) Reverse disassembly procedure and note the following: Before reassembly, ensure that all components are thoroughly cleaned and are free from scratches. Small scratches on valves and valve body bores may be removed with fine emery cloth.

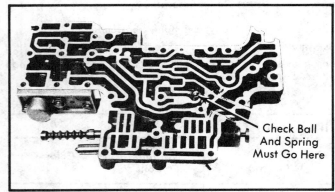

Fig. 25　View of Lower Valve Body Showing Location of Check Ball and Spring

2) Dip all valves and plugs in automatic transmission fluid before installing. Rotate valves and plugs when inserting into bores to avoid shearing off soft body castings. Ensure all valves move freely and smoothly in their bores. Ensure check ball and spring are in correct position in lower valve body before installing oil tube plate (see *Fig. 25*).

OIL PUMP

Disassembly – Remove the five attaching bolts and one screw and separate pump housings. Remove pump back plate, then mark pump drive gear and driven gear to ensure reassembly in the same position. **NOTE** – *DO NOT scratch alignment marks on pump gears.* Remove pump gears from pump body. Inspect pump gears and housing for scratches and other damage. Inspect pump bearing and seal for wear and replace if necessary.

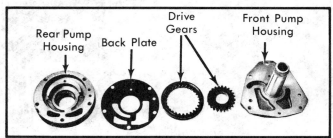

Fig. 26　Disassembled View of Oil Pump Assembly

Pump Bearing Replacement – Remove snap ring, then gently tap oil pump shaft with a plastic mallet to free shaft from bearing. Using a piece of tubing 5.9" (150 mm) long with an inside diameter of 1.46" (37 mm), knock off bearing. Install new bearing in reverse order of removal.

Reassembly – Reverse disassembly procedure and use a suitable centering tool (8790248) to center oil pump. Install a new "O" ring seal on outside of pump housing.

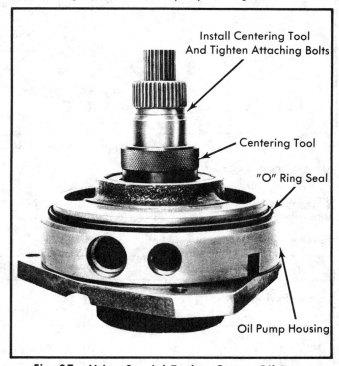

Fig. 27　Using Special Tool to Center Oil Pump

DIFFERENTIAL ASSEMBLY

Disassembly – If differential bearings require replacement, remove them from differential housing using a suitable puller.

SAAB — BORG-WARNER MODEL 35 (Cont.)

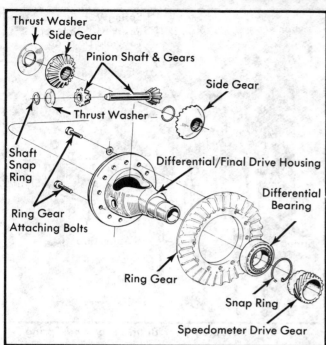

Fig. 28 **Exploded View of Differential Assembly**

NOTE — *Before left side bearing can be removed, speedometer drive gear must be pulled from housing.* Remove differential ring gear attaching bolts and separate ring gear from differential housing. Remove snap ring, then push out differential pinion gear shaft. Remove pinion gears and side gears along with thrust washers from housing.

NOTE — *If ring gear requires replacement, pinion shaft must also be replaced as they are a matched set.*

Reassembly — Install pinion gears and side gear along with thrust washers into differential housing, then install pinion shaft and lock in place with snap ring. Mount ring gear on differential housing, then install attaching bolts and tighten to specifications. **NOTE** — *Coat threads of attaching bolts with Loctite or equivalent before installation.* If removed, press new bearings onto differential housing, then install speedometer drive gear.

INNER DRIVE SHAFT ASSEMBLY

Disassembly — Remove drive shaft snap ring and press drive shaft from bearing housing. Using a screwdriver, remove oil seal from housing using care not to damage housing. On left side bearing housing, remove shaft and pull out speedometer drive assembly. On both sides, press out drive shaft bearing. If new differential bearings are to be installed, remove bearing outer race from housing using a drift.

NOTE — *A washer is located between right side race and bearing housing to improve bearing lubrication.*

Reassembly — Press new drive shaft bearing into bearing housing. If removed, press new differential bearing outer race into bearing housing. **NOTE** — *Ensure lubrication washer is installed before right side race.* Using a drift, press bearing housing oil seal into housing until it protrudes approximately .08" (2 mm) above face of housing. **NOTE** — *Drive shafts will be installed at Transaxle Reassembly.*

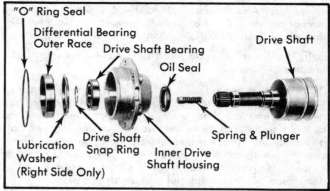

Fig. 29 **Exploded View of Inner Drive Shaft Assembly (Right Side Assembly Shown)**

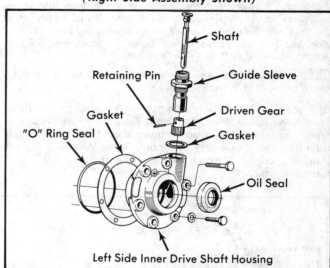

Fig. 30 **Exploded View of Speedometer Drive Assembly**

TRANSAXLE REASSEMBLY

NOTE — *Handle all parts carefully to avoid damaging bearing and mating surfaces. Lubricate all components with automatic transmission fluid. Gaskets and thrust washers may be held in place by using vaseline. Use all new gaskets and seals, and tighten all bolts evenly.* See Fig. 31 for thrust washer and bearing locations.

1) Lubricate pinion bearing housing seal rings, then loosen attaching screws of seal housing. Hold seal housing away from seal rings and press ring gear hub into pinion shaft bearing housing, then tighten seal housing attaching screws. Fit "O" ring on pinion housing. Screw locating studs into transaxle case, then install pinion housing into transaxle case. Install two attaching bolts, remove locating studs and install remaining attaching bolts and tighten all bolts to specifications.

2) Place parking pawl and spring in place, then install parking pawl shaft so that spring is locked in shaft groove. Invert transaxle case. Place shims, thrust bearing and thrust needle bearing on planetary gear unit. Coat small thrust bearing washer and sun gear rear thrust needle bearing with vaseline and attach them to inside of planetary gear unit. Install gear unit and center support into case.

NOTE — *The front and rear band are similar and may not be interchanged. The rear band may be identified by a smooth in-*

SAAB — BORG-WARNER MODEL 35 (Cont.)

ner surface. Also the designations 004N, 3004 or 1606 may appear on band. Front band has 3 grooves on the inner surface and has a 005K designation.

NOTE — *Flange on small thrust bearing washer must point towards gear unit.*

3) Install front band. Install a thrust needle bearing on each side of sun gear on sun gear shaft, then carefully insert sun gear shaft into rear clutch assembly, using care not to damage oil seal ring on shaft. Place steel washer (washer with two flats on inside) and bronze washer on rear clutch hub. Mount front clutch assembly to rear clutch assembly, then install complete clutch assembly into transaxle case, using care to avoid damage to oil seals. Install clutch assembly end plate.

4) Lubricate front and rear servo piston "O" rings with automatic transmission fluid, then install pistons into servo cylinders in transaxle case. Place long band apply strut against rear band, then place rear band apply lever in position and insert shaft from the side, at the same time holding spring in place so that shaft engages.

NOTE — *One end of spring must lie against apply lever to avoid scratching servo cylinder.*

5) Place short band apply strut against front band, then place front band apply lever in position. Place automatic adjusting screw assembly against band. Insert shaft from side through adjusting screw assembly and apply lever. Adjust spring on adjusting screw until gap between spring and lever is 1½ to 2 thread flights.

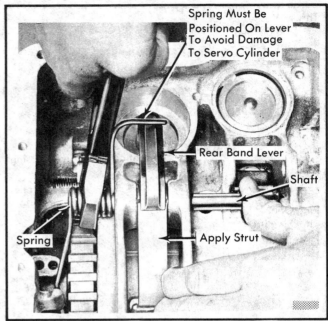

Fig. 32   Installing Rear Band Lever and Spring

6) Place gasket on torque converter housing. Install the following oil tubes into transaxle case: Governor return, main lubrication, and rear clutch. Mount converter housing to transaxle case and at the same time install contact washer onto in-

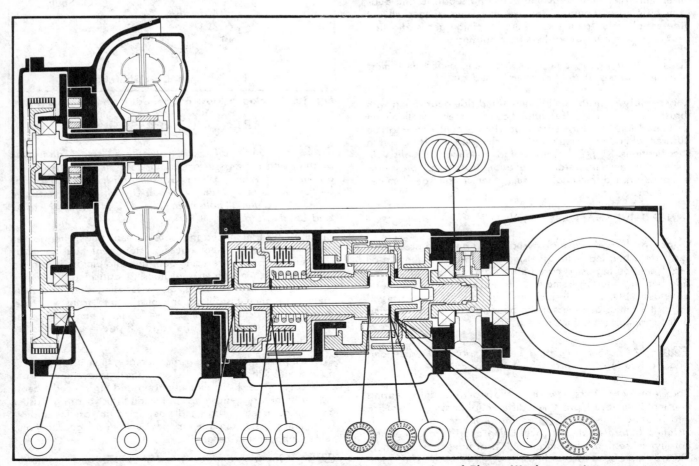

Fig. 31   Cutaway View of Transaxle Assembly Showing Location of Thrust Washers and Bearings

SAAB — BORG-WARNER MODEL 35 (Cont.)

put shaft, then install attaching bolts and tighten to specifications. Check transaxle gear unit end play as follows:

7) Mount a dial indicator on torque converter housing so that indicator tip is touching end of input shaft, then zero dial indicator. Pry forward on planetary gear unit and read gear unit end play; end play should be .01-.03" (.25-.75 mm). If end play is not within specifications, correct by adding or removing shims between ring gear and forward sun gear, or between the washer and bearing on input shaft.

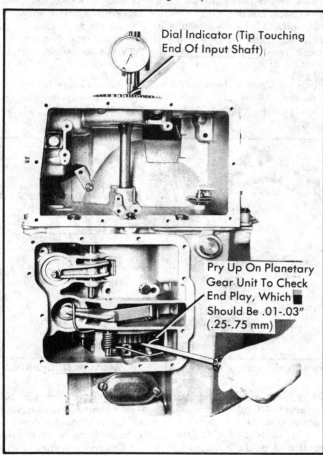

Fig. 33   Using a Dial Indicator to Measure Gear Unit End Play

8) Install torque converter and oil pump into converter housing using care not to damage oil seals, then install the two wide bore oil tubes into oil pump. Ensure that "O" ring to suction line is in place, then fit short tube between valve body assembly and torque converter housing. Install valve body assembly into converter housing and ensure oil tubes engage valve body. Ensure manual gear selector is connected. Connect throttle valve cable to converter housing, then connect throttle valve wire to valve body lever.

9) Install remaining oil tubes to valve body in the following order: Rear band (inner hole), rear band (outer hole), front band (apply), front band (release), front clutch/governor, front lubrication, main lubrication, rear clutch, and governor return. **NOTE** — *The last three oil tubes installed are connected to the three tubes previously installed into transaxle case (see Fig. 34). Install drive chain and sprockets.*

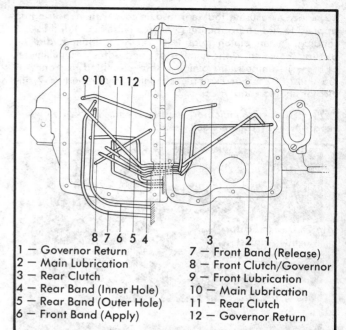

1 — Governor Return	7 — Front Band (Release)
2 — Main Lubrication	8 — Front Clutch/Governor
3 — Rear Clutch	9 — Front Lubrication
4 — Rear Band (Inner Hole)	10 — Main Lubrication
5 — Rear Band (Outer Hole)	11 — Rear Clutch
6 — Front Band (Apply)	12 — Governor Return

Fig. 34   Bottom View of Transaxle Showing Oil Tube Routing

10) Before installing differential/final drive assembly, pinion depth must be checked and adjusted as follows: **NOTE** — *Pinion bearing preload must be correctly adjusted as previously outlined before adjusting pinion depth. Also, adjustment specifications (in metric) for setting pinion depth are stamped into end face of pinion gear. See Fig. 35.*

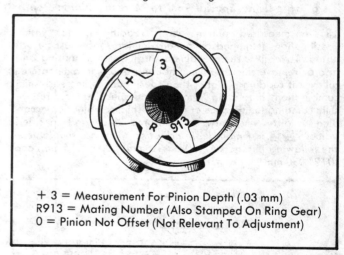

+ 3 = Measurement For Pinion Depth (.03 mm)
R913 = Mating Number (Also Stamped On Ring Gear)
0 = Pinion Not Offset (Not Relevant To Adjustment)

Fig. 35   View of Pinion Gear Showing Location of Adjustment Data

11) **NOTE** — *Pinion depth must be measured using Saab measuring instrument (8390155), which consists of a measuring jig with attached dial indicator and a gauge block for calibrating dial indicator. To calibrate indicator, place calibration stops of measuring tool against gauge block. Distance between stops and centerline of tools should be 2.362" (60 mm), which is equal to the distance from end face of pinion shaft to centerline of ring gear. Ensure that dial indicator pointer is zeroed when measuring tip touches gauge block.*

SAAB — BORG-WARNER MODEL 35 (Cont.)

12) Place measuring tool in transaxle case with measuring tip applied to flat end of pinion gear (see illustration) and take a reading. When pinion gear is correctly positioned, dial indicator should show the number of hundredths of a millimeter (+ or −) stamped into pinion with a permitted tolerance of .05 mm (.002"). For example, if pinion is stamped − 7, indicator should read − .07±.05 mm.

NOTE — *On dial indicator, positive reads clockwise, while negative reads counterclockwise.*

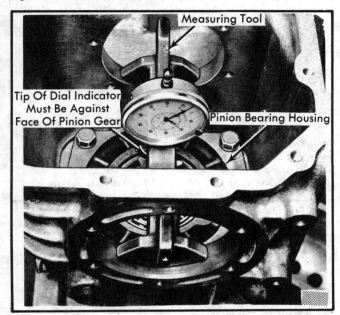

Fig. 36   Using Special Tool to Measure Pinion Depth

13) If measured pinion depth reading is not within specifications (stamped on pinion), pinion shaft must be adjusted. To adjust, remove pinion shaft bearing housing and add or remove shims between housing and transaxle case as follows: if reading is higher than specifications, increase shim combination, if reading is lower than specifications, reduce shim combination. Reduce or increase shim combination according to difference between measured value and specified value. **NOTE** — *Pinion depth adjusting shims are available in the following thicknesses: .004" (.10 mm), .006" (.15 mm) and .012" (.30 mm).*

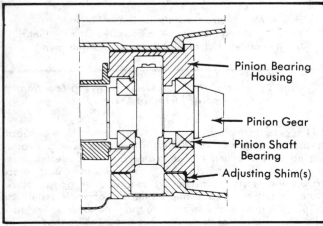

Fig. 37   Cutaway View of Pinion Bearing Housing Showing Location of Pinion Depth Shim

14) Before reinstalling pinion housing and pinion depth adjusting shims, differential bearing preload must be adjusted. Place differential/final drive assembly into transaxle case, then install left side inner drive shaft housing (side with speedometer drive) without shims and install attaching bolts and tighten to 14-18 ft. lbs. (2.0-2.5 mkg). Oil differential bearing and install right side drive shaft housing without shims and tighten attaching bolts, in two or three stages to 19 INCH lbs. (22 cmkg) while rotating differential assembly.

15) Using a feeler gauge, measure gap between right side drive shaft housing and transaxle case at two points opposite each other. Take the average of the two readings and select adjusting shims which will equal this value, then add an additional .008" (.20 mm) in shim thickness to obtain correct bearing preload.

NOTE — *Up to 4 shims may be used to obtain correct preload. Adjusting shims are available in the following thicknesses: .004" (.10 mm), .006" (.15 mm), .012" (.30 mm) and .020" (.50 mm).*

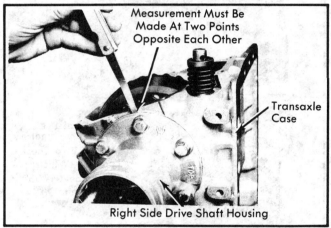

Fig. 38   Using Feeler Gauge to Measure Differential Bearing Preload

16) Remove right side drive shaft housing and lift out differential/final drive assembly. Install pinion shaft housing along with pinion depth adjusting shims, then tighten attaching bolts to specified torque. Recheck pinion depth adjustment and adjust if necessary. Reinstall differential/final drive assembly. Reinstall right side drive shaft housing along with previously selected bearing preload adjusting shims and tighten attaching bolts to 14-18 ft. lbs. (2.0-2.5 mkg). Next, ring gear backlash must be checked and adjusted as follows:

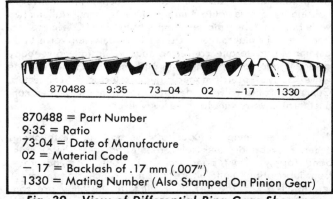

870488 = Part Number
9:35 = Ratio
73-04 = Date of Manufacture
02 = Material Code
− 17 = Backlash of .17 mm (.007")
1330 = Mating Number (Also Stamped On Pinion Gear)

Fig. 39   View of Differential Ring Gear Showing Ring Gear Adjustment Data

SAAB — BORG-WARNER MODEL 35 (Cont.)

NOTE — *Ring gear backlash adjustment specifications (in metric) are stamped into ring gear (see illustration). Also, backlash should be measured at 4 points around circumference of ring gear and must not deviate by more than .002" (.05 mm) from specified value.*

17) Mount dial indicator on transaxle case so that indicator tip is touching ring gear teeth and measure backlash. If backlash is not to specifications (stamped on ring gear), remove both drive shaft housings and move shims (as necessary) from right side housing to left side housing. Reinstall housings with shims and check backlash. If not to specifications, repeat adjustment procedure until correct backlash is obtained.

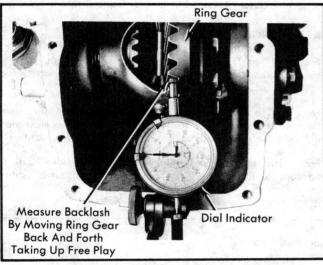

Fig. 40   Measuring Ring Gear Backlash

18) Remove both drive shaft housings, using care to keep adjusting shims with correct housing. Press drive shafts into housings and install drive shaft snap ring on each side. On left side housing, install speedometer drive assembly. Install new "O" ring in groove of each housing. Install spring and plunger in hole in end of drive shaft. Install drive shaft assemblies along with adjusting shims to transaxle case, then install attaching bolts and tighten them to specifications.

19) Install transaxle covers with new gaskets and transaxle cowlings, then install attaching bolts and tighten to specifications. Adjust rear band by loosening adjusting screw lock nut (located on outside of case on left side), then tighten adjusting screw to 10 ft. lbs. (1.4 mkg) and back screw off ¾ of a turn and tighten lock nut to specifications.

20) To adjust front band, place spacer tool 8790073 (¼" 6.35 mm rod) between adjusting screw and the boss on piston. Tighten adjusting screw to 10 INCH lbs. (1.4 mkg). Check that gap between self adjusting spring and lever is 1.5-2 thread flights.

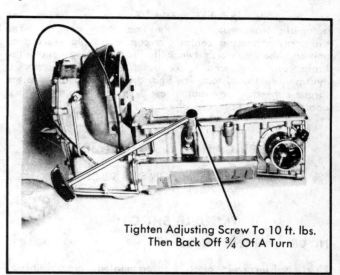

Fig. 41   Side View of Transaxle Case Showing Location of Rear Band Adjusting Screw

TIGHTENING SPECIFICATIONS

Application	Ft. Lbs. (mkg)
Converter-to-flywheel	25-30 (3.4-4.0)
Chain Cover-to-Converter Hsg.	10-15 (1.4-2.1)
Trans. Case-to-Converter Hsg.	10-15 (1.4-2.1)
Sprocket Wheel-to-Turbine Shaft	20-25 (2.7-3.4)
Sprocket Wheel-to-Input Shaft	25-30 (2.7-3.1)
Center Support Bolts	10-18 (1.4-2.5)
Selector Rod Cover	6-9 (.8-1.2)
Oil Pan Bolts	6-9 (.8-1.2)
Oil Pan Drain Plug	4-6 (.5-.8)
Pinion Shaft Nut	180-200 (25-27)
Pinion Hsg.-to-Trans. Case	20-25 (2.7-3.4)
Oil Pump Cover	17-22 (2.3-3.0)
Oil Pump-to-Converter Hsg.	13-18 (1.8-2.5)
Valve Body-to-Trans. Case	4.5-9 (1.1-1.4)
Rear Band Adjust Screw Lock Nut	30-40 (4-5.4)

SUBARU MODEL M41A

Subaru 1800

DESCRIPTION

The transaxle assembly consists of two main units; the automatic transmission and the final drive assembly. The transmission housing contains a compound planetary gear unit and one-way clutch, two multi-disc clutches, one multi-disc brake, one servo and brake band, an oil pump, and a hydraulic control system. The final drive housing contains the torque converter, governor assembly, ring and pinion gears, and the differential assembly.

LUBRICATION & ADJUSTMENT

See *AUTOMATIC TRANSMISSION SERVICING* Section.

TROUBLE SHOOTING

NO DRIVE IN ANY RANGE

Fluid level incorrect, or fluid contaminated. Manual linkage out of adjustment or improperly installed. Incorrect oil pressure. Faulty valve body. Leak in hydraulic circuit. Defective oil pump. Defective parking linkage.

NO DRIVE IN FORWARD RANGES

Transmission fluid contaminated. Incorrect oil pressure. Manual linkage out of adjustment or incorrectly installed. Faulty valve body. Defective forward or reverse clutch. Defective one-way clutch. Leak in hydraulic circuit. Poor engine performance. Faulty brakes.

NO DRIVE IN REVERSE

Transmission fluid contaminated. Incorrect oil pressure. Manual linkage out of adjustment or improperly installed. Faulty valve body. Leak in hydraulic circuit. Defective forward or reverse clutch. Reverse clutch check ball missing.

HARSH ENGAGEMENT

From "N" to "D" — Engine idle speed too high. Leak in vacuum circuit. Incorrect oil pressure. Faulty valve body. Defective forward clutch.

From 1st to 2nd Gear — Transmission fluid contaminated. Leak in vacuum circuit. Incorrect oil pressure. Incorrect stall RPM. Faulty valve body. Brake band out of adjustment.

From 2nd to 3rd Gear — Incorrect oil pressure. Leak in vacuum circuit. Faulty valve body. Brake band out of adjustment. Defective reverse clutch.

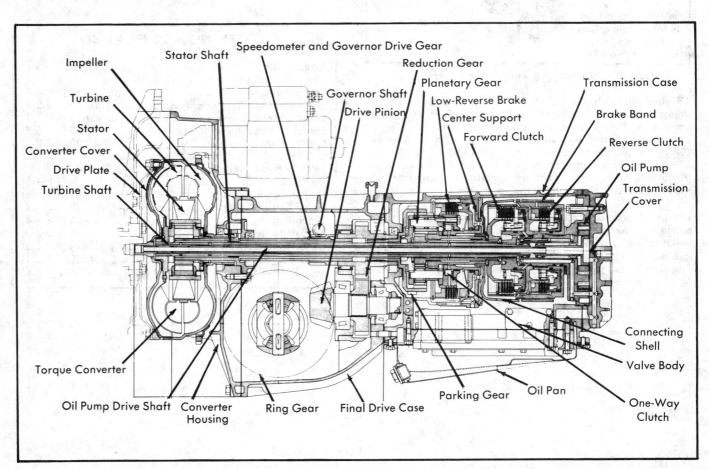

Fig. 1 *Cross-Sectional View of Subaru Model M41A Automatic Transaxle Assembly*

SUBARU MODEL M41A (Cont.)

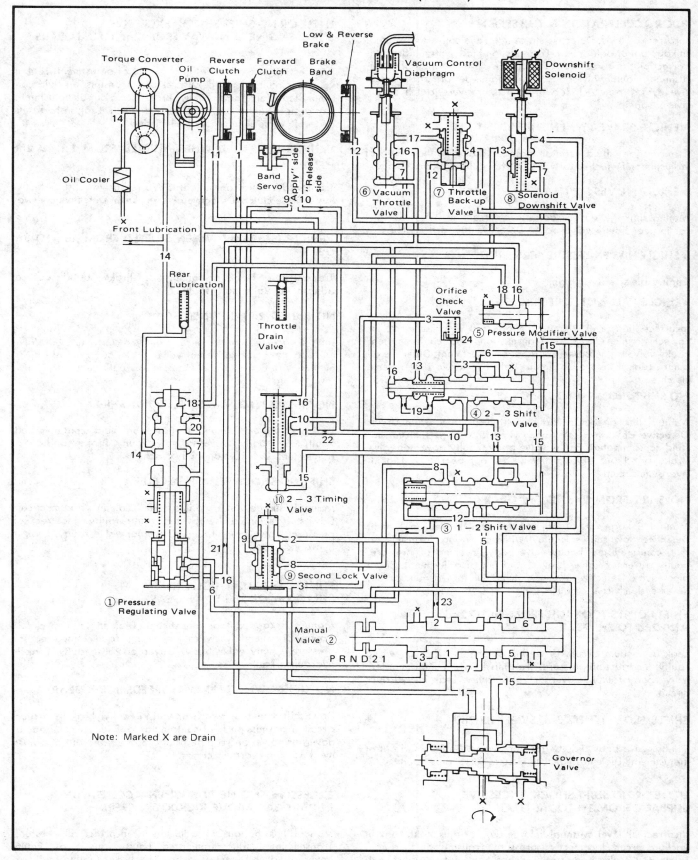

Note: Marked X are Drain

Fig. 2 Subaru Model M41A Automatic Transmission Hydraulic Circuits Diagram

SUBARU MODEL M41A (Cont.)

POOR ACCELERATION & TOP SPEED

Incorrect oil level. Defective stator in torque converter. Manual linkage out of adjustment. Transmission fluid contaminated. Incorrect oil pressure. Incorrect stall RPM. Brake band out of adjustment. Faulty valve body. Poor engine performance. Defective low-reverse clutch, forward clutch, or reverse clutch. Defective oil pump.

VEHICLE BRAKED WHEN SHIFTED INTO "R"

Transmission fluid contaminated. Brake band out of adjustment. Defective forward clutch. Faulty parking linkage.

VEHICLE MOVES IN "N"

Manual linkage out of adjustment. Transmission fluid contaminated. Faulty valve body. Defective forward clutch.

VEHICLE HAS EXCESSIVE "CREEPING"

Engine idle speed too high.

VEHICLE WILL NOT "CREEP"

Incorrect fluid level. Manual linkage out of adjustment. Incorrect engine idle RPM. Transmission fluid contaminated. Faulty valve body. Brake band out of adjustment. Defective oil pump. Leak in hydraulic circuit. Defective forward or reverse clutch.

NO SHIFT FROM 1st TO 2nd GEAR

Manual linkage out of adjustment. Leak in vacuum circuit. Defective downshift solenoid, switch or wiring. Transmission fluid contaminated. Faulty valve body. Faulty governor valve. Brake band out of adjustment. Servo pipe faulty. Leak in hydraulic circuit.

NO SHIFT FROM 2nd TO 3rd GEAR

Manual linkage out of adjustment. Leak in vacuum circuit. Defective downshift solenoid, switch or wiring. Transmission fluid contaminated. Faulty valve body. Incorrect oil pressure. Faulty governor valve. Brake band out of adjustment. Servo pipe faulty. Defective reverse clutch. Leak in hydraulic circuit. Reverse clutch check ball missing.

SHIFT POINTS TOO HIGH FROM 1st TO 2nd AND 2nd TO 3rd GEARS

Leak in vacuum circuit. Downshift solenoid, switch or wiring faulty. Incorrect oil pressure. Transmission fluid contaminated. Valve body faulty. Governor valve faulty. Leak in hydraulic circuit.

SHIFTS FROM 1st TO 3rd, SKIPPING 2nd

Faulty valve body. Faulty governor valve. Brake band out of adjustment. Leak in hydraulic circuit. Servo pipe faulty.

LITTLE OR NO SHIFT SHOCK, EXCESSIVE SLIPPAGE FROM 1st TO 2nd GEAR

Incorrect oil level. Manual linkage out of adjustment. Leak in vacuum circuit. Incorrect oil pressure. Transmission fluid contaminated. Valve body faulty. Brake band out of adjustment. Servo pipe faulty. Leak in hydraulic circuit.

LITTLE OR NO SHIFT SHOCK, EXCESSIVE SLIP & ENGINE RUNAWAY FROM 2nd TO 3rd GEARS

Incorrect oil level. Manual linkage out of adjustment. Leak in vacuum circuit. Incorrect oil pressure. Transmission fluid contaminated. Valve body faulty. Brake band out of adjustment. Servo pipe faulty. Defective reverse clutch. Leak in hydraulic circuit. Reverse clutch check ball missing.

VEHICLE IS BRAKED WHEN SHIFTED FROM 1st TO 2nd GEAR

Transmission fluid contaminated. Valve body faulty. Defective low-reverse clutch. Defective reverse clutch. Defective one-way clutch.

VEHICLE IS BRAKED WHEN SHIFTED FROM 2nd TO 3rd GEAR

Transmission fluid contaminated. Brake band out of adjustment. Valve body faulty.

NO 3rd TO 2nd DOWNSHIFT

Leak in vacuum circuit. Transmission fluid contaminated. Valve body faulty. Faulty governor valve. Brake band out of adjustment. Incorrect oil pressure. Leak in hydraulic circuit. Defective reverse clutch.

NO 2nd TO 1st OR 3rd TO 1st DOWNSHIFT

Leak in vacuum circuit. Transmission fluid contaminated. Faulty valve body. Governor valve faulty. Brake band out of adjustment. Defective one-way clutch.

SHIFTING SHOCK FELT ON DECELERATION

Manual linkage out of adjustment. Leak in vacuum circuit. Downshift solenoid, switch or wiring faulty. Incorrect oil pressure. Valve body faulty. Governor valve faulty. Leak in hydraulic circuit.

SHIFT POINTS TOO HIGH FROM 3rd TO 2nd OR 2nd TO 1st GEARS

Manual linkage out of adjustment. Leak in vacuum circuit. Downshift solenoid, switch or wiring faulty. Incorrect oil pressure. Faulty valve body. Governor valve faulty. Leak in hydraulic circuit.

NO KICKDOWN AT NORMAL SPEEDS IN 3rd GEAR

Downshift solenoid, switch or wiring faulty. Leak in vacuum circuit. Transmission fluid contaminated. Faulty valve body or governor valve. Servo pipe faulty. Brake band out of adjustment. Leak in hydraulic circuit.

EXCESSIVE ENGINE RPM WHEN ACCELERATING IN 3rd GEAR ABOVE KICKDOWN SPEED

Manual linkage out of adjustment. Incorrect oil pressure. Transmission fluid contaminated. Faulty valve body. Faulty governor valve. Defective reverse clutch. Leak in hydraulic circuit.

SUBARU MODEL M41A (Cont.)

ENGINE RUNAWAY OR TRANSMISSION SLIPPAGE ON 3rd TO 2nd GEAR KICKDOWN

Leak in vacuum circuit. Incorrect oil pressure. Transmission fluid contaminated. Valve body faulty. Brake band out of adjustment. Servo pipe faulty. Defective reverse clutch. Leak in hydraulic circuit. Reverse clutch check ball missing.

NO ENGINE BRAKING IN 1st GEAR

Manual linkage out of adjustment. Transmission fluid contaminated. Faulty valve body. Defective low-reverse clutch. Leak in hydraulic circuit. Incorrect oil pressure.

TRANSMISSION OVERHEATS

Incorrect oil level. Incorrect oil pressure. Incorrect stall RPM. Transmission fluid contaminated. Faulty valve body. Defective reverse clutch, low-reverse clutch, oil pump, or planetary gear unit. Brake band out of adjustment or defective. Leak in hydraulic circuit.

TRANSMISSION NOISY IN "N" OR "P"

Incorrect oil level. Incorrect oil pressure. Valve body faulty. Defective oil pump.

TRANSMISSION NOISY IN "R" AND ALL DRIVE RANGES

Incorrect oil level. Defective forward clutch, oil pump, one-way clutch, or Planetary gear unit. Faulty ring or pinion gear in final drive. Incorrect oil pressure. Faulty reduction gears.

TESTING

ROAD TEST

1) Before road testing, be certain that fluid level and condition, and control linkage adjustments have been checked and corrected as necessary. During test, transmission should upshift and downshift at approximately the same speeds as shown in Shift Speeds chart. All shifts may vary slightly due to production tolerances or tire size. The important factor is the quality of the shifts. All shifts should be smooth, responsive, and with no slippage or engine speed runaway.

2) Slippage or engine runaway in any gear usually indicates clutch or band problems. The slipping clutch or band in a particular gear can usually be identified by noting transmission operation in other selector positions and comparing internal units which are applied in these positions. See *Clutch and Band Application Chart.*

3) The process of elimination given can be used to detect any unit which slips and to confirm proper operation of good units, but actual cause of a malfunction cannot be easily decided. Practically any condition can be caused by leaking hydraulic circuits or sticking valves. Unless an obvious condition exists, transmission should never be disassembled until hydraulic pressure tests have been made.

Shift Speeds Chart	
Application	**Shift Points (MPH)**
Kickdown	
1-2 Upshift	31-37
2-3 Upshift	55-62
3-2 Downshift	51-57
2-1 Downshift	23-29
Half-Throttle	
1-2 Upshift	9-14
2-3 Upshift	25-32
3-2 or 3-1 Downshift	8-14
2-1 Downshift	6-11
Full Throttle	
2-1 Downshift①	25-32
Minimum Throttle	
2-1 Downshift①	25-32

① — Shifting selector from "D" to "1" range when vehicle is running at 31 MPH.

CLUTCH AND BAND APPLICATION CHART
(ELEMENTS IN USE)

Selector Lever Position	Forward Clutch	Reverse Clutch	Low-Reverse Brake	Brake Band	One-Way Clutch
P — PARK			X		
R — REVERSE		X	X		
N — NEUTRAL①					
D — DRIVE					
First Gear	X				X
Second Gear	X			X	
Third Gear	X	X			
2 — SECOND	X			X	
1 — LOW					
First	X		X		
Second	X			X	

① — All bands and clutches released and/or ineffective.

SUBARU MODEL M41A (Cont.)

STALL TEST

Testing Precautions — When making stall test, do not hold throttle open any longer than five seconds to obtain steady gauge reading. After each stall test, move selector lever to "N" and allow engine to idle for at least one minute to cool down engine and transmission. If engine speed exceeds limits shown in Stall Speeds table, release accelerator immediately as clutch or band slippage is indicated.

Testing Procedure — With engine at normal operating temperature, tachometer installed, and parking and service brakes applied, make transmission stall test in "D", "2", "1" and "R" ranges at full throttle and note maximum RPM obtained. Engine speed should be within limits shown in Stall Speeds Table.

Stall Speeds	
Application	**Stall RPM**
All Models	1800-2100

Stall Speed Too High — In all ranges: general transmission problems are indicated and a control pressure test should be made to locate faulty unit(s). In "D", "2" and "1" only: forward clutch slippage is indicated. In "D" range only: one-way clutch slippage is indicated. In "2" range only: brake band slippage is indicated. In "R" range only: slippage of reverse clutch or low-reverse brake is indicated.

Stall Speed Too Low — Converter stator one-way clutch faulty.

NOTE — *Make sure engine performance is satisfactory before condemning converter assembly. Converter is a sealed unit and cannot be overhauled, it must be replaced if defective.*

HYDRAULIC PRESSURE TESTS

Line Pressure — 1) Connect a suitable pressure gauge to line pressure checking plug on rear cover of transmission. See *Fig. 3*. Place gauge in position for viewing from drivers seat.

NOTE — *A hole is provided on front of toe-board to route gauge hose from engine compartment into drivers compartment.*

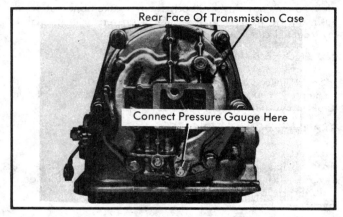

Fig. 3   Rear View of Transmission Case Showing Location of Line Pressure Checking Point

2) With engine at normal operating temperature and transmission fluid at correct level, perform line pressure test in "D", "2" and "R" ranges. Start vehicle from a standstill and slowly increase engine speed and note pressure in each range. Pressures should be approximately as shown in Line Pressure Table.

Line Pressure Test Results — 1) If the line pressure at idle is low in all ranges, faulty pressure feeding line or low oil pump discharge pressure may be assumed, due to the following: Worn oil pump or improperly adjusted internal clearances; oil leakage from oil pump, valve body, governor or transmission case; sticky pressure regulator valve.

2) If oil pressure at idle is low in "D", "2" and "1" ranges only, check for faulty or leaking forward clutch or governor assembly.

3) If oil pressure at idle is low in "P" and "R" ranges only, check for a faulty or leaking low-reverse brake assembly.

Subaru Line Pressure Table — Psi (kg/cm²)			
Range	**Throttle Opening**	**At Cut-Back Point (Under 9.5 MPH)**	**After Cut-Back Point (Over 22 MPH)**
"D"	Full Throttle Minimum Throttle	121-142 (8.5-10.0) 43-57 (3.0-4.0)	78-93 (5.5-6.5) 43-57 (3.0-4.0)
"2"	Full Throttle Minimum Throttle	145-168 (10.2-11.8) 145-168 (10.2-11.8)	84-98 (5.9-6.9) 84-98 (5.9-6.9)
"R"	Full Throttle Minimum Throttle	200-227 (14-16)	..... 67-81 (4.7-5.7)

NOTE — *Line pressures at each of "D", "2" and "R" ranges will change in steps at certain points (where pressure modifier valve functions) and these points are called the "Cut-Back Point". Before cut-back in the above table implies slow driving condition (less than 9.5 MPH) and after cut-back implies the vehicle speed of more than 22 MPH.*

SUBARU MODEL M41A (Cont.)

4) If oil pressure is high in all ranges, check for the following: Leaky vacuum tube or vacuum diaphragm, or excessive length of vacuum rod; Sticky pressure regulator valve.

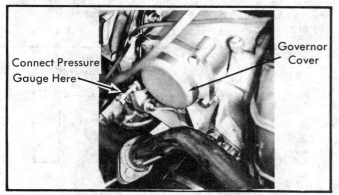

Fig. 4 View of Final Drive Housing Showing Location of Governor Pressure Checking Point

Governor Pressure — Connect pressure gauge to governor pressure plug located on right side of final drive housing, then place gauge in driver's compartment as outlined in line pressure test procedure. With engine at normal operating temperature and transmission fluid level correct, check governor pressure at the speeds shown in Governor Pressure chart with transmission in "2"

Governor Pressures Chart	
Speed (MPH)	**Psi (kg/cm²)**
Below 6	0-2.8 (0-.2)
Below 25	18-27 (1.3-1.9)
Below 50	53-67 (3.7-4.7)

TRANSAXLE REMOVAL & INSTALLATION

NOTE — *Engine and transaxle are removed from vehicle as an assembly and separated from each other after removal.*

Removal — 1) Disconnect both battery cables from battery, then disconnect ground cable from engine. Remove air cleaner and disconnect fuel line from carburetor. Drain radiator and remove all cooling system hoses. Disconnect electrical leads from the following: Alternator, oil pressure switch, radiator fan motor, distributor, thermo switch, neutral safety switch, downshift solenoid, and starter.

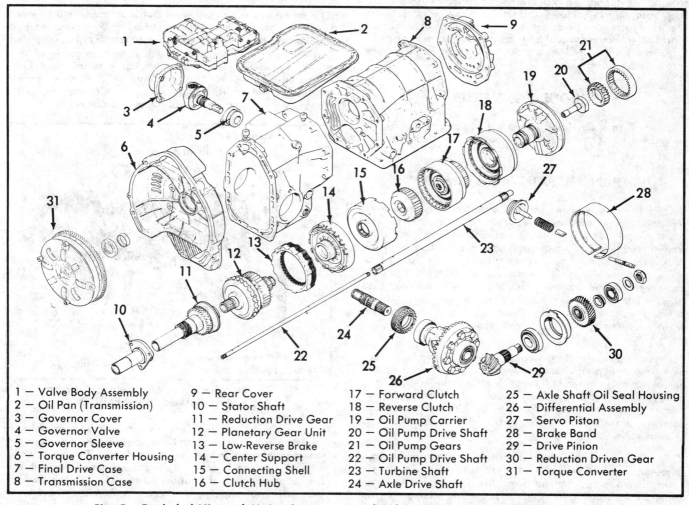

1 — Valve Body Assembly	9 — Rear Cover	17 — Forward Clutch	25 — Axle Shaft Oil Seal Housing
2 — Oil Pan (Transmission)	10 — Stator Shaft	18 — Reverse Clutch	26 — Differential Assembly
3 — Governor Cover	11 — Reduction Drive Gear	19 — Oil Pump Carrier	27 — Servo Piston
4 — Governor Valve	12 — Planetary Gear Unit	20 — Oil Pump Drive Shaft	28 — Brake Band
5 — Governor Sleeve	13 — Low-Reverse Brake	21 — Oil Pump Gears	29 — Drive Pinion
6 — Torque Converter Housing	14 — Center Support	22 — Oil Pump Drive Shaft	30 — Reduction Driven Gear
7 — Final Drive Case	15 — Connecting Shell	23 — Turbine Shaft	31 — Torque Converter
8 — Transmission Case	16 — Clutch Hub	24 — Axle Drive Shaft	

Fig. 5 Exploded View of Major Components of Subaru Automatic Transaxle Assembly

SUBARU MODEL M41A (Cont.)

2) Remove two bolts from top of radiator and lift out radiator. Remove engine stabilizer bar. Remove starter motor. Disconnect throttle cable and choke cable (if equipped) from carburetor. Disconnect speedometer cable from transaxle case. Drain automatic transmission fluid, then disconnect all oil cooler pipes from transaxle case.

3) Disconnect exhaust pipe from exhaust manifold. Disconnect manual lever from control. Remove bolts fastening front mounting bracket to engine, then install lifting sling to front and rear lifting hangers. Remove spring pin attaching drive axles to transaxle, then separate axles from transaxle case.

4) Disconnect rear crossmember from rear mount and vehicle body. Carefully lift engine and transaxle assembly from vehicle, guiding it by hand to ensure transaxle oil pan clears stabilizer. Place engine and transaxle assembly on a suitable engine stand, then remove torque converter-to-drive plate attaching bolts. **NOTE** — *Converter-to-drive plate attaching bolts are accessible through timing hole in engine.* Remove transaxle-to-engine attaching bolts, then carefully separate transaxle from engine using care not to drop torque converter.

Installation — To install, reverse removal procedure and note the following: When connecting drive axles to transaxle, align paint mark on universal joint with chamfered pin hole on drive axle. When connecting manual lever with manual shift rod, keep both the manual lever and selector lever in "N" position. The "N" position can be determined by bringing slot of manual shaft fitting hole in manual lever perpendicular to oil pan surface. Ensure oil cooler lines are flush with fittings on transaxle case before tightening them.

TORQUE CONVERTER

NOTE — *Torque converter is a sealed unit and cannot be disassembled for service. Replace if found to be defective.*

TRANSMISSION DISASSEMBLY

NOTE — *Final drive must be separated from transmission at this point. To separate, remove torque converter from converter housing, then remove turbine shaft and oil pump drive shaft from assembly by pulling straight out with pliers using care not to scar shafts. Remove bolts securing transmission case to final drive case, then disconnect neutral safety switch and clip from downshift solenoid lead wire. Remove bolt securing filler pipe to governor cover, then disconnect vacuum pipe and ground cable. Separate transmission from final drive and remove washer located on reduction drive gear.*

1) Place transmission on a work stand with oil pan facing up, then remove oil pan. Unscrew downshift solenoid and vacuum modulator by hand and remove them from transmission case, then pull out modulator rod. Carefully pry servo apply and release tubes from case. Remove attaching screws, then carefully lift out valve body assembly using care not to drop manual valve.

2) Loosen band adjusting screw lock nut, then snugly tighten adjusting screw for convenience in removing transmission rear cover. Remove rear mount from bracket on transmission. Remove bolts securing transmission rear cover, then gently tap rear mount bracket to rotate cover and remove cover and oil

pump carrier as an assembly. **NOTE** — *Be careful not to lose washers located between oil pump carrier and reverse clutch assembly.* Loosen band adjusting screw and remove band apply strut. Remove snap ring securing servo cover and remove cover, then remove piston rod by pushing it from inside of transmission case.

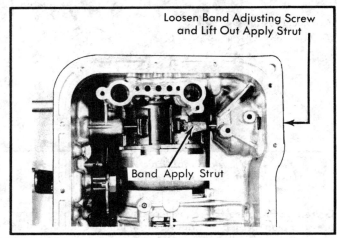

Fig. 6　Removing Band Apply Strut

3) Remove brake band, reverse clutch assembly and forward clutch assembly from transmission as a unit. Remove clutch hub and connecting shell from transmission case. Pry out snap ring and lift out center support assembly. Remove forward and reverse sun gears. Lift planetary gear assembly and low-reverse brake assembly from transmission case, then remove low-reverse brake retaining plate. If not removed with planetary gear unit, remove planetary output shaft.

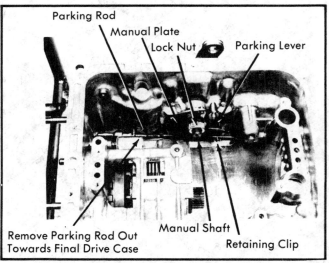

Fig. 7　Installed View of Manual Shaft and Parking Rod Assembly

4) Remove bolts securing neutral safety switch to transmission case, then remove switch and manual lever. Remove lock nut from manual shaft and remove manual plate. Remove parking rod with parking lever by pulling them out of transmission case in the direction of final drive assembly. Remove parking pawl shaft retaining clip, then remove transmission from work stand and remove parking rod support plate.

SUBARU MODEL M41A (Cont.)

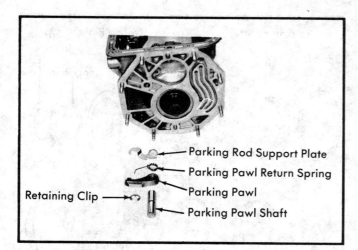

Fig. 8 Disassembled View of Parking Pawl Components

- Parking Rod Support Plate
- Parking Pawl Return Spring
- Retaining Clip → Parking Pawl
- Parking Pawl Shaft

COMPONENT DISASSEMBLY & REASSEMBLY

REVERSE CLUTCH ASSEMBLY

Disassembly — Remove clutch assembly snap ring and lift out retaining plate, drive plates, driven plates and dished plate from clutch drum. Using a suitable compressor tool, compress clutch assembly return spring and remove retaining snap ring, then remove return spring retainer and return springs. Apply compressed air to oil hole in clutch drum and remove clutch piston. Remove oil seal from clutch piston and drum.

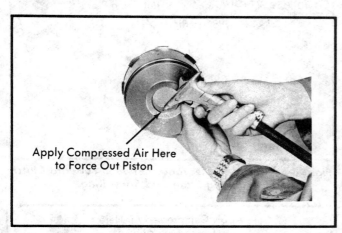

Apply Compressed Air Here to Force Out Piston

Fig. 9 Using Compressed Air to Remove Reverse Clutch Piston

Reassembly — **1)** Reverse disassembly procedure and note the following: Coat all parts with automatic transmission fluid before installation. When installing clutch plates into drum, start with the dished plate, then install a driven (steel) plate followed by a drive (lined) plate and alternate driven plates and drive plates until all plates are installed.

NOTE — *Reverse clutch assembly clutch pack consists of the dished plate, 3 driven (steel) plates and 3 drive (lined) plates. Also, when installing driven plates, be sure to align missing tooth portion with oil hole in clutch drum.*

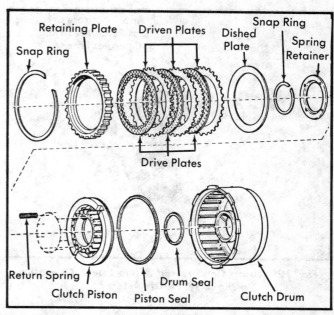

Snap Ring · Retaining Plate · Driven Plates · Dished Plate · Snap Ring · Spring Retainer · Drive Plates

Return Spring · Clutch Piston · Piston Seal · Drum Seal · Clutch Drum

Fig. 10 Exploded View of Reverse Clutch Assembly

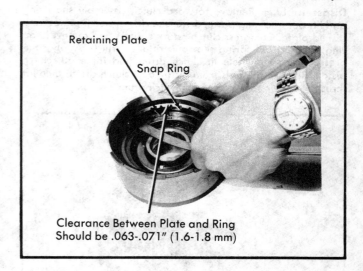

Retaining Plate

Snap Ring

Clearance Between Plate and Ring Should be .063-.071" (1.6-1.8 mm)

Fig. 11 Measuring Clearance Between Reverse Clutch Retaining Plate and Snap Ring

2) Using a feeler gauge, check clearance between retaining plate and clutch assembly snap ring. Clearance should be .063-.071" (1.6-1.8 mm). If clearance is not within specifications, correct by installing a retaining plate of different thickness.

NOTE — *Reverse clutch retaining plates are available in thicknesses of .417" (10.6 mm) to .457" (11.6 mm) in .008" (.2 mm) increments.*

3) After clutch assembly is completed, check operation by installing clutch assembly to oil pump carrier and applying compressed air to oil hole in clutch drum to ensure clutch assembly moves properly. See Fig. 12.

SUBARU MODEL M41A (Cont.)

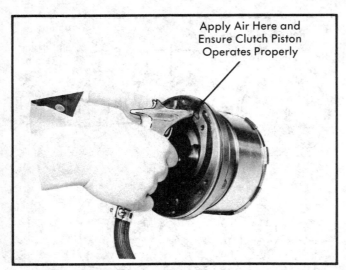

Fig. 12   Using Compressed Air to Check Operation of Reverse Clutch Assembly

FORWARD CLUTCH ASSEMBLY

Disassembly — Remove forward clutch assembly snap ring and lift out retaining plate, drive and driven clutch plates, and dished plate. Compress clutch return springs and remove snap ring, then lift out spring seat and return springs. Apply compressed air to oil hole in clutch drum and force out clutch piston. Remove oil seals from piston and clutch drum, then lift thrust bearing and washer from clutch drum.

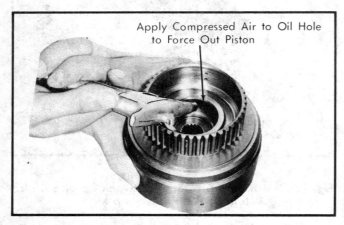

Fig. 13   Using Compressed Air to Remove Forward Clutch Piston

Reassembly — **1)** Reverse disassembly procedure and note the following: Coat all parts with automatic transmission fluid before reassembly. When installing clutch pack into clutch drum, start with the dished plate, then install a driven (steel) plate followed by a drive (lined) plate and alternate driven and drive plates until all clutch plates are installed.

NOTE — *Forward clutch pack consists of 3 driven (steel) and 3 drive (lined) plates.*

2) Check clearance between retaining plate and clutch assembly snap ring using a feeler gauge; clearance should be .040-.059" (1.0-1.5 mm).

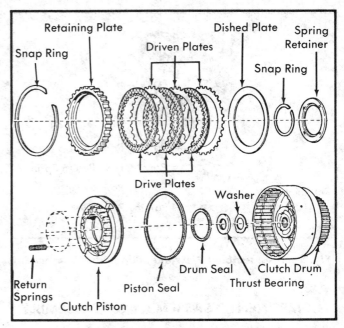

Fig. 14   Exploded View of Forward Clutch Assembly

3) With reassembly completed, install forward and reverse clutches on oil pump carrier. Apply compressed air to oil hole in forward clutch drum and ensure clutch piston operates properly.

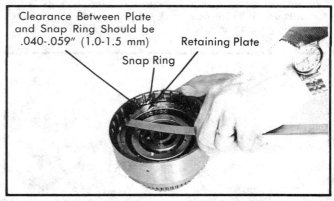

Fig. 15   Measuring Clearance Between Forward Clutch Retaining Plate and Snap Ring

Fig. 16   Using Compressed Air to Check Operation of Forward Clutch Assembly

SUBARU MODEL M41A (Cont.)

CENTER SUPPORT AND LOW-REVERSE BRAKE ASSEMBLY

NOTE — *Low-Reverse brake plates were removed at Transmission Disassembly and will be installed at Transmission Reassembly.*

Disassembly — Using a suitable compressor tool, compress low-reverse piston return spring and remove return spring snap ring, then lift out return spring and thrust ring. Apply compressed air to oil hole in center support and force low-reverse brake piston from center support. Remove oil seals from brake piston.

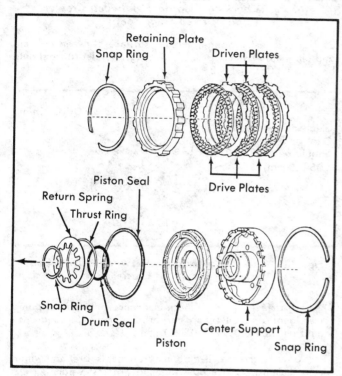

Fig. 17   Exploded View of Center Support and Low-Reverse Brake Assembly

Reassembly — Reverse disassembly procedure and note the following: Coat all parts with automatic transmission fluid before reassembly. When installing clutch piston to center support, use care not to damage piston oil seals.

GOVERNOR ASSEMBLY

NOTE — *Governor assembly is mounted in final drive case.*

Removal — Remove attaching bolts and lift off governor cover, then pull governor assembly straight out of case. Remove the 2 attaching bolts and pull governor sleeve out of case.

Disassembly — Remove screws securing governor shaft to governor housing and separate housing from shaft. Remove two snap rings and one retaining clip and remove spool valve, small weight, spring and large weight from governor housing. Remove balancing weight from housing.

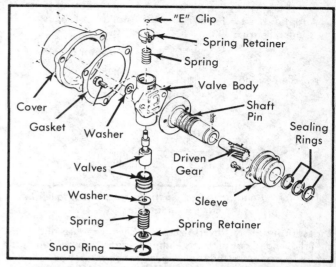

Fig. 18   Exploded View of Governor Assembly

Reassembly — Reverse disassembly procedure and note the following: Inspect all parts for wear or damage and replace as necessary. Ensure large weight moves freely in governor bore when reassembly is completed. Inspect governor shaft oil seals and replace if worn or damaged.

Installation — Reverse removal procedure and use care to prevent damage to oil seals when installing governor assembly.

OIL PUMP

Disassembly — Remove bolts and separate oil pump carrier from transmission rear cover. Mark drive and driven gears for reassembly in their original position. Inspect oil pump gears for wear or damage and replace as necessary. Also, inspect the bushing and two needle roller bearings located in pump carrier and if necessary, replace as follows:

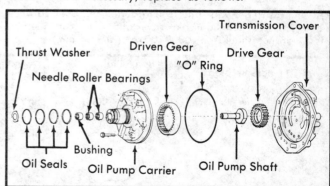

Fig. 19   Exploded View of Oil Pump and Transmission Cover Assembly

Oil Pump Bushing & Bearing Replacement — Remove the bushing and needle roller bearings at the same time using suitable removal tool (ST 399903600). To install, use suitable installation tool (ST 399543600) to drive bearings into pump carrier. See Fig. 20.

NOTE — *When installing the center needle roller bearing, adaptor (ST 398863600) must be used with installation tool to ensure center bearing is installed in the correct position. See Fig. 20.*

SUBARU MODEL M41A (Cont.)

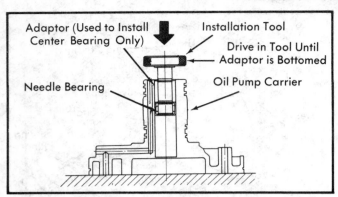

Fig. 20 Installation of Bushing and Bearings into Oil Pump Carrier

Reassembly — 1) Reverse disassembly procedure and note the following: Coat all parts with automatic transmission fluid before reassembly. Ensure alignment marks made at disassembly are aligned when installing gears. With drive and driven gears installed, check the following clearances:

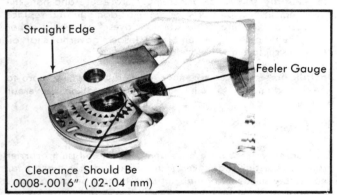

Fig. 21 Checking Clearance Between Face of Gears and Rear Cover of Transmission

2) Using a straight edge and feeler gauge, measure clearance between face of gears and rear cover of transmission. See Fig. 21. Clearance should be .0008-.0016" (.02-.04 mm).

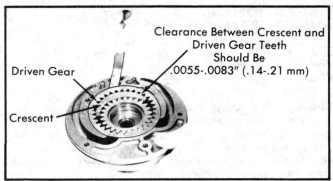

Fig. 22 Checking Clearance Between Crescent and Driven Gear Teeth

3) Using a feeler gauge, check clearance between crescent and oil pump driven gear teeth. See Fig. 22. Clearance should be .0055-.0083" (.14-.21 mm).

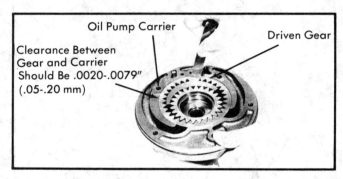

Fig. 23 Checking Clearance Between Driven Gear and Oil Pump Carrier

4) Using a feeler gauge, check clearance between oil pump driven gear and oil pump carrier. See Fig. 23. Clearance should be .0020-.0079" (.05-.20 mm).

5) If any of the preceeding measurements are not within specified limits, replace part showing greatest wear.

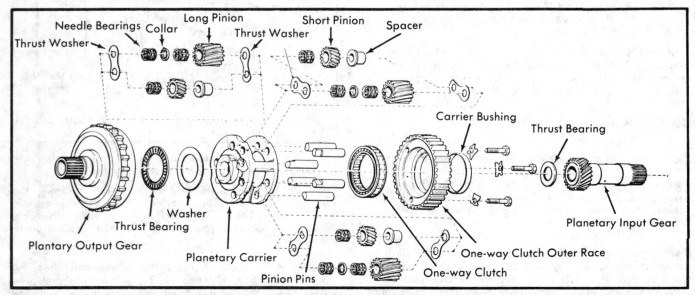

Fig. 24 Exploded View of Planetary Gear Assembly

SUBARU MODEL M41A (Cont.)

PLANETARY GEAR UNIT

Disassembly — Remove bolts securing one-way clutch outer race to planetary gear unit and separate one-way clutch from planetary gear unit, then remove one-way clutch from outer race. Press pinion pins from gear unit and remove long pinion gears, short pinion gears, thrust washers, needle roller bearings, roller bearing collars, and spacers.

Reassembly — 1) Reverse disassembly procedure using *Fig. 24* as an assembly guide and note the following:

2) Coat all parts with automatic transmission fluid. When installing one-way clutch on outer race, push "T" bar by finger to insert one-way clutch until a snap is felt, then secure retainer to outer race.

3) After reassembly, check planetary carrier-to-thrust washer clearance. Clearance should be .006-.024" (.15-.60 mm). If clearance exceeds .028" (70 mm), replace parts as necessary.

VALVE BODY ASSEMBLY

NOTE — *As valve trains are removed from each valve body bore, place individual parts in correct order and in relative position to valve body to simplify reassembly. Also, spring loaded parts should be handled carefully, as springs may jump out of place when parts are disassembled or removed.*

Disassembly — 1) Remove oil strainer bolts using a box-end wrench rather than a screwdriver and separate strainer from valve body. Remove bolts and detach lower valve body, separator plate and upper valve body. **NOTE** — *When removing separator plate, use care not to lose orifice check valve, spring, throttle relief spring and check ball.* Pull manual valve out of valve body bore.

2) Remove side plate using a box-end wrench, then remove the 1-2 shift valve and spring, 2-3 shift valve and spring, 2-3 shift plug, pressure modifier valve and spring. Remove side plate and lift out pressure regulator valve train assembly and second lock valve and spring. Remove plate and remove downshift valve and spring, throttle backup valve and spring, vacuum throttle valve and 2-3 timing valve and spring.

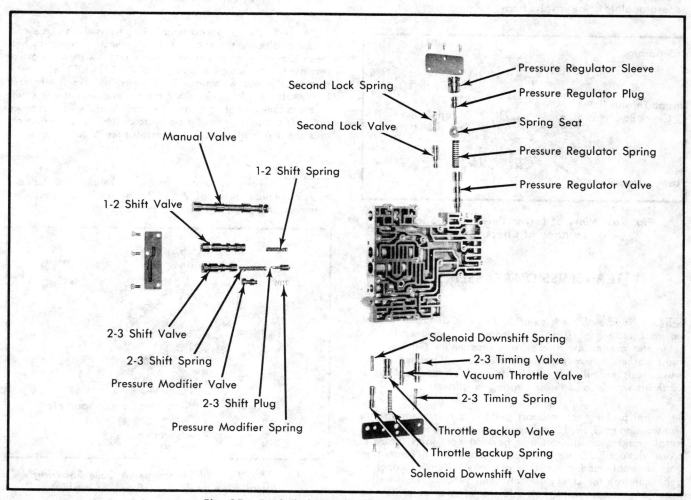

Fig. 25 Exploded View of Valve Body Assembly

SUBARU MODEL M41A (Cont.)

VALVE BODY SPRING IDENTIFICATION

Valve Spring	Length In. (mm)	Diameter In. (mm)①	Number Of Coils	Wire Thickness In. (mm)
Manual Valve	1.28 (32.4)	.24 (6.0)	15	.051 (1.3)
Press. Regulator Valve	1.69 (43.0)	.41 (10.5)	13	.047 (1.2)
Press. Modifier Valve	.73 (18.5)	.31 (8.0)	5	.016 (.4)
1-2 Shift Valve	1.26 (32.0)	.24 (6.0)	16	.024 (.6)
2-3 Shift Valve	1.61 (41.0)	.25 (6.2)	18	.028 (.7)
2-3 Timing Valve	1.28 (32.5)	.22 (5.5)	15	.028 (.7)
Throttle Back-Up Valve	1.42 (36.0)	.26 (6.5)	14	.031 (.8)
Downshift Valve	.87 (22.0)	.20 (5.0)	12	.022 (.55)
Second Lock Valve	1.32 (33.5)	.20 (5.0)	16	.022 (.55)
Throttle Relief Valve	1.06 (26.8)	.22 (5.5)	14	.036 (.9)
Orifice Check Valve	.85 (21.5)	.19 (4.8)	15	.008 (.2)

① — Mean diameter of spring coils.

Reassembly — Replace all parts in reverse order of disassembly procedure using illustrations as references. Coat all parts with automatic transmission fluid. When tightening parts be sure to observe the specified torque values. Do Not force valves into place, but lightly push them into place by hand. Ensure orifice check valve and spring, and throttle relief spring and check ball are in position before installing separator plate to lower valve body.

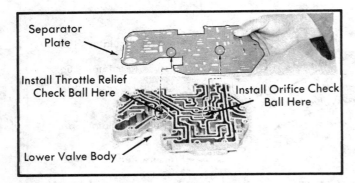

Fig. 26 View of Lower Valve Body Showing Location of Check Balls

TRANSMISSION REASSEMBLY

NOTE — *Handle all parts carefully to avoid damaging bearing and mating surfaces. Lubricate all components with automatic transmission fluid prior to reassembly. Gaskets and thrust washers may be held in place by using Vaseline. Use all new gaskets and oil seals, and tighten bolts evenly. See Fig. 36 for thrust washer and thrust bearing locations.*

1) Install parking rod support plate and return spring into transmission case, then install case onto a suitable work stand. Install parking pawl shaft and parking pawl and secure in place with circlip. Engage planetary gear unit with center support assembly and check that one-way clutch in planetary gear unit rotates clockwise only, then separate assemblies. Install planetary output shaft into transmission case, then install planetary gear unit and secure in case with snap ring.

Install low-reverse brake plates into case starting with the retainer plate followed by a drive (lined) plate, then alternate driven (steel) plates and drive plates until all brake plates are installed.

NOTE — *The low-reverse brake assembly uses three drive (lined) and three driven (steel) plates.*

2) Install center support assembly into transmission case and secure in place with snap ring. Next, measure clearance between planetary gear unit snap ring and low-reverse brake retainer plate; clearance should be .020-.047" (.50-1.2 mm). If clearance is not within specified limits, remove low-reverse brake retainer plate and install a new retainer plate of a different thickness to bring clearance within limits. With clearance correctly set, apply compressed air to oil hole in center support and check operation of low-reverse brake piston.

NOTE — *Low-reverse brake assembly retainer plates are available in thicknesses of .28" (7.2 mm) to .32" (8.2 mm) in increments of .008" (.2 mm).*

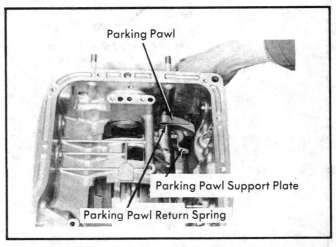

Fig. 27 View of Transmission Case Showing Installation of Parking Pawl Assembly

SUBARU MODEL M41A (Cont.)

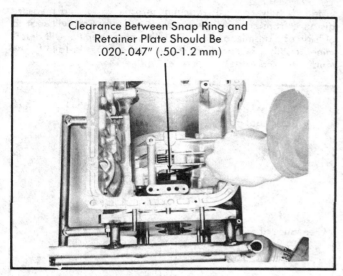

Clearance Between Snap Ring and Retainer Plate Should Be .020-.047" (.50-1.2 mm)

Fig. 28 Measuring Clearance Between Snap Ring and Low-Reverse Brake Retainer Plate

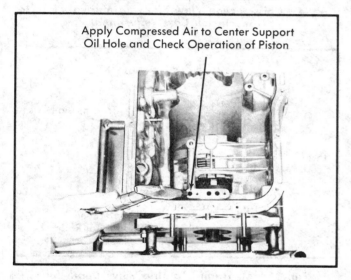

Apply Compressed Air to Center Support Oil Hole and Check Operation of Piston

Fig. 29 Using Compressed Air to Check Operation of Low-Reverse Brake Piston

3) Assemble forward clutch assembly to reverse clutch assembly, then assemble clutch hub and connecting wheel to clutch assemblies and install the complete unit into transmission case. Install brake band into transmission case and over reverse clutch drum. Before proceeding with reassembly it will be necessary to adjust total end play of transmission. Transmission end play is checked and adjusted as follows:

NOTE — *Measuring gauge block ST 398643600 must be used to check transmission total end play and reverse clutch end play.*

4) Place gauge block on rear face of transmission case, then using suitable depth gauge, measure distance "L" (from forward clutch to top of gauge block). See Fig. 30. Next, place gauge block on top of oil pump carrier (with thrust bearing installed), and measure distance "l" (from rear cover mounting surface to top of gauge block). See Fig. 31. Note both values just obtained for future reference.

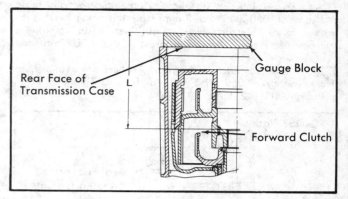

Rear Face of Transmission Case — L — Gauge Block — Forward Clutch

Fig. 30 Measuring Distance "L" for Transmission End Play Adjustment

5) Add .016" (.4 mm) to distance "L", then subtract the allowable transmission end play of .01-.02" (.25-.50 mm) from this value. Next, subtract distance "l" from value just obtained. Final value is thickness of thrust bearing to be installed. Remove reverse and forward clutch assemblies and install thrust bearing between the two assemblies, then reassemble clutch assemblies and install them into transmission case.

NOTE — *End play thrust bearings are available in thicknesses from .040" (1.0 mm) to .087" (2.2 mm) in increments of .008" (.2 mm).*

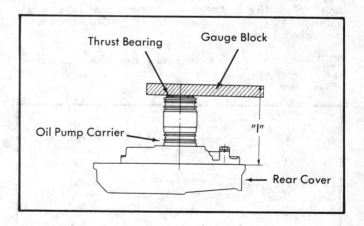

Thrust Bearing — Gauge Block — Oil Pump Carrier — "l" — Rear Cover

Fig. 31 Measuring Distance "l" for Transmission End Play Adjustment

6) Before installing oil pump carrier and rear cover assembly, reverse clutch drum end play must be checked and adjusted. With oil pump carrier and rear cover on a work bench, place gauge block on rear face of transmission case and measure distance "M" (from rear face of reverse clutch drum to top of gauge block). Next, place gauge block on oil pump face and measure distance "m" (from rear cover mounting surface to top of gauge block). To determine correct thrust washer to install, proceed as follows:

SUBARU MODEL M41A (Cont.)

7) Add .016" (.4 mm) to distance "M", then subtract allowable end play of .020-.030" (.5-.8 mm) from this value. Next, subtract distance "m" from value just obtained. Resulting value is thickness of reverse clutch drum thrust washer to be installed.

NOTE — *Reverse clutch drum thrust washers are available in thicknesses from .059" (1.5 mm) to .106" (2.7 mm) in increments of .008" (.2 mm).*

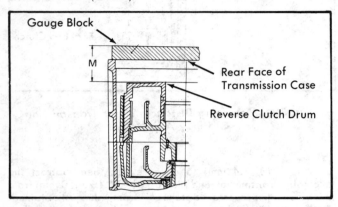

Fig. 32   Measuring Distance "M" for Reverse Clutch End Play Adjustment

8) Install correct reverse clutch drum thrust washer on oil pump carrier and retain in place with vaseline. Install oil pump carrier and rear cover assembly to transmission case and tighten attaching bolts to specifications. Install servo piston cover assembly into transmission case bore using piston rod as a guide. **NOTE** — *Use care when installing servo cover to avoid damaging "O" ring seal.* Install brake band apply strut and tighten band adjusting screw just enough to hold apply strut in place. To adjust band, tighten band adjusting screw to 6.5 ft. lbs. (.9 mkg), then back screw off TWO complete turns and tighten lock nut.

NOTE — *When adjusting brake band transmission should be in a horizontal position with the oil pan upward so that band will not jam.*

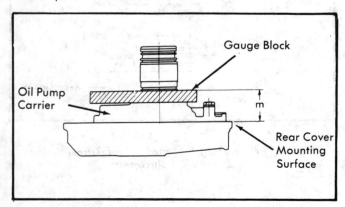

Fig. 33   Measuring Distance "m" for Reverse Clutch End Play Adjustment

9) Install manual plate onto manual shaft and using shims, adjust clearance between manual plate and transmission case to .012" (.3 mm). Install neutral safety switch. Install valve body assembly into transmission case, ensuring that groove in manual valve engages notch in manual plate. With valve body

installed, fully compress vacuum throttle valve and measure distance from end of valve where modulator rod will seat to outside of transmission case. Resulting measurement will determine length of modulator valve rod to be installed (see modulator rod table).

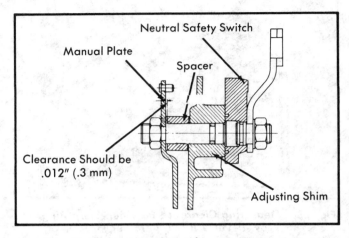

Fig. 34   Cross-Section View Showing Manual Plate to Transmission Case Adjustment

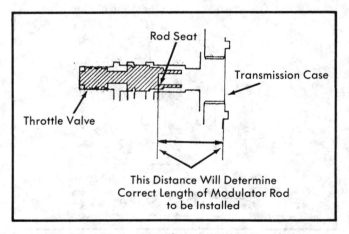

Fig. 35   Measuring Throttle Valve Depth for Modulator Rod Selection

Modulator Rod Selection Chart	
Measurement **In. (mm)**	**Rod To Use** **In. (mm)**
1.0059 (25.55) or Less	1.1417 (29)
1.0098-1.0256 (25.65-26.05)	1.1614 (29.5)
1.0295-1.0453 (26.15-26.55)	1.1811 (30)
1.0492-1.0650 (26.65-27.05)	1.2008 (30.5)
1.0689 (27.15) or More	1.2205 (31)

10) Install servo apply and release tubes, then measure the height that extends above oil pan mounting surface; maximum height allowed is .827" (21 mm). If tubes extend above specified height they will interfere with oil pan installation. If above specified height, lightly tap tubes with a soft rubber mallet to fully seat tubes. Install oil pan using a new gasket and tighten attaching bolts to specifications.

SUBARU MODEL M41A (Cont.)

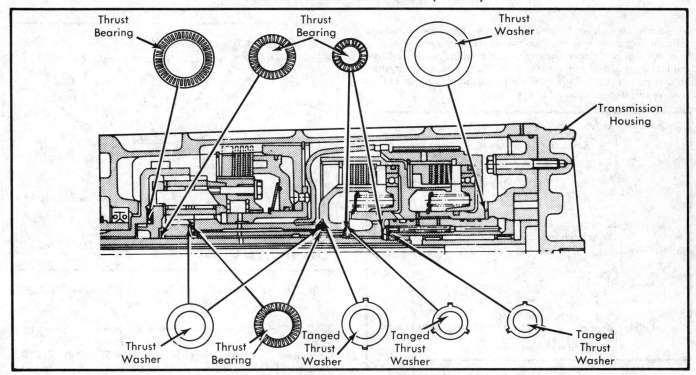

Fig. 36 Cross-Sectional View of Transmission Case Showing Thrust Washer and Thrust Bearing Locations

FINAL DRIVE ASSEMBLY

DISASSEMBLY

1) Place final drive case on a suitable work stand. Remove bolts attaching torque converter housing to case and separate housing from case. Remove governor cover and pull out governor assembly, then remove attaching bolts and pull out governor sleeve. Remove attaching bolts and lift out parking actuator assembly. Remove axle drive shaft snap rings from inside differential assembly, then remove lock plates and remove axle drive shaft oil seal housings and drive shafts as an assembly. Move differential assembly to one side and lift out of case.

2) Lock reduction drive gear in place and remove drive pinion lock nut. Place final drive housing in a suitable press with converter housing mounting surface facing up and press drive pinion from housing, then press out driven gear and bearing retainer. Invert housing in press and press out reduction drive gear. From inside of housing remove snap ring and take out speedometer driven gear, then remove second snap ring from speedometer shaft and remove steel ball from shaft. Remove speedometer shaft and oil seal from top of final drive housing. If necessary, remove stator shaft from torque converter housing.

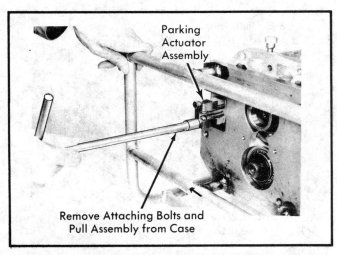

Fig. 37 Removing Parking Actuator Assembly

Fig. 38 Pressing Drive Pinion from Final Drive Case

SUBARU MODEL M41A (Cont.)

3) To disassemble differential assembly, bend back locking tabs on ring gear mounting bolt washers, then remove mounting bolts and lift ring gear from differential housing. Drive out locking pin and remove differential pinion gear shaft, then lift out pinion gears, side gears and washers. Using a puller, remove differential case bearings.

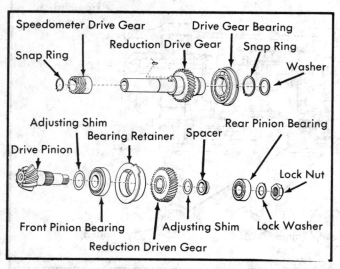

Fig. 39   Exploded View of Drive Pinion and Reduction Drive Gear Assemblies

4) If necessary to replace drive pinion front bearing, remove from shaft using suitable puller tool, then drive bearing outer race from final drive case. If necessary to replace reduction drive gear, press from shaft using an arbor press. Check all oil seals and replace as necessary.

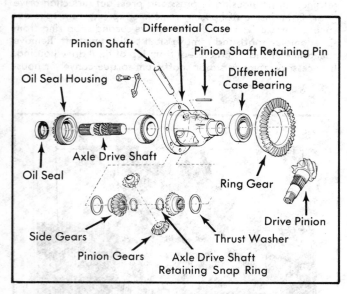

Fig. 40   Exploded View of Differential Assembly

REASSEMBLY & ADJUSTMENT

1) Press drive gear onto reduction drive gear shaft, then install speedometer governor drive gear on shaft and retain with snap ring. Press drive gear shaft into final drive case, then install final drive case on a suitable work stand.

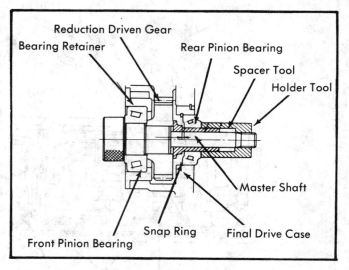

Fig. 41   Installation of Drive Pinion Bearing Preload Measuring Tools

NOTE — *Drive pinion bearing preload adjustment must now be performed. The following tools should be used to carry out adjustment: Spacer, 399913604; Master Shaft, 499912702; Holder, 399913603; Pulley, 39853600. See Fig. 41 for installation of these special tools.*

2) To set drive pinion bearing preload, install driven gear and bearing retainer into final drive case. Install front drive pinion bearing, spacer tool, and rear pinion bearing onto master shaft then install master shaft into final drive case. Install holder tool over master shaft, then hold master shaft stationary and tighten holder tool. Attach pulley to hexagonal head of holder tool, then attach a spring pull gauge to pulley. Tighten holder tool until tension on pull gauge is 6.6-8.8 lbs. (3.0-4.0 kg), this will give the correct pinion bearing preload. With preload correctly set, starting torque of drive pinion will be 10.9-14.0 INCH lbs. (12.5-16.5 cmkg).

CAUTION — *Do not overtighten holder tool. Tightening torque to give correct preload is approximately 7.2-8.7 ft. lbs. (1.0-1.2 mkg).*

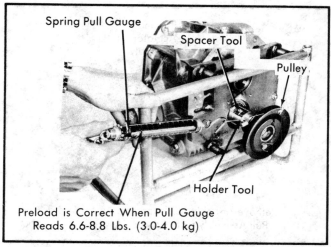

Preload is Correct When Pull Gauge
Reads 6.6-8.8 Lbs. (3.0-4.0 kg)

Fig. 42   Measuring Pinion Bearing Preload

SUBARU MODEL M41A (Cont.)

3) With special tools still installed, measure end play between spacer tool (399913604) and front pinion bearing using a dial indicator. See Fig. 43. To determine correct combination of shim and spacer needed to obtain correct pinion bearing preload, add the end play reading to the factory determined value of .397" (10.07 mm). Next, multiply the plus or minus number stamped on spacer tool by .001, then add the two totals obtained in this step together. The resulting sum is the thickness of shim plus spacer to be installed to provide correct pinion bearing preload.

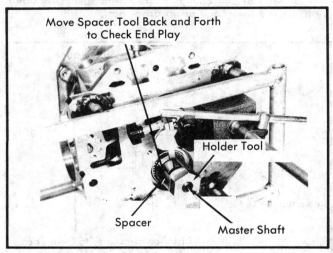

Fig. 43   Measuring End Play Between Spacer Tool and Front Pinion Bearing

NOTE — Pinion bearing preload adjusting shims are available in thicknesses of .006" (.15 mm) to .020" (.5 mm) in increments of .001" (.025 mm). Preload spacers are available in thicknesses of .378" (9.600 mm) to .385" (9.775 mm) in increments of .001" (.025 mm). The selected shim and spacer should be installed after adjusting pinion depth.

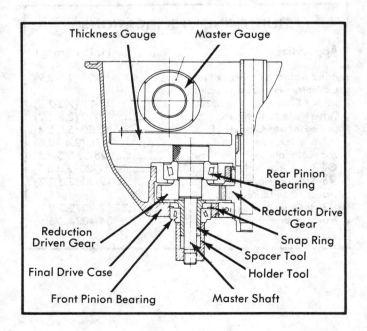

Fig. 44   Installation of Drive Pinion Depth Measuring Tools

NOTE — For drive pinion depth adjustment, pinion bearing preload measuring tools should be left installed. In addition, the following special pinion depth measuring tools should be installed as shown in Fig. 44: Thickness gauge 398643600 and Master gauge 399913601.

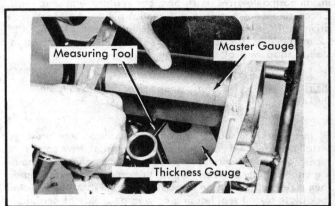

Fig. 45   Measuring Clearance Between Master Gauge and Thickness Gauge for Pinion Depth Adjustment

4) To adjust drive pinion depth, leave preload tools installed, then install thickness gauge and master gauge into final drive case. Measure and record clearance between thickness gauge and master gauge. To determine thickness of pinion depth adjusting shim(s) to be installed, proceed as follows:

Step 1: Multiply the plus or minus figure on master gauge 499917002 by .001 and record the result.
Step 2: Multiply the plus or minus figure on thickness gauge 39863600 by .001 and record the result.
Step 3: Measure clearance between master gauge and thickness gauge and record the result. See Fig. 45.
Step 4: Add totals of step 1, 2 and 3, the resulting sum is the shim thickness required for correct drive pinion depth.

5) Up to 3 adjusting shims may be installed to set pinion depth. Adjusting shims are available in thicknesses from .006" (.15 mm) to .02 (.50 mm) in increments of .001" (.025 mm).

6) Remove and disassemble all measuring tools. Install selected pinion depth adjusting shim(s) onto drive pinion, then press on front pinion bearing. Install drive pinion into final drive case. Install selected pinion bearing preload shim and spacer followed by rear pinion onto drive pinion, then install lock washer and nut and tighten nut to specifications. Install final drive case to a work stand and attach pulley and spring pull gauge to pinion lock nut. Recheck pinion bearing preload and adjust as necessary.

7) To reassemble differential assembly, proceed as follows: Install differential side gears with thrust washers and differential pinion gears into differential housing, then install pinion gear shaft. Using a dial indicator, measure backlash between pinion gears and side gears. Backlash should be .002-.006" (.05-.15 mm). If backlash is not within specifications, correct by installing side gear thrust washers of a different thickness. Align holes in differential housing with hole in pinion gear shaft and install locking pin until it is approximately .040" (1 mm) below hole.

NOTE — Side gear thrust washers are available in thicknesses from .037" (.95 mm) to .041" (1.05 mm) in increments of .001" (.025 mm).

SUBARU MODEL M41A (Cont.)

8) Press differential bearings onto differential housing. Place ring gear in position on differential housing, install NEW lock washers, then install attaching bolts and tighten them to specifications and lock in place by bending up tabs on lock washers. Install differential assembly into final drive case, then install both axle drive shafts and lock in place with snap rings. Check clearance between differential pinion shaft and axle drive shafts using a feeler gauge; clearance should be .008" (.2 mm) or less. If clearance is greater than specifications, install a snap ring of different thickness.

NOTE — *Axle drive shaft snap rings are available in 2 thicknesses: .041" (1.05 mm) and .047" (1.2 mm).*

9) Install new oil seals into axle drive shaft oil seal housings. Install ring gear side oil seal housing into final drive case, then turn reduction drive gear shaft several times and screw housing until it lightly bottoms. Repeat this procedure several times, then screw in housing on opposite side until it bottoms. Install lock plate for oil seal housing on ring gear side of final drive case, then back oil seal housing off approximately 1.5 notches and tighten housing on opposite side of case. Temporarily tighten lock plate on ring gear side, then screw in oil seal housing on other side an additional ½ to one notch and tighten lock plate.

10) Mount a dial indicator on final drive case with indicator tip touching ring gear teeth and check ring gear back lash; ring gear back lash should be .004-.007" (.10-.18 mm). If back lash is not within specifications, recheck drive pinion depth adjustment and correct as necessary. **NOTE** — *As an additional check for ring gear back lash and drive pinion depth a Gear Tooth Pattern test should also be performed.* After ring gear back lash is checked and adjusted (if necessary) tighten axle drive shaft housing locking plates to specifications.

11) Install governor assembly sleeve into final drive case with drain hole facing down, then install attaching bolts and tighten to specifications. Apply a coating of Vaseline to governor assembly needle roller bearing and oil seal lips, then install governor assembly to case. Install new gasket and install governor cover and tighten attaching bolts to specifications. Install stator shaft to torque converter housing and tighten attaching bolts, then install a new oil seal on stator shaft with flat face against shaft. Coat drive gear shaft with gear oil, then install a new gasket and attach converter housing to final drive case and tighten attaching bolts to specifications. Install parking actuator assembly into final drive case.

Final Assembly — **1)** Before reassembling cases, measure distance between end face of final drive case and end face of reduction drive gear; distance should be .776" (19.7 mm). If distance is not to specifications, a washer will have to be installed on end face of gear when reassembling cases.

NOTE — *Washers are available in the following thicknesses: .016" (.4 mm), .024" (.6 mm), .032" (.8 mm), and .040" (1 mm).*

2) Place final drive assembly on a flat surface with converter housing facing down, then install selected washer on reduction drive gear. Place a new gasket on final drive case and install transmission case, then install and tighten attaching bolts. Install turbine shaft and oil pump drive shaft into forward side of transmission case, then install torque converter to stator shaft and ensure that converter is aligned with splines of stator shaft, turbine shaft, and pump drive shaft.

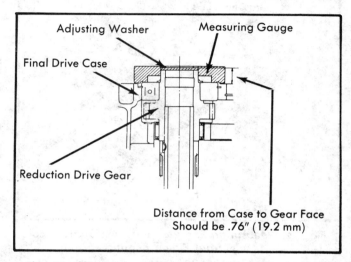

Fig. 46 Measuring Distance from Final Drive Case to End Face of Reduction Drive Gear

TIGHTENING SPECIFICATIONS

Application	Ft. Lbs. (mkg)
Band Adjust Screw Lock Nut	18-21 (2.5-2.9)
Converter Hsg.-to-Reduction Gear Case	17-20 (2.3-2.7)
Drive Plate-to-Converter	17-20 (2.3-2.7)
Drive Plate-to-Crankshaft	36-39 (5.0-5.4)
Drive Pinion Lock Nut	68-76 (9.4-10.6)
Manual Plate-to-Trans. Case	25-33 (3.5-4.5)
Oil Pump Assembly	17-20 (2.3-2.7)
Stator Shaft Flange	17-20 (2.3-2.7)
Trans. Case-to-Reduction Gear Case	17-20 (2.3-2.7)
Trans.-to-Engine	34-40 (4.7-5.5)

TOYOTA MODEL A-55

Tercel

DESCRIPTION

The transaxle assembly is a 3-speed unit attached to back of the engine. The transaxle assembly consists basically of a chain driven 3 element torque converter, 2 clutches, 3 brakes, 2 planetary gear sets, one-way clutch and a final drive assembly.

LUBRICATION & ADJUSTMENT

See *AUTOMATIC TRANSMISSION SERVICING* Section.

SERVICE (IN VEHICLE)

AXLE DRIVE SHAFTS

Removal — 1) Raise and support vehicle; remove tire and wheel. Depress brake pedal and loosen axle shaft nut. Remove brake caliper and suspend caliper from frame; DO NOT remove hydraulic line. Remove upper steering knuckle-to-suspension strut bolts. Push down on steering knuckle to separate knuckle from strut. Remove stabilizer bar (if equipped).

2) Remove axle shaft nut. Press axle shaft out of hub with puller (SST09950-20013). Separate steering knuckle from strut and draw out axle drive shaft from rear of hub. Remove stiffener plate (right side only). Remove shaft from differential with remover (SST09648-16010). Install stopper (SST09563-16010) in differential case to prevent oil leakage.

NOTE — *Do not damage rubber boots of axle driveshaft. Always carry and store shaft in level position.*

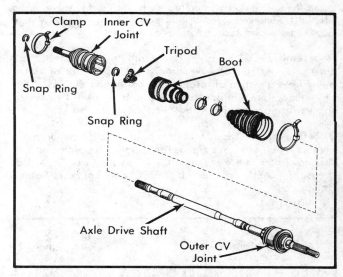

Fig. 2   Exploded View of Axle Drive Shaft Assembly

NOTE — *Before disassembling axle drive shaft, check outer CV joint for any play. If play exists at outer CV joint, replace complete axle drive shaft assembly. Outer CV joint cannot be disassembled.*

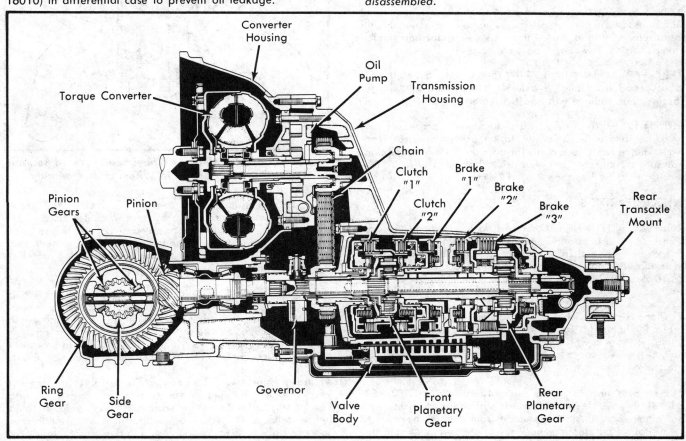

Fig. 1   Cross Sectional View of Toyota Tercel A-55 Automatic Transaxle

TOYOTA MODEL A-55 (Cont.)

Disassembly — Draw alignment marks on inner CV joint and shaft with chalk. Remove snap ring and boot clamps. Remove inner joint from shaft. Place index marks on tripod and axle shaft. Remove snap ring and tap body of tripod to drive tripod off shaft. Remove inner CV joint boot. Remove outer CV joint boot clamps and slide boot off axle shaft.

Reassembly — **1)** Slide new boots onto drive axle shaft. Place clamping rings loosely over boots with open end of clamp away from direction of rotation. Do not tighten clamps at this time. Place beveled side of tripod onto shaft with beveled splines facing outer joint and align reference marks.

2) Before tapping tripod into final position, align centers of inner and outer joints. See Fig. 3. Tap tripod into position and install new snap ring. Pack outer CV joint with 7 ozs. (200 g) of grease (supplied with boot kit). Install outer boot and tighten clamps.

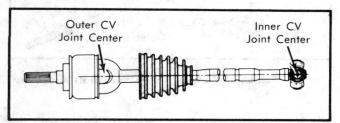

Fig. 3   Sectional View Showing Alignment of Inner and Outer CV Joint Centers

3) Pack inner CV joint with 5 ozs. (140 g) of grease (supplied with boot kit). Align reference marks made at disassembly and install inner CV joint. Install inner CV joint boot and tighten clamps. Install new snap ring on axle shaft.

NOTE — *Right axle shaft is 23.07" (586 mm) long. Left shaft is 27.09" (688 mm) long. If axle shaft does not meet length specification, replace axle shaft assembly.*

Installation — To install, reverse disassembly procedure and note the following: After installation of shafts, check front wheel alignment. Check boots for damage during installation. Measure the distance between drive shafts at transaxle. Distance should be less than 7.6" (194 mm).

WHEEL BEARINGS

Removal — **1)** Raise and support vehicle; remove tire and wheel. Apply brakes and loosen axle shaft nut. Remove brake caliper and suspend from frame with wire; DO NOT remove hydraulic line. Disconnect and remove tie rod end with remover (SST09610-20011). Disconnect and remove stabilizer bar and strut bar.

2) Place a jack and block of wood under left lower control arm and slightly lift control arm. Right side does not require lifting. Remove lower control arm-to-crossmember attaching bolt. Disconnect control arm from crossmember. Remove axle shaft nut.

3) Press axle shaft out of hub assembly with puller (SST09950-20013). Remove steering knuckle-to-suspension strut retaining bolt and separate steering knuckle from strut. Remove lower control arm from steering knuckle. Mount steering knuckle in a vise and remove dust shield, then remove inner oil seal with puller.

4) Press hub assembly out of steering knuckle with puller (SST09608-16031). Remove inner bearing and spacer from knuckle. Place reference marks on hub and disc assembly, then separate hub and disc. Place hub in vise and dislodge outer bearing from hub with hammer and chisel. Remove outer bearing with a puller. Remove scratches from hub bearing surface with oil stone.

NOTE — *Mark bearings for reassembly reference.*

Installation — **1)** Place inner bearing, spacer and outer bearing onto bearing preload holder (SST09608-16040). Coat bearings and bearing housing of steering knuckle with oil. Place assembled bearings into bearing housing and tighten nut to 90 ft. lbs. (12.5 mkg). Rotate assembly back and forth to seat bearings. Install INCH lb. torque wrench and measure bearing preload while turning nut. Bearing preload should be 3.5-8.7 INCH lbs. (4-10 cmkg). See Fig. 4.

NOTE — *Spacers are available in 20 thicknesses ranging from .316" (8.03 mm) to .346" (8.79 mm) in .0016" (.04 mm) increments.*

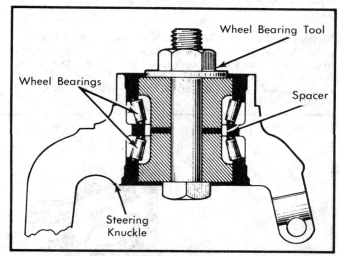

Fig. 4   Assembled View of Wheel Bearings and Bearing Preload Adjusting Tool in Wheel Hub Assembly

2) If preload is not within specifications, select and install suitable spacer and repeat procedure. Mount hub to rotor, align marks made during removal and tighten hub-to-rotor bolts. Pack bearings and bearing housing with grease. Install outer bearing and oil seal in steering knuckle. Install preselected spacer and inner bearing in steering knuckle.

3) Place steering knuckle assembly in vise and press hub assembly into knuckle with press and arbor (SST09636-20010). Do not exceed 2,205 lbs. (1,000 kg) force. With pressure applied, rotate steering knuckle to seat bearings. Attach spring pull scale to steering knuckle stopper and measure frictional force. Frictional force should be .8-1.7 lbs. (.4-.8 kg).

4) Increase force to 7,716 lbs. (3,500 kg) and turn steering knuckle to seat bearings. Attach spring pull scale to steering knuckle stopper and measure bearing preload. Preload should be .8-2.5 lbs. (.4-1.1 kg). If below specification, install thinner spacer; if above specification, install thicker spacer. Install inner oil seal with installer (SST09554-22010) until seal is recessed .156" (4 mm) from end surface. Install dust shield.

TOYOTA MODEL A-55 (Cont.)

5) Complete installation by reversing removal procedure and note the following: Install suspension components snugly. Lower vehicle to floor and bounce vehicle several times to seat suspension. Tighten suspension components with vehicle weight resting on suspension system.

TROUBLE SHOOTING

NO DRIVE IN ANY SELECTOR POSITION

Incorrect fluid level. Manual linkage incorrectly adjusted. Leaking valve body or seals. Sticking or broken valves. Defective oil pump. Defective torque converter.

NO DRIVE IN FORWARD RANGES

Manual linkage incorrectly adjusted. Low fluid level. Defective front clutch.

HARSH ENGAGEMENT

Line pressure is too high. Accumulator is defective. Check ball is defective.

DELAYED ENGAGEMENT

From "N" to "D" — Line Pressure is too low. Front clutch is worn.

From "N" to "R" — Rear clutch is worn. Brake number 3 is worn. Line pressure is too low.

NO 1-2 UPSHIFT

Governor valve is defective. 1-2 shift valve is stuck.

NO 2-3 UPSHIFT

Throttle cable is out of adjustment. Throttle valve is defective. 1-2 shift valve is defective. 2-3 shift valve is defective.

SHIFT POINTS INCORRECT

Throttle cable is out of adjustment. Throttle valve is defective. 1-2 shift valve is defective. 2-3 shift valve is defective. Tire size has been changed. Rear axle ratio has been changed.

SLIPPING ON UPSHIFTS

Clutches worn or defective. Leaking valve body. Low fluid level. Brakes worn or defective. Throttle cable out of adjustment.

HARSH UPSHIFTS

Line pressure too high. Throttle cable out of adjustment.

TESTING

ROAD TEST

1) Before road test, ensure that fluid level and condition, and control linkage adjustments have been checked and corrected as necessary. During test, transmission should upshift and downshift at approximately same speed as shown in *Shift Speed charts*. All shifts may vary slightly due to production

tolerances or tire size. The important factor is the quality of the shifts. All shifts should be smooth, responsive, and with no slippage or engine surge.

2) Slippage or engine speed runaway in any gear usually indicates clutch or brake problems. The slipping clutch or brake in a particular gear can usually be identified by noting transmission operation in other selector positions and comparing internal units which are applied in these positions. See *Clutch and Brake Application chart*.

3) With vehicle at a standstill, place selector lever in "D" and accelerate at half throttle, note 1-2 and 2-3 upshift points. Shift points should be as indicated in *Shift Speeds chart*. Repeat test with full throttle and note shift points. See *Shift Speeds chart*.

4) With selector lever in "D" and transmission in 3rd gear, check kickdown speeds for 2-1 and 3-2. See *Shift Speeds chart*. With vehicle in "D" and 3rd gear, manually shift to "2" and note braking effect of engine. If no engine braking occurs, brake number 1 is defective. Manually shift to "L" position and note braking effect of engine. If no braking occurs, brake number 3 is defective.

5) Place selector lever in "2" and accelerate vehicle at full throttle, note 1-2 upshift speed. Shift speed should be same as upshift speed with selector lever in "D". See *Shift Speeds chart*. Place selector lever in "L" position and accelerate vehicle. There should be no upshift.

Shift Speeds Chart		
Application	**Half Throttle MPH**	**Full Throttle MPH**
In "D"		
1-2 Upshift	15-17	26-36
2-3 Upshift	35-40	53-62
3-2 Downshift	19-24	49-58
2-1 Downshift	8-10	22-31
In "L"		
2-1 Downshift		22-31

STALL SPEED TEST

Testing Precautions — When making test, do not hold throttle open any longer than 5 seconds. If engine speed exceeds limits shown in *Stall Speeds* table, release accelerator immediately as clutch or brake slippage is indicated.

Testing Procedure — With engine and transmission at normal operating temperature tachometer installed and parking and service brakes applied, make transmission stall test in "D" and "R" ranges at full throttle and note maximum RPM obtained. Engine speed should be within limits shown in *Stall Speeds* table.

Stall Speed Specifications	
Application	**Stall RPM**
All Models	2050-2350

TOYOTA MODEL A-55 (Cont.)

CLUTCH AND BRAKE APPLICATION CHART

Selector Lever Position	Clutch 1	Clutch 2		Brake 1	Brake 2	Brake 3	
		Inner Piston	Outer Piston			Inner Piston	Outer Piston
D — DRIVE First Gear Second Gear Third Gear	X X X	X			X X		
2 — IMTERMEDIATE First Gear Second Gear	X X			X	X		
1 — LOW (First)	X					X	
R — REVERSE		X	X			X	X
NEUTRAL OR PARK — All clutches and brakes released and/or ineffective.							

Stall Test Results — 1) If stall speed is below specifications in both ranges, engine performance may be unsatisfactory or stator one-way clutch is not operating properly. If stall speed is more than 600 RPM below specifications, torque converter could be defective.

2) If stall speed is higher than specification in "D" range; front clutch is slipping, one-way clutch number 2 could be defective or line pressure is low. If stall speed is higher than specification in "R" range; rear clutch could be slipping, brake number 3 could be slipping or line pressure is too low.

SHIFT TIME LAG TEST

Testing Procedure — With engine and transmission at normal operating temperature, shift from "N" to "D" and note time it takes for gear engagement (use a stop watch). Repeat this test 2 or 3 times and take an average time. Repeat this test procedure shifting to "R".

Shift Time Lag Specifications	
Application	**Time Lag (Seconds)**
"N" to "D"	Less Than 1.2
"N" to "R"	Less Than 1.5

Test Results — If time lag is longer than specifications when shifting from "N" to "D", line pressure is too low or front clutch is worn. If time lag is longer than specifications when shifting from "N" to "R", rear clutch is worn, brake number 3 is worn or line pressure is too low.

HYDRAULIC PRESSURE TESTS

Governor Pressure Test — 1) Connect a pressure gauge to governor pressure test port. See Fig. 5. Raise and support front of vehicle or place vehicle on a chassis dynomomenter. With engine and transmission at normal operating temperature, place selector lever in "D" and note pressure readings at speeds indicated in Hydraulic Pressure Specifications chart.

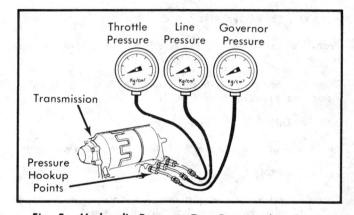

Fig. 5   Hydraulic Pressure Test Port Hookup Points

2) If pressures are not to specifications, governor valve operation is defective, governor pressure circuit is leaking or line pressure is not to specifications.

Line Pressure Test — 1) Connect a pressure gauge to line pressure test port. See Fig. 5. Apply parking brake and service brakes, then with engine and transmission at normal operating temperature, place selector lever in "D" and note pressure readings at speeds indicated in Hydraulic Pressure Specifications chart. Repeat test with selector lever in "R".

2) If test pressures were higher than specifications in all ranges; regulator valve is defective, throttle valve is defective or throttle link is out of adjustment.

3) If test pressures were lower than specifications in all ranges; oil pump is defective, regulator valve is defective, throttle valve is defective or throttle valve link is out of adjustment.

4) If test pressures were low in "D" range; front clutch is defective or "D" range circuit is leaking. If test pressures were low in "R" range; rear clutch is defective, brake number 3 is defective or "R" range circuit is leaking.

TOYOTA MODEL A-55 (Cont.)

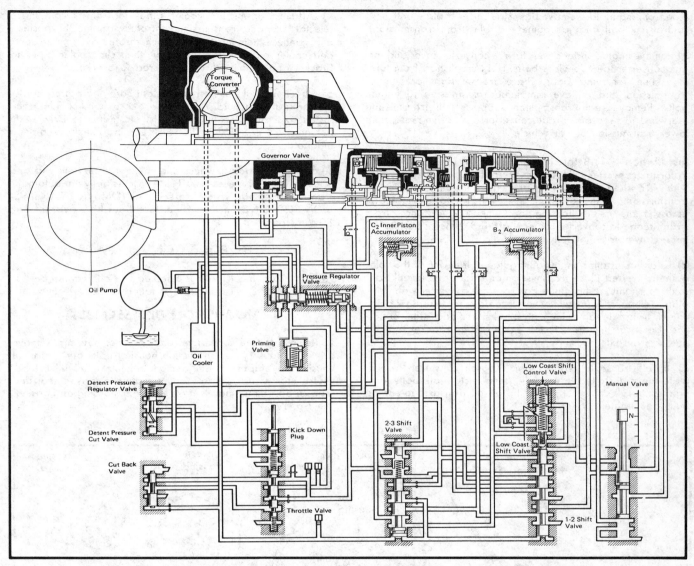

Fig. 6 *Toyota Tercel Model A-55 Automatic Transmission Hydraulic Circuits Diagram*

Hydraulic Pressure Specifications

Application	In "R"	psi (kg/cm²)	In "D"
Governor Pressure			
18 MPH			14-23 (1.0-1.6)
33 MPH			24-33 (1.7-2.3)
64 MPH			61-78 (4.3-5.5)
Line Pressure			
At Idle Speed	84-112 (5.9-6.9)		54-63 (3.8-4.4)
At Stall Speed	205-241 (14.4-16.9)		129-157 (9.1-11.1)
Throttle Pressure			
At Idle Speed	0-4.3 (0-.3)		0-4.3 (0-.3)
At Stall Speed	110-118 (7.7-8.3)		110-118 (7.7-8.3)

Throttle Pressure Test — 1) Connect a pressure gauge to throttle pressure test port. See *Fig. 5.* Apply parking and ser-

vice brakes. With engine and transmission at normal operating temperature, place selector lever in "D" and note pressure readings at speeds indicated in *Hydraulic Pressure Specifications chart.* Repeat test in "R" range.

2) If pressure readings are not to specifications, check throttle linkage adjustment.

REMOVAL & INSTALLATION

TRANSAXLE ASSEMBLY

Removal — 1) Disconnect battery ground and neutral safety switch. Partially drain radiator, then disconnect upper radiator hose at engine. Disconnect throttle linkage, transmission cooler pipes and clamps, then remove throttle linkage bracket. Disconnect cooler pipes from transmission.

2) Remove transmission-to-engine top 2 bolts and top starter bolt. Remove drive axle assemblies. *Refer to Drive Axle Assembly under SERVICE (IN VEHICLE).* Disconnect exhaust

TOYOTA MODEL A-55 (Cont.)

pipe from manifold. Remove right side stiffener plate bolt, shift control link bolt and speedometer cable (from transmission).

3) Remove engine under cover, torque converter cover and torque converter-to-drive plate bolts. Hold crankshaft from turning when removing bolts. Place transmission jack under transmission and remove remaining transmission to engine bolts. Remove rear transmission support. Pull transmission rearward to separate torque converter from drive plate, then lower transmission out of vehicle.

Installation — 1) Before installing transmission, apply grease to torque converter shaft and crankshaft. Fill torque converter with ATF fluid (about 1 quart), then install converter to transmission. With converter installed, lay a straightedge across transmission housing and measure distance from straightedge to converter center shaft. If distance is not .31" (8 mm), converter is not fully seated.

2) To aid in installation, install a guide bolt to one of the holes in the converter. Place transmission on a jack and install transaxle to engine, using guide bolt to align converter with drive plate. Temporarily install converter to drive plate using 2 bolts. Attach transaxle to engine with 2 bolts (one each side) but do not tighten at this time. Install exhaust pipe bracket to right side of transaxle housing.

3) Install transaxle rear support. Loosen converter-to-drive plate bolts installed previously, then install all bolts and tighten. Install converter cover. Install all transaxle-to-engine bolts and tighten.

4) Attach transmission cooler pipes to transmission. Place selector lever and transmission control lever in the "N" position and connect them together. Attach throttle link rod bracket and cooler pipe bracket to body, then clip cooler pipes to bracket and connect throttle link rod to bracket.

5) Attach neutral start switch, coolant hose and battery cable. Fill radiator with fluid. Apply grease to axle oil seal lip, then install axle shafts, caliper, wheels, etc. *Refer to Drive Axle Assembly under SERVICE (IN VEHICLE).* Install exhaust pipe to manifold.

6) Check and adjust wheel alignment, throttle link rod and selector lever if necessary. Fill transmission with automatic transmission fluid Type F. *Refer to AUTOMATIC TRANSMISSION SERVICING Section.* Fill differential with 1 quart of SAE 80W-90 gear oil.

TORQUE CONVERTER

NOTE — *Torque converter is a sealed unit and cannot be disassembled for service. Replace if found to be defective.*

TRANSMISSION DISASSEMBLY

1) Remove torque converter from converter housing. Remove converter housing-to-transmission housing bolts and separate housings by tapping with a mallet. Remove oil filler tube, neutral start switch, control rod, speedometer driven gear and rear support mounting. Remove extension housing and gasket. *See Fig. 7.*

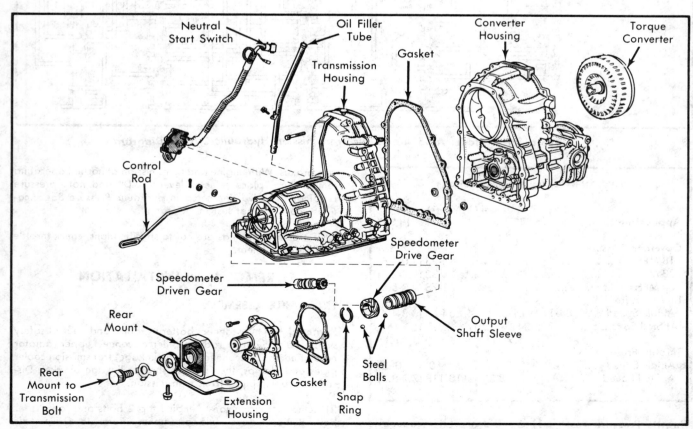

Fig. 7 Exploded View of Transmission and Converter Housing

TOYOTA MODEL A-55 (Cont.)

2) Remove snap ring and slide output shaft with speedometer drive gear out of transmission. Remove speedometer drive gear from output shaft, being careful not to lose the 2 steel balls.

3) Remove oil pan, then turn transmission over so valve body side is up. Remove oil pressure tubes by prying on both ends of tubes. Remove front valve body, with rod, then remove oil strainer. Remove valve body with plate and gaskets. Remove the 6 steel balls from transmission side of valve body.

4) Remove accumulator cover. Using compressed air, remove accumulator pistons (hold pistons from flying out). See Fig. 8. Remove accumulator piston springs. Note size and location of accumulator pistons and springs for reassembly reference. See Fig. 9.

5) Remove parking lock pawl bracket, then remove spring, pin and parking lock pawl. Loosen staked part of ring, on manual valve shaft, then rotate ring 90° to align spring pin with slot in ring. Drive out spring pin and remove manual valve shaft with detent plate, spring, ball and parking lock rod. See Fig. 10.

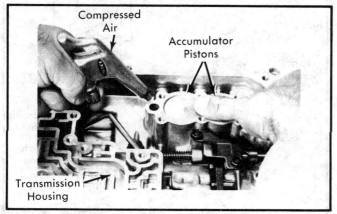

Fig. 8 Removing Accumulator Pistons with Compressed Air

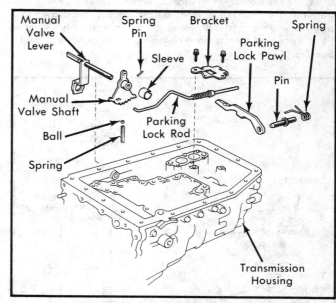

Fig. 10 Removing Parking Lock Pawl and Manual Valve Shaft Components

6) Turn transmission over so valve body side is down. Remove oil pump suction tube bracket and tube. Remove oil pump delivery tube. Remove reverse line pressure tube and throttle pressure tube by prying on both ends of tube.

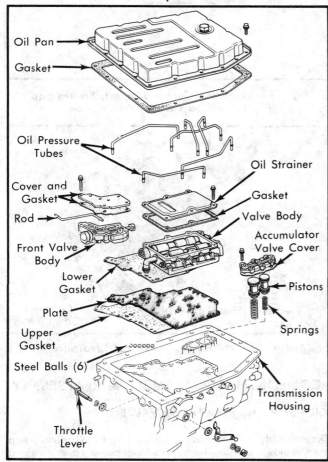

Fig. 9 Exploded View of Transmission Valve Body and Related Components

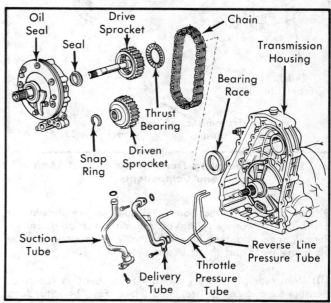

Fig. 11 Removing Oil Pump and Components from Transmission Housing

TOYOTA MODEL A-55 (Cont.)

7) Remove oil pump by loosening 3 inside bolts (do not remove) and removing all outside bolts. Remove oil pump seal. Remove snap ring from oil pump driven sprocket. Pull oil pump drive sprocket chain and driven sprocket out of transmission. Make sure oil pump drive sprocket bearing and race are removed from transmission housing. See *Fig. 11*.

8) Remove bolts attaching front support to transmission housing, then lift front support off output shaft. Remove thrust bearing with races from output shaft. Measure distance from transmission case end to top surface of clutch "1" (front clutch) drum for reassembly reference. Remove clutch "1" with thrust bearing and with race from output shaft. Withdraw front planetary gear and output shaft as an assembly. Remove thrust race and then remove clutch "2" (rear clutch) assembly. See *Fig. 12*.

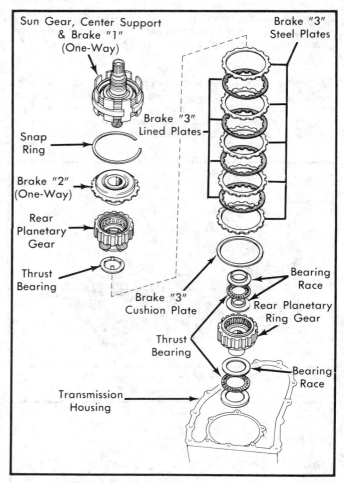

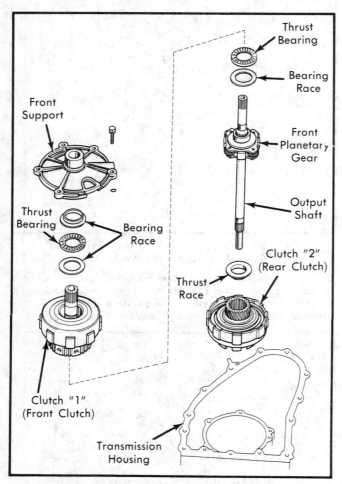

Fig. 12   Removing Transmission Output Shaft and Components

9) Remove center support bolts. Pull sun gear, center support and brake "1" (one-way) out of transmission as an assembly. Remove snap ring, then lift out brake "2" (one-way). Remove planetary gear and thrust bearing. See *Fig. 13*.

10) With rear planetary gear and thrust bearing removed, measure clearance of brake "3". See *Fig. 14*. Standard clearance is .395-.445" (10.04-11.30 mm). Note brake "3" clearance measurement for reassembly reference.

Fig. 13   Removing Center Support, Brakes and Planetary Gears from Transmission

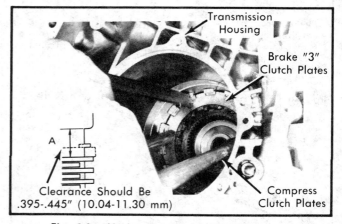

Fig. 14   Measuring Brake "3" Clearance

COMPONENT DISASSEMBLY & REASSEMBLY

OIL PUMP AND REGULATOR VALVE

Disassembly — 1) Remove large "O" ring from around pump, then remove 3 inside bolts attaching pump cover to pump body. Remove snap ring and bearing race from rear of pump body.

TOYOTA MODEL A-55 (Cont.)

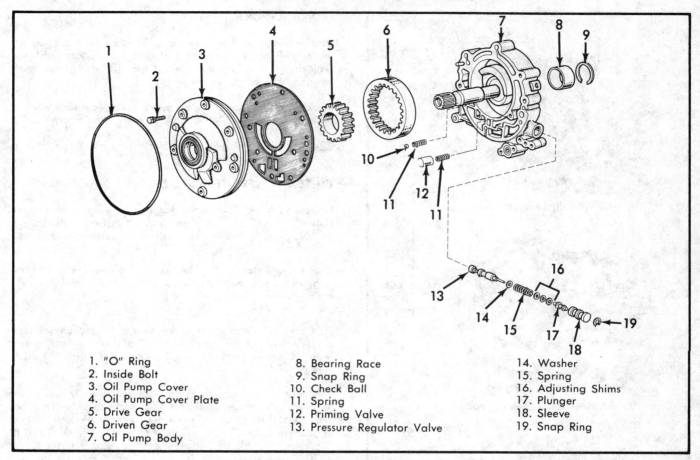

Fig. 15 Exploded View of Oil Pump and Regulator Valve Assembly

1. "O" Ring
2. Inside Bolt
3. Oil Pump Cover
4. Oil Pump Cover Plate
5. Drive Gear
6. Driven Gear
7. Oil Pump Body
8. Bearing Race
9. Snap Ring
10. Check Ball
11. Spring
12. Priming Valve
13. Pressure Regulator Valve
14. Washer
15. Spring
16. Adjusting Shims
17. Plunger
18. Sleeve
19. Snap Ring

2) Remove pump cover and plate from front of pump body, being careful not to let springs and check valves fly out. Remove check ball and spring then priming valve and spring. Remove oil pump drive and driven gears. Remove snap ring, then remove regulator valve assembly. See *Fig. 15.*

NOTE — *When adjusting shims are removed, keep shims together for reassembly.*

Inspection — Check pump cover, plate, body and gears for wear or damage. Check bearing race, bushing and pump shaft for scoring, wear or damage. Check regulator valve body (in pump body) for wear or damage. Check regulator valve and spring for damage, scoring or wear. Check priming valve, check ball and springs for wear or damage. Measure spring lengths and replace if not to specifications. See *Oil Pump Spring Length Specifications chart.*

Oil Pump Spring Specifications

Spring Application	Free Length In. (mm)	Coil Dia. In. (mm)	No. of Coils
Regulator Spring	2.126 (54.0)	.650 (16.5)	8.5
Check Ball Spring	1.032 (26.2)	.236 (6.0)	14
Priming Valve Spring	.756 (19.2)	.224 (5.7)	8

Reassembly — 1) Install oil pump driven and drive gears to pump body. Using a feeler gauge, measure clearance between a straightedge (layed across pump body) and pump gears. Clearance should be .0008-.002" (.02-.05 mm). Measure clearance between driven gear and pump body. Clearance should be .0028-.006" (.07-.15 mm). Next, measure clearance between driven gear tooth and cresent in pump body. Clearance should be .0043-.0055" (.11-.14 mm). See *Fig. 16.* If clearances are not to specifications, replace oil pump.

2) Install check ball valve spring then check ball to pump body. Install priming valve spring and priming valve to pump body. Lubricate large "O" ring with ATF fluid, then install onto pump cover. Assemble pump cover plate to pump cover and install pump cover to pump body.

NOTE — *When installing pump cover, make sure check ball and priming valve seat into pump body correctly.*

3) Temporarily install and tighten (by hand) inside bolts to retain pump cover in place. Check rotation of pump drive gear. Install pressure regulator valve, washer and spring to pump body. Assemble same number of adjusting shims as removed to plunger, then install plunger to spring in pump body. Install sleeve then snap ring.

TOYOTA MODEL A-55 (Cont.)

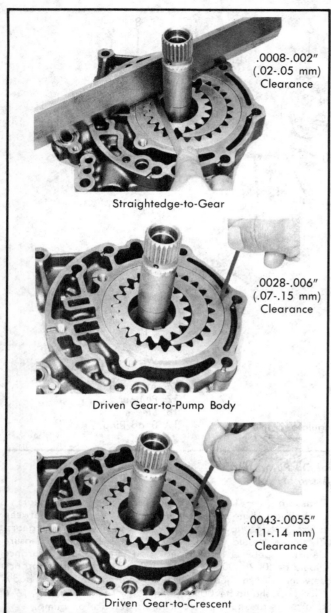

Straightedge-to-Gear

.0008-.002"
(.02-.05 mm)
Clearance

.0028-.006"
(.07-.15 mm)
Clearance

Driven Gear-to-Pump Body

.0043-.0055"
(.11-.14 mm)
Clearance

Driven Gear-to-Crescent

Fig. 16 Measuring Oil Pump Gear Clearance

INPUT SHAFT, GEARS AND CHAIN

Disassembly — Check input shaft, drive and driven gears for wear or damage. Remove snap ring, roller bearing and thrust bearing from input shaft driven gear. Check components for wear, scoring or damage. Check input shaft drive gear rear thrust bearing and race for wear or damage. Inspect chain for wear or damage. Check input shaft oil seal rings for wear or damage.

Reassembly — Replace any components found worn or damaged. Replace oil seal rings if worn or damaged. Install thrust bearing and roller bearing into input shaft driven gear and install snap ring. Install thrust bearing and roller bearing to input shaft drive gear and install snap ring. Place thrust bearing and race to rear of input shaft.

FRONT SUPPORT

Disassembly — Check mating surfaces of front support for wear or damage. Check oil seal rings on support shaft and replace if worn or damaged. Check front support shaft bushing for wear or damage.

Reassembly — Install new oil seal rings if they were worn or damaged. Install new small "O" ring to front support.

NOTE — *Oil seal ring ends are interlocking, make sure rings fit together correctly.*

CLUTCH "1" (FRONT CLUTCH)

Disassembly — 1) Remove large snap ring, then remove clutch "2" (rear clutch) hub from clutch "1" (front clutch) drum. Remove planetary ring gear with thrust bearing and race.

2) Remove 1 steel and 1 lined plate, then remove large snap ring. Remove steel plate, lined plate, steel plate and then cushion plate.

3) Compress piston return spring seat and remove small snap ring. Slowly release compressor tool and remove spring seat with all return springs. Remove piston from clutch "1" drum. See Fig. 17.

Inspection — Check clutch drum, spring retainer and piston for wear or damage. Shake piston to make sure check ball has movement, then using air pressure make sure check ball makes a good seal. Check return springs for a free length of 1.138" (28.9 mm), outside coil diameter of .276" (7.0 mm) and for 12 coils. Check steel plates for scoring or damage and lined plates for wear or burning. Check planetary ring gear, clutch "2" hub, clutch "1", drum, and all thrust bearings for wear or damage. Replace components as necessary.

Reassembly — 1) Replace "O" ring on piston, then install piston, return springs and spring seat. Compress spring seat and install small snap ring. Install cushing plate with convex side facing out of clutch drum.

2) Install steel plate first, then alternate with lined plate until all plates are installed. Install wide large snap ring. Install clutch "2" hub. Do not install narrow large snap ring, bearings or ring gear at this time. With components installed, measure clearance between last steel plate and wide snap ring. Clearance should be .014-.054" (.35-1.37 mm). If not, install thicker snap ring.

3) With proper snap ring selected, remove wide large snap ring, clutch "2" hub, 1 steel plate and 1 lined plate. Install lined plate, steel plate then selected snap ring. Install lined plate and steel plate, then install bearing race, thrust bearing, planetary ring gear, clutch "2" hub and large snap ring.

OUTPUT SHAFT & FRONT PLANETARY GEAR

Disassembly — Remove snap ring and slide planetary gears off output shaft. Check output shaft for wear or damage. Check planetary gear for wear or damage. Check planetary gear thrust play. Thrust play should be .008-.020" (.2-.5 mm). Check planetary thrust bearing and race for wear or damage. Replace components as necessary.

TOYOTA MODEL A-55 (Cont.)

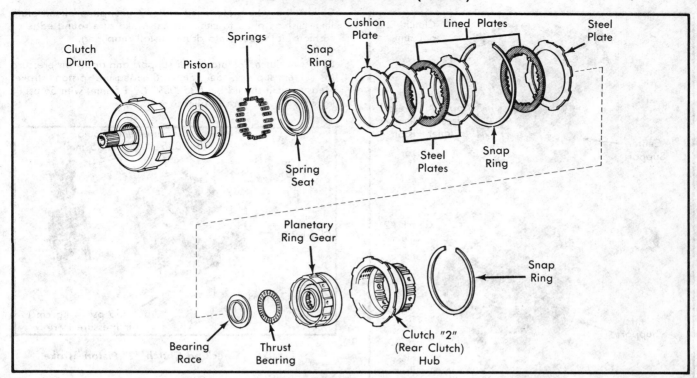

Fig. 17 Exploded View of Clutch "1" (Front Clutch)

Reassembly — To reassemble output shaft and front planetary gear, reverse disassembly procedure.

CLUTCH "2" (REAR CLUTCH)

Disassembly — 1) Remove large snap ring, then remove steel plates and lined plates noting order of removal. Compress piston return spring seat and remove small snap ring.

2) Slowly remove pressure on spring seat, then remove spring seat with all return springs. Remove inner piston then remove outer piston, See Fig. 18.

3) If pistons are difficult to remove, place clutch drum into the center support. Using air pressure applied to inner piston port, blow out inner piston. Move air pressure to outer piston port and remove outer piston. See Fig. 19.

Inspection — Check clutch drum, sun gear, spring retainer and piston for wear or damage. Make sure seal ring contacting surface and snap ring groove areas are not damaged. Shake outer piston to make sure check ball has movement. Apply air to check ball orifice, no air should leak by. Check inner piston in same manner as outer. Check return springs for a free length of 1.138" (28.9 mm), outside coil diameter of .276" (7.0 mm) and for 12 coils. Check steel plates and lined plates for burning, excessive wear or other damage.

Reassembly — 1) Install new "O" rings to inner and outer pistons (lubricate "O" rings before installation). Lubricate

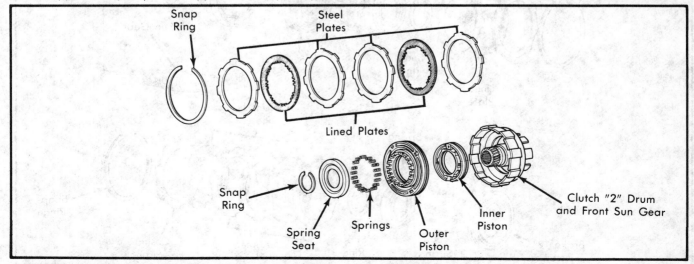

Fig. 18 Exploded View of Clutch "2" (Rear Clutch)

TOYOTA MODEL A-55 (Cont.)

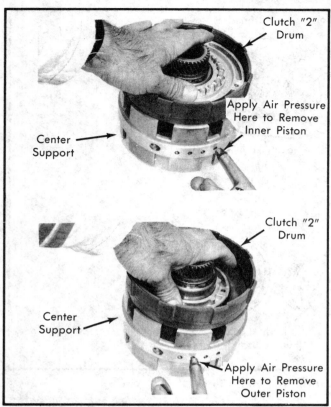

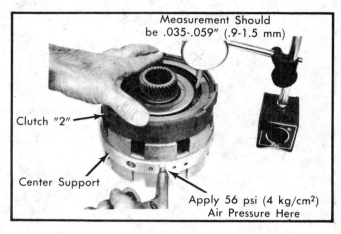

2) Install a steel plate, lined plate, 2 steel plates, lined plate then cushion plate to clutch drum. Make sure round edge of cushion plate faces into drum. Install snap ring.

3) Install clutch "2" into center support and apply air pressure to center support. See Fig. 20. Measure piston stroke. Measurement should be .035-.059" (.9-1.5 mm) with 56 psi (4 kg/cm²) air pressure applied.

Fig. 20 Checking Clutch "2" Piston Stroke

Fig. 19 Removing Inner and Outer Pistons of Clutch "2" with Compressed Air

pistons and install into clutch drum. Make sure spring seats in pistons are facing out of drum. With springs installed to pistons, install spring seat and compress to install snap ring. Make sure snap ring is seated properly before releasing spring compressor.

CENTER SUPPORT AND COMPONENTS

Disassembly — 1) Withdraw sun gear from center support. Remove front one-way clutch from center support. Remove large snap ring holding brake "1" plates, then remove steel plate, lined plate and cushion plate.

NOTE — *Keep brake "1" plates separate from brake "2" plates. They are not interchangeable.*

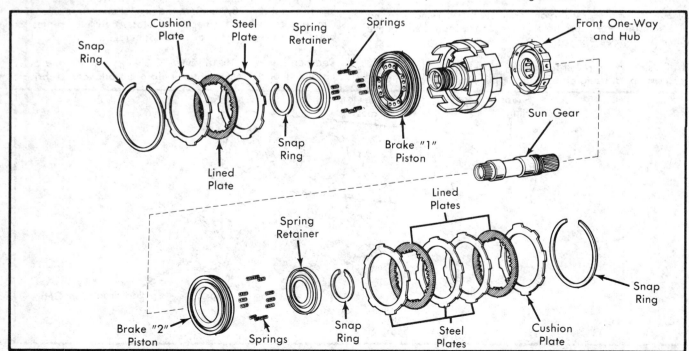

Fig. 21 Exploded View of Center Support, Brake "1", Brake "2", Sun Gear and Front One-Way Clutch

TOYOTA MODEL A-55 (Cont.)

2) Turn center support over and remove large snap ring, steel plates and lined plates for brake "2". Using a spring compressor, compress spring seat of brake "2" and remove small snap ring. Slowly release pressure and remove spring seat with springs. Apply air pressure to center support brake "2" pressure port to remove piston.

3) Turn center support over and compress spring retainer of brake "1". Remove small snap ring and slowly release compressor. Remove springs then apply air pressure to remove piston.

Inspection — Check all components for wear or damage. Check center support oil seal rings and grooves for wear or damage. Check brake "1" and brake "2" springs for a free length of .635" (16.1 mm), coil outside diameter of .276" (7.0 mm) and for 6 coils. Check front one-way clutch by inserting sun gear into clutch and checking for rotation. From sun gear tooth end, sun gear should rotate counterclockwise but lock up in clockwise rotation. Check oil seal rings on sun gear. Replace components as necessary.

Reassembly — **1)** Install new "O" rings on brake pistons and lubricate with ATF fluid. Install brake "1" piston into center support and rotate by hand to make sure it is seated correctly. Place springs on piston then spring retainer. Compress spring retainer and install small snap ring.

2) Turn center support over and install brake "2" piston, springs and retainer in same manner as brake "1". Assemble brake "2" cushion plate, lined plate and steel plate, then install them to center support. Make sure rounded edge of cushion plate faces toward center support.

3) Install brake "1" plates in same manner as brake "2". See Fig. 21 for steel plate and lined plate installation sequence. With large snap rings installed to brake plates, measure piston stroke of each brake piston.

4) Brake "1" piston stroke should be .026-.051" (.65-1.3 mm) with 56 psi (4 kg/cm²) air pressure applied. Brake "2" piston stroke should be .037-.068" (.93-1.7 mm) with 56 psi (4 kg/cm²) air pressure applied.

5) Install front one-way clutch to center support and check that clutch protrudes approximately .20" (5 mm) from cushion plate. Install sun gear to center support and check rotation of gear to confirm correct installation of front one-way clutch.

REAR ONE-WAY CLUTCH AND PLANETARY GEAR

Disassembly — Remove thrust washer from rear of planetary gear. Remove brake reaction plate from front of planetary gear. Remove snap ring, one-way clutch and thrust washer from planetary gear. See Fig. 22.

Inspection — Check one-way clutch, brake reaction plate, and thrust washers for wear or damage. Check planetary gears for smooth rotation and any damage to gear teeth. Check all thrust bearings for damage or wear.

Reassembly — **1)** Install thrust washer into planetary gear. Make sure thrust washer slot fits into slot in planetary gear. Install one-way clutch in planetary gear. Make sure lip on clutch faces out of planetary gear and rollers on clutch are inclining in a counterclockwise direction.

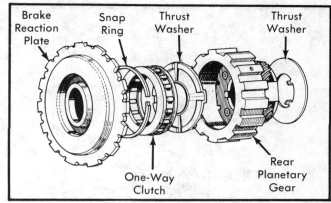

Fig. 22   Exploded View of Rear One-Way Clutch and Planetary Gear

2) Install snap ring. Place brake reaction plate on planetary gear. Hold assembly so planetary gears are facing you, then rotate planetary gears. Check for smooth rotation and that gears will only rotate in a counterclockwise direction.

BRAKE "3" PISTON

Disassembly — Compress spring retainer and remove small snap ring. Slowly release spring compressor and remove spring retainer and springs. Place shop towels on top of piston and hold piston from coming out while applying air pressure to brake "3" pressure port. See Fig. 23.

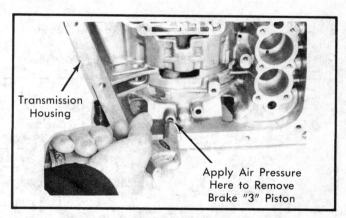

Fig. 23   Removing Brake "3" Piston with Air Pressure

Inspection — Check piston, spring retainer, snap ring and transmission housing (piston area) for wear or damage. Check bushing in transmission housing for wear or damage. Check piston springs for a free length of 1.030" (26.2 mm), coil outside diameter of .276" (7.0 mm) and for 9 coils.

Reassembly — **1)** Install a new "O" ring to piston and install piston to transmission housing. Make sure lip on piston mates with notch in transmission housing (this notch is wider than other notches).

2) Install springs and spring seat, then compress spring seat and install snap ring. See Fig. 24.

3) Check steel plates and lined plates of brake "3". Install cushion plate (concave side down toward transmission hous-

TOYOTA MODEL A-55 (Cont.)

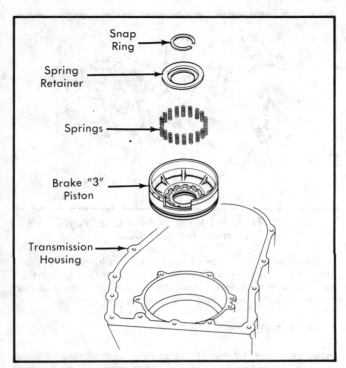

Fig. 24 Exploded View of Brake "3"

ing). Install brake plates, starting with a steel plate and alternating with lined plates until all plates are installed.

4) Measure brake "3" clearance. *Refer to Fig. 14 and to Transmission Disassembly for measuring procedures.* Clearance should be .395-.445" (10.04-11.30 mm). If

clearance is not to specifications, recheck plates for excessive wear or a damaged cushion plate. Replace components as necessary.

VALVE BODY

NOTE — *When disassembling valve body, lay removed components out in order for reassembly reference.*

Disassembly — 1) Remove manual valve from front valve body. Remove front valve body from valve body. Remove pin from cut back plug, then remove plug and cut back valve. Remove cover and gasket, then remove 2-3 shift valve seat, valve and spring.

2) Remove 1-2 shift valve and spring. Remove oil pump suction tube. Remove detent pressure cut valve plug then detent pressure cut valve. Remove detent regulator valve and spring.

3) Remove shift valve plug seat, 2-3 shift valve plug and intermediate coast shift valve. Remove snap ring, plug, low coast shift control valve and spring. Remove low coast shift control valve sleeve and valve. *See Fig. 25.*

4) From transmission housing, remove down shift plug pin then remove down shift plug. Remove spring, vibrating seat, throttle valve, spring and adjusting spacer(s). Remove throttle valve sleeve. Record number of adjusting spacers for reassembly reference. *See Fig. 26.*

Inspection — Check all components for wear, scoring or damage. Check springs against *Valve Body Spring specifications chart.*

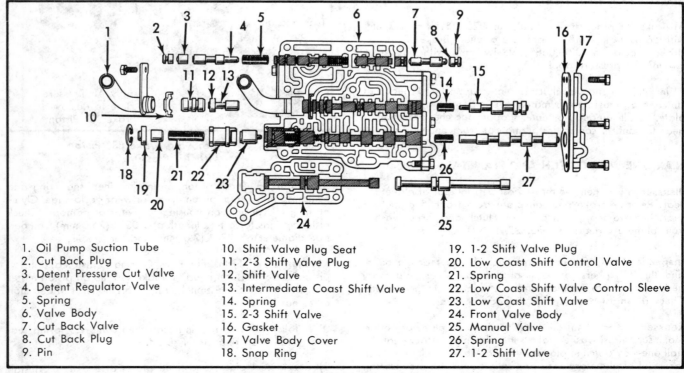

1. Oil Pump Suction Tube	10. Shift Valve Plug Seat	19. 1-2 Shift Valve Plug
2. Cut Back Plug	11. 2-3 Shift Valve Plug	20. Low Coast Shift Control Valve
3. Detent Pressure Cut Valve	12. Shift Valve	21. Spring
4. Detent Regulator Valve	13. Intermediate Coast Shift Valve	22. Low Coast Shift Valve Control Sleeve
5. Spring	14. Spring	23. Low Coast Shift Valve
6. Valve Body	15. 2-3 Shift Valve	24. Front Valve Body
7. Cut Back Valve	16. Gasket	25. Manual Valve
8. Cut Back Plug	17. Valve Body Cover	26. Spring
9. Pin	18. Snap Ring	27. 1-2 Shift Valve

Fig. 25 Exploded View of Throttle Body and Components

TOYOTA MODEL A-55 (Cont.)

VALVE BODY SPRING IDENTIFICATION

Valve Spring	Length In. (mm)	Diameter In. (mm)	Number Of Coils	Wire Thickness In. (mm)
1-2 Shift Valve Spring	1.024 (26.0)	.183 (4.65)	14.5	.020 (.5)
Low Coast Valve Spring	1.437 (36.5)	.291 (7.4)	14	.047 (1.2)
2-3 Shift Valve Spring	.870 (22.1)	.228 (5.8)	9.5	.024 (.6)
Detent Regulator				
Valve Spring	1.038 (26.36)	.276 (7.0)	10.5	.040 (1.0)
Throttle Valve Spring				
Front	1.194 (30.33)	.301 (7.65)	10	.035 (.9)
Rear	1.083 (27.5)	.268 (6.8)	10.25	.024 (.6)
Accumulator Spring				
Front	2.638 (67.0)	.616 (15.5)	12.5	.....
Rear	1.513 (38.42)	.472 (12.0)	10	.....

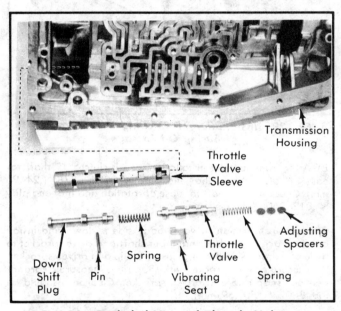

Fig. 26 Exploded View of Throttle Valve

Reassembly — **1)** Install manual valve into front valve body. Insert low coast shift valve, low coast shift control valve sleeve, low coast shift control valve, 1-2 shift valve plug, and snap ring to valve body. *Refer to Fig. 25.*

2) Insert shift valve, 2-3 shift valve plug into valve body and hold in place with shift valve plug seat (tangs on seat face into valve body). Place detent regulator valve spring, detent regulator valve, detent pressure cut valve and plug into valve body. Plug has a groove cut into it, place edge of oil pump suction tube into this groove to hold components in place. Attach suction tube to valve body with bolt. *Refer to Fig. 25.*

3) Insert 1-2 shift valve spring, 1-2 shift valve, 2-3 shift valve spring and 2-3 shift valve into valve body. Attach valve body cover, with gasket, to hold shift valves in position. Install cut back valve and plug into valve body. Insert pin into cut back valve plug. *Refer to Fig. 25.*

4) Install same number of adjusting spacers into throttle valve sleeve as removed, then install sleeve into transmission housing. Insert spring, throttle valve, spring, down shift plug and pin into transmission housing. Insert vibrating stopper into transmission housing. *Refer to Fig. 26.*

5) Attach front valve body cover to valve body.

GOVERNOR VALVE

Disassembly — Remove snap ring and washer, then pull governor valve out of governor pressure adapter. Remove bolts attaching adapter to converter housing and remove adapter. Remove retaining ring, then pull governor body support out of governor body. Remove "E" clip and governor weight. Remove valve shaft, spring and governor valve from governor body. *See Fig. 27.*

Inspection — Check all governor components for wear or damage. Check governor body support oil seal rings for wear or damage. Check governor spring for free length of .728" (18.5 mm), coil outside diameter of .295" (7.5 mm) and for 6 coils.

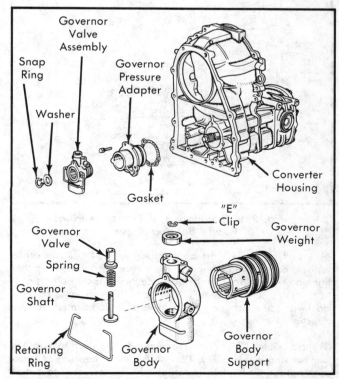

Fig. 27 Exploded View of Governor Valve Assembly

TOYOTA MODEL A-55 (Cont.)

Reassembly — To reassemble governor, reverse disassembly procedure. Make sure retaining ring holes in governor body support are aligned with holes in governor body.

TRANSMISSION REASSEMBLY

1) Install drive plate, with spacers, to crankshaft. Install front spacer, .127" (3.2 mm) thick, with beveled edge facing drive plate then install drive plate. Install rear spacer, .056" (1.4 mm) thick, with cupped edge facing converter.

2) Install thrust bearing and races then rear planetary ring gear to transmission housing. Install thrust bearing and races, then install cushion plate and steel and lined plates to transmission housing. Make sure planetary ring gear is fully seated, then measure brake "3" clearance. *Refer to Fig. 14.* Clearance should be .395-.445" (10.04-11.30 mm).

3) Install thrust washer, planetary gear, brake reaction plate, snap ring and center support to transmission housing. *Refer to Fig. 13 for plate installation sequence. See Fig. 28 for thrust bearing and bearing race installation.*

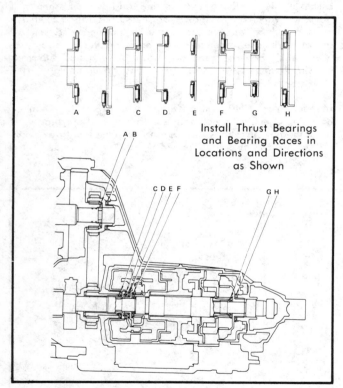

Install Thrust Bearings and Bearing and Races in Locations and Directions as Shown

Fig. 28   *Installation of Thrust Bearings and Bearing Races*

4) Install center support bolts, make sure oil holes in center support are aligned with oil holes in transmission housing then tighten center support bolts. After center support bolt installation, make sure planetary sun gear is easy to turn in a clockwise direction and hard to turn in a counterclockwise direction.

5) Install clutch "2", bearing race and output shaft to transmission housing. *Refer to Fig. 12.* Install a thrust bearing and race over output shaft, then install clutch "1" assembly to output shaft.

6) After clutch "1" installation, lay a straightedge across clutch drum and transmission housing. Measure distance from straightedge to clutch drum. Distance should be the same as distance measured during disassembly. Standard distance is .024-.063" (.6-1.6 mm).

7) Install thrust bearing and race to clutch "1" shaft. Insert bearing race into front support. Install "O" ring to transmission housing. *See Fig. 29.* Install front support to transmission housing.

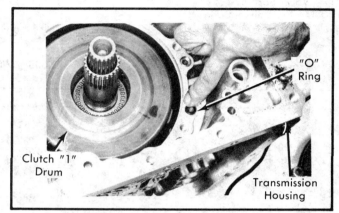

"O" Ring

Clutch "1" Drum

Transmission Housing

Fig. 29   *Installation of "O" Ring in Transmission Housing Oil Passage*

8) After front support installation, check clutch "1" shaft for ease of rotation and that end play is .0094-.0378" (.24-.96 mm). Check output shaft for ease of rotation and that end play is .012-.060" (.31-1.53 mm).

9) Place transmission so valve body side is down and install bearing race, thrust bearing, input shaft and drive sprocket to front of transmission housing. Install chain and driven sprocket, then secure driven sprocket with snap ring. Measure clearance between snap ring and driven sprocket. Clearance should be .0043-.027" (.11-.69 mm).

10) Install bearing race to input shaft, then install oil pump over input shaft. *Refer to Fig. 11.* Install throttle pressure tube then reverse line pressure tube to front of transmission housing. Use new "O" rings, install oil pump delivery tube and oil pump suction to front of transmission housing. *See Fig. 30.*

11) Install spacer and parking lock rod to manual valve lever. Install spring and ball to transmission, then place manual valve lever onto spring and compress until manual valve lever aligns with hole in transmission housing. Insert manual valve shaft through transmission housing and manual valve lever. Insert spring pin into manual valve lever. *Refer to Fig. 10.*

12) Insert pin into parking lock pawl then attach spring to pin. Install parking lock pawl assembly to transmission housing and secure with parking lock pawl bracket. Shift manual valve lever to "P" position and check the locking condition. If it does not lock properly, disassemble and check components for wear or damage and reassemble. If it locks properly, place manual shift lever in the "N" position.

13) Turn transmission over so valve body side is up. Install accumulator springs and pistons, fully seat pistons by hand. Install accumulator gasket (straight side of gasket nearest housing), then install accumulator cover. *Refer to Fig. 9.*

TOYOTA MODEL A-55 (Cont.)

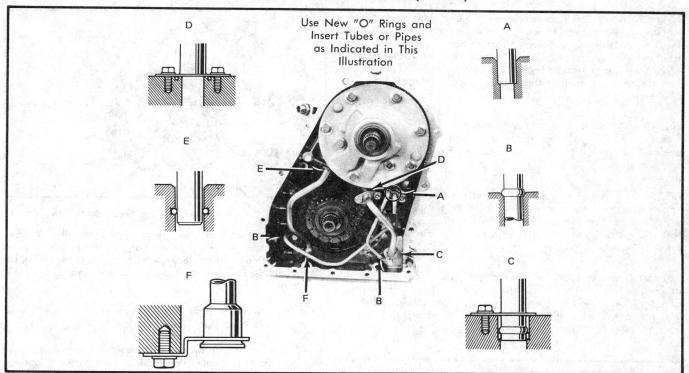

Use New "O" Rings and Insert Tubes or Pipes as Indicated in This Illustration

Fig. 30 *Installation of Oil Tubes and Pipes to Front of Transmission Housing*

Fig. 31 *Installation Locations of Valve Body Steel Balls*

14) Install steel balls into valve body on transmission side. *See Fig. 31.* Make sure vibrating stopper is still in place and install upper valve body gasket. *Refer to Fig. 9 for gasket installation sequence.* Also make sure cut back plug lock pin has not fallen out. Install valve body plate, lower gasket and valve body. When installing valve body, make sure oil pump suction pipe is fully seated in transmission housing.

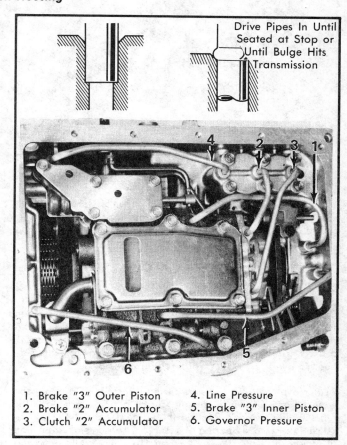

Drive Pipes In Until Seated at Stop or Until Bulge Hits Transmission

1. Brake "3" Outer Piston
2. Brake "2" Accumulator
3. Clutch "2" Accumulator
4. Line Pressure
5. Brake "3" Inner Piston
6. Governor Pressure

Fig. 32 *Installation of Oil Pressure Tubes*

TOYOTA MODEL A-55 (Cont.)

15) Install oil strainer and gasket to valve body. Attach rod to manual valve lever and to manual valve (in front valve body), then install front valve body to transmission housing. Install front valve body cover and gasket. Place a waved washer then a plain washer on throttle lever shaft. Insert throttle lever shaft into transmission, then install a plain washer, throttle lever, washers and nut.

16) Check throttle lever thrust clearance. If clearance is greater than .020" (.5 mm), install additional washers to outside of lever. Install oil pressure tubes. See Fig. 32. Install oil pan and gasket.

17) Place transmission housing-to-converter housing gasket on transmission housing (coated with sealant). Install new "O" rings into transmission housing-to-converter housing oil passages. Attach converter housing-to-transmission housing. Refer to Fig. 7.

18) Install output shaft sleeve with speedometer drive gear and balls to transmission output shaft. Secure sleeve with snap ring. Install extension housing and gasket to transmission housing. Attach transmission rear mount to rear of transmission housing.

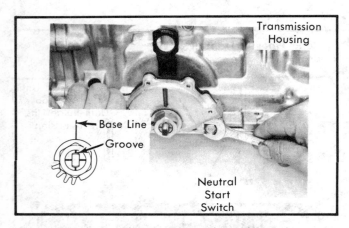

Fig. 33 Aligning Neutral Start Switch

19) Install speedometer driven gear, neutral start switch, oil filler tube and control rod to transmission. When installing neutral start switch, align switch shaft groove to neutral base line. See Fig. 33. Install torque converter.

FINAL DRIVE

DIFFERENTIAL ASSEMBLY

Disassembly — 1) Mount transmission/converter housing on support stand and remove differential cover. Measure and record ring gear backlash, ring gear runout and check tooth contact pattern. Remove and mark side bearing caps and side bearing washers. Lift out differential assembly.

2) Remove converter housing oil seals. Install INCH lb. torque wrench and measure pinion shaft bearing preload for reassembly reference. Preload should be 5.2-8.7 INCH lbs. (6-10 cmkg). Remove bearing oil reservoir. Loosen staked portion of pinion shaft nut. Remove pinion shaft nut. While removing nut, turn pinion shaft clockwise with collar (SST09556-16010). Press out pinion shaft and collapsible spacer.

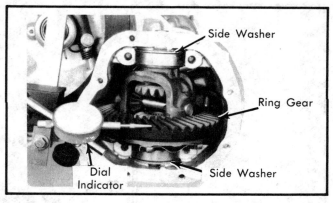

Fig. 34 Measuring Ring Gear Backlash

3) Remove pinion shaft front bearing with a puller. Remove shim and place aside for reassembly. Remove rear bearing and race. Remove differential side bearing races and mark for identification. Pull off side bearings and mark for identification.

NOTE — Differential case has indentations for insertion of puller jaws to ease side bearing removal.

4) Remove staking from ring gear bolt lock plates. Remove ring gear bolts and lock plate. Using chalk, draw alignment mark on ring gear and differential case. Tap ring gear off differential case. Tap out differential lock pin. Remove pinion shaft, pinion gears, side gears and thrust washers.

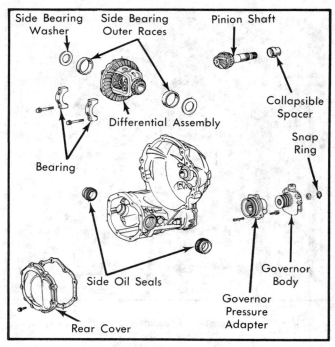

Fig. 35 Differential/Converter Housing

Reassembly — 1) Install thrust washers, side gears, pinion gears and pinion shaft. Hold 1 side gear and measure backlash of opposite side gear. Backlash should be .0016-.0094" (.04-.24 mm). If backlash is not to specification, disassemble differential case and install proper side gear thrust washers. Recheck backlash and install lock pin. Stake differential case.

TOYOTA MODEL A-55 (Cont.)

NOTE — *Side gear thrust washers are available in 6 thicknesses ranging from .059" (1.50 mm) to .069" (1.75 mm) in increments of .002" (.05 mm).*

2) Heat ring gear to 212° F (100° C). Install ring gear with marks aligned. Install new lock plates. Install and tighten nuts, then stake lock plates. Press on differential side bearings.

PINION BEARING PRELOAD

1) Measure and record thickness of pinion shim with micrometer and install shim on pinion shaft. Press on new front bearing. Slide new collapsible spacer onto pinion shaft. Install pinion shaft and collapsible spacer into transaxle housing. Press in rear bearing (do not smash collapsible spacer) until threaded portion of pinion shaft extends .12" (3 mm) above rear bearing surface.

2) Coat threaded portion of pinion shaft with oil, then install pinion shaft nut. Tighten nut to 108 ft. lbs. (15 mkg).

3) Apply gear oil to bearings and rotate pinion shaft to seat bearings with socket (SST09556-16010). Attach INCH lb. torque wrench and measure bearing preload. Preload for new bearings should be 4.3-8.7 INCH lbs. (5-10 cmkg); used bearings should be 2.6-4.3 INCH lbs. (3-5 cmkg).

4) If preload is above specification, replace collapsible spacer and test again. If preload is not to specification, gradually tighten pinion nut 5-10° at a time and measure preload after each tightening. If preload is insufficient after reaching maximum torque value of 267 ft. lbs. (37 mkg), loosen pinion nut and repeat procedure.

NOTE — *If preload is not within specifications after reaching maximum torque value, install new collapsible spacer and repeat procedure.*

RING GEAR BACKLASH

1) Mount transmission/converter housing so ring gear side of housing is down. Install outer side bearing races. Insert lower differential side bearing washer, then install differential case into housing. Tap differential into position with plastic hammer.

NOTE — *Do not interchange side bearings.*

2) Mount dial indicator. Hold upper side bearing outer race against side bearing and measure ring gear backlash. Backlash should be .0039-.0059" (.10-.15 mm). Select and install a washer which will eliminate any clearance between outer race and housing. Recheck ring gear backlash.

3) Remove differential side bearing races and washer. Measure thickness of washers with micrometer, divide by 2 and select appropriate shims of equal thickness for each side of differential assembly. Reinstall differential assembly, side bearing outer races and washers. Measure ring gear runout. If not to specification, increase or decrease washer thickness until specification is obtained. Ring gear runout should be .0028" (.07 mm).

NOTE — *Side bearing washers are available in the following thicknesses: .103-.129" (2.62-3.28 mm) in .001" (.03 mm) increments. Backlash will change about .0008" (.02 mm) with .001" (.03 mm) alteration of side bearing washers.*

4) After adjusting ring gear backlash, install side bearing caps and tighten bolts. Do not interchange bearing caps. Mount dial indicator on pinion nut and measure total ring and pinion bearing preload. Preload should be 2.6-4.3 INCH lbs. (3-5 cmkg) PLUS amount of pinion bearing preload.

GEAR TOOTH CONTACT PATTERN

NOTE — *Final adjustments to differential are made with results from gear tooth contact pattern. See Gear Tooth Contact Pattern in DRIVE AXLES Section.*

1) If excessive heel or toe contact is evident, readjust pinion shaft depth. Pinion depth is adjusted by installing thinner shim (excessive toe contact) or thicker shim (excessive heel contact). Altering thickness of pinion washer .0039" (.10 mm) will change center of tooth contact 1/8 of total tooth contact.

NOTE — *Pinion washers are available in 16 thicknesses ranging from .0591" (1.50 mm) to .0768" (1.95 mm) in .0012" (.03 mm) increments.*

2) Too much flank or face contact reveals incorrect ring gear backlash. Too much flank contact can be eliminated by installing thicker side bearing washers (adjust backlash closer to high side of specification). Too much face contact can be eliminated by installing thinner side bearing washers (adjust backlash closer to low side of specification).

NOTE — *Increase or decrease both side washers in equal amounts.*

3) After adjusting pinion depth and ring gear backlash according to gear tooth contact pattern, check ring gear backlash. Stake pinion nut and reinstall rear cover and gasket. Install differential side bearing oil seals with installer (SST09223-46011) until seal protrudes .331-.354" (8.4-9.0 mm) from housing.

TIGHTENING SPECIFICATIONS

Application	Ft. Lbs. (mkg)
Axle Shaft Nut	73-108 (10.0-15.0)
Ball Joint-to-Steering Knuckle	40-52 (5.5-7.2)
Center Support Bolts	18-20 (2.5-2.8)
Drive Plate	44-50 (6.1-6.9)
Engine Front Mount-to-Crossmember	26-39 (3.6-5.4)
Engine Rear Mount-to-Body	26-36 (3.6-5.0)
Engine-to-Converter Housing	37-57 (5.1-7.9)
Hub-to-Rotor	29-36 (4.0-5.1)
Lower Arm-to-Crossmember	51-65 (7.1-9.0)
Lower Arm-to-Strut Bar	29-39 (4.0-5.4)
Pinion Nut	109-267 (15.0-37.0)
Rear Trans. Mount-to-Ext. Hsg.	55-79 (7.6-10.9)
Ring Gear Bolts	67-75 (9.3-10.4)
Side Bearing Caps	33-39 (4.6-5.4)
Stabilizer Bracket	22-32 (3.0-4.5)
Stabilizer-to-Lower Arm	11-15 (1.6-2.0)
Strut Bar-to-Strut Bracket	55-79 (7.6-10.9)
Strut-to-Steering Knuckle	40-52 (5.5-7.2)
Transmission-to-Converter Hsg.	11-15 (1.6-2.0)

VOLKSWAGEN VANAGON

TRANSAXLE IDENTIFICATION

Transmission portion of transaxle assembly may be identified by a group of numbers stamped into top of transmission case. One of the numbers is "090", and this denotes the Volkswagen "2-planetary" type transmission. Final drive portion of transaxle assembly may be identified by a group of figures stamped into final drive housing near governor assembly. These figures consist of a 2 letter model code and a build date code.

DESCRIPTION

Transaxle assembly consists of two main units: Automatic transmission and final drive assembly. The transmission housing contains two planetary gear sets, two multi-disc clutches, one brake band and servo, one multiple-disc brake, a one-way clutch, and a hydraulic control system. The final drive housing contains the torque converter, governor assembly for transmission, ring and pinion gear, and the differential assembly.

LUBRICATION & ADJUSTMENT

See *AUTOMATIC TRANSMISSION SERVICING* Section.

TROUBLE SHOOTING

NO MOVEMENT

In Any Gear — Low fluid level. Manual lever not connected to manual valve. Torque converter disconnected from drive plate.

Main pressure valve sticking. Oil pump drive plate and/or shaft defective.

In Forward Gears — Forward clutch internal damage (worn plates, broken diaphragm spring, seals leaking, etc.). Forward planetary gear set damaged.

In First Gear in "D" or "2" — One-way clutch not holding. Forward clutch internal damage.

In First Gear in "1" — First/reverse brake plates worn or burnt.

In Second Gear — Second gear brake band out of adjustment, or burnt, or servo defective.

In Reverse — First/reverse brake plates worn or burnt. Direct/reverse clutch internal damage. Forward clutch seized in applied position.

NO UPSHIFTS

Into Second Gear — Governor drive defective. Governor dirty or improperly assembled. Accumulator cover plate loose. Valve body dirty. 1-2 shift valve sticking. Second gear brake band burnt or worn.

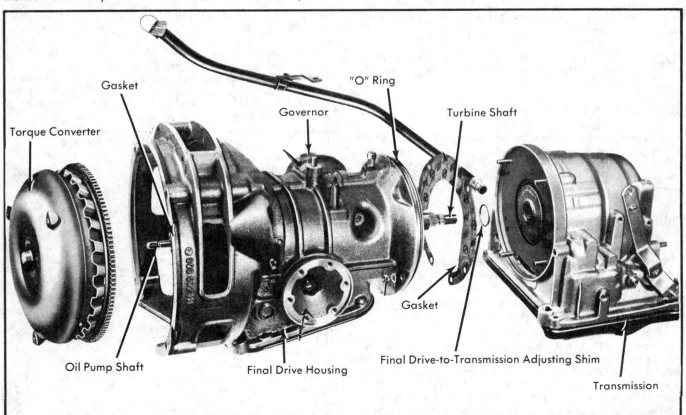

Fig. 1 Volkswagen Vanagon Automatic Transaxle Assembly

VOLKSWAGEN VANAGON (Cont.)

Into Third Gear — Governor or valve body dirty. 2-3 shift valve sticking. Transfer plate check ball missing. Oil pump bolts loose.

NO DOWNSHIFTS

Into Second Gear — Governor dirty. 2-3 shift valve sticking.

Into First Gear — Governor dirty. 1-2 shift valve sticking.

DELAYED ENGAGEMENT ON UPSHIFTS

1-2 Upshift — Low fluid level. Dirty valve body. Second gear brake band worn, burnt or out of adjustment. Second gear servo defective.

2-3 Upshift — Low fluid level. Dirty valve body. Second gear brake band worn, burnt or out of adjustment. Second gear servo defective. Direct/reverse clutch plates worn or burnt. Wrong direct/reverse clutch installed.

ERRATIC DRIVE

Low fluid level. Bushing in one-way clutch support and turbine shaft worn. Oil filter dirty.

INCORRECT SHIFT SPEEDS

Governor dirty. Valve body dirty. Planetary gears or separation plate gasket damaged.

TESTING

ROAD TEST

1) Before road testing, be certain that fluid level and condition, and control linkage adjustments have been checked and corrected as necessary. During the test, transmission should upshift and downshift at approximately the speeds shown in Shift Speeds chart. All shifts may vary somewhat due to production tolerances or tire size. The important factor is the quality of the shifts. All shifts should be smooth, responsive, and with no slippage or engine speed runaway.

2) Slippage or engine runaway in any gear usually indicates clutch, band or brake problems. The slipping unit in a particular gear can usually be identified by noting transmission operation in other selector positions and comparing which internal units are applied in those positions. See *Clutch and Band Application Chart.*

3) This process of elimination can be used to detect any unit which slips, and to confirm proper operation of good units, however, the actual cause on the malfunction usually cannot be easily decided. Practically any condition can be caused by leaking hydraulic circuits or sticking valves. Therefore, unless an obvious condition exists, do not disassemble transmission until a hydraulic pressure test has been made.

Shift Speed Specifications

Application	Shift Points (MPH)	
	Full Throttle	Kickdown
1-2 Upshift	16-21	30-32
2-3 Upshift	42-45	55-57
3-2 Downshift	25-30	52-53
2-1 Downshift	12-14	27-29

HYDRAULIC PRESSURE TEST

1) Connect a pressure gauge to main pressure test point on case (adjacent to servo cover). With transmission at normal operating temperature, place selector lever in "D", run engine at idle speed and note pressure reading on gauge.

2) Next, run engine at full throttle with vehicle speed above 25 MPH, and again note pressure reading in "D".

CLUTCH AND BAND APPLICATION CHART (ELEMENTS IN USE)

Selector Lever Position	Forward Clutch	Direct/ Reverse Clutch	First/ Reverse Brake	Second Gear Band	One Way Clutch
D — DRIVE					
First Gear	X				X
Second Gear	X			X	
Third Gear	X	X			
2 — INTERMEDIATE					
First Gear	X				X
Second Gear	X			X	
1 — LOW (First)	X		X		
R — REVERSE		X	X		

NEUTRAL OR PARK — All Clutches, brake, and band released and/or ineffective.

VOLKSWAGEN VANAGON (Cont.)

Arrow Indicates Pressure Connection

Fig. 2   View of Transmission Case Showing Main Pressure Test Point

3) Finally, with vehicle at a standstill, place selector lever in "R" position, and note reading on pressure gauge.

4) Pressures obtained in each phase of test should be approximately as shown in Main Pressure chart. If not, disassemble and clean valve body and check especially for sticking valves.

Main Pressure Specifications

Application	psi (kg/cm²)
"D" at Idle①	41-43 (2.0-3.0)
"D" at Full Throttle②	83-85 (5.8-6.0)
"R" at Idle①	108-117 (7.6-8.2)

① — With Vehicle stationary.
② — Road speed above 25 MPH. Test should be performed on a dynamometer whenever possible.

STALL SPEED

Testing Precautions — When making test, do not hold throttle open any longer than the time it takes to read tachometer. Maximum stall speed test time is 20 seconds. If engine speed exceeds limits shown in Stall Speeds table, release accelerator immediately as clutch or band slippage is indicated.

Testing Procedure — With engine at normal operating temperature, connect a tachometer. Start engine and set parking and service brakes. Place selector lever in "D". Depress accelerator briefly to full throttle and note maximum RPM obtained. Engine speed should be within limits shown in Stall Speeds table.

NOTE — Normal stall speed will drop approximately 125 RPM per 3200 feet altitude. Also, stall speed will drop slightly at high ambient temperatures.

Stall Speed Specifications

Application	Stall RPM
All Models	1950-2250

Stall Test Results — 1) If stall speed is higher than specified, forward clutch or first gear one-way clutch is slipping. If stall speed in "D" is too high, repeat stall test in "1". If RPM is within specifications, one-way clutch for first gear is defective.

2) If stall speed is approximately 200 RPM below specifications, engine performance may be unsatisfactory. If stall speed is approximately 400 RPM below specifications, torque converter stator one-way clutch is defective and complete converter should be replaced.

REMOVAL & INSTALLATION

NOTE — For Axle Drive Shaft, Constant Velocity (CV) Joint, and Axle Shaft replacement, see appropriate manual transaxle article in MANUAL TRANSAXLES Section.

TRANSAXLE ASSEMBLY

Removal — 1) Disconnect battery ground and remove fan housing grille. Remove the 3 torque converter bolts. To gain access to bolts, rotate engine until each bolt is visible in hole at top of transmission housing.

NOTE — When turning crankshaft, use a "T" handle and adapter 3052. This adapter has a pin that must engage recess on cooling fan hub.

2) Disconnect both drive shafts from transmission. Disconnect wires from starter, then remove starter. Loosen bracket for automatic transmission filler tube. Disconnect accelerator linkage, accelerator cable and selector lever cable from operating lever.

3) Install an engine support and disconnect engine ground wire. Support transmission with a jack. Remove mounting bracket bolts, then disconnect rear transmission mount from body. Remove lower engine-to-transmission bolts and lower transmission out of vehicle.

NOTE — When lowering transmission out of vehicle, torque converter must be secured to transmission so it will not slide off transmission.

Installation — To install transaxle assembly, reverse removal procedures. Make sure torque converter is fully seated on the one-way clutch support or damage to the oil pump could occur when assembly is bolted to engine.

TORQUE CONVERTER

NOTE — The torque converter is a sealed unit and cannot be disassembled for service. However, the bushing in converter hub may be replaced as follows:

BUSHING REPLACEMENT

1) Check bushing wear using an inside micrometer. Wear limit of bushing is 1.348" (34.25 mm), and maximum allowable out-of-round is .001" (.03 mm).

VOLKSWAGEN VANAGON (Cont.)

2) To replace bushing, use a suitable bushing puller to withdraw bushing from converter hub. Press new bushing into place until it is fully seated in hub.

TRANSMISSION DISASSEMBLY

NOTE — *To separate transaxle units, withdraw torque converter from final drive housing and remove oil pump shaft from center of turbine shaft. Disconnect oil filler pipe. Remove attaching nuts from transmission studs that attach final drive to transmission, then separate final drive unit from transmission case. Withdraw turbine shaft from final drive assembly pinion shaft. For final drive disassembly and reassembly, see Final Drive information at rear of this article.*

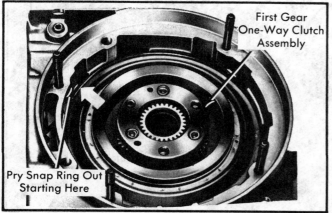

Fig. 3   Removing First Gear One-Way Clutch Assembly Retaining Snap Ring

First Gear One-Way Clutch Assembly

Pry Snap Ring Out Starting Here

1) Mount transmission assembly in a suitable work stand. Remove separation plate attaching screws and lift plate and gasket from transmission case. Remove forward annulus gear and the two thrust washers behind it from case.

2) Using a screwdriver, carefully pry large snap ring retaining first gear one-way clutch assembly from case. Lift out one-way clutch, first/reverse gear brake plates, and reverse planetary gear set as a unit.

3) Remove thrust washers, then lift the following components from case as an assembly: Sun gear, driving shell, forward planetary gear set, and forward clutch assembly.

Tap Cover Until Cover and Piston Pop Out Under Spring Pressure

Fig. 4   Removing Brake Band Servo Assembly

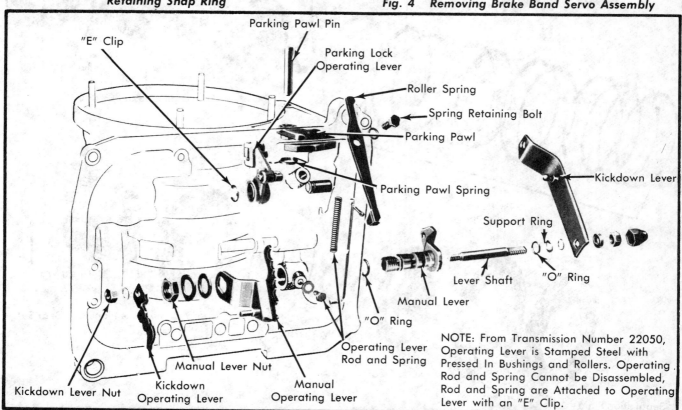

NOTE: From Transmission Number 22050, Operating Lever is Stamped Steel with Pressed In Bushings and Rollers. Operating Rod and Spring Cannot be Disassembled, Rod and Spring are Attached to Operating Lever with an "E" Clip.

Fig. 5   Bottom View of Transmission Case Showing Kickdown and Selector Linkage.

Automatic Transaxles

VOLKSWAGEN VANAGON (Cont.)

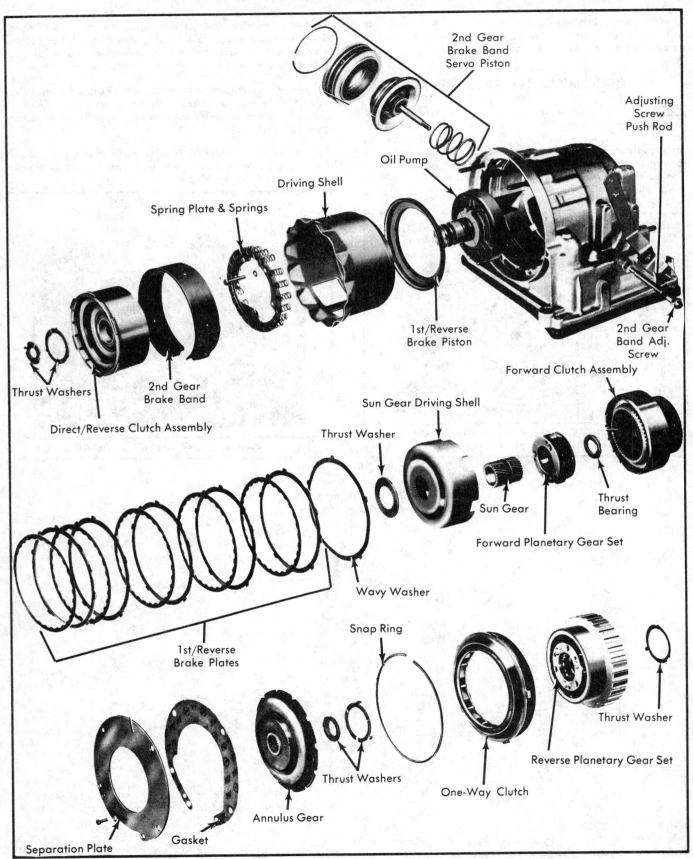

Fig. 6 Exploded View Showing Major Components of Transmission Assembly

VOLKSWAGEN VANAGON (Cont.)

4) Remove second gear brake band servo cover snap ring. Then using a rubber mallet, tap cover until cover and piston assembly pop out under spring tension.

5) Loosen second gear brake band adjusting screw locknut and remove lock nut and screw, then withdraw push rod for adjusting screw.

6) Lift out remaining planetary gear set components that are housed in first/reverse gear brake shell. Remove bolt from first/reverse brake spring plate, withdraw spring plate and springs, then pull driving shell, brake piston, and oil pump from case.

7) Invert transmission so that oil pan is facing up. Remove attaching bolts and lift off pan and gasket. Remove screws from oil strainer and separate strainer from valve body.

8) Remove the valve body attaching bolts and lift valve body assembly from case using care not to drop manual valve. Remove attaching screws from accumulator cover plate, then remove cover, spring and accumulator piston. If necessary for parts replacement, disassemble kickdown and selector linkage using *Fig. 5* as a disassembly guide.

COMPONENT DISASSEMBLY & REASSEMBLY

OIL PUMP ASSEMBLY

CAUTION — *Oil pump cover is under spring tension.*

Disassembly — **1)** Remove pump cover attaching screws and separate cover from housing. Remove check ball and spring, then lift out inner and outer pump gears along with drive plate.

2) Using needlenose pliers, unhook oil seal ring ends and carefully remove seal rings from pump housing. Remove thrust washer from pump housing.

Inspection — Wash all parts in kerosene and blow out oil passages with compressed air. Inspect all parts for wear, scoring, chipped teeth, and any other damage. Replace parts as necessary.

NOTE — *If either of the pump gears, the pump housing or cover are damaged, then entire oil pump assembly must be replaced. The drive plate, oil seal rings, and thrust washers can be replaced individually.*

Reassembly — **1)** Install thrust washer on pump housing so tangs on washer engage lug on housing. Carefully install first the large oil seal rings and then the small seal rings onto pump housing, ensuring that ring ends hook correctly.

2) Lubricate all parts with automatic transmission fluid. Install inner and outer pump gears into housing, then install drive plate with extended hub inserted into pump housing shaft opening. Install check ball and spring into housing. Align cover with housing, then install and tighten attaching screws.

NOTE — *After pump has been reassembled, insert pump shaft into pump and ensure that gears rotate freely and smoothly. Gear rotation should also be checked after oil pump is installed into transmission case.*

DIRECT/REVERSE CLUTCH

Disassembly — **1)** Using a screwdriver, pry clutch pack retaining snap ring from clutch drum. Withdraw clutch pressure plate, lined clutch plates and steel clutch plates from drum.

2) Place clutch drum in a press, apply downward pressure to piston spring retainer and remove snap ring. Release press and remove spring retainer. Using a twisting motion, remove piston with return springs from drum. Remove piston seals and springs from piston.

3) If necessary for replacement, place clutch drum in a press and drive bushing from drum hub using a suitable driver.

Inspection — **1)** Inspect friction surfaces of piston and drum for wear or damage. Check clutch drum ball valve for free movement. Inspect piston springs for wear or collapsed coils and replace as necessary.

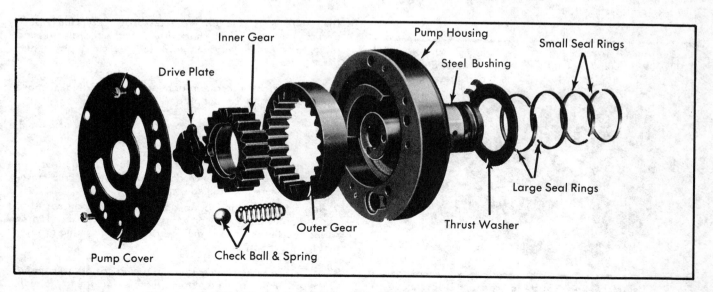

Fig. 7 Exploded View of Oil Pump Assembly

VOLKSWAGEN VANAGON (Cont.)

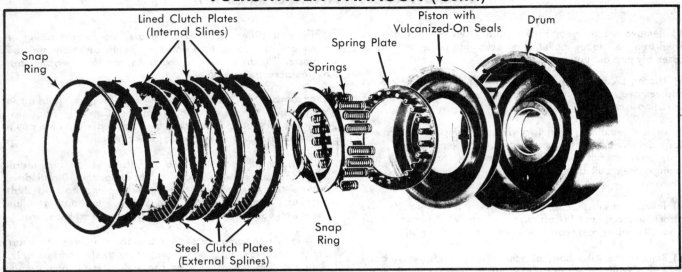

Fig. 8 Exploded View of Direct/Reverse Clutch Assembly

2) Inspect steel (external splines) clutch plates. If plates are scored or have radial grooves, they must be replaced. Plates that are only discolored can be reused.

3) Inspect lined (internal splines) clutch plates. Replace any plate that is worn, damaged or burnt.

NOTE — *New lined clutch plates must be soaked in automatic transmission fluid for at least 15 minutes prior to installation.*

Reassembly — 1) If removed, press new clutch drum bushing into drum until it is flush with outer lip of hub.

2) Lubricate piston seals with automatic transmission fluid, then install them into clutch drum with lips facing into drum. Using a stiff plastic sheet to protect seals, install piston into drum using a twisting motion. Remove plastic sheet from drum.

3) Position piston return springs on piston. Place spring retainer on springs, then compress retainer and install snap ring. Install clutch plates into drum starting with a steel (external splines) plate and alternating lined and steel plates until all clutch plates are installed.

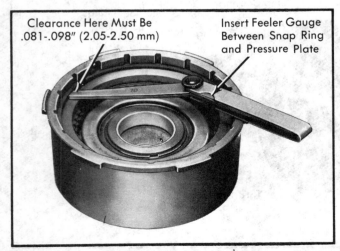

Fig. 9 Using a Feeler Gauge to Measure Direct/Reverse Clutch Pack Clearance

Direct/Reverse Clutch Plate Chart		
Application	**Steel Plates**	**Lined Plates**
All Models	4	4

4) Install pressure plate and clutch pack retaining snap ring. Using a feeler gauge, measure clearance between pressure plate and retaining snap ring. Clearance should be .081-.098" (2.05-2.50 mm); if not, remove clutch pack snap ring and replace with a snap ring of sufficient thickness to bring clearance within specifications.

NOTE — *Direct/Reverse clutch pack snap rings are available in various thicknesses from .059" (1.5 mm) to .098" (2.5 mm).*

5) Install correct thickness snap ring. Recheck clutch pack clearance to ensure correct snap ring has been installed.

FORWARD CLUTCH

Disassembly — 1) Using a screwdriver, pry clutch pack retaining snap ring from clutch drum. Then withdraw pressure plate, forward annulus gear, lined and steel clutch plates, and thrust plate.

2) Carefully pry out diaphragm spring snap ring. Remove diaphragm spring. Lift out piston.

NOTE — *It may be necessary to force piston from clutch drum using compressed air.*

Inspection — 1) Inspect clutch drum for scoring, wear, or other damage. Check clutch drum ball valve for free movement and ensure that drilling is clear.

2) Inspect diaphragm spring and piston for damage. Also, place diaphragm spring onto piston and ensure that top of spring reaches to at least the lower edge of snap ring groove; if not, replace spring.

NOTE — *The forward clutch piston sealing lips are vulcanized to the piston. Replace the piston if there is damage to the sealing lips or if there is leakage past the sealing lips.*

VOLKSWAGEN VANAGON (Cont.)

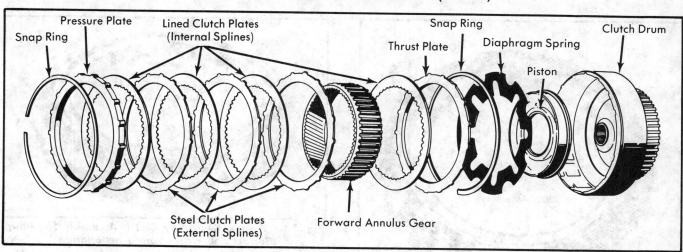

Fig. 10 Exploded View Showing Forward Clutch Assembly

3) Use direct/reverse clutch inspection procedures to inspect the lined and steel clutch plates.

NOTE — *If new lined (internal splines) clutch plates are to be installed, they must be soaked in automatic transmission fluid for at least 15 minutes prior to installation.*

Reassembly — **1)** Lubricate piston sealing lips with automatic transmission fluid, then install piston into drum using a twisting motion. Install diaphragm spring, with convex side toward piston, into clutch drum. Install retaining snap ring.

NOTE — *With snap ring installed, diaphragm spring should be lightly tensioned; if not, replace spring.*

2) Install thrust plate into drum. If one side of thrust plate is chamfered, install chamfered side toward diaphragm spring.

3) Install one lined (internal splines) clutch plate into drum, then install annulus gear so that short splines beneath its retaining ridge are engaged in the lined clutch plate. Install remaining clutch plates starting with a steel (external splines) plate and alternating lined and steel clutch plates until all plates have been installed.

Forward Clutch Plate Chart

Application	Steel Plates	Lined Plates
All Models	3	4

4) Install pressure plate and retaining snap ring into clutch drum. Next, position a dial indicator on clutch assembly so that indicator tip contacts pressure plate, then zero dial face.

5) Measure forward clutch end play by moving annulus gear up and down so that dial indicator will show play between pressure plate and snap ring.

6) Forward clutch end play should be .020-.035" (.50-.90 mm); if not, replace pressure plate with one of sufficient thickness to bring end play within specifications. After correct pressure plate is installed, recheck end play.

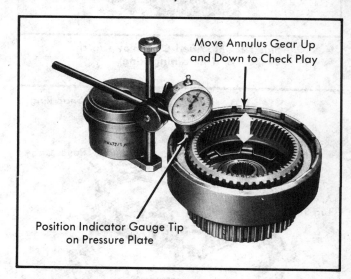

Fig. 11 Using a Dial Indicator to Measure Forward Clutch End Play

NOTE — *Forward clutch pressure plates are available in thicknesses of .236" (6.0 mm) to .299" (7.6 mm) in increments of .016" (.4 mm).*

FIRST GEAR ONE-WAY CLUTCH

Disassembly — Remove one-way clutch rollers and springs. Remove snap rings. Using a plastic mallet, carefully drive roller cage out of outer race.

Inspection — Inspect all parts for wear scoring, or other damage and replace as necessary.

NOTE — *One-way clutch has been modified and now has a retaining key to hold ring from turning in transmission housing. Previously, 5 protruding lugs served this purpose. New type clutch cannot be installed in transmission with old type clutch.*

VOLKSWAGEN VANAGON (Cont.)

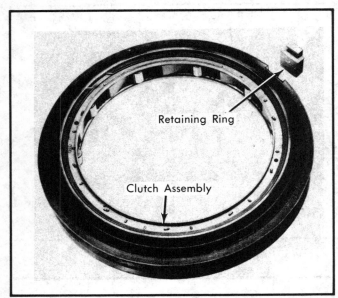

Fig. 12 Modified One-Way Clutch and Retaining Ring

Fig. 14 View of One-Way Clutch Assembly Showing Correct Roller and Spring Installation

REVERSE ANNULUS GEAR

NOTE – *Reverse annulus gear should be disassembled only if parts replacement is necessary.*

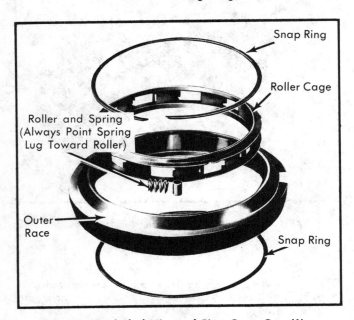

Fig. 13 Exploded View of First Gear One-Way Clutch Assembly

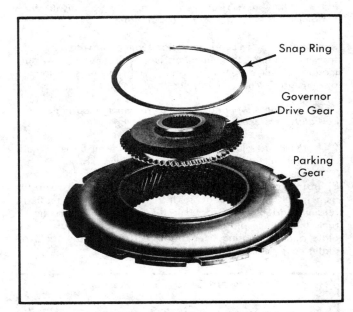

Fig. 15 Disassembled View of Reverse Annulus Gear

Reassembly – **1)** Install lower snap ring in groove of outer race. If necessary, heat outer race to 300° F (150° C), then place roller cage into race using two pair of pliers.

NOTE – *The heat from outer race will transfer quickly to roller cage, causing cage to stick inside race. If cage is not correctly positioned against lower snap ring inside race, DO NOT attempt to press it into position after cage has stuck. Carefully knock cage out of outer race and repeat procedure again after race has cooled down.*

2) Install upper snap ring. Install rollers and springs into cage as shown in *Fig. 14*.

Disassembly & Reassembly – Remove snap ring and lift governor drive gear out of parking gear. Inspect parking lock notches on parking gear and replace worn part. To reassemble, reverse disassembly procedure.

VALVE BODY ASSEMBLY

NOTE – *As valve body components are removed from each valve bore, place individual parts in correct order in relative position to valve body to simplify reassembly.*

Disassembly – **1)** Remove transfer plate-to-valve body attaching screws. Lift transfer plate and separator plate from main valve body. Withdraw the four main valve body check balls from passages in valve body.

VOLKSWAGEN VANAGON (Cont.)

VALVE BODY SPRING IDENTIFICATION

Valve Spring	Length In. (mm)	Diameter In. (mm)①	Number Of Coils	Wire Thickness In. (mm)
Throt. Pres. Limiting Valve	1.389 (35.3)	.303 (7.7)	14.5	.043 (1.1)
Main Pres. Limiting Valve	1.275 (32.4)	.303 (7.7)	11	.047 (1.2)
Main Pressure Valve	3.031 (77.0)	.468 (11.9)	16.5	.059 (1.5)
3-2 Control Valve	1.275 (32.4)	.303 (7.7)	12.5	.039 (1.0)
Throttle Pressure Valve	1.708 (43.4)	.305 (7.75)	16	.049 (1.25)
1-2 Shift Valve	1.024 (26.0)	.323 (8.2)	9.5	.031 (.8)
Converter Pressure Valve	.874 (22.2)	.303 (7.7)	8.5	.049 (1.25)
Modulator Pressure Valve	1.126 (28.6)	.305 (7.75)	11.5	.031 (.8)
2-3 Shift Valve	1.024 (26.0)	.323 (8.2)	9.5	.031 (.8)
3-2 Kickdown Valve	1.118 (28.4)	.318 (8.1)	11.5	.035 (.9)
1st/Reverse Apply Valve	1.118 (28.4)	.318 (8.1)	11.5	.035 (.9)

① — Inner diameter of coils; within a tolerance of ±.012" (.3 mm).

CAUTION — *DO NOT alter setting of adjusting screws when removing from valve body.*

2) Remove rear end cover plate and withdraw valves, springs and adjusting screws. Remove remaining end plates, one at a time, and withdraw all valves, plugs, springs and adjusting screws. Tag all parts for reassembly reference.

Inspection — 1) Wash all parts in clean kerosene and dry them with compressed air only (do not use fluffy rags, etc.). Check all parts for burrs and scores; replace assembly if damage is found.

2) When valves are clean and lubricated with fluid, they should fall freely of their own weight in respective bore; if not, check for valve or bore damage.

3) Check all valve body springs for damage or collapsed coils.

CAUTION — *Several valve body springs have similar dimensions; however, they must not be interchanged as they have different tolerances. See Valve Body Spring Identification table.*

4) Take care not to disturb settings of adjusting screws; pressures affected by these screws can only be measured and adjusted accurately on a test stand.

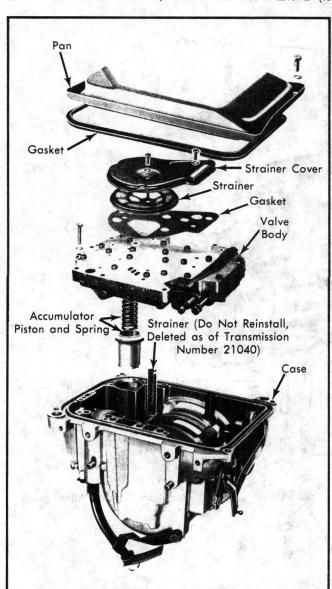

Fig. 16 *Exploded View Showing Removal of Strainers and Valve Body Assembly*

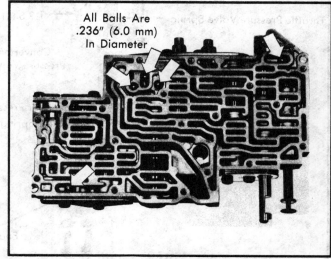

Fig. 17 *View of Main Valve Body Showing Check Ball Locations*

VOLKSWAGEN VANAGON (Cont.)

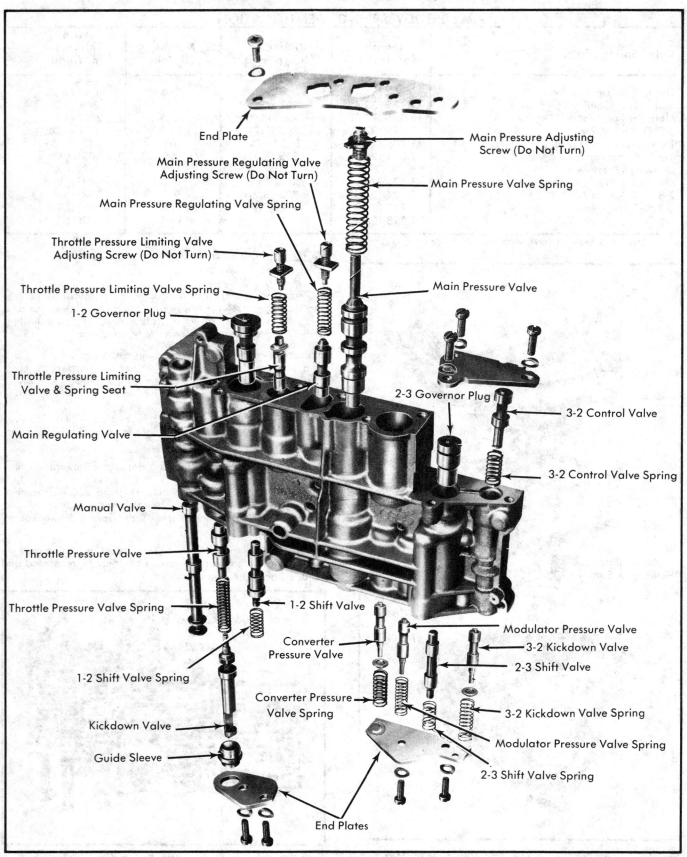

Fig. 18 Exploded View Showing Main Body Assembly Valve Trains

VOLKSWAGEN VANAGON (Cont.)

Reassembly — 1) Lubricate all parts with automatic transmission fluid and install into proper valve body bores, in reverse order of disassembly. When tightening end plate attaching screws, be careful not to overtighten them as this could easily strip the threads or distort the valve body enough to cause a valve to stick.

2) Ensure all check balls are installed in proper valve body and transfer plate passages. Install transfer plate-to-main valve body screws and tighten from center outward, taking care not to overtighten.

NOTE — *2 collar-type screws are used for attaching roller assembly to body, 3 galvanized screws are for accumulator cover plate, and the remaining 17 screws are used for transfer plate-to-main body attachment.*

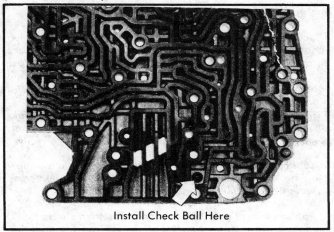

Install Check Ball Here

Fig. 19 *View of Transfer Plate Showing Check Ball Locations*

GOVERNOR ASSEMBLY

NOTE — *The governor is mounted in the final drive housing.*

Removal — Remove attaching bolts and washers and remove governor cover and "O" ring from final drive housing. Withdraw governor from housing using a clockwise twisting motion that will allow governor drive gear to disengage drive pinion gear.

Disassembly — Remove two attaching screws and withdraw thrust plate and governor housing. Remove transfer plate, balance weight, and if equipped, oil strainer. Remove "E" clips and withdraw centrifugal weight, valve, spring, and dished washer from pin.

Reassembly — Reverse disassembly procedure and note the following: If equipped, ensure that oil strainer is properly installed as shown in *Fig. 20*. Make sure angle in thrust plate is in center of housing so cover will bear against it.

Installation — Reverse removal procedure and note the following: Prior to installation, check governor oil seal and needle bearing in final drive case for damage and wear, and replace if necessary. After installation, rotate governor to engage drive gear.

BAND SERVO

Disassembly — Pull servo piston assembly out of cover, then remove "O" ring seals from outside diameter of cover. Remove retaining "E" clip and separate piston pin, accumulator spring, spring seat, and adjusting shim from servo piston. Withdraw two lip seals from piston.

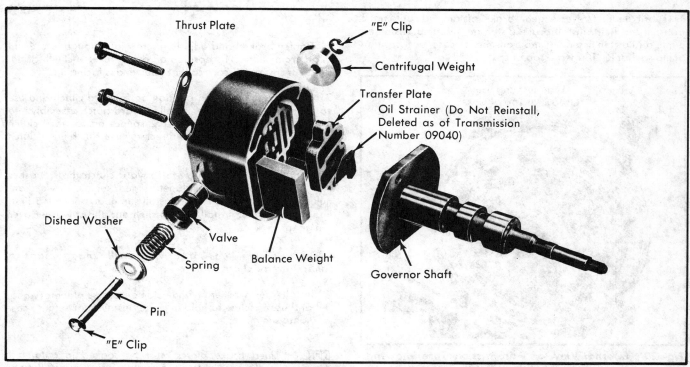

Thrust Plate

"E" Clip

Centrifugal Weight

Transfer Plate

Oil Strainer (Do Not Reinstall, Deleted as of Transmission Number 09040)

Dished Washer

Valve

Spring

Balance Weight

Governor Shaft

Pin

"E" Clip

Fig. 20 *Exploded View Showing Components of Governor Assembly*

VOLKSWAGEN VANAGON (Cont.)

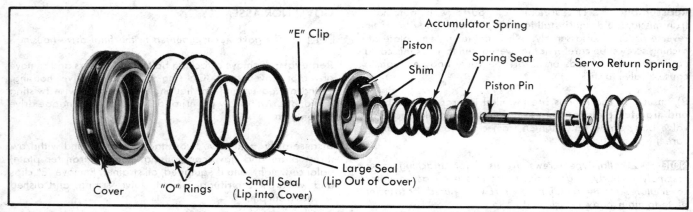

Fig. 21   Disassembled View of Servo Assembly

Inspection — Clean all parts and check for wear, scoring, or other damage. If replacement of piston is necessary, pin, spring, spring seat, and shim must also be replaced as this is serviced as an assembly only.

Reassembly — 1) Position spring seat, accumulator spring, and shim on piston pin, install assembly into servo piston, and install "E" clip onto piston.

2) Install lip seals onto piston as follows: Smaller (upper) seal is installed onto piston with lip facing upward, or into servo cover. Larger seal is installed onto piston with lip pointed downward, or out of servo cover. Lubricate assembly thoroughly and install piston into cover. Install "O" rings onto servo cover.

TRANSMISSION REASSEMBLY

1) Lubricate first/reverse gear brake piston with automatic transmission fluid. Install brake piston on oil pump. Install oil pump and piston assembly into transmission case, and position pump so that lug is toward top of case.

Lug Must Engage
Groove at Top of Case

Fig. 22   Internal View of Transmission Case Showing Brake Shell Installation

2) Install first/reverse gear brake shell into case so that lug engages in groove at top of case. Position low/reverse brake piston return springs on spring plate, insert plate into case with springs downward, then install attaching bolts and tighten to specified torque in a diagonal pattern.

NOTE — *After spring plate installation, insert pump shaft into oil pump and ensure that pump gears rotate freely; if not, remove oil pump and ensure that it is assembled correctly.*

3) Lubricate servo cover "O" rings, then install servo assembly into case and install retaining snap ring. Rotate transmission on work stand so that servo cover points down.

4) Position second gear brake band in case and ensure that it engages servo piston. Loosely install push rod for adjusting screw, then install adjusting screw and lock nut.

5) Lubricate direct/reverse clutch assembly, then install it into case, sliding it onto oil pump neck and into second gear brake band.

6) Tighten brake band adjusting screw just enough to prevent band from shifting its position on direct/reverse clutch drum. Rotate transmission case so that open end is facing up.

7) Place thrust washer in position on forward clutch and use vaseline to hold it in place. Install forward clutch assembly into direct/reverse clutch, making sure splines on forward clutch drum fully engage splines on direct/reverse clutch lined clutch plates.

8) Install forward planetary-to-forward clutch thrust washer into forward clutch. Install planetary gear set into forward annulus gear in forward clutch. Install sun gear (short end first) into gear set, then install driving shell and thrust washer over sun gear.

NOTE — *Ensure lugs of driving shell engage tabs of direct/reverse clutch drum.*

9) Install thrust washer on underside of reverse planetary gear set and use vaseline to hold in place. Install gear set into case and onto sun gear.

NOTE — *Lined brake plates must be soaked in automatic transmission fluid for at least 15 minutes prior to installation.*

VOLKSWAGEN VANAGON (Cont.)

10) Install first/reverse brake waved washer into case. Install first/reverse brake plates into case starting with a steel (external splines) plate and alternating lined (internal splines) plates and steel plates until all brake plates are installed.

First/Reverse Brake Plate Chart		
Application	Steel Plates	Lined Plates
All Models 5 5		

11) Install first gear one-way clutch assembly into transmission case, then push clutch downward while rotating reverse planetary gear set to fully engage parts.

NOTE — *With one-way clutch installed, it should not be possible to rotate reverse planetary gear set counterclockwise due to the locking action of the one-way clutch.*

12) Install one-way clutch-to-case snap ring. If all parts are correctly installed, the one-way clutch snap ring groove will be exposed. Do not attempt to force snap ring into groove of an incorrectly assembled transmission.

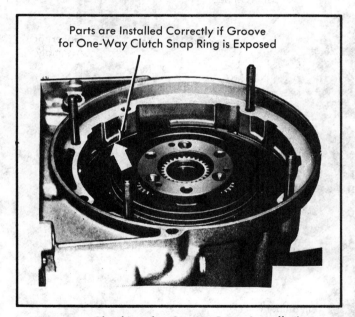

Parts are Installed Correctly if Groove for One-Way Clutch Snap Ring is Exposed

Fig. 23   Checking for Correct Parts Installation

13) Position both thrust washers on rear side of reverse planetary gear set annulus gear, then install gear into transmission case so that it fully engages planetary gear set.

14) Install separation plate gasket over case studs, place separation plate on top of gasket, then install and tighten attaching screws.

NOTE — *At this time second gear brake band must be adjusted. To adjust band, the transmission case must be horizontal to prevent band from jamming. Adjust band as follows:*

15) Tighten brake band adjusting screw to 7 ft. lbs. (1 mkg), loosen screw, then tighten again to 4 ft. lbs. (.5 mkg). Finally, back adjusting screw off 1¾ to 2 turns and tighten adjusting screw lock nut.

16) If case linkage was disassembled, reassemble in case using *Fig. 5* as an assembly guide.

17) Install a new seal on accumulator piston (lip pointing toward case), and install piston and spring into case. Install valve body assembly into case, making sure manual valve engages manual lever, and that kickdown valve engages kickdown lever. Install valve body-to-case attaching bolts and tighten from center outward.

NOTE — *Do not use sealer on oil pan gasket, as any surplus sealer may find its way into transmission fluid and cause control valves to stick.*

18) Position a new oil pan gasket on transmission case. Install oil pan, then install and tighten oil pan attaching bolts.

NOTE — *This completes assembly of transmission. Installation or turbine shaft, pump shaft and measurement of play between transmission and final drive will be made in Final Transaxle Assembly, located near end of this article.*

FINAL DRIVE

DISASSEMBLY

NOTE — *Prior to final drive disassembly, it is recommended that pinion shaft turning torque be measured. See Pinion Depth and Bearing Preload adjustment for checking procedure.*

1) Remove retaining bolts from center of axle drive flange shafts and pull drive flanges from final drive housing. Mark position of each side bearing adjusting ring on ring and housing, then measure screw-in depth of each ring in housing using a micrometer. Note measurements for reassembly reference.

2) Remove final drive pan bolts and pan, then remove side bearing adjusting ring lock plates. While supporting differential, unscrew side bearing adjusting rings, move differential to right side of case, tilt upward, and remove from final drive housing.

3) If necessary for replacement, use a hook type puller and remove oil seal from each side bearing adjusting ring.

4) If differential side bearing are to be replaced, use a drift and drive bearing outer race from each adjusting ring.

5) Loosen ring gear attaching bolts, tap on bolts with a soft hammer to break loose ring gear, then remove ring gear from differential case.

6) If side bearings require replacement, pull from case using a suitable puller. Using a screwdriver, pry differential housing cover from housing. Drive out pinion gear shaft, then withdraw differential pinion gears and thrust washers, side gears and thrust washers, and nuts for drive flange shaft retaining bolts.

VOLKSWAGEN VANAGON (Cont.)

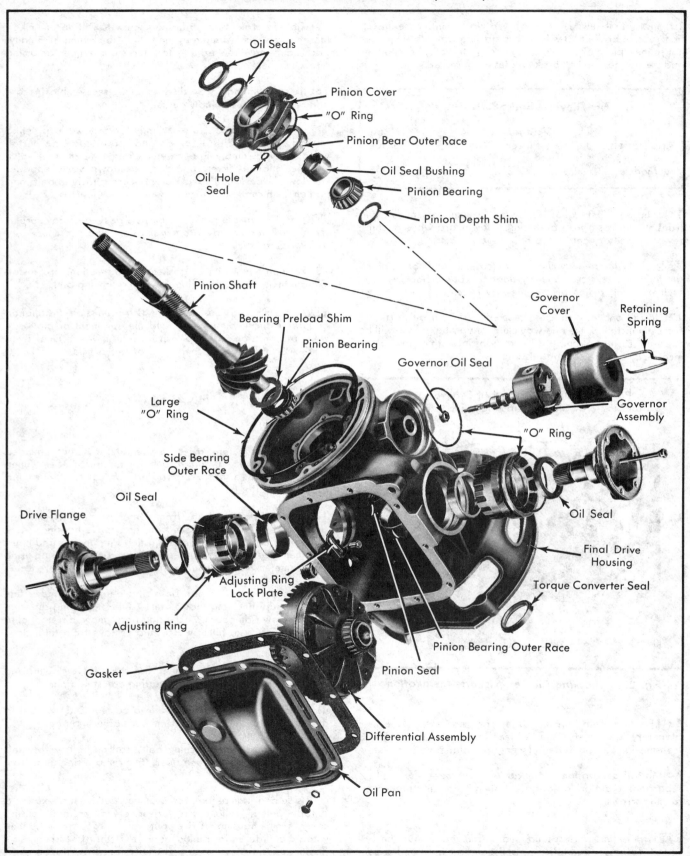

Oil Seals

Pinion Cover

"O" Ring

Pinion Bear Outer Race

Oil Hole Seal

Oil Seal Bushing

Pinion Bearing

Pinion Depth Shim

Pinion Shaft

Bearing Preload Shim

Pinion Bearing

Governor Cover

Retaining Spring

Governor Oil Seal

Large "O" Ring

Governor Assembly

"O" Ring

Side Bearing Outer Race

Oil Seal

Drive Flange

Oil Seal

Final Drive Housing

Torque Converter Seal

Adjusting Ring Lock Plate

Adjusting Ring

Pinion Bearing Outer Race

Gasket

Pinion Seal

Differential Assembly

Oil Pan

Fig. 24 Exploded View Showing Main Components of Final Drive Assembly

VOLKSWAGEN VANAGON (Cont.)

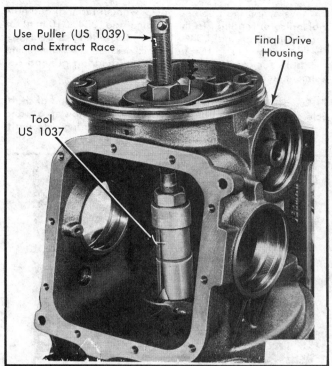

Use Puller (US 1039) and Extract Race

Final Drive Housing

Tool US 1037

Fig. 25 Removing Pinion Bearing Outer Race from Final Drive Housing

7) Remove pinion shaft cover from final drive housing. Withdraw pinion shaft from final drive housing.

8) If necessary for replacement, use a press and press pinion oil seals out of pinion cover. If pinion shaft bearings are to be replaced, press bearing outer race from pinion cover.

9) Use a hook type puller and remove pinion oil seal from final drive housing. Remove other pinion shaft bearing outer race from final drive housing using a suitable puller (US 1039 and US 1037) as shown in Fig. 25.

10) If necessary for replacement, use a press (with press plates to support bearing) and press bearings, shims and oil seal bushing from pinion shaft.

11) Finally, use suitable pullers and extract torque converter oil seal and governor oil seal from final drive housing.

REASSEMBLY & ADJUSTMENTS

Differential Assembly — 1) Inspect all thrust surfaces on differential housing, cover, ring gear, pinion gear shaft and thrust washers. Replace all worn parts. Inspect gear teeth for burrs, or excessive wear and replace as necessary.

NOTE — *If ring gear requires replacement, pinion shaft musi also be replaced as they are a matched set.*

2) Position differential side gears, large thrust washers, dished washers, drive flange retaining bolt nuts and pinion gears in differential housing. Align pinion gear holes with pinion shaft holes in housing, then drive pinion gear shaft through gears.

NOTE — *If differential pinion gear shaft does not fit tightly, replace it with a new shaft.*

3) Heat ring gear in hot oil to approximately 212° F (100° C). Place differential cover on housing. Install ring gear on housing, then install attaching bolts through cover and into ring gear. Tighten attaching bolts to specified torque.

4) If differential side bearings were removed, heat them in oil and press them onto differential housing and cover. Press side

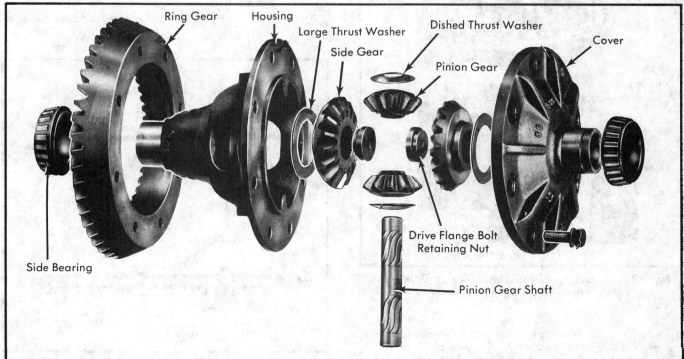

Ring Gear Housing Large Thrust Washer Side Gear Dished Thrust Washer Pinion Gear Cover

Side Bearing

Drive Flange Bolt Retaining Nut

Pinion Gear Shaft

Fig. 26 Exploded View of Differential Assembly

VOLKSWAGEN VANAGON (Cont.)

bearing outer races into position in side bearing adjusting rings.

Pinion Depth and Bearing Preload — 1) If original parts are reinstalled, use the same thickness pinion depth and bearing preload adjusting shims as were removed. For replacement ring and pinion gear set, or pinion bearings, proceed as follows:

2) Press new pinion shaft bearing outer races into final drive housing and pinion cover until they are fully seated. Install new pinion oil seal into final drive case. Install new oil seal into final drive side of pinion cover with open side of seal towards final drive housing, then install a new oil seal into transmission side of pinion cover with open side towards transmission.

3) Heat pinion shaft bearings to 212° F (100° C) in hot oil. Install both bearings (without shims) onto pinion shaft until they are seated.

4) Install pinion shaft into final drive housing. Install pinion cover on housing, then install attaching bolts and tighten to specified torque.

NOTE — *For correct pinion depth and bearing preload adjustment, measuring tools called out in the following procedures must be used.*

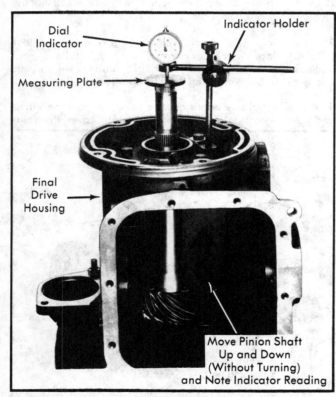

Fig. 27   *Measuring Pinion Shaft Play to Determine Total Pinion Adjusting Shim Thickness*

5) Attach a dial indicator onto final drive housing using holder (VW 387) as shown in *Fig. 27*. Then, place measuring plate (VW 385/17) on end of pinion. Zero dial indicator without preload.

6) Move pinion shaft up and down (without turning) and note dial indicator reading. To this reading add .004" (.10 mm) for bearing preload and .004" (.10 mm) for settling of bearings. The resulting sum is the total thickness of adjusting shims necessary for correct pinion depth and bearing preload adjustment. Record sum for future reference.

7) Remove pinion shaft. Press bearing from gear end of shaft. Select shims of correct thickness as determined in step **6)**, and install them on gear end of shaft. Reinstall bearing onto shaft, then install shaft into final drive housing.

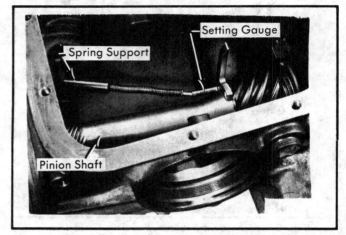

Fig. 28   *Installation of Setting Gauge on Pinion Shaft*

8) Install setting gauge (VW 385/22) on pinion as shown in *Fig. 28*, and hold in place with spring support (VW 385/19).

9) Adjust setting ring on measuring bar (VW 385/1), until distance from center of bar to ouside of ring is approximately 2.9" (74 mm).

NOTE — *Refer to Fig. 29 for the assembling of tools to measuring bar.*

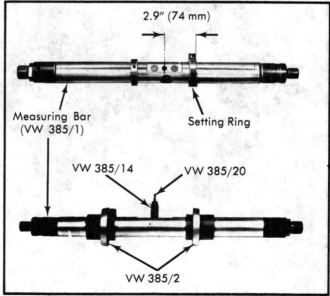

Fig. 29   *Assembling Special Measuring Tools for Pinion Depth Shim Selection*

VOLKSWAGEN VANAGON (Cont.)

10) Slide centering discs (VW 385/2) on measuring bar. Screw measuring pin (VW 385/14) into bar with .118" (3 mm) extension (VW 385/20).

11) Screw left side differential side bearing adjusting ring into final drive housing until it is flush with housing. Place measuring bar assembly in final drive housing as shown in *Fig. 30* Install right side bearing adjusting ring into final drive housing.

12) Turn knob on end of measuring bar to move centering discs outward until bar can just barely be turned by hand. Attach a dial indicator to measuring bar. Place setting block (VW 385/21) on measuring bar as shown in *Fig. 30*, then zero dial indicator without preload. Remove setting block.

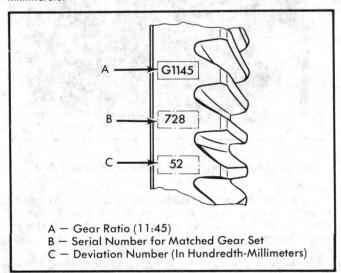

Fig. 30   Positioning of Measuring Bar in Housing

13) Rotate measuring bar until measuring pin rests against setting gauge on pinion face, then rotate bar back and forth over center. Read and record maximum dial indicator reading.

14) Add the dial indicator reading just obtained to the deviation number stamped in ring gear *(Fig. 31)*. The resulting sum is thickness of pinion depth adjusting shim to use at reassembly.

NOTE — *The ring gear deviation number is in hundredth-millimeters.*

15) Next, subtract the thickness of pinion depth shim just selected from the total pinion adjusting shim thickness obtained in step 6). The remainder is thickness of pinion bearing preload shim to use at reassembly.

NOTE — *Pinion depth and bearing preload shims are available in thicknesses from .043" (1.1 mm) to .075" (1.9 mm) in increments of .001" (.025 mm). Also, shim thickness should be measured at several points on shim prior to installation to ensure correct thickness shims are being installed.*

16) Remove measuring tools and pinion shaft from final drive housing. Press bearings from pinion shaft. Install the selected pinion bearing preload shim onto gear end of pinion shaft, then press bearing back onto shaft. Place the selected pinion depth shim on opposite end of shaft, then press remaining bearing onto shaft along with pinion oil seal bushing.

17) Install pinion shaft into final drive housing and lubricate bearings with hypoid gear oil. Reinstall measuring bar into housing and zero dial indicator with .04" (1 mm) preload.

18) Recheck pinion depth and bearing preload adjustment. If correct shims have been installed, dial indicator reading should be equal to the ring gear deviation number with a tolerance of ±.0016" (.04 mm). Remove measuring bar and side bearing adjusting rings.

19) Finally, attach a torque wrench to pinion shaft and check pinion shaft turning torque. Turning torque should be at least 12.4 INCH lbs. (14.3 cmkg).

NOTE — *Turning torque value given is for new bearings only. If used bearings are installed, turning torque should be measured prior to final drive disassembly. When assembled correctly, turning torque with used bearings should be approximately 1.7-3.5 INCH lbs. (2-4 cmkg) greater than it was prior to disassembly.*

A — Gear Ratio (11:45)
B — Serial Number for Matched Gear Set
C — Deviation Number (In Hundredth-Millimeters)

Fig. 31   Location of Deviation Number on Ring Gear

Fig. 32   Adjusting Ring Settings for Side Bearing Preload Adjustment

VOLKSWAGEN VANAGON (Cont.)

Side Bearing Preload & Ring Gear Backlash — 1) With pinion shaft correctly adjusted, install differential assembly into final drive housing. Coat "O" rings and threads of side bearing adjusting rings with multi-purpose grease and coat side bearings with hypoid gear oil.

2) Install both adjusting rings into final drive housing until they are flush with housing. Next, adjust right side (ring gear end) adjusting ring in until ring gear meshes with pinion shaft gear with no backlash, then screw left ring in and preload slightly so that side bearings have no play.

3) From this position, unscrew right adjusting ring 2½ teeth, then screw in left adjusting ring 5 teeth. This should correctly set side bearing preload and ring gear backlash.

4) To check ring gear backlash, rotate pinion shaft several times in both directions to settle bearings. Install locking sleeve (VW 521/4) with slotted sleeve (VW 521/7) in differential and secure with nut. See Fig. 33.

5) Adjust length of backlash measuring bar (VW 388) to 3.15" (80 mm). Attach correctly adjusted measuring bar to locking sleeve.

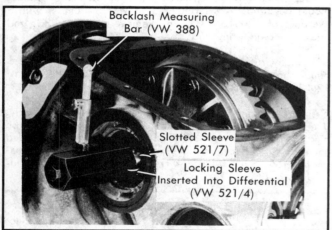

Backlash Measuring Bar (VW 388)

Slotted Sleeve (VW 521/7)

Locking Sleeve Inserted Into Differential (VW 521/4)

Fig. 33   Installation of Backlash Measuring Bar on Locking Sleeve

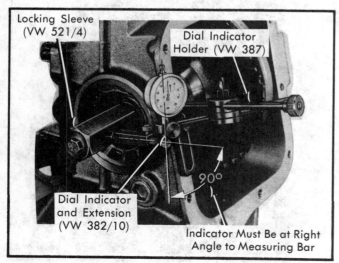

Locking Sleeve (VW 521/4)

Dial Indicator Holder (VW 387)

Dial Indicator and Extension (VW 382/10)

90°

Indicator Must Be at Right Angle to Measuring Bar

Fig. 34   Positioning of Ring Gear Backlash Measuring Tools

NOTE — Refer to Fig. 34 for positioning of ring gear backlash measuring tools.

6) Install dial indicator with .24" (6 mm) flat end extension (VW 382/10) in indicator holder (VW 387). Bolt holder to final drive housing so that indicator is located at a right angle to backlash measuring bar.

7) Turn ring gear (via pinion shaft) until measuring bar contacts dial indicator gauge pin, then turn ring gear further until indicator shows .04" (1 mm) preload. Attach locking clamp (VW 386) to pinion shaft as shown in Fig. 35, then tighten clamp screw to lock pinion shaft.

8) Turn ring gear away from dial indicator until it is stopped by the locked pinion shaft, then zero dial indicator. Next, turn ring gear towards indicator until it is again stopped by pinion shaft. Read and record indicator reading. This reading is the ring gear backlash.

9) Repeat backlash measurement procedure at three other points 90° apart around ring gear. Add the four measurements together, then divide the total by four. The resulting sum is the average ring gear backlash, which should be .006-.010" (.15-.25 mm).

NOTE — The individual backlash measurements should not vary from each other by more than .002" (.05 mm); if they do, ring gear or pinion shaft is worn or they have been improperly installed.

Pinion Shaft

Locking Clamp (VW 386)

Tighten Clamp Screw to Lock Pinion Shaft

Fig. 35   Attaching Locking Clamp to Pinion Shaft

10) If backlash is not within specifications, correct by turning both side bearing adjusting rings an equal amount in opposite directions so that bearing preload is not altered. Remove measuring tools.

11) With backlash correct, check pinion shaft turning torque. Total pinion shaft turning torque, with differential installed, should be 14.2 INCH lbs. (16.4 cmkg).

VOLKSWAGEN VANAGON (Cont.)

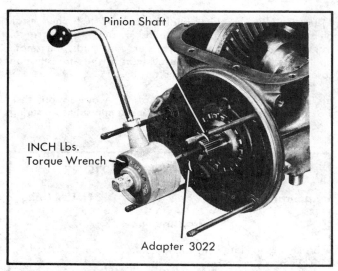

Fig. 36   Using an INCH Lbs. Torque Wrench to Measure Pinion Shaft Turning Torque

12) Install side bearing adjusting ring lock plates and tighten bolts to specified torque. Install new oil seals in adjusting rings. Install final drive oil pan using a new gasket.

13) Install a new torque converter oil seal into final drive housing. Install a new governor oil seal into housing with lip pointing toward governor, then install governor assembly.

FINAL TRANSAXLE ASSEMBLY

1) To measure play between final drive and transmission, place a straight edge on transmission attaching face of final drive housing, and using a depth gauge, measure distance from top surface of straight edge down to edge of pinion shaft oil seal bushing. Next, measure distance from top surface of straight edge to face of final drive housing. Subtract this second measurement from first measurement obtained in this step and note for future reference.

2) Place a new gasket on transmission separation plate, position straight edge on transmission case, and measure distance from top surface of straight edge down to gasket sur-

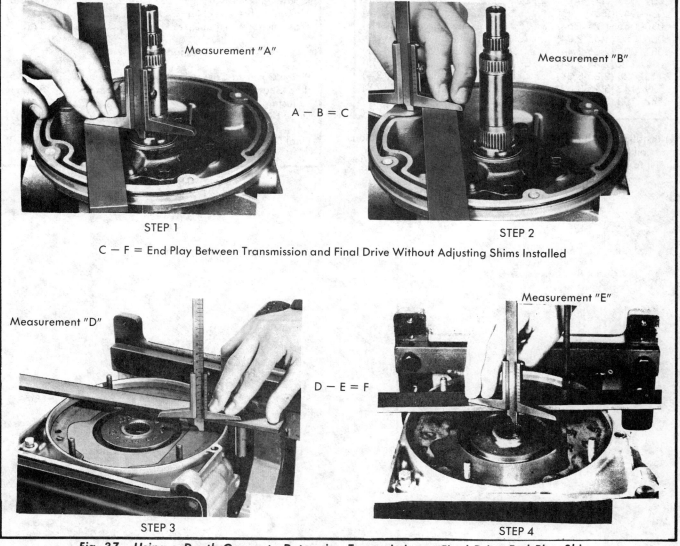

Fig. 37   Using a Depth Gauge to Determine Transmission-to-Final Drive End Play Shim

VOLKSWAGEN VANAGON (Cont.)

face. Next, measure distance from top of straight edge down to shim surface on shoulder of annulus gear flange. Subtract this measurement from first measurement obtained in this step and record for future reference.

3) Subtract the last measurement obtained in step **2)** from last measurement obtained in step **1)**. Remainder is end play (without shims) between final drive and transmission. Select proper end play shim(s) to use by finding applicable end play reading in first column of End Play Shim Chart, and obtaining shim thickness noted in second column.

NOTE — *Transmission-to-final drive end play adjusting shims are available in thicknesses of .016" (.4 mm) and .047" (1.2 mm). Combine shim thicknesses to obtain total thickness required.*

End Play Shim Selection Chart

If End Play Is In. (mm)	Install This Shim In. (mm)
.009-.033 (.23-.84)	None
.034-.049 (.85-1.24)	.016 (.4)
.050-.065 (1.25-1.64)	.032 (.8)
.066-.080 (1.65-2.04)	.048 (1.2)
.081-.096 (2.05-2.44)	.064 (1.6)
.097-.112 (2.45-2.84)	.080 (2.0)
.113-.128 (2.85-3.24)	.096 (2.4)
.129-.143 (3.25-3.64)	.112 (2.8)
.144-.153 (3.65-3.88)	.128 (3.2)

4) Install selected shim(s) into final drive case, on top of pinion shaft oil seal bushing. Next, lubricate and install sealing "O" ring into groove on transmission end of final drive housing.

5) Install turbine shaft into final drive pinion shaft, then install oil pump shaft into turbine shaft. Position a new final drive-to-transmission gasket onto transmission case studs, then mate final drive to transmission. Install final drive-to-transmission case nuts and tighten to specified torque.

6) Set torque converter carefully on one-way support, then move converter back and forth and insert into splines ensuring that it does not jam.

TIGHTENING SPECIFICATIONS

Application	Ft. Lbs. (mkg)
Transmission	
Brake Spring Plate Bolts	5 (.7)
Oil Pump Cover-to-Housing	5 (.7)
Oil Pan-to-Case	14 (1.9)
Strainer-to-Valve Body	2 (.3)
Valve Body-to-Case	3 (.4)
Kickdown Lever Nut	11 (1.5)
Manual Valve Lever Nut	14 (1.9)
Transmission-to-Final Drive	22 (3.0)
Final Drive	
Pinion Cover-to-Case	18 (2.5)
Ring Gear Bolts	52 (7.1)
Adjusting Ring Lock Plate	7 (1.0)
Drive Flange-to-Case	18 (2.5)
Converter-to-Drive Plate	29 (4.0)
Final Drive-to-Engine	22 (3.0)

Section 4
MANUAL TRANSMISSION SERVICING

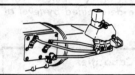

MANUAL
TRANSMISSION
SERVICING
Section 4

CONTENTS

NOTE — ALSO SEE GENERAL INDEX.

AUDI

4000
5000

LUBRICATION

SERVICE INTERVALS

All Models — Inspect transmission lubricant level when vehicle is serviced. Transmission oil does not have to be changed.

RECOMMENDED LUBRICANT

All Models — Use Multi-Grade Hypoid SAE 80W/90. In cold climates, use Multi-Grade Hypoid SAE 80.

CHECKING LUBRICANT LEVEL

All Models — Check lubricant level at fill hole. Lubricant should be slightly below bottom of fill hole.

CAPACITY

NOTE — *Transmission capacities listed below are approximate. Correct level should be determined by level at fill hole rather than by amount added.*

Transmission Refill Capacities	
Application	**Capacity (Pts.)**
4000	3.4
5000	5.5

ADJUSTMENT

GEAR LEVER

Audi 4000 — 1) Place gear shift lever in neutral. Loosen shift rod clamp nut. Check that shift finger slides freely on shift rod. Remove shift lever knob and rubber shift boot.

2) Align holes of gear shift lever housing and shift lever bearing housing. Install tool (3014), with locating pin toward front. Push shift lever into 1st/2nd cutout of tool. Tighten lower screw on tool, move shift lever and slide to left stop. Tighten upper screw on tool. Push shift lever into right cutout of tool (3rd/4th) and align shift rod and finger. Tighten clamp nut and remove tool.

3) Push shift lever into 1st gear and press to left stop. Shift lever should spring back .2-.4" (5-10 mm). If not, move shift lever housing sideways until correct deflection is reached. Check engagement of gears.

Audi 5000 — Position lever in neutral in line with 1st-2nd gear. Loosen stop plate mounting bolts and align holes in stop plate with bearing support. Tighten bolts. Loosen clamp between front and rear shift rods. Shift rods should move freely on splines. With front shift rod in neutral, install tool (3048), and ensure that locating pins fit into holes of stop plate. Tighten shift rod clamp and remove tool. Shift through all gears to see that they engage easily. Readjust stop plate if necessary.

BMW

320i
528i
633CSi
733i

LUBRICATION

SERVICE INTERVALS

All Models — Inspect transmission lubricant level when vehicle is serviced. Change transmission oil at first 600 miles, then at 30,000 miles and at 30,000 mile intervals thereafter

CHECKING LUBRICANT LEVEL

All Models — Check lubricant at filler plug hole. Lubricant should be to bottom of fill plug hole.

RECOMMENDED LUBRICANT

Use SAE 80 grade transmission gear oil.

CAPACITY

NOTE — *Transmission capacities listed below are approximate and should be used only as a guide when refilling transmission after service. Correct (final) lubricant level should be determined at fill hole rather than by amount added.*

Transmission Refill Capacities	
Application	**Capacity (Pts.)**
320i	3.0
528i	3.3
633CSi & 733i	2.3

ADJUSTMENT

LINKAGE ADJUSTMENT

NOTE — *All models use floor-mount shift with no external linkage. No adjustment is provided.*

CHRYSLER CORP. IMPORTS

Arrow	Colt
Arrow Pickup	D50 Pickup
Challenger	Sapporo
Champ	

LUBRICATION

SERVICE INTERVALS

All Models — Check oil level every 6 months, or 15,000 miles.

CHECKING LUBRICANT LEVEL

All Models — Check lubricant level at fill hole. Lubricant should be within ¼" of bottom of fill hole.

RECOMMENDED LUBRICANT

All Models — Use multipurpose gear lubricant conforming to API GL-4 quality, SAE 80W.

CAPACITY

NOTE — *Transmission refill capacities listed below are approximate. Correct level of lubricant should be determined at fill hole rather than by amount added.*

Transmission Refill Capacities	
Application	Capacity (Pts.)
Arrow & D50 Pickup	
4-Speed	4.4
5-Speed	4.8
Colt & Champ FWD	
4-Speed	4.8
Challenger, Sapporo, Colt, Arrow	
5-Speed (1600 Eng.)	4.2
5-Speed (2600 Eng.)	4.8

ADJUSTMENT

LINKAGE ADJUSTMENT

4 & 5-Speed Transmissions — Shifter is integral with transmission housing and has no external linkage. No adjustment is required.

4-Speed Transaxles — No linkage adjustment is required.

COURIER

Pickup

LUBRICATION

SERVICE INTERVALS

All Models — Change fluid after first 7,500 miles. Check fluid every 7.5 months and change every 24 months or 22,500 miles.

CHECKING LUBRICANT LEVEL

All Models — Lubricant level should be even with bottom of oil fill hole in side of transmission.

RECOMMENDED LUBRICANT

All Models — Use a gear lubricant having a rating of SAE 90 with E.P.

CAPACITY

NOTE — *Transmission capacities listed below are approximate, and correct lubricant level should be determined by level at fill hole rather than by amount added.*

Transmission Refill Capacities	
Application	Capacity (Pts.)
4-Speed	3.0
5-Speed	3.6

ADJUSTMENT

LINKAGE ADJUSTMENT

All Models — The floor shifter attaches directly into the transmission housing; therefore, no adjustment is provided.

DATSUN

200SX	510
210	810
280ZX	Pickup
310	

LUBRICATION

SERVICE INTERVALS

310 — Check oil level every 7,500 miles, and replace every 30,000 miles.

All Other Models — Check oil level every 15,000 miles.

CHECKING LUBRICANT LEVEL

All Models — Check lubricant level at filler hole. Lubricant for all models should be level with the bottom of fill hole.

RECOMMENDED LUBRICANT

All Models — Use a gear lubricant having a quality rating of API GL-4.

CAPACITY

NOTE — *Transmission capacities listed are approximate, and correct fluid level should be determined by level at fill hole rather than by amount added.*

DATSUN (Cont.)

Transmission Refill Capacities

Application	Capacity (Pts.)
200SX	
5-Speed	4.2
210	
4-Speed	2.6
5-Speed	2.5
310	
4 & 5-Speed	4.9
510	
4-Speed	3.1
5-Speed	3.6
280ZX, 810 & Pickup	
4-Speed	3.6
5-Speed	4.2

ADJUSTMENT

LINKAGE ADJUSTMENT

NOTE — *All models except 310 have a floor shift which has no external linkage and requires no linkage adjustment.*

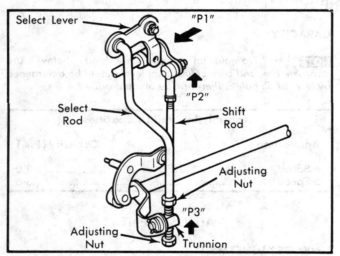

Fig. 1 4-Speed Transmission Control Linkage

310 — 1) Loosen adjusting nut on each end of control rod lever. Set shift lever in neutral. Push shift lever in direction "P1", then pull it back .31" (8 mm) for 4-speed transmissions and .45" (11 mm) for 5-speed transmissions. With select lever held in that position, move shift lever in direction "P2".

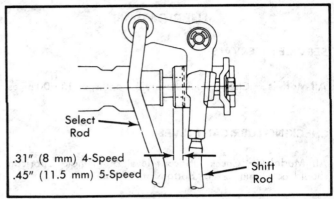

Fig. 2 Positioning Shift Lever

2) Push control rod select lever in direction "P3", and turn adjusting nut until it touches trunnion. Turn adjusting nut ¼ turn further, and lock select lever with adjusting nut on either side of lever.

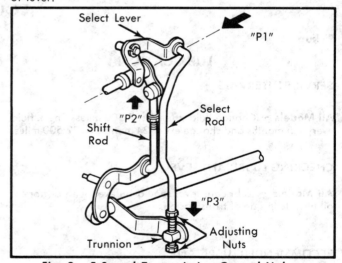

Fig. 3 5-Speed Transmission Control Linkage

FIAT

Brava
Spider 2000
Strada
X1/9

LUBRICATION

SERVICE INTERVALS

All Models — Check lubricant level every 12,500 miles and change every 30,000 miles.

CHECKING LUBRICANT LEVEL

All Models — Check lubricant level at transmission fill hole. Lubricant should be up to bottom of opening.

RECOMMENDED LUBRICANT

X1/9 — Use SAE 90W (not E.P.) gear oil with anti-wear additives.

All Other Models — Use SAE 80W/90 gear oil with anti-wear additives.

CAPACITY

NOTE — *Refill capacities given below are approximate. Use these as a guide when refilling; however, correct lubricant level should be determined by checking at fill hole.*

FIAT (Cont.)

Transmission Refill Capacities	
Application	Capacity (Pts.)
Brava & Spider	3.5
Strada	7.0
X1/9	6.3

Hatchback

LUBRICATION

SERVICE INTERVALS

All Models — Transmission oil normally does not need changing. Check periodically to ensure that level is correct.

CHECKING LUBRICANT LEVEL

All Models — Check lubricant at transmission fill hole. Correct level is when oil reaches lower edge of fill opening.

RECOMMENDED LUBRICANT

All Models — Standard Transmission Fluid, Ford part number D8DZ-19C547-A.

CAPACITY

NOTE — *Transmission capacities are approximate, and correct lubricant level should be determined by level at oil fill hole rather than by amount added.*

Transmission Refill Capacities	
Application	Capacity (Pts.)
All Models	5.0

ADJUSTMENT

NOTE — *Fiesta uses two types of shift linkages, one with a boot near the gearshift rod, and one with a cranked rod and no boot.*

CRANKED ROD SHIFTER LINKAGE ADJUSTMENT

1) Place shift shaft and lever in 4th gear position. Loosen selector rod locating bolt and pull shift lever down. Align lever with hole in selector housing and lock it with a .16" (4 mm) pin.

2) Using a suitable arbor, rotate shift shaft clockwise to stop. Tighten selector rod locating bolt. Remove arbor. Check shift operation.

NOTE — *After installation of a new gear shift mechanism, and before any adjustment is made, a new retract spring must be installed.*

ADJUSTMENT

LINKAGE ADJUSTMENT

NOTE — *All models have a floor shift which has no external linkage and requires no linkage adjustment.*

FIESTA

GEARSHIFT ROD WITH BOOT LINKAGE ADJUSTMENT

1) Remove shift rod bias spring and place shifter in 4th gear. Loosen selector rod to shift shaft bolt so that rod is free to slide.

2) Pull selector rod and shift lever down until holes in end of gear lever align with holes in selector housing. Lock in position with a .16" (4 mm) diameter pin.

3) Manufacture a spacer as shown in *Fig. 1.* Pull selector rod down and wedge spacer between rod and floor pan as shown in *Fig. 2.*

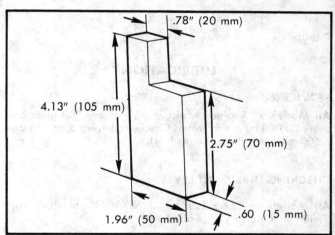

Fig. 1   Manufacture Spacer to these Dimensions

4) Using suitable mandrel, rotate shift shaft clockwise to stop. Push shift shaft into transmission case. Hold in position and lock selector rod clamp bolt. Ensure that clamp arm crossing is parallel to split tube slot.

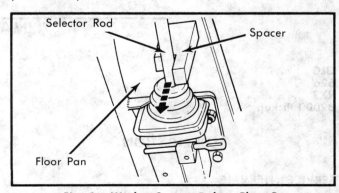

Fig. 2   Wedge Spacer Below Floor Pan

5) Remove mandrel, spacer and pin. Replace shift rod bias spring and check gear shifting operation.

HONDA

Accord
Civic
Prelude

LUBRICATION

CHECKING LUBRICANT LEVEL

All Models — With engine off, oil at operating temperature and car parked on level ground, remove oil filler plug from side of transmission. Oil level should be up to level of plug opening. If below, add oil until it comes up to the plug opening level.

SERVICE INTERVALS

All Models — Replace transmission fluid every 30,000 miles.

RECOMMENDED LUBRICANT

All Models — Use only high quality SAE 10W-40 oil for adding or changing transmission oil.

CAPACITY

NOTE — *Refill capacities given below are approximate. Correct fluid level should be checked as described previously.*

Transmission Refill Capacities	
Application	Capacity (Pts.)
All Models	5.2

ADJUSTMENT

LINKAGE ADJUSTMENT

NOTE — *Shift linkage is such that it requires no external adjustments.*

LUV

Pickup

LUBRICATION

SERVICE INTERVALS

All Models — Replace lubricant after first 7,500 miles and every 30,000 miles thereafter. Check level every 6 months and 7,500 miles (whichever occurs first).

CHECKING LUBRICANT LEVEL

All Models — Check lubricant level at fill hole. Lubricant should be to bottom edge of fill hole.

RECOMMENDED LUBRICANT

All Models — SAE 10W-30 for temperatures below 50°F (10°C); SAE 40 for temperatures above 50°F; SAE 30 for temperatures between 0° and 90°F (-18°-32°C).

CAPACITY

NOTE — *Transmission capacities listed are approximate; use these as a guide when refilling transmission. Check for proper "full" level at oil fill hole.*

Transmission Refill Capacities	
Application	Capacity (Pts.)
4-Speed	2.7
4-Speed W/Transfer Case	5.2

ADJUSTMENT

LINKAGE ADJUSTMENT

NOTE — *Shift linkage is integral with transmission housing and requires no external adjustment.*

MAZDA

GLC
626
RX7
B2000 Pickup

LUBRICATION

SERVICE INTERVALS

RX7 — Replace lubricant at first 2,000 miles, and then every 30,000 miles thereafter. Check lubricant level every 7,500 miles.

All Other Models — Replace lubricant at first 7,500 miles, and every 30,000 miles thereafter. Check lubricant level every 7,500 miles.

CHECKING LUBRICANT LEVEL

All Models — Check lubricant level at fill hole. Lubricant should be up to bottom of fill hole.

RECOMMENDED LUBRICANT

All Models — API GL-4 or GL-5 gear lubricant.

MAZDA (Cont.)

CAPACITY

NOTE — *Capacities listed are approximate. Use these as a guide when refilling transmission after service. Correct fluid level should be determined at oil fill hole.*

ADJUSTMENT

LINKAGE ADJUSTMENT

NOTE — *No external linkage adjustment is required.*

Transmission Refill Capacities	
Application	Capacity (Pts.)
GLC	
4-Speed	2.8
5-Speed	3.6
626	
4-Speed	3.0
5-Speed	3.6
RX7	3.6
B2000 Pickup	
4-Speed	3.2
5-Speed	3.6

MERCEDES-BENZ

240D

LUBRICATION

SERVICE INTERVALS

Transmission fluid has to be changed at first 1000 and 5000 miles of operation. Thereafter check and replenish fluid every 15,500 miles.

CHECKING LUBRICATION LEVEL

Check lubricant level at fill hole. Lubricant should be at bottom of fill hole.

RECOMMENDED LUBRICANT

Automatic Transmission Fluid (ATF)

CAPACITY

NOTE — *Capacity is approximate. Use as a guide only when refilling transmission after service. Correct fluid level should be determined at fill hole.*

Transmission Refill Capacities	
Application	Capacity (Pts.)
240D	3.4

ADJUSTMENT

Disconnect shift rods at shift lever. Align 3 intermediate levers at bottom of shift bracket by inserting a centering pin. *See Fig. 1.* Place transmission in neutral. Adjust shift rods so they will fit into their respective holes in intermediate levers without tension. Install lock pins, remove centering pin and check for proper operation.

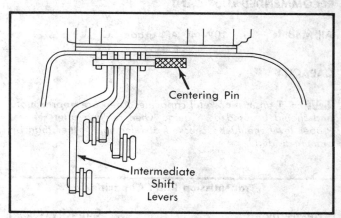

Centering Pin

Intermediate Shift Levers

Fig. 1   View Showing Shift Lever Adjustment

MG

MGB

LUBRICATION

SERVICE INTERVALS

Check oil level every 6,000 miles and change lubricant every 25,000 miles.

CHECKING LUBRICANT LEVEL

Check oil level through filler plug in side of transmission. Oil should be even with bottom of filler plug hole.

RECOMMENDED LUBRICANT

Use same oil as selected for engine; SE quality 10W/40.

CAPACITY

NOTE — *The capacities listed below are approximate amounts. The correct fluid level should be determined at the filler hole rather than by amount added.*

Transmission Refill Capacities	
Application	Capacity (Pts.)
MGB	
Without Overdrive	6.0
With Overdrive	7.2

ADJUSTMENT

LINKAGE ADJUSTMENT

No external linkage adjustment is required.

PEUGEOT

504
505
604

LUBRICATION

SERVICE INTERVALS

504 & 505 Diesel — Check transmission oil level every 3,000 miles, and replace every 18,500 miles.

505 Gasoline — Check transmission oil level every 5,000 miles, and replace every 20,000 miles.

604 — Change transmission oil at first 1,500 miles, and every 12,500 miles thereafter. Check level every 4,500 miles.

CHECKING LUBRICANT LEVEL

All Models — Transmission oil fill plug is located on side of transmission. Lubricant should be at bottom edge of fill hole.

RECOMMENDED LUBRICANT

All Models — Use 10W/40 API grade CC.

CAPACITY

NOTE — *Transmission refill capacities listed are approximate and should be used as a guide when refilling after service. Proper level should be checked at filler hole rather than by amount added.*

Transmission Refill Capacities	
Application	Capacity (Pts.)
504 & 505 Diesel 4-Speed	2.4
505 Gas 5-Speed	3.4
604 5-Speed	2.8

ADJUSTMENT

LINKAGE ADJUSTMENT

Floor Shift Models — Adjustment is accomplished by setting the 2 control levers to proper dimensions. See *Fig. 1*.

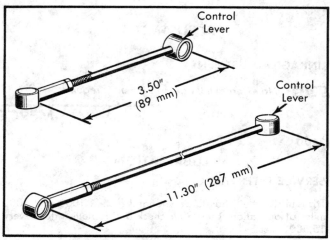

Fig. 1　Floor Shift Lever Adjustment

Column Shift Models — Adjust control link to 9.76±.004" (248±1 mm), place selector lever inside vehicle in neutral. Unscrew adjusting nut, determine free play in control arm and set rod in midway position. See *Fig. 2*. Tighten nut.

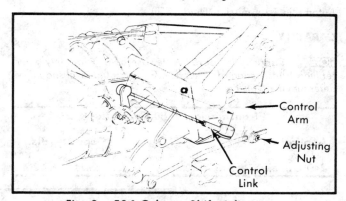

Fig. 2　504 Column Shift Adjustment

PORSCHE

911SC
924
928

LUBRICATION

SERVICE INTERVALS

911SC — Check lubricant level and clean magnetic drain plug every 15,000 miles, and replace lubricant every 30,000 miles.

924 — Check lubricant level at first 1,000 miles, then check every 15,000 miles thereafter.

924 Turbo — Check lubricant level at first 1,000 miles, then every 30,000 miles. Change lubricant every 60,000 miles.

928 — Check lubricant level and clean magnetic drain plug at first 1,000 miles. Check lubricant level every 15,000 miles and replace every 30,000 miles.

CHECKING LUBRICANT LEVEL

All Models — Transmission filler plug is located on side of transaxle housing. Since transaxle assembly houses both transmission and differential, fill unit slowly to ensure proper distribution of lubricant. Proper "full" level is just to bottom of filler plug opening.

RECOMMENDED LUBRICANT

911SC & 924 Turbo — SAE 90W transmission oil according to API GL-5 or MIL-L-2105-B specifications.

PORSCHE (Cont.)

924 — SAE 80W/90 transmission oil according to API GL-4 or MIL-L-2105 specifications.

928 — SAE 75W/90 transmission oil according to API GL-5 or MIL-L-2105-B specifications.

CAPACITY

NOTE — *Transmission refill capacities listed are approximate and should be used as a guide when refilling after service. Proper "full" level should be checked at transmission filler hole rather than by amount added.*

Transmission Refill Capacities	
Application	Capacity (Pts.)
911 SC 5-Speed	6.3
924 & 924 Turbo 5-Speed	5.3
928 5-Speed	8.0

ADJUSTMENT

LINKAGE ADJUSTMENT

NOTE — *These models do not require external linkage adjustment.*

RENAULT

Le Car

LUBRICATION

SERVICE INTERVALS

All Models — Change lubricant after first 1,000 miles, and at 12,000 mile intervals thereafter.

CHECKING LUBRICANT LEVEL

All Models — Check lubricant level at fill hole. Lubricant should be even with bottom of fill hole.

RECOMMENDED LUBRICANT

All Models — Use SAE 80 for all applications.

CAPACITY

NOTE — *Transmission capacities listed below are approximate. Correct "full" level should be determined by level at oil fill hole rather than by amount added.*

Transmission Refill Capacities	
Application	Capacity (Pts.)
Le Car	3.8

ADJUSTMENT

LINKAGE ADJUSTMENT

All Models — 1) Place shift lever into 3rd gear position. Press shift lever toward 1st-2nd gear position. Use slotted holes in stop plate to visually check clearance between end of shift lever and stop plate. Clearance should be ⅛" (3 mm).

2) Adjustments are made by placing washers between the stop plate and floor panel. The tolerance of the reverse stop should be ³⁄₁₆-⁹⁄₃₂" (5-7 mm) when the end of the shift lever is resting against stop plate.

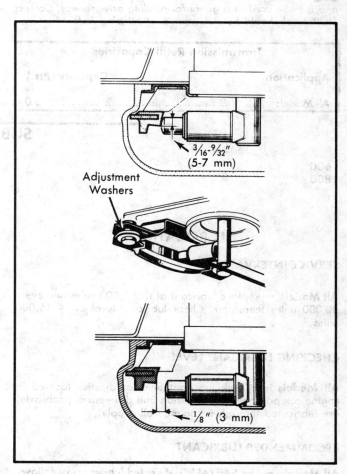

Fig. 1 Setting Shift Lever Dimension

SAAB

99
900

LUBRICATION

SERVICE INTERVALS

All Models — Change transmission lubricant and clean magnetic drain plug at first 1,000 miles. Check and adjust lubricant every 7,500 miles thereafter, except 900 Turbo, which should be checked every 5,000 miles.

CHECKING LUBRICANT LEVEL

All Models — Check fluid level with dipstick located in engine compartment. Fluid level should be between "Min" and "Max" marks on dipstick.

RECOMMENDED LUBRICANT

All Models — Use SAE 10W/30.

CAPACITY

NOTE — *The transmission refill capacity listed is approximate and is to be used as a guide for refilling after service. Correct "full" level should be determined at fill plug hole.*

Transmission Refill Capacities	
Application	**Capacity (Pts.)**
All Models	6.0

ADJUSTMENT

GEAR POSITION ADJUSTMENT

All Models — Engage reverse gear and turn ignition key to "L" (Locked). Move gear lever back and forth. The gear shift rod should have an axial movement of .06-.10" (1.5-5.5 mm) for 99 models and .12-.16" (3-4 mm) for 900 models. Adjust by moving gear lever housing forward or backward. See *Fig. 1.*

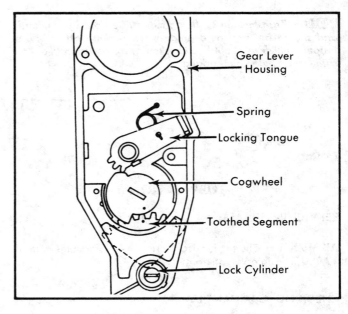

Gear Lever Housing
Spring
Locking Tongue
Cogwheel
Toothed Segment
Lock Cylinder

Fig. 1   Cutaway View of Gear Lever Lock

SUBARU

1600
1800

LUBRICATION

SERVICE INTERVALS

All Models — Replace lubricant at first 1,000 miles and every 30,000 miles thereafter. Check lubricant level every 15,000 miles.

CHECKING LUBRICANT LEVEL

All Models — Check lubricant level at dipstick located in engine compartment. Transmission and differential (transaxle) are lubricated through a common oil supply.

RECOMMENDED LUBRICANT

All Models — Use SAE (API GL-5) rated lubricants as follows: Above 90°F (32°C), use SAE 90; 20°-90°F (-29°-32°C), use SAE 85W 90; below 20°F (-29°C), use SAE 80.

CAPACITY

NOTE — *Transmission capacities shown are approximate, and should be used as a guide when refilling. Final level should be determined at dipstick rather than by amount added.*

Transmission Refill Capacities	
Application	**Capacity (Pts.)**
4-Speed	5.7
5-Speed	5.7
4-WD	6.3

ADJUSTMENT

LINKAGE ADJUSTMENT

NOTE — *All models use shift linkage which does not require external adjustment.*

TOYOTA

Celica
Corolla
Corona
Land Cruiser

Pickup
Supra
Tercel

LUBRICATION

SERVICE INTERVALS

Land Cruiser & Pickup — Check lubricant level every 7,500 miles. Replace lubricant every 30,000 miles.

All Other Models — Check lubricant level every 15,000 miles. No fluid change is required.

CHECKING LUBRICANT LEVEL

All Models — Check lubricant level at fill hole. Lubricant should be to bottom of fill hole.

RECOMMENDED LUBRICANT

All Models — Use SAE 80, 80W/90 or 90 gear oil with API rating of GL-4.

CAPACITY

NOTE — *Capacities listed are approximate, and correct fluid level should be checked at fill hole rather than by amount added.*

Transmission Refill Capacities	
Application	**Capacity (Pts.)**
Celica	
4-Speed	5.7
5-Speed	5.5
Corolla	3.6
Corona	
4-Speed	5.7
5-Speed	5.5
Land Cruiser	
Transmission	6.6
Transfer Case	3.6
Pickup	
4-Speed	4.0
5-Speed	5.5
Pickup 4-WD	
Transmission	4.0
Transfer Case	3.4
Supra	5.4
Tercel	7.0

ADJUSTMENT

LINKAGE ADJUSTMENT

All Models — Linkage is such that no external adjustment is possible.

TRIUMPH

Spitfire
TR7
TR8

LUBRICATION

SERVICE INTERVALS

All Models — Check fluid level at first 1,000 miles, then every 7,500 miles thereafter. Regular oil changes are not required.

CHECKING LUBRICANT

All Models — With vehicle standing level, remove filler plug from side of transmission. Oil level should be to bottom of plug hole. Add as necessary, allow excess to drain away, and replace plug.

RECOMMENDED LUBRICANT

All Models — Use SAE 80 API GL-4 hypoid type oil for Spitfire, SAE 75W API GL-4 hypoid type oil for TR7 and TR8.

CAPACITY

NOTE — *Capacities listed below are approximate "from dry" amounts. Determine exact "full" level at oil fill hole rather than by amount added.*

Transmission Refill Capacities	
Application	**Capacity (Pts.)**
Spitfire	
Without Overdrive	1.8
With Overdrive	3.2
TR7 & TR8 5-Speed	3.3

ADJUSTMENT

LINKAGE ADJUSTMENT

All Models — Linkage on these vehicles requires no external adjustments.

VOLKSWAGEN

Dasher   **Rabbit Pickup**
Jetta   **Scirocco**
Rabbit   **Vanagon**

NOTE — *All information labeled "Rabbit" also applies to Rabbit Pickup.*

LUBRICATION

SERVICE INTERVALS

All Models — No oil changes are required. Check oil every 15,000 miles.

CHECKING LUBRICANT LEVEL

All Models — Check lubricant level through fill plug hole in side of transmission. Lubricant should be to bottom of hole.

RECOMMENDED LUBRICANT

All Models — Use SAE 80W or 80W 90 (API GL-4).

CAPACITY

NOTE — *Transmission capacities listed are approximate, to be used as guide for refilling. Check for proper "full" level at oil fill plug hole, rather than relying strictly on amount added.*

Transmission Refill Capacities	
Application	**Capacity (Pts.)**
Dasher	3.4
Jetta & Rabbit	
4-Speed	3.2
5-Speed	4.2
Scirocco	3.2
Vanagon	7.4

ADJUSTMENT

LINKAGE ADJUSTMENT

Dasher — No external adjustments are required.

Jetta, Rabbit & Scirocco — 1) Loosen bolts holding lever housing, and pull boot off of housing. Loosen shift rod clamp bolt so selector lever moves freely on shift rod. Adjust shift finger in center of lock out plate so that an equal distance is obtained on both sides of the shift finger. See Fig. 1.

2) Adjust shift rod end so that a distance of ¾" (20 mm) for 4-speed models, or 9/32" (15 mm) for 5-speed models exists between shift finger and stop plate. See Fig. 2. Tighten shift rod clamp. Shift through gears and check for proper engagement.

Vanagon — 1) Place shift lever in neutral position. Align holes of upper lever bearing plate with holes in lower lever bearing plate.

2) Loosen shift rod clamp so selector lever moves freely on shift rod. Remove spare tire. Move shift finger of front shift rod to center of rubber stop in housing.

3) Adjust shift rod end so that a distance of ¾" (19 mm) exists between shift rod end and stop plate. Check for proper operation.

GEAR SHIFT LEVER

Jetta, Rabbit & Scirocco — Move the lever bearing assembly on its elongated bolt holes until the round holes indicated in *Fig. 3* are perfectly aligned with the corresponding round holes in lever plate and housing.

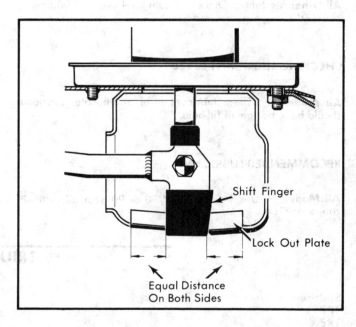

Shift Finger

Lock Out Plate

Equal Distance
On Both Sides

Fig. 1   Correct Position of Shift Finger

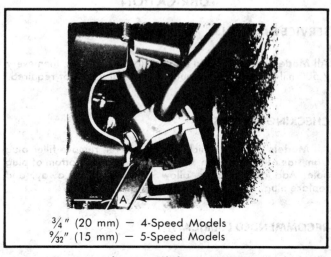

¾" (20 mm) — 4-Speed Models
9/32" (15 mm) — 5-Speed Models

Fig. 2   Adjusting Shift Finger Distance

VOLKSWAGEN (Cont.)

**Fig. 3   Adjusting Shift Lever
(Jetta, Rabbit & Scirocco)**

Dasher — Loosen nuts on plate. Move bearing plate in direction of arrows. See *Fig. 4.* Tighten nuts, shift into 2nd gear and loosen bolts holding stop plate. Adjust plate so that lever moves sideways approximately ¼-⅜" (5-10 mm) measured at knob. Tighten bolts.

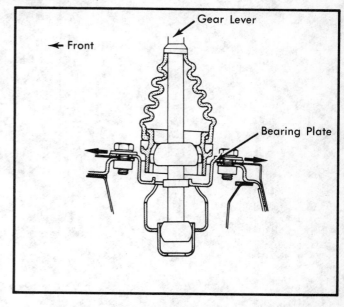

Fig. 4   Adjusting Dasher Shift Lever

VOLVO

DL	GT
GL	Coupe
GLE	Diesel

LUBRICATION

SERVICE INTERVALS

All Models — Replace transmission oil at first 600 miles. Check every 7,500 miles. Under severe driving conditions, change oil every 30,000 miles.

CHECKING LUBRICANT LEVEL

All Models — Check lubricant level at fill hole. Oil should be up to bottom of fill hole. When adding oil, allow sufficient time for oil to flow into overdrive unit.

RECOMMENDED LUBRICANT

All Models — Use Automatic Transmission Fluid, Type F.

CAPACITY

NOTE — *Refill capacities listed below are approximate, and to be used as a refilling guide; however, make certain of final "full" oil level at oil fill hole.*

Transmission Refill Capacities	
Application	**Capacity (Pts.)**
All Models Without Overdrive	1.6
All Models With Overdrive	4.8

ADJUSTMENT

All Models — No external linkage adjustment is required.

Section 5

MANUAL TRANSMISSIONS

CONTENTS

MANUAL TRANSMISSIONS Section 5

NOTE — ALSO SEE GENERAL INDEX.

Manual Transmissions

BMW 633CSi & 733i 4-SPEED

DESCRIPTION

The transmission is a Getrag type unit. This transmission is a 4-speed unit which is fully synchronized in all forward gears. All forward gears are helical cut and in constant mesh. Reverse gear is helical cut and engaged by a sliding reverse idler gear. The console shift lever actuates a single selector rod operating 4 shift rails mounted in transmission case.

LUBRICATION & ADJUSTMENT

See MANUAL TRANSMISSION SERVICING Section.

TROUBLE SHOOTING

HARD SHIFTING

Improperly adjusted clutch. Weakened synchro insert spring. Face of synchro ring in contact with hub, worn. Cones on synchro ring and gear worn or not in proper contact.

SLIPS OUT OF GEAR

Bearings worn or defective. Excessive play between gears and bearings. Play in clutch hub and sliding sleeve. Shift arm worn. Lock ball spring weak or broken. Lock ball missing.

TRANSMISSION NOISY

Low or incorrect lubricant. Gears or bearings worn or damaged. Worn clutch hub or mainshaft splines. Incorrectly meshed gears. Incorrectly assembled sliding sleeves.

TRANSMISSION REMOVAL & INSTALLATION

Removal — 1) Disconnect selector rod from gearshift lever. From inside vehicle, lift shift lever dust boot and remove circlip holding lever in position. Remove shift lever. Disconnect any exhaust system components which may interfere with transmission removal.

2) Attach clamping tool (26 1 011) to propeller shaft coupling and remove nuts. Tighten clamping tool and remove bolts holding coupling to transmission shaft coupler. Remove heat shield and bearing center bracket. On 733i models, remove web under propeller shaft tunnel.

3) On all models, remove center support bearing and bend propeller shaft so that it can be removed from front coupling and positioned out of way. Support transmission with jack and remove crossmember. Disconnect speedometer cable and housing from transmission.

4) Remove clutch slave cylinder from clutch housing, leaving hydraulic line connected. Disconnect back-up light switch wires. Remove transmission mounting nuts, pull transmission rearward and carefully remove from under vehicle.

Installation — Reverse removal procedure and note the following: Lubricate input shaft splines and release bearing groove with grease. Make sure clutch slave cylinder bleeder screw is pointing downward. Preload center bearing .080"

(2.0 mm) by moving bracket forward in slots provided. Install NEW propeller shaft coupling nuts.

TRANSMISSION DISASSEMBLY

1) Remove selector rod housing attaching bolts and separate housing from transmission case. Drive out dowel pin and separate gearshift rod from selector rod. Mount transmission on workstand and drain transmission oil. Remove attaching bolts from front cover and remove front cover from case, making sure not to lose shims.

2) Remove input shaft bearing snap ring and remove support ring and shims. Using special bearing puller (Rillex 23 2 060) installed over input shaft, pull bearing from case using care not to lose spacer. Remove countergear bearing from case using a puller. Lift lock pin cover from top of front transmission case and remove springs and lock pins. Remove back-up light switch from transmission case. Remove attaching bolts and separate front transmission case from rear case.

3) Loosen reverse idler gear shift lever screw and lift shift lever from rear transmission case. Drive retaining pins out of 3rd-4th shift fork and reverse shift fork, then pull reverse shift rail from case. Turn selector rod until 3rd-4th shift rail can be removed. Hold propeller shaft coupling flange on rear of transmission stationary and remove flange nut, then remove flange. Remove mainshaft support ring attaching screws from rear of case.

4) Heat rear transmission case to approximately 176° F (80° C), then pull the following components from case: Mainshaft, countergear shaft, reverse idler gear, 1st-2nd shift rail and all shift forks. Pull selector rod from case. Remove speedometer drive assembly screw and slide assembly from bore in rear transmission case. Pry out covers and remove detent balls and springs from bores in transmission case.

COMPONENT DISASSEMBLY & REASSEMBLY

MAINSHAFT

Disassembly — 1) From front of mainshaft, pull off input shaft and needle bearing. Remove mainshaft snap ring and slide the following off of mainshaft: Thrust washer, 4th gear synchro ring, 3rd-4th synchro hub with sleeve, 3rd gear synchro ring, 3rd gear needle bearing, and 3rd gear.

NOTE — *Mark each synchro ring to ensure reassembly with correct gear.*

2) From rear of mainshaft, press off the following parts: Speedometer gear, thrust washer, ball bearing, support ring, reverse gear, spacer, 1st gear needle bearing, 1st gear, 1st gear synchro ring, 1st-2nd synchro hub with sleeve, 2nd gear synchro ring, 2nd gear needle bearing and 2nd gear.

Reassembly — Reverse disassembly procedure and note the following: Ensure synchro rings are installed with correct gear. Recess side of 1st-2nd synchro assembly sleeve must face towards first gear.

BMW 633CSi & 733i 4-SPEED (Cont.)

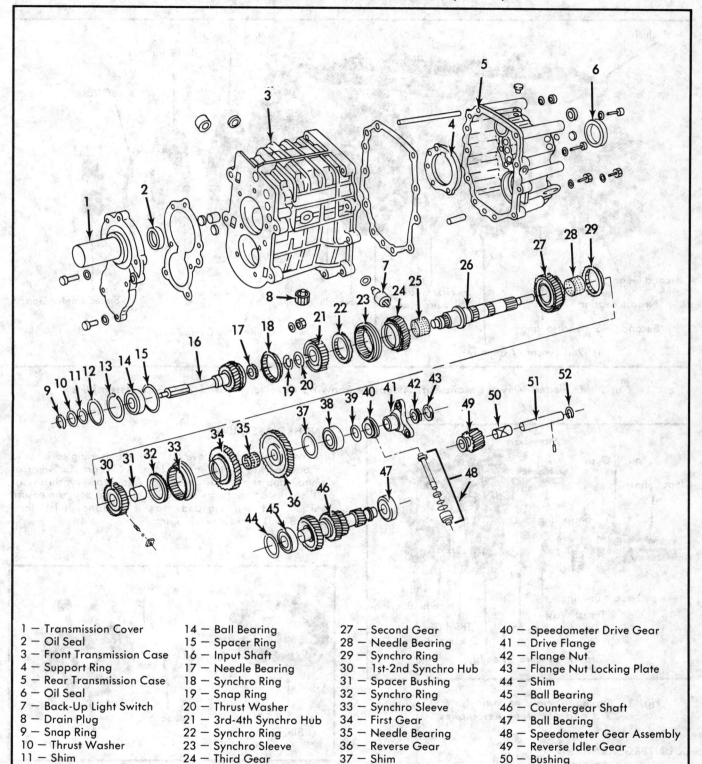

1 — Transmission Cover	14 — Ball Bearing	27 — Second Gear	40 — Speedometer Drive Gear
2 — Oil Seal	15 — Spacer Ring	28 — Needle Bearing	41 — Drive Flange
3 — Front Transmission Case	16 — Input Shaft	29 — Synchro Ring	42 — Flange Nut
4 — Support Ring	17 — Needle Bearing	30 — 1st-2nd Synchro Hub	43 — Flange Nut Locking Plate
5 — Rear Transmission Case	18 — Synchro Ring	31 — Spacer Bushing	44 — Shim
6 — Oil Seal	19 — Snap Ring	32 — Synchro Ring	45 — Ball Bearing
7 — Back-Up Light Switch	20 — Thrust Washer	33 — Synchro Sleeve	46 — Countergear Shaft
8 — Drain Plug	21 — 3rd-4th Synchro Hub	34 — First Gear	47 — Ball Bearing
9 — Snap Ring	22 — Synchro Ring	35 — Needle Bearing	48 — Speedometer Gear Assembly
10 — Thrust Washer	23 — Synchro Sleeve	36 — Reverse Gear	49 — Reverse Idler Gear
11 — Shim	24 — Third Gear	37 — Shim	50 — Bushing
12 — Shim	25 — Needle Bearing	38 — Ball Bearing	51 — Reverse Idler Gear Shaft
13 — Snap Ring	26 — Mainshaft	39 — Thrust Washer	52 — Snap Ring

Fig. 1 Exploded View of 633CSi and 733i Transmission Assembly

BMW 633CSi & 733i 4-SPEED (Cont.)

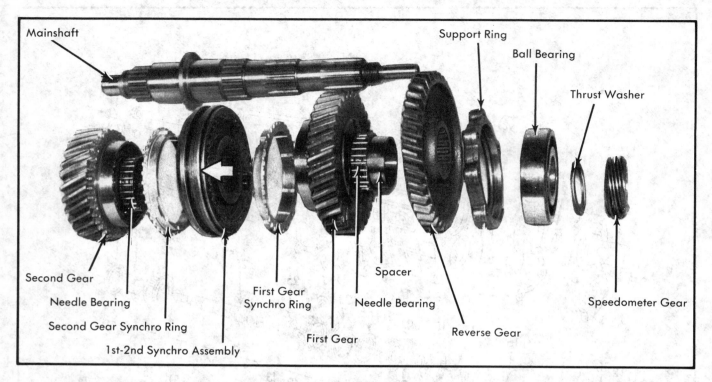

Fig. 2 *Exploded View of Mainshaft Assembly Showing Reverse, 1st and 2nd Gear Assemblies*

Mainshaft — Support Ring — Ball Bearing — Thrust Washer — Second Gear — Needle Bearing — Second Gear Synchro Ring — 1st-2nd Synchro Assembly — First Gear Synchro Ring — First Gear — Spacer — Needle Bearing — Reverse Gear — Speedometer Gear

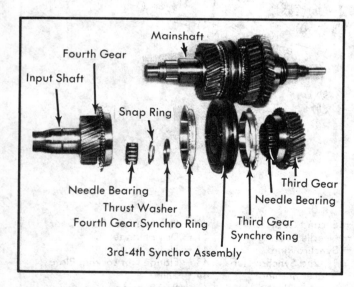

Mainshaft — Fourth Gear — Input Shaft — Snap Ring — Needle Bearing — Thrust Washer — Fourth Gear Synchro Ring — 3rd-4th Synchro Assembly — Third Gear Synchro Ring — Third Gear Needle Bearing — Third Gear

Fig. 3 *Exploded View of Mainshaft Showing 3rd and 4th Gear Assemblies*

COUNTERGEAR SHAFT

Disassembly — With gears and shaft cold, pull off bearing, then press off fourth gear. Remove snap ring from shaft and press off third gear.

Reassembly — Reverse disassembly procedure and note the following: Heat gears to approximately 250-300° F (120-150° C) before pressing them onto shaft. Also, high collar on bore of third and fourth gears must face towards second gear.

SYNCHRO ASSEMBLIES

Disassembly — Slide sleeve off synchro hub using care not to lose ball, ball seat and spring. Inspect all parts for wear or damage and replace as necessary. Also, place synchro rings on their respective gears and using a feeler gauge measure clearance between ring and gear. If clearance is less than .031" (.8 mm), replace synchro ring.

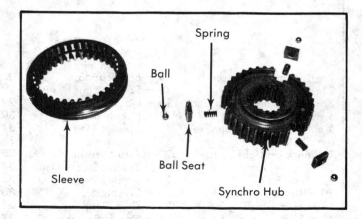

Spring — Ball — Ball Seat — Sleeve — Synchro Hub

Fig. 4 *Exploded View of Synchro Assembly*

Reassembly — Slide sleeve half-way onto hub, then install spring, ball seat (with domed side facing sleeve), and ball into position on hub and slide sleeve remaining way onto hub.

BMW 633CSi & 733i 4-SPEED (Cont.)

Fig. 5   Using Feeler Gauge to Measure
Synchro Ring-to-Gear Clearance

TRANSMISSION REASSEMBLY

1) Heat rear transmission case to approximately 176° F (80° C), then install mainshaft, countergear shaft and reverse idler gear into case. Install mainshaft support ring attaching screws through rear of case and tighten them to specifications. Install gear selector rod into case, then install shift forks onto selector rod.

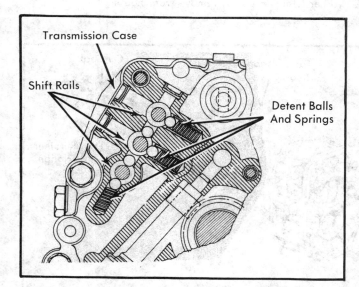

Fig. 6   Cutaway View of Rear Transmission Case
Showing Location of Detent Balls and Springs

2) Install reverse shift fork on reverse shift rail, then install spring pin through fork to retain it in position. Install detent balls and springs into position in transmission case (see Fig. 6), then slide reverse shift rail into position in case. Turn gear selector rod to reverse gear position, then install 1st-2nd gear shift rail and fork. Install 3rd-4th shift rail and fork, then

secure shift forks to rails with spring pins. Coat detent ball covers with sealant and install them into bores of case. Install reverse idler gear selector lever and tighten attaching bolt.

3) Install propeller shaft coupling flange on rear of transmission and tighten attaching nut to specifications, then install lock plate and lock in groove. Install a new seal ring on speedometer drive assembly, then install assembly into case and lock in place with retaining screw. Install back-up light switch to case using a new gasket. Install lock pins and springs into front transmission case and install cover.

4) Heat inner race of countergear shaft bearing to approximately 176°F (80°C) and press onto countergear shaft. Heat inner race of mainshaft bearing to the same temperature, then using installer tool (23 11 000) install on mainshaft. Install support ring and shims onto mainshaft and secure in place with snap ring, then install cover on transmission with 3 longer bolts at top and 3 shorter bolts at bottom. Tighten front cover attaching bolts. Using new dowel pin, connect gearshift rod to selector rod and install selector rod housing to transmission and tighten attaching bolts.

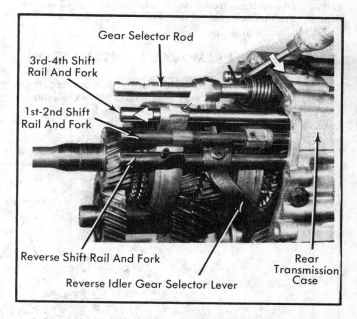

Fig. 7   Installed View of Shift Rails and Forks

TIGHTENING SPECIFICATIONS

Application	Ft. Lbs. (mkg)
Transmission-to-Engine	
8 mm Bolts	18-20 (2.5-2.7)
10 mm Bolts	34-37 (4.7-5.1)
Coupling Flange Lock Nut	72 (10.0)
Transmission-to-Clutch Housing	54-59 (7.4-8.2)
Mainshaft Support Ring Bolts	16-17 (2.2-2.4)
Front Cover-to-Transmission Bolts	18 (2.5)
Transmission Case Bolts	13-18 (1.8-2.5)

Manual Transmissions

BMW 320i 5-SPEED

DESCRIPTION

The transmission model is a Getrag 245/5. This 5-speed transmission is fully synchronized with constant mesh helical cut gears in forward speeds, and uses non-synchronized helical cut reverse gears. Shifting is accomplished through 3 shift rails and forks. Transmission case is a 3-piece design.

LUBRICATION & ADJUSTMENT

See *MANUAL TRANSMISSION SERVICING* Section.

TROUBLE SHOOTING

HARD SHIFTING

Check clutch adjustment, or check gears, shafts, bearings or synchronizers for wear or damage.

SLIPS OUT OF GEAR

Check for worn or damaged interlock, bearings or gears.

NOISE IN TRANSMISSION

Ensure noise is from transmission and not clutch. Check for proper transmission lubricant level. Check for worn or damaged bearings or gears.

TRANSMISSION REMOVAL & INSTALLATION

Removal — 1) Push up shift lever boot and foam ring, then remove circlip from shift lever ball socket. Remove exhaust bracket from transmission and exhaust pipe from manifold. Remove upper clutch housing bolts.

2) Remove propeller shaft from transmission (coupling or flexible disc remains with shaft). Remove propeller shaft center support bearing, pull shaft downward and away from centering pin.

3) Remove shift lever bearing pin and push shift lever upward. Remove clutch linkage and slave cylinder as required. Loosen angle support and remove transmission front cover plate.

4) Support engine using a block between engine and front axle subframe. Remove speedometer shaft and electrical connections. Loosen crossmember and turn steering to full right lock position. Remove remaining bolts securing transmission to engine and frame; remove transmission.

Installation — Reverse removal procedure and note the following: Use new lock nuts on propeller shaft; use suitable shims under shift lever circlip to remove play in shift lever; preload center bearing .078" (2 mm); adjust clutch pedal free play.

TRANSMISSION DISASSEMBLY

TRANSMISSION CASE

1) Remove crossmember and exhaust support bracket. Secure transmission in holding device and drain oil. Remove guide sleeve, cover, spring and locking pin from upper right front of housing. Unscrew back-up light switch.

2) Drive out pins and remove bolts and hex-head screw on rear housing. Remove front bearing race, snap ring and washer. Using a puller, remove front housing.

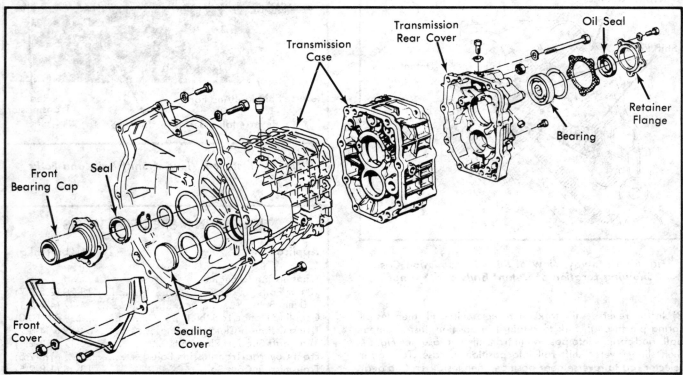

Fig. 1 Exploded View of BMW 320i 5-Speed Transmission Case Components

BMW 320i 5-SPEED (Cont.)

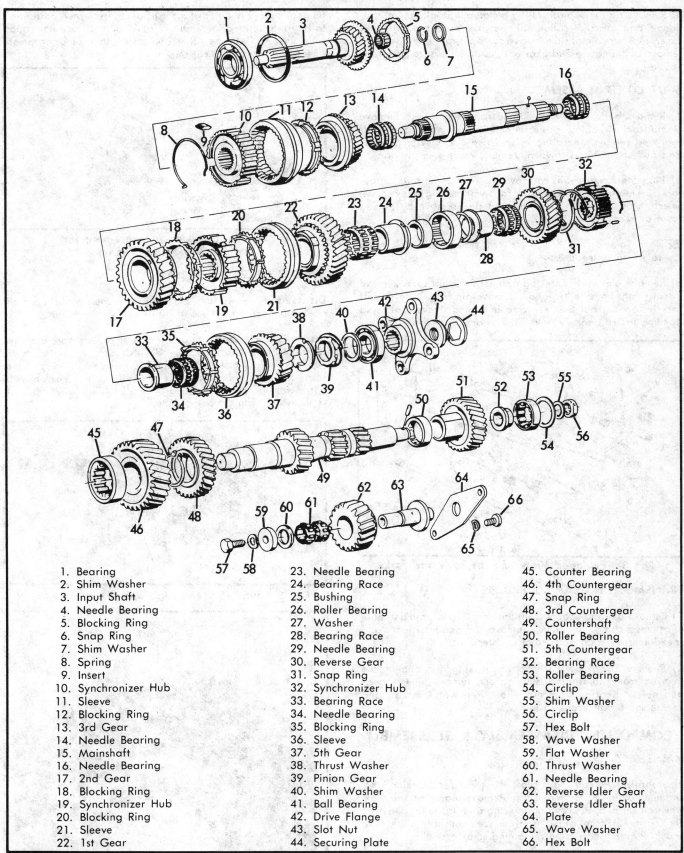

1. Bearing
2. Shim Washer
3. Input Shaft
4. Needle Bearing
5. Blocking Ring
6. Snap Ring
7. Shim Washer
8. Spring
9. Insert
10. Synchronizer Hub
11. Sleeve
12. Blocking Ring
13. 3rd Gear
14. Needle Bearing
15. Mainshaft
16. Needle Bearing
17. 2nd Gear
18. Blocking Ring
19. Synchronizer Hub
20. Blocking Ring
21. Sleeve
22. 1st Gear

23. Needle Bearing
24. Bearing Race
25. Bushing
26. Roller Bearing
27. Washer
28. Bearing Race
29. Needle Bearing
30. Reverse Gear
31. Snap Ring
32. Synchronizer Hub
33. Bearing Race
34. Needle Bearing
35. Blocking Ring
36. Sleeve
37. 5th Gear
38. Thrust Washer
39. Pinion Gear
40. Shim Washer
41. Ball Bearing
42. Drive Flange
43. Slot Nut
44. Securing Plate

45. Counter Bearing
46. 4th Countergear
47. Snap Ring
48. 3rd Countergear
49. Countershaft
50. Roller Bearing
51. 5th Countergear
52. Bearing Race
53. Roller Bearing
54. Circlip
55. Shim Washer
56. Circlip
57. Hex Bolt
58. Wave Washer
59. Flat Washer
60. Thrust Washer
61. Needle Bearing
62. Reverse Idler Gear
63. Reverse Idler Shaft
64. Plate
65. Wave Washer
66. Hex Bolt

Fig. 2 Exploded View of BMW 320i 5-Speed Transmission Gears and Shafts

Manual Transmissions

BMW 320i 5-SPEED (Cont.)

3) Remove rear lock plate. Using a clamping tool, hold output flange and unscrew collar nut. Remove output flange and cover, making note of shims. Drive out 2 pins on rear cover and remove bolt. Engage 2nd gear and, using pullers, remove rear housing.

SHIFT CONTROL ASSEMBLY

1) Remove bolts in top and side of transmission case. Remove clamp from end of lower selector rod. Pull selector rod towards rear and remove operating lever. Drive out selector arm pin and pull selector rod towards rear. Remove selector arm.

2) Push 5th-Reverse shift rod towards rear enough to expose fork. Drive out pin and remove fork with sliding sleeve. Turn selector rod until slot faces upward and remove by pulling towards rear.

NOTE — *Take care not to lose detent balls when performing the followng procedures.*

3) Remove pins in driving dog and 1st-2nd shift fork. Remove driving dog. Engage 3rd gear. Remove pin from 3rd-4th shift fork by driving out between gap in sliding sleeve tooth and opening in 3rd gear. Remove 1st-2nd and 3rd-4th shift forks.

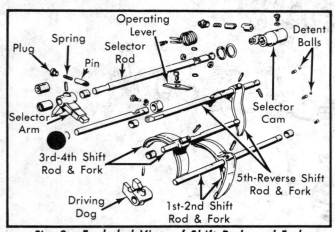

Fig. 3   Exploded View of Shift Rods and Forks

TRANSMISSION GEAR ASSEMBLIES

1) Remove pin and spacer from 5th countergear, making note of shims. Using a puller, remove 5th countergear and speedometer pinion gear from countershaft.

2) Remove 5th gear, synchronizer blocking ring and needle bearing from mainshaft. Using pullers, remove reverse gear and needle bearing from mainshaft. Remove mainshaft and countershaft from transmission case.

COMPONENT DISASSEMBLY & REASSEMBLY

MAINSHAFT

Disassembly — Pull input shaft, synchronizer blocking ring and needle bearing off mainshaft. Remove snap ring and slide synchronizer hub, sleeve, blocking ring and 3rd gear with needle bearing off front of mainshaft. Place mainshaft in a holder and press mainshaft from remaining gear assemblies.

Reassembly — Reverse disassembly procedure making note to measure distance "A" of mainshaft collar to inner bearing race

on gear assembly and distance "B" of reverse synchronizer hub to bearing bushing. *See Fig. 4.* If "A" and "B" are not equal, subtract one from the other and install shim of appropriate (measurement difference) thickness.

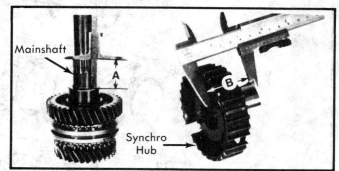

Fig. 4   Checking Measurement for Mainshaft Shim Thickness

SYNCHRONIZER ASSEMBLIES

Disassembly — Remove blocking ring, then push hub from sleeve. Separate inserts and insert springs from hub.

Inspection — Check all parts for wear or damage. Blocking rings must be replaced if tapered clutch surface is pitted or excessively worn. Place each synchronizer ring into position on its respective gear, then, using a feeler gauge, measure clearance between ring and gear. If clearance is less than .032" (.8 mm), replace synchronizer ring.

Fig. 5   Synchronizer Spring and Insert Installation

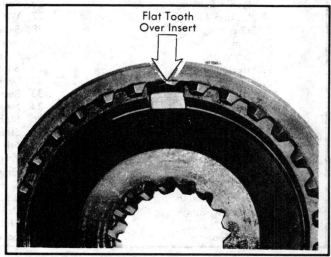

Fig. 6   Synchronizer Sleeve Installation

BMW 320i 5-SPEED (Cont.)

Reassembly — Stagger hooks on insert springs in notches in hub. Install inserts and push sleeve over hub. Install blocking ring on hub and install synchronizer on mating gear.

COUNTERSHAFT

Disassembly — Pull bearing off front of countershaft, then press off 4th gear. Remove snap ring and press off 3rd gear. Remove rear circlips making note of shims. Pull outer bearing off rear of countershaft, then press off 5th gear. Pull off inner bearing.

Inspection — Check shaft and gears for wear or damage. Lightly polish any scoring from shaft surfaces.

Reassembly — Reverse disassembly procedure by heating gears to 250-300°F (120-150°C) and then pressing gears into position.

REVERSE IDLER GEAR & SHAFT

Disassembly — Remove end plate. Unscrew hex bolt while holding shaft at front. Remove bolt and washers. Install a bolt in tapped bore and push out assembly towards rear. Separate needle bearing and gear from shaft.

Inspection — Inspect components for wear or damage and replace if necessary.

Reassembly — Reverse disassembly procedure using Loctite (or equivalent) on holding bolt.

TRANSMISSION REASSEMBLY

GEAR & SHAFT CONTROL ASSEMBLIES

1) Install mainshaft and countershaft assemblies in intermediate transmission case. Install appropriate shim, heat bearing race to about 175°F (80°C) and push onto mainshaft. Press needle bearing and reverse gear onto mainshaft. Slide 5th gear synchronizer assembly onto mainshaft.

2) Push 5th-Reverse shift rod up to spring in transmission case from input shaft end. Insert locking balls and press down, pushing rod on through to lock.

3) Insert 5th-Reverse shift fork in sliding sleeve. Install sleeve on mainshaft with pins facing out. Guide 5th-Reverse shift fork onto rod and drive in a .24 x .94" (6 x 24 mm) pin.

4) Drive sleeve against stop on mainshaft spline. Heat bearing race to about 175°F (80°C) and push on mainshaft to sleeve. Install synchronizer blocking ring, needle bearing and 5th gear onto mainshaft.

5) Install inner roller bearing and 5th countergear on countershaft. Using appropriate driver, drive bearing race onto countershaft. Install circlip and insert a .2" (5 mm) mandrel in bore hole. Measure distance between spacer and bearing race and take up countershaft end play with appropriate shims. Install locking circlip with .20 x 1" (5 x 26 mm) pin on countershaft.

6) Install washer with bevelled side out on mainshaft. Heat speedometer gear and push onto mainshaft.

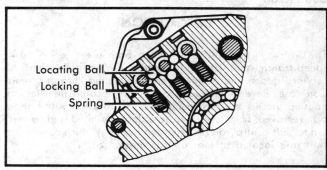

Fig. 7   Arrangement of Locating and Locking Balls

7) Install 1st-2nd and 3rd-4th shift forks. Push in 3rd-4th shift rod through shift fork to spring. Insert locating ball and locking ball and press down. Push 3rd-4th shift rod on through to lock making sure that opening on shift rod faces 5th-Reverse shift rod. Drive in a .24 x .94" (6 x 24 mm) pin.

8) Push in 1st-2nd shift rod through fork to spring in transmission case. Install driving dog. Install locating ball and locking ball and press down. Push 1st-2nd shift rod on through to lock and drive in a .24 x.94" (6 x 24 mm) pin.

9) Push in upper selector rod with opening facing out. Install selector arm with long side facing 3rd-4th shift rod.

10) Install lower selector rod with opening facing up. Install operating lever with sharp edge facing up and push in rod.

11) Install bolt in top of transmission case with Loctite (or equivalent) making sure that center engages bore of operating lever. Test operating lever for ease of movement. Push clamp onto lower selector rod with bevelled side facing shift fork.

12) Install bolt in side of transmission case with Loctite (or equivalent) making sure that center engages groove in lower selector rod. Hold 4 rollers on selector rod with grease.

TRANSMISSION CASE

Thoroughly clean all sealing surfaces, coat with Loctite (or equivalent and reverse disassembly procedure.

TIGHTENING SPECIFICATIONS

Application	Ft. Lbs. (mkg)
Transmission-to-Engine	
8 mm Bolts	18-19 (2.5-2.7)
10 mm Bolts	35-37 (4.8-5.2)
Transmission Rear Cover Bolts	18 (2.5)
Propeller Shaft Flange Nut	72 (1.0)
Rear Seal Flange Bolts	7 (1.0)
Front Cover Plate Bolts	18 (2.5)
Rubber Mount	32-35 (4.4-4.9)
Bracket	16-17 (2.2-2.4)

Manual Transmissions

CHRYSLER CORP. IMPORTS 4-SPEED

Arrow Pickup
D50 Pickup

DESCRIPTION

The Arrow Pickup and D50 Pickup both use the KM130 4-speed transmission with all forward gears synchromeshed. All forward gears, and countergear, are located in the transmission case. Reverse and idler gears are located in extension housing. Access to transmission gears is obtained with bottom pan removed. Shift lever is remote floor mounted and connected to shift control rod (in extension housing) which connects to shift rails located at rear of transmission case.

LUBRICATION & ADJUSTMENT

See *MANUAL TRANSMISSION SERVICING* Section.

TROUBLE SHOOTING

DIFFICULTY MESHING GEARS

Malfunction of gearshift lever or control shaft. Synchro rings or gear coned surfaces worn or excessive play. Synchro shift keys worn or damaged.

JUMPS OUT OF GEAR

Shifting forks worn or detent springs broken. Mainshaft or mainshaft support bearings worn or damaged. Clearance between synchro hub and sleeve excessive. Gears or gear bushings worn. Countergear worn.

NOISE IN TRANSMISSION

Lubrication oil incorrect or insufficient. Gears or bearings worn. Mainshaft spline worn or damaged.

TRANSMISSION REMOVAL & INSTALLATION

Removal — **1)** In engine compartment, remove air cleaner. Disconnect battery cables from starter, unclip cables from transmission, and move them out of way.

2) Remove bolts holding clutch housing to engine block.

3) Inside vehicle, take out console box (if equipped), and carpet. Remove dust cover retainer plate at base of shift lever. Lift up dust cover and remove four attaching bolts at lower part of extension housing and remove gearshift lever.

NOTE — *Make sure gearshift lever is in 2nd speed position before removing.*

4) With vehicle raised and supported, drain transmission. Remove speedometer cable, then disconnect transmission switch and back-up light switch. Remove bolts from rear of propeller shaft and draw shaft out of transmission. Disconnect tail pipe from tail pipe bracket and disconnect clutch cable.

5) Support rear of engine with jack, place transmission jack under transmission and remove rear supports and crossmember.

6) Remove clutch housing inspection cover and bolts attaching clutch housing to engine block. Pulling rearward and downward, remove transmission from vehicle.

Installation — **1)** To install reverse removal procedure and note the following: When installing control lever assembly, place shift lever in 2nd gear position so that nylon bushing hole is vertical. **CAUTION** — *During this operation, use care that dirt does not enter through opening.*

2) When installing clutch housing inspection cover, make sure that it is not bent. When installing shift lever dust boot, make sure cover is tightly installed to prevent noise entry into vehicle. After installing transmission, refill with SAE 80 gear oil.

TRANSMISSION DISASSEMBLY

NOTE — *Transmission case and extension housing are made of aluminum and care should be exercised when handling machined surfaces.*

1) Before proceeding with disassembly, clean exterior of transmission case. In clutch housing, use a 3/16" (4.76 mm) punch to drive out spring pin in clutch shaft. Remove clutch shaft from clutch housing and remove release fork, felt packing and return springs.

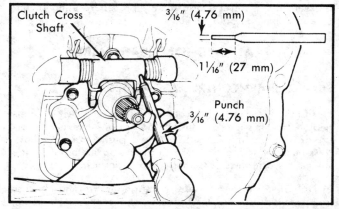

Fig. 1   Removing Spring Pin from Clutch Cross Shaft

2) From extension housing, remove speedometer locking plate and then remove speedometer driven gear assembly. Remove back-up light switch and transmission switch.

CAUTION — *When switch is removed, take care not to lose ball.*

3) Remove extension housing attaching bolts. Rotate contol lever to left and hold while pulling extension housing off to the rear. Remove bottom pan from transmission case.

4) Remove detent plugs, springs and balls. Place 1st-2nd shift rail in neutral position then remove reverse shaft rail and fork assembly together with reverse idler gear.

5) Use a 3/16" (4.76 mm) punch to drive out shift rail and fork spring pins. Pull each shift rail and selector out toward rear of case then remove shift fork. Shift rail and selector should re-

CHRYSLER CORP. IMPORTS 4-SPEED (Cont.)

main together as an assembly. Make sure interlock plungers are not lost when removing shafts.

6) Remove snap ring from rear of countergear. Remove counter reverse gear and spacer. Remove mainshaft lock nut and reverse gear from mainshaft. Remove retaining screws and then bearing retainer. Remove front bearing retainer.

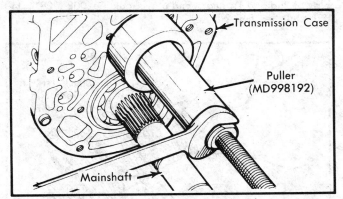

Fig. 2   Removing Countergear Rear Bearing from Transmission Case

7) Press countergear rearward and remove snap ring. Use bearing puller and remove countergear rear bearing. Remove snap ring from front of countergear bearing, then remove bearing with bearing puller. Remove countergear from transmission case. Pull input shaft pinion from front of transmission case. Remove snap rings from input shaft pinion then remove bearing with gear puller.

8) Remove mainshaft bearing snap ring and then bearing. Remove mainshaft from transmission case.

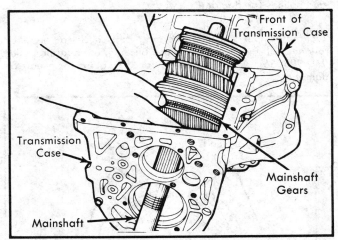

Fig. 3   Removing Mainshaft Assembly from Transmission Case

COMPONENT DISASSEMBLY & REASSEMBLY

MAINSHAFT

Disassembly — 1) Pull 1st gear, 1st-2nd synchro and 2nd gear toward rear of mainshaft. Remove snap ring from forward end of mainshaft, then remove 3rd-4th synchro and 3rd gear.

2) Using a 3/16" (4.76 mm) punch, remove pin locking the gear shifter. Remove control shaft assembly. Press gear shifter forward and pull lock pin off, being careful not to bend control shaft.

Inspection — 1) Check transmission case and extension housing for cracks and damage. Check mainshaft for worn or damaged gear area, bearing surfaces and splines. Check spacers and bearings for wear or damage. Check all bearings for smooth rolling action. Replace parts as necessary.

2) Check all gears for damaged, worn or chipped teeth. Check inside diameter for wear or damage. Check all synchro assemblies for worn or damaged teeth, cone surface, internal surface and rings.

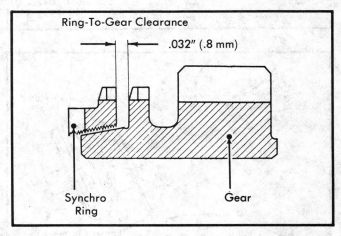

Fig. 4   Checking Synchro Ring-to-Gear Clearance

3) Check synchro ring to gear clearance on all synchro rings. See *Fig. 4.* If the clearance is not .032" (.8 mm) replace synchro ring. With hub and sleeve assembled, check that sleeve slides smoothly and that there is not excessive looseness. If either part is defective, replace both synchro sleeve and hub as an assembly.

4) Check synchro pieces for wear and damage, especially the projecting part. Check synchro springs for deterioration and breakage. Check countergear for wear or chipped teeth.

5) Check reverse idler gear and shaft for wear or damage. Check shift forks, rail and selector for wear or damage. Check clearance between shift fork and fork grove on synchro sleeve and gear. Clearance should be .004-.012" (.1-.3 mm). Check detent ball slots for wear. Check clearance between selector and lever, clearance should be .004-.012" (.1-.3 mm).

6) Check detent balls and springs for damage or breakage. Check shift rails, control lever and forks for wear, damage or breakage. If any parts do not meet above specifications, they must be replaced.

Reassembly — 1) Assemble both synchro assemblies, making sure components are positioned correctly. See *Fig. 6.*

2) Install needle bearing and and 3rd gear on front end of mainshaft. Install synchro ring and 3rd-4th synchro assembly.

CHRYSLER CORP. IMPORTS 4-SPEED (Cont.)

NOTE — *Make sure synchro rings and assemblies are installed in same position that they were removed from.*

3) Select snap ring of proper size so 3rd-4th synchro hub end play is 0-.003" (0-.07 mm). See *3rd-4th Synchronizer Hub End Play Chart.*

3rd-4th Synchronizer Hub End Play Chart

Application (Color)	Thickness In. (mm)
No Color	.085 (2.16)
Yellow	.087 (2.21)
Green	.090 (2.29)
White	.093 (2.36)

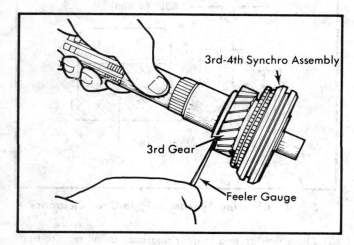

Fig. 5   Using a Feeler Gauge to Check 3rd Gear End Play

4) Check 3rd gear end play using a feeler gauge. Specified end play is .002-.008" (.04-.20 mm). See *Fig. 5*. If end play is not to specifications, check cone part of 3rd gear and coned part of 3rd-4th synchro assembly for wear. Replace components as necessary.

5) Install needle bearing, 2nd gear, synchro assembly, bearing sleeve, needle bearing, 1st gear and bearing spacer onto rear of mainshaft. Press bearing spacer forward and check end play of 2nd and 1st gears. End play should be .002-.008" (.04-.20 mm). See *Fig. 7.*

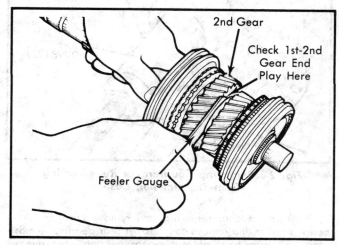

Fig. 7   Checking 1st-2nd Gear End Play

INPUT SHAFT

Inspection & Disassembly — **1)** Check front end outside and inside diameter of needle bearing area for damage or wear. Check synchro cone surface for wear or damage. Check gear and splines for damage or wear.

2) Rotate input shaft ball bearing and check for noise or roughness. If necessary to replace bearing, use bearing puller (MD-998056). Check coned surface of gear for wear or damage.

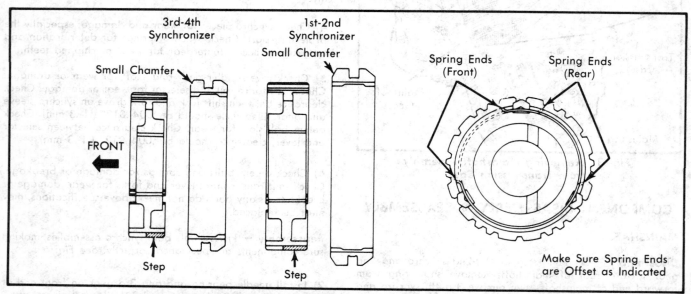

Fig. 6   Correct Position and Assembly of Synchronizer Assembly Components

CHRYSLER CORP. IMPORTS 4-SPEED (Cont.)

Reassembly — To install input shaft ball bearing, use bearing installer (MD-998029). Then install selective fit snap ring to obtain clearance between snap ring and bearing of 0-.002" (0-.05 mm). See *Input Shaft Snap Ring Chart.*

Input Shaft Snap Ring Sizes

Application (Color)	Thickness In. (mm)
White	.091 (2.30)
No Color	.092 (2.35)
Red	.094 (2.40)
Blue	.096 (2.45)

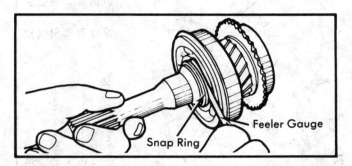

Fig. 8   Checking Input Shaft Bearing End Play

COUNTERGEAR & REVERSE IDLER

Inspection — Check gears for wear, damage or tooth failure. Check bearings and thrust washers for wear or damage. Check shafts for scoring, wear or damage.

SHIFTING MECHANISM & COMPONENTS

Inspection — Check shift rails and forks for smooth operation and excessive scoring. Check clearance between shift fork and fork groove in synchro sleeve. Clearance should be .004-.012" (.1-.3 mm). Check detent slots for wear.

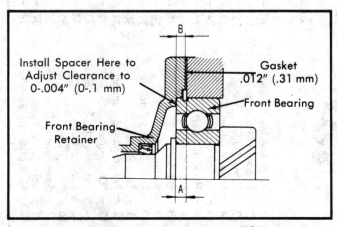

Fig. 9   Front Bearing to Retainer Clearance Measurement

Detent Spring Specifications

Application	Specification
Free Length	.744" (18.9 mm)
Compressed Length at 8.8 Lbs. (4 kg)	.598" (15.2 mm)

TRANSMISSION REASSEMBLY

1) Insert mainshaft assembly into transmission case and drive mainshaft center bearing in using installer tool (MD998067). Install needle bearing and synchro ring, then insert input shaft into front of transmission case.

2) Insert countergear into transmission case. Install snap ring to countergear front bearing, then drive bearing into case by hammering on outer race with mallet. Install snap ring to countergear rear bearing, then install into place with bearing installer (MD998199).

3) Install front bearing retainer with spacer to obtain clearance of 0-.004" (0-.1 mm). See *Fig. 9 and refer to Front Bearing Retainer Spacer Chart.* Install rear bearing retainer and tighten screws. Stake screws with punch.

Front Bearing Retainer Spacer Sizes

Application (Color)	Thickness In. (mm)
Black	.033 (.84)
No Color	.037 (.94)
Red	.040 (1.02)
White	.044 (1.12)
Yellow	.047 (1.19)
Blue	.051 (1.30)
Green	.054 (1.37)

4) Install reverse gear onto mainshaft and tighten lock nut. After tightening, lock the nut at the notch on mainshaft. Install spacer and counter reverse gear to countergear rear end. Install snap ring so reverse gear end play is 0-.003" (0-.07 mm). *Refer to Counter Reverse Gear Snap Ring Chart.*

Counter Reverse Gear Snap Ring Sizes

Application (Color)	Thickness In. (mm)
No Color	.059 (1.5)
Red	.063 (1.6)
Blue	.067 (1.7)
Green	.073 (1.85)
Yellow	.079 (2.0)

5) Install 3rd-4th and 1st-2nd shift forks onto synchro sleeves. Insert shift rails from rear of transmission case. Lock forks and rails with spring pins and install interlock plungers between

Manual Transmission

CHRYSLER CORP. IMPORTS 4-SPEED (Cont.)

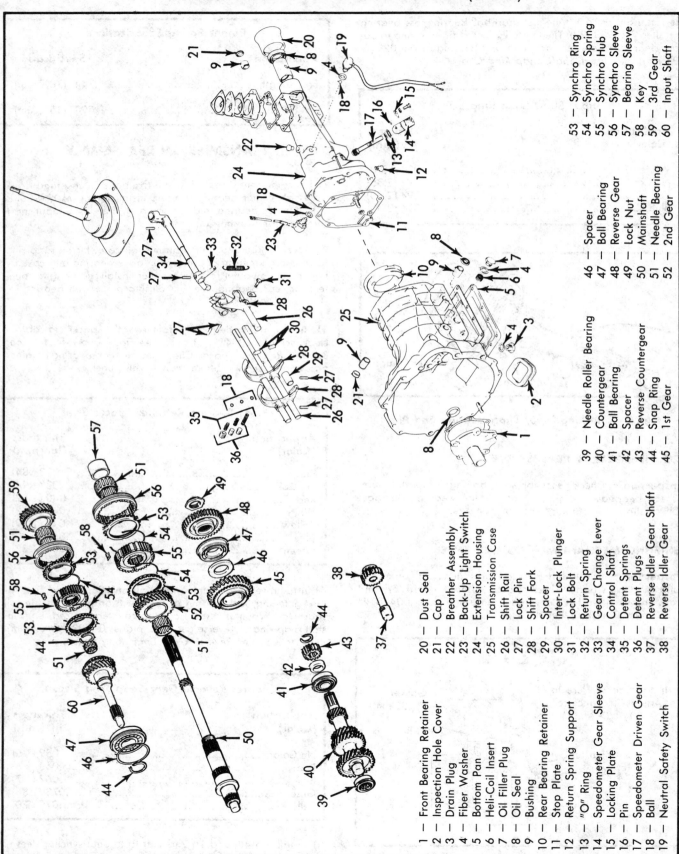

1 — Front Bearing Retainer
2 — Inspection Hole Cover
3 — Drain Plug
4 — Fiber Washer
5 — Bottom Pan
6 — Heli-Coil Insert
7 — Oil Filler Plug
8 — Oil Seal
9 — Bushing
10 — Rear Bearing Retainer
11 — Stop Plate
12 — Return Spring Support
13 — "O" Ring
14 — Speedometer Gear Sleeve
15 — Locking Plate
16 — Pin
17 — Speedometer Driven Gear
18 — Ball
19 — Neutral Safety Switch
20 — Dust Seal
21 — Cap
22 — Breather Assembly
23 — Back-Up Light Switch
24 — Extension Housing
25 — Transmission Case
26 — Shift Rail
27 — Lock Pin
28 — Shift Fork
29 — Spacer
30 — Inter-Lock Plunger
31 — Lock Bolt
32 — Return Spring
33 — Gear Change Lever
34 — Control Shaft
35 — Detent Springs
36 — Detent Plugs
37 — Reverse Idler Gear Shaft
38 — Reverse Idler Gear
39 — Needle Roller Bearing
40 — Countergear
41 — Ball Bearing
42 — Spacer
43 — Reverse Countergear
44 — Snap Ring
45 — 1st Gear
46 — Spacer
47 — Ball Bearing
48 — Reverse Gear
49 — Lock Nut
50 — Mainshaft
51 — Needle Bearing
52 — 2nd Gear
53 — Synchro Ring
54 — Synchro Spring
55 — Synchro Hub
56 — Synchro Sleeve
57 — Bearing Sleeve
58 — Key
59 — 3rd Gear
60 — Input Shaft

Fig. 10 Exploded View of Chrysler Corp. KM130 4-Speed Transmission

CHRYSLER CORP. IMPORTS 4-SPEED (Cont.)

shift rails. Spring pins should have slits in axial direction of shift rail.

6) Install reverse shift rail and fork assembly together with reverse idler gear. Insert detent ball and spring (small end toward ball) into each shift rail. Tighten all plugs to a depth of .24" (6.1 mm) then apply sealant to fill up plug holes.

7) Apply sealant to extension housing gasket, then install gasket and extension housing. When installing extension housing, turn control lever down to the left. Put sealant on extension housing bolts before installation.

8) Apply gear oil to speedometer driven gear and install with sleeve. Make sure number on sleeve (corresponding to number of teeth on gear) is in the "U" mark position when gear and

sleeve are installed. Install clamp and tighten bolt. Install back-up light switch with steel ball.

9) Install bottom pan. Fill gear shifter area with grease and install shifter lever. Fill transmission with SAE 80 gear oil.

TIGHTENING SPECIFICATIONS

Application	Ft. lbs (mkg)
Mainshaft Lock Nut	72-94 (10.0-13.0)
Pan Attaching Bolts	6-7 (0.8-1.0)
Oil Filler Plug	22-25 (3.0-3.5)
Transmission Mounting Bolts	22-30 (3.0-4.0)

CHRYSLER CORP. IMPORTS 5-SPEED

Arrow	Colt
Arrow Pickup	Sapporo
Challenger	D50 Pickup

DESCRIPTION

Transmissions are 5-speed fully synchronized type with constant mesh in all forward gears. All forward gears are helical type gears, with reverse gear using non-synchronized spur type gears. 1st through 3rd gears are located in transmission case, 4th gear is direct, 5th and reverse gears are located in extension housing. Shift lever assembly is located on top rear portion of extension housing. The model KM119 transmission is used in Arrow models with 1.6L engine only. The model KM132 transmission is used in all other models.

LUBRICATION & ADJUSTMENT

See MANUAL TRANSMISSION SERVICING Section.

TROUBLE SHOOTING

DIFFICULTY MESHING GEARS

Malfunction of gearshift lever or control shaft. Synchro rings or gear coned surfaces worn or excessive play. Synchro shift keys worn or damaged.

JUMPS OUT OF GEAR

Shifting forks worn or detent springs broken. Mainshaft or mainshaft support bearings worn or damaged. Clearance between synchro hub and sleeve excessive. Gears or gear bushings worn. Countergear worn.

NOISE IN TRANSMISSION

Lubricating oil incorrect or insufficient. Gears or bearings worn. Mainshaft spline worn or damaged.

TRANSMISSION REMOVAL & INSTALLATION

Removal — 1) In engine compartment, remove air cleaner and disconnect battery cable from starter motor. Unclip wire attached to transmission and move out of way. Remove starter motor and top 2 bolts holding clutch housing to engine block.

2) Inside vehicle, take out console box and carpet. Remove dust cover retainer plate at base of shift lever. Lift up dust cover and remove attaching bolts at lower part of extension housing and remove gearshift lever.

NOTE — Shift lever should be placed in 1st gear position before removal.

3) With vehicle raised and supported, drain transmission. Remove speedometer cable, transmission switch and back-up light switch. Remove bolts from rear propeller shaft and draw shaft out of transmission. Disconnect tail pipe from tail pipe bracket and disconnect clutch cable.

4) Place a jack under transmission for support and remove rear supports and crossmember. Remove clutch housing inspection cover and bolts attaching clutch housing to engine block. Pulling rearward and downward, remove transmission from vehicle.

Installation — 1) To install, reverse removal procedure and note the following: When installing control lever assembly, place shift lever in 1st gear position so that nylon bushing hole is vertical.

CAUTION — During this operation, use care that dirt does not enter through opening.

2) When installing clutch housing inspection cover, make sure that it is not bent. When installing shift lever dust boot, make sure cover is tightly installed to prevent noise entry into vehicle. After installing transmission, refill with SAE 80 gear oil.

TRANSMISSION DISASSEMBLY

1) Remove return clip, then clutch release bearing and carrier. Using a 3/16" (4.76 mm) punch, drive roll pin from clutch release shaft (see Fig. 1). Remove shaft, felt, return spring and clutch release arm. Remove bottom pan from transmission case. Remove back-up light switch and steel ball.

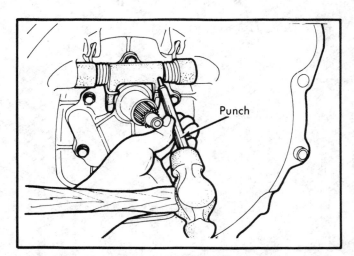

Fig. 1   Removing Roll Pin from Clutch Release Shaft

2) Remove extension housing bolts. Unscrew plug of neutral return plunger "B" (refer to Fig. 13). Move shifter down to the left (see Fig. 3). Slide extension housing from transmission case and mainshaft. On transmission model KM119, remove snap ring and withdraw speedometer drive gear then remove other snap ring and pull ball bearing from rear of mainshaft.

3) Unscrew the three detent plugs, remove springs and balls. Using a 3/16" (4.76 mm) punch, drive 3rd-4th and 1st-2nd roll pins from shift forks. Pull each shift rail toward rear of transmission until shift forks can be removed. Take out interlock plunger.

NOTE — On KM119 transmissions, remove 5th gear and ball bearing at same time the 1st-2nd shift rail is removed.

CHRYSLER CORP. IMPORTS 5-SPEED (Cont.)

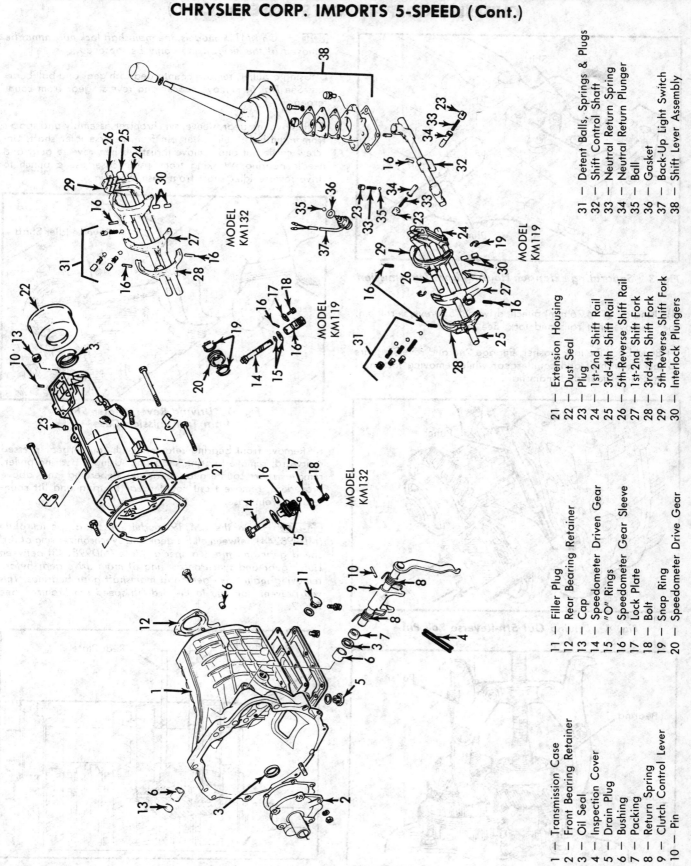

1 — Transmission Case
2 — Front Bearing Retainer
3 — Oil Seal
4 — Inspection Cover
5 — Drain Plug
6 — Bushing
7 — Packing
8 — Return Spring
9 — Clutch Control Lever
10 — Pin
11 — Filler Plug
12 — Rear Bearing Retainer
13 — Cap
14 — Speedometer Driven Gear
15 — "O" Rings
16 — Speedometer Gear Sleeve
17 — Lock Plate
18 — Bolt
19 — Snap Ring
20 — Speedometer Drive Gear
21 — Extension Housing
22 — Dust Seal
23 — Plug
24 — 1st-2nd Shift Rail
25 — 3rd-4th Shift Rail
26 — 5th-Reverse Shift Rail
27 — 1st-2nd Shift Fork
28 — 3rd-4th Shift Fork
29 — 5th-Reverse Shift Fork
30 — Interlock Plungers
31 — Detent Balls, Springs & Plugs
32 — Shift Control Shaft
33 — Neutral Return Spring
34 — Neutral Return Plunger
35 — Ball
36 — Gasket
37 — Back-Up Light Switch
38 — Shift Lever Assembly

Fig. 2 *Exploded View of Chrysler Corp. KM119 and KM132 Transmission Assembly*

CHRYSLER CORP. IMPORTS 5-SPEED (Cont.)

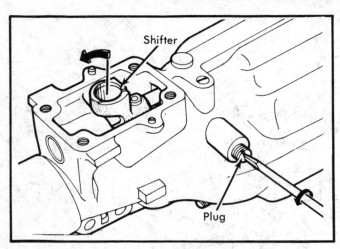

Fig. 3   Separating Extension Housing from Transmission

4) Using a $\frac{3}{16}$" (4.76 mm) punch, drive out 5th-reverse roll pin, then remove shift rails and fork. See *Fig. 4*.

5) Bend back the lock washer. Engage 2nd and reverse gears to lock mainshaft and countergear while removing lock nuts from countergear and mainshaft.

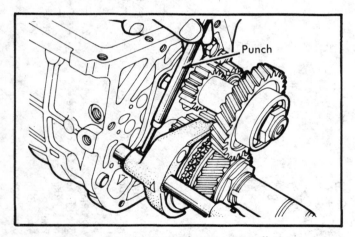

Fig. 4   Driving Out 5th-Reverse Roll Pin

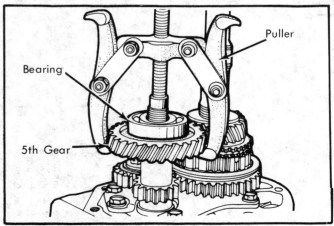

Fig. 5   Pulling 5th Gear and Bearing from Countergear

NOTE — *On KM119 models, the mainshaft lock nut cannot be removed at this time, it may only be loosened.*

6) Using a puller, remove countergear 5th gear and ball bearing. See *Fig. 5*. Remove spacer and reverse gear from countergear.

7) Remove 5th gear, sleeve, synchronizer assembly and spacer from mainshaft. Pull cotter pin from reverse idler shaft. Unscrew castle nut and remove thrust washer, reverse gear and needle bearing. Working from inside case, use a punch to drive reverse idler shaft from case. See *Fig. 6*.

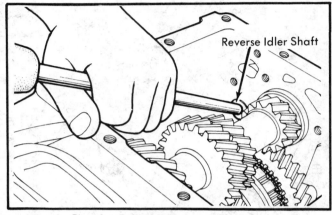

Fig. 6   Driving Reverse Idler Shaft from Transmission Case

8) Remove front bearing retainer. With countergear pressed rearward, remove bearing snap ring. Using a bearing puller, remove rear countergear bearing. Repeating the above procedure, remove front countergear bearing and lift countergear from case.

CAUTION — *On the KM119 models, insert a special plate (MD998244) between clutch gear and synchronizer ring of 3rd speed gear and insert a special plate (MD998243) between clutch gear and synchronizer ring of main drive gear before removing main drive gear and mainshaft gear bearings. This will prevent damage to the 3rd-4th speed synchronizer. See Fig. 7.*

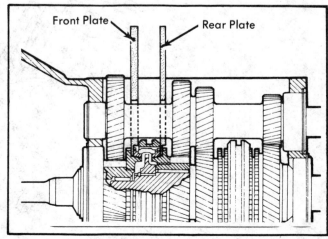

Fig. 7   Synchronizer Ring Protection Plates on KM119 Transmission

CHRYSLER CORP. IMPORTS 5-SPEED (Cont.)

9) On KM119 models, remove snap ring from countergear and remove sub-gear then spring. On both transmissions, pull input shaft/pinion gear assembly from front of case. Remove large snap ring from bearing and small snap ring from input shaft. Using a bearing puller, pull bearing off input shaft.

NOTE — *On KM119 models, slide special tool (MD998241) over mainshaft in place of bearing to support mainshaft.*

10) Remove mainshaft bearing snap ring and pull bearing from case and shaft, then remove mainshaft assembly from case. See *Fig. 8.*

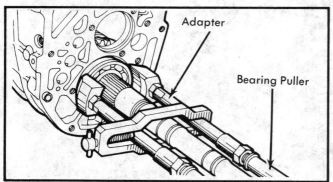

Fig. 8   Pulling Mainshaft Bearing from Transmission Case

COMPONENT DISASSEMBLY & REASSEMBLY

MAINSHAFT

Disassembly — On KM119 models, remove mainshaft nut. On both transmissions, slide 1st gear, 1st-2nd synchronizer and 2nd gear off rear of mainshaft. Remove snap ring from forward end of mainshaft. Slide 3rd-4th synchronizer and 3rd gear from mainshaft.

Inspection — **1)** Clean and inspect mainshaft and gear assemblies as follows: Check mainshaft O.D. and splines for wear or damage. Check gear teeth for wear or damage.

Check I.D. of gear. Inspect synchronizer cone surface for wear or damage.

Gears Standard Dimensions	
Application	**Specification In. (mm)**
KM119	
2nd & 3rd Gear I.D.	1.57 (39.9)
1st Gear I.D.	1.65 (42.0)
5th Gear I.D.	1.42 (36.1)
Reverse Idler Gear I.D.	1.02 (25.9)
Countergear Forward O.D.	.87 (22.0)
KM132	
1st & 2nd Gear I.D.	1.89 (48.0)
3rd & 5th Gear I.D.	1.58 (40.1)
Reverse Idler Gear I.D.	.79 (20.1)
Countergear Forward O.D.	.98 (25.0)

2) On synchronizer rings, check gear teeth and cone I.D. for wear and damage. Place ring on mating gear and measure dimension "A" as shown in *Fig. 9.* Standard value is .059" (1.5 mm) and maximum wear limit is .031" (.8 mm). With hub and sleeve assembled, check for excessive clearance and see if the parts slide smoothly.

NOTE — *If sleeve or hub need replacing, always replace them as an assembly. Check shift fork groove in sleeve for wear.*

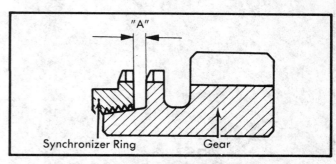

Fig. 9   Measuring Synchronizer Ring-to-Gear Clearance

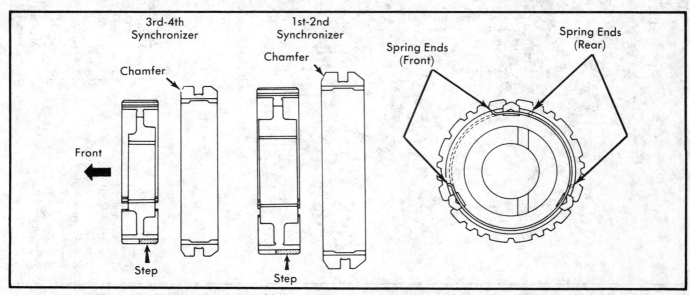

Fig. 10   Synchronizer Assembly and Spring Location (KM132 Shown — KM119 Similar)

Manual Transmissions

CHRYSLER CORP. IMPORTS 5-SPEED (Cont.)

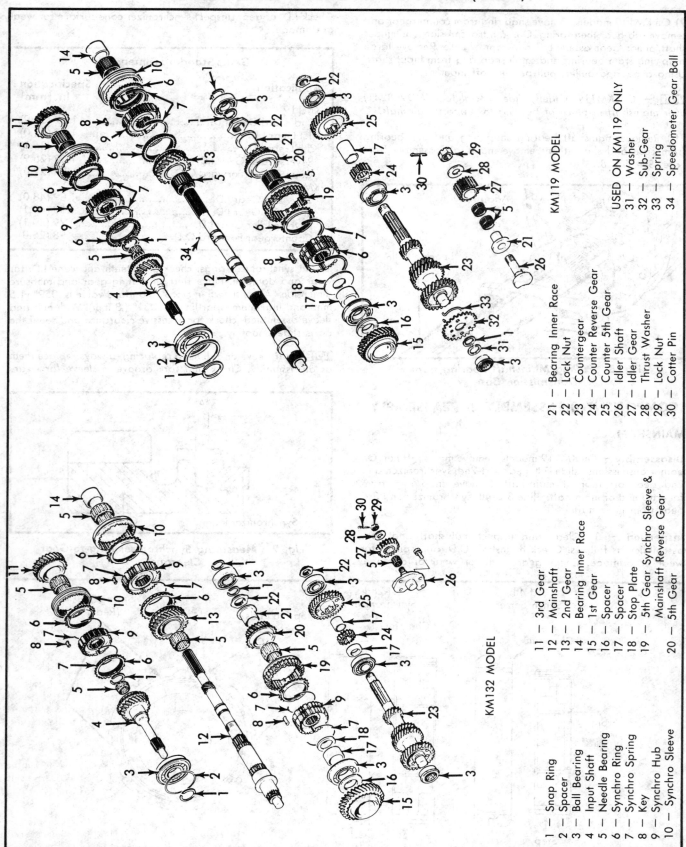

KM119 MODEL

21 — Bearing Inner Race
22 — Lock Nut
23 — Countergear
24 — Counter Reverse Gear
25 — Counter 5th Gear
26 — Idler Shaft
27 — Idler Gear
28 — Thrust Washer
29 — Lock Nut
30 — Cotter Pin

USED ON KM119 ONLY
31 — Washer
32 — Sub-Gear
33 — Spring
34 — Speedometer Gear Ball

KM132 MODEL

1 — Snap Ring
2 — Spacer
3 — Ball Bearing
4 — Input Shaft
5 — Needle Bearing
6 — Synchro Ring
7 — Synchro Spring
8 — Key
9 — Synchro Hub
10 — Synchro Sleeve

11 — 3rd Gear
12 — Mainshaft
13 — 2nd Gear
14 — Bearing Inner Race
15 — 1st Gear
16 — Spacer
17 — Spacer
18 — Stop Plate
19 — 5th Gear Synchro Sleeve &
      Mainshaft Reverse Gear
20 — 5th Gear

Fig. 11 Exploded View of Chrysler Corp. KM119 and KM132 Transmission Gear Assembly

CHRYSLER CORP. IMPORTS 5-SPEED (Cont.)

Reassembly — 1) Assemble 1st-2nd and 3rd-4th synchronizers as shown in *Fig. 10*. Place the needle bearing, 3rd gear, synchronizer ring and 3rd-4th synchronizer assembly on front of mainshaft. Check gear end play. End play should be as specified in table. See *Synchronizer Snap Ring End Play* chart.

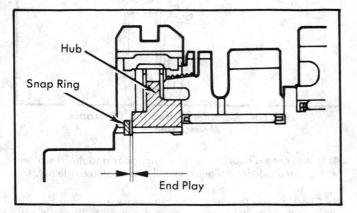

Fig. 12   Measuring Synchronizer Hub End Play

2) Place the needle bearing, 2nd gear, synchronizer assembly, bearing sleeve, needle bearing, 1st gear and bearing spacer on mainshaft from the rear end. Pressing forward with the bearing spacer, measure 1st and 2nd gear end play. End play should be the same as shown in table.

Synchronizer Snap Ring End Play	
Application	**Clearance In. (mm)**
KM119	
1st & 2nd Gear End Play	.001-.007 (.03-.19)
3rd Gear End Play	.001-.007 (.03-.19)
3rd & 4th Synchronizer Hub End Play	0-.003 (0-.08)
KM132	
1st & 2nd Gear End Play	.002-.008 (.05-.2)
3rd Gear End Play	.002-.008 (.05-.2)
3rd & 4th Synchronizer Hub End Play	0-.003 (0-.08)

INPUT SHAFT/PINION GEAR

Inspection — Check O.D. of forward end and I.D. of rear end of input shaft. Inspect tapered synchronizer surface, gear teeth and clutch disc splines for wear or damage.

Input Shaft Standard Dimensions	
Application	**Specification In. (mm)**
O.D. of Forward End	.59 (14.9)
I.D. of Rear End	1.02 (25.9)

Reassembly — Press ball bearing onto input shaft using a bearing installer (MD998029). Install a selective snap ring so there will be 0-.0024″ (0-.061 mm) clearance between bearing and snap ring.

Input Shaft Snap Ring Sizes	
Application (Color)	**Thickness In. (mm)**
KM119	
Dark Blue	.087 (2.21)
Brown	.089 (2.26)
Orange	.090 (2.29)
Blue	.092 (2.34)
Green	.093 (2.36)
KM132	
White	.091 (2.31)
No Color	.092 (2.34)
Red	.094 (2.39)
Blue	.096 (2.44)
Yellow	.098 (2.49)

NOTE — *Synchronizer snap rings are available in different sizes, from .085″ (2.15mm) to .093″ (2.36mm).*

REVERSE IDLER SHAFT

Inspection — Check shaft O.D. for wear or damage. O.D. should be .63″ (16.0 mm).

SHIFTING MECHANISMS

Inspection — Check shift fork ends for wear or damage. Check each shift rail for warpage and detent ball slot for wear. Check forward end of control finger and shift lug groove for wear.

Shift Mechanism Standard Dimensions	
Application	**Specification In. (mm)**
Shift Fork, Sleeve Groove	.197 (5.00)
Shift Fork-to-Sleeve	.004-.012 (.1-.3)
Shift Fork-to-Sleeve (5th Gear)	.006-.014 (.15-.36)
Warpage of Shift Rail	.0016 (.04) Max.
Control Finger-to-Shift Lug	.004-.012 (.1-.3)
Detent Spring Length	.744 (18.90)

EXTENSION HOUSING

Disassembly — 1) Remove locking plate, then speedometer driven gear. Remove all three screw plugs, springs, neutral return plungers ("A" and "B") and detent ball from housing. See *Fig. 13*.

2) Press gear shifter all the way forward in housing. Using a 3/16″ (4.76 mm) punch, drive roll pin from shifter. Separate shifter and control shaft by pulling shaft out front of housing.

Inspection — Inspect forward end of neutral return plunger and detent ball slot for wear. Check neutral return springs and detent spring for collapsing or breakage. Length of neutral return springs is 1.64″ (41.6 mm) and detent spring is 1.09″ (27.7 mm).

CHRYSLER CORP. IMPORTS 5-SPEED (Cont.)

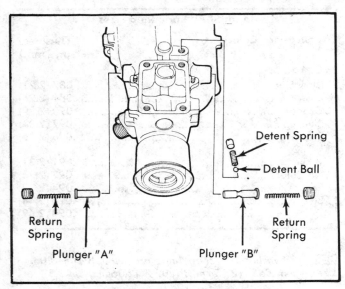

Fig. 13 Removing Neutral Return Plungers from Extension Housing

Reassembly — *See Transmission Reassembly for extension housing reassembly.*

TRANSMISSION REASSEMBLY

NOTE — *Replace all gaskets, seals and roll pins with new ones. Oil all rolling or sliding parts and grease seal lips before reassembly.*

1) Place mainshaft assembly into transmission case. Using a bearing installer, drive middle mainshaft bearing onto mainshaft and into case while holding front of mainshaft by hand. Install needle bearing and synchronizer, then slide input shaft/pinion gear assembly into transmission case with needle bearing engaging end of mainshaft.

2) On KM119 models, install spring then sub-gear onto countergear. On both transmissions, position countergear into case. Install respective snap rings on front needle bearing and rear ball bearing. Drive needle bearing and ball bearing into case. Install front bearing retainer with a bearing spacer which will give a clearance of 0-.004" (0-.1 mm) at dimension "C" (refer to Fig. 14). Apply a sealer to both sides of gasket.

Front Bearing Retainer Spacer Sizes	
Application (Color)	**Thickness In. (mm)**
All Models	
Black	.033 (.84)
No Color	.037 (.94)
Red	.040 (1.0)
White	.044 (1.1)
Yellow	.047 (1.2)
Blue	.051 (1.3)
Green	.054 (1.4)

3) Install rear bearing retainer. Place reverse idler shaft into position and install bolts to act as guides. Using a large drift, drive reverse idler shaft into case.

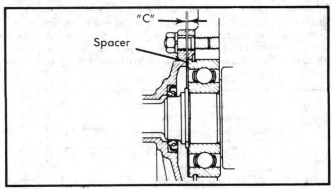

Fig. 14 Retainer-to-Bearing Clearance Measurement

4) Install needle bearing, reverse idler gear and thrust washer with ground side facing gear. Install and tighten castle nut.

5) Check to see that end play between washer and gear is .005-.011" (.12-.28 mm). Then install cotter pin in castle nut. See Fig. 15.

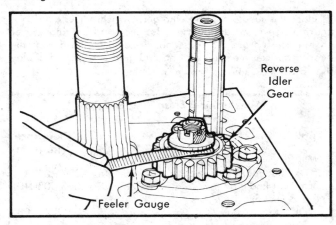

Fig. 15 Using a Feeler Gauge to Check Reverse Idler Gear End Play

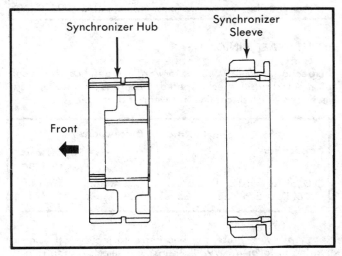

Fig. 16 5th Gear Synchronizer Assembly (KM132 Shown)

CHRYSLER CORP. IMPORTS 5-SPEED (Cont.)

6) Assemble 5th gear synchronizer. See *Fig. 16.* Install spacer, stop plate, synchronizer ring and 5th gear on mainshaft.

7) Install and tighten lock nut, staking it at a notch in mainshaft. End play measured between 5th gear and lock nut should be .001-.007" (.03-.18 mm).

8) Install spacer and 5th countergear ball bearing. Tighten lock nut and stake into notch at rear end of countergear. Engage 1st-2nd and 3rd4th shift forks in their respective synchronizer sleeves.

9) Slide lower shift rail into position and install shift fork roll pin. Install lower interlock plunger. Next install middle shift rail and roll pin. Position 5th-Reverse shift fork in synchronizer sleeve. Install upper interlock plunger.

10) Slide upper shift rail into position and install shift fork roll pin. Install all 3 detent balls and springs with small end of spring facing ball. Screw detent plugs approximately .24" (6.1 mm) into case and apply sealer to head of plugs. See *Fig. 17.*

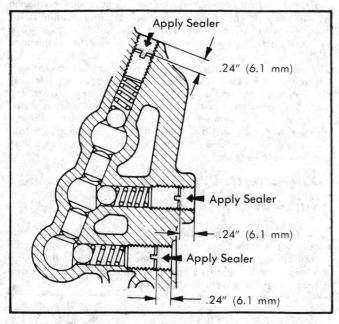

Fig. 17 Installing Detent Balls, Springs and Plugs

11) Install snap ring in forward groove of mainshaft. Install bearing retaining snap ring. Install speedometer gear snap ring and speedometer gear. Finally install snap ring.

12) Apply sealer to both sides of extension housing gasket and position on housing. While holding shifter fully to the left, slide housing onto mainshaft. Make sure forward end of control finger is snugly fitted in slot of shift lug. Apply sealer to threads of attaching bolts and tighten bolts.

13) Install neutral return plungers "A" and "B", springs and plugs. Then install detent ball, spring and plug. Screw all plugs flush with housing and apply sealer to head of plugs. See *Fig. 18.*

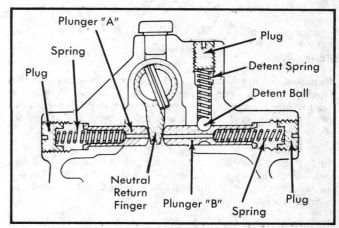

Fig. 18 Installing Neutral Return Plungers

14) Using sealer, install speedometer drive lock plate. Place steel ball in position and screw back-up light switch into housing. Install bottom pan and gasket.

TIGHTENING SPECIFICATIONS

Application	Ft. Lbs. (mkg)
Transmission Case-to-Engine Bolts	22-30 (3.1-4.2)
Countergear Lock Nut	50-72 (7.0-10.0)
Idler Shaft Lock Nut	15-43 (2.0-5.9)
Mainshaft Lock Nut	72-94 (10.0-13.0)

COURIER 4-SPEED

Pickup

DESCRIPTION

A 4-speed synchromesh type transmission is standard on Courier models. All forward gears are selective synchromesh type, reverse gear is sliding mesh type.

Shift mechanism is floor type built into the extension housing. Transmission case consists of 2 mating halves bolted together with removable extension and clutch housing.

LUBRICATION & ADJUSTMENT

See *MANUAL TRANSMISSION SERVICING* Section.

REMOVAL & INSTALLATION

REAR SEAL

Removal — Raise vehicle and support with safety stands. Disconnect drive shaft at rear axle flange. Remove center support bearing nuts and washers. Pull drive shaft rearward out of transmission and remove from vehicle. Using a suitable tool (T72J-7697), remove seal from end of extension housing.

Installation — Lubricate new seal with transmission oil and drive into position using a suitable tool (T72J-7095). Reverse removal procedure to complete assembly. Check transmission lubricant level.

REAR BUSHING

Removal — Raise vehicle and support with safety stands. Disconnect drive shaft at rear axle flange. Remove center support bearing nuts and washers. Pull drive shaft rearward out of transmission and remove from vehicle. Using suitable tool (T72J-7697), drive tool through seal until hooked portion of tool is beyond rear bushing. Turn tool screw clockwise until bushing and seal are pulled from housing.

Installation — Lubricate new bushing and position on a suitable bushing installer tool (T72J-7697-A). Drive bushing into housing. Install new seal and complete installation as previously outlined.

TRANSMISSION ASSEMBLY

Removal — 1) With gearshift lever in neutral, lift up large shift lever boot. Remove four screws securing shift lever tower to extension housing. Remove shift lever, tower, gasket and both shift lever boots. Cover shift tower opening in extension housing with a clean cloth to prevent foreign matter from entering transmission.

2) Raise vehicle and position on safety stands. Disconnect drive shaft at rear axle flange. Remove center support bearing nuts and washers. Pull drive shaft rearward out of transmission and remove from vehicle. Install a suitable tool in end of transmission to prevent oil leakage. Disconnect exhaust pipe bracket at transmission and at clutch housing. Disconnect exhaust pipe at manifold and muffler. Remove pipe and resonator.

3) Disconnect clutch lever return spring. Remove clutch slave cylinder without disconnecting hydraulic line and position out of way. Disconnect speedometer cable, back-up light wires and starter motor wires. Remove starter. Place a jack under engine, protecting oil pan with a wood block. Place a transmission jack under transmission. Remove bolts securing clutch housing to engine. Remove bolts securing crossmember to transmission and frame and remove crossmember. Lower engine jack and work clutch housing off dowels. Slide transmission rearward and lower to remove.

Installation — Make sure all mating surfaces are clean and free of burrs. To install transmission, reverse removal procedure. Adjust clutch release lever free play. Check transmission lubricant level and refill as necessary.

TRANSMISSION DISASSEMBLY

NOTE — *Transmission can be disassembled without disassembling most of the sub-assemblies.*

1) Remove clutch release bearing return spring and slide bearing off clutch housing. Remove clutch lever and boot from clutch housing. Remove clutch housing retaining bolts and separate from transmission housing. Remove gasket and input shaft bearing thrust washer. Position transmission on bench with left side down. Remove extension housing retaining bolts. Position control lever in neutral and press to left or downward as far as possible and slide extension housing off transmission.

2) Remove all nuts, bolts, and washers connecting case halves. Lift right case half off left case half. Lift countershaft assembly out. Remove input and output shafts as an assembly by rolling out from under shift forks. Separate input and output shafts after removal. To remove reverse idler, push center shift rail forward as far as possible. This will allow clearance to rotate reverse shifter as idler is removed. Remove set screw and slide out reverse idler shaft.

COMPONENT DISASSEMBLY & REASSEMBLY

INPUT SHAFT

Disassembly — Remove roller bearing assembly from inside input shaft bearing pocket. Remove bearing snap ring. Install a suitable support (T71P-4621-B) under bearing so that bearing inner race is supported and press bearing off shaft. Inspect all components for wear or damage.

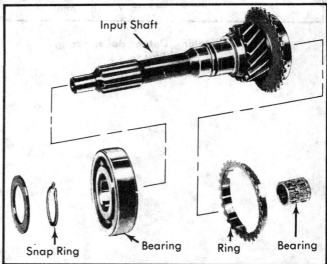

Input Shaft

Snap Ring   Bearing   Ring   Bearing

Fig. 1   Exploded View of Input Shaft Assembly

COURIER 4-SPEED (Cont.)

Reassembly — Place input shaft bearing on shaft and press into position using a suitable support (T62F-4621-A). Install snap ring and roller bearing assembly.

OUTPUT SHAFT

Disassembly — Remove snap ring at front of output shaft. Slide off 3rd and 4th gear synchronizer, synchronizer ring and 3rd gear. Mark synchronizer hub to ensure it is installed in same direction if not previously marked. Remove rear snap ring and slide off speedometer gear and drive ball. Remove front speedometer gear snap ring. Remove next snap ring (selective fit type) and thrust washer. Slide off reverse gear, output shaft bearing, 1st gear, 1st gear bushing, 1st and 2nd synchronizer and 2nd gear. Note that oil groove on synchronizer faces forward. Inspect all components for wear or damage and replace as necessary.

Reassembly — 1) Install 3rd gear, 3rd gear synchronizer ring, and 3rd and 4th synchronizer hub on front of shaft. Note marks on hub made during disassembly and install front snap ring. Slide 2nd gear and synchronizer ring on shaft. Install 1st and 2nd speed synchronizer and ring on shaft, making sure oil groove in hub faces forward. Install 1st speed synchronizer ring, 1st gear and sleeve, thrust washer, bearing and reverse gear on shaft.

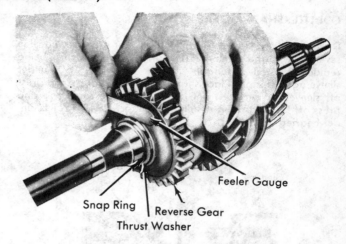

Feeler Gauge
Snap Ring
Reverse Gear
Thrust Washer

Fig. 3 Checking Reverse Gear-to-Snap Ring Clearance Using a Feeler Gauge

2) Slide selective fit thrust washer and snap ring on shaft. Using a feeler gauge (See Fig. 3), check clearance between rear face of reverse gear and thrust washer. Clearance should be 0-.004" (0-.1 mm). If clearance is not to specification, install a new thrust washer or snap ring to obtain correct clearance.

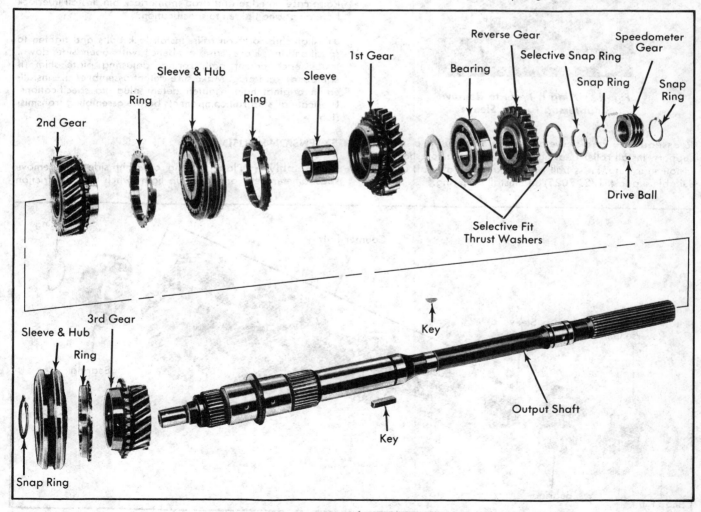

2nd Gear · Ring · Sleeve & Hub · Ring · Sleeve · 1st Gear · Bearing · Reverse Gear · Selective Snap Ring · Snap Ring · Speedometer Gear · Snap Ring

Selective Fit Thrust Washers · Drive Ball

Sleeve & Hub · Ring · 3rd Gear · Key · Key · Output Shaft · Snap Ring

Fig. 2 Exploded View of Output Shaft Assembly

COURIER 4-SPEED (Cont.)

COUNTERSHAFT & GEAR

Disassembly — Remove snap ring on rear of shaft and slide reverse gear and roller bearing off shaft. If sleeve is being replaced, install a suitable support tool (OTC-950) under sleeve against shaft. Place shaft and tool in a press and press off sleeve. To remove front bearing, remove snap ring and press off bearing using a suitable support (T71P-4621-B) under bearing.

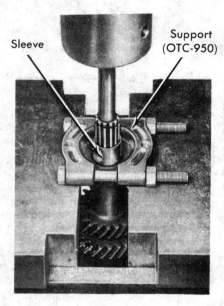

Fig. 4 Using a Press to Remove Countershaft Gear Sleeve

Reassembly — Press sleeve back into position using a suitable support. Install roller bearing and reverse gear on shaft and install snap ring. Press ball bearing on front of shaft using a suitable support (T72J-7025) and install snap ring.

SHIFT RAILS

NOTE — *All components of detent assemblies should be installed in original position. Mark or identify all components for reassembly.*

Disassembly — Remove each spring cap (one at a time) and withdraw spring, ball and adjusting plate. Now move to next spring cap to avoid mixing of components. Remove interlock plug and remove interlock pins. Remove shift fork attaching screws and withdraw shift forks and rails from case.

Reassembly — 1) Place shift fork in case and slide in 1st and 2nd gear shift rail through fork and case. Install two suitable pilot shift rails (T27J-7280) in case. Use alignment pin part of tool to align holes in pilot shift rail and 1st and 2nd gear shift rail. Rotate case up on edge and drop interlock pin into position. Remove pilot shift rail from 3rd and 4th gear shift rail bore in case.

2) Position 3rd and 4th gear shift fork in case and slide shift rail (with over-travel washer if required) into case. Use alignment pin part of tool to align holes in pilot shift rail and 3rd and 4th gear shift rail. Rotate case up on edge and drop interlock pin into position. Remove remaining pilot shift rail and install reverse shift rail and fork. Use alignment pin part of tool to align holes in pilot shift rail and reverse gear shift rail. Raise case on edge and drop in interlock pin. Install interlock bore plugs and tighten to specification.

3) Align shift forks on rails. Install lock bolts and tighten to specifications. Place case on bench with open side down. Install each detent ball, spring, adjusting plate shim (if equipped), and plug. Make sure detent assemblies are installed in original hole. Tighten detent plugs to specifications. Lubricate all shift rail components before assembling transmission.

EXTENSION HOUSING

Disassembly — Place housing on right side and remove speedometer gear and back-up light switch with the friction

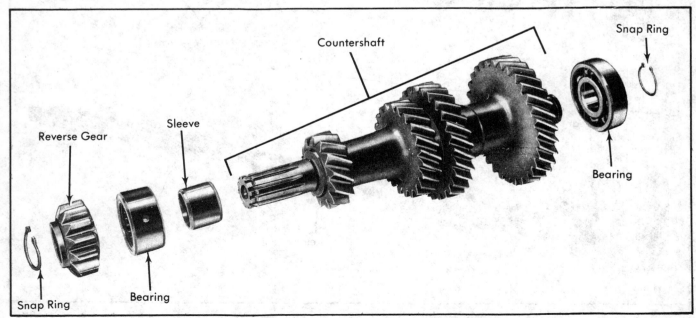

Fig. 5 Exploded View of Countershaft Gear Assembly

COURIER 4-SPEED (Cont.)

spring loaded piece. Place housing upright and remove lock bolt securing cupped control lever end to control lever rod. Remove control lever end from rod, slide rod from housing and remove key.

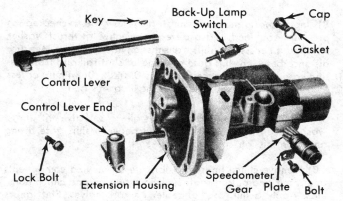

Fig. 6 *Exploded View of Extension Housing*

Reassembly — Place key in position and slide control lever rod into housing. Install rod end and lock bolt. Tighten bolt to specification. Install friction piece and back-up lamp. Lubricate speedometer gear housing seal and install speedometer gear.

SHIFT TOWER & LEVER

Disassembly — Remove three bolts securing shift lever to tower. Remove lever and components. Remove detent spring

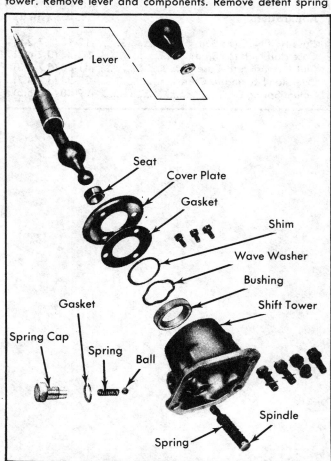

Fig. 7 *Exploded View of Shift Tower and Lever*

cap, spring and ball from tower and drop out selector lock spindle and spring.

Reassembly — If shift lever was loose in tower before disassembly, increase pressure on socket by adjusting washer thickness. Place selector lock spindle and spring in shift tower. With upward pressure held on spindle, locate positioning notch on spindle and install detent ball and spring cap. Make sure that ball is in notch in spindle and tighten spring cover to specification. Install gearshift lever on tower and tighten bolts.

TRANSMISSION REASSEMBLY

1) Make sure all components are clean, including mating surfaces on case halves. Position reverse idler gear in case and insert shaft. Install lock screw and tighten to specification. Insert input shaft roller bearing assembly in bearing pocket.

2) Place shift forks in neutral. Connect input shaft and output shaft and position in case. Place countershaft assembly in case, making sure that dowel hole in roller bearing is lined up with dowel hole in case. Gear train will rotate freely when dowel is correctly aligned. Place input shaft thrust washer (or shim) in clutch housing. Position clutch housing and gasket on left case half. Install nuts and tighten to specification.

3) Using a feeler gauge, check end play between rear face of input shaft bearing and shoulder in transmission case. Move input shaft forward as far as possible to check end play. Specified end play is 0-.004" (.1 mm). If end play is not to specification, remove clutch housing and insert another selective fit thrust washer to obtain correct end play. Repeat end play checking procedure until specified end play is obtained. Leave clutch housing in place.

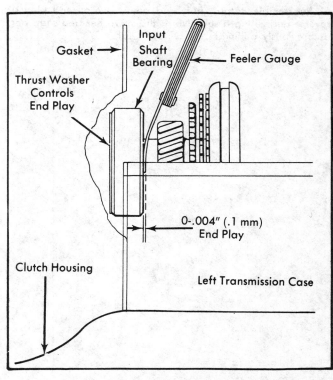

Fig. 8 *Checking Input Shaft Clearance Using a Feeler Gauge*

COURIER 4-SPEED (Cont.)

4) Shift transmission into 3rd gear. Using a feeler gauge, check clearance between synchronizer insert and the exposed edge of synchronizer ring. Specified clearance is .030-.080" (.76-2.03 mm). If clearance exceeds .080" (2.03 mm), key may pop out. See *Fig. 9.*

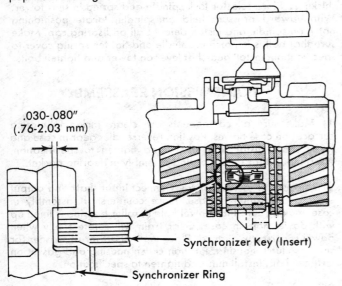

.030-.080"
(.76-2.03 mm)

Synchronizer Key (Insert)

Synchronizer Ring

Fig. 9   View Showing Synchronizer Insert Clearance

5) Remove clutch housing if clearance is excessive. Remove countershaft, input shaft and output shaft assemblies. Disassemble output shaft assembly and insert a thicker key-slotted thrust washer between output shaft bearing and 1st gear.

6) Reassemble output shaft and adjust overall end play at reverse gear using a selective fit thrust washer and snap ring as previously outlined. See *Output Shaft.*

7) Reinstall input and output shaft assemblies and countershaft gear assembly in case. Reinstall clutch housing and gasket. Recheck synchronizer insert key clearance as previously outlined.

8) Input shaft end play must also now be rechecked as previously outlined and a different selective fit thrust washer installed if necessary. Shift transmission into 4th gear. Measure distance between shift gate and end of shift rail and transmission case boss. Clearance should be 0-.028" (0-.74 mm) or less to prevent over-travel when shifting into 4th gear.

9) If clearance is excessive, install a selective fit thrust washer(s) on 3rd and 4th shift rail between shift gate fitting and transmission case boss. See *Shift Rails.*

10) Remove clutch housing. Lubricate all moving components and input and output shaft seals in extension and clutch housings. Apply a thin coat of sealer on case halves. Shift gears into neutral and assemble case halves.

11) Install nuts and tighten. Place a new gasket on case and install extension housing. Install and tighten nuts. Place clutch housing and gasket on case, then install and tighten nuts. Install clutch release lever, bearing and components in clutch housing.

TIGHTENING SPECIFICATIONS	
Application	**Ft. Lbs. (mkg)**
Case Half Nuts (To Bolt)	12-17 (1.7-2.4)
Case Half Nuts (To Stud)	23-34 (3.2-4.7)
Clutch Housing-to-Case	41-60 (5.7-8.3)
Extension Housing-to-Case	23-34 (3.2-4.7)
Detent Spring Caps	29-40 (4.0-5.5)

COURIER 5-SPEED

Pickup

DESCRIPTION

The 5-speed transmission is synchronized in all gears except reverse, which is constant mesh. All forward gears are helical type for quiet running. Reverse gear and reverse idler gear are spur type.

The transmission case is of light metal and consists of removable clutch and extension housings. Gear shifting is of direct control, floor shift type, built into the extension housing.

LUBRICATION & ADJUSTMENT

See *MANUAL TRANSMISSION SERVICING* Section.

TRANSMISSION REMOVAL & INSTALLATION

Removal — **1)** Remove console box, if equipped. Remove boot retaining screws and bolts attaching retainer cover. Place gearshift lever in neutral position and pull gearshift lever, shim and bushing straight up from gearshift lever retainer.

2) Cover shift tower opening in extension housing to avoid dropping dirt into transmission.

3) Disconnect the negative battery cable, then raise vehicle. Disconnect drive shaft at rear axle drive flange and remove drive shaft center bearing support attaching nuts, washers and lock washer.

4) Pull drive shaft to rear and disconnect from transmission, then install a suitable plug in extension housing to prevent leakage of lubricant.

5) Remove bolts attaching exhaust pipe brackets to transmission case, and bolt and nut attaching exhaust pipe hanger to clutch housing. Disconnect exhaust pipe at exhaust manifold and muffler, then remove exhaust pipe and resonator.

6) Remove clutch release cylinder and secure it to side. Remove speedometer cable from extension housing. Disconnect starter motor and back-up light switch wires.

7) Place jack under engine, protecting oil pan with wood block. Remove starter motor. Remove bolts, lock washers and flat washers attaching transmission to engine rear plate.

8) Position a transmission jack under transmission. Remove nuts and bolts attaching transmission mount to crossmember and nuts attaching crossmember to frame side rails, then remove crossmember.

9) Lower engine jack and slide transmission to rear until input shaft spline clears clutch disc. Remove transmission from vehicle.

Installation — **1)** To install, reverse removal procedure and note the following: Position gearshift lever, shim and bushing straight above gearshift lever retainer. Make sure no dirt falls into transmission while installing gearshift lever.

2) Tighten all attaching nuts and bolts. Check transmission fluid level and fill with specified fluid if necessary.

TRANSMISSION DISASSEMBLY

1) Remove nuts attaching clutch housing to transmission case and remove clutch housing and gasket. Remove drain plug and drain transmission. Clean metal filings from drain plug magnet (if necessary) then reinstall drain plug.

2) Place transmission in suitable holder. Put transmission in neutral, then remove four attaching bolts holding gearshift retainer to extension housing and remove gearshift lever retainer and gasket. Remove speedometer lock plate and driven gear assembly from extension housing.

3) Remove nuts attaching extension housing to transmission case. Raise control lever to left and slide toward rear of transmission, then slide extension housing off mainshaft.

NOTE — *Be careful not to damage oil seal.*

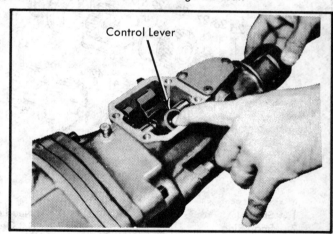
Control Lever

Fig. 1 Removing Extension Housing

4) Remove spring cap bolt, spring and friction piece from extension housing. Remove bolt attaching gearshift control lever end to control lever, then remove control lever end, key and control lever. Remove back-up light switch from extension housing.

5) Remove snap ring securing speedometer drive gear to mainshaft, slide drive gear off mainshaft, and remove lock ball and snap ring.

6) Unscrew bolts securing transmission case cover, then remove cover and gasket.

7) Mark shifter rails (for later reassembly) then remove bolts attaching shift rod ends and remove ends from shift rods.

COURIER 5-SPEED (Cont.)

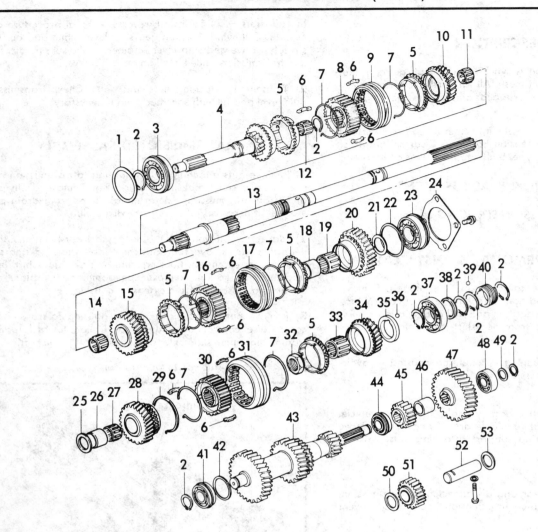

1. Shim	19. Needle Bearing	37. Mainshaft Rear Bearing
2. Snap Ring	20. 1st Gear	38. Thrust Washer
3. Main Driveshaft Bearing	21. Thrust Washer	39. Lock Ball
4. Input Shaft	22. Shim	40. Speedometer Drive Gear
5. Synchronizer Ring	23. Mainshaft Front Bearing	41. Countershaft Front Bearing
6. Synchronizer Key	24. Bearing Cover	42. Shim
7. Synchronizer Key Spring	25. Thrust Washer	43. Countershaft
8. 3rd-4th Clutch Hub	26. Bearing Inner Race	44. Countershaft Center Bearing
9. Clutch Sleeve	27. Needle Bearing	45. Counter Reverse Gear
10. 3rd Gear	28. Reverse Gear	46. Spacer
11. Needle Bearing	29. Stop Ring	47. Reverse Gear
12. Needle Bearing	30. 5th-Reverse Clutch Hub	48. Countershaft Rear Bearing
13. Mainshaft	31. Clutch Sleeve	49. Thrust Washer
14. Needle Bearing	32. Mainshaft Lock Nut	50. Thrust Washer
15. 2nd Gear	33. Needle Bearing	51. Reverse Idler Gear
16. 1st-2nd Clutch Hub	34. 5th Gear	52. Idler Gear Shaft
17. Clutch Sleeve	35. Thrust Washer	53. Thrust Washer
18. Bearing Inner Race	36. Lock Ball	

Fig. 2 Exploded View of Courier 5-Speed Transmission Showing Shafts and Gears

COURIER 5-SPEED (Cont.)

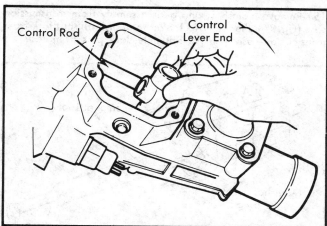

Fig. 3   Removing Control Lever End

Control Rod

Control Lever End

8) Carefully pry bearing housing from transmission case with screwdriver, then slide housing off mainshaft. Remove snap ring and washer retaining mainshaft rear bearing to mainshaft, then press main bearing from case.

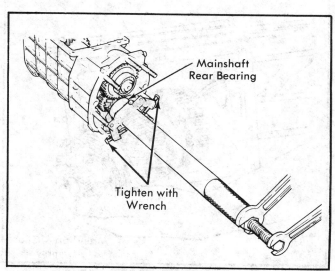

Mainshaft Rear Bearing

Tighten with Wrench

Fig. 4   Removing Mainshaft Rear Bearing

9) Remove snap ring and washer from rear end of countershaft and press countershaft bearing from case.

10) Remove 5th gear and spacer from rear of countershaft. Remove center housing attaching bolt (*Fig. 5*) and tapping housing with plastic hammer (if necessary) remove center housing.

11) Remove three spring cap bolts, detent springs and detent balls from transmission case. Remove nuts attaching covers on side of transmission case and remove covers and gaskets.

12) Remove attaching bolt from 5th-reverse shift fork and slide shaft out of transmission case. Remove attaching bolts from 1st-2nd and 3rd-4th shift forks and slide shafts from rear of transmission case.

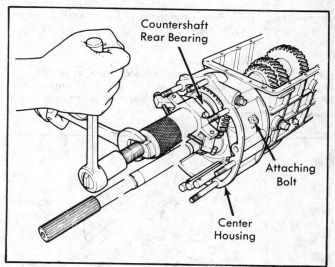

Countershaft Rear Bearing

Attaching Bolt

Center Housing

Fig. 5   Removing Countershaft Rear Bearing

13) Remove snap ring securing 5th gear to mainshaft, then remove thrust washer, 5th gear, lock ball and needle bearing from rear of mainshaft.

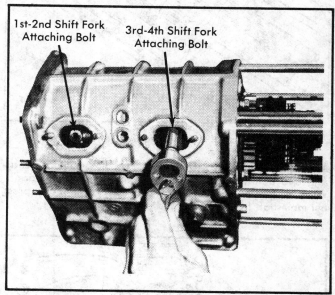

1st-2nd Shift Fork Attaching Bolt

3rd-4th Shift Fork Attaching Bolt

Fig. 6   1st-2nd and 3rd-4th Shift Fork Attaching Bolt Locations

14) Engage 2nd gear and counter reverse gear to lock mainshaft. Straighten staked part of lock nut, remove lock nut and slide reverse gear and clutch hub assembly off mainshaft.

15) Slide spacer and counter reverse gear off rear of countershaft, then remove reverse idler gear with idler gear shaft from transmission case.

16) Remove key and spacer from mainshaft. Install synchronizer ring holder (T77J-7025-E), between 4th gear synchronizer ring and synchromesh gear on mainshaft. See *Fig. 7*. Secure ring holder with two bottom cover attaching bolts.

COURIER 5-SPEED (Cont.)

Remove snap ring securing countershaft front bearing to front end of countershaft.

17) Press countershaft front bearing from case. Remove adjusting shim(s) from countershaft front bearing bore. Remove bolts attaching bearing cover to transmission case, then remove bearing cover.

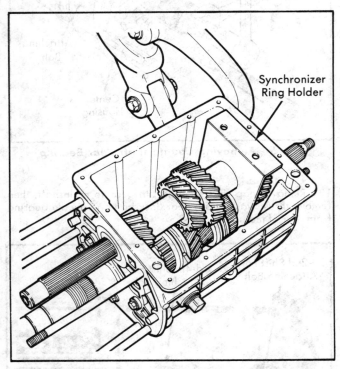

Fig. 7   Installing Synchronizer Ring Holder

18) Press countershaft center bearing from case. Remove snap ring and adjusting shims retaining mainshaft front bearing. With the special synchronizer ring holder still in place, press out mainshaft front bearing and center bearing.

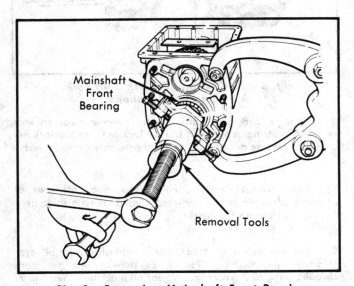

Fig. 8   Removing Mainshaft Front Bearing

19) Remove mainshaft and gear assembly from transmission case (*Fig. 10*), then remove 1st-2nd and 3rd-4th shift fork from transmission case. Remove shift inter-lock pins from case.

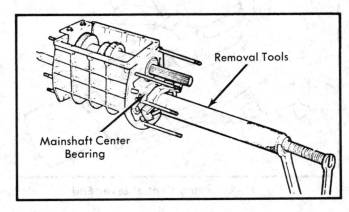

Fig. 9   Removing Mainshaft Center Bearing

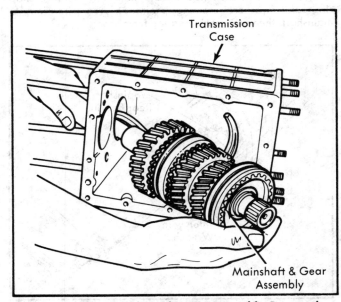

Fig. 10   Mainshaft and Gear Assembly Removal

COMPONENT DISASSEMBLY & REASSEMBLY

MAINSHAFT

Disassembly — 1) Remove snap rings from front of mainshaft, then slide 3rd-4th clutch hub and sleeve assembly, 3rd synchronizer ring, and 3rd gear off front of mainshaft.

NOTE — *Do not mix the synchronizer rings.*

2) Slide thrust washer, 1st gear, and needle bearing off rear of mainshaft. Remove needle bearing inner race, 1st-2nd clutch hub and sleeve assembly from mainshaft. If necessary, press 2nd gear from mainshaft.

Inspection — 1) Check mainshaft for warpage by mounting shaft between "V" blocks and applying a dial indicator several

COURIER 5-SPEED (Cont.)

places along shaft. If warpage exceeds .001" (.03 mm) replace shaft.

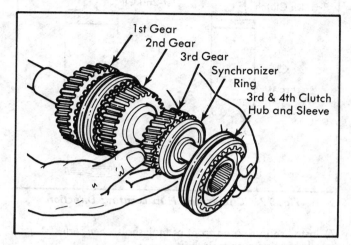

Fig. 11   Mainshaft Disassembly

2) Clean bearings by rotating in solvent until all lubricant is removed. Dry with compressed air.

NOTE – *Do not allow bearing to rotate while drying with compressed air.*

3) Check bearings for wear and make sure they rotate smoothly. Check for worn, broken or missing teeth on all gears. Replace if necessary.

4) Check gear teeth on synchronizer rings. Inspect rings for wear by fitting the ring evenly to cone and measuring the clearance between the side faces with a feeler gauge. See *Fig. 12.* If clearance is less than .031" (.8 mm), replace ring or gear.

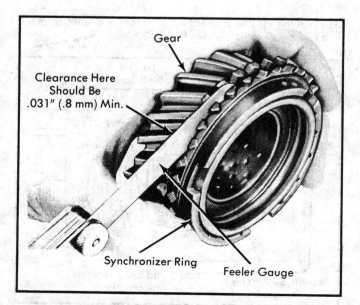

Fig. 12   Measuring Synchronizer Ring Clearance

5) Inspect contact between inner surface of ring and cone surface of gear. If contact is poor, correct by applying a lapping compound to surfaces and lap until proper fit is obtained.

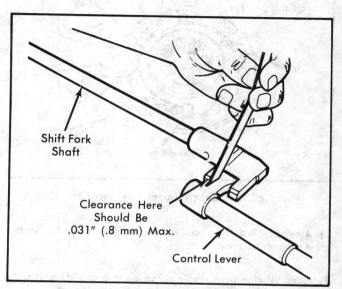

Fig. 13   Measuring Shift Fork-to-Control Lever Clearance

6) Using a feeler gauge, check and ensure that clearance between shift fork shaft and control lever is less than .031" (.8mm) as shown in *Fig. 13.* Check that clearance between shift forks and clutch sleeve is less than .020" (.5mm) as shown in *Fig. 14.* If clearance exceeds specifications, replace parts as necessary.

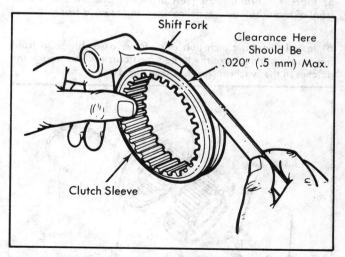

Fig. 14   Measuring Shift Fork-to-Sleeve Clearance

Reassembly – 1) Assemble 1st-2nd clutch hub to sleeve. Place the 3 synchronizer keys into the clutch hub key slots and install the key springs. See *Fig. 15.*

NOTE – *The open end of the key springs should be kept 120° apart in order to keep spring tension on each key uniform.*

COURIER 5-SPEED (Cont.)

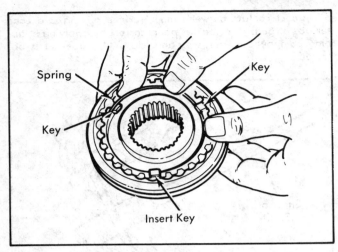

Fig. 15   *Synchronizer Key Location*

2) Assemble 3rd-4th and 5th synchronizer assembly in the same manner as 1st-2nd.

3) Place synchronizer ring on 2nd gear and slide unit onto mainshaft with synchronizer ring toward rear of shaft.

4) Press 1st gear needle bearing inner race and 1st-2nd clutch hub/sleeve assembly onto mainshaft with clutch hub oil grooves toward front of mainshaft.

NOTE — *Make sure the three synchronizer keys engage the notches in second synchronizer ring.*

5) Place synchronizer ring on 3rd gear and slide unit onto front of mainshaft with synchronizer ring toward front.

6) Install 3rd-4th clutch hub and sleeve assembly onto front mainshaft, making sure the three synchronizer keys engage the notches in the synchronizer ring. See *Fig. 16.*

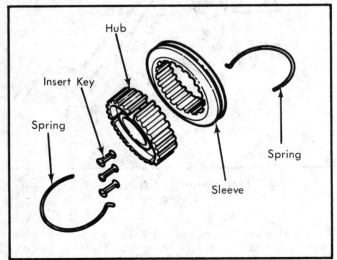

Fig. 16   *Exploded View of Sychromesh Assembly*

NOTE — *The direction of the 3rd-4th clutch hub and sleeve assembly should be as shown in Fig. 17.*

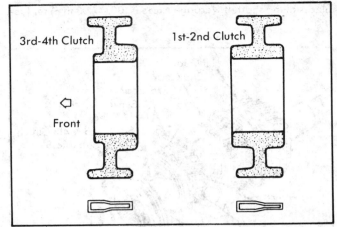

Fig. 17   *Clutch and Hub Locating Direction*

7) Install snap ring on front of mainshaft, then slide 1st gear needle bearing onto mainshaft.

8) Place synchronizer ring on 1st gear and slide unit onto mainshaft with synchronizer ring facing front of shaft.

9) Rotate the 1st gear as necessary to engage the three notches in the synchronizer ring with the synchronizer keys. Install the original thrust washer on the mainshaft.

TRANSMISSION REASSEMBLY

1) Make sure all components are clean and properly lubricated. Install mainshaft and gear assembly in case, then place needle bearing on front end of mainshaft.

2) Place synchronizer ring on input shaft, then install input shaft on front end of mainshaft, making sure the three synchronizer keys in the 3rd-4th synchromesh unit engage the notches in the synchronizer ring.

3) Place the 1st-2nd and 3rd-4th shift fork in groove of clutch hub and sleeve assembly. See *Fig. 18.*

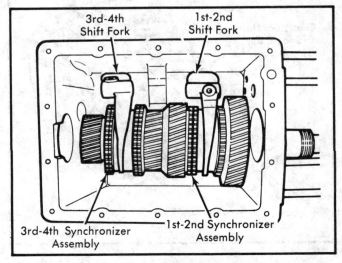

Fig. 18   *Installing Shift Forks*

COURIER 5-SPEED (Cont.)

4) Press inner race of countershaft center bearing onto countershaft, then position countershaft gear in case, making sure countershaft gears engage each gear of mainshaft assembly.

5) Check mainshaft thrust play by measuring the depth of mainshaft front bearing bore in clutch housing. Then measure thickness of mainshaft front bearing. The difference between the two measurements indicates the thickness of the adjusting shims needed.

6) Standard thrust play is 0-.004" (0-.1 mm). Adjusting shims are available in .004" (.1 mm) and .012" (.3 mm) sizes.

7) Install synchronizer ring tool (as used in disassembly), between 4th synchronizer ring and the synchromesh gear on mainshaft. Place mainshaft and mainshaft front bearing into proper bearing bore and press into place.

8) Install mainshaft bearing snap ring, then check countershaft thrust play in same manner as described for mainshaft thrust play. Standard end play and adjusting shims are same as that for mainshaft.

9) With tool still in place between 4th synchronizer ring and synchromesh gear, press countershaft front and center bearings into bearing bores.

10) Secure countershaft front bearing with snap ring then remove ring holder tool. Install bearing cover to transmission case and tighten bolts.

11) Install reverse idler gear. Slide reverse gear and spacer onto countershaft.

12) Install spacer, key, reverse gear, and clutch hub assembly onto mainshaft. Install new lock nut (hand tight). Engage 2nd and reverse gear to lock mainshaft rotation, then tighten lock nut to specification. Stake lock nut into place.

13) Place 2nd-3rd clutch sleeve in third gear. Check clearance between synchronizer key and edge of ring with feeler gauge. Clearance should not exceed .079" (2.0 mm). If clearance does exceed this amount, synchronizer key can pop out of position. Adjust clearance by using select fit thrust washer fitted between mainshaft front bearing and 1st gear. Thrust washers are available in the following sizes: .098" (2.5 mm), .118" (3.0 mm) and .138" (3.5 mm). After correcting clearance, bend tab of lock washer.

14) Install needle bearing and lock ball on mainshaft. Position 5th synchronizer ring on 5th gear and slide assembly onto mainshaft with synchronizer ring toward front of mainshaft.

15) Install thrust washer at rear of 5th gear, then place snap ring behind thrust washer. Check clearance between thrust washer and snap ring. If clearance exceeds .004" (.1 mm), correct by using select fit thrust washer. Thrust washers are available in the following sizes: .236" (6.0 mm), .244" (6.2 mm), 252" (6.4 mm), .256" (6.5 mm), .260" (6.6 mm), .264" (6.7 mm), .268" (6.8 mm), .276" (7.0 mm) and .283" (7.2 mm).

16) Press countershaft rear bearing into case, then install thrust washer and snap ring at rear of bearing and check clearance between thrust washer and snap ring with feeler gauge. If clearance is not within .004" (.1 mm), select appropriate thrust washer to obtain correct clearance. Thrust washers are available in the following sizes: .079" (2.0 mm), .083" (2.1 mm) and .087" (2.2 mm).

17) Repeat the procedure for rear main bearing. Clearance between thrust washer and snap ring on rear bearing is 0-.006" (0-.15 mm). Thrust washers are available in the following sizes: .079" (2.00 mm), .085" (2.15 mm) and .091" (2.30 mm).

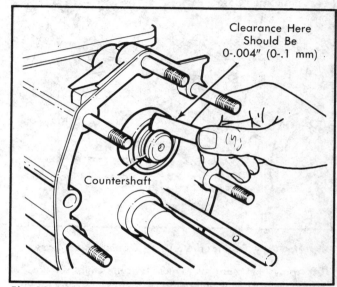

Clearance Here Should Be 0-.004" (0-.1 mm)

Countershaft

Fig. 19   Measuring Countershaft Rear Bearing End Play

18) Slide 1st-2nd, 3rd-4th, and 5th-reverse shift fork shafts into case from rear. Lock shift forks on shafts with lock nuts. Install three detent balls and springs in case and screw in spring cap bolts.

19) Install two covers and gaskets on side of transmission, then tighten attaching bolts. Apply a thin coat of sealer to con-

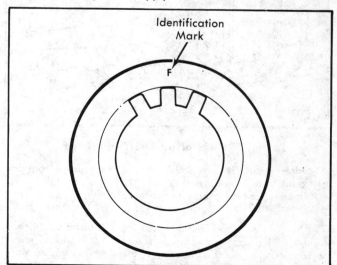

Identification Mark

F

Fig. 20   5th Gear Identification Mark Location

COURIER 5-SPEED (Cont.)

tacting surfaces of center housing and transmission case. Position the center housing on the case and align the reverse idler gear shaft boss with center housing attaching bolt boss. Install and tighten center housing attaching bolt. Install the countershaft 5th gear on the countershaft. Make sure "F" mark on gear is toward front of shaft.

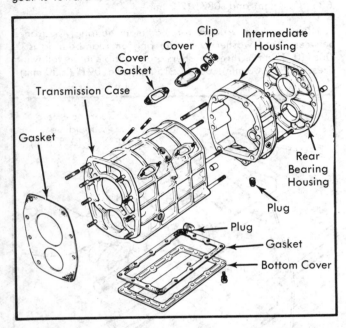

Fig. 21   Exploded View of Transmission Case

20) Apply thin coat of sealer to contacting surfaces of bearing housing and center housing. Position housing on studs of center housing, then install shift fork shaft ends onto proper shift fork shafts (note marks made during disassembly). Tighten bolts, then install snap ring, lock ball, speedometer drive gear and snap ring on mainshaft.

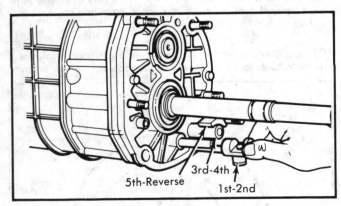

Fig. 22   Installing Shaft Fork Ends

21) Insert gearshift control lever through holes from front side of extension housing. Install Woodruff key, then install control lever end on control lever, and secure with bolt.

22) Place spring and friction piece in extension housing and tighten spring cap bolt to housing. Apply a thin coat of sealer to contacting surfaces of bearing housing and extension housing. Place gearshift control lever as far to left as possible and install extension housing on studs. Tighten attaching nuts.

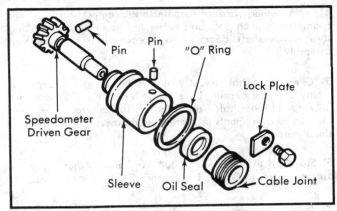

Fig. 23   Disassembled View of Speedometer Driven Gear Assembly

23) Insert speedometer driven gear assembly into extension housing and secure with bolt and lock plate. Install gearshift lever retainer and gasket on extension housing, then tighten attaching bolts.

24) Check input shaft bearing clearance by measuring depth of bearing bore in clutch housing and measuring bearing thickness. The difference between the measurements indicates the required shim thickness. Standard clearance is 0-.004" (0-.1 mm), if a shim is needed to obtain correct clearance, the following sizes are available: .004" (.1 mm) and .012" (.3 mm).

25) Install clutch housing on transmission. Install back-up light switch.

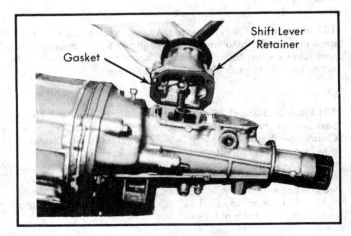

Fig. 24   Installing Gearshift Lever Retainer

TIGHTENING SPECIFICATIONS

Application	Ft. Lbs. (mkg)
Detent Spring Plugs	29-40 (4.0-5.5)
Mainshaft Nut	116-173 (16.0-24.0)
Shift Rod End-to-Shift Rod Bolt	20-25 (2.8-3.5)
Transmission-to-Clutch Housing	41-60 (5.7-8.3)

DATSUN 210, 810 & PICKUP 4-SPEED

TRANSMISSION IDENTIFICATION

Three models of the center support-type transmissions are used: F4W56A, F4W60L and F4W71B. The F4W56A transmission is used on 210 models equipped with the 1.2 liter engine only. The F4W60L transmission is used on 210 models equipped with the 1.4 liter or 1.6 liter engines. The F4W71B transmission is used on 810 and pickup models. All transmissions may be identified by a serial number stamped on a pad located on top of clutch housing.

DESCRIPTION

Transmissions are 4-speed, fully synchronized, constant mesh-type units, using helical type gears in all forward ranges, and sliding mesh spur type gears in reverse range. Transmission consists of three main parts: A transmission case with integral clutch housing, an adapter plate (center support) to which all gears and shafts are installed, and an extension housing. The adapter plate supports mainshaft, countergear, idler shaft, and 3 shift rods, and is bolted at the front to transmission case and at the rear to the extension housing by means of through bolts.

LUBRICATION & ADJUSTMENT

See MANUAL TRANSMISSION SERVICING Section.

TROUBLE SHOOTING

Hard Shifting — With hard shifting check clutch adjustment first. If clutch adjustment is correct, check for worn gears, shaft, bearing, and/or sliding part. Also check for damaged synchronizer.

Slips Out of Gear — Check for worn or damaged interlock plunger, check ball, check ball spring, fork rod ball groove, bearing, and gear.

Noisy Operation — Make sure noise is from transmission and not clutch. If transmission is noisy, check for correct level and type of lubricant. Check for oil leaks and clogged breather cap. Check for worn or damaged bearings, bushings, and gears.

TRANSMISSION REMOVAL & INSTALLATION

Removal — 1) Disconnect battery ground cable, remove console (if equipped) and shift lever boot. Place transmission in neutral. Remove snap ring or nut from control lever pin. Remove control lever pin and control lever.

2) Raise vehicle and remove exhaust pipe. Disconnect wires to high gear detecting switch and back-up light switch. Disconnect speedometer cable from extension housing.

3) On 4-WD pickups, disconnect wires from 4-WD indicator switch. Disconnect propeller shaft between transmission and transfer case. Remove front differential carrier crossmember. Disconnect propeller shaft between transfer case and front differential carrier.

4) On all other models, disconnect propeller shaft from transmission. On all models, remove clutch cylinder from transmission case. Support engine and transmission. Remove rear engine mounting bolts and crossmember bolts. Remove starter and transmission case-to-engine mounting bolts.

5) Slide transmission to rear away from engine. Remove transmission from vehicle.

Installation — 1) Install transmission in reverse order of removal, noting these points: Before installation, clean mating surfaces of transmission case and rear of engine block.

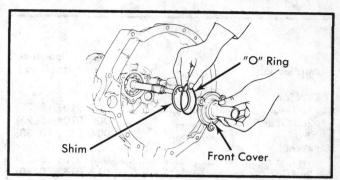

Fig. 1 Removal of Front Cover on F4W56A and F4W60L Transmissions

2) Apply grease to splines of clutch hub, input shaft, and moving surfaces of control lever and striking rod. Lubricate oil seal lip and bushing of extension housing before installing propeller shaft. Make sure transmission is filled with proper type and amount of gear oil.

TRANSMISSION DISASSEMBLY

1) Drain oil and remove release bearing and lever. Remove back-up light and high gear switches. Remove speedometer driven gear and sleeve. Remove nut or "C" ring and stopper pin bolt from extension housing. Remove plug, return spring, reverse check spring and plunger from extension housing.

2) Remove front cover, "O" ring, adjusting shim and bearing snap ring (if equipped) from front of transmission case. Remove extension housing bolts. Turn striking lever clockwise on transmission F4W56A or counterclockwise on all other transmissions and remove extension housing.

NOTE — *On transmission F4W71B, make sure that countergear thrust washer is removed after front cover is removed.*

3) Remove adapter plate from transmission case by tapping on transmission case with a mallet. On transmissions F4W56A and F4W60L, remove countergear thrust washer.

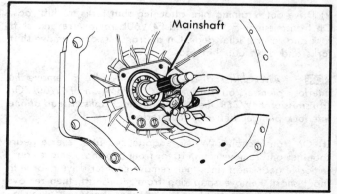

Fig. 2 Removal of Front Cover on F4W71B Transmission

DATSUN 210, 810 & PICKUP 4-SPEED (Cont.)

COMPONENT DISASSEMBLY & REASSEMBLY

GEAR ASSEMBLY

NOTE — *During disassembly, check gear end play. For specifications, see Gear End Play Chart.*

Gear End Play	
Application	**Clearance In. (mm)**
F4W56A	
1st Gear	.006-.010 (.15-.25)
2nd Gear	.006-.010 (.15-.25)
3rd Gear	.004-.012 (.10-.30)
F4W60L	
1st Gear	.006-.010 (.15-.25)
2nd Gear	.012-.016 (.30-.40)
3rd Gear	.006-.014 (.15-.35)
F4W71B	
1st Gear	.011-.013 (.27-.34)
2nd Gear	.005-.007 (.13-.19)
3rd Gear	.005-.015 (.13-.37)

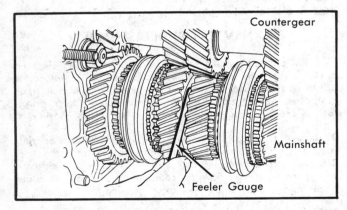

Fig. 3   Checking Gear End Play with a Feeler Gauge

Disassembly — 1) Mount adapter plate in a holding fixture. Remove detent plugs, springs and balls. On transmission F4W56A, detent ball and spring for reverse shift rod is removed after shift rod is removed.

2) Drive out retaining pins attaching shift forks to shift rods. On transmissions F4W56A and F4W60L, remove reverse shift fork and reverse idler gear. On all transmissions, remove shift forks and drive out shift rods.

NOTE — *After shift rods are removed, be sure to remove the interlock plungers on transmissions F4W56A and F4W60L. On transmission F4W71B, there are 2 interlock balls instead of one interlock plunger between shift rods.*

3) On transmission F4W71B, engage 2nd and reverse gears together and remove countergear front bearing. Remove counter drive gear snap ring, then remove counter drive gear with input shaft. Remove snap ring from mainshaft, then remove 3rd-4th synchro assembly and 3rd gear. Release staking on mainshaft nut and remove nut with thrust washer and reverse gear.

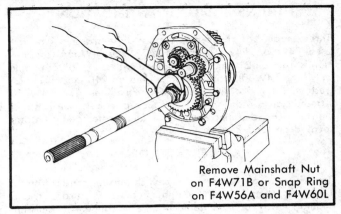

Remove Mainshaft Nut on F4W71B or Snap Ring on F4W56A and F4W60L

Fig. 4   Removing Mainshaft from Adapter Plate

4) On transmissions F4W56A and F4W60L, remove reverse gear snap ring from mainshaft and remove thrust washer with reverse gear. On transmission F4W60L, remove bearing retainer. On all transmissions, remove mainshaft and countergear together by lightly tapping on rear of mainshaft while holding onto mainshaft and countergear.

5) On transmission F4W60L, remove snap ring from mainshaft. On transmission F4W56A, remove needle bearing, thrust washer and steel ball. On transmissions F4W56A and F4W60L, remove 3rd-4th synchro assembly, 3rd gear and needle bearing from front of mainshaft.

6) On all transmissions, remove thrust washer, 1st gear, needle bearing, bushing, 1st-2nd synchro assembly, 2nd gear and needle bearing from mainshaft. Remove snap ring, thrust washer and ball bearing from input shaft.

NOTE — *Be sure not to lose pilot needle bearing in end of input shaft.*

7) On transmissions F4W56A and F4W60L, remove needle bearing and thrust washer from front of countergear. Remove snap ring, counter reverse gear and ball bearing from rear of countergear.

8) On transmission F471B, remove snap ring, counter reverse gear and ball bearing from rear of countergear. Remove bearing retainer plate, then remove idler shaft from adapter plate. On transmissions F4W56A and F4W60L, remove idler shaft snap ring then tap idler shaft from adapter plate.

Inspection — 1) Wash all components in solvent. Check transmission case and extension housing for cracks or damage. If extension housing bushing is worn or damaged, replace extension housing and bushing as an assembly.

NOTE — *Do not wash or soak oil seal in cleaning solvent.*

2) Check all bearings for smooth operation and for signs of wear or damage, replace as necessary. Check all gears for wear or damage. Check shafts for wear, damage or bending. Replace components as necessary.

3) Check gear end play, condition of gears, condition of thrust washers and bushings. Replace components as necessary.

DATSUN 210, 810 & PICKUP 4-SPEED (Cont.)

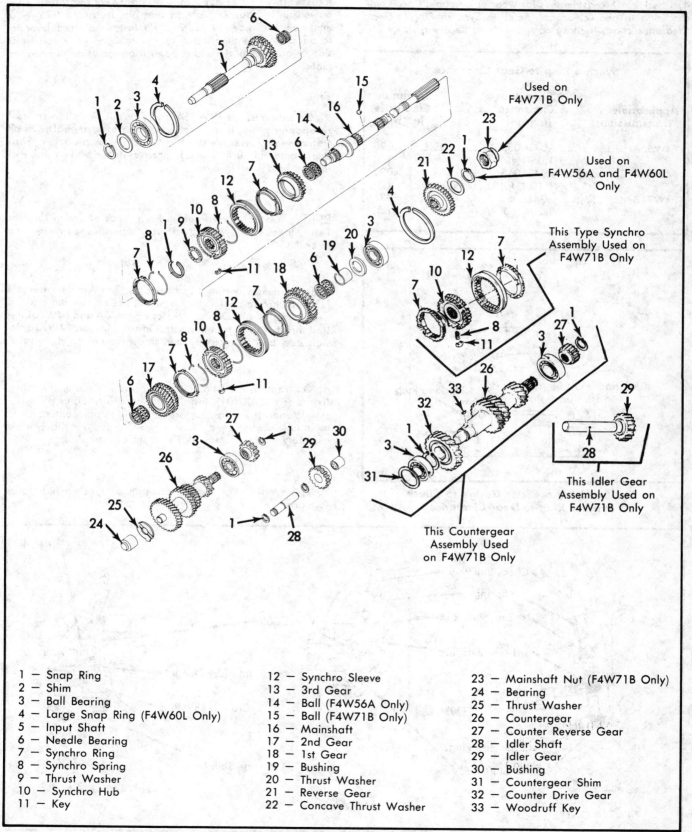

Used on F4W71B Only

Used on F4W56A and F4W60L Only

This Type Synchro Assembly Used on F4W71B Only

This Idler Gear Assembly Used on F4W71B Only

This Countergear Assembly Used on F4W71B Only

1 — Snap Ring	12 — Synchro Sleeve	23 — Mainshaft Nut (F4W71B Only)
2 — Shim	13 — 3rd Gear	24 — Bearing
3 — Ball Bearing	14 — Ball (F4W56A Only)	25 — Thrust Washer
4 — Large Snap Ring (F4W60L Only)	15 — Ball (F4W71B Only)	26 — Countergear
5 — Input Shaft	16 — Mainshaft	27 — Counter Reverse Gear
6 — Needle Bearing	17 — 2nd Gear	28 — Idler Shaft
7 — Synchro Ring	18 — 1st Gear	29 — Idler Gear
8 — Synchro Spring	19 — Bushing	30 — Bushing
9 — Thrust Washer	20 — Thrust Washer	31 — Countergear Shim
10 — Synchro Hub	21 — Reverse Gear	32 — Counter Drive Gear
11 — Key	22 — Concave Thrust Washer	33 — Woodruff Key

Fig. 5 *Exploded View of Datsun 4-Speed Transmission Gear Assembly*

DATSUN 210, 810 & PICKUP 4-SPEED (Cont.)

4) Check synchro assemblies for wear or damage. Check synchro ring to gear clearance. *Refer to Synchro Ring-to-Gear Clearance chart.* Replace components as necessary.

Synchro Ring-to-Gear Clearance		
Application (Transmission)	Standard Clearance In. (mm)	Minimum Clearance In. (mm)
F4W56A	.041-.055 (1.05-1.40)	.020 (.5)
F4W60L	.043-.055 (1.10-1.40)	.020 (.5)
F4W71B	.047-.063 (1.20-1.60)	.031 (.8)

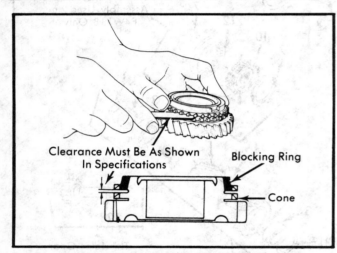

Clearance Must Be As Shown In Specifications — Blocking Ring — Cone

Fig. 6 Using a Feeler Gauge to Check Synchro Ring-to-Gear Clearance

Reassembly — 1) On transmission F4W71B, install new dowel pin in adapter plate so that pin protrudes .295" (7.5 mm) from each side of adapter plate. Install mainshaft bearing to adapter plate then install oil gutter. Bend gutter on front side of adapter plate and expand it on rear side of adapter plate.

2) On transmissions F4W56A and F4W60L, install idler shaft to adapter plate, then install snap ring to idler shaft. On all transmissions, assemble synchro assemblies by placing synchro sleeve onto hub. Install keys to grooves in hub, then install springs to hold keys in place.

NOTE — *Do not hook front and rear ends of spring to same key. Make sure synchro assembly operates correctly and smoothly.*

3) Install needle bearing, 2nd gear, 1st-2nd synchro assembly (with synchro ring), 1st gear bushing, needle bearing and 1st gear to mainshaft. On transmissions F4W56A and F4W60L, install thrust washer to mainshaft. On transmission F4W71B, install steel ball (lubricated) then thrust washer to mainshaft.

4) On transmission F4W71B, install adapter plate to holding fixture (KV31100401). Install mainshaft to adapter plate. Install Woodruff key to countergear, then install countergear to mainshaft. Install needle bearing, 3rd gear, 3rd-4th synchro assembly (with synchro ring) to front of mainshaft.

NOTE — *Make sure short protrusion of synchro hub faces forward.*

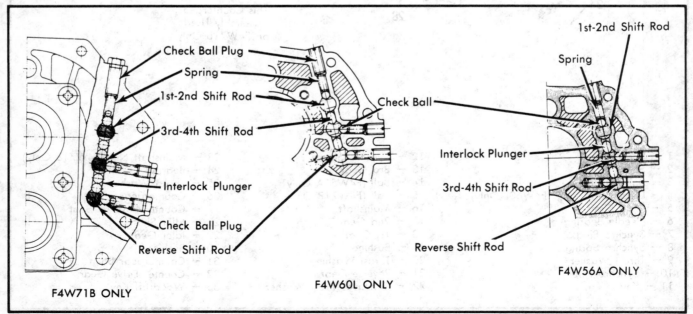

Check Ball Plug — Spring — 1st-2nd Shift Rod — 3rd-4th Shift Rod — Interlock Plunger — Check Ball Plug — Reverse Shift Rod

F4W71B ONLY

Check Ball

F4W60L ONLY

1st-2nd Shift Rod — Spring — Interlock Plunger — 3rd-4th Shift Rod — Reverse Shift Rod

F4W56A ONLY

Fig. 7 Cross Section of Positions of Shift Rods, Forks, Check Balls, Spings, Plugs and Interlock Plungers in Adapter Plate of All Transmissions

DATSUN 210, 810 & PICKUP 4-SPEED (Cont.)

5) Install thrust washer and snap ring to front of mainshaft. Select snap ring that will minimize clearance. Snap rings for transmission F4W71B are available in 3 sizes: .055" (1.4 mm), .059" (1.5 mm) and .063" (1.6 mm). On transmission F4W56A and F4W60L, install mainshaft bearing. Install needle bearing, 3rd gear, 3rd-4th synchro assembly (with synchro ring) to front of mainshaft. On transmission F4W56A, install steel ball and thrust washer (lubricated) to front of mainshaft. On transmission F4W60L, install snap ring to mainshaft that eliminates clearance. *Refer to Mainshaft Front Snap Ring chart.*

Mainshaft Front Snap Rings	
Snap Ring No.	Thickness In. (mm)
1	.061-.063 (1.55-1.60)
2	.063-.065 (1.60-1.65)
3	.065-.067 (1.65-1.70)

6) On transmission F4W71B, install 3rd-4th front synchro ring to synchro assembly. Apply gear oil to input shaft pilot bearing and install to mainshaft. Install input shaft with countergear to mainshaft and adapter plate. Install mainshaft drive gear to mainshaft. Make sure that inner diameter of gear that protrudes, faces toward rear.

7) Install counter drive gear to countergear and install snap ring that will minimize clearance. Snap rings are available in .055" (1.4 mm), .059" (1.5 mm) and .063" (1.6 mm) sizes. Install countergear front bearing.

8) Install reverse gear to mainshaft, then plain washer and mainshaft nut. Tighten mainshaft nut temporarily. Install counter reverse gear and snap ring that will minimize clearance. Snap rings are available in .055" (1.4 mm), .059" (1.5 mm), .063" (1.6 mm) and .067" (1.7 mm) sizes. Install idler gear, engage 2nd and reverse gears and tighten mainshaft nut. Stake nut after tightening.

9) On transmission F4W56A, install bearing onto input shaft, making sure bearing clears snap ring groove. Install thrust washer (concave side facing bearing) then install snap ring, making sure snap ring fits into groove.

10) On transmission F4W60L, install bearing onto input shaft, making sure snap ring groove is clear. Install bearing spacer and install snap ring that eliminates end play. *Refer to Input Shaft Bearing Snap Ring Chart.*

Input Shaft Bearing Snap Rings	
Snap Ring No.	Thickness In. (mm)
1	.053-.055 (1.34-1.40)
2	.055-.057 (1.40-1.46)
3	.057-.060 (1.46-1.52)
4	.060-.062 (1.52-1.58)
5	.062-.065 (1.58-1.64)
6	.065-.067 (1.64-1.70)
7	.067-.069 (1.70-1.76)

11) On transmissions F4W56A and F4W60L, install bearing to rear of countergear. Install original thrust washer to countergear and install into transmission case. Using special countergear height gauge (ST23050000) and a feeler gauge, check clearance between countergear rear bearing and height gauge. End play should be 0-.008" (0-.2 mm) on transmission F4W56A or .004-.008" (.1-.2 mm) on transmission F4W60L. See Fig. 8.

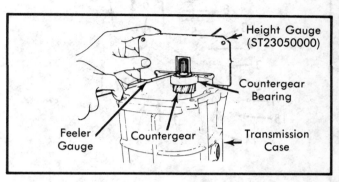

Fig. 8 Determining Countergear Shim Thickness on F4W56A and F4W60L Transmissions

12) If clearance is not to specifications, select thrust washer thickness to obtain specified clearance. Thrust washers are available in 8 different sizes, ranging from .087-.089" (2.20-2.25 mm) up to .100-.102" (2.55-2.60 mm) in .002" (.05 mm) increments.

13) With correct thrust washer selected, remove countergear from transmission case. Install counter reverse gear to countergear and install snap ring to countergear groove.

14) Install synchro ring to input shaft and install input shaft to mainshaft. Be sure that pilot bearing is in place before input shaft installation. Assemble mainshaft and countergear together and install them to adapter plate. Use a puller to pull mainshaft into adapter plate. Tapping mainshaft and countergear with a mallet will aid in installation.

NOTE — *Be sure to hold gear assemblies from dropping during installation.*

15) Make sure that snap ring groove on mainshaft rear bearing clears adapter plate. Install snap ring to mainshaft rear bearing, then install bearing retainer and screws. Stake screws after installation. Install reverse gear and thrust washer to rear of mainshaft, then install snap ring. Make sure concave side of thrust washer faces reverse gear.

16) On all transmissions, install 1st-2nd and 3rd-4th shift forks to synchro assemblies. Install 1st-2nd shift rod to adapter plate and place in neutral position. Install interlock plunger in adapter plate. Install 3rd-4th shift rod, place in neutral position and install interlock plunger.

NOTE — *On transmission F4W71B, there are 2 interlock balls instead of 1 interlock plunger.*

17) Install reverse shift rod, fork and idler gear to adapter plate. Install check balls, springs and plugs to adapter plate. Apply sealant to plugs after installation. Install new retaining pins to all shift forks, Apply gear oil to all sliding surfaces and make sure all components operate properly.

DATSUN 210, 810 & PICKUP 4-SPEED (Cont.)

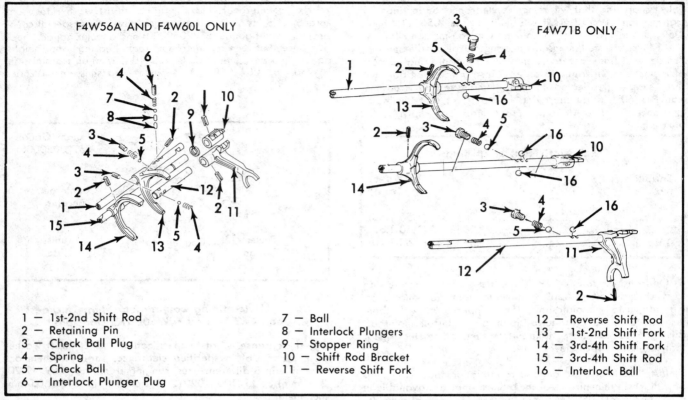

F4W56A AND F4W60L ONLY

F4W71B ONLY

1 — 1st-2nd Shift Rod	7 — Ball	12 — Reverse Shift Rod
2 — Retaining Pin	8 — Interlock Plungers	13 — 1st-2nd Shift Fork
3 — Check Ball Plug	9 — Stopper Ring	14 — 3rd-4th Shift Fork
4 — Spring	10 — Shift Rod Bracket	15 — 3rd-4th Shift Rod
5 — Check Ball	11 — Reverse Shift Fork	16 — Interlock Ball
6 — Interlock Plunger Plug		

Fig. 9   Exploded View of Shift Rods and Forks

18) On all transmissions, make sure all mating surfaces are cleaned, then apply sealant to mating surfaces. On transmissions F4W56A and F4W60L, install countergear thrust washer selected. Apply grease to thrust washer before installation. Slide transmission case onto adapter plate by tapping with mallet.

19) Install mainshaft bearing and countergear needle bearing. Make sure mainshaft rotates freely, then install snap ring to input shaft bearing.

20) On transmission F4W56A and F4W60L, select front cover shim by measuring distance from front of transmission case (where front cover bolts) to input shaft bearing, then refer to *Front Cover Shim chart* for shim thickness. See Fig. 10. On transmission F4W71B, select countergear front bearing shim by measuring distance from front bearing to transmission case and selecting shim thickness from *Countergear Front Shim chart*. See Fig. 11.

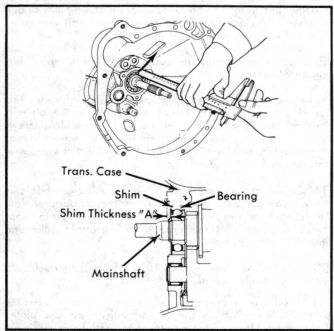

Trans. Case

Shim

Bearing

Shim Thickness "A"

Mainshaft

Fig. 10   Determining Front Bearing Shim Thickness (On F4W56A and F4W60L Transmissions)

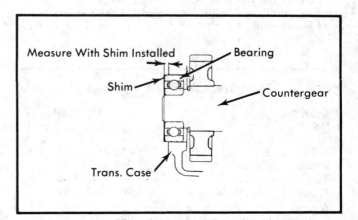

Measure With Shim Installed

Bearing

Shim

Countergear

Trans. Case

Fig. 11   Determining Countergear Shim Thickness (On F4W71B Transmission)

DATSUN 210, 810 & PICKUP 4-SPEED (Cont.)

Front Cover Shims

Shim No.	Measurement A In. (mm)	Thickness In. (mm)
F4W56A		
1	.203-.207 (5.16-5.25)	.004 (.1)
2	.207-.211 (5.25-5.35)	.008 (.2)
3	.211-.215 (5.25-5.45)	.012 (.3)
F4W60L		
1	.238-.240 (6.05-6.10)	.020 (.50)
2	.240-.242 (6.10-6.15)	.022 (.55)
3	.242-244 (6.15-6.20)	.024 (.60)
4	.244-.246 (6.20-6.25)	.026 (.65)
5	.246-.248 (6.25-6.30)	.028 (.70)
6	.248-.250 (6.30-6.35)	.030 (.75)
7	.250-.252 (6.35-6.40)	.032 (.80)

Countergear Front Shims

Shims①	Measurement A In. (mm)	Thickness In. (mm)
1	.135-.138 (3.42-3.51)	.004 (.10)
2	.131-.134 (3.32-3.41)	.008 (.20)
3	.127-.130 (3.22-3.31)	.012 (.30)
4	.123-.126 (3.12-3.21)	.016 (.40)
5	.119-.122 (3.02-3.11)	.020 (.50)
6	.115-.118 (2.92-3.01)	.024 (.60)

① — Countergear front shims do not have a number stamped on shim, but use part number. Basic number is 32218 with suffix starting at E9000 for smallest shim up to E9005 for largest shim.

TRANSMISSION REASSEMBLY

1) With adapter plate and gear assembly installed in transmission case (as done in previous steps to determine shim thickness), install shim, "O" ring, snap ring (if equipped), then front cover to transmission case.

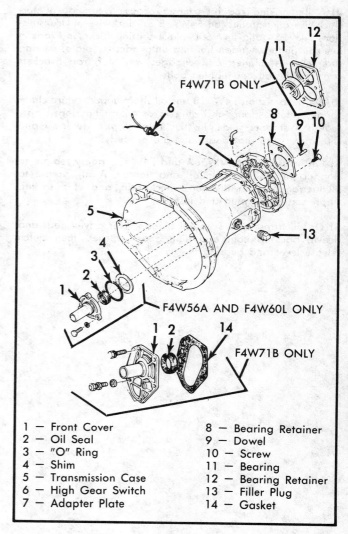

F4W71B ONLY

F4W56A AND F4W60L ONLY

F4W71B ONLY

1 — Front Cover
2 — Oil Seal
3 — "O" Ring
4 — Shim
5 — Transmission Case
6 — High Gear Switch
7 — Adapter Plate
8 — Bearing Retainer
9 — Dowel
10 — Screw
11 — Bearing
12 — Bearing Retainer
13 — Filler Plug
14 — Gasket

Fig. 12 Exploded View of Transmission Case Components

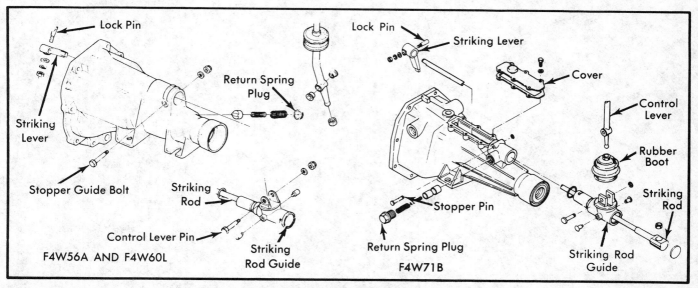

F4W56A AND F4W60L

F4W71B

Fig. 13 Exploded View of Extension Housing Components

DATSUN 210, 810 & PICKUP 4-SPEED (Cont.)

2) With striking rod in extension housing turned counter-clockwise on transmission F4W71B or clockwise on transmissions F4W56A and F4W60L, place shifting forks and rods in neutral. Slide extension housing onto adapter plate, making sure lever is aligned and engages with shift rod brackets correctly. Install and tighten bolts.

3) On transmission F4W71B, install the plunger, return check spring, return spring and plug to extension housing. Apply sealant to stopper guide pin, then install stopper guide pin and clip. Make sure that gears operate properly.

4) On transmissions F4W56A and F4W60L, apply sealant to stopper pin bolt, install bolt and tighten. Apply grease to plunger and install with reverse check spring and return spring. Apply sealant to plug and install.

5) On all transmissions, install speedometer driven gear and sleeve, back-up light and high gear switches, then clutch release lever and bearing.

TIGHTENING SPECIFICATIONS

Application	Ft. Lbs. (mkg)
Bearing Retainer	
F4W60L	5-7 (0.7-1.0)
F4W71B	12-17 (1.6-2.3)
Extension Housing-to-Transmission Case	12-16 (1.6-2.2)
Mainshaft Nut (F4W71B)	101-123 (14.0-17.0)
Transmission-to-Engine	
F4W56A, F4W60L	12-16 (1.6-2.2)
F4W71B	
Upper Bolts (4)	32-43 (4.4-5.9)
Lower Bolts (2)	7-9 (0.9-1.2)

DATSUN 510 4-SPEED

TRANSMISSION IDENTIFICATION

Only one 4-Speed transmission is used on this model, a F4W63L. Transmission case and clutch housing are integral with a separate extension housing. Transmission case is provided with a bottom cover for easy servicing.

DESCRIPTION

Transmission is a 4-speed fully synchronized constant mesh with helical cut gears in forward range and a sliding mesh spur cut gear in reverse. Transmission uses a three rail shift linkage.

LUBRICATION & ADJUSTMENT

See MANUAL TRANSMISSION SERVICING Section.

TROUBLE SHOOTING

Hard Shifting — Shifting linkage out of adjustment, worn or damaged. Fork rods bent or binding in transmission case. Synchronizer sleeves tight on hubs or synchronizer springs weak or broken. Wrong or no transmission oil. Clutch out of adjustment or low on fluid.

Slips Out of Gear — Incorrect shifting. Shifting linkage out of adjustment. Transmission incorrectly assembled. Worn interlock and check balls or weak springs. Blocking rings worn. Check shift linkage, check balls and interlock springs and balls.

Noisy Operation — Make sure noise is from transmission. Check for incorrect or insufficient transmission oil. Check for gears, bearings or synchronizer assemblies worn or damaged.

TRANSMISSION REMOVAL & INSTALLATION

Removal — 1) Disconnect battery ground cable and, if equipped, disconnect catalytic converter sensor harness and harness protector. Remove exhaust system components necessary for removal clearance. Disconnect speedometer cable and electrical connectors from case. Disconnect propeller shaft from rear axle and withdraw from transmission.

2) From inside vehicle, remove gear shift lever. From under vehicle, support engine with jack and transmission with transmission jack. Remove bolts from crossmember to transmission and bolts from crossmember to frame.

3) Remove starter and clutch slave cylinder. Lower transmission and remove bolts securing transmission to gussets (if equipped). Remove bolts securing transmission to engine. Slide transmission rearward and lower it out of vehicle.

Installation — To install transmission, reverse removal procedure. Make sure transmission has the correct type and amount of transmission oil. Make sure clutch adjustment is correct.

TRANSMISSION DISASSEMBLY

1) Drain transmission oil. With transmission supported, remove dust cover, clutch release lever and release bearing. Remove speedometer gear, reverse light switch and neutral or high gear detecting switch (if equipped).

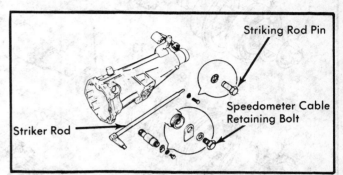

Fig. 1   Exploded View of Extension Housing Assembly

2) With transmission gears in neutral position, remove the striking rod pin from shifting linkage. Remove bolts securing extension housing to transmission case and slide extension housing off transmission. Remove bolts securing front cover to transmission case.

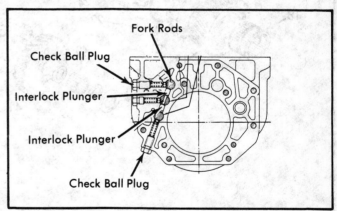

Fig. 2   Cross Section View of Balls and Interlock Plungers in Case

3) Remove bottom cover. Remove check ball plugs and springs. Using a drift, remove pins securing shifting forks to fork rods. Remove fork rods, interlock plungers and shifting forks.

4) Mesh mainshaft gears at two places to lock mainshaft and remove lock nut from mainshaft. Remove reverse gear and reverse gear hub.

5) Using a countershaft guide (ST23100000), drive countershaft from transmission case. Remove countergear and countershaft with needle bearings and washers.

NOTE — Countershaft is supported by needle bearings.

Manual Transmissions

DATSUN 510 4-SPEED (Cont.)

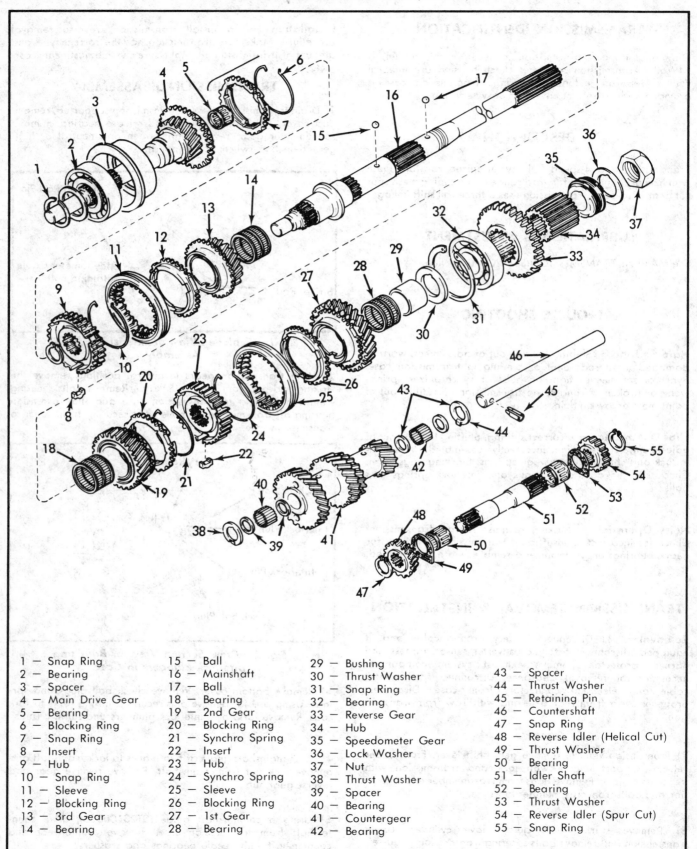

1 — Snap Ring	15 — Ball	29 — Bushing	43 — Spacer
2 — Bearing	16 — Mainshaft	30 — Thrust Washer	44 — Thrust Washer
3 — Spacer	17 — Ball	31 — Snap Ring	45 — Retaining Pin
4 — Main Drive Gear	18 — Bearing	32 — Bearing	46 — Countershaft
5 — Bearing	19 — 2nd Gear	33 — Reverse Gear	47 — Snap Ring
6 — Blocking Ring	20 — Blocking Ring	34 — Hub	48 — Reverse Idler (Helical Cut)
7 — Snap Ring	21 — Synchro Spring	35 — Speedometer Gear	49 — Thrust Washer
8 — Insert	22 — Insert	36 — Lock Washer	50 — Bearing
9 — Hub	23 — Hub	37 — Nut	51 — Idler Shaft
10 — Snap Ring	24 — Synchro Spring	38 — Thrust Washer	52 — Bearing
11 — Sleeve	25 — Sleeve	39 — Spacer	53 — Thrust Washer
12 — Blocking Ring	26 — Blocking Ring	40 — Bearing	54 — Reverse Idler (Spur Cut)
13 — 3rd Gear	27 — 1st Gear	41 — Countergear	55 — Snap Ring
14 — Bearing	28 — Bearing	42 — Bearing	

Fig. 3 Exploded View of Transmission Gears and Shafts

DATSUN 510 4-SPEED (Cont.)

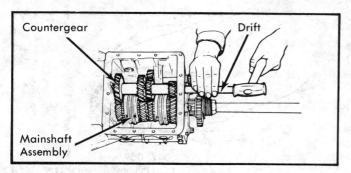

Fig. 4   Driving Countershaft from Case

6) Remove snap ring and reverse idler gear (from inside transmission case) then slide idler shaft with second reverse idler gear from transmission case. Remove bolts securing mainshaft bearing retainer then remove mainshaft. Remove bearing from input shaft and then remove input shaft from transmission case.

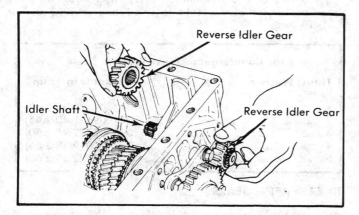

Fig. 5   Rear View of Case Showing Removal of Reverse Idler Gears and Shaft

COMPONENT DISASSEMBLY & REASSEMBLY

INPUT SHAFT

Disassembly — Remove snap ring and spacer from front of input shaft. Remove bearing from input shaft using a puller.

Inspection — Check input shaft splines for wear or damage. Check bearing inner and outer race for wear, burrs or other damage. Check bearing for smooth operation. Replace bearing if any damage or wear is detected.

Reassembly — Using a press and bearing driver, press bearing onto input shaft. Install a spacer so that clearance between snap ring and spacer is minimum. *See table for spacer thickness.*

Input Shaft Spacer Table	
Spacer	Thickness In. (mm)
1	.059-.061 (1.49-1.55)
2	.061-.064 (1.55-1.62)
3	.064-.066 (1.62-1.68)
4	.066-.069 (1.68-1.74)
5	.069-.071 (1.74-1.80)
6	.071-.073 (1.80-1.86)
7	.073-.076 (1.86-1.92)

MAINSHAFT

Disassembly — 1) From front end of mainshaft remove snap ring, 3rd-4th synchronizer assembly, third gear, and bearing. From rear of shaft, remove nut, tab washer, speedometer gear and drive ball (or retaining snap rings). Slide reverse gear and hub from end of mainshaft.

2) Position adaptor plates against front side of first gear, and press off first gear along with ball bearing. Place adaptor plates against front side of second gear, and press off second gear along with first gear bushing and 1st-2nd synchronizer assembly.

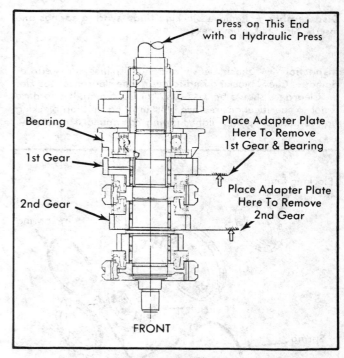

Fig. 6   Press Points for Mainshaft Gear Removal

Inspection — Check gears for wear or damage, replace if necessary. Check bearings for damage, wear and smooth operation, replace if necessary.

Reassembly — 1) From rear of mainshaft, install 2nd gear bearing, 2nd gear, blocking ring and 1st-2nd synchronizer assembly. Drive 1st gear bushing onto mainshaft with brass drift. Also install 1st gear needle bearing, 1st gear, steel ball, and thrust washer.

DATSUN 510 4-SPEED (Cont.)

2) Press bearing with bearing retainer onto mainshaft with an adaptor plate. Install reverse gear hub, reverse gear, ball, speedometer gear, lock washer and nut on mainshaft. Tighten nut temporarily.

3) From front of mainshaft, install 3rd gear bearing, 3rd gear, blocking ring, and 3rd-4th synchronizer assembly. Install a snap ring so that clearance between snap ring and synchronizer hub is at a minimum (see *table* for *snap ring thickness*).

Synchronizer Snap Ring Table

Snap Ring	Thickness In. (mm)
1	.055-.057 (1.40-1.45)
2	.057-.059 (1.45-1.50)
3	.059-.061 (1.50-1.55)
4	.061-.063 (1.55-1.60)
5	.063-.065 (1.60-1.65)

SYNCHRONIZER ASSEMBLY

Disassembly — Remove blocking rings, synchro springs and inserts. Slide hub from sleeve.

Inspection — Check sleeve and hub splines for wear or damage. Check blocking ring-to-gear cone clearance (*See Fig. 8*). Clearance should be .047-.059" (1.2-1.5 mm). If clearance is not to specifications replace blocking ring and lap blocking ring-to-gear cone with light lapping compound if necessary.

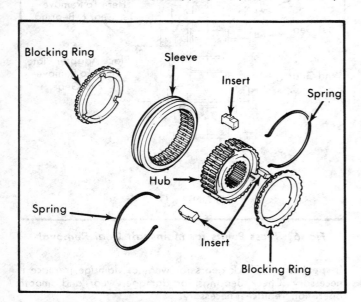

Fig. 7   Exploded View of Synchronizer Assembly

Reassembly — Slide hub into sleeve and place inserts in slots of hub, between sleeve and hub. Install springs, one on each side, to retain inserts.

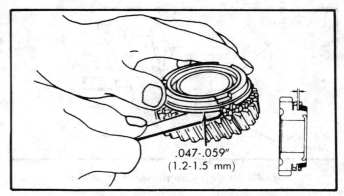

.047-.059"
(1.2-1.5 mm)

Fig. 8   Using a Feeler Gauge to Check Blocking Ring-to-Gear Cone Gap

COUNTERGEAR

Inspection — Countergear is a one piece casting. Inspect gear teeth for wear or damage, countershaft for wear or damage and bearings for damage and smooth operation. When installing countergear into transmission case, select thrust washer (rear) so that end play is in the specified range of .002-.006" (.05-.15 mm).

Rear Countergear Thrust Washer Table

Thrust Washer	Thickness In. (mm)
1	.093-.094 (2.35-2.40)
2	.094-.096 (2.40-2.45)
3	.096-.098 (2.45-2.50)
4	.098-.100 (2.50-2.55)
5	.100-.102 (2.55-2.60)

IDLER SHAFT & GEARS

Disassembly — Remove snap ring, thrust washer, bearing and gear. Inspect idler shaft, gears, bearings and thrust washers for wear or damage. Replace if necessary.

Reassembly — **1)** There are 2 idler gears on the idler shaft, one is spur type and one is helical type. Idler shaft has 2 snap ring grooves, one thin and one wide. Slide the spur type gear onto the end of idler shaft with the wide snap ring groove and install snap ring.

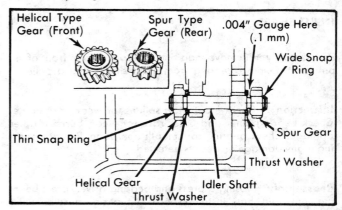

Fig. 9   Cross-Sectional View of Reverse Idler in Case.

DATSUN 510 4-SPEED (Cont.)

2) From front of idler shaft, slide thrust washer and bearing onto idler shaft. Insert idler shaft into transmission and install bearing, thrust washer and helical type gear onto idler shaft. Insert a .004" (.1 mm) feeler gauge between spur type gear and thrust washer. With gauge in place, push idler gear forward as far as it will go. Select a snap ring with a thickness to give gear end play of .004-.012" (.1-.3 mm).

Idler Gear Snap Ring Table

Snap Ring	Thickness In. (mm)
1	.045-.049 (1.15-1.25)
2	.053-.057 (1.35-1.45)
3	.049-.053 (1.25-1.35)
4	.057-.061 (1.45-1.55)
5	.041-.045 (1.05-1.15)

TRANSMISSION REASSEMBLY

1) With components reassembled as previously described, install input shaft to transmission case, then install input shaft bearing. Install mainshaft and bearing retainer. Install idler shaft with second reverse gear into case, then install reverse idler gear and snap ring.

2) Install countergear with bearings and washers, then drive countergear shaft into case. Make sure needle bearings do not fall out. Install reverse gear and hub to mainshaft. Mesh mainshaft gears at 2 places and install mainshaft lock nut.

3) Align 1st-2nd and 3rd-4th shift forks with respective synchronizer sleeves. Insert 1st-2nd shift rod into case and through fork, install retaining pin into fork and rod.

4) Place assembly in neutral position. Install one interlock plunger into bore, then install 3rd-4th shift rod into case and shift fork, locking into place with retaining pin.

5) Place 3rd-4th shift rod in neutral position and install second interlock plunger into bore. Install reverse shift rod into case and through shift fork, and lock into place with retaining pin.

6) Install detent balls and springs through 3 bores in case, coat bore plugs with sealant then install bore plugs and tighten.

TIGHTENING SPECIFICATIONS

Application	Ft. Lbs. (mkg)
Clutch Housing-to-Engine	29-35 (4.0-4.8)
Extension Housing	10-13 (1.4-1.8)
Front Cover	6-7 (.8-1.0)
Mainshaft Nut	65-80 (9.0-11.0)

DATSUN 200SX, 280ZX, 810 & PICKUP 5-SPEED

DESCRIPTION

The transmission is a type FS5W71B with fully synchronized constant mesh gears. All forward gears are of the helical type. Fifth gear (overdrive gear) rides freely on the mainshaft. The countershaft 5th gear is fitted to the countershaft by splines. The 5th gear synchronizer system is also on the rear of the mainshaft. Placing the control lever in the 5th gear position will bring the reverse and 5th gear coupling sleeve on the mainshaft into mesh with the countershaft gear. The reverse and 5th synchronizer hub is fitted to the mainshaft by splines. The main components of the transmission are: transmission case, adapter plate and rear extension housing.

LUBRICATION & ADJUSTMENT

See MANUAL TRANSMISSION SERVICING Section.

TRANSMISSION REMOVAL & INSTALLATION

Removal — 1) Disconnect battery ground cable, remove console (if equipped) and shift lever boot. Place transmission in neutral. Remove snap ring and control lever pin from transmission striking rod guide. Remove control lever.

2) Raise vehicle and remove exhaust pipe. Disconnect wires at back-up light switch, 5th gear indicator switch and neutral switch (if equipped). Disconnect speedometer cable from extension housing.

3) On 4-WD pickups, disconnect wires from 4-WD indicator switch. Disconnect propeller shaft between transmission and transfer case. Remove front differential carrier crossmember. Disconnect propeller shaft between transfer case and front differential carrier.

4) On all other models, disconnect propeller shaft from transmission. On all models, remove clutch cylinder from transmission case. Support engine and transmission. Remove rear engine mounting bolts and crossmember bolts. Remove starter and transmission case-to-engine mounting bolts.

5) Slide transmission to rear away from engine. Remove transmission from vehicle.

NOTE — *Care should be taken when removing transmission not to strike any adjacent parts or main drive shaft.*

Installation — Install transmission in the reverse of removal procedure, noting the following:
- Clean mating surfaces of engine rear plate and transmission case.
- Apply a light coat of grease to spline parts of clutch disc and main drive gear.
- Fill transmission with recommended gear oil to the level of the filler hole.

TRANSMISSION DISASSEMBLY

1) Drain oil, remove dust cover and release bearing. Remove back-up light switch, speedometer driven gear and front cover. Remove countershaft front bearing shim. Remove main drive bearing snap ring.

2) Remove rear extension, using a standard puller. Separate transmission case from adapter plate, using a soft hammer.

COMPONENT DISASSEMBLY & REASSEMBLY

GEAR ASSEMBLY

Disassembly — 1) Drive out retaining pins from fork rods, using a pin punch. Remove three check ball plugs and drive out fork rods, from adapter plate by tapping lightly on the front of the rods.

2) With gears engaged, remove countershaft front bearing, using a suitable puller. Remove countergear snap ring and remove counterdrive gear and main drive gear assembly.

3) Remove snap ring and thrust washer from mainshaft. Remove 3rd and 4th synchronizer assembly, remove 3rd gear. Remove snap ring and speedometer gear and bearing from the rear of the mainshaft.

4) Release staking on countershaft and mainshaft nuts, loosen nuts. Remove countershaft nut. Using suitable puller, remove countershaft 5th gear and bearing. Remove counter reverse idler gear and spacer. Remove countershaft (by tapping lightly at the rear end).

5) Remove reverse idler gear snap ring and reverse idler gear. Remove snap ring on mainshaft bearing. Remove mainshaft end bearing with a suitable puller, (KV 32101330).

6) Remove mainshaft nut, thrust washer, mainshaft reverse gear, overdrive synchronizer and overdrive gear. Remove mainshaft gear assembly and countershaft.

NOTE — *Countershaft and mainshaft nuts should be discarded and replaced with new nuts.*

Inspection — 1) Wash all parts in a suitable cleaning solvent and check for wear, damage or other faulty conditions.

NOTE — *Do not clean, wash or soak oil seals in solvent.*

2) Check transmission case and extension housing for cracks, or other faulty conditions. If rear extension housing bushing is worn or cracked, replace extension housing and bushing as an assembly.

3) Measure gear backlash of mainshaft and counter gear. *Refer to Gear End Play Chart for measurement limits.* Record gear end play measurements for reassembly reference.

Gear End Play Measurements	
Application	**In. (mm)**
1st Gear	.011-.013 (.27-.34)
2nd Gear	.005-.008 (.12-.19)
3rd Gear	.005-.015 (.12-.37)
5th Gear	.004-.007 (.10-.17)
Reverse Gear	.002-.020 (.05-.50)

DATSUN 200SX, 280ZX, 810 & PICKUP 5-SPEED (Cont.)

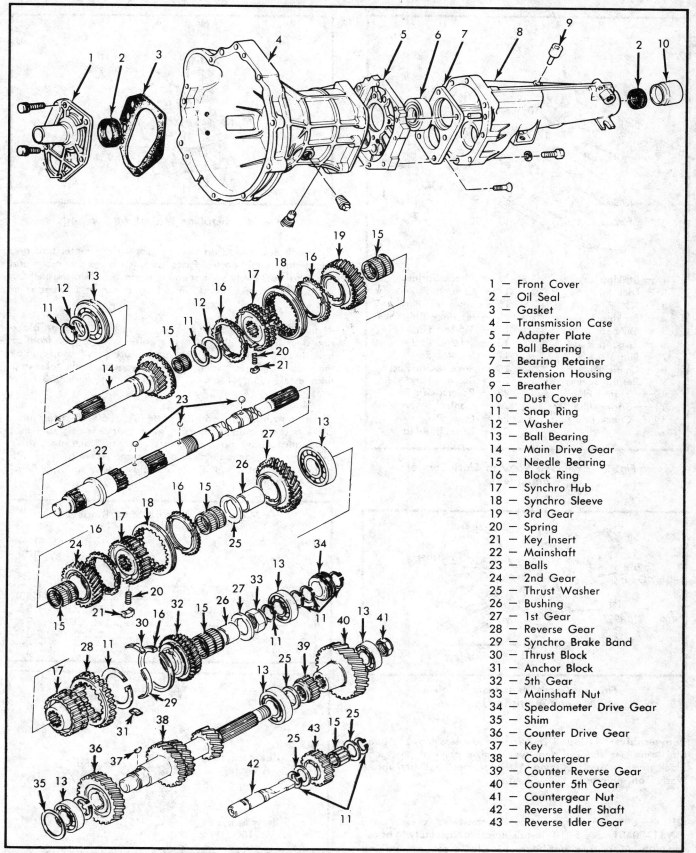

1 — Front Cover
2 — Oil Seal
3 — Gasket
4 — Transmission Case
5 — Adapter Plate
6 — Ball Bearing
7 — Bearing Retainer
8 — Extension Housing
9 — Breather
10 — Dust Cover
11 — Snap Ring
12 — Washer
13 — Ball Bearing
14 — Main Drive Gear
15 — Needle Bearing
16 — Block Ring
17 — Synchro Hub
18 — Synchro Sleeve
19 — 3rd Gear
20 — Spring
21 — Key Insert
22 — Mainshaft
23 — Balls
24 — 2nd Gear
25 — Thrust Washer
26 — Bushing
27 — 1st Gear
28 — Reverse Gear
29 — Synchro Brake Band
30 — Thrust Block
31 — Anchor Block
32 — 5th Gear
33 — Mainshaft Nut
34 — Speedometer Drive Gear
35 — Shim
36 — Counter Drive Gear
37 — Key
38 — Countergear
39 — Counter Reverse Gear
40 — Counter 5th Gear
41 — Countergear Nut
42 — Reverse Idler Shaft
43 — Reverse Idler Gear

Fig. 1 *Exploded View of Datsun FS5W71B 5-Speed Transmission Assembly*

DATSUN 200SX, 280ZX, 810 & PICKUP 5-SPEED (Cont.)

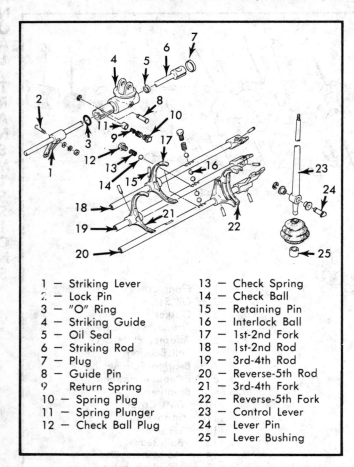

1 —	Striking Lever	13 —	Check Spring
2 —	Lock Pin	14 —	Check Ball
3 —	"O" Ring	15 —	Retaining Pin
4 —	Striking Guide	16 —	Interlock Ball
5 —	Oil Seal	17 —	1st-2nd Fork
6 —	Striking Rod	18 —	1st-2nd Rod
7 —	Plug	19 —	3rd-4th Rod
8 —	Guide Pin	20 —	Reverse-5th Rod
9 —	Return Spring	21 —	3rd-4th Fork
10 —	Spring Plug	22 —	Reverse-5th Fork
11 —	Spring Plunger	23 —	Control Lever
12 —	Check Ball Plug	24 —	Lever Pin
		25 —	Lever Bushing

Fig. 2   Exploded View of Shift Control Components

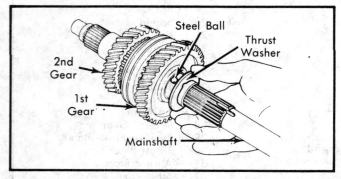

Fig. 3   Component Installation (on Mainshaft)

Reassembly — 1) Install 2nd gear needle bearing, 2nd gear block ring, 1st and 2nd gear synchronizer assembly, 1st gear block ring, 1st gear bushing, 1st gear, steel ball and thrust washer on mainshaft. (See Fig. 3).

2) Place adapter plate on transmission press stand (KV31100401). See Fig. 4. Install mainshaft assembly to adapter plate. Make sure that bearing is placed squarely against shaft and press into place.

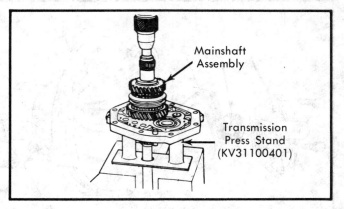

Fig. 4   Installing Mainshaft Assembly

3) Install new Woodruff keys in grooves in countershaft and tap lightly until seated. Place adapter plate assembly and mainshaft assembly so that countershaft rear bearing rests on transmission press stand. Install countershaft into adapter plate.

4) Install 3rd gear needle bearing, mainshaft 3rd gear, block ring and 3rd and 4th gear synchronizer assembly on front of mainshaft. Install thrust washer and secure with a snap ring of the proper thickness. Snap rings are available in the following thicknesses: .055" (1.4 mm), .059" (1.5 mm) and .063" (1.6 mm).

5) Using transmission adapter plate (ST23860000), press main drive bearing onto main drive gear shaft, making sure that snap ring groove on shaft clears bearing. Place main drive bearing spacer on main drive bearing and secure bearing with a snap ring that will eliminate end play. See Main Drive Bearing Snap Ring Chart.

Main Drive Bearing Snap Rings	
No.	**Thickness In. (mm)**
1	.0680 (1.73)
2	.0709 (1.80)
3	.0736 (1.87)
4	.0764 (1.94)
5	.0791 (2.01)
6	.0819 (2.08)

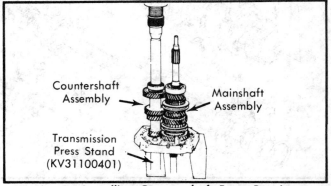

Fig. 5   Installing Countershaft Front Bearing

DATSUN 200SX, 280ZX, 810 & PICKUP 5-SPEED (Cont.)

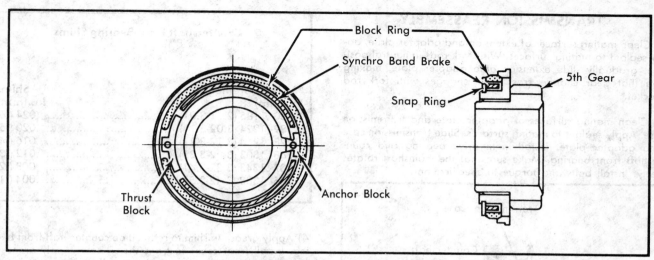

Fig. 6   Exploded View of Overdrive Gear Assembly

6) Install countershaft front bearing onto countershaft. See *Fig. 5.* Install countershaft and mainshaft into adapter plate and place adapter plate in a vise. Position synchronizer ring, band brake, thrust block and anchor block on overdrive clutch gear. Install circlip. See *Fig. 6.* Install snap ring, spacer, needle bearing. reverse idler gear, spacer and snap ring.

7) Install 5th and reverse synchronizer assembly, 5th gear, steel ball and thrust washer on the rear of mainshaft. Install counter reverse gear, counter 5th gear, bearing and new countershaft nut. Tighten mainshaft and countershaft nuts.

8) Install 1st and 2nd, 3rd and 4th shift forks into grooves on coupling sleeves. Slide 1st and 2nd fork rod through adapter plate and 1st and 2nd shifter fork. See *Fig. 7.* Secure rod to shift fork with a new retaining pin. Install check ball, check spring and plug. Apply sealant to plug before installing. Align notch in 1st and 2nd fork rod with check ball.

NOTE — *Long end of shift fork, for 1st and 2nd gear is placed on the countergear side.*

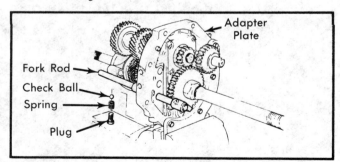

Fig. 7   Installing 1st and 2nd Shift Fork Rod

9) Slide 3rd and 4th fork rod through adapter plate and 3rd and 4th shift fork and secure with a new retaining pin. Install check ball, spring and plug. Apply sealant to plug before installing. Align notch in 3rd and 4th fork rod with check ball. See *Fig. 8.*

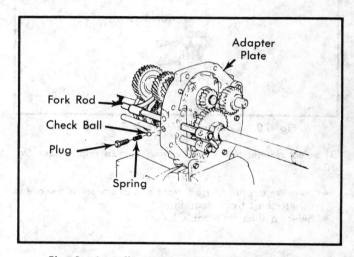

Fig. 8   Installing 3rd and 4th Shift Fork Rod

10) Place reverse shift fork in reverse idler gear. Slide reverse fork rod through reverse shift fork and adapter plate and secure with a new retaining pin. Install check ball, spring and plug. Apply sealant to plug before installing. Align notch in reverse fork rod with check ball. See *Fig. 9.*

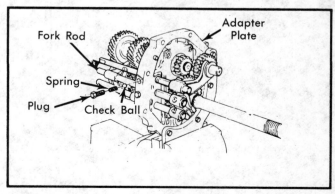

Fig. 9   Installing Reverse Shift Fork Rod

DATSUN 200SX, 280ZX, 810 & PICKUP 5-SPEED (Cont.)

TRANSMISSION REASSEMBLY

1) Clean mating surfaces of extension and adapter plate, apply sealant to mating surfaces. With fork rods in neutral position, gradually slide extension onto adapter plate, making sure that gear change cross lever engages with fork rod bracket.

2) Clean mating surfaces of adapter plate and transmission case. Apply sealant to mating surfaces. Slide transmission case onto adapter plate. Install main drive bearing and countershaft front bearing. Make sure that the mainshaft rotates freely. Install bolts and torque to specifications.

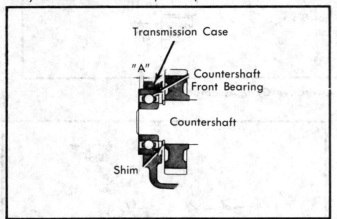

Fig. 10   Countershaft Front Bearing Shim

3) Select countershaft front bearing shim as follows: *See Fig. 10.*

- Measure depth "A" from front end of transmission case to countershaft front bearing.
- Select a shim from table below.

Countershaft Front Bearing Shims	
"A" Measurement In. (mm)	**Shims** In. (mm)
.1150-.1185 (2.91-3.01)	.024 (.6)
.1189-.1224 (3.02-3.11)	.020 (.5)
.1228-.1264 (3.12-3.21)	.016 (.4)
.1268-.1303 (3.22-3.31)	.012 (.3)
.1307-.1343 (3.32-3.41)	.008 (.2)
.1346-.1382 (3.42-3.51)	.004 (.1)

4) Apply grease to shim to retain it on countershaft front bearing. Install front cover to transmission case. Apply grease to reverse select return plunger and install in rear extension. Install speedometer pinion assembly on rear extension. Apply grease to release bearing. Temporarily install control lever and shift control lever. Shift transmission through all gears to ensure correct operation.

TIGHTENING SPECIFICATIONS

Application	Ft. Lbs. (mkg)
Bearing Retainer-to-Adapter	14-18 (1.9-2.5)
Countergear Nut	72-94 (10.0-13.0)
Mainshaft Nut	101-123 (14.0-17.0)

DATSUN 210 5-SPEED

DESCRIPTION

The Datsun FS5W60A transmission is a 5-speed, fully synchronized, constant mesh unit that uses helical type gears on 1st through 5th speeds. Reverse gear is sliding mesh, spur type gear. Transmission assembly consists of three main parts: transmission case, adapter plate and extension housing. The adapter plate supports the mainshaft, countergear, idler shaft and fork rods. Adapter plate is bolted to rear of transmission case, extension housing is bolted to adapter plate and transmission case.

LUBRICATION & ADJUSTMENT

See *MANUAL TRANSMISSION SERVICING* Section.

TRANSMISSION REMOVAL & INSTALLATION

Removal — 1) Disconnect battery ground cable, remove console and floor hole cover. Detach rubber boots. Place transmission in neutral. Remove snap ring and control lever pin from transmission striking rod guide. Remove control lever. Raise vehicle, remove exhaust pipe. Disconnect wires at; back-up switch, neutral switch, high gear switch and overdrive switch.

2) Remove clutch cylinder from transmission case. Disconnect speedometer cable. Remove drive shaft and plug opening in rear of extension housing. Support engine and transmission. Remove rear engine mounting bolts and crossmember bolts. Remove starter, then remove transmission-to-engine attaching bolts.

3) Slide transmission to the rear away from engine. Remove transmission from vehicle.

NOTE — *Care should be taken when removing transmission not to strike any adjacent parts or main drive shaft.*

Installation — Install transmission in the reverse of removal procedure, paying attention to the following:

- Clean mating surfaces of engine rear plate and transmission.
- Apply a light coat of grease to spline parts of clutch disc hub and to input shaft.
- Fill transmission with recommended gear oil, to the level of the filler hole.

TRANSMISSION DISASSEMBLY

1) Drain oil, remove dust cover and release bearing. Remove back-up switch, neutral switch, speedometer driven gear and front cover.

2) Remove nut and stopper pin bolt from extension housing. Remove return spring plug, spring and plunger from extension housing. Remove reverse check sleeve assembly. Remove "O" ring, spacer and snap ring from front of input shaft. See *Fig. 1.*

3) Remove extension housing with puller. Separate transmission case from adapter plate by tapping on transmission case with mallet while holding onto rear of mainshaft. Install adapter plate to a holding fixture and remove thrust washer from countergear. See *Fig. 2.*

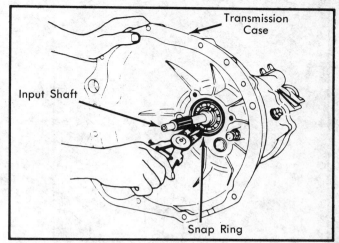

Fig. 1 Removing Snap Ring from Input Shaft

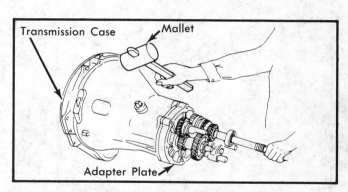

Fig. 2 Removing Transmission Case from Adapter Plate

COMPONENT DISASSEMBLY & REASSEMBLY

GEAR ASSEMBLY

NOTE — *Check gear clearance and end play before disassembly. See Inspection.*

Disassembly — 1) Drive out retaining pins from shift rods, using a punch. Remove 3 check ball plugs, and drive out shift rods from adapter plate (by tapping lightly on front ends of shift rods). Remove shift forks.

NOTE — *Be careful not to lose the 3 detent balls and 2 interlock plungers.*

2) Remove snap ring from mainshaft end bearing then remove bearing with a puller. Remove other end bearing snap ring. Engage 1st and reverse gears at same time then loosen staking on countergear nut. Remove countergear nut. See *Fig. 4.*

3) Remove small snap ring, large snap ring holder and large snap ring from mainshaft. Remove 5th gear and bearing from mainshaft with counter 5th gear. Remove snap ring and 5th-Reverse synchro assembly. Remove reverse gear with needle bearing from mainshaft and reverse gear from countergear at same time.

Manual Transmissions

DATSUN 210 5-SPEED (Cont.)

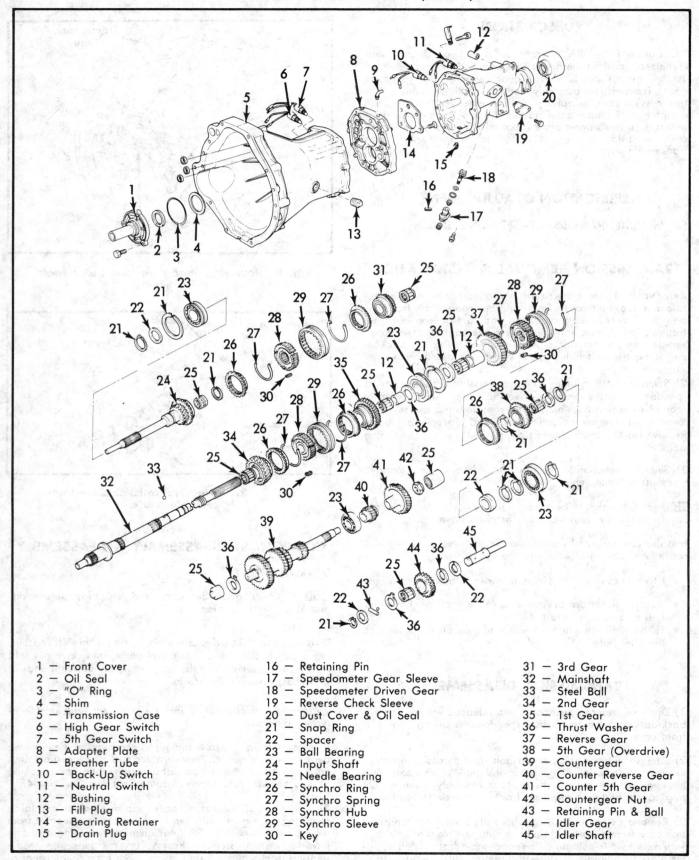

1 — Front Cover	16 — Retaining Pin	31 — 3rd Gear
2 — Oil Seal	17 — Speedometer Gear Sleeve	32 — Mainshaft
3 — "O" Ring	18 — Speedometer Driven Gear	33 — Steel Ball
4 — Shim	19 — Reverse Check Sleeve	34 — 2nd Gear
5 — Transmission Case	20 — Dust Cover & Oil Seal	35 — 1st Gear
6 — High Gear Switch	21 — Snap Ring	36 — Thrust Washer
7 — 5th Gear Switch	22 — Spacer	37 — Reverse Gear
8 — Adapter Plate	23 — Ball Bearing	38 — 5th Gear (Overdrive)
9 — Breather Tube	24 — Input Shaft	39 — Countergear
10 — Back-Up Switch	25 — Needle Bearing	40 — Counter Reverse Gear
11 — Neutral Switch	26 — Synchro Ring	41 — Counter 5th Gear
12 — Bushing	27 — Synchro Spring	42 — Countergear Nut
13 — Fill Plug	28 — Synchro Hub	43 — Retaining Pin & Ball
14 — Bearing Retainer	29 — Synchro Sleeve	44 — Idler Gear
15 — Drain Plug	30 — Key	45 — Idler Shaft

Fig. 3   *Exploded View of Datsun FS5W60A 5-Speed Transmission Assembly*

DATSUN 210 5-SPEED (Cont.)

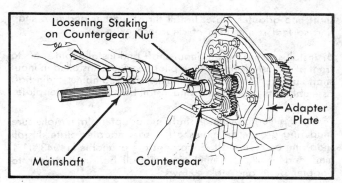

Fig. 4 Loosening Staking on Countergear Nut

4) Remove thrust washer from countergear. Remove bearing retainer screws from adapter plate, then remove retainer plate. Remove mainshaft rear bearing snap ring. Drive mainshaft, with countergear, out of adapter plate by tapping on end of mainshaft with a mallet. See Fig. 5.

NOTE — *Be careful to hold both the mainshaft and countergear from falling when removing from adapter plate.*

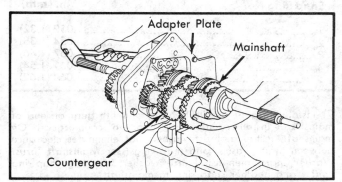

Fig. 5 Removing Mainshaft and Countergear from Adapter Plate

5) Remove idler shaft snap ring and spacer. Tap idler shaft out of adapter plate just enough so that retaining pin can be driven out of idler shaft. Remove retaining pin, then remove idler shaft from adapter plate. Remove thrust washers, spacer, idler gear and needle bearing from idler shaft.

6) From front of mainshaft, remove snap ring. Then remove synchro assembly, 3rd gear and needle bearing. Pull mainshaft bearing from mainshaft rear end. Remove thrust washer, 1st gear, needle bearing, bushing, synchro assembly, 2nd gear and needle bearing together.

7) On input shaft, remove snap ring, spacer and bearing. On countergear, press bearing off.

Inspection — 1) Wash all parts in a suitable cleaning solvent and check for wear, damage or other faulty conditions.

NOTE — *Do not clean, wash or soak oil seals in solvent.*

2) Check transmission case and rear extension for cracks, distortion or other faulty conditions. If rear extension bushing is worn or cracked, replace extension housing and bushing as an assembly.

3) If bearing race or ball surfaces are worn, rough or out-of-round, replace bearings. Replace needle bearing and taper roller bearing if worn or damaged.

4) Check gears for wear, chips or cracks. Measure gear end play on all gears. *Refer to Fig. 6 and see Gear End Play Chart* for specifications.

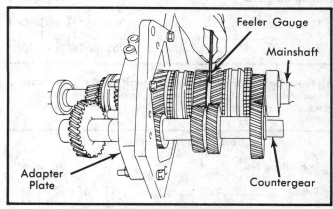

Fig. 6 Checking Gear End Play

Gear End Play

Application	In. (mm)
1st Gear	.006-.010 (.15-.25)
2nd Gear	.012-.016 (.30-.40)
3rd Gear	.006-.014 (.15-.35)
5th Gear	.012-.016 (.30-.40)
Reverse Gear	.012-.022 (.30-.55)
Countergear	.004-.008 (.10-.20)
Idler Gear	0-.008 (0-.20)

5) Check mainshaft for binding, cracks or wear. Check synchro rings for cracks, wear or damage. Replace as necessary. Check synchro ring to gear clearance. Clearance should be .043-.055" (1.1-1.4 mm). See Fig. 7.

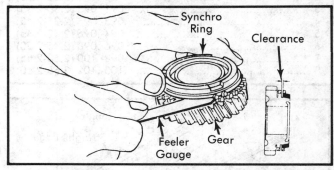

Fig. 7 Checking Synchro Ring to Gear Clearance

6) Replace oil seal if sealing lip is deformed, cracked or spring is out of position. Check oil seal lip contact face on shaft; if necessary, replace seal and shaft as a set.

Reassembly — 1) Install needle bearing, 2nd gear, 1st-2nd synchro assembly, bushing, needle bearing, 1st gear and thrust washer onto mainshaft. Press roller bearing onto mainshaft.

2) Place needle bearing, 3rd gear, 3rd-4th synchro assembly to front end of mainshaft. Place a snap ring on front of mainshaft that will allow a minimum of clearance between synchro hub and snap ring. See Mainshaft Front End Snap Ring Chart.

DATSUN 210 5-SPEED (Cont.)

Mainshaft Front End Snap Rings

Snap Ring No.	In. (mm)
1	.061-.063 (1.55-1.60)
2	.063-.065 (1.60-1.65)
3	.065-.067 (1.65-1.70)

3) Press ball bearing onto input shaft (make sure bearing clears snap ring groove) and install snap ring that elimates all clearance. *See Input Shaft Snap Ring Chart.*

Input Shaft Snap Rings

Snap Ring No.	In. (mm)
1	.053-.055 (1.34-1.40)
2	.055-.057 (1.40-1.46)
3	.057-.060 (1.46-1.52)
4	.060-.062 (1.52-1.58)
5	.062-.065 (1.58-1.64)
6	.065-.067 (1.64-1.70)
7	.067-.069 (1.70-1.76)

4) Install countergear and thrust washer into transmission case. Select thrust washer by placing a straight edge across rear of transmission case and using a feeler gauge to measure clearance between countergear and straight edge. *See Fig. 8.* With thrust washer in place, end play should be .004-.008" (.1-.2 mm). *See Countergear Thrust Washer Chart.*

Countergear Thrust Washers

Thrust Washer No.	In. (mm)
1	.087-.089 (2.20-2.25)
2	.089-.091 (2.25-2.30)
3	.091-.093 (2.30-2.35)
4	.093-.094 (2.35-2.40)
5	.094-.096 (2.40-2.45)
6	.096-.098 (2.45-2.50)
7	.098-.100 (2.50-2.55)
8	.100-.102 (2.55-2.60)

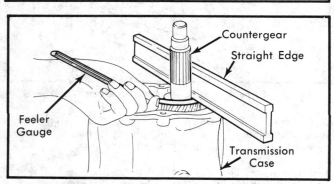

Fig. 8 Checking Countergear End Play

5) After selecting appropriate thrust washer, remove countergear from transmission case. Assemble idler shaft by installing thrust washers, needle bearing, idler gear and thrust washer. Insert new retaining pin to idler shaft. Install idler shaft into adapter plate. Install thrust washer and fit a snap ring so that a minimum of clearance exists.

6) Install synchro ring to input shaft and install input shaft to front of mainshaft (make sure pilot bearing is installed in input shaft before installing to mainshaft). Combine mainshaft assembly with countergear and install both into adapter plate.

7) Use a puller to pull mainshaft into adapter plate. Make sure snap ring groove, in mainshaft, clears adapter plate. Install snap ring on mainshaft. Snap rings are available in .043" (1.1 mm) and .047" (1.2 mm) sizes. Install bearing retainer to adapter plate and stake screws.

8) Place thrust washer, bushing, needle bearing and reverse gear on end of mainshaft. Install counter reverse gear to countergear. Install 5th-Reverse synchro assembly to mainshaft and install snap ring that eliminates clearance between synchro hub and snap ring. *See 5th-Reverse Snap Ring Chart.*

5th-Reverse Snap Rings

Snap Ring No.	In. (mm)
1	.052 (1.32)
2	.054 (1.38)
3	.057 (1.46)
4	.061 (1.54)
5	.064 (1.62)

9) Install 5th gear needle bearing and 5th gear on end of mainshaft. Install counter 5th gear to countergear. On mainshaft, install a thrust washer that eliminates clearance between thrust washer and snap ring (*see Mainshaft Thrust Washer Chart*), then install thrust washer, snap ring, snap ring holder and another snap ring to mainshaft.

Mainshaft Thrust Washers

Thrust Washer No.	In. (mm)
1	.310 (7.87)
2	.313 (7.94)
3	.315 (8.01)
4	.318 (8.08)
5	.321 (8.15)
6	.324 (8.22)

10) Engage 1st and reverse gears at same time then tighten countergear nut. Stake countergear nut. Measure gear end play and make sure that it is to specifications. Install a .045" (1.15 mm) snap ring to front end of mainshaft end bearing. Install mainshaft end bearing to mainshaft. Install a thick snap ring onto mainshaft that eliminates play between bearing and snap ring. Snap rings are available in 2 sizes, .045" (1.15 mm) and .047" (1.2 mm).

11) Install 5th-Reverse shift rod into its shift fork and install in adapter plate. Place 5th-Reverse shift fork in neutral and install interlock plunger in adapter plate. Install 3rd-4th shift rod into 5th-Reverse fork and install new snap ring to 3rd-4th shift rod.

12) Install 3rd-4th shift rod to adapter plate and its shift fork. Place 3rd-4th shift rod in neutral, install interlock plunger to

DATSUN 210 5-SPEED (Cont.)

adapter plate. Install 1st-2nd shift rod to its shift fork and install in adapter plate. Secure shift forks and shift rods with new retaining pins. *Refer to Fig. 9.*

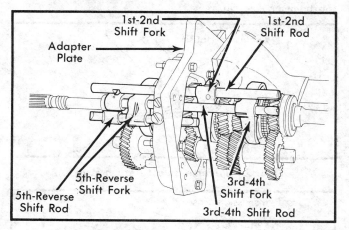

Fig. 9   Shift Rod and Shift Fork Installation

NOTE — *Be sure to install interlock plunger when installing adjacent shift rods to adapter plate. Properly align 3rd-4th shift fork with groove in synchro sleeve. Also align 1st-2nd and 5th-Reverse shift forks with synchro sleeve before installing.*

13) Install detent balls, springs and plugs. Apply sealer to plugs before installation. *See Fig. 10.* Apply gear oil to sliding surfaces and make sure all shift forks, rods and gears operate properly.

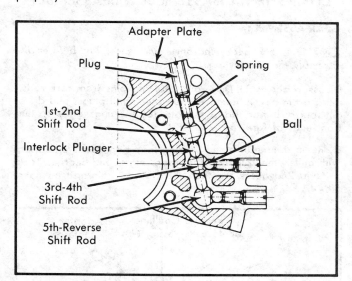

Fig. 10   Interlock Plungers, Detent Balls, Springs and Plug Installation

TRANSMISSION REASSEMBLY

1) Clean mating surfaces of adapter plate and transmission case. Apply sealant to cleaned surfaces. Install countergear thrust washer selected previously. Apply grease to sliding surface of thrust washer. Install adapter plate to transmission case, lightly tapping with mallet. Install input shaft bearing snap ring.

2) Clean mating surfaces of adapter plate and extension housing, apply sealant to cleaned surfaces. Place striking rod in neutral, turn striking guide clockwise, then set striking lever and shift arm. Align shift arm pin with groove in shift rod and install extension housing to adapter plate. Install bolts and tighten. Grease plunger and install it in extension housing. Install return spring and plug.

3) Select front cover shim by measuring distance from front end of transmission case to input shaft bearing outer race. See *Fig. 11.* Select shim that will give an end play of .219-.220" (5.55-5.59 mm). *Refer to Front Cover Shim Chart.* Install front cover to transmission case.

4) Install front cover to transmission case.

Front Cover Shims

Shim No.	Measurement A In. (mm)	Shim Thickness In. (mm)
1	.238-.240 (6.05-6.10)	.020 (.50)
2	.240-.242 (6.10-6.15)	.022 (.55)
3	.242-.244 (6.15-6.20)	.024 (.60)
4	.244-.246 (6.20-6.25)	.026 (.65)
5	.246-.248 (6.25-6.30)	.028 (.70)
6	.248-.250 (6.30-6.35)	.030 (.75)
7	.250-.252 (6.35-6.40)	.032 (.80)

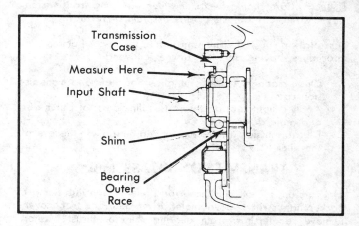

Fig. 11   Measuring Front Cover for Shim Selection

TIGHTENING SPECIFICATIONS

Application	Ft. Lbs. (mkg)
Transmission Case-to-Engine	12-16 (1.6-2.2)
Countergear Nut	36-43 (5.0-6.0)
Front Cover	7-12 (1.0-1.6)
Extension Housing	12-16 (1.6-2.2)

DATSUN 510 5-SPEED

DESCRIPTION

The Datsun FS5W63A transmission is a 5-speed, fully synchronized, constant mesh unit that uses helical type gears on 1st through 5th speeds. Reverse gear is sliding mesh, spur type of gear. Transmission assembly consists of three main parts: transmission case, adapter plate and extension housing. The adapter plate supports the mainshaft, countergear, idler shaft and fork rods. Adapter plate is bolted to rear of transmission case, extension housing is bolted to adapter plate and transmission case.

LUBRICATION & ADJUSTMENT

See *MANUAL TRANSMISSION SERVICING* Section.

TRANSMISSION REMOVAL & INSTALLATION

Removal — 1) Disconnect battery ground cable, remove console and floor hole cover. Detach rubber boots. Place transmission in neutral. Remove snap ring and control lever pin from transmission striking rod guide. Remove control lever. Raise vehicle, remove exhaust pipe. Disconnect wires at; back-up light switch, top and neutral switches.

2) Remove clutch cylinder from transmission case. Disconnect speedometer cable. Remove drive shaft and plug opening in rear extension housing. Support engine and transmission. Remove rear engine mounting bolts and crossmember bolts. Remove starter, remove tranmission-to-engine attaching bolts.

3) Slide transmission to the rear away from engine. Remove transmission from vehicle.

NOTE — *Care should be taken when removing transmission, not to strike any adjacent parts or main drive shaft.*

Installation — Install transmission in the reverse of removal procedure, paying attention to the following:

- Clean mating surfaces of engine rear plate and transmission case.
- Apply a light coat of grease to spline parts of clutch disc and main drive gear.
- Fill transmission with recommended gear oil, to the level of the filler hole.

TRANSMISSION DISASSEMBLY

1) Drain oil, remove dust cover and release bearing. Remove backup light switch, speedometer driven gear and front cover. Remove countershaft from bearing shim or thrust washer. Remove mainshaft bearing snap ring. *See Fig. 1.*

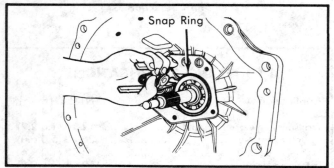

Fig. 1   Removing Main Drive Bearing Snap Ring

2) Remove reverse select return plug, spring and plunger from rear extension. *See Fig. 2.* Remove extension housing with puller. Separate transmission case from adapter plate, using soft hammer. *See Fig. 3.*

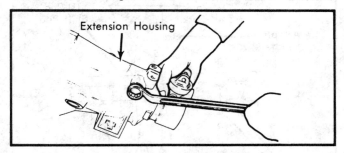

Fig. 2   Reverse Select Return Plug

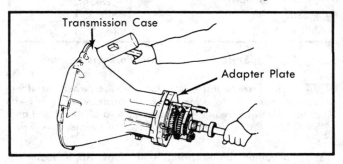

Fig. 3   Removing Transmission Case

COMPONENT DISASSEMBLY & REASSEMBLY

GEAR ASSEMBLY

NOTE — *Check gear clearance and end play before disassembly. See Inspection.*

Disassembly — 1) Drive out retaining pins from fork rods, using a pin punch. Remove three check ball plugs, and drive out fork rods from adapter plate, (by tapping lightly on the front ends of fork rods).

2) Remove mainshaft end bearing snap ring. Remove bearing with puller, then remove other snap ring of end bearing. Lock 1st and 2nd gears together, then loosen mainshaft nut. See Fig. 4.

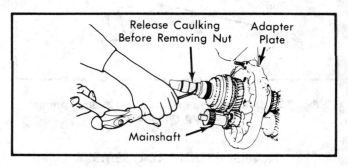

Fig. 4   Removing Mainshaft Nut

3) Remove mainshaft nut, speedometer drive gear and steel ball. Remove following components together: synchro hub and reverse gear, 1st gear with needle bearing and bushing, idler gear with needle bearing. *See Fig. 5.*

DATSUN 510 5-SPEED (Cont.)

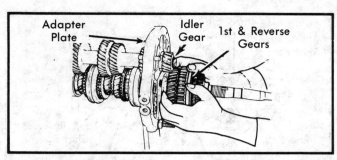

Fig. 5   Removing Idler, 1st and Reverse Gears From Mainshaft and Idler Shaft

4) Remove snap ring and thrust washer from countergear. Remove counter 1st gear (using gear puller) from countergear. Using a puller (KV32101310), pull mainshaft out about .4" (10 mm), then remove input shaft and countergear. See Fig. 6.

NOTE — *When removing thrust washer, be careful not to lose ball.*

5) Remove thrust washer, steel ball, 2nd gear and needle bearing from mainshaft. Using a bearing puller (ST30031000), remove bushing, 2nd-3rd synchro assembly, 3rd gear and needle bearing.

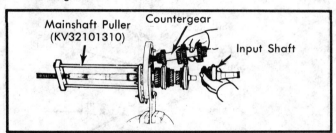

Fig. 6   Removing Input Shaft and Countergear

6) On front of mainshaft, remove snap ring, 4th-5th synchro assembly and 5th gear. On input shaft, remove snap ring and spacer, then press bearing off. On countergear, remove shim and press front bearing off. From rear of countergear, remove snap ring, spacer, and counter 1st gear, then press bearing off. On idler shaft, remove washers, gear, needle bearings, spacer and retaining pin.

Inspection — **1)** Wash all parts in a suitable cleaning solvent and check for wear, damage or other faulty conditions.

NOTE — *Do not clean, wash or soak oil seals in solvent.*

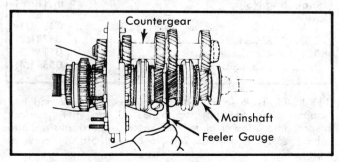

Fig. 7   Measuring Gear End Play

2) Check transmission case and rear extension for cracks, distorsion or other faulty conditions. If rear extension bushing is

worn or cracked, replace extension housing and bushing as an assembly.

3) If bearing race or ball surfaces are worn, rough or out-of-round, replace bearings. Replace needle bearing and taper roller bearing if worn or damaged.

4) Check all gears for excessive wear, chips or cracks. Measure gear end play on all gears. See Fig. 7. End play of gears should be as specified. See *Mainshaft Gear End Play Chart.*

Mainshaft Gear End Play	
Application	**End Play In. (mm)**
1st Gear	.011-.015 (.27-.37)
2nd Gear	.008-.012 (.20-.30)
3rd Gear	.002-.006 (.05-.15)
5th Gear	.002-.008 (.05-.20)
Reverse Idler Gear	.006-.016 (.15-.40)

5) Check shaft for binding, cracks or wear. Check and replace synchro ring that is deformed or cracked. Check synchro ring-to-gear clearance, with synchro ring in place on gear cone and pushed towards gear. See Fig. 8. Clearance should be .047-.059" (1.2-1.5 mm).

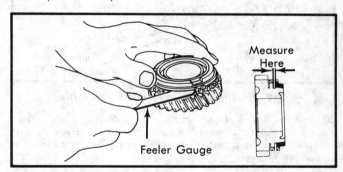

Fig. 8   Measuring Synchro Ring-to-Gear Clearance

6) Replace oil seal if sealing lip is deformed, cracked or spring is out of position. Check oil seal lip contact face on shaft; if necessary replace seal and shaft as a set.

Reassembly — **1)** Position 5th gear needle bearing, 5th gear, synchro ring and 4th-5th gear synchro assembly on front of mainshaft. Fit snap ring in groove on mainshaft that eliminates clearance. *Refer to Front Mainshaft Snap Ring Chart.*

Front Mainshaft Snap Rings	
Snap Ring No.	**Thickness In. (mm)**
1	.055-.057 (1.40-1.45)
2	.057-.059 (1.45-1.50)
3	.059-.061 (1.50-1.55)
4	.061-.063 (1.55-1.60)
5	.063-.065 (1.60-1.65)

2) Install 3rd gear needle bearing, 3rd gear, 3rd gear synchro ring and 2nd-3rd synchro assembly on mainshaft. Then install 2nd gear bushing and mainshaft bearing thrust washer on mainshaft. Install 2nd gear synchro ring, needle bearing, 2nd gear, steel ball and thin thrust washer.

DATSUN 510 5-SPEED (Cont.)

Input Shaft Bearing Snap Rings	
Snap Ring No.	Thickness In. (mm)
1	.059–.061 (1.50–1.56)
2	.061–.064 (1.56–1.62)
3	.064–.066 (1.62–1.68)
4	.066–.069 (1.68–1.74)
5	.069–.071 (1.74–1.80)
6	.071–.073 (1.80–1.86)
7	.073–.076 (1.86–1.92)

3) Press input shaft bearing on mainshaft, ensuring that snap ring is in groove on shaft and clears bearing. Install input shaft bearing spacer and secure input shaft bearing with a snap ring that eliminates clearance. *Refer to Input Shaft Bearing Snap Ring Chart.*

4) Press countergear front and rear bearings onto countergear. When positioning thrust washers on idler gear shaft, make sure brown surfaces are facing toward the gear.

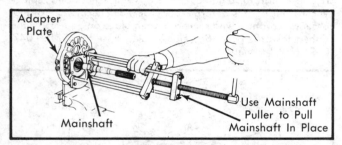

Fig. 9   Installing Mainshaft Assembly

5) Install mainshaft assembly into adapter plate. Place mainshaft nut onto mainshaft. Pull mainshaft assembly into adapter until the thrust washer-to-bearing clearance reaches about .4" (10 mm).

6) Install synchro ring on cone surface of input shaft and install input shaft with pilot bearing on front of mainshaft. Install countergear assembly into adapter plate, with mainshaft in input shaft. Pull mainshaft assembly into adapter plate together with input shaft and countergear assemblies.

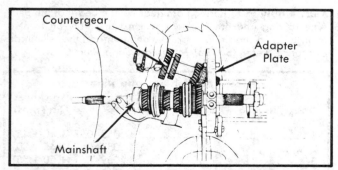

Fig. 10   Installing Countergear to Adapter Plate

7) Press counter 1st gear onto countergear. Place spacer on rear end of counter 1st gear and secure with snap ring.

8) Remove mainshaft nut, then install steel ball and thick thrust washer to rear of mainshaft. Install synchro hub with reverse gear, 1st gear with needle bearing and bushing and idler gear togther with needle bearing.

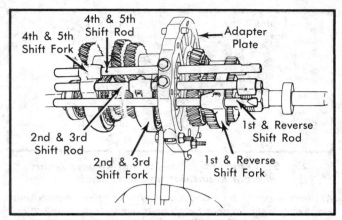

Fig. 11   Installing Shift Forks and Shift Rods

9) Install mainshaft nut, engage 1st and 2nd gears at same time, tighten mainshaft nut. Stake mainshaft nut to groove in mainshaft with punch. Install a .043" (1.1 mm) snap ring to front side of mainshaft end bearing.

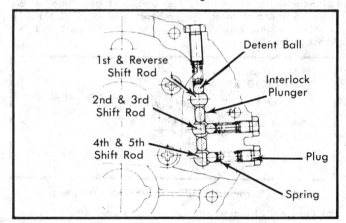

Fig. 12   Cross Section of Adapter Plate Showing Detent Balls, Springs, Plugs and Interlock Plungers

10) Install mainshaft end bearing and install a thick snap ring to mainshaft that eliminates end play. *Refer to Mainshaft End Bearing Snap Ring Chart.*

Mainshaft End Bearing Snap Rings	
Snap Ring No.	Thickness In. (mm)
1	.043 (1.1)
2	.047 (1.2)
3	.051 (1.3)
4	.055 (1.4)

11) Install 1st-Reverse shift rod into its shift fork and into adapter plate. Set shift rod to neutral and insert interlock plunger into adapter plate. Now insert 2nd-3rd shift rod into adapter plate and install 2nd-3rd and 4th-5th shift forks to shift rod.

12) Set 2nd-3rd shift rod to neutral and install interlock plunger into adapter plate. Insert 4th-5th shift rod into adapter plate and its shift fork. Secure all shift forks and shift rods with new retaining pins.

DATSUN 510 5-SPEED (Cont.)

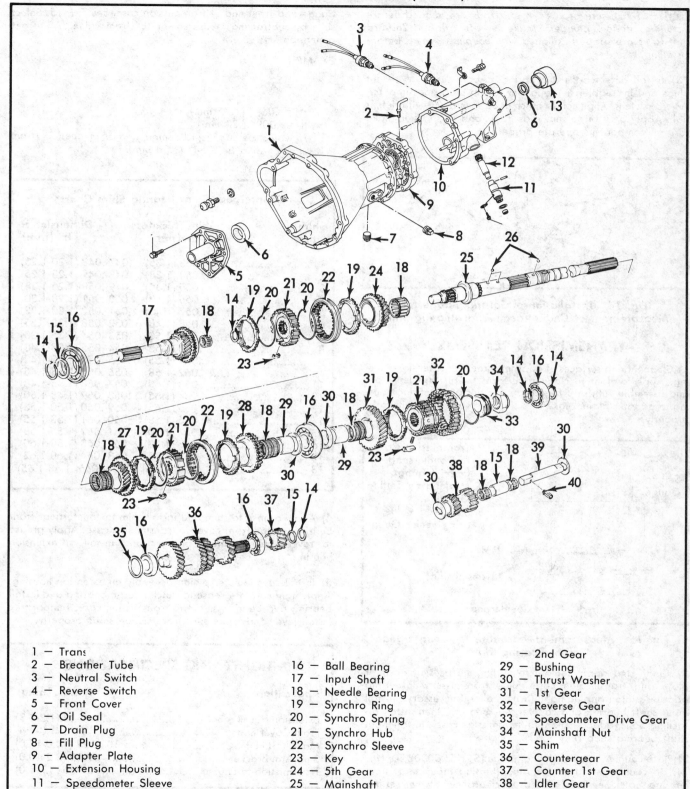

1 — Trans
2 — Breather Tube
3 — Neutral Switch
4 — Reverse Switch
5 — Front Cover
6 — Oil Seal
7 — Drain Plug
8 — Fill Plug
9 — Adapter Plate
10 — Extension Housing
11 — Speedometer Sleeve
12 — Speedometer Driven Gear
13 — Dust Cover
14 — Snap Ring

16 — Ball Bearing
17 — Input Shaft
18 — Needle Bearing
19 — Synchro Ring
20 — Synchro Spring
21 — Synchro Hub
22 — Synchro Sleeve
23 — Key
24 — 5th Gear
25 — Mainshaft
26 — Steel Balls
27 — 3rd Gear

— 2nd Gear
29 — Bushing
30 — Thrust Washer
31 — 1st Gear
32 — Reverse Gear
33 — Speedometer Drive Gear
34 — Mainshaft Nut
35 — Shim
36 — Countergear
37 — Counter 1st Gear
38 — Idler Gear
39 — Idler Shaft
40 — Retaining Pin

Fig. 13 Exploded View of Datsun FS5W63A Transmission Assembly

DATSUN 510 5-SPEED (Cont.)

NOTE — *Make sure grooves in shift rods are aligned before installing interlock plungers. Make sure 4th-5th and 2nd-3rd shift forks are properly aligned with coupling sleeves before installing.*

13) Install detent balls and springs. Apply sealer to detent plugs and install plugs. The longer detent plug goes into 1st-Reverse detent. Align center notch in each shift rod with detent ball. Apply gear oil to shift rods, forks and gears, then make sure all components operate properly.

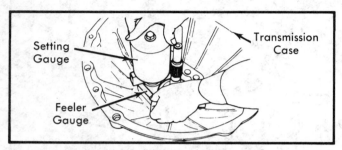

Fig. 14   Installation of Setting Gauge for Measurement of Countergear Front Bearing Shim

TRANSMISSION REASSEMBLY

1) Clean mating surfaces of adapter plate and extension housing. Apply sealant to cleaned surfaces. Align shift lever pin and assemble with shift fork in groove. Install extension housing to adapter plate. Make sure shift lever operates shift forks properly.

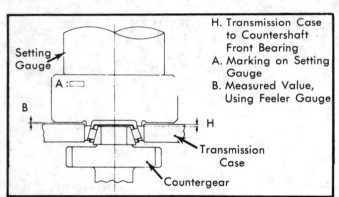

Fig. 15   Measurement Procedure for Countergear Front Bearing Shim

2) Clean and apply sealant to mating surfaces of adapter plate and transmission case. Slide transmission case onto adapter plate (tapping lightly with mallet if necessary). Install input shaft bearing and countergear bearing, then install attaching bolts (adapter plate to transmission case). Install input shaft bearing snap ring.

3) Place counter bearing setting gauge (ST22500000), see Fig. 14, on countergear front bearing (turning input shaft until bearing seats). See Fig. 14. Measure clearance between setting

gauge and front end of transmission case. See Fig. 15. Select shim by subtracting measurement "B" from value "A" to get dimension "H".

EXAMPLE:

$$H = A - B$$

A = .069" (1.75 mm)
B = .009" (.22 mm)
H would be .048" (1.23 mm) and shim needed (from chart) would be .054" (1.38 mm).

Countergear Front Bearing Shim Chart		
Shim No.	Shim Thickness In. (mm)	Dimension H In. (mm)
1	.053 (1.35)	.047-.048 (1.20-1.23)
2	.054 (1.38)	.048-.049 (1.23-1.25)
3	.055 (1.40)	.049-.050 (1.25-1.28)
4	.056 (1.43)	.050-.051 (1.28-1.30)
5	.057 (.145)	.051-.052 (1.30-1.33)
6	.058 (1.48)	.052-.053 (1.33-1.35)
7	.059 (1.50)	.053-.054 (1.35-1.38)
8	.060 (1.53)	.054-.055 (1.38-1.40)
9	.061 (1.55)	.055-.056 (1.40-1.43)
10	.062 (1.58)	.056-.057 (1.43-1.45)
11	.063 (1.60)	.057-.058 (1.45-1.48)
12	.064 (1.63)	.058-.059 (1.48-1.50)
13	.065 (1.65)	.059-.060 (1.50-1.53)
14	.066 (1.68)	.060-.061 (1.53-1.55)
15	.067 (1.70)	.061-.062 (1.55-1.58)
16	.068 (1.73)	.062-.063 (1.58-1.60)
17	.069 (1.75)	.063-.064 (1.60-1.63)
18	.070 (1.78)	.064-.065 (1.63-1.65)

4) Apply grease to shim and install shim to countergear front bearing. Install front cover to transmission case. Apply grease to reverse select return plunger and install in extension housing.

5) Install speedometer pinion assembly on extension housing. Apply light coat of grease to clutch release bearing and install bearing and bearing sleeve to transmission case. Temporarily install lever and make sure transmission shifts properly.

TIGHTENING SPECIFICATIONS

Application	Ft. Lbs. (mkg)
Extension Housing Bolts	9-13 (1.3-1.8)
Front Cover Bolts	9-13 (1.3-1.8)
Mainshaft Nut	101-123 (14.0-17.0)
Shift Arm Bracket	59-72 (8.2-10.0)
Transmission-to-Engine	27-36 (3.7-5.0)

FIAT BRAVA 5-SPEED

DESCRIPTION

Transmission is a 5-speed, fully synchronized, constant mesh type unit. Forward mainshaft gears are helical cut and are in constant contact with corresponding gears on countergear, while reverse gears are spur type and engaged by a sliding reverse idler gear. The case assembly consists of four main parts: Clutch housing, front case (containing front mainshaft and countergear bearings), main case (containing gears, shafts, and rear bearings), and extension housing (containing shifter assembly and speedometer driven gear).

LUBRICATION & ADJUSTMENT

See MANUAL TRANSMISSION SERVICING Section.

TROUBLE SHOOTING

HARD SHIFTING

Improperly adjusted clutch. Weakened synchro insert spring. Face of synchro ring in contact with insert, worn. Cones on synchro ring and rear and gear worn or not in proper contact.

SLIPS OUT OF GEAR

Bearings worn or defective. Excessive play between gears and collars. Play in clutch hub and sliding sleeve. Shift arm worn. Lock ball spring weak or broken.

TRANSMISSION NOISY

Low or incorrect lubricant. Gears or bearings worn or damaged. Worn gears or collars. Worn clutch hub or mainshaft splines. Incorrectly meshed gears.

TRANSMISSION REMOVAL & INSTALLATION

Removal — 1) Disconnect negative battery cable, and clamp securing exhaust pipe to exhaust manifold. Working from inside of vehicle, pry up console center insert, disconnect wiring from cigarette lighter. Pull on selector handle to disengage retainer and remove handle with boot and center console piece attached. Slacken parking brake adjustment and set parking brake to its highest position, then pull parking brake handle from lever. Remove 3 screws holding center console in place and remove console. Remove 3 screws from plastic cover, lift cover slightly and remove rubber boot. Place gear selector in neutral, remove 3 bolts from locking ring and remove locking ring.

2) Raise vehicle on a hoist and disconnect propeller shaft from flexible joint on transmission output flange; place shaft out of the way. Disconnect electrical leads from switch on back of extension housing. Position a transmission jack under transmission and secure with a safety strap, then suitably support engine for transmission removal.

3) Remove starter bolts and position starter out of the way. Remove return spring from clutch release lever, disconnect clutch operating cable from lever, and slide out of transmission case. Disconnect remaining electrical leads from case and speedometer cable from extension housing. Remove flywheel cover from front of clutch housing, and exhaust pipe support from case.

4) Remove bolts attaching transmission mount to body, then withdraw transmission-to-engine attaching bolts. Separate transmission from engine and move rearward. Tilt rear of transmission downward slightly to allow input shaft to clear clutch assembly. Lower transmsision out of vehicle.

CAUTION — *DO NOT allow input shaft to press against clutch diaphragm springs.*

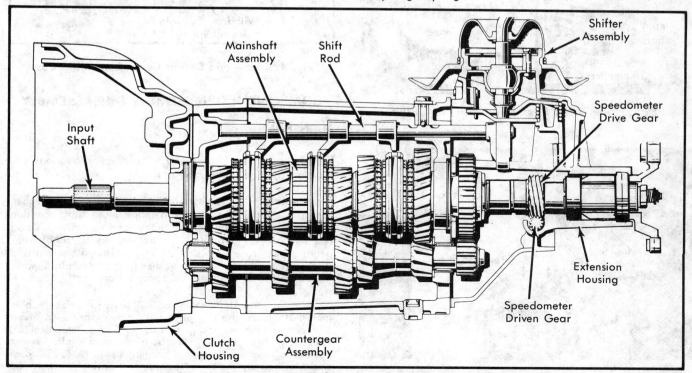

Fig. 1 Cutaway View of Fiat Brava 5-Speed Transmission

FIAT BRAVA 5-SPEED (Cont.)

Installation — Reverse removal procedure and note the following: Fill transmission to correct level with specified lubricant, and adjust clutch pedal free play if necessary.

TRANSMISSION DISASSEMBLY

1) Remove transmission drain plug and drain lubricant. Place transmission in a holding fixture. Remove snap ring, ring, seal, nut and washer from end of output shaft. Remove output shaft yoke. Remove retaining bolt and withdraw speedometer driven gear assembly and gasket from extension housing. Remove shifter assembly and gasket from extension housing. Remove extension housing-to-main case bolts and remove extension housing and gasket from main case.

2) Disengage clutch release lever from ball stud on clutch housing, remove bearing support, then withdraw release lever. Remove clutch housing-to-front case bolts and withdraw clutch housing and gasket. On front of case, remove large snap ring from outer race of front bearing. On rear of case, remove snap ring retaining speedometer drive gear and slide gear off output shaft.

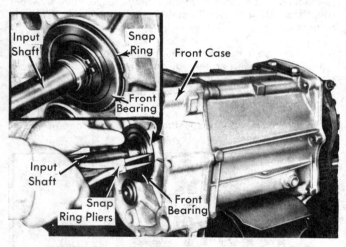

Fig. 2   Removing Bearing-to-Case Snap Ring

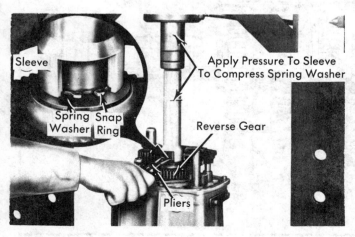

Fig. 3   Using a Press to Remove Mainshaft Snap Ring

3) Place transmission in a press with output shaft upward. Position a suitable sleeve (A.70350) over output shaft and apply pressure to sleeve with press to compress spring washer. Remove output shaft snap ring, release press, and withdraw washer. Move transmission again to holding fixture. Remove bolt and lock washer from reverse shift fork, withdraw fork and reverse idler gear along with spacer from reverse shift rod. Withdraw reverse gear from mainshaft.

4) Remove bolt and lock washer retaining extension on 3rd-4th shift rod and remove extension. Remove snap ring from rear of countergear and withdraw counter reverse gear and washer. Remove detent ball cover from case and withdraw detent balls and springs. Remove key from output shaft and slide main case off assembly. Remove bolts and lock washers from shift forks, withdraw shift rods, then lift mainshaft and countergear out of front housing.

NOTE — *Position shift forks back on shift rods after removal for reassembly reference.*

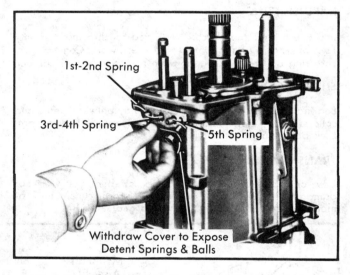

Fig. 4   Removing Detent Cover from Main Case

COMPONENT DISASSEMBLY & REASSEMBLY

MAINSHAFT

NOTE — *On later models, the loose roller bearings are replaced by caged roller bearings.*

Disassembly — **1)** Remove input shaft from mainshaft, then withdraw needle bearings from inside input shaft. Position mainshaft in a soft-jawed vise with rear end upward. Using two screwdrivers opposite one another, pry mainshaft rear bearing inner race from shaft. Withdraw thrust bearing and 2 races, 1st gear and thrust washer from mainshaft. Remove the 122 roller bearings and 2 spacers from shaft.

2) Remove snap ring retaining 1st-2nd synchronizer hub to mainshaft. Place shaft in press with plates positioned under 2nd gear and press 2nd gear and 1st-2nd synchronizer off mainshaft. Remove 134 roller bearings from shaft. Reverse position of shaft in press and position sleeve (A.70159) over shaft and apply pressure to compress spring washer and remove snap ring.

FIAT BRAVA 5-SPEED (Cont.)

Fig. 5 Removing Rear Bearing Inner Race from Shaft

Pry Race Up Using 2 Screwdrivers

3) Withdraw 3rd-4th synchronizer hub from mainshaft, then remove 3rd gear from shaft using a suitable puller. Remove snap ring retaining 5th synchronizer to mainshaft, remove 5th gear from shaft using a suitable puller. Place input shaft in press, position a suitable sleeve (A.70350) over end, apply pressure to spring washer and remove snap ring. Using a puller, withdraw front bearing along with 2 inner races from input shaft.

Inspection — Check mainshaft gears for wear, chipping, or other damage, and also inspect corresponding gears on countergear. Check shafts for wear or distortion; minor distortions can be corrected, however, replace shaft if badly distorted. Inspect synchronizer parts for wear or damage to teeth, splines, and other contacting surfaces. If any part is found worn or damaged, replace.

Mainshaft Specifications

Application	Clearance In. (mm)
Gear Lash	.004 (.10)
Ball Bearing Radial Play①	.002 (.05)
Ball Bearing End Play①	.020 (.50)
Shaft Misalignment①	.002 (.05)
1st Gear and Bushing Clearance	.002-.004 (.05-.10)
2nd & 3rd Gear on Mainshaft	.002-.004 (.05-.10)
Reverse Shaft & Gear Bushing	.002-.004 (.05-.10)

① — Max. Limits

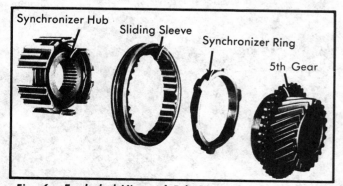

Fig. 6 Exploded View of 5th Gear and Synchronizer

Synchronizer Hub
Sliding Sleeve
Synchronizer Ring
5th Gear

Reassembly — 1) Position front bearing along with two inner races over input shaft and press into place. Position spring washer and snap ring over shaft against bearing, and using

sleeve used in disassembly, compress spring washer and install snap ring.

2) Place mainshaft in soft-jawed vise with front end facing upward. Install 5th gear and synchronizer ring on shaft and against shoulder. Install 5th synchronizer hub onto assembly aligning synchronizer ring with hub and tap hub in place using a brass drift. Install hub retaining snap ring on mainshaft. Place sliding sleeve onto assembly with beveled teeth on sleeve toward 5th gear.

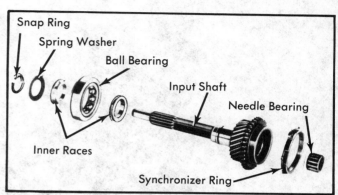

Snap Ring
Spring Washer
Ball Bearing
Input Shaft
Needle Bearing
Inner Races
Synchronizer Ring

Fig. 7 Exploded View of Input Shaft Assembly

3) Install 3rd gear with synchronizer ring onto mainshaft and against 5th synchronizer. Position 3rd-4th synchronizer hub onto mainshaft and tap into place using brass drift. Make sure ring engages synchronizer hub correctly and install sliding sleeve onto hub with grooved side down. Place spring washer and snap ring on mainshaft. Using sleeve tool used for disassembly, compress spring washer and install snap ring.

4) Turn mainshaft so rear end faces upward. Coat 2nd gear area of mainshaft with grease and position 2 rows of 67 roller bearings onto shaft. Install 2nd gear on shaft, being careful not to disturb needle bearings. Place synchronizer ring on 2nd gear, install synchronizer hub onto assembly and tap hub in place using a brass drift. Make sure ring engages synchronizer hub correctly and install snap ring.

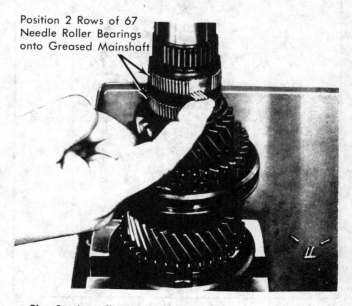

Position 2 Rows of 67 Needle Roller Bearings onto Greased Mainshaft

Fig. 8 Installing 2nd Gear Bearings on Mainshaft

FIAT BRAVA 5-SPEED (Cont.)

5) Install flat washer on mainshaft, then grease 1st gear area of shaft. Position 1 row of 61 roller bearings onto shaft. Install spacer, then position 2nd row of 61 roller bearings onto shaft. Place sliding sleeve on 3rd-4th synchronizer hub, position synchronizer ring into hub, then install 1st gear into assembly. Install thrust washer, thrust bearing and bearing race on shaft. Position rear mainshaft bearing inner race over end of shaft and tap into place using a brass drift.

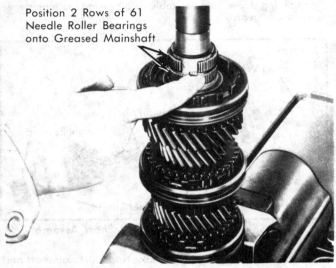

Position 2 Rows of 61 Needle Roller Bearings onto Greased Mainshaft

Fig. 9   Installing 1st Gear Bearings on Mainshaft

TRANSMISSION REASSEMBLY

1) If removed, install countergear roller bearings into front housing and main case. Install mainshaft rear ball bearing into

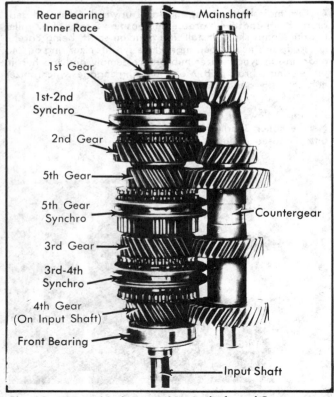

Rear Bearing Inner Race — Mainshaft
1st Gear
1st-2nd Synchro
2nd Gear
5th Gear
5th Gear Synchro
3rd Gear
3rd-4th Synchro
4th Gear (On Input Shaft)
Front Bearing
Countergear
Input Shaft

Fig. 10   Assembled View of Mainshaft and Countergear

Install Ball into Bore and Against 5th Shift Rod
Sliding Sleeve
Shift Rod
Shift Fork

Fig. 11   Installation of 5th Gear Shift Rod

main case. With open end of front housing facing upward, install tabbed thrust washer into slots of case, against bearing. Making sure grooved side of washer is facing gear. Position needle bearing into end of input shaft, then install on mainshaft. Couple mainshaft and countergear, then position both shafts into front housing.

2) Remove Allen screw from detent bore of front housing. Position 5th gear shift fork on 5th gear sliding sleeve, then install 5th gear shift rod through fork and into front housing. Install detent ball into detent bore of housing and against 5th gear shift rod. Place 3rd-4th fork in position on 3rd-4th synchronizer sleeve and install 3rd-4th shift rod through fork and into front housing. Position detent pin into detent bore and against 3rd-4th shift rod. Place 1st-2nd shift fork into position on 1st-2nd sliding sleeve and install 1st-2nd shift rod through fork and into front housing. Install and tighten Allen screw in detent bore of front housing. Tighten all shift fork set screws.

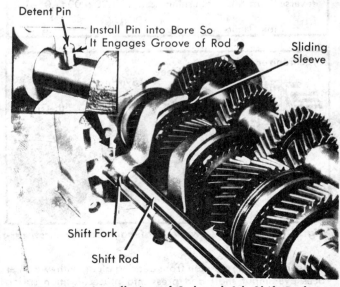

Detent Pin
Install Pin into Bore So It Engages Groove of Rod
Sliding Sleeve
Shift Fork
Shift Rod

Fig. 12   Installation of 3rd and 4th Shift Rod

FIAT BRAVA 5-SPEED (Cont.)

3) Coat countergear thrust washer with grease and position over countergear rear bearing in main case, making sure grooved side of washer will face countergear. Position main case over mainshaft, countergear, and shift rods, and into place on front housing. Install rear mainshaft bearing inner race over mainshaft and tap into place in bearing with a brass drift. Place washer and retainer plate over mainshaft, install reverse idler shaft into case, place tab of retainer plate into groove of reverse idler shaft, then secure plate with retaining screws.

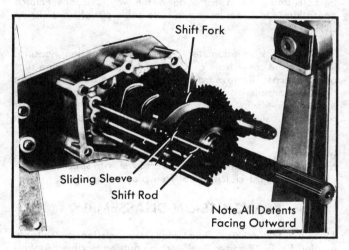

Fig. 13 Installation of 1st and 2nd Shift Rod

4) Install detent balls and springs into detent bores of main case and secure with cover plate. Position counter reverse gear on countergear shaft, place washer over gear, and install snap ring. Install extension for 3rd-4th shift rod onto shift rod,

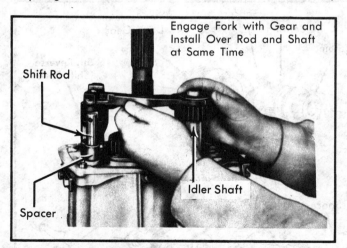

Fig. 14 Installing Reverse Fork and Idler Gear

then install and tighten retaining bolt. Position reverse gear key in mainshaft, install reverse gear onto shaft. Place spacer on reverse shift rod, position reverse shift fork and reverse idler gear onto shift rod and idler shaft, then secure fork to rod with set screw. Position spring washer and snap ring over mainshaft. Using sleeve tool used at disassembly, compress washer and install snap ring.

5) Slide speedometer drive gear and collar over output shaft and secure with snap ring. On front of case, install large front bearing-to-case snap ring in bearing outer race. Install clutch housing with new gasket and seal on front of case. Install retaining bolts, then install clutch lever and release bearing.

6) Install extension housing with new gasket on rear of case. Install and tighten attaching bolts. Place 2 ends of shifter spring in slotted plate in extension housing, turn spring over onto support, then install shifter assembly. Install speedometer driven gear and output flange.

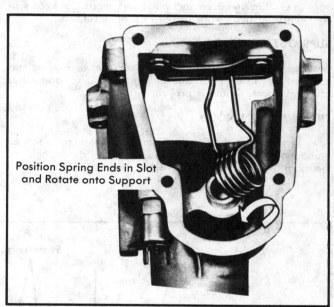

Fig. 15 Installing Shift Lever Spring

TIGHTENING SPECIFICATIONS

Application	Ft. Lbs. (mkg)
Detent Ball Retainer Cover Bolts	18 (2.5)
Clutch Housing-to-Engine Bolts	62 (8.5)
Shift Fork Bolts	15 (2.0)
Retainer Cover Nut	7 (1.0)
Gearshift Support Nut	18 (2.5)

FIAT SPIDER 2000 5-SPEED

DESCRIPTION

Transmission is a 5-speed fully synchronized constant mesh type. Forward gears are helical cut and are in constant mesh with corresponding gears on countershaft. The transmission case is in 4 parts, clutch housing, main case, rear housing and shift tower. The rear housing contains the 5th and reverse gears. The main housing has an oil pan which can be removed for inspection of inner housing and gear components.

LUBRICATION & ADJUSTMENTS

See *MANUAL TRANSMISSION SERVICING* Section.

TROUBLE SHOOTING

HARD SHIFTING

Improperly adjusted clutch. Weakened synchro insert spring. Face of synchro ring in contact with insert, worn. Cones on synchro ring and gear worn or not in proper contact.

SLIPS OUT OF GEAR

Bearings worn or defective. Excessive play between gears and collars. Play in clutch hub and sliding sleeve. Shift arm worn. Lock ball spring weak or broken.

TRANSMISSION NOISY

Low or incorrect lubricant. Gears or bearings worn or damaged. Worn gears or collars. Worn clutch hub or mainshaft splines. Incorrectly meshed gears.

TRANSMISSION REMOVAL & INSTALLATION

Removal — 1) Disconnect negative battery terminal. Working from inside the vehicle, untie leather boot from around shift lever. Remove shift lever extension from stub by giving a sharp tug to lever.

2) Raise vehicle on hoist and disconnect propeller shaft from flexible joint on transmission output flange and position shaft out of the way. Disconnect electrical leads from back-up light switch. Support engine for transmission removal. Remove starter bolts and position starter out of the way. Disconnect clutch operating cable from lever and slide cable out of transmission case.

3) Disconnect speedometer cable from extension housing. Remove front cover from clutch housing and exhaust pipe support from case. Remove transmission mount-to-body bolts, then remove transmission-to-engine attaching bolts and separate transmission from engine. Moving rearward, tilt rear of transmission slightly down to allow input shaft to clear clutch assembly. Lower transmission out of vehicle.

Installation — Reverse removal procedure and note the following: Fill transmission to correct level with specified lubricant, and adjust clutch pedal free play if necessary.

TRANSMISSION DISASSEMBLY

1) Drain transmission fluid, place transmission on suitable holding fixture. Remove 3 self-locking nuts on flexible coupling and remove from flange. Remove clutch return spring and rear crossmember. Remove clutch release fork and throw-out bear-

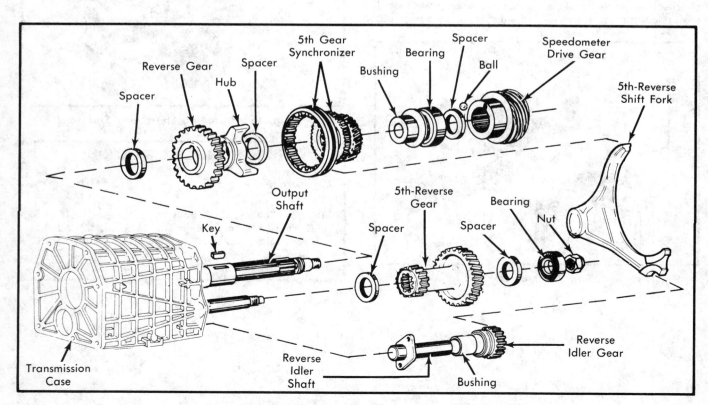

Fig. 1   View Showing 5th-Reverse Gear Components

FIAT SPIDER 2000 5-SPEED (Cont.)

ing. Remove clutch housing bolts and remove housing, gasket and seal.

2) Remove speedometer gear from extension housing. Remove 4 nuts from shift tower and remove tower by pushing shift lever forward until tab on dog clears engaging lever in rear housing. Remove snap ring, spacer, seal and spring from rear yoke. Use suitable socket and remove nut and washer, then use suitable puller to remove yoke from output shaft.

3) Remove 10 nuts from oil pan and remove pan and gasket. Remove 6 nuts from extension housing (1 nut is located inside transmission case and can be removed after oil pan is removed). Remove extension housing from case, as housing is removed, guide gear selector and engaging lever out of fork shafts. Remove gasket and seal from extension housing.

4) Remove bolt from 5th-Reverse shift fork. Slowly remove shaft from case. As shaft is removed, detent ball will drop into case. Lock transmission in 2 gears and loosen nut and bolt on ends of countershaft. Remove cover on side of case and remove detent springs and balls. Remove bolt from 3rd-4th shift fork and slowly remove shaft from case. Remove detent dowels from case and remove 1st-2nd shift fork bolt and remove shaft from case.

5) Remove speedometer drive gear, ball, spacer and bearing from output shaft. Remove nut, bearing and spacer from countershaft. Use a plastic hammer and tap 5th-reverse gear from countershaft, along with reverse sliding gear from its shaft. Remove spacer, bushing, shift fork and 5th gear synchronizer assembly from output shaft. Remove spacer, hub and reverse gear from output shaft.

6) Remove bolt, washer and lock washer from front of countershaft. Using a plastic mallet, tap on front of countershaft until front bearing can be removed from case, then tap on rear bearing until it is free of case. Remove countershaft from case. Remove 3rd-4th shift fork and 1st-2nd shift fork. Remove 3 screws from rear bearing retainer, remove retainer and bearing. Remove mainshaft rearward and out of case. Pull input shaft from front of case.

COMPONENT DISASSEMBLY & REASSEMBLY

MAINSHAFT

Disassembly — 1) Remove 3rd gear synchronizer sleeve. From rear of mainshaft, remove bushing, 1st gear, 1st-2nd synchronizer assembly and 2nd gear. Place mainshaft in press with plates positioned under shoulder of shaft. Position sleeve tool (A.70159) over shaft and apply pressure to compress spr-

ing washer. Remove snap ring, spring washer and synchronizer hub from mainshaft and 3rd gear assembly.

NOTE — *Do not support mainshaft assembly on 3rd gear when compressing spring washer.*

2) Position sleeve tool (A.70159) on 3rd gear assembly and apply pressure to compress spring. Remove snap ring, synchronizer, spring and spring retainer from gear. Remove 3rd gear from mainshaft. Remove synchronizer sleeve from 5th gear assembly. Remove and discard snap ring. Using tool (A.70166), remove synchromesh ring. Remove springs, lock and stop from 5th gear.

NOTE — *Disassembly and reassembly procedures for 1st-2nd gear assemblies are same as 3rd gear except 3rd gear is assembled on mainshaft.*

Inspection — Check mainshaft for straightness. Maximum runout should not exceed .002" (.05 mm). Check splines for damage, remove burrs and nicks with file or emery cloth. Check bearing surfaces for nicks or burrs. Check gears for chipped teeth. Check synchronizer crown teeth for flatness, check sleeves for nicks or burrs. Check 1st gear-to-bushing clearance. It should be .002-.004" (.05-.10 mm). Replace if worn. Check 2nd-3rd gear-to-mainshaft clearance. Clearance should be .002-.004" (.05-.10 mm). Replace if worn.

Reassembly — 1) Lightly coat all parts with oil. Install ONLY 3rd gear on mainshaft. On 1st, 2nd and 3rd gear assemblies, install spring retainer on gear with cup side facing away from gear. Install spring and synchronizer with small end of synchronizer facing away from gear.

2) Using sleeve tool (A.70159), compress spring assembly and install snap ring. Make sure synchronizer sleeve can be moved along gear and springs back when released. Place 5th gear with gear side down on bench. Install lock into slot in gear. Install stop and 2 springs.

3) Carefully spread synchromesh ring and install around assembled parts so open end is positioned over stop. Using tool (A.70166), install new snap ring with dog end installed in slot of gear. Install synchronizer sleeve. Place mainshaft in press with plates positioned under shoulder of shaft.

4) Install synchronizer hub, spring washer and snap ring. Position sleeve tool (A.70159) over shaft and apply pressure to compress spring washer, then seat snap ring in groove. Remove mainshaft assembly from press.

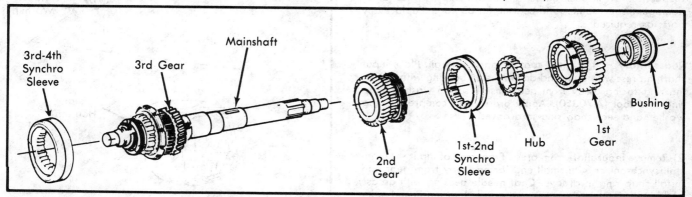

Fig. 2 Exploded View of Mainshaft Assembly

FIAT SPIDER 2000 5-SPEED (Cont.)

5) Install 2nd gear assembly, synchronizer sleeve and hub, 1st gear assembly and bushing on output end of mainshaft. Carefully assemble all parts making sure synchronizer sleeve straddles synchronizers on 1st and 2nd gear assemblies. Install synchronizer sleeve on 3rd gear assembly.

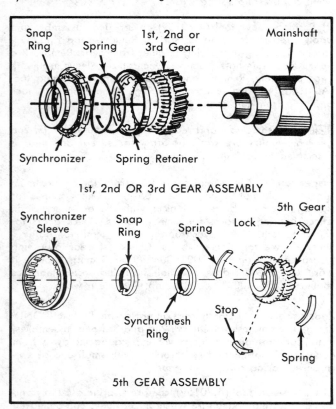

1st, 2nd OR 3rd GEAR ASSEMBLY

5th GEAR ASSEMBLY

Fig. 3   Exploded View of Synchronizer Assemblies

INPUT SHAFT

Disassembly — Using press and tool (A.70350), compress spring washer on front of input shaft and remove snap ring. Remove input shaft from press. Remove spring washer and bearing. From rear of input shaft remove snap ring, synchronizer, needle bearing, washer and snap ring.

Inspection — Inspect gears for wear, chipping, or other damage. Inspect splines and bearing for damage. Replace any parts as required.

Reassembly — 1) Lightly coat all parts with oil. Place input shaft in press with gear end down. Install bearing with retaining ring facing away from gear. Install spring washer, snap ring and tool (A.70350). Apply pressure to compress spring washer and seat snap ring in groove.

2) Remove input shaft from press. From rear of input shaft, install synchronizer with small end facing away from gear and install snap ring in groove. Coat needle bearing with grease and install snap ring, washer and needle bearing in end of input shaft.

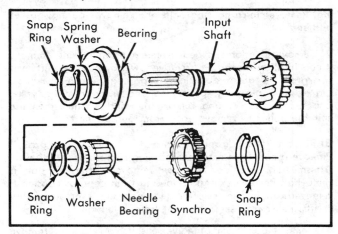

Fig. 4   View of Input Shaft

ENGAGING LEVER

NOTE — *Disassemble engaging lever ONLY if damaged or binding.*

Disassembly — 1) Remove 2 bolts and lock washers and remove attaching cover and gasket. Slowly slide engaging lever rod out side of rear housing.

2) As rod is withdrawn, carefully remove spring, spring retainer, engaging lever, spring and thrust washer. Remove thrust washer from rear housing.

Inspection — Check engaging rod lever for straightness, excessive wear and/or damage. Check that dog is not bent or damaged. Replace if worn, damaged or bent. Check all springs for tension and/or wear. Replace as required.

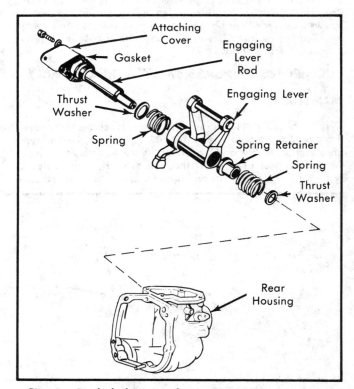

Fig. 5   Exploded View of Engaging Lever Assembly

FIAT SPIDER 2000 5-SPEED (Cont.)

Reassembly — 1) Install thrust washer in rear housing. Slowly install engaging lever rod and assemble thrust washer, spring, engaging lever, spring retainer and spring on engaging lever rod.

2) Install attaching cover with new gasket, lock washers and bolts and tighten bolts. Check side-to-side travel of engaging lever making sure it returns to center position when released.

SHIFT TOWER

NOTE — *Disassemble shift tower ONLY if damaged or binding and only to the extent of replacing damaged parts.*

Disassembly — 1) Remove shifter boot. Remove 4 nuts and lock washers and remove cover and gasket. Do not remove reverse lockout screw or lock nut unless damaged. Remove 3 nuts and lock washers and remove bearing cover.

2) Remove nut and washer from bearing and remove bearing, socket cover, cover and spring. Lift shift lever from shift tower and remove spring clip. Remove bolt and lock washer and slide shift shaft out rear of shift tower, then remove dog. Remove bearing cap and bearing only if worn or damaged.

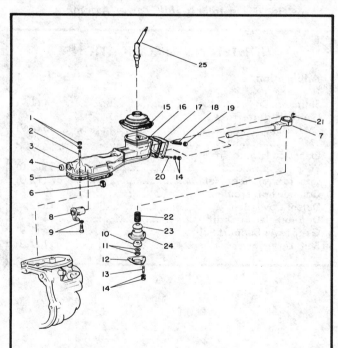

1 — Nut and Lock Washer	14 — Nut and Lock Washer
2 — Stud	15 — Shifter Boot
3 — Shift Tower	16 — Gasket
4 — Bearing Cap	17 — Cover
5 — Gasket	18 — Reverse Lockout Screw
6 — Bearing	19 — Lock Nut
7 — Shift Shaft	20 — Stud
8 — Dog	21 — Spring Clip
9 — Bolt and Lock Washer	22 — Spring
10 — Bearing	23 — Cover
11 — Nut and Washer	24 — Bearing Socket
12 — Bearing Cover	25 — Shift Lever
13 — Stud	

Fig. 6   Exploded View of Shift Tower Assembly

Inspection — Check all parts for excessive wear and/or damage. Check that shifter shaft is not bent. Check for free movement without binding or excessive play. Replace parts as required.

Reassembly — 1) Install bearing and bearing cap if removed. Install shifter shaft into shift tower and into dog. Install lock washer and bolt and tighten bolt. Install spring clip on shifter shaft and install shift lever.

2) Install spring, cover, socket cover, bearing, washer and nut and tighten nut. Install bearing cover, 3 lock washers and nuts and tighten nuts. If reverse lockout screw was removed, install screw and lock nut in shift tower.

3) Adjust by placing shift lever in 5th-Reverse gate position. Screw in reverse lockout screw until it contacts shift lever, then back out 3 turns and tighten lock nut. Install cover with new gasket and install 4 lock washers and nuts and tighten nuts. Install shifter boot.

TRANSMISSION REASSEMBLY

1) Insert mainshaft into case. Make sure there is a bearing in input shaft end, then install shaft into case. Place output shaft rear bearing into position, install bearing retainer and fasten with 3 screws, tighten screws with impact driver. Check for free movement of input and output shaft. Check operation of synchro assemblies.

2) Install 1st-2nd and 3rd-4th shift forks in their respective position on mainshaft. Install countershaft into case. Install end bearings, install washer and bolt on front of countershaft and tighten.

3) Install reverse idler shaft on case and tighten screws with impact driver. Place spacer and key on output shaft. Slide reverse gear, hub and spacer on output shaft. Install spacer on countershaft. Partially slide 5th-reverse gear assembly on countershaft and 5th gear on output shaft. Place 5th-reverse shift fork on its respective sleeve. Slide gears into position on shafts, tap on 5th-reverse gear until it is fully seated on countershaft.

4) Place spacer, bearing and nut on rear of countershaft, finger tighten the nut. Place bushing, bearing, spacer, ball and speedometer drive gear on rear of output shaft. Install 1st-2nd shift shaft into case, install bolt and tighten to 14 ft. lbs. (1.9 mkg). Install long detent dowel. Install 3rd-4th shift shaft into case, install detent, install bolt and tighten to 14 ft. lbs. (1.9 mkg).

5) Install 2 detent balls and springs for shift shafts, then install side cover. Lock transmission gears, tighten countershaft front bolt to 87 ft. lbs. (12.0 mkg). Tighten rear countershaft nut to 69 ft. lbs. (9.5 mkg). Install 5th-reverse shift shaft, install bolt and tighten to 14 ft. lbs. (1.9 mkg).

FIAT SPIDER 2000 5-SPEED (Cont.)

6) Install new seal in extension housing and place new extension housing gasket in place on transmission. Move selector lever rearward, guide gear selector lever into shift shafts as housing is mated to transmission. Install bolts and tighten to specifications. Coat rear output splines with grease and install yoke. Install washer and nut, tighten nut to 108 ft. lbs. (14.9 mkg), then place spring, seal, spacer and snap ring on rear of output shaft, coat seal with grease.

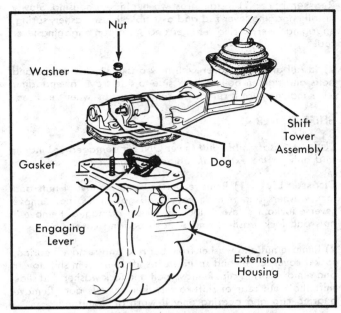

Fig. 8 Installing Shift Tower Assembly

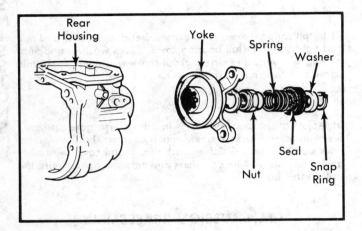

Fig. 7 Exploded View of Yoke Assembly

7) Install new gasket for shift tower on extension housing. Move shift lever forward, then place shift tower on extension housing, move shift lever rearward to engage dog on engaging lever, install washers and nuts, tighten to specifications.

8) Install new clutch housing gasket and seal. Coat spring washer with grease and install on input shaft. Install bolts and tighten. Install release fork, throw-out bearing and return spring. Refill transmission with SAE 90 gear oil to proper fluid level.

TIGHTENING SPECIFICATIONS

Application	Ft. Lbs. (mkg)
Shift Fork Bolt	14 (1.9)
Clutch Hsg.-to-Trans.	
M10	36 (4.9)
M8	18 (2.4)
Extension Hsg.-to-Trans.	18 (2.4)
Yoke Nut	108 (15.0)
Countershaft Rear Nut	87 (12.0)
Countershaft Front Bolt	69 (9.5)
Detent Cover Bolt	18 (2.4)
Dog-to-Selector Shaft Bolt	14 (1.9)
Gear Lever Support Bolt	14 (1.9)
Shift Lever Lower Locking Nut	11 (1.5)

LUV 4-SPEED

Pickup (Exc. 4-WD)

DESCRIPTION

Transmission is a floor shifted, fully synchronized 4-Speed unit with block ring type synchronizers and a sliding mesh type reverse. The unit consists of a case with integral clutch housing, center support, rear extension, and gears. A shifter cover, located on top of rear extension housing, contains the transmission control mechanism. The case, center support and rear extension case are aluminum alloy to reduce weight.

LUBRICATION & ADJUSTMENT

See *MANUAL TRANSMISSION SERVICING* Section.

TROUBLE SHOOTING

HARD SHIFTING

Improperly adjusted clutch. Weakened insert spring. Face of blocker ring, in contact with insert, worn. Cones on blocker ring and gear worn or not in proper contact.

SLIPS OUT OF GEAR

Bearings worn or defective. Excessive play between gears and collars. Play in clutch hub and sliding sleeve. Shift arm worn. Lock ball spring weak or broken.

TRANSMISSION NOISY

Low or incorrect lubricant. Gears or bearings worn or damaged. Worn gears or collars. Worn clutch hub or mainshaft splines. Incorrectly meshed gears.

TRANSMISSION REMOVAL & INSTALLATION

Removal — 1) Disconnect negative battery terminal. Slide gearshift boot up on lever and remove lever attaching bolts, then withdraw lever. Remove starter attaching bolts and place starter out of way.

2) Raise vehicle on hoist. Disconnect exhaust pipe hanger at transmission, speedometer cable at extension housing, battery ground cable at transmission and propeller shaft from rear axle. Remove propeller shaft and either drain transmission fluid or install plug in extension housing to prevent fluid loss.

3) Remove return spring from clutch fork. Remove bolts attaching flywheel cover and remove frame bracket-to-transmission rear mount bolts. Raise engine and transmission as required and remove crossmember-to-frame bracket bolts. Remove rear mounting from extension housing.

4) Lower engine and transmission assembly and support rear of engine with support stand. Disconnect electrical connectors at back-up light and CRS (Federal models) switches. Remove transmission-to-engine attaching bolts. Pull transmission straight back until disengaged from clutch, tip front of transmission down and remove transmission from vehicle.

Installation — Reverse removal procedure and note the following: Adjust clutch cable and clutch pedal height if required. Refill transmission to correct fluid level.

TRANSMISSION DISASSEMBLY

1) Disconnect retaining springs from throw-out bearing and remove bearing, dust cover and clutch fork. Remove 4 front bearing retainer bolts and remove retainer, gasket and spring washer.

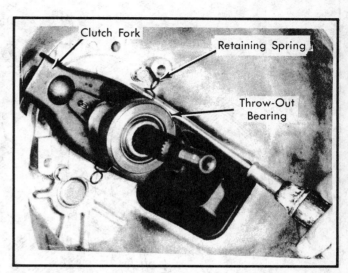

Fig. 1   Removing Throw-Out Bearing & Clutch Fork

2) Remove speedometer gear attaching bolt and take out speedometer driven gear assembly. Unscrew shifter cover bolts and remove cover and gasket.

3) Remove back-up light switch and CRS switch (if equipped). Remove rear extension attaching bolts, then remove extension and gasket.

4) Remove thrust washers and reverse idler gear from reverse idler gear shaft, then remove snap rings, speedometer drive gear and key from mainshaft.

5) Drive out roll pin from reverse shifter fork and remove shifter fork and reverse gear. Remove snap ring from outer edge

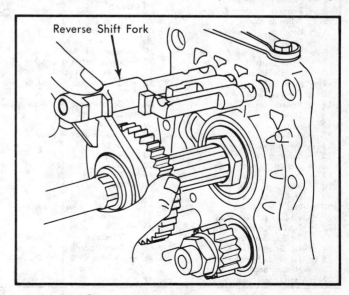

Fig. 2   Removing Reverse Gear

Manual Transmissions

LUV 4-SPEED (Cont.)

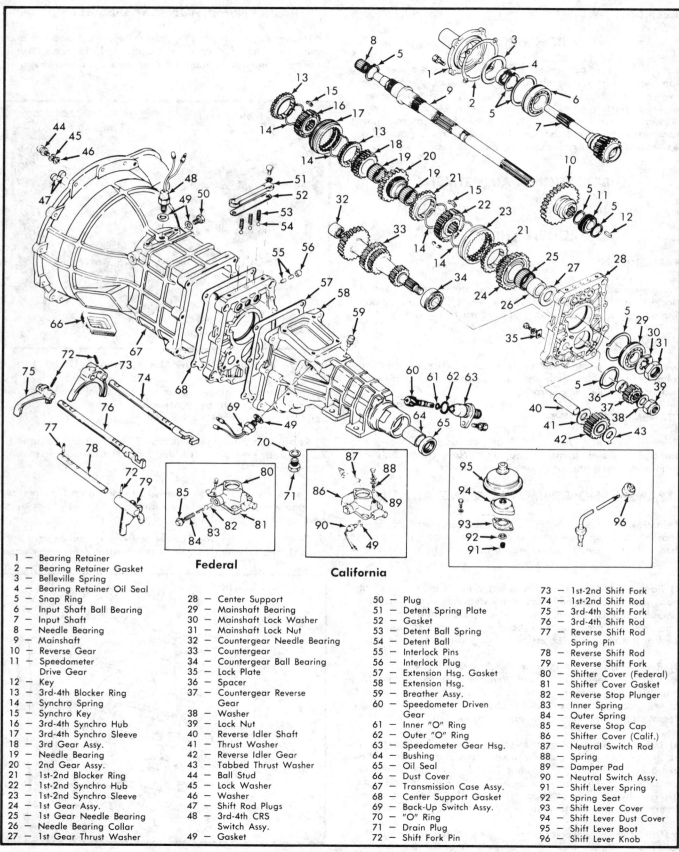

1 — Bearing Retainer	28 — Center Support	50 — Plug
2 — Bearing Retainer Gasket	29 — Mainshaft Bearing	51 — Detent Spring Plate
3 — Belleville Spring	30 — Mainshaft Lock Washer	52 — Gasket
4 — Bearing Retainer Oil Seal	31 — Mainshaft Lock Nut	53 — Detent Ball Spring
5 — Snap Ring	32 — Countergear Needle Bearing	54 — Detent Ball
6 — Input Shaft Ball Bearing	33 — Countergear	55 — Interlock Pins
7 — Input Shaft	34 — Countergear Ball Bearing	56 — Interlock Plug
8 — Needle Bearing	35 — Lock Plate	57 — Extension Hsg. Gasket
9 — Mainshaft	36 — Spacer	58 — Extension Hsg.
10 — Reverse Gear	37 — Countergear Reverse	59 — Breather Assy.
11 — Speedometer	Gear	60 — Speedometer Driven
Drive Gear	38 — Washer	Gear
12 — Key	39 — Lock Nut	61 — Inner "O" Ring
13 — 3rd-4th Blocker Ring	40 — Reverse Idler Shaft	62 — Outer "O" Ring
14 — Synchro Spring	41 — Thrust Washer	63 — Speedometer Gear Hsg.
15 — Synchro Key	42 — Reverse Idler Gear	64 — Bushing
16 — 3rd-4th Synchro Hub	43 — Tabbed Thrust Washer	65 — Oil Seal
17 — 3rd-4th Synchro Sleeve	44 — Ball Stud	66 — Dust Cover
18 — 3rd Gear Assy.	45 — Lock Washer	67 — Transmission Case Assy.
19 — Needle Bearing	46 — Washer	68 — Center Support Gasket
20 — 2nd Gear Assy.	47 — Shift Rod Plugs	69 — Back-Up Switch Assy.
21 — 1st-2nd Blocker Ring	48 — 3rd-4th CRS	70 — "O" Ring
22 — 1st-2nd Synchro Hub	Switch Assy.	71 — Drain Plug
23 — 1st-2nd Synchro Sleeve	49 — Gasket	72 — Shift Fork Pin
24 — 1st Gear Assy.		
25 — 1st Gear Needle Bearing		
26 — Needle Bearing Collar		
27 — 1st Gear Thrust Washer		

73 — 1st-2nd Shift Fork	
74 — 1st-2nd Shift Rod	
75 — 3rd-4th Shift Fork	
76 — 3rd-4th Shift Rod	
77 — Reverse Shift Rod	
Spring Pin	
78 — Reverse Shift Rod	
79 — Reverse Shift Fork	
80 — Shifter Cover (Federal)	
81 — Shifter Cover Gasket	
82 — Reverse Stop Plunger	
83 — Inner Spring	
84 — Outer Spring	
85 — Reverse Stop Cap	
86 — Shifter Cover (Calif.)	
87 — Neutral Switch Rod	
88 — Spring	
89 — Damper Pad	
90 — Neutral Switch Assy.	
91 — Shift Lever Spring	
92 — Spring Seat	
93 — Shift Lever Cover	
94 — Shift Lever Dust Cover	
95 — Shift Lever Boot	
96 — Shift Lever Knob	

Federal

California

Fig. 3 Exploded View of LUV 4-Speed Transmission Assembly

LUV 4-SPEED (Cont.)

of input shaft bearing. Slide off center support assembly from transmission case. Drive out roll pins from 3rd-4th and 1st-2nd shift forks.

NOTE — *Be careful not to damage shift forks when removing roll pins.*

6) Remove detent spring plate, springs and balls from center support. Slide out 1st-2nd and 3rd-4th shift rods and remove shift forks. Remove reverse shift rod through front of case as it is fitted with detent interlock pins located between shifter rods in center support.

7) Move both synchros rearward to lock mainshaft. It may be necessary to tap synchros with hammer handle to engage them both. Straighten tab on lock washer and remove lock nut and washer from mainshaft.

8) Remove locking nut, washer, countergear reverse gear and collar from rear of countergear. Remove countergear bearing snap ring by expanding snap ring and tapping on front face of center support. Remove mainshaft rear bearing snap ring and remove center support.

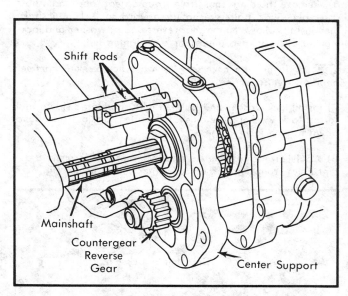

Fig. 4 Removing Center Support from Transmission Case

COMPONENT DISASSEMBLY & REASSEMBLY

MAINSHAFT

Disassembly — 1) Separate input shaft, needle bearing and blocker ring from mainshaft. Using adapter plate tool (J-22912) and an arbor press, remove rear bearing from mainshaft. Remove thrust washer, 1st gear, needle bearing, collar and blocker ring.

2) Remove 1st-2nd synchro assembly. Remove 2nd gear, blocker ring and needle bearing. Remove snap ring, 3rd-4th synchro assembly and blocker ring. Remove 3rd gear and needle bearings. Remove snap ring from input shaft and press bearing off shaft. Using adapter plate tool (J-22912) and an arbor press, remove countergear bearing from countergear.

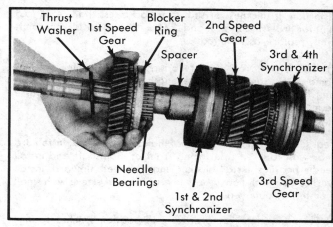

Fig. 5 Mainshaft Components

Inspection — 1) Check mainshaft for wear, scoring or excessive runout. Maximum mainshaft runout is .002" (.05 mm). Check all gear teeth and splines for wear and/or damage. Check all bearings for smooth operation.

2) Check synchro assemblies for wear by holding blocker ring against cone section of gear and measuring clearance. If clearance exceeds .032" (.08 mm), replace blocker ring. Measure inside diameter of 1st, 2nd and 3rd gears. Measurements should be 1.773-1.776" (45.0-45.1 mm) for 1st gear; 1.615-1.619" (41.0-41.1 mm) for 2nd and 3rd gear.

3) Measure width of 1st gear and collar. If more than .0197" (.5 mm) clearance, replace gear. Measure outside diameter of reverse idler gear shaft and inside diameter of gear bushing. Shaft diameter is .866" (22.0 mm). If more than .006" (.15 mm) clearance, replace bushing. Measure clearance between synchro-clutch hub splines and mainshaft splines in normal direction of rotation.

4) If clearance exceeds .008" (.2 mm), replace synchro-clutch hub. Check grooves in shift arms and blocks for wear and/or

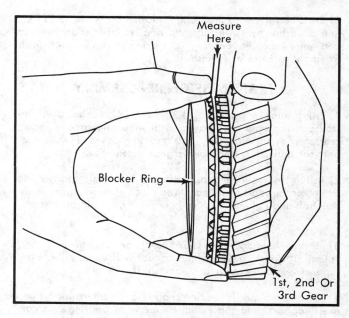

Fig. 6 Measuring Blocker Ring Clearance

Manual Transmissions

LUV 4-SPEED (Cont.)

distortion. If thickness of shift arm pad is less than .256" (6.5 mm) for 3rd-4th shift arm and .276" (7.0 mm) for all other shift arms, replace as required.

5) Check shift rod detent springs for weakening and/or damage. Measure spring free length. If less than 1.083" (27.5 mm) for all forward gears, or 1.051" (26.7 mm) for reverse gear, replace springs as required.

Reassembly — 1) Hold front of mainshaft upward. Install 3rd gear with tapered side facing front of mainshaft and install needle bearing. Install blocker ring with teeth upward. Install synchro hub with heavy boss toward face of sleeve with small chamfer on outer edge.

2) Place keys into key grooves and position synchro springs into hole inside face of hub. Make sure hub and sleeve slide smoothly. Install 3rd-4th synchro assembly on mainshaft with face of sleeve with small chamfer on outer edge facing rearward. Install snap ring.

3) Hold rear of mainshaft upward. Install 2nd gear and needle bearing with taper surface of gear facing rearward on mainshaft. Install blocker ring with teeth downward. Install 1st-2nd synchro assembly with small chamfer on sleeve facing front of mainshaft. Install synchro hub with chamfer on inner edge toward face of sleeve with large chamfer on outer edge.

4) Place keys into key grooves and position synchro springs into hole in either side face of hub. Make sure hub and sleeve slide smoothly. Install blocker ring with teeth rearward. Install collar, needle bearing and 1st gear with tapered side of gear facing front of mainshaft.

5) Install 1st gear thrust washer with grooved side facing 1st gear on mainshaft. Place rear bearing on mainshaft with snap ring groove facing front of mainshaft. Press bearing onto shaft using adapter plate tool (J-22912) and an arbor press. Place input shaft bearing on input shaft with snap ring groove facing front of input shaft.

6) Press bearing onto shaft using adapter plate tool (J-22912) and an arbor press. Install snap ring on input shaft bearing and install needle bearing, blocker ring and input shaft assembly to front of mainshaft.

TRANSMISSION REASSEMBLY

1) Using adapter plate tool (J-22912) and an arbor press, install bearing onto countergear with snap ring groove facing rear of transmission. Install snap rings in grooves of center support for mainshaft and countergear assemblies.

2) Install reverse idler gear shaft with lock plate groove side into center support from rear. Install lock plate into groove, install bolt and tighten. Mesh countergear with mainshaft assembly.

3) Install holding tool (J-26545-5) on countergear and mainshaft assembly. Place holding tool in vise and slide center support on countergear and mainshaft.

4) Expand mainshaft bearing snap ring in center support and press support onto shaft until countergear bearing is in contact with its snap ring.

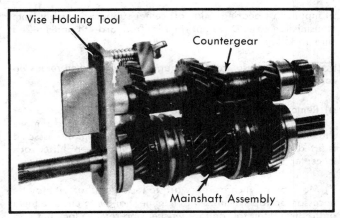

Fig. 7   Installing Center Support

5) Expand countergear bearing snap ring and press center support further until the mainshaft and countergear snap rings snap into their grooves.

6) Remove holding tool from countergear and mainshaft assembly. Slide both synchros rearward to lock mainshaft, then install collar, countergear reverse gear, washer and locking nut on rear of countergear and tighten nut.

NOTE — *It may be necessary to tap synchros with hammer handle to engage gears.*

7) Install lock washer and lock nut with chamfered side of nut facing lock washer on mainshaft. Tighten lock nut and bend down tab on lock washer.

8) Apply grease to 2 detent interlock pins and insert into detent holes from middle hole of center support. *See Fig. 8.*

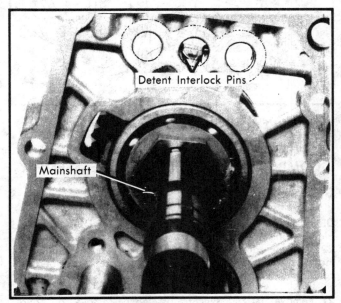

Fig. 8   Installing Detent Interlock Pins

9) Place shift forks into position on synchronizer grooves then install 1st-2nd and 3rd-4th shifter rods through holes in center support and shift forks from front side of center support.

LUV 4-SPEED (Cont.)

10) Insert three detent balls and springs in center support, then install gasket and detent plate and tighten bolts to specification. Install roll pins in 1st-2nd and 3rd-4th shift fork.

NOTE — *Use block of wood to support ends of shift rods when driving in roll pins.*

11) Place gasket on transmission case and install center support with mainshaft, countergear and input shaft assembly, making sure to align dowel pin holes with dowel pins correctly. Install input shaft bearing snap ring.

12) Assemble reverse shifter fork to reverse gear and install on reverse shifter rod from rear of center support. Install roll pin in reverse shifter fork.

13) Install reverse idler tabbed thrust washer with tab pointing downward and into notch in center support. Install reverse idler gear with undercut teeth rearward.

Fig. 9 Installing Reverse Idler Gear

Thrust Washer Tab

14) Install speedometer drive gear snap ring and Woodruff key on mainshaft, then install speedometer drive gear on shaft, aligning gear with key. Install snap ring.

15) Coat outer reverse idler thrust washer with grease and install in extension housing with tab pointing downward into notch in housing. Check gear backlash. It should not exceed .016" (.4 mm) for all gears. If not, replace gears as required.

16) Place gasket on center support and install extension housing. Make sure to align dowel pin correctly. Install and tighten bolts. Install back-up light and CRS (Federal models) switches.

17) Install gasket and gear shift cover on extension housing and tighten bolts to specification, then install speedometer driven gear to rear extension and tighten bolt.

18) Install spring washer on shaft, with dished face toward input shaft gear bearing. Install input shaft bearing retainer gasket and retainer. Tighten bolts.

NOTE — *The 2 shorter bolts are used on countergear front bearing side of bearing retainer.*

19) Install dust cover, clutch fork and throw-out bearing with retaining springs. Install drain plug and refill transmission with correct fluid.

TIGHTENING SPECIFICATIONS

Application	Ft. Lbs. (mkg)
Countergear Lock Nut	108 (14.9)
Mainshaft Lock Nut	94 (13.0)
Detent Plate Bolts	14 (1.9)
Extension Housing-to-Center Support Bolts	27 (3.7)
Shift Cover Bolts	14 (1.9)
Input Shaft Bearing Retainer	14 (1.9)

Manual Transmissions

LUV 4-SPEED WITH INTEGRAL TRANSFER CASE

Pickup (4-WD)

DESCRIPTION

Transmission is a floor shifted, fully synchronized 4-speed unit with block ring type synchronizers and a sliding mesh type reverse. This unit consists of a transmission case with integral clutch housing, center support, transfer case with transfer side case and gears. A shifter cover, located on top of transfer case, contains the transmission control mechanism. Another shifter cover located on the transfer side case contains the range and four wheel drive shifting mechanism.

LUBRICATION & ADJUSTMENT

See *MANUAL TRANSMISSION SERVICING* Section.

TROUBLE SHOOTING

HARD SHIFTING

Improperly adjusted clutch. Weakened insert spring. Face of blocker ring, in contact with insert, worn. Cones on blocker ring and gear worn or not in proper contact.

SLIPS OUT OF GEAR

Bearings worn or defective. Excessive play between gears and collars. Play in clutch hub and sliding sleeve. Shift arm worn. Lock ball spring weak or broken.

TRANSMISSION NOISY

Low or incorrect lubricant. Gears or bearings worn or damaged. Worn gears or collars. Worn clutch hub or mainshaft splines. Incorrectly meshed gears.

TRANSMISSION REMOVAL & INSTALLATION

Removal — 1) Disconnect battery negative terminal. Slide gearshift boot up on lever and remove lever attaching bolts. Disconnect transfer gear shift lever return spring. Remove both gear shift levers.

2) Remove starter attaching bolts and lay starter out of way. Raise vehicle on hoist. Disconnect exhaust pipe from manifold and at hanger on transmission. Disconnect speedometer cable at transfer case, ground cable at transmission and propeller shaft from rear axle. Disconnect front propeller shaft and remove both shafts from vehicle.

3) Disconnect clutch fork return spring, then remove clutch cable from hooked portion of fork. Pull cable forward through stiffener bracket. Remove the lower 2 bolts to stone guard, then remove the 3 bolts attaching transmission rear mount to frame.

4) Raise engine and transmission just enough so the 4 crossmember-to-frame bolts can be removed. Remove the 2 transfer case rear mounting bolts, then remove bolts attaching transfer side case to transfer case and remove transfer side case.

NOTE — *Be sure not to lose shift rod detent spring and ball from transfer side case.*

5) Remove stud bolt from transfer case then lower engine and transmission, supporting rear of engine. Disconnect electrical connectors at back-up light and CRS (Federal models) switches. Remove 4 bolts holding shift cover to transfer case and remove cover and gasket.

6) Remove all bolts attaching transmission to engine then remove transmission with transfer case. To ease removal, turn transfer case side of transmission downward, slide transmission backward until clear of clutch, then tilt front of transmission down and slide forward and out of vehicle.

Installation — To install, reverse removal procedure while noting the following: Install transmission with transmission shift lever in neutral and transfer case shift lever in 4H position. Fill transmission with suitable amount and type of lubricant and make sure clutch fork and pedal height are to specifications.

TRANSMISSION DISASSEMBLY

1) Remove retainer springs, throw-out bearing and clutch fork. Remove 4 bolts holding bearing retainer to transmission case and remove bearing retainer, gasket and spring washer. Remove speedometer gear bolt, bushing and driven gear assembly.

2) Remove back-up light and CRS (Federal models) switches. Remove snap ring from input shaft bearing. Remove 8 bolts holding transfer case, center support and transmission case together. Separate transmission case from center support and transfer case.

3) Remove pin from reverse shifter fork. Remove 4 bolts attaching transfer countershaft lock plate, then remove lock plate and shim. Remove center support from transfer case.

4) Drive pins out from 3rd-4th and 1st-2nd shift forks. Remove detent spring plate from center support, then remove detent springs and balls. Remove 1st-2nd and 3rd-4th shift rods from center support and then remove shift forks. Remove reverse shifter rod rearward.

NOTE — *When shifter rods are removed, be careful not to lose detent interlock pins. Pins are located between shifter rods in center support.*

5) Move both synchronizers rearward to prevent mainshaft from turning. Remove mainshaft lock nut with spacer. Remove transfer clutch hub, transfer input gear, roller bearing, collar, thrust washer, shim and reverse gear from rear of mainshaft.

6) Remove countergear lock nut, washer and collar from rear of countergear. Remove countergear snap ring by inserting snap ring pliers into hole in center support. Tap on front of center support while expanding snap ring. Remove center support while expanding mainshaft rear bearing snap ring.

COMPONENT DISASSEMBLY & REASSEMBLY

MAINSHAFT

Disassembly — 1) Separate input shaft gear, needle bearing and blocker ring from mainshaft assembly. Using bearing removal tool (J-22912) and an arbor press, remove rear bearing from mainshaft.

LUV 4-SPEED WITH INTEGRAL TRANSFER CASE (Cont.)

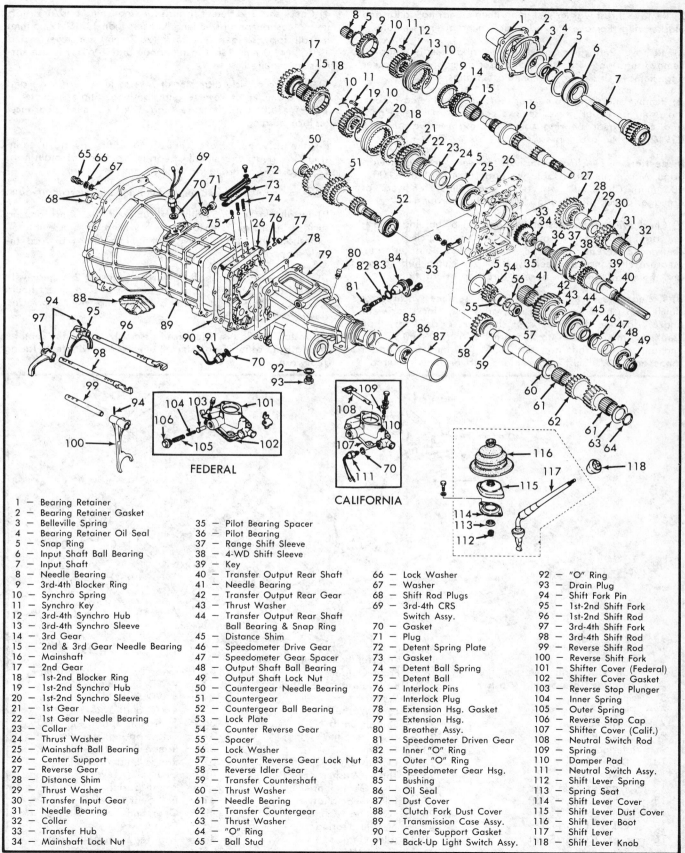

FEDERAL

CALIFORNIA

1 — Bearing Retainer			
2 — Bearing Retainer Gasket			
3 — Belleville Spring	35 — Pilot Bearing Spacer	66 — Lock Washer	92 — "O" Ring
4 — Bearing Retainer Oil Seal	36 — Pilot Bearing	67 — Washer	93 — Drain Plug
5 — Snap Ring	37 — Range Shift Sleeve	68 — Shift Rod Plugs	94 — Shift Fork Pin
6 — Input Shaft Ball Bearing	38 — 4-WD Shift Sleeve	69 — 3rd-4th CRS	95 — 1st-2nd Shift Fork
7 — Input Shaft	39 — Key	Switch Assy.	96 — 1st-2nd Shift Rod
8 — Needle Bearing	40 — Transfer Output Rear Shaft	70 — Gasket	97 — 3rd-4th Shift Fork
9 — 3rd-4th Blocker Ring	41 — Needle Bearing	71 — Plug	98 — 3rd-4th Shift Rod
10 — Synchro Spring	42 — Transfer Output Rear Gear	72 — Detent Spring Plate	99 — Reverse Shift Rod
11 — Synchro Key	43 — Thrust Washer	73 — Gasket	100 — Reverse Shift Fork
12 — 3rd-4th Synchro Hub	44 — Transfer Output Rear Shaft	74 — Detent Ball Spring	101 — Shifter Cover (Federal)
13 — 3rd-4th Synchro Sleeve	Ball Bearing & Snap Ring	75 — Detent Ball	102 — Shifter Cover Gasket
14 — 3rd Gear	45 — Distance Shim	76 — Interlock Pins	103 — Reverse Stop Plunger
15 — 2nd & 3rd Gear Needle Bearing	46 — Speedometer Drive Gear	77 — Interlock Plug	104 — Inner Spring
16 — Mainshaft	47 — Speedometer Gear Spacer	78 — Extension Hsg. Gasket	105 — Outer Spring
17 — 2nd Gear	48 — Output Shaft Ball Bearing	79 — Extension Hsg.	106 — Reverse Stop Cap
18 — 1st-2nd Blocker Ring	49 — Output Shaft Lock Nut	80 — Breather Assy.	107 — Shifter Cover (Calif.)
19 — 1st-2nd Synchro Hub	50 — Countergear Needle Bearing	81 — Speedometer Driven Gear	108 — Neutral Switch Rod
20 — 1st-2nd Synchro Sleeve	51 — Countergear	82 — Inner "O" Ring	109 — Spring
21 — 1st Gear	52 — Countergear Ball Bearing	83 — Outer "O" Ring	110 — Damper Pad
22 — 1st Gear Needle Bearing	53 — Lock Plate	84 — Speedometer Gear Hsg.	111 — Neutral Switch Assy.
23 — Collar	54 — Counter Reverse Gear	85 — Bushing	112 — Shift Lever Spring
24 — Thrust Washer	55 — Spacer	86 — Oil Seal	113 — Spring Seat
25 — Mainshaft Ball Bearing	56 — Lock Washer	87 — Dust Cover	114 — Shift Lever Cover
26 — Center Support	57 — Counter Reverse Gear Lock Nut	88 — Clutch Fork Dust Cover	115 — Shift Lever Dust Cover
27 — Reverse Gear	58 — Reverse Idler Gear	89 — Transmission Case Assy.	116 — Shift Lever Boot
28 — Distance Shim	59 — Transfer Countershaft	90 — Center Support Gasket	117 — Shift Lever
29 — Thrust Washer	60 — Thrust Washer	91 — Back-Up Light Switch Assy.	118 — Shift Lever Knob
30 — Transfer Input Gear	61 — Needle Bearing		
31 — Needle Bearing	62 — Transfer Countergear		
32 — Collar	63 — Thrust Washer		
33 — Transfer Hub	64 — "O" Ring		
34 — Mainshaft Lock Nut	65 — Ball Stud		

Fig. 1 Exploded View Showing LUV 4-Speed Transmission Case & Transfer Case with Shifting Mechanism

LUV 4-SPEED WITH INTEGRAL TRANSFER CASE (Cont.)

2) Remove thrust washer, 1st gear, needle bearing, collar and blocker ring. Remove 1st-2nd gear synchronizer assembly.

3) Remove 2nd gear, blocker ring and needle bearing. Remove snap ring, 3rd-4th synchronizer assembly and blocker ring. Remove 3rd gear and needle bearings.

4) Remove snap ring from input shaft gear and remove bearing using an arbor press. Remove countershaft reverse gear and countergear bearing using bearing removal tool (J-22912) and an arbor press.

Inspection — 1) Check mainshaft for wear, scoring or warpage. Maximum permissable warpage of mainshaft is .002" (.05 mm). Check all gear teeth and splines for wear or damage. Check all bearings for smooth operation.

2) Check synchronizer assemblies for wear by holding blocker ring against cone section of gear and measuring clearance. If clearance exceeds .032" (.8 mm), replace blocker ring. Measure clearance between synchronizer clutch hub splines and mainshaft splines in normal direction of rotation.

3) If clearance exceeds .008" (.2 mm), replace synchronizer clutch hub. Check grooves in shift arms and blocks for wear and/or damage. If thickness of shift arm pads is less than .256" (6.5 mm) for 3rd-4th shift arm; .276" (7.0 mm) for 1st-2nd and reverse shift arm and .236" (6.0 mm) for transfer range and 4-WD shift arm, replace shift arms as required.

4) Check shift rod detent springs for weakening and/or distortion. Measure spring free length. If less than 1.083" (27.5 mm) for all forward gears; 1.051" (26.7 mm) for reverse and 1.615" (41.0 mm) for transfer range and 4-WD, replace springs as required.

5) Measure outside diameter of reverse idler gear shaft and inside diameter of reverse gear bushing. Shaft diameter is 1.379" (35.0 mm). If more than .008" (.2 mm) clearance, replace bushing.

Reassembly — 1) Place front of mainshaft upward, then install 3rd gear and needle bearing on front of mainshaft. Tapered side of 3rd gear facing front.

NOTE — *Front and rear needle bearings are interchangeable.*

2) Install blocker ring with teeth upward over synchronizing surface of 3rd gear. Install 3rd-4th synchronizer assembly on mainshaft with face of sleeve with light chamfer rearward. Install snap ring.

3) Turn rear of mainshaft upward and install 2nd gear with needle roller bearing. Tapered surface of 2nd gear should face rear of mainshaft. Install blocking ring with teeth facing downward.

4) Install 1st-2nd synchronizer assembly with light chamfer facing front of mainshaft. Install blocker ring with teeth facing rearward.

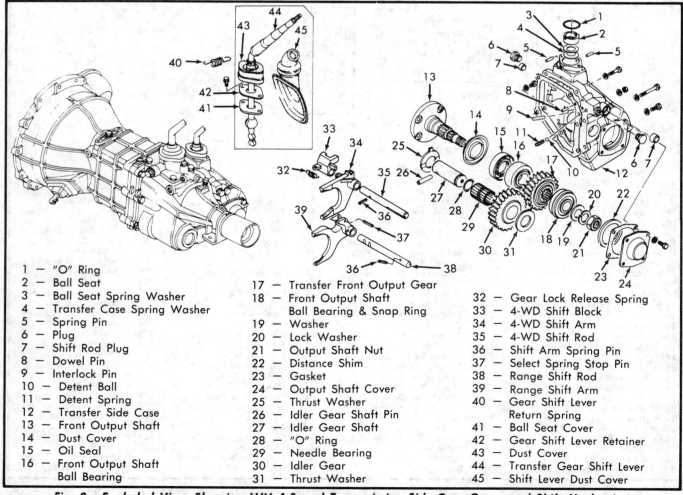

1 — "O" Ring	17 — Transfer Front Output Gear	32 — Gear Lock Release Spring
2 — Ball Seat	18 — Front Output Shaft	33 — 4-WD Shift Block
3 — Ball Seat Spring Washer	Ball Bearing & Snap Ring	34 — 4-WD Shift Arm
4 — Transfer Case Spring Washer	19 — Washer	35 — 4-WD Shift Rod
5 — Spring Pin	20 — Lock Washer	36 — Shift Arm Spring Pin
6 — Plug	21 — Output Shaft Nut	37 — Select Spring Stop Pin
7 — Shift Rod Plug	22 — Distance Shim	38 — Range Shift Rod
8 — Dowel Pin	23 — Gasket	39 — Range Shift Arm
9 — Interlock Pin	24 — Output Shaft Cover	40 — Gear Shift Lever
10 — Detent Ball	25 — Thrust Washer	Return Spring
11 — Detent Spring	26 — Idler Gear Shaft Pin	41 — Ball Seat Cover
12 — Transfer Side Case	27 — Idler Gear Shaft	42 — Gear Shift Lever Retainer
13 — Front Output Shaft	28 — "O" Ring	43 — Dust Cover
14 — Dust Cover	29 — Needle Bearing	44 — Transfer Gear Shift Lever
15 — Oil Seal	30 — Idler Gear	45 — Shift Lever Dust Cover
16 — Front Output Shaft	31 — Thrust Washer	
Ball Bearing		

Fig. 2　Exploded View Showing LUV 4-Speed Transmission Side Case Gears and Shift Mechanism

LUV 4-SPEED WITH INTEGRAL TRANSFER CASE (Cont.)

5) Install collar, needle roller bearing and 1st gear on mainshaft. Tapered side of gear should face front of mainshaft. Install 1st gear thrust washer with grooved side facing 1st gear.

6) Install rear bearing onto mainshaft using bearing removal tool (J-22912) and an arbor press. Make sure snap ring groove in bearing is facing front of mainshaft. Install ball bearing onto input shaft using bearing removal tool (J-22912) and an arbor press. Make sure snap ring groove is facing front of transmission.

7) Install snap ring on input shaft. Install needle bearing, blocker ring and input shaft assembly onto front of mainshaft assembly.

TRANSFER CASE

Disassembly — 1) Remove reverse idler gear and reverse shift arm. Remove range shift sleeve and pilot needle bearing from rear of output shaft.

2) Lightly tap transfer countershaft assembly out through shaft hole in transfer case. Expand rear output shaft front bearing snap ring, then remove output shaft assembly.

3) Remove "O" ring, thrust washer, countergear, needle roller bearing and thrust washer from transfer countershaft.

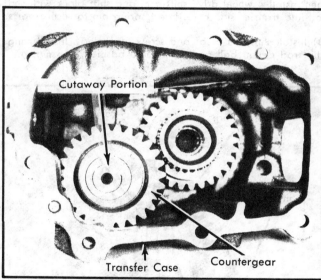

Fig. 3 Alignment of Transfer Countershaft in Transfer Case

4) Remove rear output shaft nut, then press rear bearing off output shaft using bench press. Remove spacer, speedometer drive gear and key from output shaft.

5) Remove output shaft front bearing with thrust washer and rear output gear from output shaft (use bench press). Remove output gear needle roller bearing and 4 wheel drive shift sleeve from output shaft.

Inspection — 1) Check output shaft for wear or scoring. Check splines for damage. Light scoring or damage can be corrected with an oil stone, otherwise replace shaft.

2) Measure outside diameter of reverse idler shaft. Measure inside diameter of idler gear bushing. If difference between the two measurements (clearance) is more than .008" (.2 mm), replace bushing.

Reassembly — 1) If removed, install new oil seal to transfer case and output shaft front bearing snap ring to transfer case.

2) Install 4 wheel drive shift sleeve, with heavy chamfered side toward output gear, on rear of output shaft. Install needle roller bearing, output gear and thrust washer on output shaft. Make sure grooved side of thrust washer faces output gear.

3) Install output shaft front bearing onto output shaft, making sure snap ring groove is turned rearward. Install shim, with grooved side toward front bearing, speedometer drive gear key, drive gear and spacer to output shaft.

4) Press output shaft rear bearing, with sealed face facing rearward, on output shaft. Install output shaft nut and tighten. Stake nut to groove in shaft.

5) Apply grease to needle roller bearings and both faces of thrust washers. Install thrust washer on countershaft by aligning finger on washer with cutaway portion of shaft, then install needle roller bearing, countergear, needle roller bearing, thrust washer and "O" ring to transfer countergear.

NOTE — *Thrust washer oil grooves should face countergear.*

6) Install output shaft assembly into transfer case by expanding front bearing snap ring into transfer case groove far enough so front bearing can be inserted. Allow snap ring to engage bearing groove.

7) Install transfer countershaft assembly into transfer case. Make sure cutaway portion at front end of countershaft is positioned correctly. The finger on thrust washer, on rear of shaft, should be aligned with groove in transfer case. See *Fig. 3* and *Fig. 4*.

8) Grease output shaft pilot bearing, and install bearing and range shift sleeve on output shaft. Make sure end of sleeve with heavy chamfering is toward front of transfer case.

9) Install reverse idler gear and reverse shift arm. Install idler gear so that shift arm fitting groove is turned toward rear of transfer case.

Fig. 4 Alignment of Thrust Washer on Transfer Countershaft in Transfer Case

TRANSFER SIDE CASE

Disassembly — 1) Remove range shift rod detent spring, detent ball and plug from each shift rod. Remove spring pin from the 4 wheel drive shift arm.

LUV 4-SPEED WITH INTEGRAL TRANSFER CASE (Cont.)

2) Hold range shift rod in the high position, at the same time drive out the 4 wheel drive shift rod from the rear side. The plug will come out at same time.

3) Remove shift arm and shift block. Remove detent ball, spring and interlock spring from transfer side case.

NOTE — *Detent ball may pop out as shift rod is removed, be careful not to lose ball.*

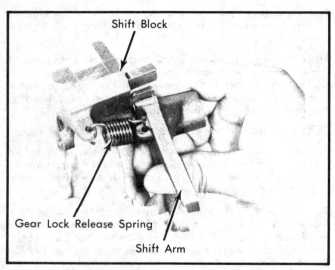

**Fig. 5   Assembling 4-WD
Shift Arm With Shift Block**

4) Remove spring pin from range shift arm and remove range shift rod with plug through front side. Remove shift arm and dowel pin from idler shaft.

5) Remove idler shaft by inserting a bolt (M8x1.25) into threaded hole and pulling idler shaft out. Remove thrust washers, idler gear and needle roller bearing.

6) Remove output shaft cover and shim. Use a pin wrench (J-29042) to hold flanged part of front output shaft from turning, then remove output shaft nut, spring washer and plain washer.

7) Remove output gear from transfer side case. Remove output shaft front and rear bearings using suitable bearing removal tools (J-8092 and J-29040).

NOTE — *Remove front bearing with oil seal.*

8) Remove gear lock release spring from the 4 wheel drive shift arm, then disconnect shift arm and shift block. Remove pin from range shift arm.

Inspection — Inspect shafts and shift forks for wear, scoring or damage. Check bearings for smoothness of operation and for wear. Check all gears for wear or damage. Replace as necessary.

Reassembly — **1)** Install range shift arm so that slit in spring pin is turned in opposite direction as fingers of shift arm. Assemble 4-WD shift arm with shift block, then install gear lock release spring. See Fig. 5.

2) Using suitable installer tools (J-8092 and J-29040), drive front output shaft rear bearing into transfer side case until it contacts snap ring. Install output gear.

3) Using installer tools, drive output shaft front bearing into transfer side case until it contacts output gear. Install output shaft oil seal.

4) Install output shaft, plain washer, spring washer and output shaft nut. Use pin wrench to hold shaft from turning and tighten output shaft nut. Install shim in transfer side case, then install output shaft cover and tighten bolts.

5) Apply grease to both sides of idler gear thrust washer and install with grooved face toward gear. Make sure tab on washer aligns with notch in case. Grease idler gear needle bearing and install bearings on gear. Make sure heavier bossed end is turned toward front. Install idler shaft.

6) Install dowel pin into transfer side case. Dowel should protrude .355-.433″ (9-11 mm). Install range shift arm and shift rod, then install spring pin to hold in place.

7) Install interlock pin, 4 wheel drive shift rod detent spring and detent ball into case. Hold range shift rod in high range, then install 4 wheel drive shift arm and shift block with shift rod into transfer side case. Insert spring pin to secure parts.

8) Install shift rod plugs and screw type plugs. Install range shift rod detent ball and spring into position. See Fig. 6.

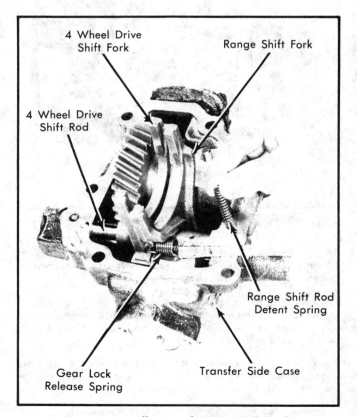

**Fig. 6   Installation of 4-WD Shift Rod,
Fork, Range Shift Rod, Range Shift Fork
and Detent Spring**

LUV 4-SPEED WITH INTEGRAL TRANSFER CASE (Cont.)

TRANSMISSION REASSEMBLY

1) If removed, install countershaft reverse gear and countergear ball bearing with snap ring groove facing rear of transmission. Use adapter (J-22912) and bench press to install bearing. If removed, install snap rings in countergear and mainshaft snap ring grooves of center support.

2) Mesh gears of mainshaft and countergear together, then install onto a suitable holding fixture (J-26545-5). Install holding fixture in a vise, then install center support. While installing center support, expand mainshaft snap ring and press center support onto mainshaft and countergear until countergear bearing hits its snap ring.

3) Expand countergear snap ring and press center support further until both snap rings fit into grooves. Remove holding fixture from mainshaft and countergear. Move both synchronizers rearward to prevent mainshaft from turning.

4) Install collar, washer and lock nut to rear of countergear. Install reverse gear shim on mainshaft with undercut teeth facing rearward.

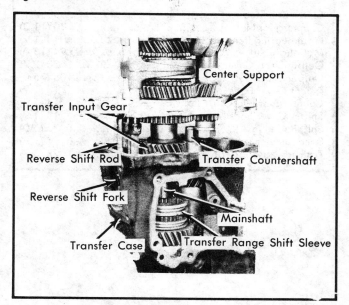

**Fig. 7   Installation of Center Support
to Transfer Case**

5) Install transfer input gear thrust washer on mainshaft with grooved side facing input gear. Install collar, needle bearing and input gear on mainshaft. Input gear should be installed with teeth facing rearward.

6) Install transfer clutch hub on mainshaft with grooved side facing input gear. Install lock nut on mainshaft and tighten. Caulk lock nut. Install spacer to mainshaft.

7) Apply grease to 2 interlock pins and insert into detent holes from middle hole of center support. Install 1st-2nd shifter fork and 3rd-4th shifter fork into grooves in synchronizer assembly.

8) Install 3rd-4th shifter rod from rear of center support through middle hole and then into 1st-2nd and 3rd-4th shifter forks. Align spring pin hole in shifter fork with hole in shifter rod.

NOTE — *The 3rd-4th shifter rod can be identified by 2 detent grooves on side of rod.*

9) Install 1st-2nd shifter rod from rear of center support, through 1st-2nd shifter fork and align hole in rod to hole in shifter fork. Install reverse shifter rod from rear of center support. Install 2 spring pins in 1st-2nd and 3rd-4th shifter forks.

NOTE — *Make sure shifter rod is supported, by round bar against end of shifter rod, when installing spring pins.*

10) Install detent balls, detent spring, gasket and retainer on top of center support. Place transfer case upright and on wooden blocks. Install center support assembly and gasket into the transfer case. See *Fig. 7*. Before installing, apply a thin coat of grease to end of reverse shift rod, mainshaft and transfer countershaft. When installing center support to transfer case, make sure following parts are installed together in following order:

- Reverse shift rod to reverse shift arm.
- Mainshaft to output shaft.
- Transfer countershaft to countershaft hole fitting.
- Input gear to transfer countergear is engaged.
- Range shift sleeve to clutch hub is engaged.
- Dowel pins fit into dowel pin holes.

11) Install spring pin in reverse shifter fork. Tighten 4 bolts attaching center support to transfer case evenly. Measure how much transfer countershaft protrudes from center support. Select distance shim so thrust clearance will be .004-.014" (.10-.35 mm). See *Fig. 8*.

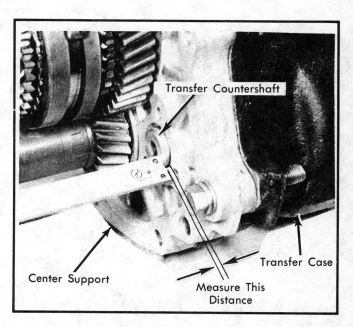

**Fig. 8   Measuring Transfer Countershaft for
Distance Shim Selection**

LUV 4-SPEED WITH INTEGRAL TRANSFER CASE (Cont.)

Transfer Countergear Distance Shims

Countergear Measurement	Shim Thickness	Color Code
.106-.114" (2.7-2.9 mm)	.118" (3.0 mm)	Red
.114-.122" (2.9-3.1 mm)	.126" (3.2 mm)	Orange
.122-.130" (3.1-3.3 mm)	.134" (3.4 mm)	No Color
.130-.138" (3.3-3.5 mm)	.142" (3.6 mm)	Green
.138-.142" (3.5-3.6 mm)	.150" (3.8 mm)	Blue

12) Remove bolts attaching center support to transfer case, then install transfer countergear shim selected and lock plate. Install transmission case and gasket to transfer case and center support. Make sure dowel pin and dowel pin hole are aligned. Tighten the 8 bolts.

13) Install back-up light switch and the CRS switch (if equipped). Install speedometer driven gear to rear of transfer case.

NOTE — *To prevent damage to "O" ring when installing, coat "O" ring with oil.*

14) Install front bearing retainer seal. Install snap ring to input shaft bearing. Apply grease to bearing retainer spring washer and install in bearing retainer.

NOTE — *Install spring washer so dished face is toward bearing outer race.*

15) Install bearing retainer to front of transmission case. Apply sealer to threads of bolt installed in lower left corner of retainer, then install the other 3 bolts and tighten.

16) Install ball stud to transmission case. Install dust boot, clutch fork and throw-out bearing. Install retaining springs. Apply grease to input shaft splines, shift fork support and shift block. Make sure hook on clutch fork is installed on support correctly. Install drain plug on transfer case.

NOTE — *Transfer side case is installed after transmission is installed in vehicle. See Removal and Installation for installation of transmission.*

17) With transmission installed in vehicle, install transfer side case studs to transmission. Install transfer side case to transfer case by aligning grooves in shift arms and sleeve. Install with shift arms and shift sleeves held in the 4H position.

TIGHTENING SPECIFICATIONS

Application	Ft. Lbs. (mkg)
Clutch Ball Stud-to-Case	30 (4.1)
Countergear Nut	80 (11.0)
Front Bearing Retainer Bolts	14 (1.9)
Mainshaft Nut	94 (13.0)
Output Shaft Cover Bolts	20 (2.7)
Output Shaft Nut	108 (15.0)
Detent Cover Bolts	14 (1.9)
Countergear Lock Plate Bolts	14 (1.9)
Shifter Cover Bolts	14 (1.9)
Shift Rod Plugs	36 (5.0)
Speedometer Hsg. Retainer Bolt	14 (1.9)
Transfer Case-to-Transmission Case Bolts	27 (3.7)

MAZDA 4 & 5-SPEED

DESCRIPTION

The 4 and 5 speed transmissions are fully synchronized in all forward gears. Synchronizers are of the blocker type and provide for smooth gear engagement. Gear selection is accomplished by direct control from the floor mounted shift lever. On all models, clutch housing is integral with transmission case. The center support plate is mounted between transmission case and extension housing on 4-speed models, and between transmission case and intermediate housing on 5-speed models and is the main gear support.

LUBRICATION & ADJUSTMENT

See MANUAL TRANSMISSION SERVICING Section.

TROUBLE SHOOTING

HARD SHIFTING

Improperly adjusted clutch. Weakened synchro insert spring. Face of synchro ring in contact with insert, worn. Cones on synchro ring and gear worn or not in proper contact.

SLIPS OUT OF GEAR

Bearings worn or defective. Excessive play between gears and collars. Play in clutch hub and sliding sleeve. Shift arm worn. Lock ball spring weak or broken.

TRANSMISSION NOISY

Low or incorrect lubricant. Gears or bearings worn or damaged. Worn gears or collars. Worn clutch hub or mainshaft splines. Incorrectly meshed gears.

TRANSMISSION REMOVAL & INSTALLATION

Removal — 1) Disconnect negative battery cable. Place transmission in neutral. Remove gearshift knob, boot, cover and gasket. Remove console (if equipped). Remove gearshift lever, wave washer, shim and bushing straight up and away from gearshift lever retainer.

2) Remove 2 upper bolts from clutch housing. Disconnect clutch slave cylinder (if equipped) and position out of way. Remove nuts and disconnect air pipe and air duct from thermal reactor. Disconnect air duct hanger and remove air duct from silencer. Remove thermal reactor cover (if equipped).

3) Raise vehicle and support with stands. Drain transmission fluid. Remove propeller shaft. Remove exhaust pipe hangers from transmission. Disconnect clutch cable from clutch release lever (if equipped). Disconnect back-up light switch and starter motor wiring connectors.

4) Disconnect top switch and overdrive switch wires (if equipped). Remove starter motor. Disconnect speedometer cable at extension housing. Remove dust cover from clutch housing (if equipped). Place jack with wood block under rear of engine. Remove transmission support-to-crossmember attaching nuts.

5) Raise engine and transmission slightly with jack. Remove crossmember bolts and remove crossmember (if required). Remove transmission attaching bolts, slide transmission

rearward until input shaft clears clutch disc, then carefully remove transmission from under vehicle.

Installation — To install, reverse removal procedure, ensuring that splines in input shaft align with those in clutch disc.

TRANSMISSION DISASSEMBLY

1) Clean exterior of transmission assembly. On GLC models, remove clutch cross-shaft bolt, cross-shaft, release lever, spring and throw-out bearing. On all other models, remove dust cover, throw-out bearing and clutch release fork. Remove front cover bolts (or nuts) and remove front cover, shim, gasket and oil seal.

2) Remove snap ring from input shaft and countershaft. Remove gearshift lever retainer and gasket from extension housing. Remove extension housing bolts and slide extension housing off mainshaft with control lever positioned to the left as far as possible. Remove control lever end attaching bolt and remove control lever end and control rod from housing.

3) Remove speedometer driven gear assembly, back-up light switch and overdrive switch from extension housing. Remove top switch from transmission case. On 4-speed, remove speedometer drive gear snap ring from mainshaft and slide drive gear off mainshaft. Remove lock ball.

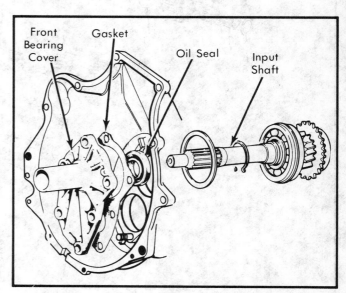

Fig. 1 Exploded View of Front Bearing Cover and Input Shaft Assembly

4) On 4 and 5-speed, separate transmission case from bearing plate/intermediate housing using push tool (49 0305 430) or by tapping input shaft with plastic faced hammer. Remove bearing from transmission case. Using bearing puller tool (49 0710 520), remove countershaft front bearing from countershaft.

5) On 5-speed, remove speedometer drive gear snap ring from mainshaft and slide drive gear off mainshaft. Remove lock ball and drive gear positioning snap ring. On 4-speed, remove 3

MAZDA 4 & 5-SPEED (Cont.)

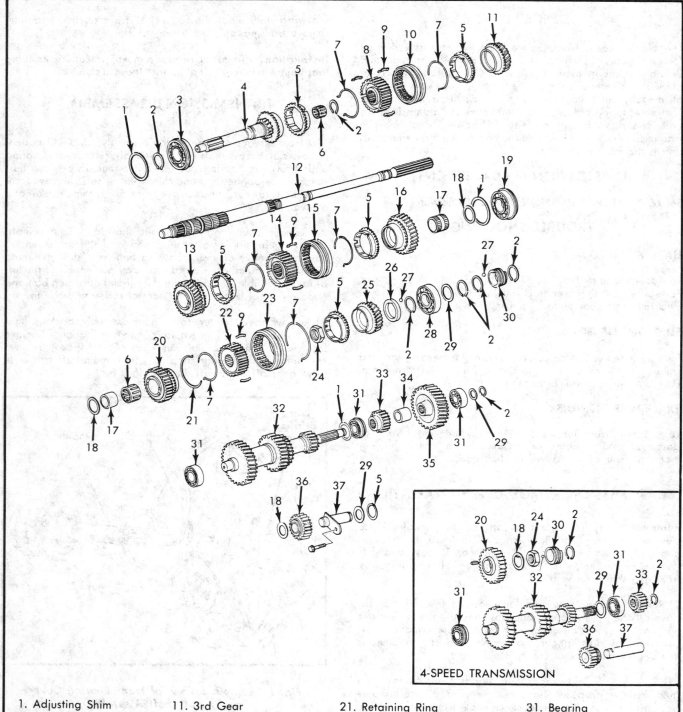

1. Adjusting Shim
2. Snap Ring
3. Bearing
4. Input Shaft
5. Synchro Ring
6. Bearing
7. Synchro Key Spring
8. 3rd & 4th Clutch Hub
9. Synchro Key
10. Hub Sleeve
11. 3rd Gear
12. Mainshaft
13. 2nd Gear
14. 1st & 2nd Clutch Hub
15. Hub Sleeve
16. 1st Gear
17. Gear Sleeve
18. Thrust Washer
19. Bearing
20. Reverse Gear
21. Retaining Ring
22. 5th & Reverse Clutch Hub
23. Hub Sleeve
24. Lock Nut
25. 5th Gear
26. Thrust Washer
27. Locking Ball
28. Bearing
29. Adjusting Washer
30. Speedometer Drive Gear
31. Bearing
32. Countershaft
33. Counter Reverse Gear
34. Spacer
35. Counter 5th Gear
36. Reverse Idler Gear
37. Idler Gear Shaft

Fig. 2 Exploded View of Mazda 4 and 5-Speed Transmission Gears and Shafts

MAZDA 4 & 5-SPEED (Cont.)

spring cap bolts and remove springs and shift locking balls. On 5-speed, remove shift rod end attaching bolts and remove shift rod ends.

6) Separate bearing plate from intermediate housing by lightly tapping housing with plastic faced hammer. On 4-speed, remove reverse shift rod, shift fork assembly and reverse gear from bearing plate. Remove shift fork set screws. Remove shift rods and forks by pushing shift rods rearward through shift forks and bearing plate.

7) Remove reverse shift rod locking ball, spring and interlock pins from bearing plate. On 5-speed, remove 3 spring cap bolts and remove springs and shift locking balls. Remove 3 shift rod snap rings. Remove shift fork attaching bolts, shift fork rods and shift forks. Remove lock ball, spring and interlock pins.

NOTE — On 5-speed, be careful not to lose lock ball when removing 5th-Reverse shift rod.

8) On 4-speed, straighten lock washer tab and secure mainshaft with holding tool (49 0259 440) and loosen lock nut using suitable wrench. Remove reverse gear and key from mainshaft. Remove countershaft snap ring and counter reverse gear. Remove bearing cover and reverse idler gear shaft from bearing plate.

9) Using plastic faced hammer, tap rear end of mainshaft and countershaft assemblies and remove from bearing plate, being careful not to damage shafts. Remove bearings from bearing plate. On 5-speed, remove mainshaft and countershaft snap rings and adjusting washers. Remove rear bearings using bearing removal tool (49 0839 425C).

10) From rear of mainshaft, remove snap ring, thrust washer, lock ball, 5th gear, synchro ring, counter 5th gear and spacer. Engage clutch sleeves into 1st and reverse gear to lock mainshaft assembly. Mount bearing plate in vise. Remove lock nut caulking using a chisel.

11) Remove and discard lock nut using suitable wrench. Remove 5th-Reverse clutch hub assembly, reverse gear, needle bearing, inner race, thrust washer, counter reverse gear, snap ring, thrust washers and reverse idler gear. Using plastic faced hammer, tap rear end of mainshaft and countershaft assemblies and remove from bearing plate. Remove bearing cover and bearings from bearing plate.

COMPONENT DISASSEMBLY & REASSEMBLY

MAINSHAFT

Disassembly — 1) On 4-speed, remove thrust washer, 1st gear, sleeve and synchro ring from mainshaft. Remove snap ring from front of mainshaft. Using arbor press, remove 3rd-4th clutch hub and sleeve assembly, synchro ring and 3rd gear from front of mainshaft. Reposition mainshaft in press and remove 1st-2nd clutch hub and sleeve assembly, synchro ring and 2nd gear from rear of mainshaft.

2) On 5-speed, remove snap ring from front of mainshaft. Remove 3rd-4th clutch hub assembly, synchro ring, 3rd gear, thrust washer, synchro ring, 1st gear, needle bearing, inner race, 1st-2nd clutch hub assembly, synchro ring and 2nd gear.

Mainshaft Inspection — Inspect mainshaft for runout by positioning a dial indicator along the shaft in several places. If runout exceeds .0012" (.03 mm), straighten shaft using press or replace. Inspect all other surfaces and splines for wear and/or damage.

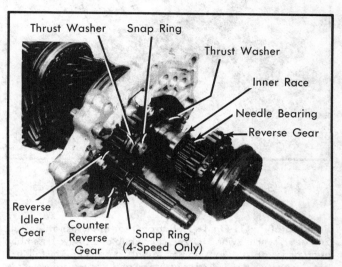

Fig. 3   Removing Reverse and Counter Reverse Gear Assemblies

Synchronizer Inspection — Inspect unit for worn or damaged parts. Install synchronizer ring evenly to gear cone and measure clearance between side faces of ring and gear with feeler gauge. If clearance is less than .031" (.8 mm), replace synchronizer ring or gear. Inspect contact between ring and gear using machinist blue on cone surface of gear. If contact pattern is poor, correct by lapping surfaces together or by replacing ring or gear. Check synchronizer key spring for tension. Ensure that clutch sleeve slides easily on clutch hub. Check clearance between shift fork and clutch using feeler gauge. Clearance limit is .020" (.5 mm).

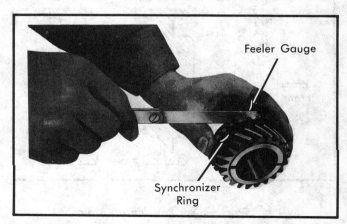

Fig. 4   Checking Synchronizer Ring Clearance with Feeler Gauge

Bearing Housing Inspection — Place a straight edge across the bearing housing, measure clearance between straight edge and each bearing with a feeler gauge. Clearance should be 0-.002" (0-.05 mm), if not within limits, install correct shim. See Fig. 5.

MAZDA 4 & 5-SPEED (Cont.)

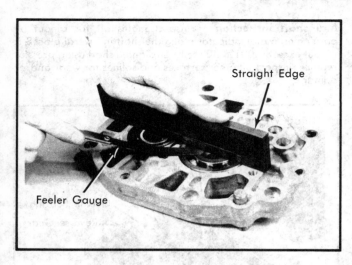

Fig. 5 Checking Bearing Housing Clearances

Reassembly — 1) On 4-speed, from rear of mainshaft, install 2nd gear, synchro ring, 1st-2nd clutch hub and sleeve assembly using arbor press. Reposition mainshaft in press and install 3rd gear, synchro ring, 3rd-4th clutch hub and sleeve assembly. Install snap ring on front of mainshaft and install synchro ring, sleeve, 1st gear and thrust washer.

2) On 5-speed, install 2nd gear, synchro ring, 1st-2nd clutch hub assembly, inner race, needle bearing, 1st gear, synchro ring, thrust washer, 3rd gear, synchro ring and 3rd-4th clutch hub assembly. Install snap ring on front of mainshaft. On 4 and 5-speed, install input shaft with needle bearing onto mainshaft.

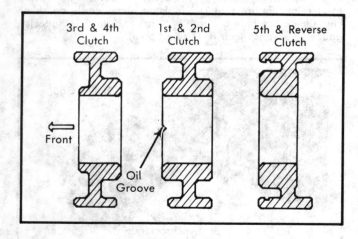

Fig. 6 Synchronizer Position on Mainshaft

TRANSMISSION REASSEMBLY

1) On 4 and 5-speed, install countershaft and mainshaft rear bearings into bearing plate and check clearance between bearing plate bore and bearing height. If clearance exceeds .004" (.1 mm), replace adjusting shim. Using arbor press, install countershaft and mainshaft assembly into bearing plate.

2) Install bearing cover and reverse idler gear shaft. On 4-speed, install reverse gear with key onto mainshaft and chamfer on teeth of gear facing rearward. Secure mainshaft with holding tool (49 0259 440) and install and tighten lock nut using suitable wrench.

3) Bend over lock washer tab. Install countershaft reverse gear and snap ring. On 5-speed, install thrust washer, reverse idler gear, thrust washer and snap ring on reverse idler shaft. Check clearance between thrust washer and snap ring using feeler gauge.

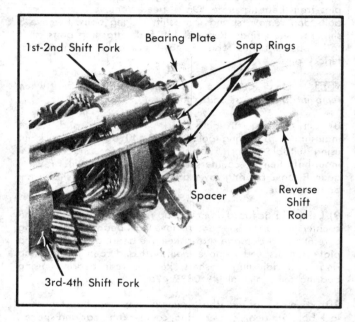

Fig. 7 Assembled View of Reverse Shift Fork and Shift Rod Assemblies

4) If clearance exceeds .004-.012" (.1-.3 mm), replace thrust washer. Thrust washers are available in .106" (2.6 mm), .110" (2.8 mm) and .118" (3.0 mm) sizes. On 4 and 5-speed, install counter reverse gear and spacer (5-speed only) on countershaft. On 5-speed, install thrust washer, reverse gear, needle bearing and sleeve on rear end of mainshaft.

5) Install 5th-Reverse clutch hub and sleeve and new lock nut on mainshaft. Engage clutch sleeves into 1st and reverse gear to lock mainshaft assembly. Tighten mainshaft lock nut using suitable wrench and caulk lock nut. Install synchro ring, 5th gear, counter 5th gear, thrust washer, lock ball and snap ring to rear end of mainshaft.

6) Check clearance between mainshaft thrust washer and snap ring using feeler gauge. If clearance exceeds .004-.012" (.1-.3 mm), replace thrust washer. Thrust washers are available in .252" (6.4 mm), .256" (6.5 mm), .260" (6.6 mm), and .264" (6.7 mm) sizes. Install mainshaft rear bearing using wrench tool (49 1243 465A).

7) Install adjusting washer and snap ring. Check clearance between mainshaft adjusting washer and snap ring using feeler gauge. If clearance exceeds .004" (.1 mm), replace adjusting washer. Adjusting washers are available in .075" (1.9 mm), .079" (2.0 mm), .083" (2.1 mm) and .087" (2.2 mm) sizes.

MAZDA 4 & 5-SPEED (Cont.)

8) Install countershaft rear bearing using bearing installer tool (49 0500 330). Install countershaft thrust washer and snap ring. Check clearance between thrust washer and snap ring using feeler gauge. If clearance exceeds .004" (.1 mm), replace thrust washer. Thrust washers are available in .083" (2.1 mm), .087" (2.2 mm), .091" (2.3 mm) and .094" (2.4 mm) sizes.

9) On 4 and 5-speed, install reverse shift spring and locking ball into bearing plate. Push ball down using screwdriver and install reverse shift rod, shift fork and reverse idler gear (4-speed only) at same time. Install washer and snap ring (5-speed only).

10) Install 1st-2nd and 3rd-4th shift forks onto clutch sleeves. Using guide tools (49 0862 350 & 49 0187 451A), install each shift fork rod and interlock pin. Align bolt holes in both shift forks and rods. Install and tighten lock bolts. Install snap rings onto shift rods (5-speed only).

NOTE — *On 4-speed, make sure that spacer is installed in position on reverse shift fork rod.*

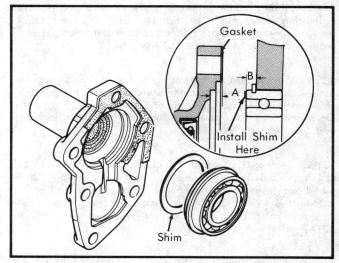

Fig. 9   View of Front Case Showing Front Bearing End Play Shim Location

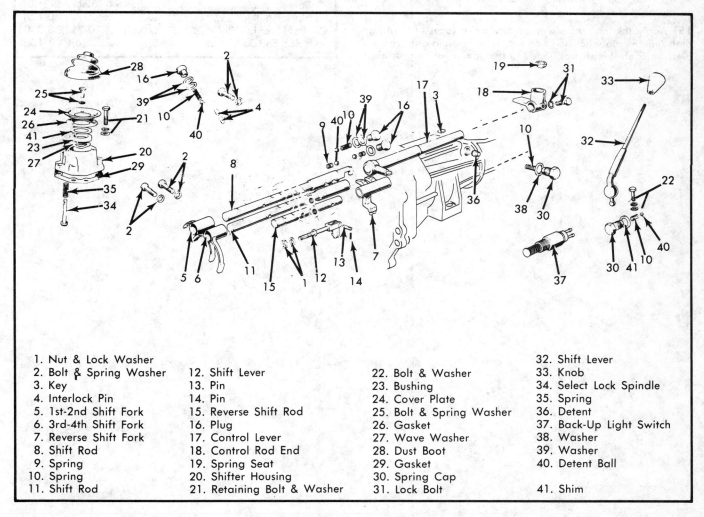

1. Nut & Lock Washer	12. Shift Lever	22. Bolt & Washer	32. Shift Lever
2. Bolt & Spring Washer	13. Pin	23. Bushing	33. Knob
3. Key	14. Pin	24. Cover Plate	34. Select Lock Spindle
4. Interlock Pin	15. Reverse Shift Rod	25. Bolt & Spring Washer	35. Spring
5. 1st-2nd Shift Fork	16. Plug	26. Gasket	36. Detent
6. 3rd-4th Shift Fork	17. Control Lever	27. Wave Washer	37. Back-Up Light Switch
7. Reverse Shift Fork	18. Control Rod End	28. Dust Boot	38. Washer
8. Shift Rod	19. Spring Seat	29. Gasket	39. Washer
9. Spring	20. Shifter Housing	30. Spring Cap	40. Detent Ball
10. Spring	21. Retaining Bolt & Washer	31. Lock Bolt	41. Shim
11. Shift Rod			

Fig. 8   Exploded View of 4-Speed Transmission Shift Control Linkage (5-Speed Shift Control Linkage Similar)

MAZDA 4 & 5-SPEED (Cont.)

11) Install shift locking balls and springs into respective bores in bearing plate. Install and tighten spring cap bolts. On 4-speed, apply thin coat of sealer on contact surfaces of bearing plate and transmission case and assemble.

12) On 5-speed, apply thin coat of sealer on contact surfaces of bearing plate and intermediate housing and assemble. Install shift rod ends to shift rods and install and tighten bolts. On 4 and 5-speed, install speedometer drive gear, lock ball and snap ring on mainshaft.

13) On 5-speed, apply thin coat of sealer on contact surfaces of bearing plate and transmission case, and assemble. On 4-speed and 5-speed, install input shaft bearing, using bearing installer tool (49 0500 330), and install snap ring. Install countershaft front bearing, using bearing installer tool (49 0180 321A).

14) Install speedometer driven gear assembly, lock plate and bolt into extension housing and tighten bolt. Install control lever through holes from front side of extension housing. Install control lever end, control lever and tighten bolt. Install back-up light switch, top switch and overdrive switch.

15) Apply thin coat of sealer on contact surfaces of bearing plate/intermediate housing and extension housing and assemble with control lever positioned to the left as far as possible.

Install and tighten bolts, making sure control rod operates properly. Install gearshift lever retainer and gasket to extension housing.

16) Lubricate lip of oil seal inside front cover and install front cover to transmission case. Check clearance between bearing outer race and front cover using feeler gauge. If clearance exceeds .004" (.1 mm), replace adjusting shim. Adjusting shims are available in .006" (1.5 mm) and .012" (.30 mm) sizes.

17) On GLC models, install throw-out bearing, spring, release lever, cross-shaft and cross-shaft bolt and tighten bolt. On all other models, install throw-out bearing, clutch release fork and dust cover.

TIGHTENING SPECIFICATIONS

Application	Ft. Lbs. (mkg)
Shift Fork Bolts	9-12 (1.2-1.6)
Spring Cap Bolts	7-11 (1.0-1.5)
Mainshaft Lock Nut	
4-Speed	116-174 (16.0-24.0)
5-Speed	94-152 (13.0-21.0)
Interlock Pin Plug	7-11 (1.0-1.5)
Control Lever End Bolt	20-25 (2.8-3.4)
Shift Rod End Bolts	6-9 (.8-1.2)

MERCEDES-BENZ 4-SPEED

240D

DESCRIPTION

Transmission is a fully synchronized, 4-speed unit, that uses helical gears. Main components of transmission are: Transmission case, extension housing, front cover and gearshift housing.

LUBRICATION & ADJUSTMENT

See MANUAL TRANSMISSION SERVICING Section.

TROUBLE SHOOTING

HARD SHIFTING

Clutch not releasing. Check for proper adjustment, deformed clutch disc, seized or damaged pilot bearing. Incorrect or insufficient lubricant. Linkage or levers worn or damaged.

JUMPS OUT OF GEAR

Worn or damaged shift forks. Detent balls and springs worn or broken. Worn or damaged synchro assemblies. Improper thrust clearances.

NOISY OPERATION

Improper or insufficient lubricant. Worn or damaged bushings, bearings and/or gears. Damaged splines.

NOTE — *When checking transmission for noise, ensure that it is not coming from other parts of the drive line.*

TRANSMISSION REMOVAL & INSTALLATION

Removal — **1)** Disconnect battery ground cable. Remove rear crossmember, after supporting transmission on a suitable jack or stand. Remove exhaust pipe and support bracket. Loosen drive shaft center bearing, remove driveshaft-to-transmission bolts. Push driveshaft towards the rear.

2) Remove tachometer drive from the rear of the transmission. Remove clutch slave cylinder and pull, (with lines) towards the rear, until rod is released from clutch housing. Remove shift linkage from transmission shift levers. Remove starter.

3) Remove transmission-to-intermediate flange attaching bolts, (removing the two upper bolts last). Pull transmission out horizontally, until input shaft is clear of clutch. Then remove in a downward direction.

Installation — Installation of transmission is the reverse of removal procedure. Torque clamping nut on propeller shaft to 22 ft. lbs. (3 mkg). Bleed slave cylinder and check hydraulic fluid level. Check clutch adjustment and shift linkage adjustment.

TRANSMISSION DISASSEMBLY

1) Remove clutch release bearing and arm. Remove clutch housing-to-transmission nuts and remove clutch housing with slave cylinder from transmission.

2) Drain transmission oil and remove reverse shifting lever. Remove locking clip and washer from reverse shifting shaft, then remove gearshift housing bolts. Tap gearshift housing from dowel pin and push shift forks toward transmission to remove them from shift rockers. Tilt gearshift housing down and then lift up to remove. *See Fig. 3.*

3) Remove bolts attaching front cover and remove. Note the shims for input shaft and countershaft. Remove universal flange slot nut and universal flange from rear of transmission. Then remove extension housing bolts and extension housing.

NOTE — *If the extension housing (with a machined depth of .157" (4mm)) is to be replaced, a cover with the same dimensions must be used.*

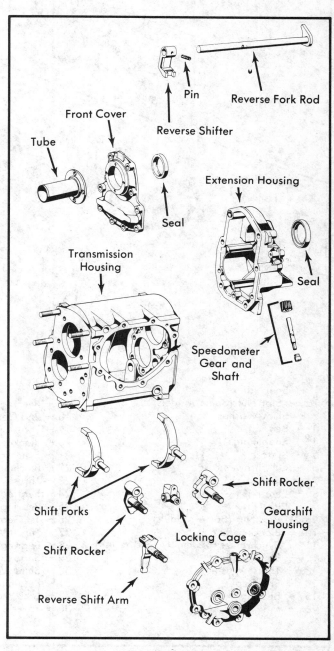

Fig. 1 Exploded View of Transmission Housing

MERCEDES-BENZ 4-SPEED (Cont.)

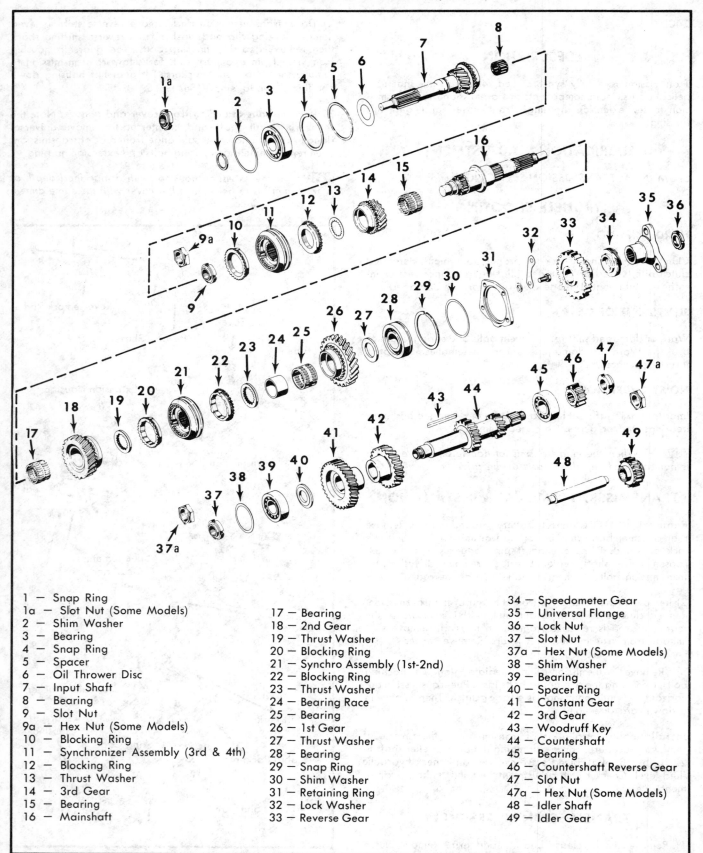

1 — Snap Ring
1a — Slot Nut (Some Models)
2 — Shim Washer
3 — Bearing
4 — Snap Ring
5 — Spacer
6 — Oil Thrower Disc
7 — Input Shaft
8 — Bearing
9 — Slot Nut
9a — Hex Nut (Some Models)
10 — Blocking Ring
11 — Synchronizer Assembly (3rd & 4th)
12 — Blocking Ring
13 — Thrust Washer
14 — 3rd Gear
15 — Bearing
16 — Mainshaft

17 — Bearing
18 — 2nd Gear
19 — Thrust Washer
20 — Blocking Ring
21 — Synchro Assembly (1st-2nd)
22 — Blocking Ring
23 — Thrust Washer
24 — Bearing Race
25 — Bearing
26 — 1st Gear
27 — Thrust Washer
28 — Bearing
29 — Snap Ring
30 — Shim Washer
31 — Retaining Ring
32 — Lock Washer
33 — Reverse Gear

34 — Speedometer Gear
35 — Universal Flange
36 — Lock Nut
37 — Slot Nut
37a — Hex Nut (Some Models)
38 — Shim Washer
39 — Bearing
40 — Spacer Ring
41 — Constant Gear
42 — 3rd Gear
43 — Woodruff Key
44 — Countershaft
45 — Bearing
46 — Countershaft Reverse Gear
47 — Slot Nut
47a — Hex Nut (Some Models)
48 — Idler Shaft
49 — Idler Gear

Fig. 2 Exploded View of Main and Countershaft Components

MERCEDES-BENZ 4-SPEED (Cont.)

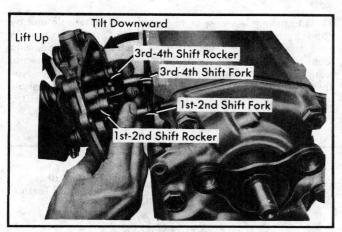

Fig. 3   Removing Gearshift Housing Cover

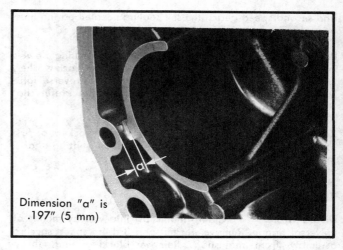

Dimension "a" is .197" (5 mm)

Fig. 4   Machined Rear Cover

4) Remove speedometer gear. Remove reverse gear from mainshaft. Pull idler shaft from transmission housing while holding idler gear in position. Remove slot nut from rear of countershaft then remove reverse gear from countershaft. Remove shifter forks. Remove pin on reverse fork rod and push shifter as far forward as possible. Remove fork rod from rear while removing shifter from forward direction. Remove holding ring and shims from mainshaft bearing.

5) Pull input shaft out of housing in a forward direction. Use care that 4th gear synchronizer and needle bearing between input shaft and mainshaft are not dropped. Place 3rd and 4th gear synchronizer into 3rd gear position. Push mainshaft towards the rear and remove mainshaft in a forward direction. Using same procedures, remove countershaft.

COMPONENT DISASSEMBLY & REASSEMBLY

GEARSHIFT HOUSING

Disassembly — Remove gear shifting shaft and washers from gearshift housing. Remove shifting rockers and shift fingers from inside of shift cover. Remove bolt for locking cage and carefully force locking cage from locating pin in gearshift housing and remove.

Inspection — If shift rocker shafts for third and fourth speed or shift finger for reverse leaks oil, "O" rings must be replaced with new ones. If oil leaks from shaft of shift rocker for first

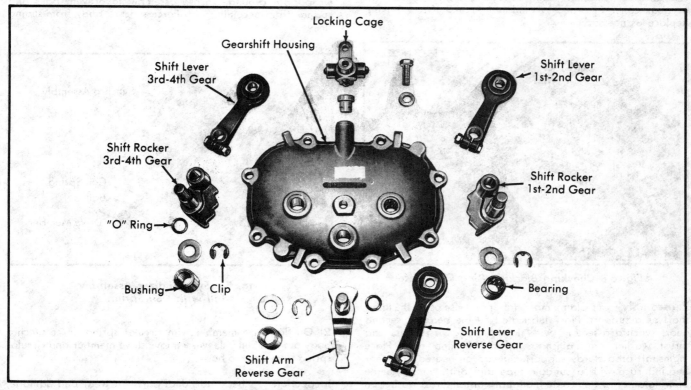

Fig. 5   Exploded View of Gearshift Housing Cover

MERCEDES-BENZ 4-SPEED (Cont.)

and second speed gears, the self sealing needle bearing must be replaced.

Reassembly — 1) Push locking cage with locating dowels into gearshift housing and secure with screw and lock washer. Grease shafts of shift rockers and shift finger for reverse lightly with grease and install gearshift housing. Be careful that "O" rings are not damaged.

2) Place washers and shifting levers on shift rockers of first and second, and third and fourth position shifting shafts. Install reverse shifting lever to reverse shift arm.

MAINSHAFT

Disassembly — 1) Clamp mainshaft into vise by means of universal flange. Remove slot nut and 3rd-4th speed synchro assembly from mainshaft. Remove blocking ring, thrust washer, and third gear from mainshaft. Remove third gear bearing. Clamp input shaft with roller bearings in vise and use to hold mainshaft. Remove thrust washer, 1st gear and needle bearings from mainshaft.

NOTE — *Use soft covers on vise jaws to protect input shaft.*

2) Place mainshaft loosely in vise so that second gear rests on jaws of vise. Tap on top of mainshaft until first gear bearing is free of mainshaft. Remove first gear bearing, thrust washer, blocking ring, synchro assembly and thrust washer from mainshaft. Remove second gear, blocking ring and needle bearing from mainshaft.

Inspection — Check all parts for wear or damage. Place all blocking rings with their respective gears and measure clearance between short teeth of blocking ring and short teeth of gear cone. Clearance should not exceed .02" (.5 mm). Replace as neessary.

Fig. 6   Checking Blocking Ring Clearance

Reassembly — 1) Clamp mainshaft into a vise using the input shaft as a support. Place lubricated needle bearing, second gear, synchro assembly (with flange facing first gear) and thrust washer on mainshaft. Install blocking ring. Place mainshaft on a sturdy support and tap on heated first gear bearing race with a suitable tube and drift. Install needle bearing and first gear onto mainshaft. Install thrust washer on mainshaft.

2) Slide assembly sleeve on mainshaft and tighten slot nut by hand. Turn mainshaft around and clamp assembly sleeve in vise. Lubricate third gear needle bearing and slide onto mainshaft with third gear. Install thrust washer, with internal teeth See *Fig. 7.*, and blocking ring on mainshaft. Place synchronizer assembly for 3rd and 4th gear onto mainshaft (machined groove of synchronizer assembly must face 3rd gear). Install and tighten slot nut on mainshaft.

Fig. 7   Thrust Washer Installation

SYNCHRONIZER ASSEMBLY

Disassembly — 1) Two types of synchro assemblies are used, one is a ball with coil spring and the other is a flat drive member with circular spring. On the ball with coil spring type, wrap cloth around synchro assembly to prevent balls and springs from becoming lost. Force synchro body from sliding sleeve.

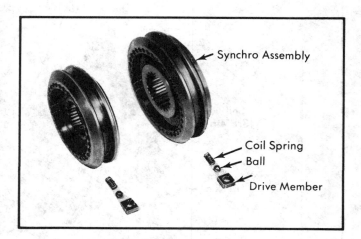

**Fig. 8   Synchronizer Assembly
Ball with Coil Spring**

2) On flat drive member with circular spring, force synchro body out of sliding sleeve. Remove drive member and circular spring from synchro body.

Inspection — Check individual parts for wear and damage, replace as necessary.

MERCEDES-BENZ 4-SPEED (Cont.)

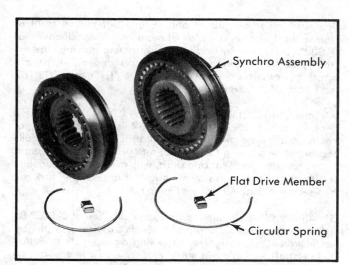

**Fig. 9 Synchronizer Assembly
with Circular Spring**

Reassembly — 1) On ball with coil spring type, insert springs and drive members into synchro body and slide into sliding sleeve. Place one ball in drive member at a time and push forward.

NOTE — *Drive members are chamfered on one edge for 1st and 2nd speed. Chamfered edge should face 2nd gear.*

2) On flat drive member with circular spring, install drive member with circular springs on synchro body and slide into sliding sleeve. Ensure that sleeve and body are properly oriented. See *Fig. 10* and *Fig. 11.*

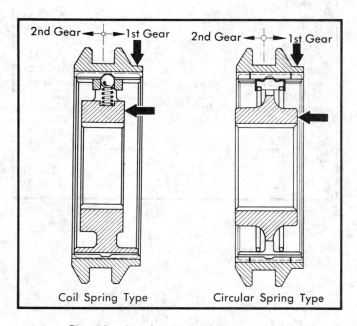

**Fig. 10 Synchronizer Body Installation
(1st and 2nd Gear)**

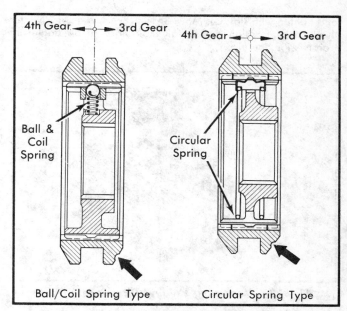

**Fig. 11 Synchronizer Body Installation
(3rd and 4th Gear)**

COUNTERSHAFT

Disassembly — Using suitable press, place countershaft third gear on a support and press out shaft. Remove Woodruff key.

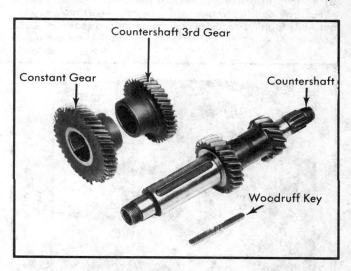

Fig. 12 Countershaft Assembly

Inspection — Inspect components for wear or damage and replace as necessary.

Reassembly — Install Woodruff key and press gears onto countershaft in reverse of removal. Make sure no material is scraped from Woodruff key. Gears should mate flush to each other.

TRANSMISSION REASSEMBLY

Mainshaft — 1) Install countershaft into transmission housing. Slide the assembly sleeve over rear end of mainshaft

Manual Transmissions

MERCEDES-BENZ 4-SPEED (Cont.)

and tighten with slot nut. Move 3rd-4th synchro assembly into third speed position and install mainshaft, at an angle, in transmission housing.

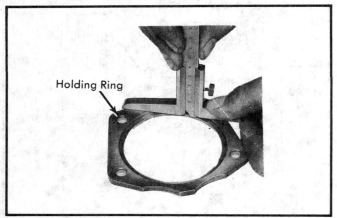

Fig. 13   Measuring Holding Ring Recess Depth

2) Insert needle bearings into input shaft and slide fourth speed blocking ring onto cone of input shaft gear. Install input shaft into transmission housing from front, while lifting mainshaft until bearing journal will slide into the needle bearings without forcing.

3) Remove assembly sleeve from rear mainshaft and install radial ball bearing. Make sure that input shaft does not slip out while tapping on bearing. Install front and rear radial ball bearings of countershaft. Raise countershaft to ease installa-

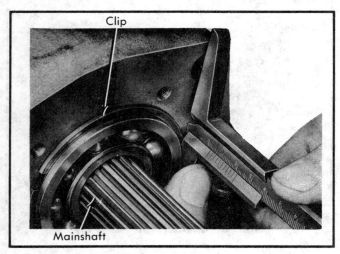

Fig. 14   Measuring Height on Mainshaft Clip

tion. Lock gear assemblies and tighten slot nut on front of countershaft. Adjust end play of mainshaft to specification of 0-.002" (0-.05 mm) by adding or subtracting spacing washers (shims) between holding ring and snap ring on mainshaft. Spacing washers are available in .004" (.1 mm), .008" (.2 mm), and .012" (.3 mm) thickness.

4) Insert correct thickness washers and install holding ring over mainshaft and tighten screws. Slide reverse gear, of countershaft, onto countershaft and attach with nut. Carefully secure nut by peening pinch collar into groove in countershaft. Install reverse idler gear and shaft, with milled surface up, into transmission housing. Install mainshaft reverse shifter, fork rod and secure with nut. Install extension housing.

5) Adjust end play of input shaft to specification of 0-.002" (0-.05 mm) by measuring depth of recess in front cover, with gasket installed, and height of snap ring on input shaft. Adjust countershaft end play in same maner. Add correct spacing washers and install front cover.

Gearshift Housing — Install new gasket and place reverse shifter in center position. Install shift forks and guide gearshift housing onto transmission housing dowel guides. Make sure gearshift housing is seated against transmission housing and install bolts. Install reverse shift lever.

Clutch Housing — Slide clutch housing complete with slave cylinder and pressure line onto studs of transmission housing and force over flange of front transmission cover. When clutch housing and transmission housing are mated flush, install nuts and tighten. Attach clutch release bearing and arm.

TIGHTENING SPECIFICATIONS

Application	Ft. Lbs. (mkg)
Gearshift Housing	
Bolts	11 (1.5)
Locking Cage	18 (2.5)
Slot Nuts	
Countershaft	109 (15)
Input Shaft	109 (15)
Mainshaft (Front)	58 (8)
Universal Flange	109 (15)
Transmission Cover Bolts	
Front	
M10	33 (4.5)
M7	11 (1.5)
Rear	
M10	33 (4.5)
M7	11 (1.5)

MGB 4-SPEED

DESCRIPTION

Transmission is a 4-speed fully synchronized unit. Clutch housing is intergal with transmission case. Main components of the transmission are: Transmission case/clutch housing, extension housing and remote shift control housing.

LUBRICATION & ADJUSTMENT

See MANUAL TRANSMISSION SERVICING Section.

TROUBLE SHOOTING

HARD SHIFTING

Clutch not releasing properly. Check for proper adjustment, deformed clutch disc, seized or damaged pilot bearing. Incorrect or insufficient lubricant. Gearshift lever retainer binding or improperly lubricated. Gear selector rods and/or forks damaged.

JUMPS OUT OF GEAR

Worn or damaged shift forks. Detent balls and springs worn or broken. Worn or damaged synchro assemblies. Improper thrust clearance between gears.

NOISY OPERATION

Improper or insufficient lubricant. Worn or damaged bushings, bearings and/or gears. Worn splines.

NOTE — When checking transmission for noise, ensure that it is not coming from other parts of the drive line.

TRANSMISSION REMOVAL & INSTALLATION

NOTE — Engine and transmission are removed as a unit and separated after removal.

Removal — 1) Raise and support vehicle. Drain transmission oil. Disconnect and remove propeller shaft by disconnecting at rear axle and sliding out of transmission housing. Disconnect clutch slave cylinder pushrod from throw-out bearing fork. Tie up cylinder clear of transmission. Remove speedometer cable from rear of extension housing.

2) Remove bolts securing rear crossmember to body and lower engine-transmission assembly until transmission rests on fixed body crossmember. Remove engine rear crossmember from transmission extension housing. Withdraw rear crossmember from body. Remove gearshift lever knob and rubber cover from transmission tunnel. Remove remote control box complete with lever.

3) In engine compartment, disconnect all wires, hoses and physical connections between body and engine. Drain cooling system and engine oil. Attach suitable lifting device to engine and pull forward to clear fixed body crossmember, then upward to clear engine compartment. With engine and transmission removed as a unit and placed on suitable stand, remove bolts securing transmission to engine and separate transmission from engine.

NOTE — Ensure that no strain is placed on clutch pressure plate or disc during removal or installation. Even slight pressure on pressure plate springs may result in clutch failure at high speed.

Installation — To install, reverse removal procedure and replenish all fluids.

TRANSMISSION DISASSEMBLY

Disassembly — 1) Remove lock nut and washer from clutch release lever. Remove dust boot and lever from clutch housing. Remove nut, spring washer and pin from engine rear support. Remove dipstick, drain plug and speedometer drive pinion. Use gear-bearing puller to remove propeller shaft flange from rear of extension housing. Remove remote control shift lever housing, transmission side cover and inter-lock plate with its bracket.

2) Remove side cover, remove detent plugs, washers, springs and plungers. Remove the locating screws from the selector forks. Remove nuts and washers securing front cover, remove cover, gasket and input shaft bearing shims.

NOTE — Do not remove front oil seal, unless it is evident that seal is leaking.

3) Before removing countergear, measure countergear thrust clearance. Clearance should be .002-.007" (.05-.18 mm). Record actual measurement for reference on reassembly. Use a soft metal drift to drive countershaft out the front of transmission case, and allow countergear to rest on bottom of case. Remove mainshaft from transmission case, using a suitable puller.

Fig. 1 Measuring Countergear Thrust Clearance

COMPONENT DISASSEMBLY & REASSEMBLY

INPUT SHAFT

Inspect input shaft bearing and splined surfaces for wear and damage. While holding input shaft in one hand, rotate bearing with other hand and check for roughness or noise. If necessary to replace front bearing, place input shaft (drive end) into soft jawed vise and remove snap ring, then remove shaft nut, noting that nut has left hand threads. Press old bearing off shaft and press on new bearing.

MGB 4-SPEED (Cont.)

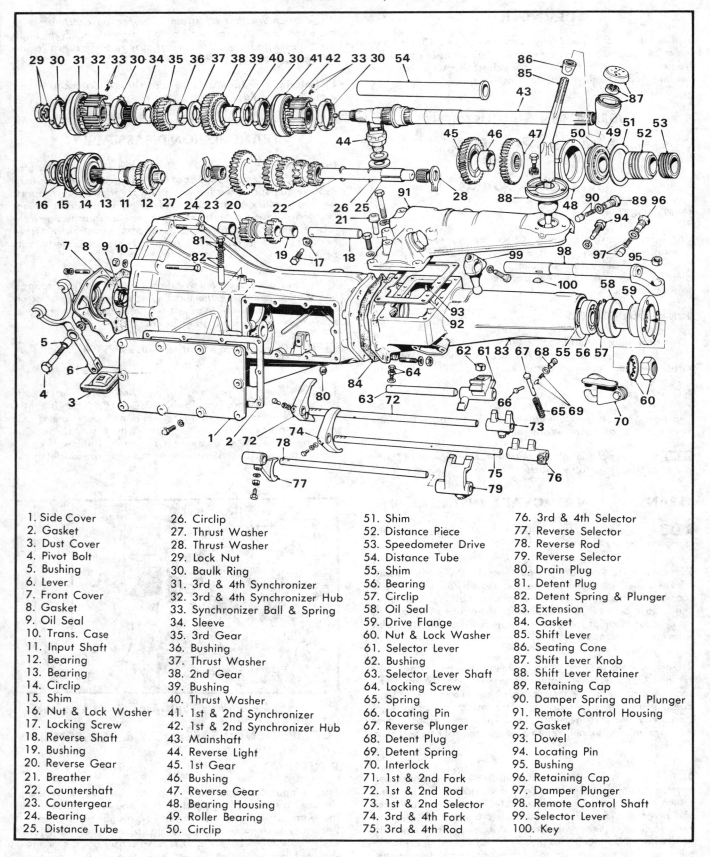

Fig. 2 Exploded View of MGB Transmission Assembly

1. Side Cover
2. Gasket
3. Dust Cover
4. Pivot Bolt
5. Bushing
6. Lever
7. Front Cover
8. Gasket
9. Oil Seal
10. Trans. Case
11. Input Shaft
12. Bearing
13. Bearing
14. Circlip
15. Shim
16. Nut & Lock Washer
17. Locking Screw
18. Reverse Shaft
19. Bushing
20. Reverse Gear
21. Breather
22. Countershaft
23. Countergear
24. Bearing
25. Distance Tube

26. Circlip
27. Thrust Washer
28. Thrust Washer
29. Lock Nut
30. Baulk Ring
31. 3rd & 4th Synchronizer
32. 3rd & 4th Synchronizer Hub
33. Synchronizer Ball & Spring
34. Sleeve
35. 3rd Gear
36. Bushing
37. Thrust Washer
38. 2nd Gear
39. Bushing
40. Thrust Washer
41. 1st & 2nd Synchronizer
42. 1st & 2nd Synchronizer Hub
43. Mainshaft
44. Reverse Light
45. 1st Gear
46. Bushing
47. Reverse Gear
48. Bearing Housing
49. Roller Bearing
50. Circlip

51. Shim
52. Distance Piece
53. Speedometer Drive
54. Distance Tube
55. Shim
56. Bearing
57. Circlip
58. Oil Seal
59. Drive Flange
60. Nut & Lock Washer
61. Selector Lever
62. Bushing
63. Selector Lever Shaft
64. Locking Screw
65. Spring
66. Locating Pin
67. Reverse Plunger
68. Detent Plug
69. Detent Spring
70. Interlock
71. 1st & 2nd Fork
72. 1st & 2nd Rod
73. 1st & 2nd Selector
74. 3rd & 4th Fork
75. 3rd & 4th Rod

76. 3rd & 4th Selector
77. Reverse Selector
78. Reverse Rod
79. Reverse Selector
80. Drain Plug
81. Detent Plug
82. Detent Spring & Plunger
83. Extension
84. Gasket
85. Shift Lever
86. Seating Cone
87. Shift Lever Knob
88. Shift Lever Retainer
89. Retaining Cap
90. Damper Spring and Plunger
91. Remote Control Housing
92. Gasket
93. Dowel
94. Locating Pin
95. Bushing
96. Retaining Cap
97. Damper Plunger
98. Remote Control Shaft
99. Selector Lever
100. Key

MGB 4-SPEED (Cont.)

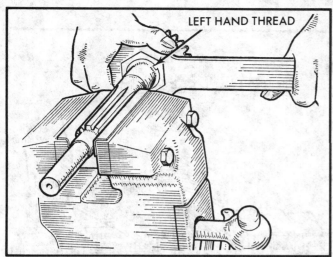

LEFT HAND THREAD

Fig. 3   Removing Input Shaft Nut

COUNTERGEAR

Inspection — Inspect needle bearings and bearing surfaces for wear or damage. If necessary to replace one roller bearing assembly, it is advisable to replace both. If shaft or gear requires replacement, replacement of countergear as an assembly is desirable.

MAINSHAFT

Disassembly — **1)** Remove 3rd and 4th gear synchronizer assembly. Unlock locking tabs and remove mainshaft lock nut. Remove shaft sleeve, 3rd gear and interlocking washer. Remove 2nd gear and thrust washer. Remove 1st and 2nd gear synchronizer assembly, speedometer drive gear Woodruff key and spacer. Press 1st gear, reverse gear bearings and bearing housings from mainshaft.

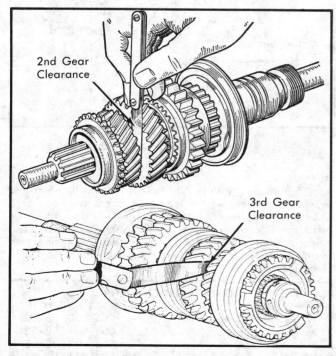

2nd Gear Clearance

3rd Gear Clearance

Fig. 4   Measuring 2nd and 3rd Gear Thrust Clearance

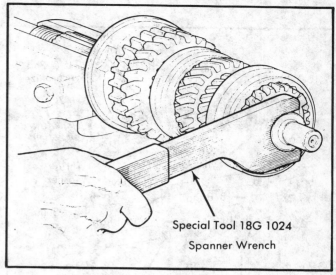

Special Tool 18G 1024

Spanner Wrench

Fig. 5   Removing Mainshaft Front Lock Nut

2) Remove synchro rings from synchro assemblies. Place shop towel around synchro assemblies to catch all detent balls and springs, then press synchro sleeve off of hub.

Inspection — **1)** Thoroughly clean, dry and examine all components for wear, distortion, deterioration and thread damage. Pay particular attention to the following: Bushings fitted to throw-out bearing fork; 3rd gear and reverse gear should be checked for wear or damage. Check bearings on input shaft, mainshaft and rear extension housing. Also examine needle roller bearings of input shaft and countergear.

2) Check springs of each synchro hub, shaft locating block, reverse gear shaft and reverse plunger detent. Comparisons should be made with new springs to determine condition of old. Examine interlock arms for burrs and for tightness of the rivet. Ensure that all oilways are clear, by blowing air through them.

Reassembly — **1)** Lubricate all contact surfaces with oil and smear inside of each gear with Moly Disulphide Grease. Use special tool 18G 222, 18G 1026 or heavy rubber band to assemble synchro hubs and sleeves. Press rear bearing into its housing. Fit speedometer drive gear to shaft with Woodruff key.

2) Assemble 1st-2nd synchro onto mainshaft followed by synchro ring and rear thrust washer. Install 2nd gear bushing and ensure that lugs face forward and that oil hole in bushing is aligned with oil hole in shaft. Install 2nd gear and inter-lock washer such that inter-lock engages with lugs in the bushing.

Manual Transmissions

MGB 4-SPEED (Cont.)

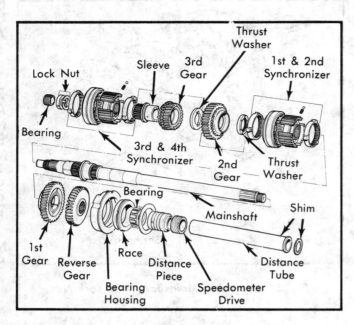

Fig. 6   Exploded View of Mainshaft

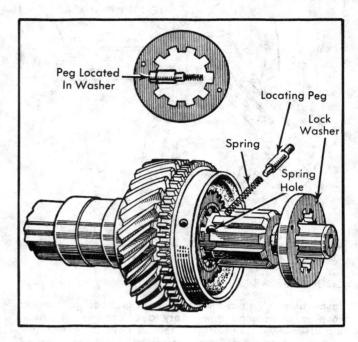

Fig. 8   Securing Mainshaft Front Gears

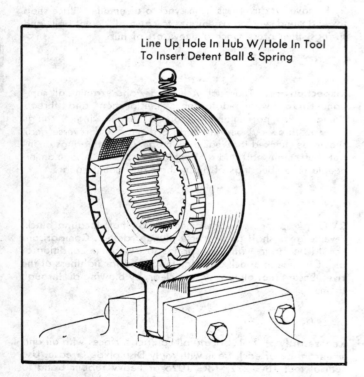

Line Up Hole In Hub W/Hole In Tool
To Insert Detent Ball & Spring

**Fig. 7   Assembling Synchronizer Using Special Tool
18G 1026**

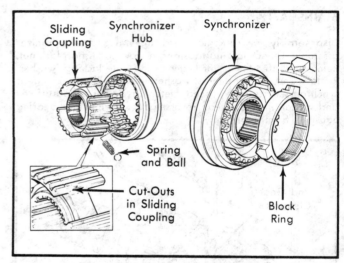

Fig. 9   Exploded View of Synchronizer

4) Position gear so that hole in cone is in line with retaining peg, depress peg (with thin drift punch) and fit thrust washer to allow peg to lock washer in position. Check thrust clearance of 2nd and 3rd gear. Thrust washers come in 4 sizes, which are listed in table. After selecting and installing correct thrust washers, install 3rd and 4th gear rear synchronizer ring; then install 3rd and 4th synchronizer assembly and front synchronizer ring.

3) Install 3rd gear bushing, lugs first, and ensure that lugs engage inter-lock washer. Also make sure that oil hole and cut-away in bushing are in alignment with holes in shaft. Place retaining pin spring in shaft and 3rd gear on bushing with coned surface facing forward.

Gear Thrust Clearance	
Application	**In. (mm)**
1st Gear	.005-.008 (.13-.20)
2nd Gear	.005-.009 (.13-.23)
3rd Gear	.005-.007 (.13-.18)
Countergear	.002-.007 (.05-.18)

MGB 4-SPEED (Cont.)

Gear Thrust Washer Sizes

Application	Thickness In. (mm)
1.	.002 (.05)
2.	.005 (.13)
3.	.010 (.25)

TRANSMISSION REASSEMBLY

1) With thrust clearance recorded on disassembly, determine (from table) correct thrust washer which will give correct thrust clearance of .002-.003" (.05-.08 mm) and install countergear assembly into bottom of gearbox.

Countergear Thrust Washer Sizes

Application	Thickness In. (mm)
1	.119-.121 (3.04-3.09)
2	.123-.125 (3.12-3.17)
3	.127-.129 (3.21-3.26)
4	.130-.132 (3.30-3.35)
5	.133-.135 (3.38-3.43)

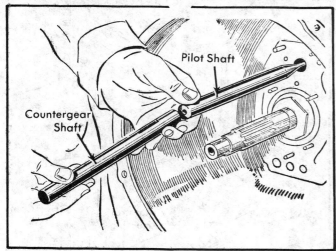

Fig. 10   Installing Pilot Shaft and Countergear Shaft

2) Install input shaft into front of gearbox. Insert mainshaft into gearbox. Use extension housing gasket to align dowel, in bearing housing. Slide input and mainshaft together. Insert dummy countershaft into countergear. Install countergear shaft through front of gearbox, pushing out dummy shaft to rear.

NOTE — Ensure that cut-away portion of shaft is facing front of transmission when installing countershaft.

3) Assemble reverse gear on its shaft and secure shaft with locating bolt. Install input shaft bearing shims. Align cut-away portion of countershaft with edge of front cover. Clean cover and inspect it for burrs, particularly around its bore. Install front cover over end of input shaft and push cover over studs.

NOTE — Input shaft front cover should glide easily over input shaft, without binding at stud holes. If difficulty is encountered, relieve stud holes in area of binding.

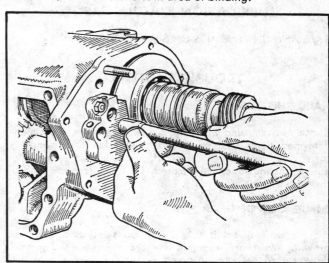

Fig. 11   Assembling Shift Rail Shafts into Rear Block

4) On rear of gearbox, bolt shaft locating block and insert three springs and balls. Assemble selectors to their shafts and lock in place with locating bolts. Lock bolt heads with security wire. Depress spring loaded balls of locating block (at rear of gearbox) and insert each shifting rail shaft. Position each shifting fork in gearbox in following order: reverse, 1st-2nd and 3rd-4th. Install spacer to 3rd-4th shift rail shaft. Push each shaft through its respective fork and align holes in shafts with holes in forks. Secure each fork with locating bolt.

5) Replace gearbox side cover. Place spacer on mainshaft and fit extension housing to gearbox, while engaging remote control shift rod with shift rails. Secure shift lever with Woodruff key and locating bolt. Install speedometer drive pinion gear. Install gearbox dip stick, drain plug and rear flange with nut. Refill transmission with clean oil.

TIGHTENING SPECIFICATIONS

Application	Ft. Lbs. (mkg)
Drive Flange Nut	150 (20.7)
Remote Control Shift Cover	8.5 (1.2)
Transmission-to-Engine	15-20 (2.1-2.8)

Manual Transmissions

MGB WITH OVERDRIVE 4-SPEED

DESCRIPTION

Transmission is a fully synchronized 4-speed unit, with an overdrive unit attached to the rear of the transmission case. Main components of the transmission are: Transmission case/clutch housing, remote control shift housing and overdrive adapter.

LUBRICATION & ADJUSTMENT

See MANUAL TRANSMISSION SERVICING Section

TROUBLE SHOOTING

HARD SHIFTING

Clutch not releasing properly. Check for proper adjustment, deformed clutch disc, seized or damaged pilot bearing. Incorrect or insufficient lubricant. Gearshift lever retainer binding or improperly lubricated. Gear selector rod and/or forks damaged.

JUMPS OUT OF GEAR

Worn or damaged shift forks. Detent balls and springs worn or broken. Worn or damaged synchro assemblies. Improper thrust clearance between gears.

NOISY OPERATION

Improper or insufficient lubricant. Worn or damaged bushings and/or gears. Worn splines.

NOTE — *When checking transmission for noise, ensure that it is not coming from other parts of the drive line.*

TRANSMISSION REMOVAL & INSTALLATION

NOTE — *Engine and transmission are removed as a unit and separated after removal*

Removal — 1) Raise and support vehicle. Drain transmission oil. Disconnect and remove propeller shaft by disconnecting at rear axle and sliding out of transmission housing. Disconnect clutch slave cylinder pushrod from throw-out bearing fork. Tie up cylinder clear of transmission. Remove speedometer cable from rear of overdrive unit.

2) Remove bolts securing rear crossmember to body and lower engine-transmission assembly until transmission rests on fixed body crossmember. Remove engine rear crossmember from transmission. Withdraw rear crossmember from body. Remove gearshift lever knob and rubber cover from transmission tunnel. Remove remote control box, complete with gear lever.

3) In engine compartment, disconnect all wires, hoses and connections between body and engine. Drain coolant and engine oil. Attach engine to hoist, and pull forward to clear fixed body crossmember, then upward to clear engine compartment. With engine and transmission removed, place on a stand,

Installation — To install, reverse removal procedure and refill engine and transmission. Refill engine coolant.

TRANSMISSION DISASSEMBLY

1) Drain oil from transmission. Remove overdrive unit, remote control assembly (noting the two dowel locating pins). Select 4th gear and lift out interlock arm assembly. See *Fig. 1.* Slide the overdrive pump driving cam from the mainshaft and remove driving ball from pocket in the mainshaft.

2) Remove the pump cam circlip and overdrive adapter. Remove side cover and the three detent plugs, washers, springs and plungers. Remove selector rod locking screws, remove selector rods and lift out selector forks. Remove clutch lever and front cover. Remove the reverse shaft locking screw and remove the reverse shaft, from the rear of the transmission.

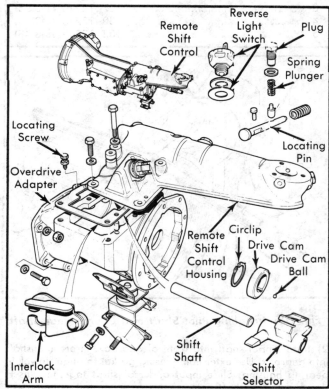

Fig. 1   Exploded View of Overdrive Adapter Assembly

3) Remove the countershaft from the transmission case. Place the countergear at the bottom of the case. Remove rear bearing housing from the rear of the transmission case and withdraw mainshaft assembly.

NOTE — *If necessary, use a press to remove mainshaft from case. Use a soft metal drift to drive input shaft out front of transmission, from inside of the case.*

MGB WITH OVERDRIVE 4-SPEED (Cont.)

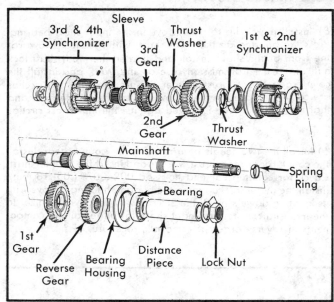

Fig. 2   Exploded View of Mainshaft

COMPONENT DISASSEMBLY & REASSEMBLY

Disassembly — 1) Remove the lock nut from the input shaft, (left hand threads). Press the input shaft out of the bearing, remove circlip from bearing and remove bearing. Remove the lock nut from the mainshaft, remove 3rd gear, sleeve and thrust washer. Remove the 2nd gear and thrust washer. Remove the 1st and 2nd synchronizer. See Fig. 2.

2) Remove the rear lock nut from the mainshaft. Support the 1st gear and press out the shaft. Remove the spring ring from the mainshaft. Using a cloth to catch the balls and springs, push the synchronizer hub from the sliding coupler.

Inspection of Block Rings — Check the block rings with the mating tapers on the gears; if the ring contacts the edge of the gear before tapers are fully engaged, replace the block rings.

Countergear — Inspect needle bearings and bearing surfaces for wear or damage. If necessary to replace one roller bearing assembly, it is advisable to replace both. If shaft or gear requires replacement, replace countergear as an assembly.

Mainshaft — Check all components for wear, distortion and thread damage. Check the bushings fitted to the throw-out bearing fork, 3rd and reverse gears for wear.

Reassembly — 1) Install the synchronizer hub into tool (18G 1026) and align one of the spring pockets with the hole in the tool. Install the spring and ball, rotate the hub to secure the ball and spring. Align the cut-outs in the sliding coupling with those in the hub, and slide the hub from the tool to the coupling. See Fig. 3.

2) Install the block rings to the synchronizers.

NOTE — *The block rings are not interchangable. The 3rd-4th block rings are identified by fillets at the base of the lugs.*

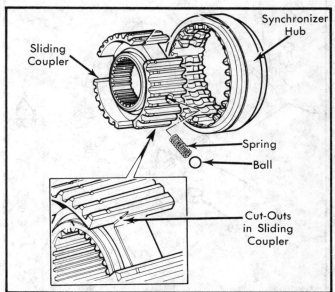

Fig. 3   Exploded View of Sliding Coupler and Synchronizer Hub

3) Install the 1st and reverse gear, (with the large diameters facing each other). Push the reverse gear towards the 1st gear and check 1st gear end float. The 1st gear end float should be .005-.008" (.13-.20 mm). Press bearing housing assembly onto the shaft. Install the distance piece onto the mainshaft, install lock nut and tighten.

4) Install the 1st and 2nd synchronizer on the mainshaft (the groove in the sliding coupling must be adjacent to the 2nd gear). Install the 2nd gear and thrust washer. Install the 3rd gear sleeve and thrust washer as an assembly, install nut and tighten. Check end float of 2nd and 3rd gears. The 2nd gear end float should be .005-.009" (.13-.23 mm); 3rd gear end float should be .005-.007" (.13-.18 mm).

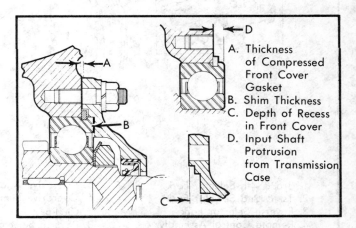

Fig. 4   Measuring Shim Thickness for Input Shaft Bearing/Front Cover

Manual Transmissions

MGB WITH OVERDRIVE 4-SPEED (Cont.)

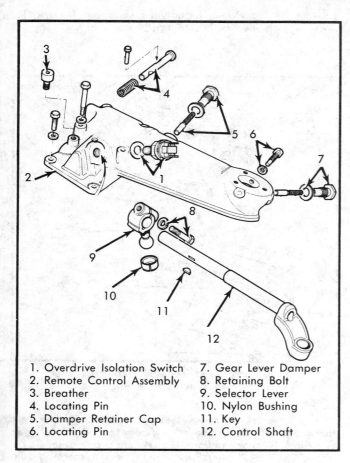

1. Overdrive Isolation Switch
2. Remote Control Assembly
3. Breather
4. Locating Pin
5. Damper Retainer Cap
6. Locating Pin
7. Gear Lever Damper
8. Retaining Bolt
9. Selector Lever
10. Nylon Bushing
11. Key
12. Control Shaft

Fig. 5 Exploded View of Remote Control Assembly

5) Install the circlip to the groove in the input shaft bearing. Press the bearing on the input shaft, with the circlip towards the front of the shaft. Install and tighten the input shaft lock nut. Stand the transmission case on the front, and install the countergear front thrust washer. Ensure that the two circlips are correctly placed in the grooves inside the countergear and that the distance tube is seated against the innermost circlip.

6) Install the two needle bearings onto the countergear. Install the countergear rear thrust washer and insert the countershaft. Check for countergear end float of .002-.007″ (.05-.18 mm). Install the mainshaft, aligning the bearing housing groove with its locating dowel. Install the 3rd and 4th gear synchronizer to the mainshaft. Install the input shaft. Install remaining components in reverse order of removal procedure.

TIGHTENING SPECIFICATIONS

Application	Ft. Lbs. (mkg)
Remote Control Cover	8.5 (1.2)
Transmission-to-Engine	15-20 (2.1-2.8)

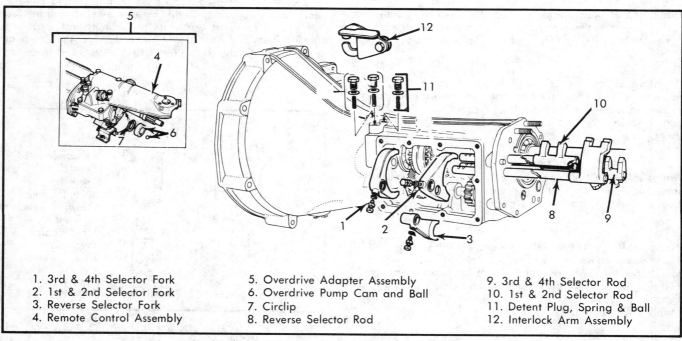

1. 3rd & 4th Selector Fork
2. 1st & 2nd Selector Fork
3. Reverse Selector Fork
4. Remote Control Assembly
5. Overdrive Adapter Assembly
6. Overdrive Pump Cam and Ball
7. Circlip
8. Reverse Selector Rod
9. 3rd & 4th Selector Rod
10. 1st & 2nd Selector Rod
11. Detent Plug, Spring & Ball
12. Interlock Arm Assembly

Fig. 6 Exploded View of Shift Rod and Forks

PEUGEOT 4 & 5-SPEED

504
505
604

DESCRIPTION

The 4 and 5-speed transmissions have a split aluminum case. Access to gear assembly is with one half of the case removed. All forward gears are of the helical type which provide for quiet operation. All forward gears are also synchronized for smooth gear engagement. Shift linkage is floor mounted with external linkage. On 4-speed transmissions, reverse gears are located in the extension housing. On 5-speed transmissions, 5th gear is located in the extension housing along with reverse gears.

LUBRICATION & ADJUSTMENT

See MANUAL TRANSMISSION SERVICING Section.

TROUBLE SHOOTING

HARD SHIFTING

Improperly adjusted clutch. Excessive input shaft end play. Face of synchro hub in contact with cone, worn. Synchro cones worn, damaged, distorted or not in proper contact.

SLIPS OUT OF GEAR

Bearings worn or defective. Excessive play between gears and synchro cage. Play in synchro hub. Shift arm worn. Lock ball spring weak or broken. Lock ball missing.

TRANSMISSION NOISY

Low or incorrect lubricant. Gears or bearings worn or damaged. Worn gears or synchro cage. Excessive input shaft end play. Worn synchro hub or splines. Incorrectly meshed gears.

TRANSMISSION REMOVAL & INSTALLATION

Removal — 1) Remove hood, battery with tray, ignition coil, starter, radiator, expansion tank and windshield washer bottle. Disconnect heater hoses, fuel lines, throttle controls, vacuum lines and all chassis-to-engine electrical wires. Remove air cleaner and ducting for fuel injection or carburetor.

2) On models with air conditioning, remove and set aside under hood air conditioning components. DO NOT disconnect hoses or pressure connections. Disconnect electrical leads to compressor, pressure switch, thermostat and electric cooling fan. Remove receiver-drier, condenser and compressor from mountings and position off to right side of vehicle.

3) On models with power steering, remove power steering pump and set aside leaving hoses connected. On all models, remove upper clutch housing-to-engine mounting bolts and inspection plates. Disconnect engine mounts. Disconnect exhaust pipe from manifold and remove muffler and exhaust pipe supporting brackets with heat deflector.

4) Attach engine hoisting sling and raise engine until transmission contacts tunnel. On 604 models, fit propeller shaft tube support between muffler and body and tighten to support tube. Remove steering coupling clamp bolts and replace with slightly longer bolts. Lower front crossmember 1.2" (30 mm), leaving steering rack attached.

5) Pull engine forward slightly and carefully lift engine and transmission assembly from vehicle. Remove lower clutch housing-to-engine bolts and place engine on workstand. Separate engine from transmission assembly.

NOTE — *Clutch slave cylinder and release assembly remains with clutch housing during removal.*

Installation — Reverse removal removal procedures and note the following: Lubricate input shaft splines and clutch release bearing guide with grease (Molykote or equivalent). Refill transmission with correct fluid to proper level. Make any linkage adjustments as required.

TRANSMISSION DISASSEMBLY

1) Place transmission on its side with clutch release fork facing upward. From clutch housing remove clutch release fork. From side of transmission, remove back-up light switch. Now remove bolts securing clutch housing to gearbox.

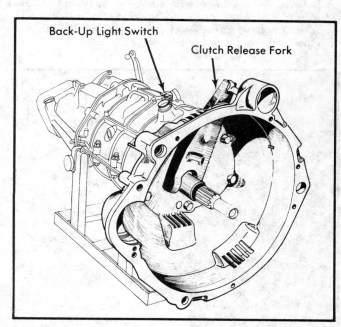

Fig. 1   Front View of Transmission Clutch Housing

2) On extension housing, remove speedometer driven gear. Place shift control lever in the neutral position. On 4-speed transmissions, remove bolts which secure extension housing to gearbox. Remove extension housing with plastic mallet if necessary. On 5-speed transmissions, remove rear cover plate and gasket. Remove extension housing-to-gearbox bolts, install special tool 8.0314M and remove housing from transmission.

3) On 4-speed transmissions, remove bearing retainer bolts, then remove 8 bolts which secure 2 halves of transmission gearbox together and remove upper half of gearbox. On 5-speed transmissions, remove 5th driven gear with suitable puller. Remove shim washer, spacer and 5th drive gear with needle bearing from rear of countershaft. Mark position of 5th/reverse synchronizer assembly for reassembly reference.

PEUGEOT 4 & 5-SPEED (Cont.)

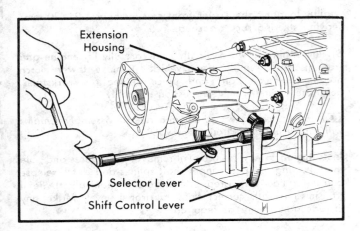

Fig. 2   Withdrawing Extension Housing & Related Parts

4) Engage 5th gear and drive out rollpin from selector fork and shaft. Reset gear in neutral position and remove 5th/reverse synchronizer assembly, selector fork and 5th gear snub shaft. Remove intermediate housing bolts and remove housing from transmission. Remove bearing thrust plate bolts. Remove 12 bolts which secure 2 halves of transmission gearbox together and remove upper half of gearbox.

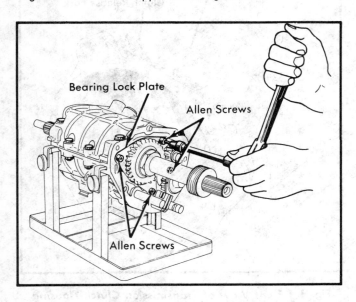

Fig. 3   Disconnecting Rear Bearing Lock Plate

COMPONENT DISASSEMBLY & REASSEMBLY

COUNTERGEAR

Disassembly — On 4-speed transmissions, from small end of countergear, remove snap ring, washer, gear and bearing outer race. If it is necessary to remove front or rear bearing inner race, use suitable press and adapter plate. On 5-speed transmissions, use suitable press and adapter plate to press off front and rear bearings.

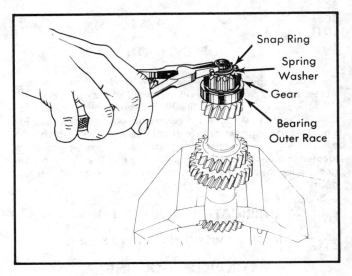

Fig. 4   Removing Parts From Countershaft

Inspection & Reassembly — Clean all parts in suitable solvent and blow dry with compressed air. To reassemble, reverse disassembly procedure.

MAINSHAFT

Disassembly — **1)** Shift and hold 3rd-4th speed synchro sleeve into 3rd gear position. While holding in this position, separate input shaft from mainshaft. Remove needle bearing (caged unit) from either input shaft or mainshaft. Place mainshaft in vise, rear end downward, and remove grease from teeth of 3rd-4th synchro, without damaging synchro hub or ring. Mark hub and sleeve, with sharp pointed brass rod, for reassembly reference.

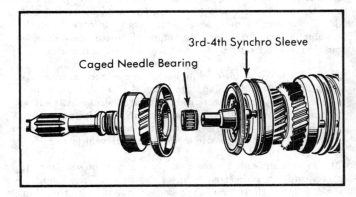

Fig. 5   Input Shaft Separated from Mainshaft

2) Remove 3rd-4th synchro sleeve. From input end of mainshaft, remove snap ring and washer from 3rd-4th synchro hub. While holding mainshaft reverse gear with special spanner wrench SJ 214, unscrew mainshaft rear lock nut.

PEUGEOT 4 & 5-SPEED (Cont.)

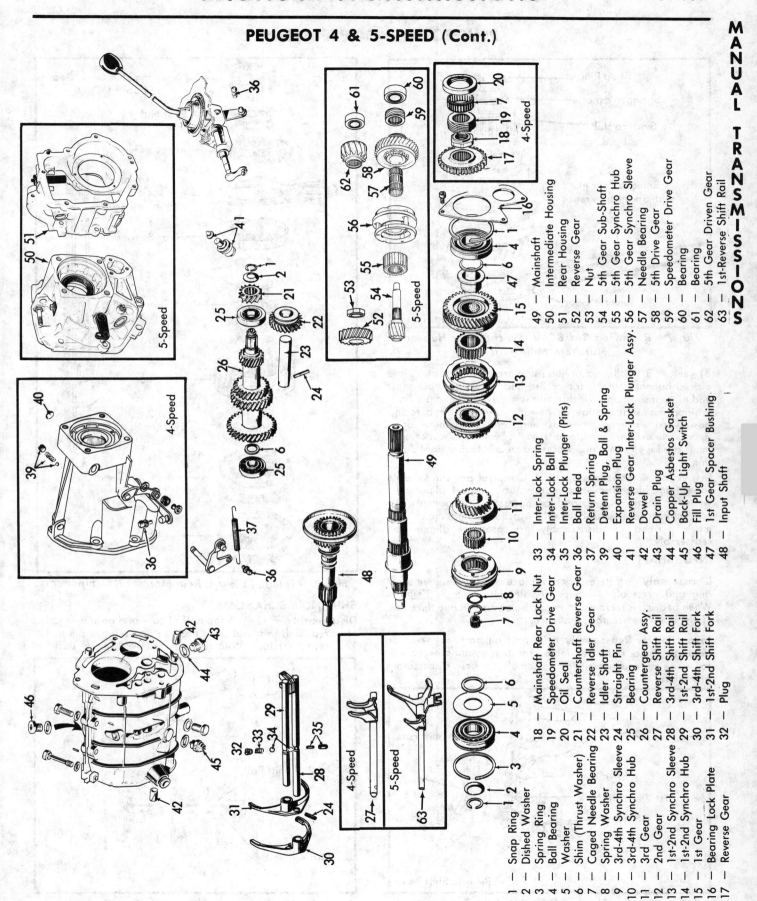

1 — Snap Ring
2 — Dished Washer
3 — Spring Ring
4 — Ball Bearing
5 — Washer
6 — Shim (Thrust Washer)
7 — Caged Needle Bearing
8 — Spring Washer
9 — 3rd-4th Synchro Sleeve
10 — 3rd-4th Synchro Hub
11 — 3rd Gear
12 — 2nd Gear
13 — 1st-2nd Synchro Sleeve
14 — 1st-2nd Synchro Hub
15 — 1st Gear
16 — Bearing Lock Plate
17 — Reverse Gear

18 — Mainshaft Rear Lock Nut
19 — Speedometer Drive Gear
20 — Oil Seal
21 — Countershaft Reverse Gear
22 — Reverse Idler Gear
23 — Idler Shaft
24 — Straight Pin
25 — Bearing
26 — Countergear Assy.
27 — Reverse Shift Rail
28 — 3rd-4th Shift Rail
29 — 1st-2nd Shift Rail
30 — 3rd-4th Shift Fork
31 — 1st-2nd Shift Fork
32 — Plug

33 — Inter-lock Spring
34 — Inter-lock Ball
35 — Inter-lock Plunger (Pins)
36 — Ball Head
37 — Return Spring
39 — Detent Plug, Ball & Spring
40 — Expansion Plug
41 — Reverse Gear Inter-Lock Plunger Assy.
42 — Dowel
43 — Drain Plug
44 — Copper Asbestos Gasket
45 — Back-Up Light Switch
46 — Fill Plug
47 — 1st Gear Spacer Bushing
48 — Input Shaft

49 — Mainshaft
50 — Intermediate Housing
51 — Rear Housing
52 — Reverse Gear
53 — Nut
54 — 5th Gear Sub-Shaft
55 — 5th Gear Synchro Hub
56 — 5th Gear Synchro Sleeve
57 — Needle Bearing
58 — 5th Drive Gear
59 — Speedometer Drive Gear
60 — Bearing
61 — Bearing
62 — 5th Gear Driven Gear
63 — 1st-Reverse Shift Rail

Fig. 6 Exploded View of Peugeot Transmission Assembly

PEUGEOT 4 & 5-SPEED (Cont.)

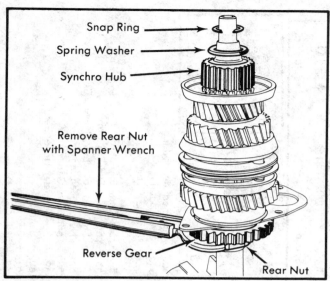

Fig. 7   Removing 3rd & 4th Synchronizer Hub and Nut from Mainshaft

3) Remove 3rd-4th synchro hub using press with adapter plate placed beneath outer edge of 3rd gear. Press on input shaft end of mainshaft until synchro hub is removed from mainshaft. Position mainshaft upside down with input shaft end facing downward. Press on mainshaft end until speedometer drive gear is removed from mainshaft. Make sure mainshaft components are layed out in order of removal and facing right direction.

Inspection & Reassembly —   Clean all parts in suitable solvent and blow dry with compressed air. Inspect all parts for wear or damage and replace necessary components. To reassemble, reverse disassembly procedure and make sure marks scribed on disassembly are properly aligned on reassembly.

INPUT SHAFT

Disassembly — If necessary to replace bearing, remove snap ring and press off old bearing with suitable tool. **NOTE** — *When bearing is removed, pay particular attention to thickness of shims for reassembly reference.*

Inspection & Reassembly — Inspect all parts for wear or damage. Check roller bearing by rotating by hand and check for noise or roughness. To reassemble, reverse disassembly procedure.

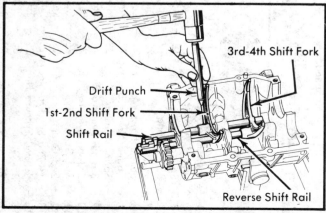

Fig. 8   Using a Drift Punch to Remove Straight Pins from Shift Forks

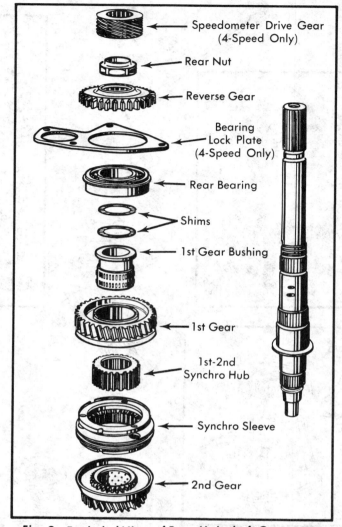

Fig. 9   Exploded View of Rear Mainshaft Components

SHIFTING MECHANISMS

Disassembly — 1) With top half of case and gear assemblies removed, shift into 2nd gear position and remove pin in 1st-2nd gear shift fork. With fork pin removed, move shift rail

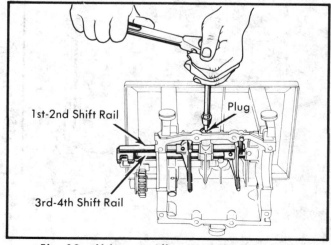

Fig. 10   Using an Allen Wrench to Remove Detent/Interlock Plug

PEUGEOT 4 & 5-SPEED (Cont.)

(shaft) back to neutral. Shift 3rd-4th shift rail into 4th gear position and remove pin in shift fork. Return shift rail to neutral.

2) Lay bottom half of transmission case on right side and remove detent plug from side of case. **NOTE** — *Remove plug by using 5 mm Allen wrench.* Now remove shift rail for 1st-2nd gear, then remove shift rail for 3rd-4th gears. **NOTE** — *As shift rails are removed, catch detent ball and spring.*

3) Turn case on its side and remove reverse detent plug from side of case. Remove reverse shift fork. Remove interlock balls, pin and plunger by inserting a .273" (6.9 mm) diameter punch which is 8.97" (227.8 mm) long into detent interlock plug hole. Push parts out of bore and catch interlock ball and plunger. From 3rd-4th shift rail, remove interlock pin. From reverse idler gear shaft, drive out straight pin using punch and remove shaft by pushing it inside case.

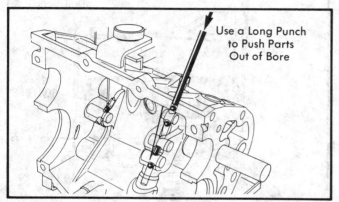

Use a Long Punch to Push Parts Out of Bore

Fig. 11   Removing Detent/Interlock Balls and Plunger

Inspection — Check neutral ball lock for positive locking action by moving selector lever in both directions. Also check that neutral ball lock plug is flush with case. If ball lock is inoperative, remove plug and inspect ball and spring. Clean all parts in suitable solvent and blow dry with compressed air. Inspect all parts for wear or damage and replace necessary components. **NOTE** — *When installing plugs into case, use some form of sealant.*

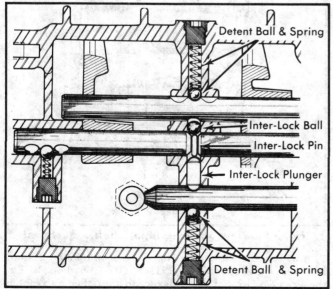

Detent Ball & Spring

Inter-Lock Ball

Inter-Lock Pin

Inter-Lock Plunger

Detent Ball & Spring

Fig. 12   Cutaway View of Transmission Showing Detent and Interlock Mechanisms

Reassembly — **1)** Install reverse idler shift rail, by using mallet and taking care to align pin holes. **NOTE** — *Manufacturer recommends using new straight pin, to hold shift rail in place.* Turn case on its side so that fill plug hole is facing upward. Install reverse idler gear, together with its shift fork. Through reverse shift rail hole, on side of case, insert detent ball and spring. Use sealer on detent plug threads and install plug into reverse detent hole.

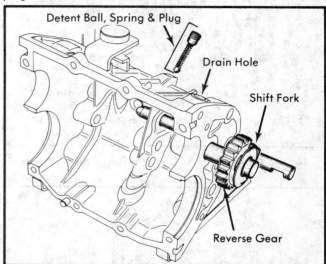

Detent Ball, Spring & Plug

Drain Hole

Shift Fork

Reverse Gear

Fig. 13   Reverse Idler Gear and Detent Assembly Positions in Transmission Case Half

2) Flip case over to other side. Install 3rd-4th reverse inter-lock plunger. Grease and install inter-lock pin into 3rd-4th shift rail.

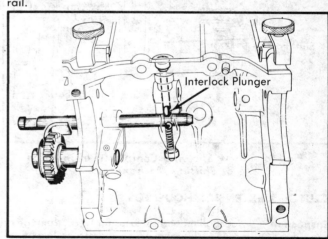

Interlock Plunger

Fig. 14   Interlock Plunger Position in Case Half

3) Turn case to face upward and install 1st-2nd shift fork (larger of two) and 3rd-4th shift rail into gearbox through two shift forks, until shaft is flush with ball lock hole. Into this hole, insert one detent spring and ball. Use drift punch to compress spring and ball assembly and slide shift rail forward until punch can be released and ball not jump out of hole.

4) Shift 3rd-4th shift rail into neutral and install straight pin into 3rd-4th shift fork (at forward end of case). Place case on right side. Through detent inter-lock hole, insert inter-lock ball. Now insert 1st-2nd shift rail through rear of case. Through detent inter-lock hole, insert detent ball, spring and secure with detent plug. **NOTE** — *Be sure to use sealant on detent plug threads. Now secure 1st-2nd shift fork with straight pin.*

PEUGEOT 4 & 5-SPEED (Cont.)

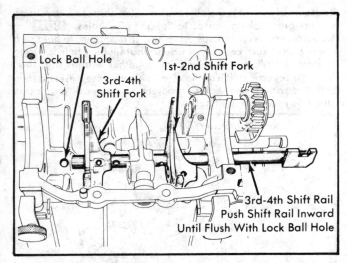

Fig. 15   Installing 3rd & 4th Shift Rail and Fork

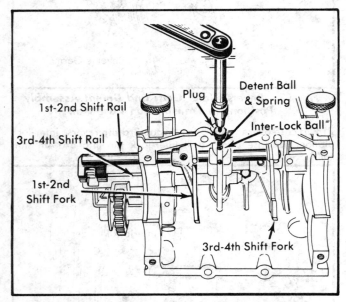

Fig. 16   View Showing Completed Installation of Shifting Mechanisms

CLUTCH & EXTENSION HOUSINGS

Inspection — Inspect all mating surfaces for wear, damage or warpage. On extension housing, if it is necessary to replace rear oil seal, remove old seal by using pry bar and install new seal by using press. On both housings, if it is necessary to replace rear bushing, use press to remove old bushing and install new one. On extension housing, if bushing was replaced, install new oil seal.

TRANSMISSION ADJUSTMENT & REASSEMBLY

Adjustments — 1) Install clutch housing onto gear case, then position on support base. Install input shaft in housing, install special tool 80310FZ and 80314G into countershaft bearing hole. See Fig. 17. Adjust dial indicator with upper edge of No. 3 synchronizer cone. Then rotate input shaft 1 revolution and set dial indicator to zero on highest spot located in 1 revolution.

2) Move dial indicator support until stem rests on surface of gauge. See Fig. 17. Now take a reading of dial indicator, the clearance found will be the amount of shims to be inserted between input shaft and front bearing.

Example:

Dial indicator reading	.023" (.58 mm)
1 Deflector washer	.006" (.15 mm)
1 Shim	.008" (.20 mm)
1 Shim	.010" (.25 mm)
Total shims needed	.024" (.60 mm)

NOTE — *Round shims to the nearest .002" (.05 mm)*

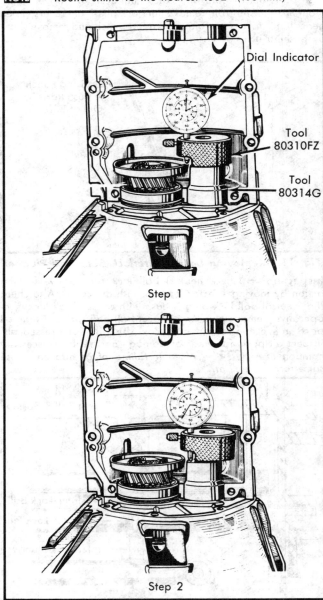

Fig. 17   View Showing Input Shaft Adjustment

3) Install needle bearing into input shaft. Install the mainshaft into case. Install special tool 80314K, 80310J and 80310FZ as shown in Fig. 18. Set dial indicator to zero, then turn dial indicator support until indicator finger is in contact with upper edge of No. 2 synchronizer cone. The clearance obtained in-

PEUGEOT 4 & 5-SPEED (Cont.)

dicates the thickness of shims to be inserted between 1st gear and rear bearing.

NOTE — *Round shims to the nearest .002" (.05 mm). Shims are available in .006" (.15 mm) to .020" (.50 mm) sizes.*

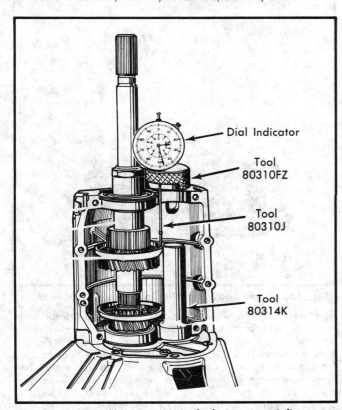

Fig. 18   View Showing Mainshaft Bearing Adjustment

4) Install left housing in suitable holding fixture. Install countergear shaft into case. Position right housing to left housing, install bolts and hand tighten only. On 4-speed transmissions, install bolts to end bearing plate. On 5-speed transmissions, install countershaft bearing plate and hand tighten bolts. Press down on countershaft and turn to seat bearing.

5) On 4-speed transmissions, install clutch housing with 4 bolts and tighten. On 5-speed transmissions, tighten side bearing bolts and countershaft bearing retainer bolts to same torque, in that order. On 4 and 5-speed transmissions, install special tool 80310EZ with dial indicator attached into countershaft bore. Rotate dial indicator 1 complete revolution. Runout between outer bearing face and face of transmission case halves must not exceed .001" (.03 mm). If runout exceeds limit, realign bearing outer race by tapping gently with soft-faced mallet.

6) With dial indicator in place on countershaft bore, set indicator to .08" (2.0 mm). Now move the indicator so finger rests on the front face of the housing. See *Fig. 19*. Note dial indicator reading, add .004" (.10 mm) to this reading for bearing preload. Now subtract .08" (2.0 mm) the result is the amount of shims to be installed between bearing and countershaft.

NOTE — *The result should be rounded to the nearest .002" (.05 mm).*

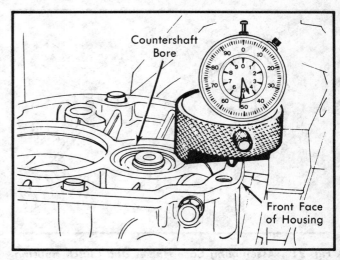

Fig. 19   Checking For Countershaft Bearing Preload

Reassembly — 1) Install needle bearing into rear of input shaft and assemble input shaft to mainshaft. Shift 3rd-4th synchro into neutral position. Mesh teeth of countergear with teeth of mainshaft and while holding assembly together in this manner, install assembly into transmission case.

NOTE — *As gear assembly is installed into bottom of case, make sure that shift forks engage with synchro sleeves.*

NOTE — *Apply a thin coat of sealer to faces of case halves.*

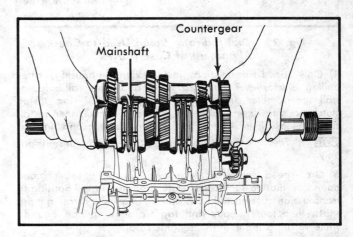

Fig. 20   Installing Countergear and Mainshaft into Case

2) With countergear and mainshaft installed, install bearing outer races to each end of countergear. Assemble two halves of transmission case together. Install clutch housing. Rotate input shaft while tapping lightly on outside of transmission case. Tighten case half bolts.

3) Rotate transmission up onto clutch housing face and on rear extension housing side of case, use dial indicator to discover whether two halves of case are flush with one another. If case halves are more than .002" (.05 mm), difference in height, loosen case half bolts and try to align case halves, then tighten bolts.

PEUGEOT 4 & 5-SPEED (Cont.)

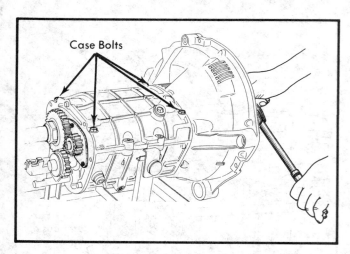

Fig. 21   Assembling Case Halves and Clutch Housing

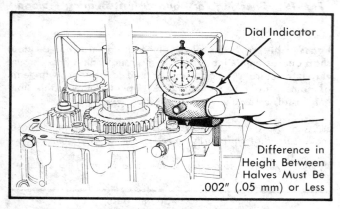

Fig. 22   Dial Indicator Being Used to Check Alignment of Case Halves

4) On 4-speed transmissions, install extension housing, after pulling selector lever rearward. Install and tighten all bolts. Install speedometer driven gear, sleeve, and "O" ring. Inside clutch housing, insert rubber cup onto pivotball, then install clutch release lever. Install back-up light switch and tighten.

NOTE — *The following steps pertain to 5-speed transmissions only.*

5) On 5-speed transmissions, apply a thin coat of sealing compound on mating surfaces of clutch housing. Install housing to transmission case, install bolts and tighten while rotating input shaft, then loosen bolts and tap transmission half housing while rotating input shaft. Retighten bolts.

6) Position transmission with clutch housing resting on support pad. Apply a thin coat of sealing compound on intermediate housing and place in position on transmission case. Make sure to engage shift levers into shift detents. Tighten bolts and nuts. Install 5th-reverse sub-shaft on countershaft with marks made at disassembly towards reverse gear. Install 5th-reverse synchronizer assembly (with shift fork attached) onto 5th-reverse sub-shaft. Install new rollpin into shift fork and shift rod.

7) Set gears in neutral position, install 5th drive gear, needle bearing and spacer. Press bearing on 5th driven gear, now place 5th gear on a hotplate. Place a piece of soft solder on top of the bearing, when the solder melts, install the gear on the output shaft. See *Fig. 23.*

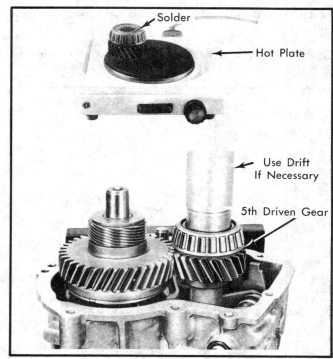

Fig. 23   View Showing 5th Driven Gear Installation

8) Place .16" (4 mm) shims in output shaft bore of rear housing, then press bearing race into housing. Place rear housing on intermediate housing and install 3 bolts as shown in *Fig. 24.* Rotate mainshaft and tighten 3 bolts by hand. Check housing for squareness. Use a feeler gauge and check clearance between intermediate housing and rear housing. Calculate required shims as follows: Take .16" (4 mm) shims that were installed in rear housing, subtract measurement obtained from clearance between intermediate and rear housing. The difference plus a pre-load of .04" (.10 mm) is the amount of shims to be used for shimming output shaft.

Fig. 24   Location of 3 Bolts to be Installed in Intermediate Housing

PEUGEOT 4 & 5-SPEED (Cont.)

NOTE — *Shims are available from .060-.120" (1.5-3.0 mm) in .002" (.05 mm) increments.*

9) Remove rear housing and remove output bearing race and test shims from housing. Reinstall housing to transmission. Place dial indicator stem on countershaft and set to zero. Now remove housing and install countershaft bearing with correct shim pack. Place special tool 8.0314K in a vise, then place bearing and dial indicator on tool as shown in *Fig. 25*. Take

reading, subtract .002" (.05 mm) from this measurement. The result is the required amount of shims to be used for countershaft. Place shim(s) on countergear stub shaft.

10) Install output shaft shims, bearing race and oil seal into housing. Coat face of rear housing with sealing compound, install housing to transmission case and tighten bolts to specifications. Install speedometer gear. Install end cover with a new gasket.

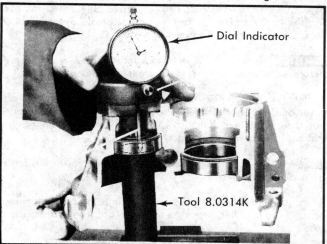

Dial Indicator

Tool 8.0314K

Fig. 25 View Showing Countershaft Shim Measurement

TIGHTENING SPECIFICATIONS

Application	Ft. Lbs. (mkg)
Mainshaft Lock Nut	40 (5.5)
Clutch Housing-to-Trans. Case	20 (2.8)
Case Half Bolts	11 (1.5)
Extension Housing-to-Trans. Case	11 (1.5)
Propeller Shaft Hsg.-to-Extension Hsg.	44 (6.0)
Intermediate Hsg.-to-Transmission	13 (1.8)

TOYOTA 4-SPEED — MODEL H42

Land Cruiser

DESCRIPTION

The Toyota model H42 transmission is a four speed unit, synchronized in all forward gears due to the use of blocker type synchronizer assemblies. All forward transmission gears are helical cut and in constant mesh; reverse gears are spur cut type and are engaged by a sliding reverse idler gear.

NOTE — *For Transfer Case service and repair procedures see appropriate article in OVERDRIVES & TRANSFER CASE Section.*

LUBRICATION & ADJUSTMENT

See *MANUAL TRANSMISSION SERVICING* Section.

TROUBLE SHOOTING

HARD SHIFTING

Clutch not releasing. Check for proper adjustment, deformed clutch disc, seized or damaged pilot bearing. Incorrect or insufficient lubricant. Gearshift lever retainer binding or improperly lubricated. Shift forks worn or damaged. Shift shafts bent.

JUMPS OUT OF GEAR

Worn or damaged shift forks. Detent balls and springs worn or broken. Worn or damaged synchro assemblies. Improper thrust clearance between gears.

NOISY OPERATION

Improper or insufficient lubricant. Worn or damaged bushings, bearings and/or gears. Worn splines.

NOTE — *When checking transmission for noise, ensure that it is not coming from other parts of the drive line.*

TRANSMISSION REMOVAL & INSTALLATION

Removal — 1) Raise and support vehicle. Drain gear oil from transmission case and from transfer case. On models with the fuel tank located under front seats, also drain fuel from tank.

2) On all models, remove transmission skid plate. Disconnect the following from transmission/transfer case assembly: Propeller shafts, speedometer cable, and parking brake cable.

3) On models with fuel tank under the front seats, remove front seats, seat frames and console box. Then, remove rear heater pipe clamp, fuel tank cover and fuel tank.

4) On all models, remove shift lever knobs, dust boots and transmission shift lever. Remove transmission cover.

5) Disconnect electrical wiring and vacuum hoses (if necessary) from transmission/transfer case assembly. Remove attaching bolts, then remove transmission/transfer case assembly from vehicle.

NOTE — *If necessary, separate transfer case from transmission case as follows:*

6) Remove shift lever guide (direct drive only), then remove transfer case shift lever and rod as an assembly. Remove back-up light switch from transmission case.

CAUTION — *Back-up light switch must always be removed before separating transfer case from transmission case.*

7) Remove transfer case cover and gasket and power take-off cover and gasket. Remove stake marks from transmission output shaft nut, then hold power take-off companion flange stationary and remove output shaft nut.

NOTE — *When removing transmission output shaft nut, have front drive engaged.*

8) Remove the five transfer case-to-transmission case attaching bolts. Using a puller, separate transfer case from transmission case.

CAUTION — *When separating transfer case from transmission case, hold power take-off gear to prevent it from dropping out of case.*

Installation — 1) To install, reverse removal procedure and note the following: After transfer case is attached to transmission case, stake transmission output shaft nut in place.

2) With transmission/transfer case assembly installed in vehicle, fill both the transmission case and transfer case with gear oil and adjust shift linkage. See *MANUAL TRANSMISSION SERVICING* Section.

TRANSMISSION DISASSEMBLY

1) Remove transmission rear bearing retainer and spacer. Remove transmission shift cover assembly and side cover. Remove front bearing retainer from transmission case.

2) Remove countershaft front bearing retaining snap rings (inner and outer), then remove bearing from transmission case using a suitable puller. Using the same procedure, remove countershaft rear bearing and thrust washer.

3) Drive input shaft assembly and bearing from case. Remove output shaft bearing snap ring, then pull bearing from transmission case with a puller.

4) Hold first gear tightly against the other gears to prevent gear from sliding off, then lift output shaft assembly from transmission case. See *Fig. 2*. Lift countershaft from case.

5) Drive reverse idler gear shaft out rear of case using care not to lose Woodruff key. Lift reverse idler gear from bottom of transmission case. Remove reverse shift arm assembly from case.

TOYOTA 4-SPEED — MODEL H42 (Cont.)

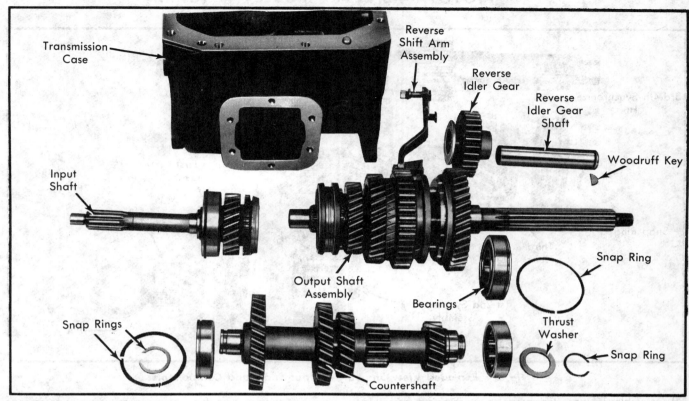

Fig. 1 Disassembled View of Land Cruiser 4-Speed Transmission Assembly

Fig. 2 Lifting Output Shaft Assembly from Transmission Case

COMPONENT DISASSEMBLY & REASSEMBLY

OUTPUT SHAFT ASSEMBLY

Disassembly — 1) From rear of output shaft remove first gear thrust washer, then slide off first gear and needle bearing using care not to lose pin. Slide 1st-2nd synchronizer assembly from output shaft.

2) Remove snap ring from front of output shaft, then slide off 3rd-4th synchronizer hub. Pull third gear and bushing off shaft using care not to lose ball. Finally, slide second gear and needle bearing off output shaft.

3) To disassemble synchronizer assembly, slide synchronizer hub sleeve from hub, then remove key springs and keys.

Inspection — 1) Check output shaft surfaces for wear and damage. Inspect output shaft bushing for excessive wear and damage. Also, check bushing-to-third gear oil clearance (clearance between outer diameter of bushing and inner diameter of gear). Clearance should be .003-.005" (.07-.12 mm).

2) Inspect gears for wear or damage to teeth, thrust faces, inside diameter and coned surfaces. Inspect output shaft ball bearing and needle bearings for wear and damage.

3) Assemble synchronizer ring on 3rd gear and check ring-to-gear clearance as shown in *Fig. 3*. Clearance should be .031" (.8 mm). Repeat measurement for 4th gear ring.

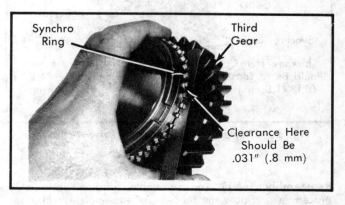

Fig. 3 Measuring 3rd and 4th Gear to Synchronizer Ring Clearance

TOYOTA 4-SPEED – MODEL H42 (Cont.)

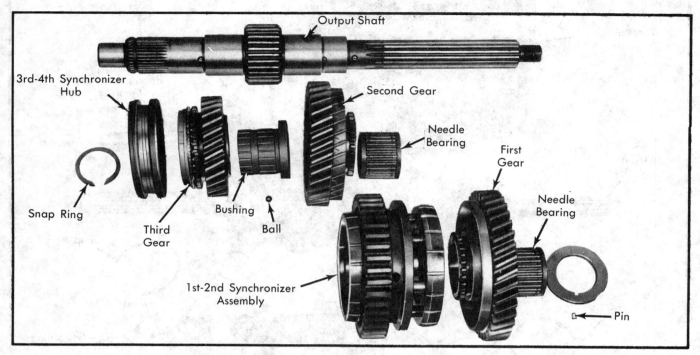

Fig. 4 Exploded View Showing Output Shaft and Components

4) Assemble 1st and 2nd gears to synchronizer assembly. Measure thickness of synchronizer ring protruding from gears as shown in *Fig. 5*. Thickness for 1st gear ring should be at least .110″ (2.8 mm) and for 2nd gear ring at least .071″ (1.8 mm).

5) Inspect splines of synchronizer hub and hub sleeve for damage and wear. Inspect the center humped part of keys for damage and wear. Inspect key springs for weakening and damage.

6) Finally, insert shift forks into their respective synchronizer hub sleeve and measure clearance between shift fork and sleeve. Clearance should be less than .032″ (.8 mm).

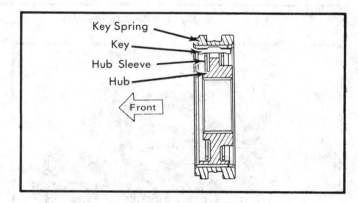

Fig. 6 Cross-Sectional View of Synchro Assembly

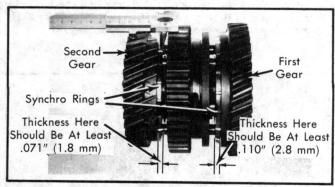

Fig. 5 Checking 1st and 2nd Gear Synchronizer Ring Wear

Reassembly — 1) To reassemble, reverse disassembly procedure and note the following: Reassemble synchronizer assembly as shown in *Fig. 6* and ensure that key springs are positioned so that end gaps will not be in line.

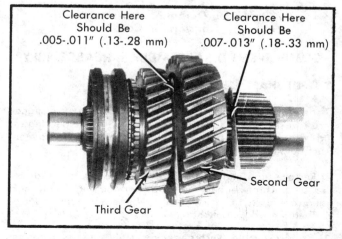

Fig. 7 Measuring 2nd and 3rd Gear Thrust Clearance

TOYOTA 4-SPEED – MODEL H42 (Cont.)

2) To install bushing on output shaft, place ball in hole of output shaft, then slide bushing onto shaft, aligning groove of bushing with ball.

3) Install thickest possible snap ring on front of output shaft that will provide a gear thrust clearance of .007-.013" (.18-.33 mm) for second gear and .005-.011" (.13-.28 mm) for third gear. See Fig. 7.

SHIFT COVER ASSEMBLY

Disassembly – 1) Remove attaching bolts and lift off shift lever retainer and gasket. Remove the three detent springs and balls. Shift forks and shafts into neutral position.

2) Invert shift cover assembly and drive out spring pin retaining 3rd-4th shift fork to shift fork shaft. Drive out 3rd-4th shift fork shaft together with expansion plug using a brass drift. Remove 3rd-4th shift fork and interlock pin.

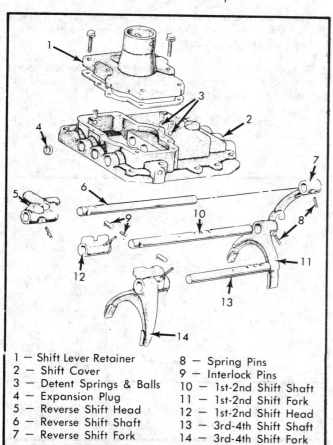

1 — Shift Lever Retainer
2 — Shift Cover
3 — Detent Springs & Balls
4 — Expansion Plug
5 — Reverse Shift Head
6 — Reverse Shift Shaft
7 — Reverse Shift Fork
8 — Spring Pins
9 — Interlock Pins
10 — 1st-2nd Shift Shaft
11 — 1st-2nd Shift Fork
12 — 1st-2nd Shift Head
13 — 3rd-4th Shift Shaft
14 — 3rd-4th Shift Fork

Fig. 8   Exploded View of Shift Cover Assembly

3) Using a long drift, drive spring pins from 1st-2nd shift fork and shift head. Rotate 1st-2nd shift fork shaft one-half turn, then drive shaft out front of cover using care not to lose interlock pin. Remove 1st-2nd shift fork and shift head.

4) Drive spring pins from reverse shift fork and shift head. Pull reverse shift fork shaft out of shift cover through back-up light switch mounting hole. Remove reverse shift fork, shift head and interlock pin.

5) If necessary to disassemble reverse shift head, remove cotter pin and remove spring and lock ball from bore in shift head. Next, remove "C" washer and pull out reverse shift return plunger and spring.

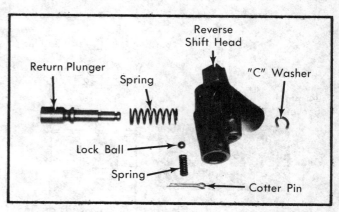

Fig. 9   Disassembled View of Reverse Shift Head

Inspection – Inspect shift fork shafts and heads for bending and wear or damage at sliding surfaces. Check shift cover bores for wear or damage. Inspect detent balls and springs for wear or damage.

Reassembly – Reverse disassembly procedure ensuring that shift forks and heads are correctly positioned before installing shift forks. Coat expansion plugs with a suitable sealer and install in shift cover. Plugs must not be driven in more than .10" (2.5 mm) below cover surface.

INPUT SHAFT

Inspection – Inspect input shaft gear teeth, splines, coned surfaces, and bearing for damage and wear. Check inner surface of input shaft for damage and wear. Also, inspect needle bearings for wear and replace bearings as a set if necessary.

Input Shaft Bearing Replacement – Remove snap ring and press off old bearing. Press new bearing in position and select a snap ring of proper thickness to provide the minimum amount of axial play. Snap rings are available in 2 thicknesses: .130-.135" (3.31-3.42 mm) and .126-.130" (3.20-3.31 mm). Install snap ring, ensuring that it is fully seated in groove.

COUNTERSHAFT ASSEMBLY

Inspection – Inspect countergear teeth for wear and damage. Inspect front and rear bearings for wear and damage and replace if necessary. If rear bearing requires replacement, press bearing inner race from countershaft. Install new inner race on countershaft using a press.

NOTE – *Make sure to position new inner race so that its flanged side will be towards front of countershaft.*

REVERSE IDLER GEAR & SHAFT

Inspection – Inspect reverse idler gear, bushing and shaft for wear and damage. Also, check oil clearance between gear and shaft. Clearance should be .0063" (.16 mm). If bushing requires replacement, proceed as follows:

Manual Transmissions

TOYOTA 4-SPEED — MODEL H42 (Cont.)

Reverse Idler Gear Bushing Replacement — Using press with a 24 mm socket, press bushings from gear. Using the same tools, press new bushings into the gear. Press bushings into gear until each bushing is .039" (1 mm) from gear end face.

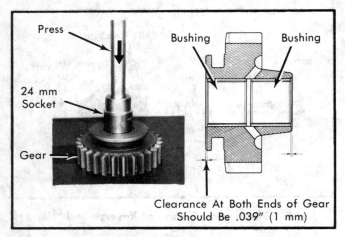

Fig. 10   Replacing Reverse Idler Gear Bushing

REVERSE SHIFT ARM

Inspection — Inspect shift arm shoe for damage or wear. Shoe thickness should be at least .32" (8.1 mm). Inpect shift arm at shoe mounting end and pivot mounting end for wear or damage. Check for maximum clearance of .028" (.7 mm) between shoe and reverse idler gear slot.

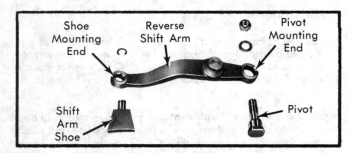

Fig. 11   Disassembled View of Reverse Shift Arm

TRANSMISSION REASSEMBLY

1) Position reverse idler gear in transmission case. Install Woodruff key in reverse idler gear shaft, then install shaft into case and through gear. Install reverse shift arm assembly.

NOTE — *Ensure punch mark on end of reverse shift arm pivot is positioned straight up before locking pivot nut.*

2) Lay countershaft in bottom of transmission case. Install output shaft assembly into transmission case. Drive output shaft rear bearing onto shaft and into case bore until it is fully seated.

3) Install the 17 needle bearings into input shaft bore and use grease to hold them in place. Assemble synchronizer ring to synchronizer hub on input shaft. Using a plastic hammer, drive input shaft into transmission case.

NOTE — *Use care not to damage synchronizer ring when installing input shaft.*

4) Align countershaft with bores in case, then start rear bearing onto shaft and into case bore. Position front bearing on countershaft. Drive bearings onto shaft and into case bores by alternately tapping them with a plastic hammer.

5) Install thrust washer and snap ring on rear of countershaft. Install large (outer) snap ring on countershaft front bearing. Select thickest snap ring that will properly fit groove on front end of countershaft, then install this snap ring on shaft.

NOTE — *Countershaft selective fit snap rings are available in the following thicknesses: .0807-.0827" (2.05-2.10 mm), .0846-.0866" (2.15-2.20 mm) and .0886-.0906" (2.25-2.30 mm).*

6) Install front bearing retainer and tighten attaching bolts. Install transmission side cover. Install rear bearing retainer and spacer.

7) Place shift cover assembly and all gears in neutral position. Position shift cover assembly on transmission case, then install and tighten attaching bolts.

8) Temporarily install transmission shift lever into shift cover assembly. While rotating input shaft check the shifting and output shaft rotational relationship.

9) If abnormal noise develops while turning input shaft, correct by adjusting reverse shift arm pivot within range of 0° to 45° of marker point (punch mark). See *Fig. 12*.

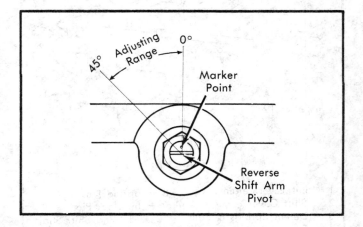

Fig. 12   Reverse Shift Arm Pivot Adjustment

TIGHTENING SPECIFICATIONS

Application	Ft. Lbs. (mkg)
Shift Cover-to-Case	22-33 (3.0-4.5)
Front Bearing Retainer-to-Case	7-12 (1.0-1.6)
Transfer Case-to-Transmission	36-58 (5.0-8.0)
Clutch Housing-to-Transmission	36-58 (5.0-8.0)
Output Shaft Rear Nut	80-101 (11.0-14.0)

TOYOTA 4-SPEED — MODEL L43

Pickup

DESCRIPTION

Transmission is a 4-speed unit, fully synchronized in all forward gears due to the use of blocker type synchronizer assemblies All forward transmission gears are helical cut and are in constant mesh; reverse gears are spur cut type and are engaged by a sliding reverse idler gear. Floor mounted shifter is linked to transmission through a control rod on side of case.

LUBRICATION & ADJUSTMENT

See MANUAL TRANSMISSION SERVICING Section.

TROUBLE SHOOTING

HARD SHIFTING

Clutch not releasing properly. Worn or damaged shift linkage components. Control shaft linkage bent, damaged, or loose.

Synchro mechanisms worn or broken. Worn or damaged shift interlock parts in shift cover. Incorrect or insufficient lubricant.

SLIPS OR JUMPS OUT OF GEAR

Shift linkage components worn or loose. Weak, loose, or worn shift mechanism in shift cover. Worn or damaged bearings on mainshaft. Synchro mechanism worn. Worn gear bushings. Engine mounting loose or broken. Propeller shaft bent or out of balance.

TRANSMISSION NOISE

NOTE — Make sure noise is not produced by other assemblies.

If noise can be stopped by depressing clutch pedal, noise is in transmission or clutch. Before removing transmission, test drive

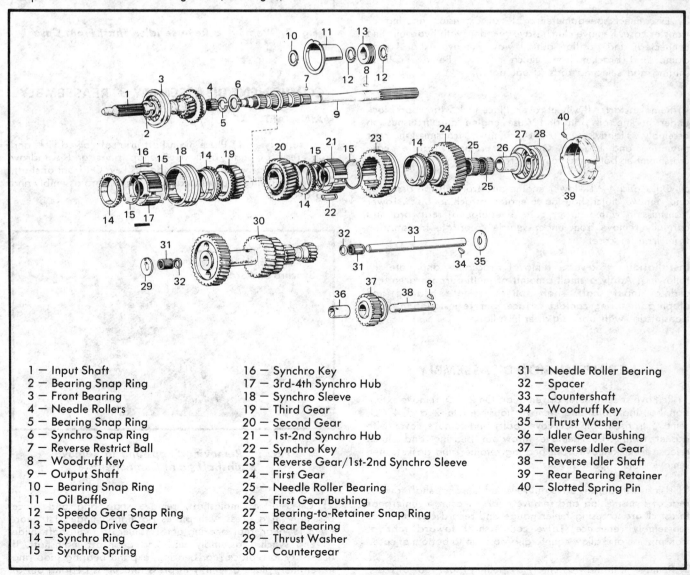

1 — Input Shaft
2 — Bearing Snap Ring
3 — Front Bearing
4 — Needle Rollers
5 — Bearing Snap Ring
6 — Synchro Snap Ring
7 — Reverse Restrict Ball
8 — Woodruff Key
9 — Output Shaft
10 — Bearing Snap Ring
11 — Oil Baffle
12 — Speedo Gear Snap Ring
13 — Speedo Drive Gear
14 — Synchro Ring
15 — Synchro Spring

16 — Synchro Key
17 — 3rd-4th Synchro Hub
18 — Synchro Sleeve
19 — Third Gear
20 — Second Gear
21 — 1st-2nd Synchro Hub
22 — Synchro Key
23 — Reverse Gear/1st-2nd Synchro Sleeve
24 — First Gear
25 — Needle Roller Bearing
26 — First Gear Bushing
27 — Bearing-to-Retainer Snap Ring
28 — Rear Bearing
29 — Thrust Washer
30 — Countergear

31 — Needle Roller Bearing
32 — Spacer
33 — Countershaft
34 — Woodruff Key
35 — Thrust Washer
36 — Idler Gear Bushing
37 — Reverse Idler Gear
38 — Reverse Idler Shaft
39 — Rear Bearing Retainer
40 — Slotted Spring Pin

Fig. 1 Exploded View of Toyota L43 Transmission Gears and Shafts

TOYOTA 4-SPEED — MODEL L43 (Cont.)

to determine in which gears noise is most apparent. Make sure transmission is filled with proper lubricant.

TRANSMISSION REMOVAL & INSTALLATION

Removal (2 & 4-WD) — 1) Disconnect negative battery cable. Remove floor mat and shifter boot(s). Depress transmission shift lever retainer cap, rotate counterclockwise and remove shift lever. Depress transfer case shift lever collar, compress snap ring and remove shift lever (if equipped).

2) Disconnect accelerator linkage at carburetor. Remove clutch hydraulic line bracket from engine, leaving hydraulic line connected. Raise vehicle and support on safety stands. Remove front and/or rear propeller shaft(s) from vehicle. Disconnect back-up light and 4-WD indicator switch (if equipped) wiring connector(s).

3) Disconnect speedometer cable at extension housing or transfer case. Remove clutch slave cylinder (with hydraulic line connected) and position out of way. Remove exhaust pipe clamp and bracket from clutch housing. Remove column shifting and selecting rods (if equipped).

4) Remove starter flywheel cover. Place jack with wood block under engine oil pan and raise engine and transmission assembly slightly. On 2-WD, remove transmission rear mounting and bracket. On 4-WD, remove transfer case crossmember bolts and remove crossmember.

5) On 2 and 4-WD, lower engine and transmission assembly and remove clutch housing-to-engine attaching bolts. Lower transmission with transfer case (if equipped) rearward and carefully remove from under vehicle. Separate transmission from transfer case.

Installation — Reverse removal procedure and note the following: Apply a small amount of multi-purpose grease to end of input shaft, shaft splines, release bearing and diaphragm spring contact surfaces before installation. Refill transmission with lubricant after installation.

TRANSMISSION DISASSEMBLY

1) Remove speedometer driven gear. On 2-WD, remove extension housing bolts and remove housing. On 2 and 4-WD, remove transmission side cover bolts and remove cover with gasket from case. Remove throw-out bearing and clutch release fork. Remove front bearing retainer and gasket, then remove clutch housing.

2) Using drift punch, drive out reverse idler gear shaft toward rear of transmission and remove gear. Measure countergear thrust clearance using feeler gauge and record clearance for reassembly reference. Drive countershaft toward rear of transmission and allow countergear to drop to bottom of case.

3) Remove mainshaft assembly by pulling it out rear of case. Remove synchro ring from input shaft, then align flat portion

of input shaft with countergear and remove input shaft by pulling out through front of case. Remove countergear from transmission case.

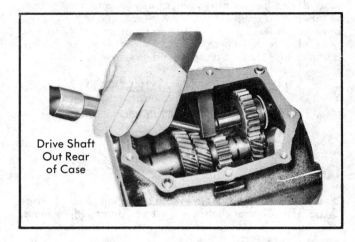

Drive Shaft Out Rear of Case

Fig. 2   Removing Reverse Idler Shaft From Case

COMPONENT DISASSEMBLY & REASSEMBLY

MAINSHAFT

Disassembly — 1) Place mainshaft in a soft-jawed vise, and from rear of shaft, remove 2 snap rings and withdraw speedometer drive gear and Woodruff key. On front of shaft, remove snap ring and withdraw 3rd-4th synchro assembly and 3rd gear.

Remove Snap Ring Then Slide Off Synchro and 3rd Gear

Fig. 3   Removing Snap Ring to Remove Mainshaft Front Components

2) On rear of mainshaft, remove snap ring and place assembly in a press with plates positioned under 1st gear. Press 1st gear, rear bearing and retainer off mainshaft. Slide 1st-2nd synchro assembly and 2nd gear off mainshaft. If necessary to replace rear bearing, expand bearing snap ring in retainer, place assembly in press and press bearing out of retainer.

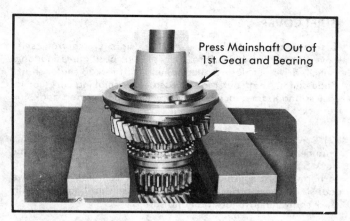

Fig. 4   Removing Mainshaft Rear Components

Inspection — 1) Check all gear surfaces for wear or damage. Inspect synchronizer ring contacting surfaces of gears for wear, and place each synchronizer ring on respective gears and check braking effect and clearance. With pressure applied to ring, it should not rotate. If ring rotates, check clearance between ring and gear. Clearance should be .031" (.8 mm); if not, replace as necessary. If clearance is within specifications and ring slips, apply lapping compound to ring and gear, and rotate parts together to restore braking feature.

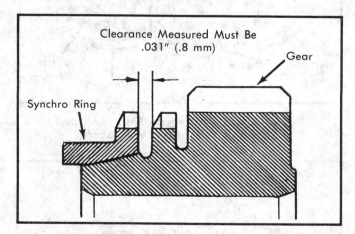

Fig. 5   Measuring Synchro Ring-to-Gear Clearance

2) Check all synchronizer parts for wear or damage to splines, sliding surfaces, and thrust surfaces. Check clearance between shift forks and sliding sleeves. Maximum clearance is .039" (1.0 mm).

3) Inspect mainshaft splines, snap ring grooves, bearing contact surfaces, and oil seal lip contact surface for wear, scoring, or other damage. Check mainshaft for warpage by placing shaft between 2 centers and checking runout with a dial indicator. Maximum allowable out of round is .002" (.06 mm).

NOTE — *Deflection (warpage) is one-half dial indicator reading.*

Reassembly — 1) To assemble synchronizer units, lubricate sliding sleeves with gear oil and insert synchronizer hub, taking care to align key slots. Place shifting keys into assembly and install key springs.

NOTE — *When installing springs, ends should be positioned 120° apart to insure uniform tension on all keys.*

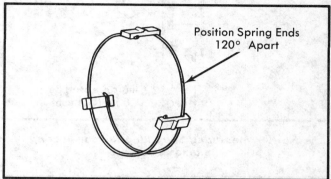

Fig. 6   Installing Synchro Springs Correctly

2) Coat 2nd gear with gear oil and install over rear end of mainshaft. Position a synchronizer ring against 2nd gear, then install 1st-2nd synchronizer assembly, making sure to align grooves of synchronizer ring with keys in hub. Position drive ball into mainshaft hole. Install roller bearings and bushing into 1st gear, position a synchronizer ring against gear, then install onto mainshaft. Take care to align ball in shaft with groove of bushing.

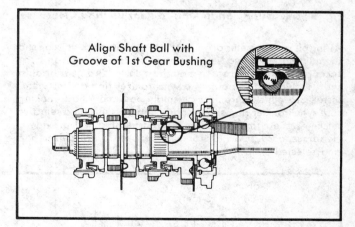

Fig. 7   Cross-Sectional View of Drive Ball and 1st Gear Bushing Alignment

3) Install baffle and snap ring into rear bearing retainer, then while expanding snap ring, use a press to install bearing into retainer. Make sure a 0-.004" (0-.1 mm) clearance exists between snap ring and retainer. Install bearing and retainer onto mainshaft using press. Install a selective thickness snap ring onto mainshaft that will provide a clearance of 0-.006" (0-.15 mm) between rear bearing and selected snap ring.

TOYOTA 4-SPEED — MODEL L43 (Cont.)

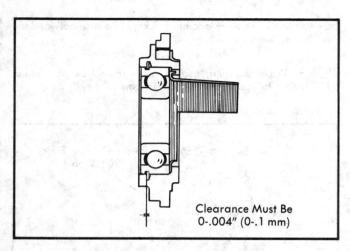

Fig. 8   Measuring Snap Ring-to-Rear Bearing Retainer Clearance

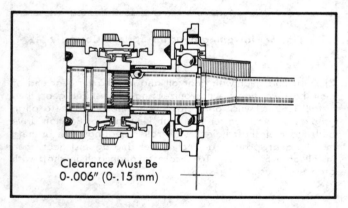

Fig. 9   Measuring Snap Ring-to-Rear Bearing Clearance

4) Install speedometer drive gear and 2 snap rings on rear end of mainshaft, making sure the manufacturers mark on gear faces rearward. On front of mainshaft, install 3rd gear against shaft shoulder, then position a synchronizer ring against gear. Install 3rd-4th synchronizer assembly onto mainshaft, making sure synchronizer ring slots engage hub keys. Install a selective thickness snap ring to retain sychronizer that will provide a clearance of 0-.006" (0-.15 mm) between synchronizer hub and selected snap ring.

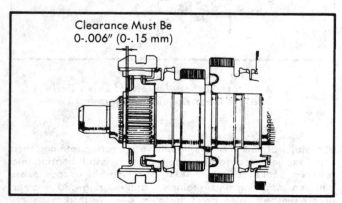

Fig. 10   Measuring Snap Ring-to-3rd-4th Synchro Hub Clearance

SHIFT COVER

Disassembly — 1) Remove back-up light switch from shift cover. Move 3rd-4th shift fork to 4th gear position. Using long punch, drive out slotted pin retaining shift fork to shifter shaft. Slide shifter shaft out rear of case cover, making sure not to lose spring loaded lock ball. Remove lock ball, spring and 2 interlock pins from cover.

2) Drive slotted pin out of 1st-2nd shift fork and shaft in same manner as 3rd-4th assembly. Remove shift fork, then withdraw lock ball and spring from side cover. Loosen and remove shift arm pivot lock nut and remove shift arm from side cover. Drive out slotted spring pin and remove reverse shift head and shift fork shaft. Remove lock ball and spring.

3) Loosen and remove reverse restrict ball retaining bolt, and withdraw reverse restrict spring and ball from housing. Remove wire and shift lever lock bolt, then pull shift and select lever shaft towards rear side of cover to remove.

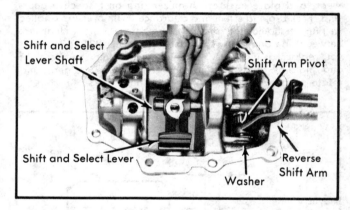

Fig. 11   Installing Reverse Shift Lever and Shift and Select Lever With Shaft

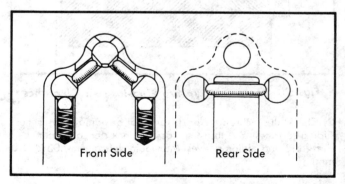

Fig. 12   Cross-Sectional View of Cover Showing Shift Interlock Pin Positions

Reassembly — 1) Install shift arm pivot onto reverse shift arm and insert into case. Assemble shift and selector shaft with shift and selector lever, and secure with lock bolt and wire. Insert reverse shift fork shaft compression spring and lock ball into case, insert fork shaft from rear side, then secure shift head with slotted spring pin.

NOTE — Align fork shaft positioning groove with shift interlock pin groove.

TOYOTA 4-SPEED — MODEL L43 (Cont.)

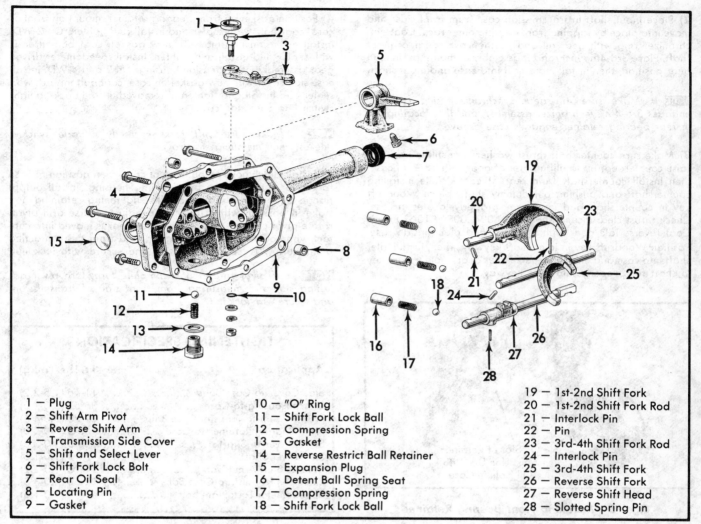

1 — Plug	10 — "O" Ring	19 — 1st-2nd Shift Fork
2 — Shift Arm Pivot	11 — Shift Fork Lock Ball	20 — 1st-2nd Shift Fork Rod
3 — Reverse Shift Arm	12 — Compression Spring	21 — Interlock Pin
4 — Transmission Side Cover	13 — Gasket	22 — Pin
5 — Shift and Select Lever	14 — Reverse Restrict Ball Retainer	23 — 3rd-4th Shift Fork Rod
6 — Shift Fork Lock Bolt	15 — Expansion Plug	24 — Interlock Pin
7 — Rear Oil Seal	16 — Detent Ball Spring Seat	25 — 3rd-4th Shift Fork
8 — Locating Pin	17 — Compression Spring	26 — Reverse Shift Fork
9 — Gasket	18 — Shift Fork Lock Ball	27 — Reverse Shift Head
		28 — Slotted Spring Pin

Fig. 13 Exploded View of Transmission Case Cover and Floor Shift Linkage Assembly

2) Align reverse shift arm knob with reverse shift fork shaft, then install "O" ring, washers and nut onto shift arm pivot. Install lock ball, compression spring, reverse restricting ball bolt and gasket into case. Install shift interlock pin into rear side of case cover.

NOTE — *Arm pivot adjustment will be made after transmission is reassembled.*

3) Install compression spring and locking ball into front side of cover. Assemble shift fork and 1st-2nd shift fork shaft in cover and secure fork with slotted spring pin. Align shift fork shaft positioning groove with shift interlock pin groove. Install 2 shift interlock pins into front side of case cover. Install compression spring and locking ball, assemble shift fork with 3rd-4th shift fork shaft and secure fork with slotted spring pin.

TRANSMISSION REASSEMBLY

1) Install spacer and needle bearing cage into each end of countergear. Position dummy shaft into countergear assembly. Coat both ends of gear with grease and place thrust washers on front and rear ends of countergear, making sure selective

thrust washer is positioned on rear end of countergear. Position countergear in case. Using feeler gauge, measure clearance between rear thrust washer and case. Clearance should be .004-.008" (.10-.20 mm). If not, install thicker or thinner rear thrust washer as required. Lay countergear on bottom of case.

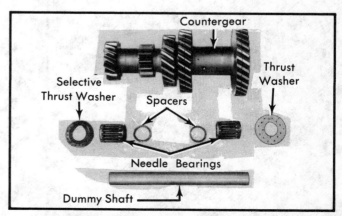

Fig. 14 Exploded View of Countergear and Shaft

TOYOTA 4-SPEED — MODEL L43 (Cont.)

2) Place input shaft in transmission case from front side, and move into place by tapping front bearing outer race. Coat synchronizer ring with gear oil and position over gear of input shaft. Place 3rd-4th synchronizer assembly of mainshaft in high gear position, then install mainshaft into case and input shaft.

NOTE — *Make sure 4th gear synchronizer ring correctly engages 3rd-4th synchronizer assembly, and that locating pin in rear bearing retainer engages case groove.*

3) Make sure countershaft thrust washers are still in position, raise countergear up to align bores of gear with bores of case, then install countershaft from rear of case. While installing countershaft and pushing out dummy shaft, place Woodruff key in countershaft and insure key properly locates in case. Check thrust clearance, it should be .004-.008" (.10-.20 mm). Coat reverse idle gear with lubricant and place inside case. Position Woodruff key in idler shaft keyway. Then, install idler shaft into case and through reverse idler gear, making sure key in shaft fits properly into case keyway.

— Oil Slot of Retainer Must Line Up With Oil Hole in Case

Fig. 15 Installing Front Bearing Retainer

4) Position gasket on front bearing retainer, mount on front of case, coat bolts with sealer and install and tighten. On 2-WD, install extension housing with new gasket, coat bolt threads with sealer and install and tighten. Install speedometer driven gear assembly into extension housing. On 2 and 4-WD, install case side cover with new gasket on case, coat bolt threads with sealer and install and tighten. If removed, install back-up light switch into case side cover.

NOTE — *Make sure shift forks correctly engage synchro sleeves when installing side cover.*

5) Install clutch housing on front of case, then position release fork and clutch release bearing into housing. Install output flange on output shaft, and after tightening retaining nut, stake in position with a punch. To adjust reverse arm pivot, rotate pivot clockwise so reverse idler gear is moved into contact with countergear or first gear, and from this contacting point, turn 90° counterclockwise and secure with lock nut.

NOTE — *If pivot rotates one complete turn, turn pivot adjusting slot 60° measuring from front side of transmission, and secure with lock nut.*

TIGHTENING SPECIFICATIONS

Application	Ft. Lbs. (mkg)
Side Cover-to-Case Bolts	11-16 (1.5-2.2)
Clutch Housing-to-Case	36-51 (5.0-7.0)
Transmission-to-Transfer Case Bolts	22-33 (3.0-4.5)
Front Bearing Retainer-to-Case	3-5 (.40-.70)
Select Lever-to-Shaft	3-5 (.40-.70)
Shift Lever Shaft	7-12 (1.0-1.6)
Reverse Shift Arm Pivot	11-16 (1.5-2.2)
Extension Housing-to-Case Bolts	22-33 (3.0-4.5)
Speedometer Lock Plate Bolt	7-12 (1.0-1.6)

TOYOTA 4 & 5-SPEED — MODELS T40 & T50

Corolla

TRANSMISSION IDENTIFICATION

The T40 & T50 transmission, can be identified from other Toyota transmissions by its ribbed aluminum transmission case; this is the only transmission type currently using the split (two piece) transmission case.

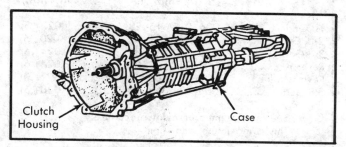

Clutch Housing

Case

Fig. 1   Exterior View of Transmission Case

DESCRIPTION

Transmissions are four or five speed, fully synchronized units, in which all gears are helical cut and in constant mesh. Gear engagement is accomplished through the use of three blocker-type synchronizer assemblies. The floor shift lever operates a single control rod in the extension housing, which in turn is connected to the shifting rails in the rear of the transmission case. Access to transmission internal parts is accomplished by separating transmission case halves.

LUBRICATION & ADJUSTMENT

See MANUAL TRANSMISSION SERVICING Section.

TROUBLE SHOOTING

HARD SHIFTING

Clutch may not be operating properly. Improper contact or wear between synchro ring and gear coned surface. Shifting key may be worn or damaged.

TRANSMISSION SLIPS OUT OF GEAR

Shift fork worn or spring (for lock ball) broken. Input and output bearings worn or damaged. Clearance between synchro hub No. 2 and synchro sleeve splines is excessive. Drive gear (2nd, 3rd, 4th and 5th) worn or its bushing worn. Clearance excessive between synchro hub No. 1 and 1st-reverse gear splines. Countergear or its bearings worn.

NOISE IN TRANSMISSION

Lubricating oil incorrect or insufficient. Gears or bearings worn or damaged. Output shaft splines worn. Bushings for 2nd gear, 1st gear or idler gear worn.

TRANSMISSION REMOVAL & INSTALLATION

Removal — 1) Remove shift lever from inside of vehicle and disconnect battery at ground terminal. Drain transmission lubricant and disconnect back-up light switch wire. Remove exhaust pipe clamp at clutch housing and disconnect exhaust pipe at manifold. Remove starter motor.

2) Remove lower clutch housing cover/stiffener plate. Disconnect clutch slave cylinder from housing, leaving hydraulic line connected. Mark propeller shaft and rear flange for orientation and remove propeller shaft. Disconnect speedometer cable and remove transmission rear support member bolts.

3) Support transmission and engine and remove bolts attaching clutch housing to engine. Move transmission rearward and lower from vehicle, clear of clutch assembly.

Installation — Lightly grease friction surfaces and reverse removal procedure. Ensure that propeller shaft and rear flange marks are aligned. Refill transmission lubricant.

TRANSMISSION DISASSEMBLY

CLUTCH HOUSING

Release spring clips and remove clutch release fork and bearing. Loosen bolts evenly and remove clutch housing from transmission. Use care not to damage oil seal lip or to drop cone washers between transmission and housing.

EXTENSION HOUSING

Remove speedometer driven gear retainer bolt and take out shaft sleeve and driven gear. Remove six housing bolts and take care when removing extension housing that output spline does not damage rear oil seal.

TRANSMISSION CASE

1) Remove back-up light switch and plate holding shift fork shaft detent balls and springs. Remove bolts holding case halves together and separate case halves by tapping on protrusion of right case half with plastic hammer. Be sure to retain detent ballss, springs and lock ball between cases and counterger bearing.

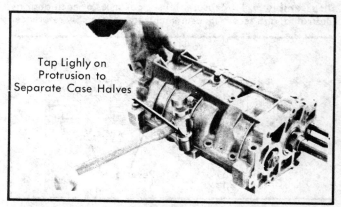

Tap Lighly on Protrusion to Separate Case Halves

Fig. 2   Using a Hammer to Separate Case Halves

TOYOTA 4 & 5-SPEED — MODELS T40 & T50 (Cont.)

2) With left half of case removed, lift mainshaft from right half of case, then lift out countergear assembly. Using suitable pin punch, drive out pins holding shift forks to shafts. Note that pin holding No. 1 fork is driven out through hole in case. Place all shafts in neutral position and pull individually from rear of case.

Remove snap rings holding speedometer drive gear in position and remove drive gear. Use suitable chisel to relieve staked part of lock nut at rear of mainshaft and remove lock nut using suitable tool (09326-20011).

Transmission Gear Thrust Clearances		
Application①	**Standard** In. (mm)	**②Wear Limit** In. (mm)
1st Gear	.006-.011 (.15-.28)	.020 (.5)
2nd Gear	.006-.010 (.15-.25)	.020 (.5)
3rd Gear	.006-.012 (.15-.30)	.024 (.6)
Reverse	.008-.012 (.20-.30)	.024 (.6)
Reverse Idler	.002-.020 (.05-.50)	.039 (1.0)
5th Gear	.006-.011 (.15-.28)	.020 (.5)

① — See text for measurement procedure.
② — This is maximum wear limit.

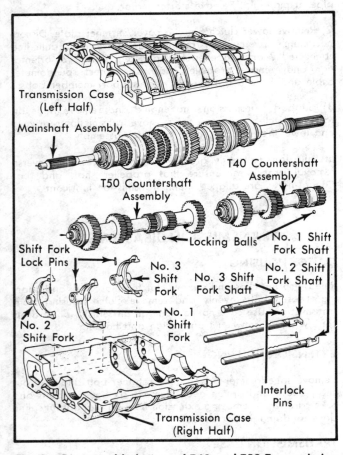

Fig. 3 Disassembled View of T40 and T50 Transmission

COMPONENT DISASSEMBLY & REASSEMBLY

MAINSHAFT

Disassembly — 1) Measure thrust clearances of each gear as illustrated, and record measurements for reassembly reference.

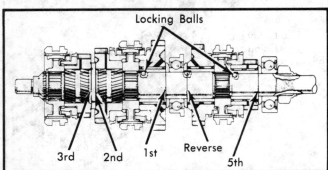

Fig. 4 Thrust Clearance Measurement Points

Fig. 5 Using Special Tool to Remove Mainshaft Nut

2) On 4-speed models, remove spacer and shift stop plate. On 5-speed models, remove rear bearing, bushing, needle bearing, 5th gear with synchronizing ring, and locking ball. On all models, remove No. 3 clutch hub and sleeve, reverse gear, needle bearing, and bushing by pressing down on output shaft while supporting reverse gear with vise jaws.

3) Remove center bearing, bushing, needle bearing, 1st gear, and synchronizer ring. Remove and retain locking ball, then press output shaft from 1st gear assembly using same procedure as for reverse gear. Remove snap ring from front of shaft, then press No. 2 clutch hub and sleeve with 3rd gear and synchronizer ring from shaft.

NOTE — *When pressing gear assemblies from mainshaft, support shaft with hand to prevent dropping shaft when it clears hub splines. Retain all locking balls.*

Inspection — 1) Inspect output shaft for wear, damage or distortion. Minimum thickness of flange between 2nd and 3rd gear is .157" (4.0 mm). Minimum diameter of 2nd and 3rd gear journals is 1.488" (37.8 mm). Check shaft deflection at speedometer drive gear journal while rotating shaft. Maximum deflection is .002" (.06 mm).

TOYOTA 4 & 5-SPEED — MODELS T40 & T50 (Cont.)

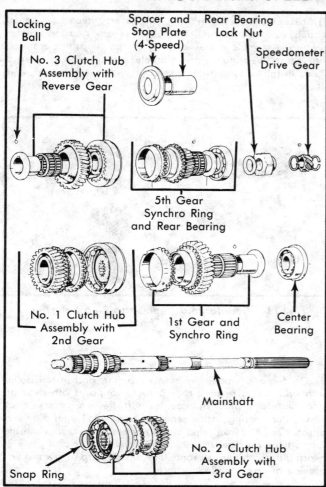

Fig. 6   Disassembled View of Mainshaft Assembly

2) Check each gear, bushing and bearing surface for wear or damage. Refer to table for specifications to check inside gear limits. Note that oil clearance for 2nd and 3rd gear is .004" (.10 mm). Disassemble clutch hubs using care not to mix parts and inspect for wear or damage. Check clearance limit of .039" (1.0 mm) between shift fork and sleeve grooves. Groove maximum width is .335" (8.5 mm).

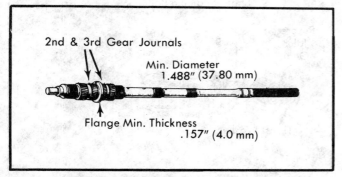

Fig. 7   Mainshaft Inspection Points

3) Check synchronizer rings for wear or damage and braking effect. Ring should stick to gear cone when turned and pressed against cone. Standard clearance between synchronizer ring and gear is .039-.079" (1.0-2.0 mm). Minimum clearance is .031" (.8 mm). Replace ring and/or gear as required. Inspect shift keys and springs for wear or damage and replace if necessary.

Gear Bearing Surface Inside Diameter Wear Limit	
Application	**Specification In. (mm)**
1st	1.66 (42.15)
2nd	1.50 (38.15)
3rd	1.50 (38.15)
5th	1.42 (36.06)
Reverse	1.66 (42.15)

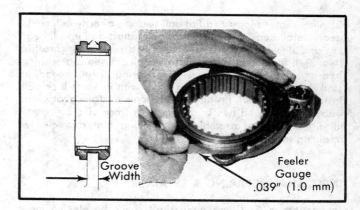

Fig. 8   Checking Shift Fork Groove Clearance

Fig. 9   Synchronizer Ring Braking Check

Reassembly — 1) Assemble synchronizer assemblies individually, ensuring that key spring ends are staggered. Note location and identification of each synchronizer assembly.

TOYOTA 4 & 5-SPEED — MODELS T40 & T50 (Cont.)

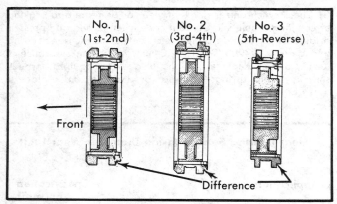

Fig. 10   View Showing Synchronizer Identification

2) From rear of mainshaft, slide 2nd gear on shaft. With synchro No. 2 assembled, including synchro rings, slide assembly on shaft from rear. Slide on 1st gear, with coned surface facing front of shaft. Install bearing sleeve lock ball in mainshaft. Slide 1st gear roller bearing and sleeve on from rear of shaft and install them inside 1st gear.

3) Slide center support radial ball bearing directly behind 1st gear. Install bearing sleeve lock ball in shaft and install bearing and sleeve. Install reverse gear and reverse synchro hub (No. 3). If five speed transmission, install 5th gear, its bushing, bearing, sleeve lock ball and rear bearing. If four speed, install dished washer and spacer tube, with its shaft lock ball. Install shim and nut. Install the speedometer drive gear along with drive ball and two snap rings. On front of shaft, install third gear, synchro assembly with blocking rings, and selective retaining snap ring.

INPUT SHAFT, BEARING & RETAINER

Inspection — 1) Check input shaft spline by placing input shaft into clutch disc and checking that shaft slides smoothly. Make sure there is no excessive play.

2) Check input shaft bearing by pressing on front of bearing and rotating input shaft. If there is abnormal resistence or noise, it will be necessary to replace bearing with new one. To replace bearing, use snap ring pliers and remove front snap ring. Use press and suitable adapter (09506-10010), to press off old bearing. Use suitable adapter (09316-60010) to press on new bearing. Select a suitable selective thickness snap ring which will engage securely in groove and eliminate play between bearing and shaft.

3) Check front bearing retainer and oil seal for wear or damage. If seal shows evidence of leakage, it must be replaced. Also check mating surfaces of transmission case and clutch housing.

COUNTERGEAR, REVERSE IDLER GEAR & SHAFT

Inspection — 1) Check countergear faces and bearings for wear or damage. To replace front bearing, remove bearing lock plate and take off snap ring. Use suitable puller to remove old bearing and press new bearing in position by supporting inner race and pressing on countershaft.

2) To replace reverse bearing and reverse gear on 4-speed models, remove snap ring and pull off reverse gear and center bearing. Assemble center bearing to rear bearing, ensuring that center bearing larger diameter roller cage is toward front. Install a snap ring which will give the minimum end clearance.

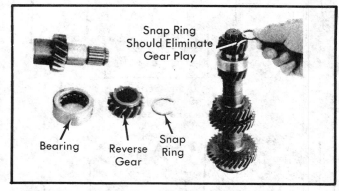

Fig. 11   Countergear Rear Snap Ring Selection (4-Speed Shown)

3) On 5-speed models, remove snap ring and install puller with adapter to remove rear bearing. Support 5th gear on steel plate and press out countershaft. Remove reverse gear and center bearing. Install center bearing with larger diameter of roller cage to front, and install reverse gear. Using suitable support for rear bearing, hold up reverse gear and press in bearing and 5th gear at same time. Install snap ring which will provide minimum end clearance.

NOTE — *Snap rings for 4-speed models are available in 2 thicknesses: .075-.077" (1.90-1.95 mm) and .071-.073" (1.80-1.85 mm). There are 3 thicknesses available for 5-speed models: .079-.081" (2.00-2.05 mm), .071-.073" (1.80-1.85 mm) and .063-.065" (1.60-1.65 mm).*

4) Measure reverse idler thrust clearance between case and gear. Standard clearance is .002-.020" (.05-.50 mm) with a maximum limit of .039" (1.0 mm). Remove shaft and gear with thrust washers. Bushing bore wear limit is .634" (16.1 mm) and shaft diameter wear limit is .626" (15.9 mm). If installing new bushing, ensure that oil holes in bushing and gear line up.

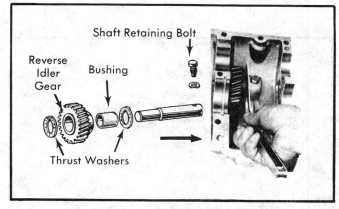

Fig. 12   Measuring Reverse Idler Gear Thrust Clearance

TOYOTA 4 & 5-SPEED – MODELS T40 & T50 (Cont.)

SHIFT FORK SHAFTS & SELECTOR SHAFT

Inspection – Check sliding action of shift fork shafts and selector shaft. Shafts should move freely without binding or excessive play.

EXTENSION HOUSING

Inspection – **1)** Inspect speedometer gear and oil seal for wear or damage. Replace inner seal and outer "O" ring as necessary. Inspect rear oil seal and bushing for wear or damage. If seal replacement is required, use puller (09308-00010) to remove old oil seal and installer (09325-12010) to drive in new seal.

2) To replace rear bushing, heat extension housing to 176-212° F (80-100° C) and drive out old bushing with special tool (09307-12010). Ensure that oil hole is positioned at top of housing and use same tool to install new bushing to proper depth of .59" (15.0 mm) below end of extension housing. Install new seal and apply multi-purpose grease to seal lips.

TRANSMISSION REASSEMBLY

SHIFTING RAILS & FORKS

Apply multi-purpose grease to interlock pins and insert in case. Insert center (No. 2) shift shaft and fork to the neutral position. Insert No. 1 shaft and fork, then No. 3 shaft and fork (short shaft) to the neutral position. Install all 3 shift fork pins, then pull center shaft out to the 3rd speed position. No. 1 and No. 2 shaft should NOT move.

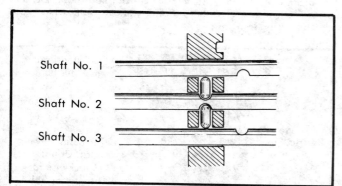

Fig. 13   Cutaway View of Case Showing Detent Pin and Fork Shaft Installation

TRANSMISSION CASE

1) Apply multi-purpose grease to input shaft needle bearings and assemble input shaft to output shaft. Line up synchronizer grooves and shift forks to the neutral position. Ensure that shifting keys are lined up with key slots in synchronizer rings. Install mainshaft assembly in right half of transmission case.

2) Install countergear assembly in case and insert locking ball in case groove. Clean case joining surfaces and bearing recesses. Apply liquid sealer to case joining faces and bolt threads. Install left half of case to right half and tighten bolts gradually in sequence. See Fig. 14.

3) Check front end of input shaft to see that there is approximately .012" (.3 mm) play radially. Check to see that shift rods move smoothly to all gear selections.

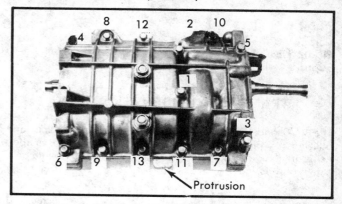

Fig. 14   Transmission Case Bolt Tightening Sequence

EXTENSION HOUSING & CLUTCH HOUSING

1) Apply liquid sealer to both sides of gasket. Place gasket on rear of transmission housing and carefully install extension housing. Shift selector shaft should engage in No. 2 fork shaft. Install and tighten extension housing bolts. Note that Black restrict pin is on RIGHT side and White pin is on LEFT side of selector housing.

2) Install shift lever retainer on extension housing. Apply multi-purpose grease to oil seal lip in clutch housing and to washers. Install cone washers in recesses with dished side to rear of transmission. Apply liquid sealer to joining surfaces and install clutch housing on transmission.

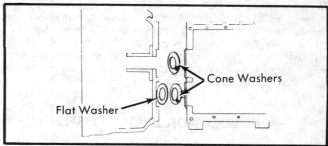

Fig. 15   Transmission Case-to-Clutch Housing Cone and Flat Washer Installation

NOTE – *When installing transmission on clutch housing, ensure that pilot shaft splines do not damage lip of oil seal.*

3) Tighten housing bolts evenly in 3 or 4 steps in a criss-cross pattern. Apply multi-purpose grease to sliding surfaces and install clutch release fork and bearing. Install shift rail detent balls, springs and retainer plate. Install back-up light switch.

TIGHTENING SPECIFICATIONS

Application	Ft. Lbs. (mkg)
Mainshaft Lock Nut	33-72 (4.5-10.0)
Reverse Idler Shaft Retaining Bolt	10-13 (1.3-1.8)
Case Half Bolts	14-15 (1.8-2.2)
Extension Housing-to-Case Bolts	22-33 (3.0-4.5)
Clutch Housing-to-Case Bolts	22-33 (3.0-4.5)
Clutch Housing-to-Engine	37-57 (5.0-8.0)
Restrict Pins	27-31 (3.7-4.3)

TOYOTA 4 & 5-SPEED — MODELS W40 & W50

Celica
Corona
Pickup (Exc. 4-WD)
Supra

TRANSMISSION IDENTIFICATION

The W40 and W50 transmissions are the only transmissions utilizing a 4-piece transmission case assembly. Main components are the clutch housing, main case, intermediate plate and extension housing.

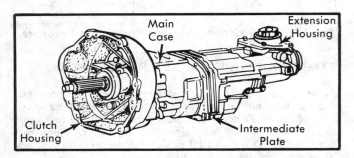

Fig. 1   Exterior View of W40 and W50 Transmission

DESCRIPTION

Transmissions are 4 or 5-speed, fully synchronized units. All forward gears are helical cut and in constant mesh. Reverse gear is spur cut and, on 4-speed models, is not in constant mesh. Reverse idler gear is sliding type. On 5-speed models, reverse and 5th gears are in constant mesh and are mounted on rear side of intermediate plate (inside extension housing). Floor shifter actuates a single control rod in extension housing operating 3 shift rails mounted in intermediate plate and main case.

LUBRICATION & ADJUSTMENT

See MANUAL TRANSMISSION SERVICING Section.

TROUBLE SHOOTING

HARD SHIFTING

Clutch not disengaging properly. Bushings in cross shaft worn or damaged. Synchro rings making faulty contact with gear cone. Synchro worn or pitted.

SLIPS OUT OF GEAR

Improper meshing of gears due to shift rails being out of adjustment. Shift forks worn or ball locks broken. Excessive play in synchro hub No. 2. Output shaft or drive gear worn. Reverse idler gear or its bushing worn. Countergear or its bushing or shaft worn.

TRANSMISSION NOISY

Gears or bearings worn or damaged. Insufficient or incorrect lubricant. Mainshaft splines worn or damaged. Reverse idler gear bushing worn.

TRANSMISSION REMOVAL & INSTALLATION

Removal — 1) Disconnect battery negative terminal. On Celica models, disconnect accelerator linkage from bracket on firewall. On all other models, disconnect accelerator linkage at engine. Remove shift lever and retainer from inside of vehicle. Raise and support vehicle. Drain transmission. Remove clutch slave cylinder (with hydraulic line connected) and position out of way.

2) Remove exhaust pipe clamp and bracket from clutch housing. Disconnect back-up light switch wire. Remove propeller shaft from vehicle, marking shaft and differential yokes for reassembly reference. Plug extension housing to prevent fluid loss. Place jack with wood block under engine oil pan and raise engine and transmission assembly slightly and remove rear engine support.

3) Remove stiffner plates (if equipped), remove starter. Disconnect speedometer cable. Lower jack and remove engine-to-clutch housing bolts. Detach transmission from engine by moving rearward until clear of vehicle.

Installation — To install reverse removal procedure and refill transmission.

TRANSMISSION DISASSEMBLY

CLUTCH & EXTENSION HOUSING

1) Drain transmission and remove clutch release bearing and arm. From inside of clutch housing remove bolts which hold clutch housing to transmission case.

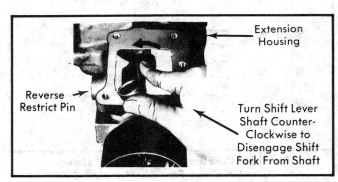

Fig. 2   Removing Shift Lever from Shift Fork Shaft

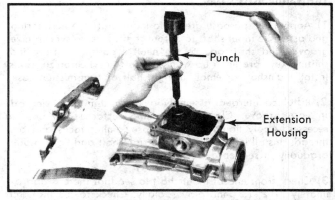

Fig. 3   Using a Punch to Remove Shift Lever Pin

TOYOTA 4 & 5-SPEED — MODELS W40 & W50 (Cont.)

2) From the extension housing, remove speedo driven gear and control shift lever retainer cover. From below shift lever cover, remove reverse restrict pin (on side of extension housing). Remove back-up light switch (if equipped).

3) Remove bolts from extension housing, turn shift lever counterclockwise (as viewed from rear), tap housing with a plastic hammer and pull housing from case.

TRANSMISSION CASE

1) Remove front bearing retainer, countershaft cover and spacer. Use snap ring pliers to remove snap ring from input shaft bearing and countershaft front bearing.

2) Use drift punch and hammer to separate center support from transmission case. Place support in soft-jawed vise and from side of support, remove detent plugs and springs.

NOTE — *Input shaft, countergear and all associated parts will be retained on center support.*

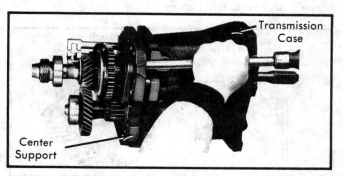

Fig. 4   Using a Hammer and Drift to Separate Center Support from Transmission Case

3) Use straight punch to drive out slotted pins which hold shift forks to shift fork shafts. Remove shift fork shaft from center support and remove shift forks from shift fork shafts.

NOTE — *Use care not to lose 2 interlock pins and 3 interlock balls.*

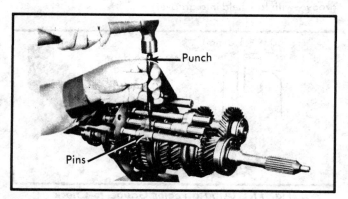

Fig. 5   Using a Punch to Drive Out Shift Fork Pins

4) Remove snap ring holding speedometer drive gear on shaft. Remove speedometer gear making sure not to lose lock ball beneath gear. Use bearing puller (SST 09950-00010) to remove mainshaft rear bearing. Remove snap ring which was in front of rear bearing.

5) On four speed models, remove reverse idler retaining bolt and tang, then withdraw idler gear and shaft out toward the front. Remove snap ring from mainshaft center bearing, then while pushing shafts from rear side, pull mainshaft and countergear assemblies out front side of support.

6) On five speed models, remove snap ring from countershaft and use a suitable bearing puller (SST 09950-20010) to remove countergear rear bearing. Remove countershaft fifth gear and countershaft reverse gear. Remove snap ring from mainshaft and withdraw fifth gear, synchro ring, needle roller bearing, and fifth gear bearing inner race.

CAUTION — *Do not lose ball which locks 5th gear inner race.*

Fig. 6   Removing 5th Gear from Mainshaft

7) Remove reverse gear and synchronizer assembly from mainshaft. Remove reverse idler gear by removing bolt and tang which retains shaft to support, then pulling reverse idler shaft, gear, and spacer towards the rear.

8) Remove retainer and snap ring from mainshaft center bearing. Push countergear cylindrical roller bearing outer race toward rear and remove bearing, then remove countergear from center support. Pull input shaft and synchro ring from mainshaft, then withdraw mainshaft from center support.

Fig. 7   Removing Countergear and Bearing from Support

COMPONENT DISASSEMBLY & REASSEMBLY

MAINSHAFT

Disassembly — From front end of mainshaft, remove retaining snap ring and withdraw synchro assembly and third

TOYOTA 4 & 5-SPEED — MODELS W40 & W50 (Cont.)

gear. On rear end of shaft, remove bearing snap ring, and with plates positioned under first gear, use a press to remove bearing and 1st gear. Remove 1st gear needle bearing, inner race, lock ball and synchro ring. Remove reverse gear and 1st-2nd synchro assembly from shaft, then remove 2nd gear and synchro ring.

Inspection — 1) Use "V" block or shaft holding fixture to measure mainshaft runout. Runout should not exceed .002" (.05 mm). Inspect all bearing and gear installation surfaces for damage or wear. Inspect flanges and bearing inner races for wear or damage.

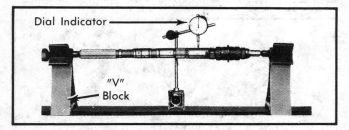

Fig. 8   Using a Dial Indicator to Check Shaft Runout

2) Inspect mainshaft flanges and bearing inner races for wear or damage according to specifications listed in following table:

Mainshaft Specifications	
Application①	**Specification In. (mm)**
Flange "A"	.189 (4.80)
Flange "B"	.179 (4.55)
Flange "C"	.152 (3.85)
Flange O.D.②	1.606 (40.8)

① — Designation in *Fig. 9*.
② — Wear limit.

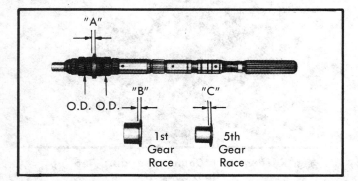

Fig. 9   View of Mainshaft Showing Wear Check Points

3) Inspect all gear toothed surfaces, thrust faces, inside diameter surfaces and coned parts for wear and/or damage. Inspect mainshaft rear bearing and needle roller bearing surfaces for wear, damage and following oil clearances (difference between I.D. of gear and O.D. of shaft):

Gear Oil Clearance		
Application	**Standard In (mm)**	**Wear Limit In (mm)**
W50		
1st & 5th	.0007-.002 (.02-.05)	.0024 (.06)
2nd & 3rd	.002-.004 (.05-.10)	.006 (.15)
W40		
1st	.0004-.002 (.010-.05)	.006 (.15)
2nd & 3rd	.002-.004 (.05-.10)	.008 (.20)

4) Check braking effect of synchro rings by installing ring into respective gear and trying to rotate ring while pressing inward. If ring does not rotate, braking effect is correct. If ring does rotate check clearance between teeth of ring and teeth of gear for clearance of .039-.079" (1.0-2.0 mm). **NOTE** — *Maximum wear limit is .031" (.8 mm).* If clearance is incorrect, it will be necessary to replace synchro ring. If clearance is correct, it is possible to lap in ring (using lapping compound), to create proper amount of friction.

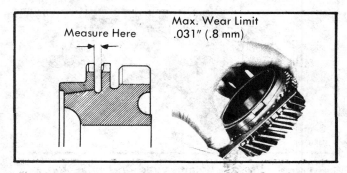

Fig. 10   Using a Feeler Gauge to Check Synchronizer Ring-to-Gear Clearance

5) Inspect splines on both synchro hubs and sleeves for wear or damage. Inspect keys for rounded corners and for wear or damage. Also check key springs. Inspect contact surfaces between hub sleeves and shift forks. Clearance should be no more than .039" (1.0 mm) as measured between fork and groove, with fork held into groove.

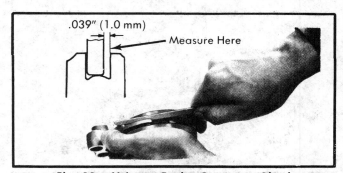

Fig. 11   Using a Feeler Gauge to Check Shift Fork-to-Sleeve Clearance

Reassembly — 1) Fit synchro sleeve No. 2 onto hub No. 2 in direction illustrated. Make sure sleeve slides smoothly over hub. Insert three shift keys into keyways between hub and sleeve and assemble two key retaining springs. Insert synchro assembly onto mainshaft until it rests against shaft shoulder.

TOYOTA 4 & 5-SPEED — MODELS W40 & W50 (Cont.)

Use press or soft-faced hammer to seat assembly, making sure synchro ring slots are aligned with shifting keys. Secure hub No. 2 on shaft with snap ring. Select thickness of snap ring for 0-.002" (0-.05 mm) clearance (axial play).

ing inner race and install them as a unit onto mainshaft until inner race end face rests against hub No. 2. Make sure inner race slot is aligned with lock ball. Be sure to have synchro ring slots aligned with shifting keys.

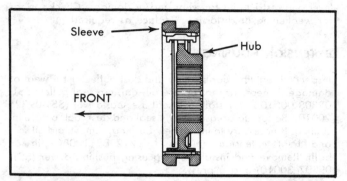

Fig. 12   Cross-Sectional View of No. 2 Synchronizer (3rd and 4th Synchronizer Assembly)

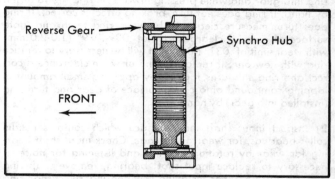

Fig. 14   Cross-Sectional View of Synchronizer No. 1 (Reverse/1st and 2nd Synchronizer Assembly)

Snap Ring Sizes	
Mark①	**Thickness In. (mm)**
No Mark	.078-.080 (2.00-2.05)
0	.080-.082 (2.05-2.10)
1	.082-.084 (2.10-2.15)
2	.084-.086 (2.15-2.20)
3	.086-.088 (2.20-2.25)
4	.088-.090 (2.25-2.30)
① — Actual mark on snap ring.	

2) Measure 3rd gear thrust clearance. Clearance should be .0059-.0098" (.15-.25 mm). Grease outer mainshaft surface and fit No. 2 synchro ring into 2nd gear and assemble onto mainshaft. Fit No. 1 synchro hub onto reverse gear, making sure reverse gear is assembled in correct direction and that it slides smoothly inside of gear. Install 3 shift keys into keyways of hub and install 2 retaining springs. Install synchro assembly onto mainshaft, making sure synchro ring slots are aligned with shift keys, then press synchro assembly on until resting against mainshaft shoulder.

Thrust Clearance .0059-.0098" (.15-.25 mm)

Fig. 15   Installation of Synchronizer No. 1 and 2nd Gear Thrust Clearance Check

4) Install bearing onto mainshaft using a press. **CAUTION** — Bearing must be installed so that outer snap ring groove of bearing faces rearward. On four speed models only, install a bearing-to-shaft selective snap ring that will provide 0-.002" (0-.05 mm) bearing axial play. On all models, measure thrust clearance between thrust surface of first gear and bearing; clearance should be .0059-.0098" (.15-.25 mm).

NOTE — Wear limit is .0118" (.30 mm).

Thrust Clearance .0059-.0098" (.15-.25 mm)

Fig. 13   Using a Feeler Gauge to Measure 3rd Gear Thrust Clearance

3) Measure 2nd gear thrust clearance for .0059-.0098" (.15-.25 mm). **NOTE** — Wear limit is .0118" (.30 mm). Fit inner race lock ball into mainshaft hole and hold ball in place with heavy grease. Assemble 1st gear, synchro ring No. 2, bearing, bear-

Thrust Clearance .0059-.0098" (.15-.25 mm)

Fig. 16   Using a Feeler Gauge to Measure 1st Gear Thrust Clearance

Manual Transmissions

TOYOTA 4 & 5-SPEED — MODELS W40 & W50 (Cont.)

INPUT SHAFT

1) Inspect gear teeth, splines and coned parts for wear or damage. Check braking effect of synchro ring by installing ring into gear and while pressing inward on ring, try to turn it by hand. If ring does not turn, braking effect is correct. If ring does turn, measure clearance between ring teeth and tooth surface of gear. If clearance is not .039-.079" (1.0-2.0 mm) with wear limit of .031" (.8 mm), it will be necessary to replace ring with new one. If replacing ring or when clearance is correct and ring still turns, lap ring by applying small amount of lapping compound onto coned surface of gear and turn ring (installed into gear) by hand.

2) Inspect input shaft inner surface which contacts needle roller bearings, for wear or damage. Check input shaft bearing for wear by rotating bearing and listening for noise. If necessary to replace input shaft bearing, remove snap ring and use a press. When installing new bearing, select snap ring which will allow minimum axial play, refer to table.

Input Shaft Snap Ring Size	
Mark On Snap Ring	Thickness In. (mm)
0	.080-.082 (2.05-2.10)
1	.082-.084 (2.10-2.15)
2	.084-.086 (2.15-2.20)
3	.086-.088 (2.20-2.25)
4	.088-.090 (2.25-2.30)
5	.090-.092 (2.30-2.35)

COUNTERGEAR

1) Inspect teeth of countergear for wear or damage. Inspect front bearing and rear bearing for wear or damage. Inspect roller bearing and inner race for wear or damage. If necessary to replace front bearing, remove snap ring and use bearing puller (SST-09602 35011) to remove bearing. To install new bearing, use adapter plate (SST 09515 20010) and a press. Install snap ring.

2) Install rear bearing on 4-speed models using same procedure for front bearing replacement. On 5-speed models, remove center bearing inner race using puller (SST 09950 20010) and remove race from shaft. Install inner race using adapter plate (SST 09515 20010) and a press.

REVERSE IDLER GEAR

Inspect teeth and bushing for wear or damage. If necessary to replace bushing, remove and install bushing using bushing driver (SST 09222-30010, four speed) or (SST 09222-40011, five speed) and a press.

NOTE — *After installation, it may be necessary to ream bushing to proper size of .780-.790" (19.8-20.1 mm) for four speed models, or .986-1.026" (25.0-26.1 mm) for five speed models. When installing new bushing into gear, align oil hole of bushing with oil groove of gear.*

SHIFT COMPONENTS

Inspect sliding surfaces of shaft for wear and/or damage. Inspect springs, balls, interlock pins and reverse restrict pins for wear and/or damage. Inspect contacting surface between shift lever and restrict pins for wear and/or damage. Check springs for weakening or distortion. Replace as required.

EXTENSION HOUSING

Inspect oil seal lip, rear bushing and dust deflector for wear or damage. If necessary to replace oil seal, use seal puller (SST-09308 00010). To install new seal use seal driver (SST-09325 20010). Be sure to grease new oil seal and dust seal, before installing. If necessary to install new bushing, remove old oil seal and heat extension housing to 212°F (100°C) in oil bath. Remove and install bushing using bushing driver (SST-09307 30010) and a press.

NOTE — *Before installing new bushing, make sure oil hole of bushing is aligned with oil groove.*

TRANSMISSION REASSEMBLY

TRANSMISSION CASE

1) Clamp center support in a soft-jawed vise. Grease needle bearings of input shaft and position shaft and synchro ring onto mainshaft. On five speed models, mate countergear with mainshaft and install both onto center support simultaneously; retain both shafts with snap rings installed on rear bearings.

2) On four speed models, install mainshaft into support and install retaining snap ring into center bearing outer race. Install countergear into support and in mesh with mainshaft, then from rear side of support, install cylindrical roller bearing and spacer onto gear.

NOTE — *After installing snap ring, press inward on bearing until flush with surface of support.*

3) On all models, install mainshaft bearing retainer on rear of center support. Assemble reverse idler gear and spacer on idler shaft, and on four speed models, secure with snap ring. Insert reverse idler assembly into support and retain with tang and lock bolt. On 5-speed, position reverse idler gear oil hole rearward.

NOTE — *Steps 4) through 6) apply to 5-speed only. If working on 4-speed, proceed to step 7).*

4) Measure reverse idler thrust clearance between gear and shaft. Clearance should be .0059-.0098" (.15-.25 mm). Install No. 3 synchro hub onto reverse gear, making sure reverse gear is assembled in correct direction and that it slides smoothly. Install 3 shift keys into keyways of hub and install 2 retaining springs. Install No. 3 synchro assembly onto mainshaft until resting against inner race of bearing in center support.

NOTE — *If synchro hub cannot be fitted onto shaft easily, lightly tap hub using soft-faced hammer.*

TOYOTA 4 & 5-SPEED — MODELS W40 & W50 (Cont.)

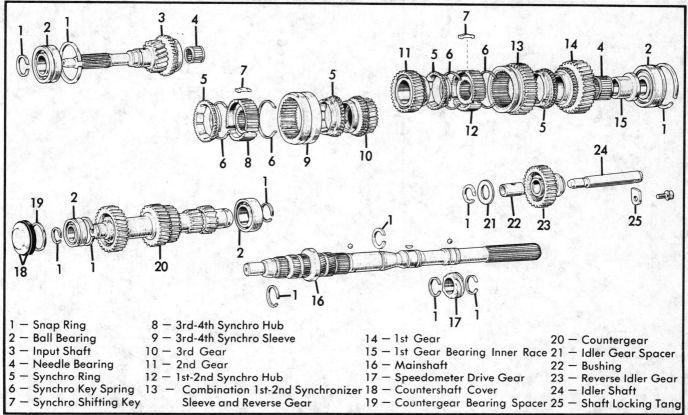

1 — Snap Ring	8 — 3rd-4th Synchro Hub
2 — Ball Bearing	9 — 3rd-4th Synchro Sleeve
3 — Input Shaft	10 — 3rd Gear
4 — Needle Bearing	11 — 2nd Gear
5 — Synchro Ring	12 — 1st-2nd Synchro Hub
6 — Synchro Key Spring	13 — Combination 1st-2nd Synchronizer
7 — Synchro Shifting Key	Sleeve and Reverse Gear

14 — 1st Gear	20 — Countergear
15 — 1st Gear Bearing Inner Race	21 — Idler Gear Spacer
16 — Mainshaft	22 — Bushing
17 — Speedometer Drive Gear	23 — Reverse Idler Gear
18 — Countershaft Cover	24 — Idler Shaft
19 — Countergear Bearing Spacer	25 — Shaft Locking Tang

Fig. 17 *Exploded View of W40 4-Speed Transmission Gears and Shafts*

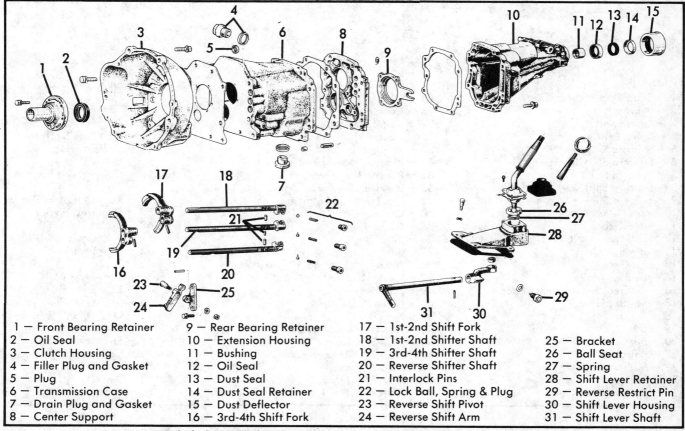

1 — Front Bearing Retainer	9 — Rear Bearing Retainer
2 — Oil Seal	10 — Extension Housing
3 — Clutch Housing	11 — Bushing
4 — Filler Plug and Gasket	12 — Oil Seal
5 — Plug	13 — Dust Seal
6 — Transmission Case	14 — Dust Seal Retainer
7 — Drain Plug and Gasket	15 — Dust Deflector
8 — Center Support	16 — 3rd-4th Shift Fork

17 — 1st-2nd Shift Fork	25 — Bracket
18 — 1st-2nd Shifter Shaft	26 — Ball Seat
19 — 3rd-4th Shifter Shaft	27 — Spring
20 — Reverse Shifter Shaft	28 — Shift Lever Retainer
21 — Interlock Pins	29 — Reverse Restrict Pin
22 — Lock Ball, Spring & Plug	30 — Shift Lever Housing
23 — Reverse Shift Pivot	31 — Shift Lever Shaft
24 — Reverse Shift Arm	

Fig. 18 *Exploded View of W40 Transmission Case and Gear Shifting Components*

Manual Transmissions

TOYOTA 4 & 5-SPEED — MODELS W40 & W50 (Cont.)

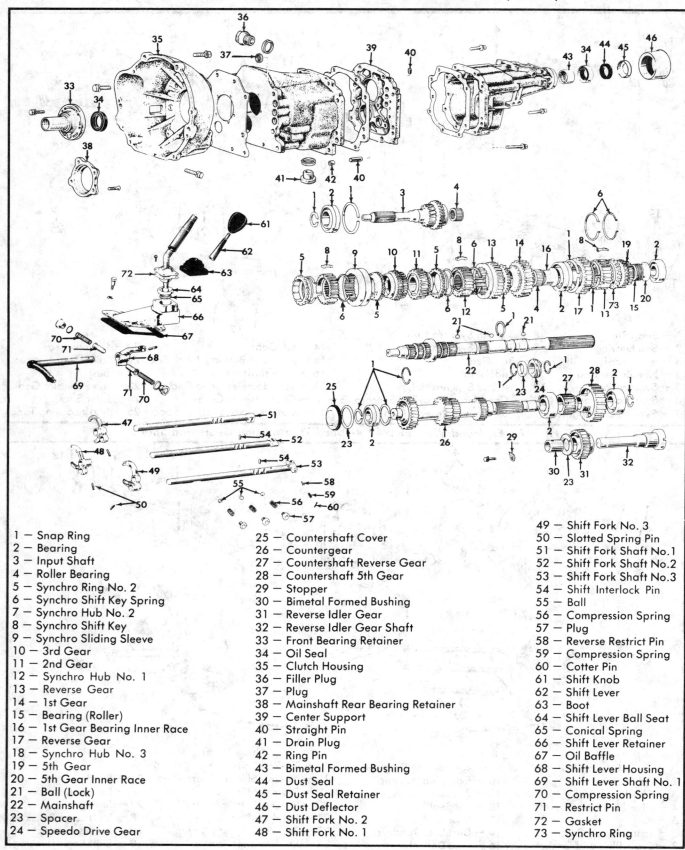

1 — Snap Ring	25 — Countershaft Cover	49 — Shift Fork No. 3
2 — Bearing	26 — Countergear	50 — Slotted Spring Pin
3 — Input Shaft	27 — Countershaft Reverse Gear	51 — Shift Fork Shaft No.1
4 — Roller Bearing	28 — Countershaft 5th Gear	52 — Shift Fork Shaft No.2
5 — Synchro Ring No. 2	29 — Stopper	53 — Shift Fork Shaft No.3
6 — Synchro Shift Key Spring	30 — Bimetal Formed Bushing	54 — Shift Interlock Pin
7 — Synchro Hub No. 2	31 — Reverse Idler Gear	55 — Ball
8 — Synchro Shift Key	32 — Reverse Idler Gear Shaft	56 — Compression Spring
9 — Synchro Sliding Sleeve	33 — Front Bearing Retainer	57 — Plug
10 — 3rd Gear	34 — Oil Seal	58 — Reverse Restrict Pin
11 — 2nd Gear	35 — Clutch Housing	59 — Compression Spring
12 — Synchro Hub No. 1	36 — Filler Plug	60 — Cotter Pin
13 — Reverse Gear	37 — Plug	61 — Shift Knob
14 — 1st Gear	38 — Mainshaft Rear Bearing Retainer	62 — Shift Lever
15 — Bearing (Roller)	39 — Center Support	63 — Boot
16 — 1st Gear Bearing Inner Race	40 — Straight Pin	64 — Shift Lever Ball Seat
17 — Reverse Gear	41 — Drain Plug	65 — Conical Spring
18 — Synchro Hub No. 3	42 — Ring Pin	66 — Shift Lever Retainer
19 — 5th Gear	43 — Bimetal Formed Bushing	67 — Oil Baffle
20 — 5th Gear Inner Race	44 — Dust Seal	68 — Shift Lever Housing
21 — Ball (Lock)	45 — Dust Seal Retainer	69 — Shift Lever Shaft No. 1
22 — Mainshaft	46 — Dust Deflector	70 — Compression Spring
23 — Spacer	47 — Shift Fork No. 2	71 — Restrict Pin
24 — Speedo Drive Gear	48 — Shift Fork No. 1	72 — Gasket
		73 — Synchro Ring

Fig. 19 Exploded View of W50 5-Speed Transmission Components

TOYOTA 4 & 5-SPEED — MODELS W40 & W50 (Cont.)

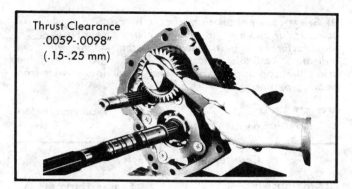

Thrust Clearance
.0059-.0098"
(.15-.25 mm)

Fig. 20   Using a Feeler Gauge to Measure Thrust Clearance (Reverse Idler Gear)

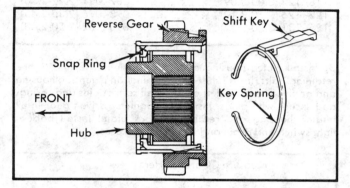

Fig. 21   Cross-Sectional View of Synchronizer No. 3 (5th and Reverse Assembly)

5) Install inner race lock ball into hole of mainshaft, by using heavy grease to hold ball in place. Assemble 5th gear, synchro ring, needle roller bearings and inner race into a set and slide this set onto mainshaft until inner race end face rests against synchro hub No. 3.

CAUTION — *Make sure inner race groove is aligned with lock ball and that synchro ring slots are aligned with shift keys.*

6) Secure 5th gear set on mainshaft with snap ring which will allow minimum axial play. *(See table.)* Measure 5th gear thrust clearance for standard of .0039-.0098" (.10-.25 mm) and wear limit of .0118" (.30 mm).

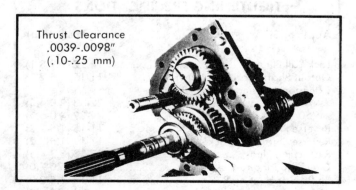

Thrust Clearance
.0039-.0098"
(.10-.25 mm)

Fig. 22   Using a Feeler Gauge to Measure 5th Gear Thrust Clearance

Selective 5th Gear Snap Rings	
Mark①	Thickness In. (mm)
1	.074-.076 (1.89-1.94)
2	.077-.079 (1.95-2.00)
3	.079-.081 (2.01-2.06)
4	.081-.083 (2.07-2.12)
5	.084-.086 (2.13-2.18)
6	.086-.088 (2.19-2.24)
7	.089-.091 (2.25-2.30)
8	.091-.093 (2.31-2.36)
9	.093-.095 (2.37-2.42)
10	.096-.098 (2.43-2.48)
11	.098-.100 (2.49-2.54)
12	.100-.102 (2.55-2.60)
13	.103-.105 (2.61-2.66)

① — Actual mark on snap ring.

7) Install countershaft reverse gear until it rests against inner bearing using driver (SST 09310 35010). Select snap ring of correct thickness and install on countershaft. Install snap ring on mainshaft and drive bearing onto mainshaft using bearing driver (SST 09515 20010 & 09309 35010). Assemble spacer, ball and speedometer drive gear onto mainshaft and secure with snap ring. Use heavy grease to prevent ball from falling out of hole in mainshaft.

Selective Countergear Bearing Snap Rings	
Mark①	Thickness In (mm)
1	.079-.081 (2.00-2.05)
2	.071-.073 (1.80-1.85)
3	.063-.065 (1.60-1.65)
4	.055-.057 (1.40-1.45)

① — Actual mark on snap ring.

8) Position shift forks into place on appropriate synchronizer sleeves and make sure each synchronizer is in neutral position. Install shift fork shafts, along with greased interlock pins into bores of center support and shift forks. Install lock balls and springs into bores of support, coat plugs with sealer, and install and tighten. At this time, install new slotted spring pins into shift forks and shafts to secure assemblies.

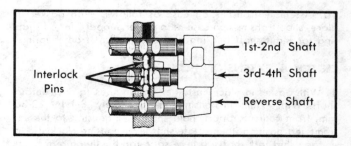

Fig. 23   Relationship of Shift Shafts in Case (4-Speed Model)

TOYOTA 4 & 5-SPEED — MODELS W40 & W50 (Cont.)

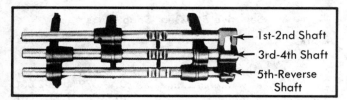

1st-2nd Shaft
3rd-4th Shaft
5th-Reverse Shaft

Fig. 24   Relationship of Shift Shafts in Case (5-Speed Models)

9) On four-speed models only, assemble reverse shift arm on bracket, tighten nut finger tight, then install assembly on center support. Drive in slotted spring pin to secure assembly. Shift to reverse position and check mesh between idler gear and reverse gear; if properly meshed, front face of idler gear will be aligned with, or slightly behind, front face of reverse gear. If not, rotate shift arm pivot until proper mesh is obtained, then tighten lock nut.

NOTE — When properly meshed, slot in shift arm pivot will be at a right angle to center support.

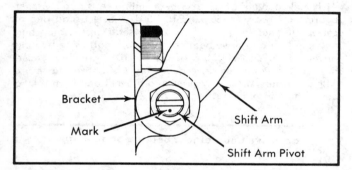

Bracket
Mark
Shift Arm
Shift Arm Pivot

Fig. 25   View Showing Reverse Idler Gear Adjustment

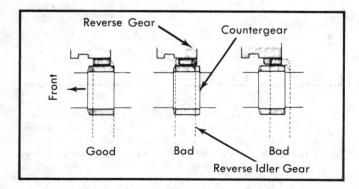

Reverse Gear
Countergear
Front
Good   Bad   Bad
Reverse Idler Gear

Fig. 26   Proper Reverse Idler Gear Position

10) Assemble transmission case as follows: With gasket in place, slide transmission case onto center support. Install snap ring for input shaft bearing and countershaft front bearing.

CLUTCH & EXTENSION HOUSING

1) With gasket in place, install extension housing over output shaft. With extension housing approximately .8-1.1" (20-30 mm) from center support, hold shift lever housing to the extreme left position, then rotate shift lever housing clockwise to engage shift fork shafts. If necessary, tap lightly on rear housing to bring it flush against center support. Install bolts and tighten to specifications.

2) Select countershaft front spacer by pressing firmly in on countergear and measuring depth of front bearing. **NOTE** — Manufacturer suggests measuring this depth with dial indicator. Available spacers are listed in following table, select the appropriate spacer and install spacer with front bearing retainer.

CAUTION — Make sure oil return hole is aligned before tightening bearing retainer bolts.

Countergear Spacer Selection

If Clearance Is In. (mm)	Spacer Thickness Is In. (mm)
.113-.118 (2.87-2.99)	.081-.085 (2.05-2.15)
.118-.122 (3.00-3.09)	.087-.091 (2.22-2.30)
.122-.126 (3.10-3.19)	.093-.096 (2.35-2.45)
.126-.131 (3.20-3.32)	.098-.102 (2.50-2.60)

3) Install clutch housing onto transmission case and tighten retaining bolts. Install shift lever retainer on extension housing, and on five speed models only, install restrict pins and springs, and secure with plugs. Install speedometer driven gear in extension housing and retain with lock plate. Install back-up light switch and drain and fill plugs into case.

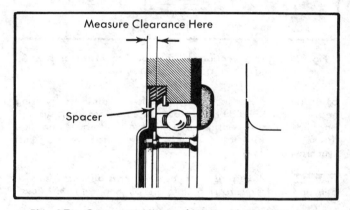

Measure Clearance Here
Spacer

Fig. 27   Cutaway View of Front of Case Showing Countergear Clearance and Spacer Position

TIGHTENING SPECIFICATIONS

Application	Ft. Lbs. (mkg)
Lock Ball Plugs	14-22 (1.9-3.1)
Output Shaft Bearing Retainer	11-15 (1.5-2.2)
Extension Housing Bolts	
W40	22-33 (3.0-4.5)
W50	29-39 (4.0-5.5)
Reverse Pivot Lock Nut	11-15 (1.5-2.2)
Reverse Shift Arm Bracket	11-15 (1.5-2.2)
Restrict Pin Plugs	27-33 (3.7-4.5)
Clutch Housing-to-Case Bolts	37-50 (5.0-7.0)
Shift Lever Housing Bolts	11-14 (1.5-2.0)
Front Bearing Retainer Bolts	5-6 (.60-.90)
Clutch Housing-to-Engine Bolts	37-50 (5.0-7.0)

TRIUMPH SPITFIRE 4-SPEED

DESCRIPTION

Transmission is a four-speed unit with synchromesh in all forward gears. Access to transmission gear train is through top cover of transmission. Gear shift mechanism is mounted on extension housing with a single tube connected to gear shift mechanism in transmission case.

LUBRICATION & ADJUSTMENT

See *MANUAL TRANSMISSION SERVICING* Section.

TROUBLE SHOOTING

HARD SHIFTING

Clutch not releasing properly. Check for adjustment, deformed clutch disc, seized or damaged pilot bearing. Incorrect or insufficient lubricant. Gearshift lever retainer binding or improperly lubricated. Gear selector rods and/or forks damaged.

JUMPS OUT OF GEAR

Worn or damaged shift forks. Detent balls and springs worn or broken. Worn or damaged synchro assemblies. Improper thrust clearance between gears.

NOISY OPERATION

Improper or insufficient lubricant. Worn or damaged bushings, bearings or gears. Worn splines.

NOTE — *When checking transmission for noise, ensure that it is not coming from other parts of the drive line.*

TRANSMISSION REMOVAL & INSTALLATION

Removal — 1) Raise vehicle and disconnect battery. Remove gearshift lever knob. If vehicle is equipped with overdrive, pry off knob cap and disconnect leads from switch. Loosen lock nut and unscrew gearshift knob. Remove transmission cover from floorboard on inside of vehicle.

2) Remove propeller shaft cover from transmission tunnel inside vehicle. Mark position of propeller shaft with flange. Disconnect propeller shaft from flange. Remove pinch bolt, then remove slave cylinder. Drain transmission. Place a jack under oil pan with a piece of wood between jack and oil pan. Raise jack to support engine.

3) Disconnect exhaust pipe from support bracket on transmission. Remove rear transmission mounting nuts. Remove restraining cable housing. Remove all accessible lower clutch housing bolts. Raise hood and remove starter. From inside vehicle, disconnect back-up light leads, overdrive leads (if equipped), and seat belt warning system. Remove transmission mount and remaining clutch housing bolts. Remove transmission from vehicle.

Installation — To install transmission, reverse removal procedure.

TRANSMISSION DISASSEMBLY

1) With transmission removed, separate clutch housing from transmission. Remove 3 springs from countergear shaft thrust washer. Remove top cover and spool interlock plate. Support transmission in a vise and remove back-up light switch and seat belt warning switch (if equipped). Drive out roll pin from gear shift selector rod.

2) Remove speedometer pinion housing and pinion from extension housing. Hold propeller shaft flange with a suitable tool and remove retaining nut and washer. Remove flange. Place transmission in reverse, making sure selector shaft pins clear interlock spool and shift forks. Remove extension housing-to-case bolts. Remove exhaust pipe support bracket from housing (if equipped).

3) Remove housing from transmission, making sure selector pins do not catch on case and countergear does not fall out of position. With housing removed, remove gasket. Remove mainshaft spacer, and oil seal and bearing from rear of extension housing.

4) Slide selector shaft rearward in housing until it contacts rear plug. Tap end of shaft to remove plug. Slide selector shaft rearward until yoke is exposed. Drive out roll pin securing yoke to shaft. Note that roll pin hole is in a horizontal position to prevent detent pin from locking in hole, then remove selector shaft through front of housing. Remove plug, detent plunger, spring, and "O" ring from housing.

5) Remove selector shaft and shift forks from case. Remove countergear shaft and allow countergear to drop into case. Connect a slide hammer to end of input shaft and pull shaft out of case (see *Fig. 1*). Remove bearing and spacer from mainshaft. Remove 4th gear synchro ring.

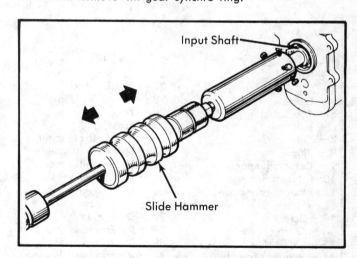

Fig. 1   Removing Input Shaft with Slide Hammer

6) Connect a suitable mainshaft centering tool (18G 47BP) to front of transmission case and connect it to mainshaft (see *Fig. 3*). Remove reverse idler gear bolt and remove reverse idler gear shaft. Remove idler gear and spacer. Remove bearing snap ring from mainshaft, then remove larger snap ring from outside of bearing. Remove bearing, shim, smaller snap ring and speedometer gear from mainshaft. Remove centering tool and mainshaft assembly. Remove countergear and thrust washers. Remove reverse operating lever.

TRIUMPH SPITFIRE 4-SPEED (Cont.)

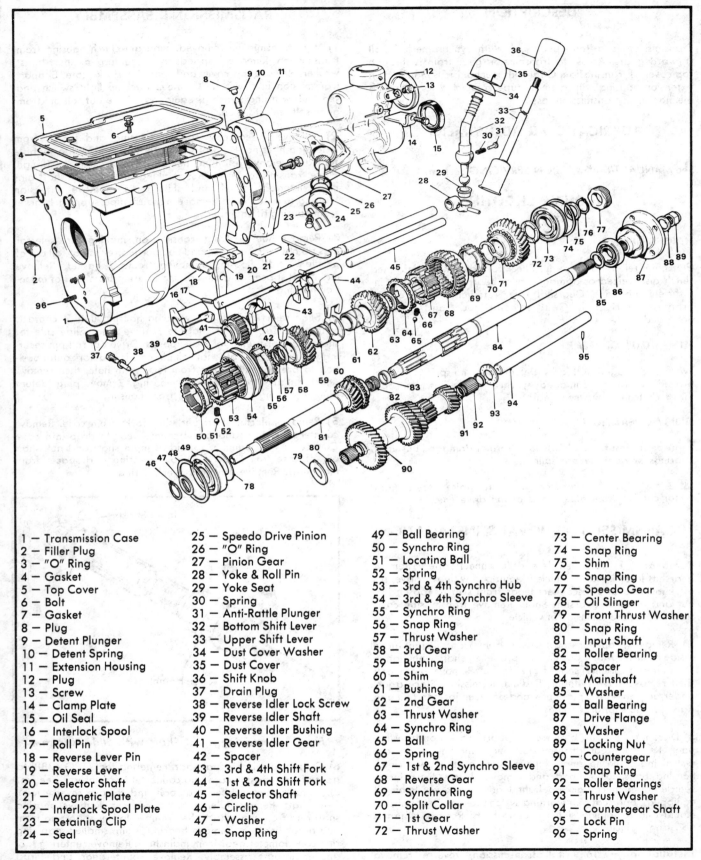

1 — Transmission Case	25 — Speedo Drive Pinion	49 — Ball Bearing	73 — Center Bearing
2 — Filler Plug	26 — "O" Ring	50 — Synchro Ring	74 — Snap Ring
3 — "O" Ring	27 — Pinion Gear	51 — Locating Ball	75 — Shim
4 — Gasket	28 — Yoke & Roll Pin	52 — Spring	76 — Snap Ring
5 — Top Cover	29 — Yoke Seat	53 — 3rd & 4th Synchro Hub	77 — Speedo Gear
6 — Bolt	30 — Spring	54 — 3rd & 4th Synchro Sleeve	78 — Oil Slinger
7 — Gasket	31 — Anti-Rattle Plunger	55 — Synchro Ring	79 — Front Thrust Washer
8 — Plug	32 — Bottom Shift Lever	56 — Snap Ring	80 — Snap Ring
9 — Detent Plunger	33 — Upper Shift Lever	57 — Thrust Washer	81 — Input Shaft
10 — Detent Spring	34 — Dust Cover Washer	58 — 3rd Gear	82 — Roller Bearing
11 — Extension Housing	35 — Dust Cover	59 — Bushing	83 — Spacer
12 — Plug	36 — Shift Knob	60 — Shim	84 — Mainshaft
13 — Screw	37 — Drain Plug	61 — Bushing	85 — Washer
14 — Clamp Plate	38 — Reverse Idler Lock Screw	62 — 2nd Gear	86 — Ball Bearing
15 — Oil Seal	39 — Reverse Idler Shaft	63 — Thrust Washer	87 — Drive Flange
16 — Interlock Spool	40 — Reverse Idler Bushing	64 — Synchro Ring	88 — Washer
17 — Roll Pin	41 — Reverse Idler Gear	65 — Ball	89 — Locking Nut
18 — Reverse Lever Pin	42 — Spacer	66 — Spring	90 — Countergear
19 — Reverse Lever	43 — 3rd & 4th Shift Fork	67 — 1st & 2nd Synchro Sleeve	91 — Snap Ring
20 — Selector Shaft	44 — 1st & 2nd Shift Fork	68 — Reverse Gear	92 — Roller Bearings
21 — Magnetic Plate	45 — Selector Shaft	69 — Synchro Ring	93 — Thrust Washer
22 — Interlock Spool Plate	46 — Circlip	70 — Split Collar	94 — Countergear Shaft
23 — Retaining Clip	47 — Washer	71 — 1st Gear	95 — Lock Pin
24 — Seal	48 — Snap Ring	72 — Thrust Washer	96 — Spring

Fig. 2 Exploded View of Triumph Spitfire 4-Speed Transmission

TRIUMPH SPITFIRE 4-SPEED (Cont.)

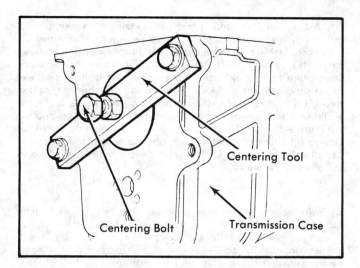

Fig. 3   Centering Mainshaft for Disassembly

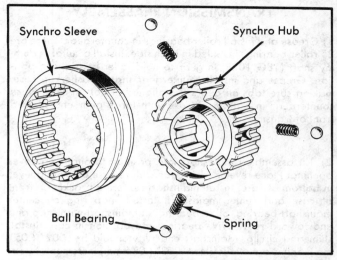

Fig. 4   Synchromesh Assembly (3rd & 4th Gear Shown)

COMPONENT DISASSEMBLY & REASSEMBLY

MAINSHAFT

Disassembly — 1) Remove 1st gear and thrust washer. Remove both portions of split collar. Remove 3rd and 4th gear synchro hub and sleeve assembly from opposite end of shaft. Remove synchro ring. Remove snap ring retaining 3rd gear and carefully slide off gear, bushing, thrust washer and snap ring.

2) Slide off 2nd gear and bushing, then remove synchro ring. Remove shim. Using a magnet, remove shim locating ball from recess in mainshaft. Remove spring from recess in mainshaft. Slide off 1st and 2nd gear synchro hub and sleeve.

3) Mark position of synchro hub on sleeve for both units. This will make sure each sleeve is installed in original position on hub. Slide sleeves off hubs, making sure three balls and three springs are retained from each hub. Check in each spring hole to make sure that a shim has not been installed under spring. If a shim has been installed, make sure it is installed in original position.

Reassembly — 1) Assemble synchro assemblies, making sure marks made during disassembly are aligned. Install any shims that were in spring recess in synchro hub. Install 1st and 2nd gear synchro assembly on mainshaft, then install synchro ring. Install locating ball and spring for shim, then install shim, making sure it is aligned with ball. Install 2nd gear and bushing. Position bushing so that collar is toward front of transmission.

2) Install 3rd gear, bushing and thrust washer. Position washer so that rim is toward front of transmission. Install snap ring so that inclined end faces forward and ends of snap ring align with edge of mainshaft spline. Install synchro ring and 3rd and 4th gear synchro assembly. Position synchro assembly so that larger boss of hub is toward front of transmission. Install remaining synchro ring, split collars and 1st gear thrust washer.

3) With mainshaft assembled, check the following clearances: Countershaft end play .007-.015" (.178-.381 mm). End play between 1st gear split collars and thrust washer should be .004-.013" (.102-.33 mm). End play for 2nd gear should be .002" (.051 mm). End play for 3rd gear should be .002-.006" (.051-.152 mm). End play for 2nd and 3rd gears is end play on bushing. Now check end play of 2nd and 3rd gear bushings on mainshaft. End play should be .006" (.152 mm). If end play is not to specification, it can be adjusted by adding shims. Shims are available in .003" (.076 mm) increments (see Fig. 5).

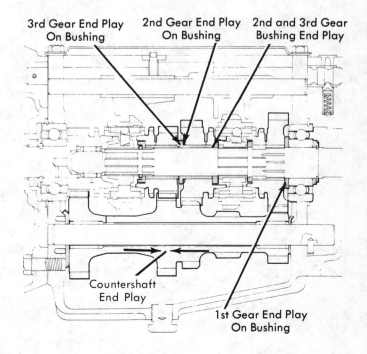

Fig. 5   Mainshaft End Play Measuring Points

TRIUMPH SPITFIRE 4-SPEED (Cont.)

TRANSMISSION REASSEMBLY

1) Grease and install roller bearings in countergear. There are 25 roller bearings installed in each side. Install a suitable dummy shaft (18G 1028) in gear to hold roller bearings in position. Grease and install countergear thrust washers in case, making sure tabs on gears are aligned in slots in case. Place countergear in bottom of case with large gear end toward front of transmission.

2) Tilt assembled mainshaft into position through top cover opening. Place reverse idler gear with reverse operating lever in bottom of case. Install mainshaft centering bracket on front of case and center mainshaft. Install snap ring on center mainshaft bearing. Slide bearing on mainshaft with snap ring end toward rear. Drive bearing into position in case. Install shim and circlip. Mainshaft end play should be .002" (.051 mm). Shims are available in .003" (.076 mm) increments to obtain correct end play.

3) Install speedometer drive gear onto mainshaft. Remove mainshaft centering bracket. Install roller bearing, spacer, synchro ring, and input shaft. Place countergear in position in case, taking care not to move thrust washers out of position. Push in countergear shaft and at the same time, push out dummy shaft. Install reverse idler gear, idler shaft and spacer. Place shift forks and shaft in position on mainshaft.

4) Install nylon plug, detent spring and plunger in extension housing. Install selector shaft in position in housing, making sure yoke roll pin hole does not lock with detent plunger. Place yoke in position on shaft and align roll pin holes. Drive in roll pin using a hammer and punch. Slide selector shaft forward in extension housing, then install plug at rear of housing.

5) Make sure mating faces of extension housing and transmission case are clean. Install a new gasket on transmission case. Install spacer on mainshaft. Place extension housing in position making sure selector spool is correctly installed. Install and tighten extension housing to case bolts. Install exhaust pipe bracket and lock plate. Install rear bearing and a new oil seal in rear of extension housing. Make sure seal is installed with lip toward transmission. Lubricate seal lip and install drive flange. Hold flange with a suitable tool. Install flange retaining nut and washer and tighten to specification. Install roll pin in front end of selector rail, making sure pin is installed in the center.

6) Install speedometer drive pinion and back-up light switch. Install 3 springs in front of transmission case. Install clutch housing gasket and clutch housing. Make sure input shaft splines do not damage seal. Install clutch fork and release bearing. Install drain plug and fill transmission through top opening to specified level. Install spool interlock plate, gasket and top cover.

TIGHTENING SPECIFICATIONS

Application	Ft. Lbs. (mkg)
Clutch Housing-to-Case	32 (4.4)
Extension Housing-to-Case	20 (2.8)
Transmission Cover	9 (1.2)
Cover Plate-to-Top Cover	9 (1.2)
Flange Nut (Exc. Midget)	120 (16.6)
Flange Nut (Midget)	100 (13.8)
Shift Fork-to-Selector Shaft	10 (1.4)
Reverse Idle Shaft Lock Bolt	14 (1.9)

TRIUMPH TR7 & TR8 5-SPEED

DESCRIPTION

Transmission is a 5-speed unit with single rail gear selector. Gear shift remote control unit is mounted on extension housing. Main components of transmission are: clutch housing, transmission case, extension housing and remote control housing.

LUBRICATION & ADJUSTMENT

See *MANUAL TRANSMISSION SERVICING* Section.

TRANSMISSION REMOVAL & INSTALLATION

Removal — 1) Disconnect battery and remove gear shift lever. Raise vehicle and place on safety stands. Disconnect propeller shaft at flange and tie shaft out of way. On TR7 models, remove propeller shaft safety strap before disconnecting shaft. On TR8 models, remove exhaust system, leaving tail pipes loosely in postion. On TR7 models, remove exhaust down pipe.

2) Disconnect speedometer cable and disconnect electrical plug for the back-up light. On TR7 models, remove starter heat shield. Place jack (with wooden block) under oil pan, then raise jack slightly to support engine. Remove oil pan protection plate, then remove bolts securing clutch slave cylinder and pipes to engine and clutch housing. On TR8 models, remove clutch slave cylinder heat shield before removing clutch slave cylinder.

3) Remove bolts attaching transmission crossmember to frame and lower engine/transmission sightly. On TR7 models, disconnect starter wires then remove starter. Place transmission jack under engine. On TR7 models, remove clutch housing-to-engine

bolts, then carefully lower and remove transmission from vehicle.

4) On TR8 models, remove all clutch housing-to-engine bolts except 3, then remove the 4 bolts attaching flywheel cover plate to clutch housing. Remove remaining 3 bolts and carefully lower transmission out of vehicle.

Installation — To install transmission, reverse removal procedures.

TRANSMISSION DISASSEMBLY

1) Remove clutch pivot bolt, clutch fork and clutch housing. Remove front cover, shims, gasket and bearing cups. Remove rear flange, using a suitable puller. Remove Nyloc nut from selector rail coupling pin (through access hole in rear extension housing). See *Fig. 1.*

2) Remove 5th gear spool retainer. Remove extension housing, retaining drive shaft for pump. Remove plastic cap and unscrew breather from main case. Remove selector rail clip, clips from 5th gear fork pivot pins and remove pins. See *Fig. 2.*

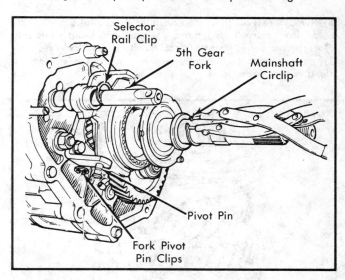

Fig. 2   Removing 5th Gear

3) Slide spool back and remove fork assembly. Remove 5th gear synchronizer hub retaining circlips, selective washer, hub backplate and hub. Remove 5th gear with caged needle bearings and thrust washer. Install four studs 2.3″ (60mm) long into the two top and two bottom bolt holes of the main case.

4) Remove circlip from countershaft 5th gear and retaining collar. Remove reverse shaft. Turn transmission case on end and insert in stand or vise, with front of case at the top. Remove spool retainer from main case. Remove bolts holding the center plate to the main case. Remove case from center plate. See *Fig. 3.*

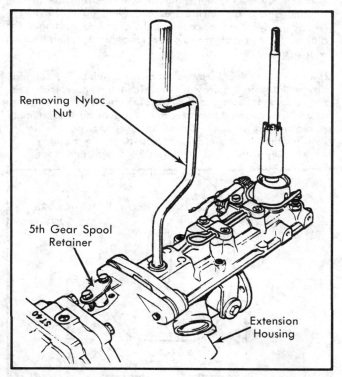

Fig. 1   Removing Nyloc Nut from Selector Rail

TRIUMPH TR7 & TR8 5-SPEED (Cont.)

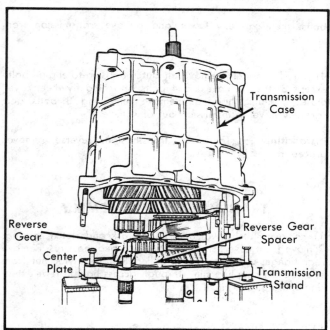

Fig. 3 Removing Transmission Case from Center Plate

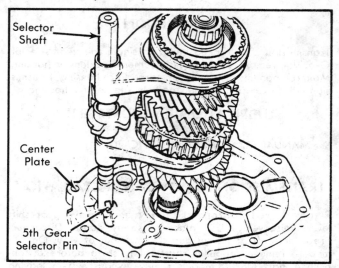

Fig. 5 Removing Selector Shaft from Mainshaft

5) Remove reverse gear and distance piece. Tilt countershaft away from mainshaft, remove countershaft, input shaft and synchronizer cone. Rotate selector rail counterclockwise until 1st gear selector pin releases reverse crossover lever. Remove clip and pivot. See Fig. 4.

COMPONENT DISASSEMBLY & REASSEMBLY

MAINSHAFT

Disassembly — 1) Remove circlips from behind center bearing, then remove bearing using a press. Remove the following from rear of mainshaft: 1st gear, bushing, 1st gear synchronizer cone, 1st and 2nd gear synchronizer hub, 2nd gear synchronizer cone and 2nd gear.

2) Using a suitable press, remove 3rd gear, 3rd gear synchronizer, distance piece and pilot bearing.

Reassembly — 1) Install 2nd gear, synchronizer cone (green), 1st and 2nd gear synchronizer hub (with outer slot facing rearward), synchronizer cone and 1st gear and bushing to the rear of the mainshaft. Press on center bearing; retain bearing with a circlip.

2) 1st gear end float is controlled by the bushing. The bushings are available in 5 different sizes. To determine correct size, assemble the following to the rear of the mainshaft: 2nd gear, 1st and 2nd gear synchronizer hub, 1st gear bushing, dummy spacer and circlip. See Fig. 6. Push spacer back against circlip, allowing the bushing maximum end float. The bushing must rotate easily with .0002-.002" (.005-.05 mm) end float.

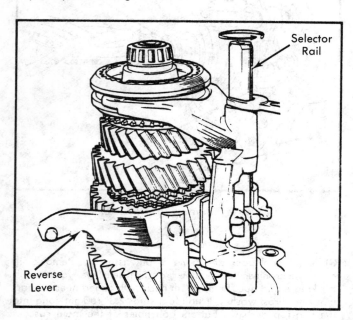

Fig. 4 Removing Mainshaft and Selector Shaft

6) Remove detent screw, spring and ball. Rotate selector shaft clockwise to align 5th gear selector pin with slot in center plate. Remove mainshaft and selectors as an assembly. Remove selectors from mainshaft. See Fig. 5.

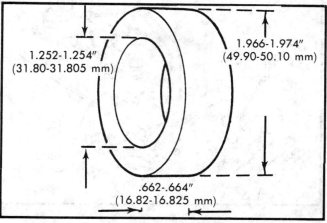

Fig. 6 Dimensions of Dummy Bearing

TRIUMPH TR7 & TR8 5-SPEED (Cont.)

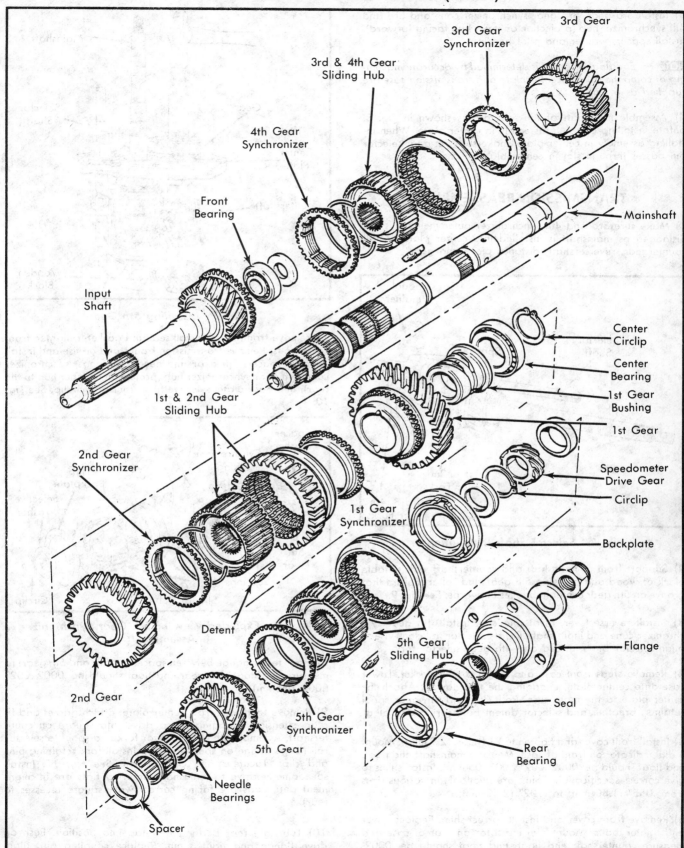

Fig. 7 Exploded View of Mainshaft

TRIUMPH TR7 & TR8 5-SPEED (Cont.)

3) Install 3rd gear, 3rd gear synchronizer cone and 3rd and 4th synchronizer hub (projection on inner hub facing forward). Install spacer, washer and pilot bearing.

NOTE — *End float of gears is determined by accurate machining of components. The center plate and transmission case are supplied as a unit.*

4) Assemble mainshaft of the selectors as shown in *Fig. 8.* before installing complete assembly in center plate. When installing assembly in center plate, make sure 5th gear selector pin passes through slot in center plate.

TRANSMISSION REASSEMBLY

1) Make sure 3rd and 4th synchronizer outer member is not dislodged as mainshaft is installed into center plate. Install countergear, reverse shaft, distance piece and gear.

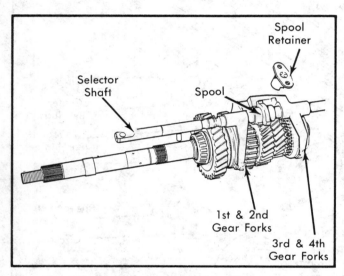

Fig. 8   Selector Shaft Installations

2) Support front of mainshaft and countershaft with suitable block of wood and press on 5th gear and collar. Ensure that groove on 5th gear center hub faces outwards. *See Fig. 9.*

3) Install reverse lever, pivot and clip. Install 4th gear synchronizer cone and input shaft. Rotate selector rail clockwise to align selector pin with 3rd and 4th gear selector fork.

4) Remove studs from case and install a new gasket. Lower case onto center plate, engaging the two dowels. Attach the center plate to the main case. Refit 3rd and 4th gear spool retainer, breather and selector detent ball, spring and plug.

5) Install front cover and tighten to 21 ft. lbs. (2.9 mkg). Mount a dial indicator on front of case. Measure mainshaft end float. End float should be .0002-.002" (.005-.05 mm). Install shims to give correct specification. Shims are available in various sizes from .055" (1.40 mm) to .102" (2.59 mm).

6) Remove front cover and install correct shim. Replace cover and tighten bolts. Mount dial indicator on rear of case and measure countershaft end float. End float should be .0002-.002" (.005-.05 mm). Countershaft shims are available in various sizes from .067" (1.69 mm) to .117" (2.99 mm).

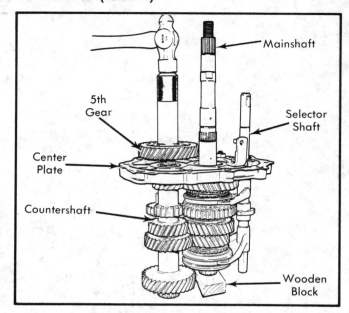

Fig. 9   Installing 5th Gear

7) Remove front cover. Install seal and gasket; retighten front cover bolts. Remove transmission from stand or vise and install selective spacer, 5th gear and needle bearings, synchronizer cone, 5th gear synchronizer hub (projection on inner hub to the rear), hub back plate, selective fit washer and circlip. *See Fig. 10.*

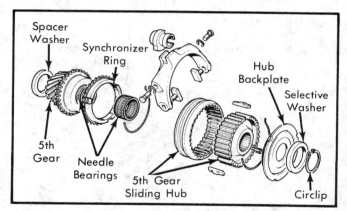

Fig. 10   Exploded View of 5th Gear Synchronizer Assembly

8) Insert feeler gauge between spacer washer and 5th gear; to measure end float. 5th gear end float should be .0002-.002" (.005-.055mm).

9) Remove four bolts from center plate, attach gasket and fit rear extension engaging pump drive into square on countershaft. Assemble 5th gear selector fork and spool to selector rail (large flange on spool to fork). Install fork retaining pins and clips. Locate spring clip on rail. *See Fig. 11.* Install speedometer drive to mainshaft, ensuring flats are in alignment and leads are facing correct way, square recesses to rear).

10) Lubricate rear bearing and tap into position. Push on drive flange and tighten nut. Replace coupling pin, plain washer and Nyloc nut. Install clutch housing and clutch fork and bearing.

TRIUMPH TR7 & TR8 5-SPEED (Cont.)

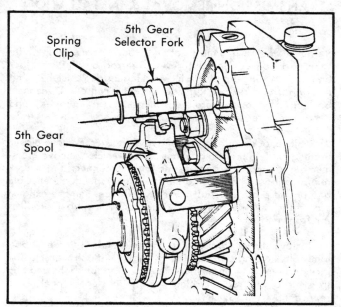

Fig. 11 *Installing 5th Gear Selector Spool and Fork*

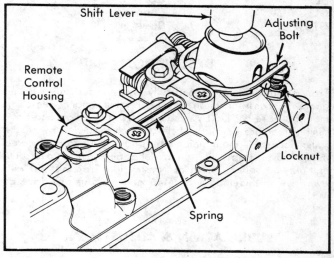

Fig. 12 *Adjusting Gear Lever Bias Spring*

ADJUSTING GEAR LEVER BIAS SPRINGS

1) With transmission assembled, place transmission in 3rd gear. Adjust the bolts to position both legs of spring .020" (.5 mm) clear of lever cross pin. Apply light pressure to lever (in left hand direction). Adjust right hand bolt downward until right hand spring leg just makes contact with cross pin.

2) Repeat operation on other side. Return lever to neutral and rock across gate. Lever should return to 3rd/4th gate. Tighten lock nuts. *See Fig. 12.*

TIGHTENING SPECIFICATIONS

Application	Ft. Lbs. (mkg)
Clutch Housing-to-Transmission Case	55 (7.5)
Bias Spring Bracket Bolts	5 (.7)
Coupling Flange Nut	150 (20)
Front Bearing Cover Bolts	21 (2.9)
Reverse Pivot Pin Nut	21 (2.9)

Manual Transmissions

VOLVO 4-SPEED

DL   GLE
GL   Coupe
GT   Diesel

DESCRIPTION

Transmission is a four speed fully synchronized unit with all gears in constant mesh except reverse gear. Gears on mainshaft are carried by needle rollers. Input shaft and drive pinion gear are an integral shaft which is carried by needle rollers located in main pinion gear and a ball bearing located in rear cover. Depending on model application, an overdrive unit may be bolted to rear of transmission. Transmissions with overdrive are identified as M46 and without overdrive as M45.

LUBRICATION & ADJUSTMENT

See *MANUAL TRANSMISSION SERVICING* Section.

TROUBLE SHOOTING

HARD SHIFTING

Clutch may not release fully due to deformed clutch disc or being out of adjustment. Pilot bearing seized, damaged or dry. Selector plate damaged. Shift forks bent.

SLIPS OUT OF GEAR

Selector plate damaged or worn. Detent balls and springs worn or broken. Shift forks bent or worn. Transmission and clutch housing misaligned.

NOISY OPERATION

Insufficient or wrong type lubricant. Worn or damaged bushings and/or gears. Worn splines.

NOTE — *When checking transmission for noise, ensure that it is not coming from other parts of the drive line.*

SERVICE (IN VEHICLE)

NOTE — *The following procedure is for "M45" transmissions (without overdrive).*

TRANSMISSION REAR OIL SEAL

Removal — Jack up rear of vehicle and place on floor stands. Drain transmission oil and disconnect propeller shaft "U" joint. Remove flange nut. Using a suitable puller (2261), pull flange from mainshaft. With suitable tool (5069), pull oil seal from rear cover.

Installation — Using suitable tool (5064), drive new oil seal into rear cover with seal lip facing rear cover. Install flange onto mainshaft using suitable tool (5149) and tighten nut to specification. Reverse removal procedure for remaining components and refill transmission with oil.

TRANSMISSION REMOVAL & INSTALLATION

Removal — 1) Disconnect battery ground cable. From under vehicle, disconnect gearshift lever from rod by removing lock bolt and pressing out pivot pin. Working inside vehicle, lift shift lever boot and remove left side of center console. Disconnect back-up light and overdrive connectors (if equipped) and remove reverse detent plate.

2) Remove lock ring and lift out gearshift lever. Remove plastic bushing and rubber ring. From under vehicle, remove crossmember at rear of transmission and disconnect clutch fork return spring and release cable. Disconnect speedometer cable and unbolt propeller shaft from drive flange. Remove exhaust pipe attachment to bell housing and unhook rubber supports for front muffler.

3) Remove starter from engine and take out all except 2 bottom bolts holding bell housing to engine. Attach transmission jack and support transmission. Remove 2 bottom bolts and pull transmission to rear, turning slightly to clear tunnel while separating from vehicle.

Installation — To install, reverse removal procedure.

TRANSMISSION DISASSEMBLY

1) Fit transmission in suitable work stand and drain lubricant. Remove back-up light switch and overdrive switch (if equipped). Remove transmission top cover and lift out detent spring and ball. Remove selector plate assembly, return spring, gasket, glide washers and shifter lock pin.

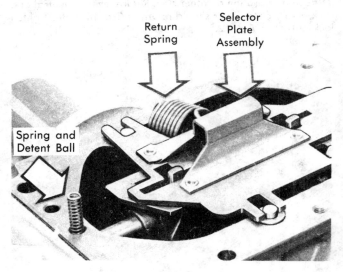

Fig. 1   Selector Plate Assembly

2) On M46 transmission, remove overdrive unit from intermediate flange. On all models, remove gearshift carrier assembly. On M46, remove sleeve over gearshift rod joint and knock out rear pin. Turn rod and knock out front pin, then remove rod. Unbolt intermediate housing from transmission and remove with gasket and shims.

VOLVO 4-SPEED (Cont.)

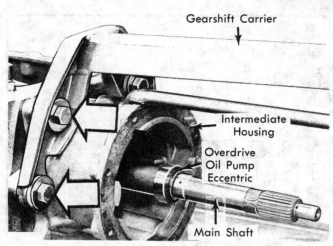

Fig. 2 Removing Gearshift Carrier Assembly (M46 Shown; M45 Similar)

3) On all models, remove selector rail, shifter and shift forks. On M45, use suitable adapter (5149) and socket to remove flange nut, then pull off flange. Remove speedometer driven gear and take off rear cover with gasket and shims. Remove speedometer drive gear.

4) On M46, remove lock ring and pull off overdrive oil pump eccentric. Catch and retain drive key. Remove lock ring and spacer ring for main shaft bearing. On all models, place adapter (2985) between input shaft and front synchro ring. Using puller and adapters (5058, 5147 and 5148) as required, pull off mainshaft bearing and remove thrust washer.

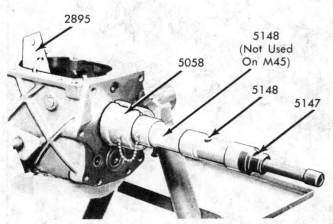

Fig. 3 Removing Mainshaft Bearing (M46 Shown; M45 Similar)

5) Remove clutch fork, bell housing, gasket and shims. On cast iron housing models, remove intermediate shaft rear bearing race by tapping shaft back until race is free, then tap forward until front race can be removed. On aluminum housing models, tap shafts only enough to install puller (5177), and remove races.

6) On all models, pull out input shaft, then remove 4th gear synchro ring. Lift out mainshaft, intermediate shaft, and reverse gear and shaft. It may be necessary to tap reverse gear shaft back for removal. Remove reverse gear shift fork and seal for selector rail. Using puller (5131), remove intermediate shaft bearings.

COMPONENT DISASSEMBLY & REASSEMBLY

MAINSHAFT

Disassembly — 1) Remove 1st gear, needle bearings and 1st gear synchro ring from mainshaft. Remove synchro sleeves and synchro rings from each end of mainshaft.

2) Remove circlips retaining each synchro hub. Using suitable tool (2853), press off 2nd gear and 1st-2nd synchro hub. Reverse shaft and press off 3rd gear and 3rd-4th synchro hub. Clean and inspect all parts for wear or damage, replace as necessary.

Reassembly — 1) Assemble synchro sleeve assemblies, making sure insert springs are correctly installed. Using suitable tool (2852), install 3rd gear and synchro ring, then 3rd-4th synchro hubs on mainshaft. Install lock ring.

2) Using same tool, install 2nd gear and synchro ring and 1st-2nd synchro hub on mainshaft, then install lock ring. Install 1st gear and synchro ring.

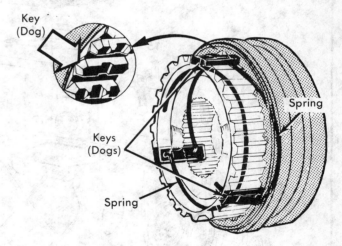

Fig. 4 View of Synchro Hub

TRANSMISSION REASSEMBLY

1) Using suitable drivers (5064, 5065, 2867 and 1801), install seals in bell housing, rear cover (M45 only) and selector rail hole. Install intermediate shaft end bearings (if removed) noting that small end bearing is different for diesel applications.

2) On aluminum housing models, determine intermediate shaft preload. Place intermediate shaft in housing and use drift (5180) to install bearing races. Install bell housing with gasket and tighten bolts to 25-35 ft. lbs. (3.4-4.8 mkg). Turn transmission vertically so bell housing is down and tap rear race in position so that clearance is gone and shaft turns sligtly sluggish.

VOLVO 4-SPEED (Cont.)

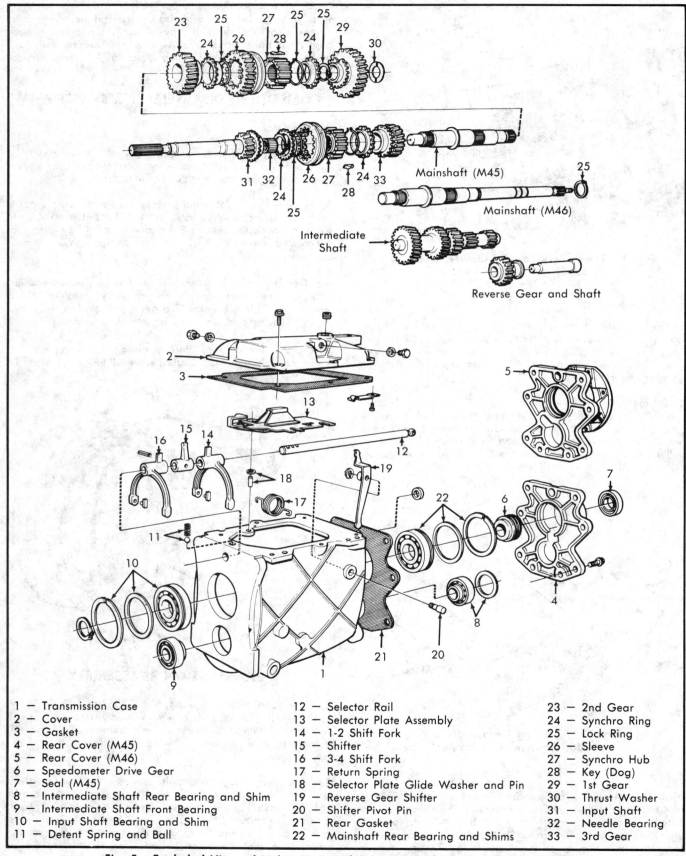

1 — Transmission Case	12 — Selector Rail	23 — 2nd Gear
2 — Cover	13 — Selector Plate Assembly	24 — Synchro Ring
3 — Gasket	14 — 1-2 Shift Fork	25 — Lock Ring
4 — Rear Cover (M45)	15 — Shifter	26 — Sleeve
5 — Rear Cover (M46)	16 — 3-4 Shift Fork	27 — Synchro Hub
6 — Speedometer Drive Gear	17 — Return Spring	28 — Key (Dog)
7 — Seal (M45)	18 — Selector Plate Glide Washer and Pin	29 — 1st Gear
8 — Intermediate Shaft Rear Bearing and Shim	19 — Reverse Gear Shifter	30 — Thrust Washer
9 — Intermediate Shaft Front Bearing	20 — Shifter Pivot Pin	31 — Input Shaft
10 — Input Shaft Bearing and Shim	21 — Rear Gasket	32 — Needle Bearing
11 — Detent Spring and Ball	22 — Mainshaft Rear Bearing and Shims	33 — 3rd Gear

Fig. 5 *Exploded View of Volvo M45 and M46 4-Speed Transmission Assembly*

VOLVO 4-SPEED (Cont.)

3) Using a depth gauge, measure distance to outer race from rear surface of housing. Add measured distance to gasket thickness of .010" (.25 mm) plus preload of .001-.003" (.03-.08 mm). Select a shim within this range and set aside for reassembly. Shims are available in the following thicknesses: .002" (.05 mm), .004" (.10 mm), .006" (.15 mm), .014" (.35 mm), .020" (.50 mm), .027" (.70 mm) and .039" (1.0 mm).

4) Remove bell housing and gasket, then remove intermediate shaft. *See DISASSEMBLY procedures.* On all models, install reverse gear shifter and lock ring. Install reverse gear and shaft. Shaft end should be at least .002" (.05 mm) below housing face.

5) Adjust clearance between reverse gear and shift fork to give .004-.040" (.10-1.0 mm) clearance. Adjust by tapping shift fork pivot pin in or out with a punch. Place intermediate shaft in bottom of housing, then position mainshaft in housing. With positioning lock ring fitted to bearing, fit thrust washer and bearing on mainshaft.

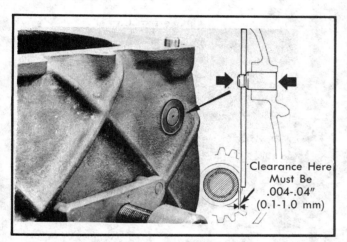

Fig. 6 Adjusting Clearance Between Reverse Gear and Shift Fork

6) Ensure that gears do not interfere with each other and use press tool (2831) to press mainshaft bearing into position. If bearing does not align correctly, use spacer between tool spindle and housing front end. Press in until positioning ring is flush with housing face.

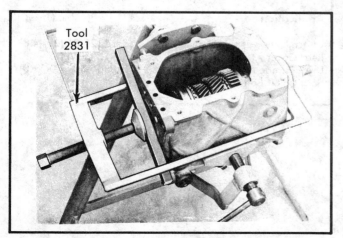

Fig. 7 Installing Mainshaft Bearing

7) On M46, install lock ring on mainshaft and insert key for oil pump eccentric. Install eccentric and lock ring. On all models, grease and install input shaft roller bearings, then position 4th gear synchro ring in synchro hub. Push input shaft into position on mainshaft. Lift intermediate shaft so that bearings are correctly positioned in housing.

8) Pull out input shaft so that spacer ring can be installed on bearing, then push shaft in so ring is against housing. On cast iron housing models, install outer bearing races for intermediate shaft bearings. On aluminum housing models, use depth gauge and measure distance from front of input bearing to surface of housing, then measure distance from bell housing surface to bottom of bearing seat.

9) Add .01" (.25 mm) to bell housing distance, then subtract distance of input bearing extension above housing. Choose shims to give .0004-.008" (.01-.20 mm) end play. Shims are available in the following thicknesses: .024" (.60 mm), .029" (.75 mm), .035" (.90 mm) and .039" (1.0 mm).

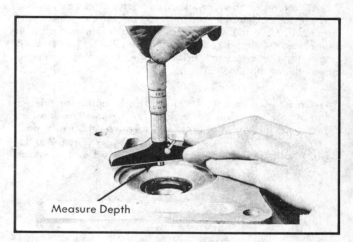

Measure Depth

Fig. 8 Measuring Clutch Housing Surface to Bearing Seat

10) On all models, attach bell housing with shims, clutch fork and release bearing. Turn transmission to vertical position with bell housing DOWN. On aluminum housing models, tap intermediate bearing race in with drift (5180) until clearance is gone and slight drag is felt on shaft when rotated.

11) On cast iron housing models, determine shim thickness requirement for intermediate shaft to give .001" (.025 mm) to .004" (.10 mm) axial clearance. Measure distance from rear housing surface to intermediate shaft outer race and add gasket thickness of .010" (.25 mm). Subtract axial clearance of .001" (.025 mm) to .004" (.10 mm) to determine shim thickness. Shims are available in the following thicknesses: .002" (.05 mm), .004" (.10 mm), .006" (.15 mm), .014" (.35 mm), .020" (.50 mm), .027" (.70 mm) and .039" (1.0 mm).

12) Measure distance from mainshaft bearing to housing rear surface, and distance from rear cover surface to bottom of rear bearing seat. Allow for gasket thickness of .010" (.25 mm) and select mainshaft shim thickness to give .0004-.008" (.01-.20 mm) axial clearance. Shims are available in the following thicknesses: .024" (.60 mm), .029" (.75 mm), .035" (.90 mm) and .039" (1.0 mm).

Manual Transmissions

VOLVO 4-SPEED (Cont.)

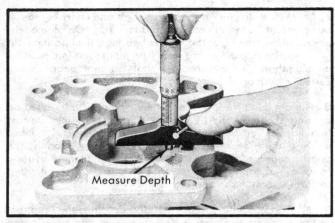

Fig. 9 Measuring Rear Housing Surface to Bearing Seat

13) On all M45 models, install speedometer drive gear, gasket and previously determined shim pack. Drive gear flange must face toward bearing. Grease mainshaft rear shim and place in rear cover, then install rear cover. Tighten 2 outer (lower) bolts finger tight, then install drive flange. Install speedometer driven gear with new "O" ring.

14) On all M46 models, install shift forks and gear selector rail. Position gasket and shim pack for intermediate shaft on transmission housing. Use grease to keep mainshaft shim pack in place and install intermediate housing. Tighten 2 outer (lower) bolts finger tight. Install gearshift rod and sleeve on joint.

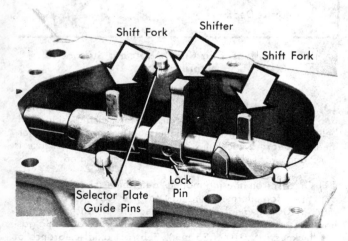

Fig. 10 Installing Shift Forks and Shifter

15) On all models, install gearshift carrier and tighten rear cover bolts to 25-35 ft. lbs. (3.5-4.8 mkg). On M45, install shift forks and gear selector rail. Install overdrive on M46. On all models, install lock pin for shifter and glide washers for selector plate assembly. Install selector plate assembly and return spring.

16) Install gearshift lever without lock screw and lock ring to check operation. Hold selector plate down with palm of hand and check gearshift operation. Correct as necessary, then remove gearshift lever. Install detent ball and spring, then install top cover with new gasket. Install overdrive switch, back-up light switch and wires at overdrive solenoid as applicable. Fill with transmission fluid.

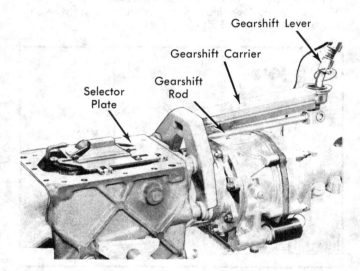

Fig. 11 Checking Gearshift Operation (M46 Shown)

TIGHTENING SPECIFICATIONS

Application	Ft. Lbs. (mkg)
Clutch Housing-to-Transmission	25-35 (3.5-4.8)
Rear Cover Attaching Bolts	25-35 (3.5-4.8)
Drive Flange Nut	65-80 (9.0-11.0)
Shift Cover Bolts	11-18 (1.5-2.5)

Section 6

MANUAL TRANSAXLES

CONTENTS

MANUAL TRANSAXLES
Section 6

NOTE — ALSO SEE GENERAL INDEX.

AUDI 4000 & VOLKSWAGEN DASHER 4-SPEED

DESCRIPTION

Transaxle is a four speed fully synchronized unit with independent front suspension. Transmission has helical cut gears which are in constant mesh with the exception of reverse gear. Mainshaft is carried at front end by a needle bearing in final drive housing and at rear by a ball bearing in transmission case. Countershaft incorporates axle drive pinion gear and is carried by a straight roller bearing at pinion gear end and by a ball bearing in transmission case. Pinion gear drive depth is controlled by a spacing shim at transmission end of countershaft. Differential assembly is carried by taper roller bearings located in final drive housing and final drive housing side plate. Shims located behind outer roller bearing races control backlash and preload of differential assembly bearings. Axle drive flanges press into differential assembly and are retained by bolts.

LUBRICATION & ADJUSTMENT

See *MANUAL TRANSMISSION SERVICING* Section.

SERVICE (IN VEHICLE)

AXLE DRIVE SHAFTS

NOTE — *Vehicle weight must be resting on wheels to remove axle shaft nut.*

Removal — 1) Remove axle shaft nut. Raise and support vehicle; remove tire and wheel. Disconnect and remove exhaust pipe from exhaust manifold and transaxle bracket on right side of engine. Remove Allen bolts connecting inner constant velocity (CV) joint to differential case drive flange.

2) Mark position of right ball joint flange to control arm. Remove ball joint from control arm and pull pivot mounting outward while removing right drive shaft. Press out drive shaft and guide shaft out of hub, past transaxle.

NOTE — *Axle drive shafts should be disassembled ONLY to replace defective rubber boots. If boots are replaced, check all components for wear or damage and replace as complete assembly.*

Disassembly — 1) On inner CV joint, remove circlip from axle shaft and drive protective cap from CV joint. Place axle shaft in holder (VW402) and press CV joint from shaft with adapter (VW408a), supporting hub to prevent damage. Pivot hub and cage assembly out of inner joint, then push out and remove balls. Align ball hub grooves with cage and remove hub.

NOTE — *Inner CV joint and ball hub are matched sets. DO NOT interchange with outer joint. Also, balls of CV joints cannot be interchanged between CV joints.*

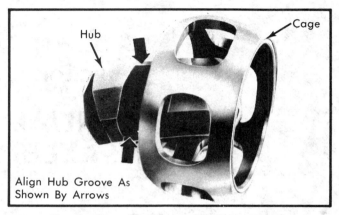

Align Hub Groove As Shown By Arrows

Fig. 2   Removing Inner CV Joint Ball Hub

2) Remove and discard inner boot clamp and boot. On outer CV joint, spread circlip inside ball hub and drive CV joint off axle shaft with brass drift; tap on hub. Mark position of ball hub and outer joint, then tilt cage and remove each ball. Align cage perpendicular to joint. Align 2 large openings of cage with raised portions of joint and remove cage and hub. Position 1 retainer of hub in large opening and remove hub by tilting outward. Remove and discard outer boot and clamp.

Reassembly — 1) To reassemble CV joints, reverse disassembly procedure and note the following: Lubricate joints with 3 ozs. (90 g) of molybdenum disulphide grease. After inserting balls into inner CV joint hub and cage, insert hub and cage into joint perpendicularly. Chamfer of ball hub splines must face larger diameter of joint. Then rotate ball and cage into position and ensure CV joint wide ball groove and narrow hub groove are on same side of joint. *See Fig. 3.* Joint is correctly assembled if hub can move over shaft splines by hand.

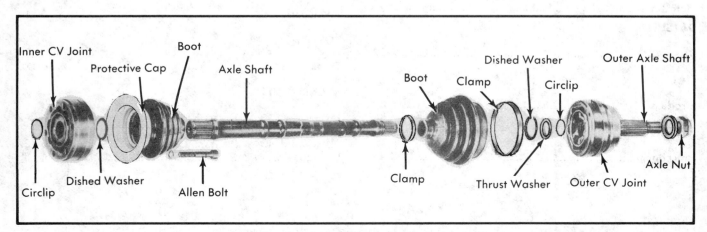

Fig. 1   Exploded View of Axle Shaft Assembly

AUDI 4000 & VOLKSWAGEN DASHER 4-SPEED (Cont.)

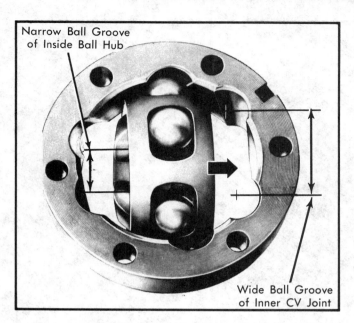

Fig. 3 Installing Ball Hub and Cage in Inner CV Joint

2) Outer CV joint alignment marks must match after reassembly. Replace dust boots and clamps. Install CV joints onto drive axle shaft with inside ball hub chamfer facing shaft. Outer CV joint must be assembled with dished washer concave side facing thrust washer and convex side of thrust washer facing CV joint. See *Fig. 4.*

3) Inner CV joint must be assembled with dished washer concave side facing CV joint when installed on shaft. Install boot clamps with open end facing opposite direction of normal rotation. Always use new circlips to retain CV joints on shafts.

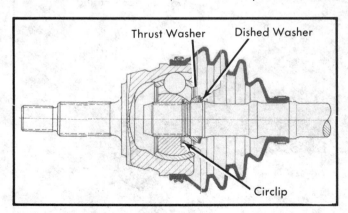

Fig. 4 Cutaway View of Outer CV Joint Showing Installation of Dished and Thrust Washers

Installation — To install, reverse removal procedure and note the following: After installing right shaft, align ball joint with mark made at removal and tighten nuts. Check camber setting and adjust if necessary.

FRONT WHEEL BEARINGS

Removal — 1) With vehicle supported and drive axle shafts removed, remove stabilizer bar clamps. Remove caliper

mounting bolts and hang caliper from frame with wire; DO NOT disconnect hydraulic line. Remove brake disc and ball joint bolt. Press off tie rod and remove ball joint from hub.

2) Support suspension strut with jack and remove upper strut retaining nuts from inside engine compartment. Remove strut assembly from vehicle and mount in holding fixture. Press out wheel hub with hub remover (VW295 & 295a). Remove circlips from both sides of bearing housing and press out bearing (toward outboard end of housing). Remove inner wheel bearing race from hub.

NOTE — *Wheel bearing must be replaced. Removal procedure destroys wheel bearing for reuse.*

Installation — To install, reverse removal procedure and note the following: Offset portion of stabilizer bar must be installed facing downward.

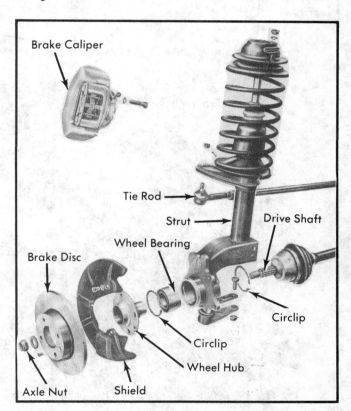

Fig. 5 Exploded View of Front Suspension Strut Assembly

INNER DRIVE FLANGE OIL SEALS

Removal — Disconnect inner CV joint from drive flange and support drive axle out of the way. Insert a long drift punch into 1 drive flange hole to prevent drive flange movement, then remove drive flange retaining bolt. Place drip pan under transaxle housing and pull out drive flange. Pry out oil seal.

Installation — Lightly lubricate seal lips and fully seat seal with driver (30-212). Install drive flange and tighten drive flange retaining bolt. Install drive axle and tighten bolts. Check and add lubricant to transaxle, if required.

Manual Transaxles

AUDI 4000 & VOLKSWAGEN DASHER 4-SPEED (Cont.)

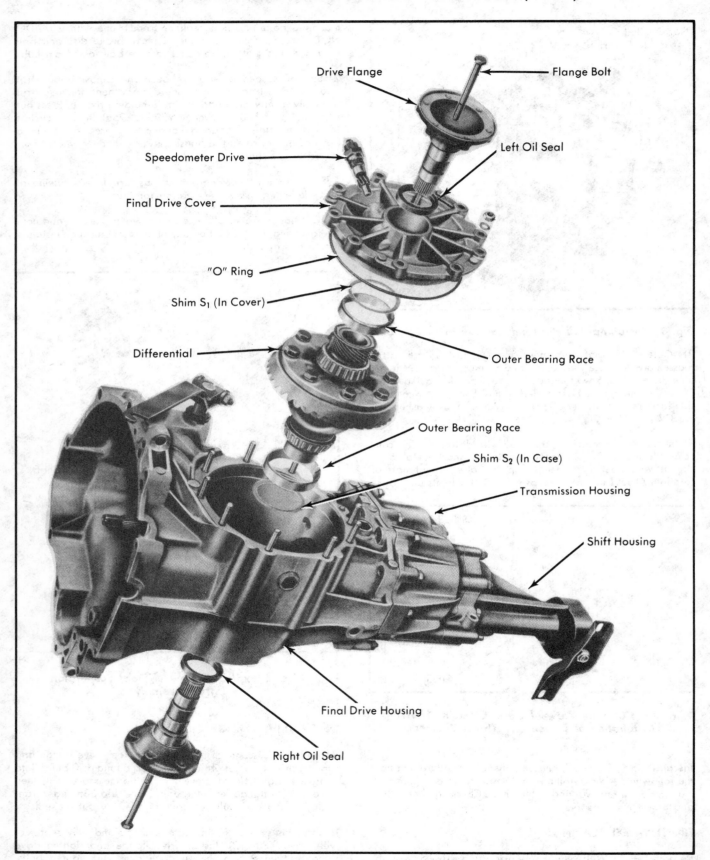

Drive Flange

Flange Bolt

Speedometer Drive

Left Oil Seal

Final Drive Cover

"O" Ring

Shim S₁ (In Cover)

Differential

Outer Bearing Race

Outer Bearing Race

Shim S₂ (In Case)

Transmission Housing

Shift Housing

Final Drive Housing

Right Oil Seal

Fig. 6   View Showing Main Components of Transaxle Assembly

AUDI 4000 & VOLKSWAGEN DASHER 4-SPEED (Cont.)

TRANSAXLE REMOVAL & INSTALLATION

Removal — 1) Disconnect battery ground strap. Disconnect exhaust pipe from transaxle bracket and engine. Remove square bolt and press shifter coupling from rear of transmission shifting shaft. Unhook clutch cable and disconnect speedometer cable.

2) Disconnect CV joints at inner drive flanges. Remove starter, front mounting plate and transaxle mounting bolts. Disconnect back-up light wires. Support transaxle on floor jack and remove crossmember mount. Lever transaxle away from engine and lower out of vehicle.

Installation — 1) Install crossmember to transaxle. Raise transaxle and install crossmember bolts (do not tighten). Slide transaxle up to engine and install mounting bolts. Install front mounting plate and starter. Install CV joint Allen screws and tighten. Tighten crossmember mounting bolts.

2) Install shift rod coupling bolt and install lock wire. Connect exhaust pipe, allowing 3/8" (10 mm) between pipe and floor pan. Reconnect back-up light wires and battery ground strap.

NOTE — *Always use longer hex head bolt when replacing shift rod coupling instead of original square head bolt. Secure with safety wire.*

TRANSAXLE DISASSEMBLY

1) Mount transaxle on suitable work fixture and drain fluid. Remove shift housing, gasket and shim from transaxle case. Retain shim and gasket for future use for determining differential pinion depth setting.

2) Carefully pull 3rd/4th gear selector rod away from transmission housing until interlock can be removed. Remove interlock and push rod back into neutral position. Lock shafts by engaging 1st and reverse shift rails.

3) Install mainshaft support bar (30-211) and tighten bolt until it touches mainshaft. Remove circlip and thrust washer from mainshaft. Remove mainshaft bearing with puller (30-207). Remove transmission housing attaching bolts and transmission housing from final drive housing. Drive out dowel pins.

4) Remove drive flange attaching bolt and remove drive flange as previously outlined. Remove final drive cover bolts and pry off final drive cover. Remove differential.

NOTE — *DO NOT drop magnet from rear of final drive cover.*

COMPONENT DISASSEMBLY & REASSEMBLY

SHIFT HOUSING ASSEMBLY

NOTE — *Shift housing shim and gasket thickness will have to be determined if any of the following items are replaced: Mainshaft ball bearing, pinion shaft ball bearing, transmission case or shift housing.*

Disassembly — Pull selector shaft from shift housing. Using suitable arbor press and tool (VW418a), press transmission rear mount from shift housing. With a drift, drive out inner bushing. Pry oil seal from nose of shift housing. Using suitable tool (VW439), press outer bushing from nose of shift housing.

Reassembly — 1) Using suitable tool (32-102), drive outer bushing into nose of shift housing until flush. Using same tool, install oil seal in same manner. Turn housing end for end and drive inner bushing in until flush with same tool. Install new rear mount onto nose of housing using press and suitable tool (VW455). Slide selector shaft into housing assuring that spring presses inner shift lever in direction of 3rd and 4th gear selector shaft.

2) Mount a dial indicator on measuring tool (VW382/7), then zero dial indicator with .12" (3 mm) preload. Measure distance between mainshaft bearing and gear carrier housing (*Dimension "A" in Fig. 7*). Measure distance between pinion bearing and gear carrier housing (*Dimension "B" in Fig. 7*). Then measure distance between end face of gearshift housing and shim contact surface in gearshift housing (*Dimension "C" in Fig. 7*).

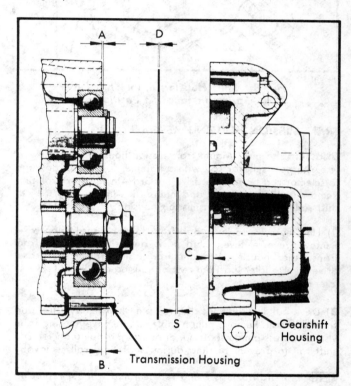

Fig. 7 Cutaway View Showing the Various Dimensions for Gearshift Housing Shim and Gasket Selections

3) To compute shim thickness (*Dimension "S" in Fig. 7*), add dimension "A" to dimension "C", then subtract dimension "B" from this total. Use only 1 shim and always use shim closest to required value.

NOTE — *Gearshift housing shims are available in thicknesses from .018" (.45 mm) to .030" (.75 mm) in increments of .002" (.05 mm). Use shims with code letter "A" which are flat on one side.*

4) To determine housing gasket thickness (*Dimension "D" in Fig. 7*), measure projection of mainshaft bearing (*Dimension "A" in Fig. 7*). If dimension "A" is .008-.010" (.20-.25 mm), use a gasket .012" (.30 mm) thick or if "A" is .011-.013" (.28-.33 mm), use a gasket .016" (.41 mm) thick.

AUDI 4000 & VOLKSWAGEN DASHER 4-SPEED (Cont.)

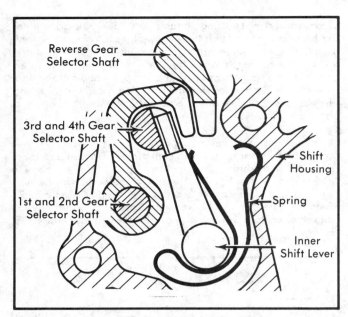

**Fig. 8   Shift Housing Inner Shift Lever
Spring Installation Position**

TRANSMISSION HOUSING ASSEMBLY

Disassembly — 1) Mount transmission housing in soft-jawed vise. Support selector rod with a hammer to prevent damage to selector rod bore, then drive out 3rd/4th shift fork roll pin. Remove 3rd/4th shift fork and mainshaft while pulling 3rd/4th shift rail out rear of transmission housing.

2) Unscrew reverse lever bolt from top of transmission case. Remove reverse lever, shift fork and shift rail pin from transmission housing. Working from inside transmission case, drive reverse idler shaft out rear of housing and lift out reverse idler gear.

3) Drive out 1st/2nd shift dog roll pin, then remove shift dog from shift rail. Remove pinion shaft nut. Remove housing from vise and press pinion shaft out of bearing, tapping on 1st/2nd shift rail to prevent binding during shaft and rail removal.

NOTE — *If transaxle is being reassembled without replacing parts, readjustment of pinion depth is not necessary. However, if transaxle case, transmission housing, pinion bearing, 1st gear needle bearing or ring and pinion gear set are replaced,*

pinion depth MUST be checked and shim replaced if required. See *Drive Pinion Depth* in this article.

Reassembly — 1) Using a press and arbor (VW426), press in pinion shaft and pinion bearing race with 1st/2nd shift fork and rail properly engaged. Install reverse gear and press in reverse shaft. Insert reverse shift rail, roll pin and relay lever. Install reverse lever bolt with washer and push relay lever in toward case.

2) Turn lever bolt until it aligns with relay lever hole. Back off bolt until starting thread engages with threaded hole in lever, then tighten bolt to 25 ft. lbs. (3.5 mkg). Select reverse gear position several times. If lever and reverse gear do not move easily through full range of movement, repeat adjustment of reverse relay lever.

3) Place 1st/2nd shift dog on shift rail and install roll pin. Install mainshaft and 3rd/4th shift fork into case. Place selector rod in neutral position and install 3rd/4th roll pin.

NOTE — *If mainshaft bearing was replaced with a new bearing, shift housing gasket and shim thickness must be calculated. See Shift Housing Assembly.*

4) Engage 3rd/4th shift fork with synchro sleeve on mainshaft (wider shoulder of shift fork facing 4th gear). Slide mainshaft and shift fork into transmission housing. Insert 3rd/4th shift rail through shift fork and install spring pin. Pull 3rd/4th shift rail out rear of transmission far enough to install lock pin. Install shim washer and circlip on transmission end of mainshaft.

5) Engage 1st and reverse gears and tighten pinion shaft nut to specifications. Check that shift rods work correctly and that forks are properly engaged prior to assembling gear case to transaxle case.

MAINSHAFT ASSEMBLY

Disassembly — Remove circlip and shim from mainshaft. Slide 4th gear and needle bearing from shaft. Remove inner circlip and press off 3rd/4th synchro assembly and 3rd gear from mainshaft. Remove split cage needle roller for 3rd gear.

Reassembly — 1) Engage synchro inserts into synchro hub and install synchro sleeve over hub. Install synchro spring with bend end in synchro insert. Install spring on opposite side of hub with bend staggered 120°. Press synchro rings onto 3rd and 4th gears by hand and measure clearance between ring and gear. Clearance should be .053-.075″ (1.35-1.90 mm) with wear limit of .020″ (.50 mm).

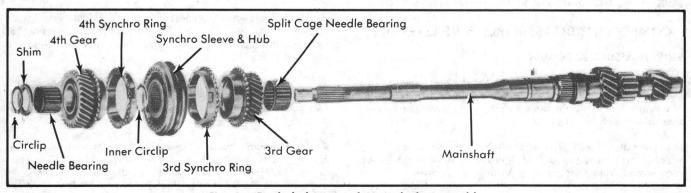

Fig. 9   Exploded View of Mainshaft Assembly

AUDI 4000 & VOLKSWAGEN DASHER 4-SPEED (Cont.)

2) Lubricate and install 3rd gear split cage needle roller on mainshaft. Place 3rd gear on mainshaft and press on synchro assembly with hub chamfer facing 3rd gear. Install inner circlip and press synchro hub back against circlip.

3) Slide needle bearing and 4th gear on mainshaft. Install shim and circlip. Using a feeler gauge, measure clearance between shim and 4th gear. Clearance should be .004-.016" (.10-.40 mm). Shim as necessary, staying on low side of range.

NOTE — *Mainshaft and shims have corresponding flats. Shims are available in thicknesses of .136" (3.45 mm), .140" (3.55 mm), and .144" (3.65 mm).*

PINION SHAFT ASSEMBLY

Disassembly — Using a gear puller, pull inner pinion bearing race, pinion depth shim (S_3) and 1st gear from pinion shaft. Next, pull 2nd gear and synchro assembly. Remove circlip from shaft and pull off 3rd gear. Press off 4th gear and remove roller bearing from pinion shaft.

NOTE — *Prior to reassembly, drive pinion shaft, 3rd gear and 4th gear must be absolutely free of oil and grease. These gears are heated to approximately 250° F (120° C) prior to being pressed onto pinion shaft.*

Reassembly — 1) Slide roller bearing onto shaft. Press 4th gear onto shaft using suitable plate (VW402). Press 3rd gear onto shaft and measure clearance between edge of circlip groove and face of 3rd gear with a feeler gauge. If clearance is less than .063" (1.6 mm), use a circlip which is .059" (1.5 mm) thick. If it is greater than .063" (1.6 mm), use a circlip which is .063" (1.6 mm) thick.

2) Assemble synchro hub and sleeve so that hub cutouts match grooved tooth of sleeve splines. Hub teeth have a groove cut on front face of hub. This groove must face 1st gear. Install synchro spring with bend end in synchro insert. Install spring on opposite side of hub with bend end staggered 120°. Press synchronizer rings onto 1st/2nd gears by hand and measure clearance between ring and gear. Clearance should be .043-.067" (1.1-1.7 mm) with a wear limit of .020" (.50 mm).

NOTE — *Synchronizer ring for 1st gear has 110° tooth angle and is identified by 3 teeth missing around circumference. This synchronizer ring MUST be installed for 1st gear ONLY. If ring is damaged, replace with standard synchronizer ring. Special ring is not available as replacement part.*

3) Place 2nd gear, needle bearing and synchro ring on pinion shaft. Align cutouts in synchro ring with synchro inserts and press on synchro hub assembly. Install 1st gear, spacing collar, needle bearing, pinion depth shim (S_3) and press on inner pinion bearing race.

NOTE — *If pinion bearing or spacing collar were replaced, pinion shim (S_3) thickness must be calculated. See Drive Pinion Depth in this article.*

FINAL DRIVE HOUSING

Disassembly — 1) Remove clutch release bearing guide sleeve. Using suitable tool (VW681), pry out mainshaft oil seal. Working from transmission side of final drive housing, insert suitable drift tools (VW431 & VW439) and drive mainshaft sleeve out clutch side of housing. Working from clutch side of housing, insert suitable tools (VW431 & VW439) and drive mainshaft needle bearing out transmission side of housing.

2) From hole located in side cover flange, remove dowel pin retaining pinion roller bearing outer race. Using suitable tools (VW295 & 30-205), drive bearing race out clutch side of final drive housing.

Reassembly — 1) With grooved side of bearing race facing transmission and dowel pin hole aligned with hole in housing, drive bearing race into housing using suitable tools (VW295 & 30-205). Install dowel pin which retains bearing race. Dowel pin will project .012" (.3 mm) above side cover flange when properly engaged with hole in roller bearing race.

2) From clutch side of housing, drive in mainshaft sleeve and oil seal. From transmission side of housing, drive in mainshaft needle bearing using suitable tools (VW295 & VW295a).

DIFFERENTIAL ASSEMBLY

Disassembly — 1) Using a puller and adapter (VW295a), pull off side bearings. Remove speedometer drive gear and bushing with bearing. Remove ring gear attaching bolts and tap ring gear off differential housing.

NOTE — *Ring gear and pinion must be replaced as matched set.*

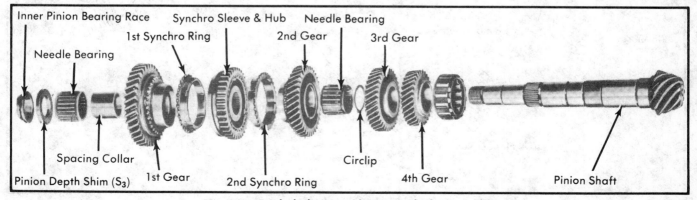

Fig. 10 Exploded View of Pinion Shaft Assembly

Manual Transaxles

AUDI 4000 & VOLKSWAGEN DASHER 4-SPEED (Cont.)

2) Remove pinion shaft circlips and drive out pinion shaft. Rotate differential side gears with aid of drive flanges to housing opening and remove pinion gears. Remove drive flanges, drive flange nuts, side gears and thrust washer.

NOTE — *If differential housing is stamped with one-piece plastic thrust washer symbol, ONLY that thrust washer can be installed.*

Reassembly — 1) Coat thrust washer and gears with transmission fluid and install thrust washer in housing. Place side gears and drive flange nuts into differential housing. Install pinion gears, rotate drive flange to align pinion shaft and insert pinion shaft. Install pinion shaft circlips.

2) Heat ring gear to 212° F (100° C) and place on differential housing. Center with drift, then install and tighten bolts. Heat side bearings to same temperature and press onto differential. Place speedometer gear and bushing on differential. Insert a .06" (1.4 mm) thick shim in bushing. Press bushing, shim and drive gear on as a unit, then remove shim.

NOTE — *Shim assures correct alignment of drive gear and bushing as they are pressed on.*

TRANSAXLE REASSEMBLY & ADJUSTMENTS

DRIVE PINION DEPTH

1) Assemble pinion shaft with standard .157" (4 mm) shim (S₃) installed. Place pinion shaft in transmission case and torque pinion shaft nut to 14-22 ft. lbs. (2-3 mkg). With 4 nuts, mount transmission case to final drive housing. Mount tensioner tool (VW297/8) on rear of transmission housing as shown in *Fig. 12.* Place a 36 mm socket over pinion nut and lock in place with knurled screw.

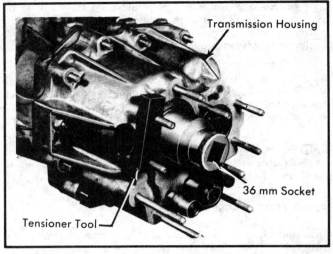

Fig. 12   *Installation of Tensioner Tool on Transmission Housing*

NOTE — *If assembly was originally equipped with gasket between final drive and transmission housing, gasket must be present when making measurement. Before starting measurement, be sure ball bearing is pressed in fully.*

2) Assemble measuring bar (VW385/1) and position sliding set ring until it is approximately 2" (50 mm) from center of bar. Complete assembly of measuring bar. *See Fig. 13.* Install dial indicator and set dial indicator to .157" (4 mm) preload. Zero gauge by removing master gauge (VW385/23).

NOTE — *Turn knurled adjusting knob on end of measuring bar to move setting ring back to stop.*

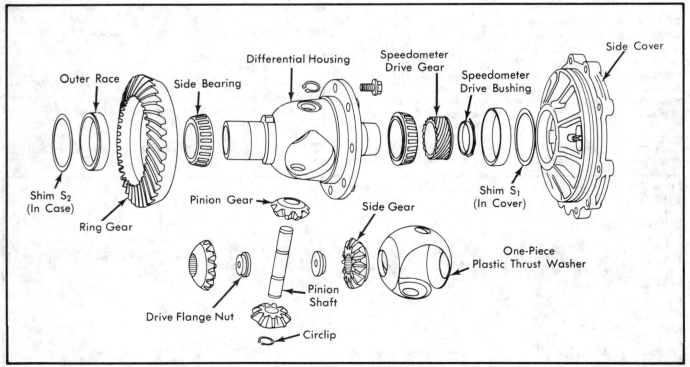

Fig. 11   *Exploded View of Differential Assembly*

AUDI 4000 & VOLKSWAGEN DASHER 4-SPEED (Cont.)

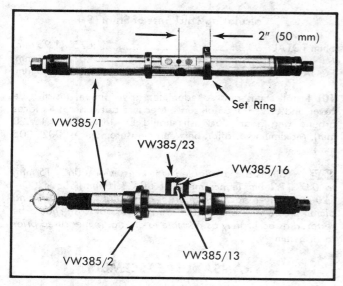

Fig. 13 Assembling Pinion Depth Measuring Tool

3) Place end plate (VW385/17) on end of drive pinion and install measuring bar in housing. Install final drive side cover together with bearing outer race and tighten bolts to 18 ft. lbs. (2.5 mkg). Do not strike cover as this may upset dial indicator setting. Pull second centering ring outward until measuring bar can just be turned by hand. See Fig. 14.

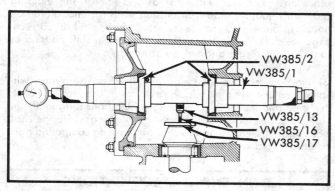

Fig. 14 Sectional View Showing Installation of Measuring Tools Used to Obtain Pinion Depth Reading

4) Rotate measuring bar until maximum dial indicator deflection is reached and note measurement. Determine production deviation marked on ring gear in .01 mm.

NOTE — *Production gears will not have this mark, however service gears will show three sets of figures, the last of which is the production deviation. A marking of 25 indicates .25 mm deviation (r).*

Typical Pinion Depth Shim (S₃) Calculations
$$(S_3 = e - r + x)$$

Dial Indicator Deflection (e) ①	.035″	(.90 mm)
MINUS Production Deviation (r)	.018″	(.45 mm)
PLUS Standard Pinion Test Shim (x)	.157″	(4.0 mm)
EQUALS Pinion Depth Shim (S_3)	.174″	(4.45 mm)

① — MINUS .078″ (2 mm) preload factor.

5) Disassemble measuring tools and remove pinion shaft. Remove pinion depth shim from pinion shaft and install NEW shim of appropriate thickness. Install pinion with correct shim installed and check reading with dial indicator. With correct shim installed, reading should be production deviation ±.0015″ (.04 mm).

NOTE — *In this sample calculation, 2 shims must be used to obtain correct clearance. Install thinner shim between thicker shim and inner bearing race. Shims are available in thicknesses of .150″ (3.80 mm) to .205″ (5.2 mm) in addition to thin shim of .006″ (.15 mm).*

BACKLASH & SIDE BEARING PRELOAD

1) Remove differential oil seals and outer roller bearing races from final drive housing and side cover. Remove bearing shims (S₁ & S₂) from behind bearing races. Place a .047″ (1.2 mm) shim (S₂) in final drive housing and press bearing race in housing using suitable tools (VW295 & 30-205). Press bearing race in side cover without shim (S₁).

2) With open side of final drive housing facing up, install differential assembly (without speedometer drive gear) so ring side is on side cover side of transaxle housing. Install side cover attaching bolts and diagonally tighten them to 18 ft. lbs. (2.5 mkg).

3) Place end disc (VW385/17) on flange end of differential assembly. Install a dial indicator so foot will rest on end disc with a .039″ (1.0 mm) preload. On bottom side of transaxle, install locking sleeve (VW521/4) into differential assembly. Move differential sleeve up and down noting total measurement for total shims required (both sides) on dial indicator. DO NOT rotate differential while taking measurements or bearings will settle causing an incorrect reading. Using the following example, calculate total shims required for bearing preload:

Calculating Differential Preload

Up and Down Measurement	.012″	(.30 mm)
PLUS Preload Constant	.016″	(.40 mm)
PLUS Housing Shim (S₂)	.047″	(1.20 mm)
EQUALS Shim Total	.075″	(1.90 mm)

4) Remove side cover and press out bearing race. Install shim (S₁) which is a total of preload constant plus measured value for a total of .028″ (.70 mm). Reinstall bearing race and side cover.

NOTE — *Differential rotating torque MUST be at least 23 INCH lbs. (25 cmkg) with new roller bearings.*

5) Install transmission housing and pinion shaft to final drive housing. Ensure .047″ (1.2 mm) shim is installed on housing side. Screw measuring bar (VW388) into locking sleeve (VW521/4). Mount dial indicator extension onto measuring bar so extension extends 2.8″ (71 mm) above measuring bar. Mount dial indicator with contact foot touching tip of extension.

6) With pinion shaft locked as previously described, *See Drive Pinion Depth,* rotate ring gear as far as it will turn and zero dial indicator. Rotate ring gear in opposite direction and read dial indicator for backlash. Loosen locking sleeve and pinion locking device, take 3 more readings at 90° intervals.

AUDI 4000 & VOLKSWAGEN DASHER 4-SPEED (Cont.)

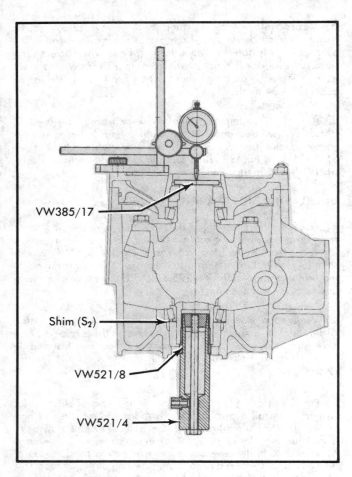

VW385/17

Shim (S₂)

VW521/8

VW521/4

Fig. 15 Cutaway View of Final Drive Housing Showing Backlash Measuring Tool Installation

NOTE — *If measurements differ more than .002" (.06 mm), ring gear and pinion are not installed properly.*

7) Using the following example, determine average backlash:

Calculating Average Backlash

1st Measurement	.016" (.41 mm)
PLUS 2nd Measurement	.017" (.42 mm)
PLUS 3rd Measurement	.017" (.42 mm)
PLUS 4th Measurement	.016" (.41 mm)
Total Measurement	.066" (1.66 mm)
Total Divided By 4	
EQUALS Average Backlash	.016" (.41 mm)

8) Determine thickness of shim (S_2) located in final drive housing in following manner:

Calculating Thickness of Shim (S_2)

Shim Inserted	.047" (1.20 mm)
MINUS Average Backlash	.016" (.41 mm)
PLUS Lift Constant	.006" (.15 mm)
EQUALS Shim (S_2)	.037" (.94 mm)

9) Determine thickness of shim (S_1) located in side cover in following manner:

Calculating Thickness of Shim (S_1)

Shim TOTAL	.075" (1.90 mm)
MINUS Shim (S_2)	.037" (.94 mm)
EQUALS Shim (S_1)	.038" (.96 mm)

10) Install shims and speedometer drive pinion. Install side cover and drive flange oil seals. Measure backlash at 4 places around ring gear. Backlash should be .004-.008" (.10-.20 mm). Maximum variation between measurements is .002" (.05 mm).

NOTE — *Shims are available in thicknesses of .006" (.15 mm) to .047" (1.2 mm) in increments of .004" (.10 mm) above .008" (.20 mm). Given backlash figure is only valid for new ring and pinion. If old ring and pinion are reused, backlash should be restored as accurately as possible to old figure measured prior to disassembly.*

TRANSAXLE REASSEMBLY

1) Using suitable sealing compound, slide transmission assembly into final drive housing and tighten attaching nuts.

NOTE — *Transmissions are mounted using a gasket WITHOUT sealing compound. Method used in production (sealing compound or gasket) must always be used for reassembly.*

2) Having previously determined gasket and shim thickness, place gasket on transmission studs and shim in shift housing. Start shift housing onto transmission studs far enough to hold housing. Slide and rotate selector shaft until it correctly engages shift rails in transmission case. Push shift housing up to transmission case and tighten attaching nuts.

3) Place differential assembly into final drive housing with speedometer drive pinion facing side cover. Use new side cover "O" ring and install side cover, tightening bolts diagonally. Install speedometer drive gear and drive flanges. Flange shaft bolts must be cleaned and coated with locking compound prior to installing and tightening.

TIGHTENING SPECIFICATIONS

Application	Ft. Lbs. (mkg)
Inner Drive Flange Bolt	14 (2.0)
Engine-to-Transaxle	40 (5.5)
Inner Drive Flange-to-CV Joint	33 (4.6)
Brake Caliper Bolts	36 (5.0)
Top Strut Nut	18 (2.5)
Ball Joint-to-Control Arm	47 (6.5)
Ball Joint Nut	36 (5.0)
Axle Nut	
Audi 4000	167 (23)
Dasher	174 (24)
Transmission Hsg.-to-Final Drive Hsg.	18 (2.5)
Gearshift Hsg.-to-Transmission Hsg.	18 (2.5)
Final Drive Cover	18 (2.5)
Pinion Shaft Nut	72 (10)
Reverse Lever Bolt	25 (3.5)
Ring Gear Bolts	
Type "A" With Lock Washer	40 (5.5)
Type "B" Without Lock Washer	50 (7.0)

AUDI 5000 5-SPEED

DESCRIPTION

Transmission is a 5-speed unit and is fully synchronized in all forward gears. Gears are helical cut and are in constant mesh with the mating gears, which are located on the pinion shaft. The 5th gear assembly is housed in a separate housing, which is attached to the rear of the main gear housing. The final drive uses hypoid ring and pinion gears. The drive axles use 2 "U" joints (1 on inboard side and 1 on outboard side). The "U" joints are of the constant velocity (CV) type.

SERVICE (IN VEHICLE)

AXLE DRIVE SHAFTS

NOTE — *Vehicle weight must be resting on wheels to remove axle shaft nut.*

Removal — Remove axle shaft nut. Raise and support vehicle; remove tire and wheel. Remove drive shaft shield (right side). Remove Allen bolts connecting inner constant velocity (CV) joint to differential case drive flange. Press out drive shaft and guide shaft out of hub, past transaxle. Remove locking compound from shaft splines.

NOTE — *Axle drive shafts should be disassembled ONLY to replace defective rubber boots. If boots are replaced, check all components for wear or damage and replace as complete assembly.*

Disassembly — 1) On inner CV joint, remove circlip from axle shaft and drive protective cap from CV joint. Place axle shaft in holder (VW402) and press CV joint from shaft with adapter (VW411), supporting hub to prevent damage. Pivot hub and cage assembly out of inner joint, then push out and remove balls. Align ball hub grooves with cage and remove hub.

NOTE — *Inner CV joint and ball hub are matched sets. DO NOT interchange with outer joint. Also, balls of CV joints cannot be interchanged between CV joints.*

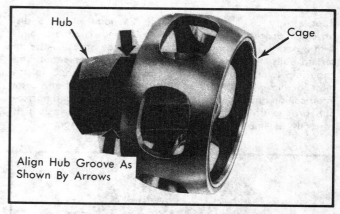

Fig. 2 Removing Inner CV Joint Ball Hub

2) Remove and discard boot clamp and boot. On outer CV joint, spread circlip inside ball hub and drive CV joint off axle shaft with brass drift; tap on hub. Mark position of ball hub and outer joint, then tilt cage and remove each ball. Align cage perpendicular to joint, align 2 large openings of cage with raised portions of joint and remove cage and hub. Position 1 retainer of hub in large opening and remove hub by tilting outward. Remove and discard boot and clamp.

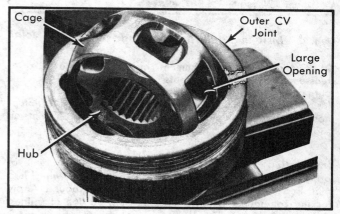

Fig. 3 Removing Outer CV Joint Ball Hub

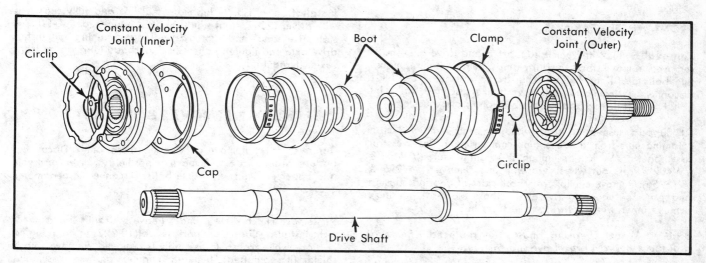

Fig. 1 Exploded View of Front Axle Drive Shaft

Manual Transaxles

AUDI 5000 5-SPEED (Cont.)

Reassembly — 1) To reassemble CV joints, reverse disassembly procedure and note the following: Lubricate joints with 3 ozs. (90 g) of molybdenum disulphide grease. After inserting balls into inner CV joint hub and cage, insert hub and cage into joint perpendicularly. Chamfer of ball hub splines must face larger diameter of joint. Then rotate ball and cage into position and ensure CV joint wide ball groove and narrow hub groove are on same side of joint. *See Fig. 4.* Joint is correctly assembled if hub can move over shaft splines.

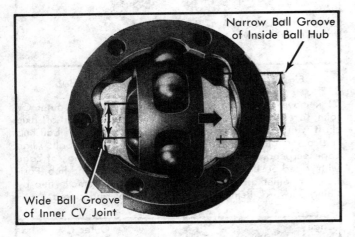

Fig. 4   Installing Ball Hub and Cage in Inner CV Joint

2) Outer CV joint alignment marks must match after reassembly. Replace dust boots and clamps. Install CV joints onto drive axle shaft with inside ball hub chamfer facing shaft. Install boot clamps with open end facing opposite direction of normal rotation. Always use new circlips to retain CV joints on shafts.

Installation — To install drive axle shaft, reverse removal procedure and note the following: Drive shaft and wheel hub must be free of oil, grease, and old locking compound. Apply locking compound to outer .203" (5 mm) portion of splines, then install shaft. Allow locking compound to harden for 1 hour before moving vehicle.

FRONT WHEEL BEARINGS

Removal — 1) With vehicle supported and drive axle shafts removed, remove stabilizer bar clamps. Remove caliper mounting bolts and hang caliper from frame with wire; DO NOT disconnect hydraulic line. Remove brake disc and ball joint bolt. Press off tie rod and remove ball joint from knuckle.

2) Support suspension strut with jack and remove 3 strut retaining nuts from inside engine compartment. Remove strut assembly from vehicle and mount in holding fixture (VW401 & VW402). Press out wheel hub with hub remover (VW295 & VW295a). Remove circlips from both sides of bearing housing and press out bearing (toward outboard end of housing). Remove inner wheel bearing race from hub.

NOTE — *Wheel bearing must be replaced. Removal procedure destroys wheel bearing for reuse.*

Installation — To install, reverse removal procedure.

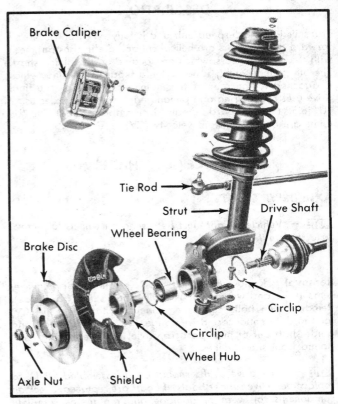

Fig. 5   Exploded View of Front Suspension Strut Assembly

INNER DRIVE FLANGE OIL SEALS

Removal — Disconnect inner CV joint from drive flange and support drive axle out of the way. Insert a long drift punch in 1 drive flange hole to prevent drive flange movement, then remove drive flange retaining bolt. Place a drip pan under transmission housing and pull out drive flange. Pry out oil seal.

NOTE — *Replacement of oil seal on right side requires removal of splash guard.*

Installation — Lightly lubricate seal lips and fully seat seal with driver (2062; right side seal also requires tool 30-20). Install drive flange and tighten drive flange retaining bolt. Install drive axle and tighten bolts. Check and add lubricant to transaxle, if required.

TRANSAXLE REMOVAL & INSTALLATION

Removal — 1) Remove air cleaner (diesel only). Disconnect battery ground cable. Remove windshield washer reservoir and upper engine-to-transaxle bolts. Disconnect speedometer cable.

2) Remove clutch slave cylinder (leave hydraulic line connected). Install a suitable support device (10-222) to hold engine in place while transaxle assembly is removed. Remove splash shield (if equipped) beneath engine/transaxle assembly. Remove front exhaust pipe.

AUDI 5000 5-SPEED (Cont.)

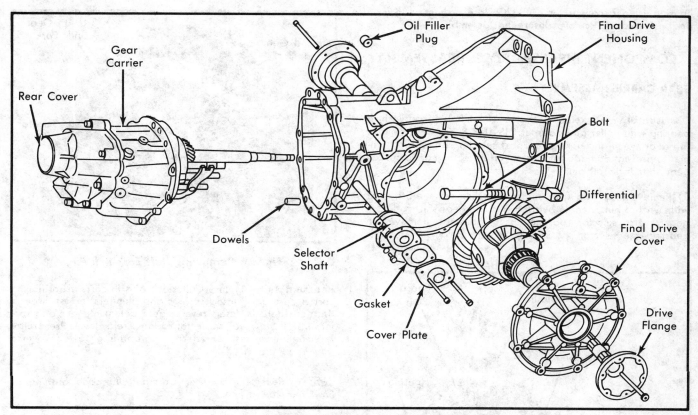

Fig. 6 Exploded View of Transaxle Components

3) Remove right side guard plate. Disconnect drive axle shafts from drive flanges and support on top of subframe. Disconnect wire from back-up light switch. Disconnect shift linkage from transaxle case.

4) Remove lower engine-to-transaxle bolts, starter and guard plate from subframe. Lift transaxle slightly and remove transaxle supports. Remove rear subframe mounting bolts. Remove right transaxle bracket, then remove transaxle from below.

Installation — Reverse removal procedure and note the following:

- Lubricate mainshaft splines lightly with grease.
- Make sure transaxle seats on engine dowels.
- Adjust shift linkage as necessary.

TRANSAXLE DISASSEMBLY

CAUTION — *If final drive housing or pinion bearings are to be replaced and deviation "r" is not marked on ring gear, position of pinion shaft must be measured before removing gear assembly. See Drive Pinion Depth adjustment under Transaxle Reassembly & Adjustment in this article.*

1) Mount transaxle in suitable holding fixture and drain oil. Remove selector shaft. Remove final drive-to-gear carrier bolts, drive out dowel pins and separate gear carrier from final drive.

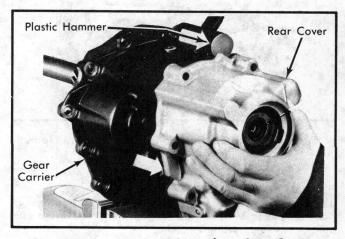

Fig. 7 Removing Rear Cover from Gear Carrier

2) Mount gear carrier in a soft-jaw vise with rear cover facing up. Remove cap from end of rear cover by driving a screwdriver into center of cap and prying up, then remove bolt from end of mainshaft.

3) Reposition gear carrier in vise, clamping lower portion of gear carrier. Remove cover attaching bolts and drive cover from gear carrier with plastic hammer. Remove mainshaft inner bearing race.

4) Remove drive flange retaining bolt and drive flange. Remove final drive cover attaching bolts and pry cover from

AUDI 5000 5-SPEED (Cont.)

housing using 2 screwdrivers. DO NOT lose magnet on rear of final drive cover. Remove differential assembly.

COMPONENT DISASSEMBLY & REASSEMBLY

GEAR CARRIER ASSEMBLY

Disassembly — 1) Remove 5th gear clutch hub and mainshaft bearing with puller and adapter (US1078 & VW431). Remove 5th gear synchronizer ring. Support selector rod with a hammer to prevent damage to selector rod bore, then drive out 5th gear shift fork roll pin.

2) Remove snap ring from mainshaft, then remove 5th gear with synchro hub, needle bearing and 5th gear shift fork (5th gear/reverse selector rod remains in housing). Remove 5th gear/reverse selector rod stop screws from side of housing.

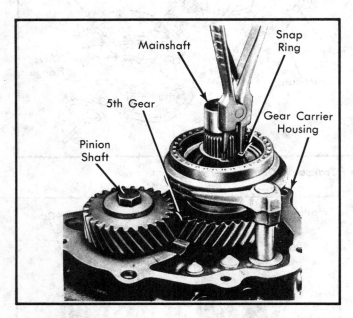

Fig. 8   Removing Snap Ring Retaining 5th Gear Components on Mainshaft

3) Clamp 4th gear/pinion shaft in soft-jaw vise and remove bolt from pinion shaft. Remove 5th gear from pinion shaft with puller, then remove adjusting shim.

4) Reposition gear carrier in vise by clamping carrier housing. Drive out 1st/2nd gear selector fork roll pin, while supporting with hammer. Turn selector fork up and drive out 3rd/4th shift fork roll pin, while supporting with hammer. Pull out 3rd/4th selector rod (shift fork remains in synchro hub) without losing small interlock pin. Remove reverse relay lever boot.

5) Partially pull out pinion shaft and mainshaft and remove mainshaft assembly with 3rd/4th gear shift fork attached. Unhook reverse gear spring clip and move it out of the way. Lift up pinion shaft just enough to remove 1st/2nd gear selector rod and shift fork. Remove pinion shaft from gear carrier.

Fig. 9   Removing Shift Fork Roll Pins

Reassembly — 1) Insert interlock pins in correct position in carrier case bore. Insert springs and plungers for 1st through 4th gear detents. Insert reverse gear detent plunger and spring. Install 5th/reverse selector rod and relay lever. Press relay lever until lever rests on selector rod and in groove of reverse gear. See Fig. 10.

NOTE — *Reverse relay lever bolt and threaded bushing of lever must be in line.*

2) Tighten adjusting screw against stop on threaded bushing. Press relay lever against screw and loosen screw until tip of threads can be heard to engage in threaded bushing. Tighten screw to 25 ft. lbs. (3.4 mkg). Select reverse gear several times and check that relay lever moves easily in all positions. Relay lever should be centered over reverse gear detent.

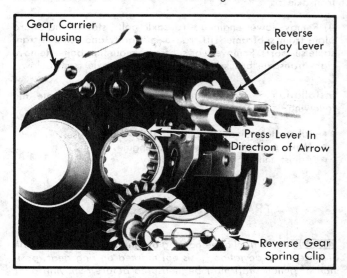

Fig. 10   Adjusting Reverse Relay Lever

3) Make sure reverse gear spring clip is out of the way, then partially install pinion shaft into gear carrier. Install 1st/2nd gear shift fork selector rod, then press pinion shaft into housing until fully seated. Connect reverse gear spring clip and make sure reverse gear is disengaged.

AUDI 5000 5-SPEED (Cont.)

4) Install 3rd/4th gear shift fork with slot in 5th/reverse gear selector rod. Press off mainshaft inner bearing race, then partially install mainshaft into housing. Insert 3rd/4th gear shift fork into clutch sleeve and press mainshaft into housing until fully seated. Move selector rods into neutral position and check for proper position of interlock pins.

5) Install 3rd/4th gear shift rod and insert small interlock pin (coated with grease). Lock 3rd/4th gear shift fork and selector rod with roll pin. Install selector rod stop screws into carrier housing using new gaskets.

6) Position gear carrier assembly in soft-jaw vise, with jaws clamped on 4th gear on pinion shaft. Using a depth gauge, measure dimension "A" as shown in *Fig. 11* to determine correct 5th gear adjusting shim to install. Select correct 5th gear adjusting shim using the following table:

Pinion Shaft 5th Gear Adjusting Shim	
If "A" Is **In. (mm)**	**Use This Shim** **In. (mm)**
.331-.339 (8.4-8.6)	.043 (1.1)
.343-.350 (8.7-8.9)	.055 (1.4)
.354-.362 (9.0-9.2)	.067 (1.7)
.366-.374 (9.3-9.5)	.079 (2.0)
.378-.386 (9.6-9.8)	.091 (2.3)

NOTE — *See Fig. 8 for Dimension "A" measurement.*

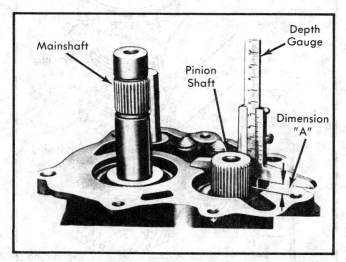

Fig. 11   Measuring Dimension for Selection of 5th Gear Pinion Shaft Adjusting Shim

7) Install selected 5th gear adjusting shim, then heat 5th gear to 250°F (120°C) and slide onto pinion shaft until seated. Install washer and bolt on end of pinion shaft and tighten bolt. Collar of washer must face pinion head.

8) Clamp mainshaft in soft-jaw vise so that mainshaft and pinion shaft are vertical. Heat mainshaft bearing inner race to 250°F (120°C) and slide it onto mainshaft until seated.

9) Install 5th gear with synchronizer hub, needle bearing and shift rod onto mainshaft. Install shift fork roll pin into fork and selector rod. Select a snap ring that will provide a maximum mainshaft end play of .002" (.05 mm), then install snap ring into mainshaft groove.

NOTE — *Mainshaft snap rings are available in the following thicknesses: .050" (1.35 mm), .055" (1.40 mm) and .060" (1.45 mm).*

10) Install 5th gear synchronizer ring. Heat 5th gear clutch hub to 250°F (120°C) and install it on mainshaft until fully seated. Drive on mainshaft bearing inner race, then install guide sleeve and new gasket on gear carrier housing. Install rear cover on carrier housing.

11) Drive on the other half of the mainshaft bearing inner race. Install washer and bolt on end of mainshaft and tighten bolt. Install and tighten rear cover mounting bolts. Install new rear cover cap.

MAINSHAFT ASSEMBLY

Disassembly — Remove snap ring from end of shaft. Remove 4th gear thrust washer, 4th gear, 4th gear needle bearing, synchro ring and snap ring. Using a press, press off 3rd gear, synchro ring, 3rd/4th gear synchro assembly and 3rd gear needle bearing.

Reassembly — **1)** Inspect all components for wear or damage and replace as necessary. Install 3rd gear needle bearing on mainshaft. Place synchro assembly, 3rd gear synchronizer ring and 3rd gear in correct relation atop each other.

NOTE — *Turn synchronizer ring so that grooves are in line with hollow keys. Also, groove on synchronizer hub or wide collar must face 4th gear.*

2) Press mainshaft into 3rd gear and synchronizer assembly. To determine correct snap ring to install, use a feeler gauge to measure 3rd/4th gear synchronizer hub end play as shown in *Fig. 12*. Install a snap ring that will allow an end play of 0-.002" (0-.05 mm).

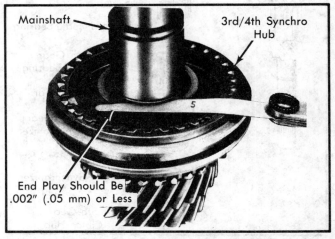

Fig. 12   Checking 3rd/4th Gear Synchronizer Hub End Play

Manual Transaxles

AUDI 5000 5-SPEED (Cont.)

NOTE — *3rd/4th gear synchronizer hub end play snap rings are available in the following thicknesses: .059" (1.5 mm), .061" (1.56 mm) and .064" (1.62 mm).*

3) Install synchronizer ring on 4th gear side of synchronizer hub, then install 4th gear needle bearing, 4th gear, thrust washer and snap ring. Measure clearance between thrust washer and snap ring. Clearance should be .008-.013" (.20-.35 mm). If not, correct by installing a different thickness snap ring.

NOTE — *4th gear end play snap rings are available in the following thicknesses: .065" (1.65 mm), .067" (1.70 mm) and .069" (1.75 mm).*

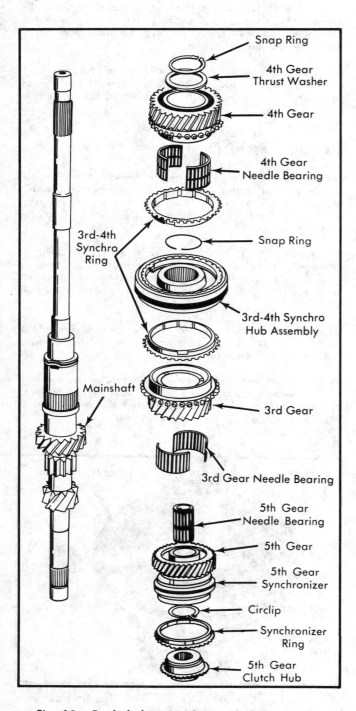

Fig. 13 *Exploded View of Mainshaft Assembly*

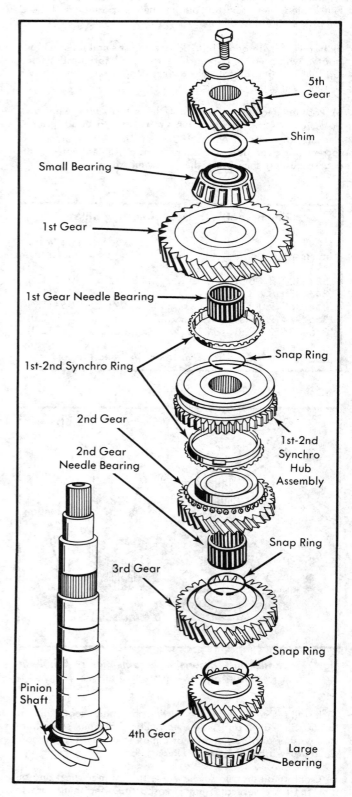

Fig. 14 *Exploded View of Pinion Shaft Assembly*

AUDI 5000 5-SPEED (Cont.)

PINION SHAFT

Disassembly — 1) Mount pinion shaft assembly into a suitable holding fixture then using a press, remove small inner bearing and 1st gear by pressing from shaft.

2) Remove 1st gear needle bearing and synchro ring. Remove snap ring, then press off 1st/2nd gear synchro hub assembly, 2nd gear synchro ring and 2nd gear.

3) Remove 2nd gear needle bearing, snap ring, then press off 3rd gear. Remove circlip, then remove 4th gear snap ring and press off 4th gear and large bearing from shaft.

Reassembly — 1) Ensure all gears and shaft are oil-free and replace any damaged or defective parts. Press large bearing onto pinion shaft. Heat 4th gear to 250° F (120° C), slide gear onto pinion shaft (shoulder facing 3rd gear) and press until fully seated.

NOTE — *After approximately 3 minutes, press 4th gear onto shaft again to ensure correct adjustment of end play. After 4th gear has cooled, continue reassembly procedure.*

2) Measure 4th gear end play with a feeler gauge and adjust end play to no more than .0008" (.02 mm) with correct snap ring. Snap rings are available in sizes from .088" (2.24 mm) to .094" (2.40 mm) in .0008" (.02 mm) increments.

3) Install a .094" (2.4 mm) snap ring into second snap ring groove of pinion shaft. Heat 3rd gear to 250°F (120°C) and slide gear onto shaft with shoulder toward 2nd gear. Press gear onto shaft until seated against snap ring, then install retaining snap ring. Using a feeler gauge, measure 3rd gear end play as shown in *Fig. 15*. End play should be 0-.002" (0-.05 mm). If not, install a different retaining snap ring.

NOTE — *3rd gear end play snap rings are available in the following thicknesses: .065" (1.65 mm), .067" (1.70 mm) and .069" (1.75 mm).*

4) Oil second gear needle bearing and install on shaft. Place 2nd gear, 2nd gear synchro ring and synchro hub assembly atop one another. Press all components onto pinion shaft. Measure synchronizer hub assembly end play with a feeler gauge. End play should be 0-.0016" (0-.04 mm). Adjust end play with a suitable snap ring.

NOTE — *1st/2nd synchronizer hub end play snap rings are available in the following thicknesses: .059" (1.50 mm), .061" (1.55 mm) and .063" (1.60 mm).*

5) Install remaining synchronizer ring onto hub. Oil and install 1st gear needle bearing, then slide 1st gear onto pinion shaft. Press pinion shaft small bearing onto shaft until fully seated.

SYNCHRONIZER ASSEMBLIES

Disassembly — Remove snap ring and separate synchronizer hub from sleeve. Use care not to lose or damage synchronizer keys and springs.

Inspection — Check all parts for wear or damage. Using a feeler gauge, check synchronizer rings for wear as shown in *Fig. 16*. Clearance "a" should be .039-.075" (1.0-1.9 mm) for 5th gear synchro or .039-.067" (1.0-1.7 mm) for all others.

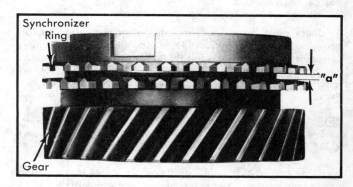

Fig. 16 Checking Synchronizer Rings for Wear

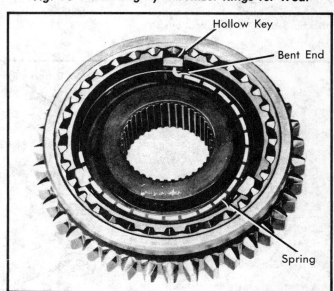

Fig. 17 Assembled View of Synchronizer Assembly

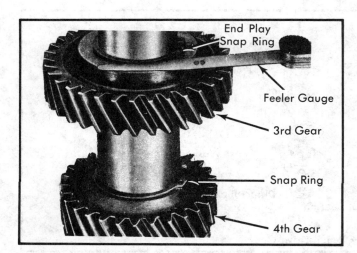

Fig. 15 Checking 3rd Gear End Play

AUDI 5000 5-SPEED (Cont.)

Reassembly — Reverse disassembly procedure and use *Fig. 17* as an assembly guide. Install springs offset 120°. Bent end of spring must engage in hollow key.

DIFFERENTIAL

Disassembly — 1) Place differential assembly in a vise. Remove ring gear bolts and ring gear. Pry speedometer gear off with a screwdriver. Using a puller, remove roller bearings from both ends of differential.

2) Drive out pinion shaft lock pin with a punch. Now drive out pinion shaft with a punch. Rotate differential gear set and remove pinion gears, side gears and thrust washers through opening in differential housing.

Reassembly — 1) Lubricate pinion gears and side gears with transmission oil. Position side gears with shims in housing. Stick thrust washers to pinion gears with grease, then position pinion gears in housing. Install pinion gear shaft, making sure lock pin hole in shaft and housing is aligned.

CAUTION — *Side gears, pinion gears and thrust washers must not be interchanged.*

2) Check pinion and side gear adjustment by pushing pinion gears outward and check play of side gears. Adjustment is correct if no play can be felt by hand, but differential gears can be turned easily without binding. If adjustment is not as specified, correct by installing thicker or thinner side gear shims.

NOTE — *Side gear shims are available in the following thicknesses: .020" (.5 mm), .024" (.6 mm), .028" (.7 mm) and .032" (.8 mm).*

3) Install correct side gear adjusting shims, then install pinion gear shaft lock pin. Heat ring gear to approximately 212°F (100°C), then position ring gear in place on differential housing. Pull ring gear into place with attaching bolts, then tighten attaching bolts to specifications.

4) Heat differential side bearings to approximately 212°F (100°C), then press them onto each end of differential housing. Install speedometer drive gear onto differential housing.

TRANSAXLE REASSEMBLY & ADJUSTMENTS

PINION SHAFT ADJUSTMENTS

1) Install pinion shaft bearing outer races into final drive housing and gear carrier **without** shims. Install assembled gear carrier to final drive housing and tighten attaching bolts.

2) Place magnetic measuring plate (VW 385/17) onto rear end of pinion shaft, then mount a dial indicator to gear carrier as shown in *Fig. 20*. Zero dial indicator with .039" (1 mm) preload. Move pinion shaft up and down (without turning shaft) and record indicator reading.

CAUTION — *Turning pinion shaft during measurement will cause bearings to settle, giving an inaccurate reading.*

3) Remove gear carrier from final drive housing. To determine total thickness of shims necessary to obtain correct pinion depth and bearing preload, add the constant preload value of .012" (.30 mm) to the dial indicator reading just obtained. Resulting sum is total thickness of required shims.

4) Remove pinion shaft bearing outer race from gear carrier, then install a shim of total shim thickness determined in step **3)** behind outer race and reinstall race into gear carrier. Install gear carrier to final drive housing and tighten attaching bolts. Turn pinion shaft several times in each direction to settle bearings.

5) Adjust clamping ring on measuring bar (VW 385/1) so that dimension "a" in *Fig. 19* is 1.97" (50 mm). Then assemble the following measuring tools onto measuring bar as shown in bottom portion of *Fig. 19*:

- Dial Indicator
- Centering Discs VW 385/2 and 3
- Measuring Pin VW 385/14
- Measuring Pin Extension VW 385/15
- Setting Gauge VW 385/27

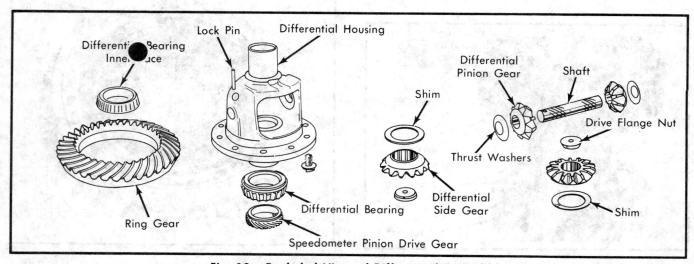

Fig. 18 Exploded View of Differential Assembly

AUDI 5000 5-SPEED (Cont.)

6) With all tools assembled to bar, zero dial indicator with .039" (1 mm) preload and remove setting gauge (VW 385/27). Move clamping ring back to stop. Place magnetic measuring plate (VW 385/17) on end of pinion shaft. Install assembled measuring bar into final drive housing with centering disc (VW 385/2) facing final drive cover. Install final drive cover and secure with 4 bolts.

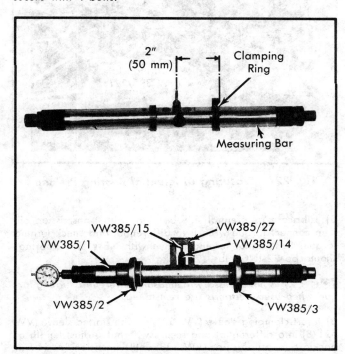

Fig. 19 Assembling Measuring Tools for Pinion Depth Shim Selection

7) Turn knob on end of measuring bar to move clamping ring and the other centering disc (VW 385/3) outward, until bar can just barely be turned by hand.

8) Rotate measuring bar until measuring pin extension rests squarely against magnetic plate on pinion shaft. Then rotate bar back and forth over center. Read and record maximum dial indicator reading.

9) To determine correct pinion depth adjusting shim(s) to install behind bearing outer race in gear carrier, add the deviation number stamped on ring gear to the dial indicator reading obtained in step **8**).

NOTE — *Deviation number stamped on ring gear is in hundredth-millimeters. So a marking of 25 would be .25 mm.*

10) To determine thickness of shim to install under pinion bearing outer race in final drive housing, subtract thickness of pinion depth shim determined in step **9**) from total pinion shim thickness obtained in step **3**).

NOTE — *Shims for outer race installed in gear carrier are available in thicknesses of .008" (.20 mm) to .045" (1.15 mm) in various increments. Shims for outer bearing race in final drive housing are available in thicknesses of .009" (.24 mm) to .056" (1.41 mm) in various increments.*

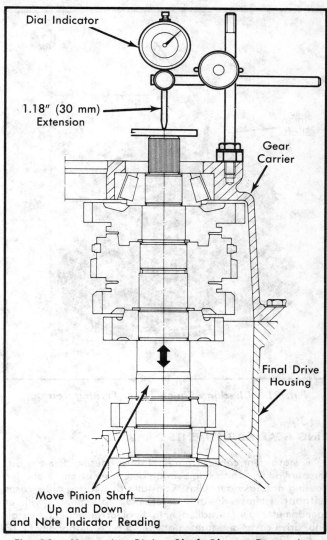

Fig. 20 Measuring Pinion Shaft Play to Determine Total Pinion Adjusting Shim Thickness

11) Remove measuring bar assembly from final drive housing. Separate gear carrier from final drive housing. Remove pinion shaft bearing outer race from gear carrier and final drive housing, then install selected shims with outer race back into carrier and housing.

12) Install gear carrier to final drive and tighten attaching bolts. To check adjustment, reinstall measuring bar assembly and recheck measurements. If correct shims have been installed, dial indicator reading (counterclockwise) should be the ring gear deviation number with a tolerance of ± .0016" (.04 mm).

13) To check pinion bearing preload, lubricate pinion bearings with transmission oil, then check pinion shaft turning torque with a torque wrench. Pinion shaft turning torque with NEW bearings installed should be 17-34 INCH lbs. (20-40 cmkg). Turning torque with USED bearings installed should be 2.6-5.2 INCH lbs. (3-6 cmkg). See Fig. 21.

14) If turning torque is not within specifications, sufficient shim thickness for bearing preload and bearing settling has not been allowed.

Manual Transaxles

AUDI 5000 5-SPEED (Cont.)

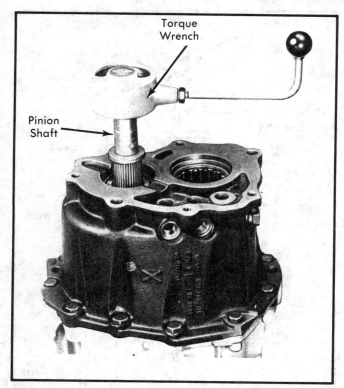

Fig. 21   Checking Pinion Shaft Turning Torque

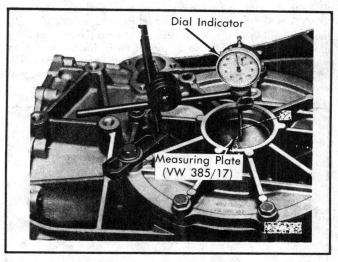

Fig. 22   Measuring Differential Bearing Preload

RING GEAR ADJUSTMENTS

1) Remove gear carrier from final drive housing. Remove differential oil seals and side bearing outer races from final drive housing and take out shims. Reinstall side bearing outer races **without** shims. Install differential assembly (without speedometer gear installed) into final drive housing. Install final drive cover and tighten attaching bolts diagonally to 18 ft. lbs. (25 mkg).

NOTE — Differential assembly is installed with ring gear side away from final drive cover.

2) Position magnetic measuring plate (VW 385/17) and dial indicator as shown in Fig. 22, then zero dial indicator with .039" (1 mm) preload. Move differential assembly up and down and note dial indicator reading.

CAUTION — Do not rotate differential while taking measurement as bearing will settle and make measurement inaccurate.

3) To the dial indicator reading obtained in step 2), add the constant preload value of .020" (.50 mm). Resulting sum is thickness of shims necessary for correct differential bearing preload.

4) Remove measuring tools and final drive housing cover. Remove differential side bearing outer race from cover, then reinstall race with a shim of the thickness obtained in step 3) behind it. Reinstall final drive housing cover.

5) Lubricate differential side bearings with transmission oil, then connect torque wrench to differential and check turning torque. Differential turning torque with NEW side bearings should be 22 INCH lbs. (25 cmkg).

NOTE — It is not necessary to measure differential turning torque when used bearings are reinstalled.

6) Insert clamping sleeve (VW 521/4) with slotted sleeve (VW 521/8) into differential and secure with nut. Adjust length of backlash measuring bar (VW 388) until dimension "A" in Fig. 23 is 3.11" (79 mm).

7) Attach measuring bar to clamping sleeve. Install dial indicator in holder (VW 387) and bolt holder to final drive housing as shown in Fig. 23.

NOTE — Dial indicator must be installed so that its foot will contact end of measuring bar at a 90° angle.

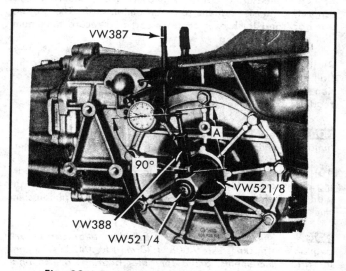

Fig. 23   Positioning of Ring Gear Backlash Measuring Tools

AUDI 5000 5-SPEED (Cont.)

8) Turn ring gear to take up backlash. Zero dial indicator and clamp in holder. Turn ring gear in opposite direction until it is stopped and note indicator reading. This reading is ring gear backlash.

9) Check ring gear at 4 locations (90° apart) around circumference of ring gear. Add measurements together, then divide by 4. Resulting sum is average ring gear backlash. Ring gear backlash should be .004-.008" (.10-.20 mm).

NOTE — *Difference between 4 ring gear backlash measurements must not exceed .002" (.06 mm). If measurements differ more than this, ring gear is incorrectly installed or final drive housing is damaged.*

10) To determine thickness of shim to install behind differential bearing outer race in final drive housing cover (opposite ring gear side), subtract the average ring gear backlash from the total shim thickness obtained in step **3)**. To this value add the constant preload value of .006" (.15 mm). Resulting sum is the thickness of ring gear adjusting shim to install in final drive housing cover.

NOTE — *Ring gear adjusting shims for final drive housing cover are available in thicknesses from .006" (.15 mm) to .047" (1.2 mm) in various increments.*

11) To determine thickness of ring gear adjusting shim to install behind differential side bearing outer race in final drive housing (ring gear side), subtract thickness of shim determined in step **10)** from the total ring gear adjusting shim thickness determined in step **3)**.

FINAL ASSEMBLY

1) Lightly coat joints of gear carrier and final drive housings with sealing compound. Mate units together and tighten bolts to specifications. Coat selector shaft with sealing compound, install into case and tighten bolts.

2) Place differential assembly into final drive housing. Install differential cover magnet at the bottom. Install both drive flanges and tighten bolts. Install speedometer driven gear and adapter.

3) Install clutch release shaft, spring and bearing assembly into clutch housing. Lubricate release shaft with suitable grease.

TIGHTENING SPECIFICATIONS

Application	Ft. Lbs. (mkg)
Axle Shaft Nut	202 (28.0)
Inner CV Joint Bolts	58 (8.0)
Upper Strut Retaining Nuts	18 (2.4)
Gear Carrier-to-Final Drive	18 (2.4)
Selector Shaft Cover Plate	7 (.9)
Drive Flange Bolts	18 (2.4)
Final Drive Cover	18 (2.4)
Mainshaft End Bolt	36 (4.9)
5th Gear End Bolt	36 (4.9)
Relay Lever Bolt	25 (3.4)
Ring Gear Bolt	72 (9.9)
Transaxle-to-Engine	40 (5.5)

CHAMP & COLT 4 & 4x2-SPEED

DESCRIPTION

Two types of transaxle assemblies are used, the KM 160 and KM 165. Both types are fully synchronized and incorporate an input shaft, intermediate shaft and output shaft. The major difference is that the KM 165 has a high and low gear on the input shaft which allows 2 speed ranges that can be selected. The differential assembly consists of a differential drive gear in mesh with output shaft gear, side gears and pinion gears.

LUBRICATION & ADJUSTMENT

See MANUAL TRANSMISSION SERVICING Section

SERVICE (IN VEHICLE)

AXLE SHAFTS

Removal — 1) Remove front wheel dust cap and loosen lock nut. Raise vehicle and remove tires and undercover panel.

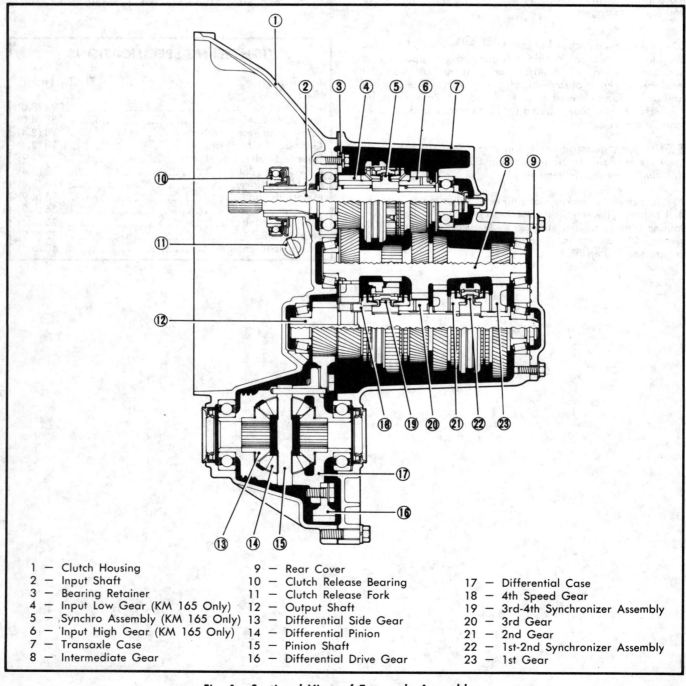

1 — Clutch Housing	9 — Rear Cover	
2 — Input Shaft	10 — Clutch Release Bearing	17 — Differential Case
3 — Bearing Retainer	11 — Clutch Release Fork	18 — 4th Speed Gear
4 — Input Low Gear (KM 165 Only)	12 — Output Shaft	19 — 3rd-4th Synchronizer Assembly
5 — Synchro Assembly (KM 165 Only)	13 — Differential Side Gear	20 — 3rd Gear
6 — Input High Gear (KM 165 Only)	14 — Differential Pinion	21 — 2nd Gear
7 — Transaxle Case	15 — Pinion Shaft	22 — 1st-2nd Synchronizer Assembly
8 — Intermediate Gear	16 — Differential Drive Gear	23 — 1st Gear

Fig. 1 Sectional View of Transaxle Assembly

CHAMP & COLT 4 & 4x2-SPEED (Cont.)

Remove lower ball joint and strut from lower control arm. Drain transaxle fluid.

2) Use suitable tool and insert between transaxle case and Double Offset Joint (D.O.J.). Apply pressure to the tool handle and force axle shaft from transaxle.

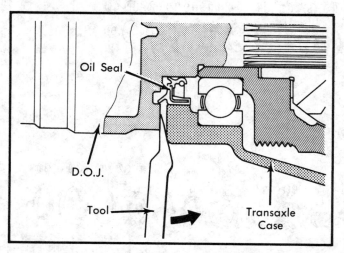

Fig. 2   View of Drive Axle Removal

NOTE — *Replace D.O.J. side retainer ring each time the drive shaft is removed from transaxle case.*

3) Force drive shaft out of hub with axle puller (CT-1003). When the drive shaft is forced out, do not let spacer fall out of hub (inner side).

Disassembly — Remove inner joint boot. Remove circlip from joint and remove outer race. Remove snap ring and inner race. Remove cage and balls as an assembly.

NOTE — *Do not disassemble inner bearing assembly as they are mated parts and should not be disturbed.*

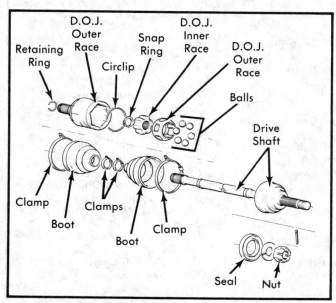

Fig. 3   Exploded View of Drive Shaft

Reassembly — To assemble, reverse disassembly procedure and note the following: Apply grease to inner and outer races. Install CV joint assembly on shaft with chamfered edge of inner race facing outer edge of shaft. Install new boots and place boot clamps 3.5" (90 mm) apart.

Installation — To install, reverse removal procedure and note the following: Install a new D.O.J. side retainer ring.

WHEEL BEARINGS

Removal — **1)** Remove drive shaft and brake assembly from hub. Remove tie rod end from knuckle. Disconnect knuckle from upper strut and lower control arm. Remove hub and knuckle as an assembly.

2) Mount hub and knuckle assembly in a vise and drive hub from knuckle with soft hammer. Remove brake disc. Using a hammer and drift, drive out inner and outer bearing races.

Installation — **1)** Drive outer races of inner and outer bearings into knuckle. Apply grease to knuckle, oil seals and bearings. Mount brake disc to hub and tighten bolts evenly. Install outer wheel bearing, then press in outer oil seal. Hold inner race of outer bearing with bearing holder (MB990776-A), then press hub into knuckle.

NOTE — *Wheel bearing preload adjustment MUST be performed without inner oil seal installed.*

2) Install inner wheel bearing and install spacer selection gauge (MB990768) into hub assembly. Tighten nut to approximately 14 ft. lbs. (2.8 mkg). Rotate hub and gauge assembly several times to seat bearings. Install dial indicator and load indicator by .19" (5 mm). Zero indicator, hold threaded stud of gauge and back off axle nut until travel no longer registers on indicator.

3) Note indicator reading and repeat procedure. Average both readings and select proper spacer. Remove gauge, install inner oil seal and complete installation by reversing removal procedure. Spacer MUST be installed on end of hub with chamfered side facing knuckle.

NOTE — *Spacers are available in 5 thicknesses from .139" (3.55 mm) to .159" (4.03 mm) in .012" (.12 mm) increments.*

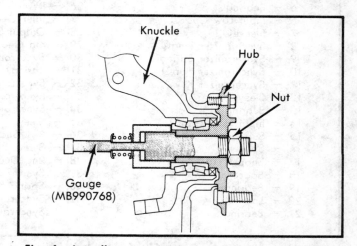

Fig. 4   Installing Gauge to Measure Bearing Preload

CHAMP & COLT 4 & 4x2-SPEED (Cont.)

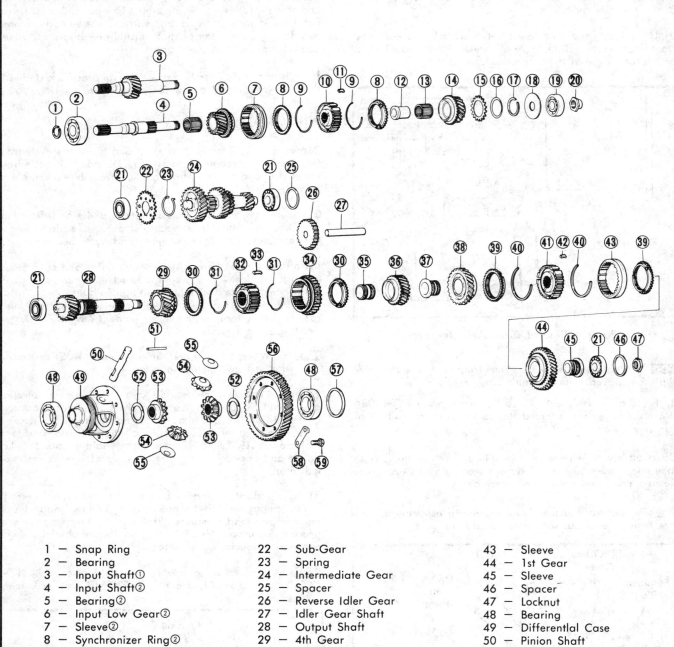

1 — Snap Ring	22 — Sub-Gear	43 — Sleeve
2 — Bearing	23 — Spring	44 — 1st Gear
3 — Input Shaft①	24 — Intermediate Gear	45 — Sleeve
4 — Input Shaft②	25 — Spacer	46 — Spacer
5 — Bearing②	26 — Reverse Idler Gear	47 — Locknut
6 — Input Low Gear②	27 — Idler Gear Shaft	48 — Bearing
7 — Sleeve②	28 — Output Shaft	49 — Differential Case
8 — Synchronizer Ring②	29 — 4th Gear	50 — Pinion Shaft
9 — Synchronizer Spring②	30 — Synchronizer Ring	51 — Lock Pin
10 — Synchronizer Hub②	31 — Spring	52 — Spacer
11 — Synchronizer Key②	32 — Synchronizer Hub	53 — Differential Side Gear
12 — Sleeve②	33 — Synchronizer Key	54 — Differential Pinion
13 — Bearing②	34 — Synchronizer Sleeve	55 — Washer
14 — Input High Gear②	35 — Sleeve	56 — Differential Drive Gear
15 — Sub-Gear②	36 — 3rd Gear	57 — Spacer
16 — Spacer	37 — Sleeve	58 — Lock Washer
17 — Snap Ring②	38 — 2nd Gear	59 — Bolt
18 — Spacer	39 — Synchronizer Ring	
19 — Bearing	40 — Spring	
20 — Locknut	41 — Synchronizer Hub	① — KM 160 Only.
21 — Bearing	42 — Synchronizer Key	② — KM 165 Only.

Fig. 5 Exploded View of Transaxle Gear Components

CHAMP & COLT 4 & 4x2-SPEED (Cont.)

TRANSAXLE REMOVAL & INSTALLATION

Removal — 1) Disconnect battery negative cable. Remove the following parts from transaxle: Clutch cable, speedometer cable, back-up light switch, starter, front roll rod and 4 top engine-to-transaxle mounting bolts.

2) From under vehicle, remove dust cover and disconnect shift rod and extension. Drain transaxle fluid. Remove drive shafts. Disconnect range selector cable. Remove engine rear cover and remove coupling bolt at each end of front roll rod. Loosen engine side roll rod bracket. Connect suitable engine lift to engine, remove remaining engine-to-transaxle mounting bolts.

3) Remove transaxle mount insulator-to-mount bracket nuts. Loosen transaxle mount bracket. Lower and remove transaxle.

Installation — To install, reverse removal procedure and note the following: The coupling bolt at each end of front roll rod should be temporarily tightened at installation. After the transaxle has been installed, tighten bolts to specifications.

TRANSAXLE DISASSEMBLY

1) Remove clutch cable bracket and transaxle mounting bracket. Remove back-up light switch. Remove steel ball and spring from case. Remove rear cover and remove spacers from bearings. Remove transaxle case. Place shift rails in neutral, remove plugs from side of case and remove springs and 3 steel balls.

2) Remove reverse idler shaft and gear. Remove reverse shift lever assembly and shift rail. Remove 3rd-4th shift rail spacer collar. Using a flat punch, re... e spring pins from 1st-2nd and 3rd-4th shift forks. Remov... t-2nd shift rail from case. Shift fork and rail cannot be re... ed from case as a unit. Remove 3rd-4th shift rail from case. Remove 1st-2nd shift rail and fork with 3rd-4th shift rail.

3) Shift 3rd-4th synchronizer sleeve to 4th gear position and remove output shaft assembly. Remove differential assembly. Remove input shaft poppet plug, spring and ball (KM 165). Remove input shaft bearing retainer. Remove input shaft assembly and shift rail and fork (KM 165) with intermediate shaft. Remove shift shaft spring retainer.

4) Pull out shift shaft spring pin with pliers, then remove shift shaft through case hole. When shift shaft is removed, place finger over control finger hole to prevent poppet ball from falling out. Remove control finger, springs, spacer, poppet spring and ball.

5) Remove selector finger lock pin, selector shaft and selector finger (KM 165). Place identification mark on bearing outer race and remove bearing. Outer race MUST be installed in original position. Remove speedometer driven gear assembly.

COMPONENT DISASSEMBLY & REASSEMBLY

INPUT SHAFT

Disassembly (KM 160) — Remove snap ring from front bearing. Use suitable tool and press off bearing. Remove staking from lock nut on rear of shaft. Remove lock nut and bearing from rear of shaft.

Inspection — Check splines for damage and wear. Check oil seal area for damage or wear.

NOTE — *Bearing must be replaced. Removal destroys bearing beyond serviceability.*

Reassembly — Using suitable tool, press front bearing onto input shaft and install snap ring. Snap rings are available in 3 sizes, use the thickest one that will fit. Install spacer on rear of shaft with stepped side facing rear of bearing. Install bearing onto shaft with suitable tool. Install lock nut and tighten. Stake lock nut only at the notch on shaft. See *Fig. 7.*

NOTE — *The shaft rear end will interfere with the breather if deformed by staking, resulting in breakage.*

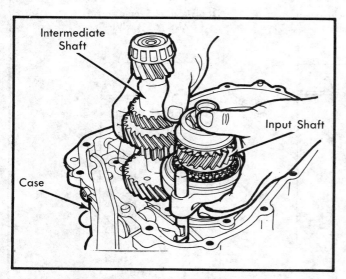

Fig. 6 Removing Input Shaft and Intermediate Shaft from Case

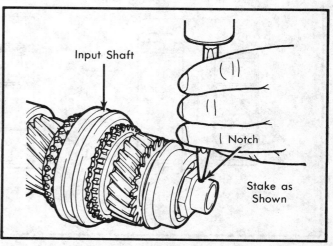

Fig. 7 Staking Input Shaft Lock Nut

CHAMP & COLT 4 & 4x2-SPEED (Cont.)

Disassembly (KM 165) — Remove front bearing snap ring. Use suitable puller and remove bearing. Remove staking at rear lock nut and remove lock nut. Support low gear between press plates and press input shaft from gears.

Inspection — Check splines for wear or damage. Check oil seal fitting area for damage or wear. Check gear bearing surface for wear or scoring.

Reassembly — 1) Install front bearing onto input shaft using suitable tool and install snap ring. Snap rings are available in 3 sizes, use the thickest ring that will fit. Install synchronizer assembly onto input shaft. Install sub-gear onto input shaft in the following order: Install sub-gear onto high gear and apply oil to entire surface. Install cone spring in direction shown in *Fig. 8.* Install new snap ring.

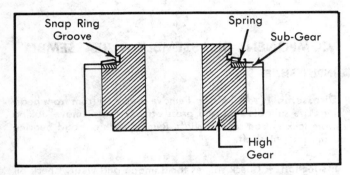

Fig. 8   View of Correct Sub-Gear Installation

2) Install low gear and needle bearing onto shaft. Install synchronizer ring and synchronizer assembly on shaft and check for proper operation. Install high gear and bearing onto shaft. Install spacer with stepped side facing rear bearing and install bearing. Install rear nut and tighten. Stake nut.

INTERMEDIATE SHAFT

Disassembly — Use suitable puller and remove front bearing from shaft. Remove sub-gear and spring. Remove rear bearing using same puller as used on front.

Inspection — Inspect gears for wear or damage. Replace any defective parts as required.

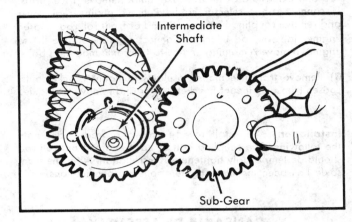

Fig. 9 . View of Sub-Gear Installation

Reassembly — Install sub-gear spring in position on intermediate shaft. *See Fig. 9.* Install sub-gear onto shaft. Press on new bearings with suitable tool. Replace outer bearing races.

OUTPUT SHAFT

Disassembly — Remove staking on rear nut and remove lock nut from shaft. Use suitable puller and remove front and rear bearing. Remove 1st gear, 1st-2nd synchronizer assembly and 2nd gear. Remove 2nd gear sleeve, 3rd gear, sleeve, 3rd-4th synchronizer and 4th gear.

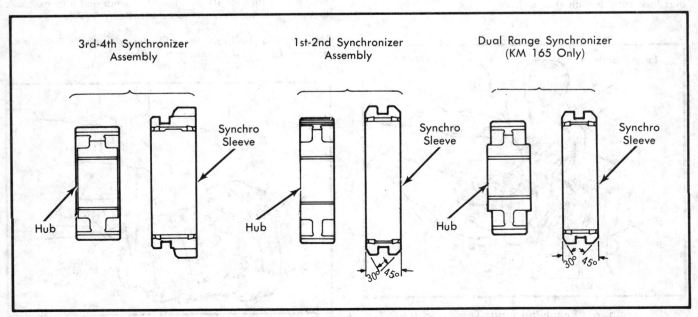

Fig. 10   View of Synchronizers in Proper Assembled Order

CHAMP & COLT 4 & 4x2-SPEED (Cont.)

Inspection — Check output shaft for wear or damage. Check gear wear areas for scoring or excessive wear.

Reassembly — 1) Assemble synchronizer assemblies as shown in *Fig. 10.* Install 4th gear onto output shaft. Install synchronizer ring. Use suitable tool and press 3rd-4th synchronizer assembly onto shaft. Check 4th gear for smooth rotation on output shaft.

NOTE — *Oil all moving parts with sufficient oil during reassembly.*

2) Install synchronizer ring onto output shaft. Install 3rd gear onto output shaft. Install 2nd gear bushing onto output shaft. Check that 3rd gear rotates freely on shaft. Install 2nd gear. Install synchronizer ring. Install 1st-2nd synchronizer assembly onto output shaft. Check that 2nd gear rotates freely on shaft. Install synchronizer ring.

3) Install 1st gear bushing into 1st gear and press 1st gear onto output shaft. Using suitable tool, press front and rear bearings onto shaft. Install lock nut and tighten. Stake lock nut securely.

DIFFERENTIAL ASSEMBLY

Disassembly — Using suitable puller remove side bearings from differential assembly. Remove bolts from ring gear and tap gear from differential. Pull lock pin from pinion shaft and remove shaft from differential carrier. Remove pinion and side gears from differential carrier. Mark gears for proper installation.

Inspection — Check splines for damage or wear. Check gears for chipped or worn teeth.

Reassembly — 1) Press bearings onto both ends of differential carrier. Place spacers on the back side of side gears and place gears into differential carrier. Place washers behind pinion gears and install pinion gears meshing with side gears at the same time. Install pinion shaft.

2) Measure backlash between pinion and side gears. *See Fig. 11.* Backlash should be 0.003" (0.076 mm). Install spacers of equal size on both sides to arrive at the proper backlash. Install ring gear and tighten bolts to specifications.

NOTE — *Always use new lock washers when reassembling ring gear.*

TRANSAXLE REASSEMBLY

1) Place differential assembly into transaxle case. Adjust end play as follows: Place .080" (2 mm) of Plastigage on bearing surface as shown in *Fig. 12.* Install transaxle case and tighten bolts to specifications. Now remove transaxle case and measure Plastigage. Select proper shim to give an end play of 0-.006" (0-.15 mm).

2) Turn sub-gear in direction of arrow stamped on gear to align .31" (8 mm) holes of sub-gear and intermediate gear. When holes are aligned, insert bolt of same diameter (long enough to maintain alignment).

3) Mesh input and intermediate shaft together and place into transaxle case. On KM 165 transaxle, install shift detent and spring and tighten end plug. On all transaxles, install input bearing retainer. Pull out the sub-gear aligning bolt and install output shaft.

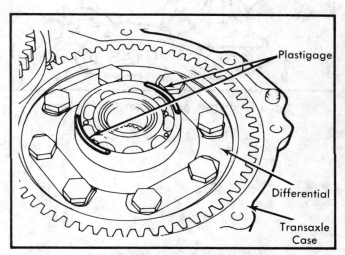

Fig. 12 *Measuring Differential Play*

4) Install 1st-2nd and 3rd-4th shift rail into case. Install shift forks and install spring pins. Install reverse shift rail. Install detents and springs (spring with white marking is for reverse shift rail). Install reverse gear, shaft and fork. Measure distance "A". *See Fig. 13.* Specified distance should be 1.44-1.53" (36.6-58.8 mm). Replace reverse shift lever if not within specifications.

5) Install clutch housing gasket in place on transaxle. Place shims for differential bearing in case with grease. Install clutch housing to transaxle case. Install bolts and tighten to specifications. Install intermediate and output shaft bearing races in case and press them into place by hand. Install output shaft rear seal into case. Determine shims for rear cover by the following method: Use a depth gauge and measure the dif-

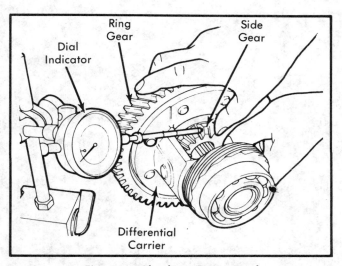

Fig. 11 *Checking Pinion and Side Gear Backlash*

Manual Transaxles

CHAMP & COLT 4 & 4x2-SPEED (Cont.)

ference between the transaxle case and rear bearing. *See Fig. 14.* Add .004" (.1 mm) to the measurement obtained. The result is the amount of shims to be used for rear cover. Install cover and tighten bolts.

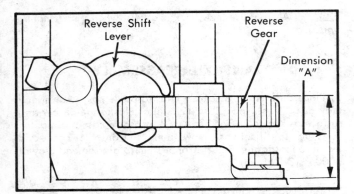

Fig. 13   Measuring Reverse Idler Gear

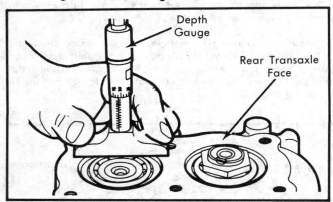

Fig. 14   Measuring for Rear Cover Shims

TRANSAXLE SPECIFICATIONS

Application	In. (mm)
Synchronizer Ring-to-Gear	.032 (.8) Max.
Shift Lever-to-Rail	.002-.008 (.05-.20)
Ring Gear-to-Drive Shaft Spline	.002-.007 (.05-.18)
Ring Gear-to-Case	.001-.003 (.03-.08)
Pinion Gear-to-Side Gear Backlash	0-.003 (0-.08)
Differential Case End Play	0-.006 (0-.15)

TIGHTENING SPECIFICATIONS

Application	Ft. Lbs. (mkg)
Rear Cover	14-17 (1.9-2.4)
Engine-to-Transaxle	
Bolt with Washer	22-25 (3.0-3.5)
All Others	32-40 (4.4-5.5)
Clutch Housing-to-Transaxle	26-30 (3.6-4.2)
Input Shaft Lock Nut	65-79 (9.0-10.9)
Output Shaft Lock Nut	65-79 (9.0-10.9)
Ring Gear	47-54 (6.5-7.5)

DATSUN 310 4 & 5 SPEED

DESCRIPTION

The Datsun 310 transaxle assembly contains the clutch, transmission and final drive (differential). The main unit consists of 4 major subassemblies: Primary gear cover, clutch housing, transmission case and transmission cover. Transmission is a 4-speed (F4WF60A) or a 5-speed (F5WF60A) unit, fully synchronized in all foward gears. All forward gears are helically cut and in constant mesh. Final drive is directly coupled to transmission and housed in transmission case. Transmission and final drive are lubricated from a common oil supply. Constant velocity (CV) joints are used on both ends of drive axle shafts.

LUBRICATION & ADJUSTMENT

See *MANUAL TRANSMISSION SERVICING* Section.

SERVICE (IN VEHICLE)

WHEEL BEARINGS

Removal — 1) Raise and support front of vehicle. Remove wheel. Disconnect brake line from caliper, plug line and remove caliper assembly.

2) Remove cotter pin, nut and washer from axle shaft. Using suitable puller, remove stub axle and brake rotor from axle shaft as an assembly. Remove output flange-to-axle shaft attaching bolts and remove axle shaft assembly from vehicle.

3) Remove cotter pin and ball joint stud nut. Using ball joint driver and hammer, drive ball joint out of steering knuckle. Remove 4 bolts securing knuckle to strut and remove knuckle from vehicle.

4) Remove bolts attaching rotor to stub axle and press stub axle out of rotor. Using press or bearing puller, remove outer bearing and seal from stub axle. Use a hammer and brass drift to drive outer and inner bearing races out of knuckle.

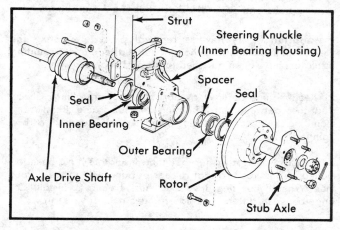

Fig. 1 Exploded View of Steering Knuckle and Stub Axle Assembly

Installation — 1) Using suitable installer tools, press or drive inner and outer bearing races into steering knuckle.

2) It is now necessary to determine required thickness of bearing spacer. Place outer bearing on base (KV40100700-3 or equivalent) and place steering knuckle over it so bearing seats in outer race. Then, slide inner bearing over dummy shaft (KV40100700-1 or equivalent), and place shaft bearing in knuckle with end of shaft in outer bearing and inner bearing in inner race.

3) Slide weight (KV40100700-2 or equivalent) over dummy shaft and down onto knuckle. Turn knuckle back and forth to seat bearing. Assemble suitable dial indicator with contact button resting on top of dummy shaft, and set indicator to zero. Pull upward on shaft until it reaches end of travel, rotate it 1 revolution and record maximum deflection of indicator needle.

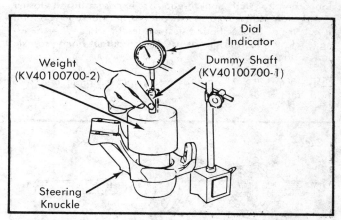

Fig. 2 Determining Required Spacer Thickness

4) To determine required spacer thickness, add recorded dial indicator reading to metric thickness dimension stamped on side of flange on end of dummy shaft.

5) Select required spacer. Spacers are available in 18 sizes, ranging from .291-.293" (7.38-7.44 mm) to .331-.333" (8.40-8.46 mm) in .002" (.06 mm) increments. For size identification, spacers are numbered "05" (smallest) through "22" (largest).

6) Pack grease seals and bearings with suitable bearing grease. Install outer grease seal and press outer bearing onto stub axle. Install rotor on stub axle. Place knuckle in position on stub axle, install spacer and press inner bearing onto stub axle and knuckle assembly until it just bottoms. Install inner seal.

7) Clamp axle shaft in a vise with splined end up. Set stub axle and knuckle on shaft and align splines. Using a soft hammer, tap on stub axle until washer and nut can be installed. Tighten nut to specification.

8) Spin assembly in both directions to check for free rotation. Check bearing preload at hub nut. If end play is present or preload is less than specification, install smaller spacer. If preload is greater than specification, install larger spacer.

9) To install knuckle on vehicle, reverse removal procedures and note the following: Bleed brake system.

DATSUN 310 4 & 5 SPEED (Cont.)

AXLE SHAFTS

Removal — 1) Raise and support front of vehicle. Remove wheel. Remove cotter pin, nut and washer from axle shaft. Remove output flange-to-axle shaft attaching bolts and place shaft on steering rack.

2) Using suitable puller, force axle shaft out of stub axle and knuckle assembly. Remove shaft from vehicle.

CAUTION — *Take care not to damage grease seals when removing or installing axle shaft.*

Installation — Insert splined end of axle shaft into stub axle and knuckle and align splines. If necessary, lightly hammer on flanged end of shaft until threads are exposed. Install washer and tighten shaft nut to specification. Check bearing preload at nut. If not as specified, adjust as described in Wheel Bearings — Installation in this article. Install output flange-to-axle shaft attaching bolts.

NOTE — *Install "O" rings between output flange and axle shaft before connecting.*

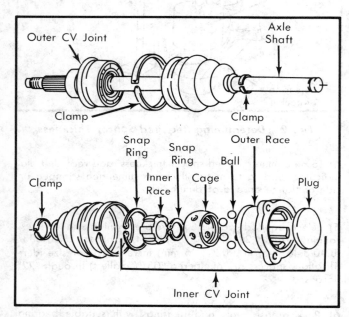

Fig. 3 *Exploded View of Axle Shaft Components*

CONSTANT VELOCITY (CV) JOINTS

NOTE — *Inner CV joint can be disassembled and serviced, outer CV joint is non-serviceable and must be replaced as an assembly. Remove axle shaft from vehicle before disassembling.*

Disassembly — Place axle shaft in a soft-jawed vise. Cut large clamp off of inner boot and slide boot back on shaft. Remove large snap ring and slide outer race off of shaft. Remove balls from cage. Turn cage ½ turn and slide off of inner race. Remove small snap ring and tap inner race off of shaft.

Reassembly — To reassemble, reverse disassembly procedure and note the following: Repack CV joint with suitable grease and install new clamp on boot.

TRANSAXLE REMOVAL & INSTALLATION

NOTE — *If equipped with air conditioning, disconnect compressor without removing lines and lay on top of engine.*

Removal — 1) Engine and transmission must be removed as a unit, then separated. Assembly is removed from above vehicle. Remove hood. Remove battery and drain engine coolant.

2) Remove carburetor air cleaner. Disconnect accelerator cable from carburetor. Disconnect engine ground strap, ignition coil wire, distributor wires and engine wiring harness at connectors. Disconnect fusible links.

3) Disconnect ignition coil ground cable at clutch housing. Disconnect fuel and fuel return hoses, upper and lower radiator hoses, heater inlet and outlet and Master-Vac hose. Remove carbon canister hoses and air pump cleaner hose.

4) Remove air pump air cleaner, carbon canister and auxiliary fan. Remove washer tank, radiator grille, radiator and fan motor assembly. Remove clutch cylinder from clutch housing.

5) Remove right and left buffer rods and unhook speedometer cable. Remove spring pins and free transmission shift and select rods. Attach engine removal brackets (10005M4900) and (10006M4900) to cylinder block.

6) Attach suitable engine hoist to lifting brackets. Disconnect exhaust tube at manifold and rear engine mounting clamp. Disconnect right and left drive shafts from differential side flanges by removing bolts. Remove bolt securing radius link.

7) Lower transmission shift and select rods. Disconnect mounting insulator bolts. Remove nuts holding front mounting insulators to sub-frame. Remove bolts holding rear mounting insulator to transmission case.

8) Lift engine and transaxle assembly up and away from vehicle. Remove primary drive gear assembly from transaxle. Remove starter and transmission mounting bracket. Remove attaching bolts and separate clutch housing from engine.

Installation — 1) Reverse removal procedure noting the following: Remove lifting chain or cable after engine mounting insulators have been attached to support engine weight.

2) Keep engine as level as possible when installing. Check clearance between clutch housing and sub-frame. Right front mounting insulator must be installed with stamped arrow pointing upward.

3) Install buffer rods after mounting insulators have been installed. Adjust rods so that rubber packing will not be deformed. When connecting drive axle shaft, be sure to install "O" rings between differential side flanges and drive shafts.

TRANSAXLE DISASSEMBLY

PRIMARY GEAR

1) Thoroughly clean transmission case, then remove back-up light and top detecting switch (if equipped). Mount transmis-

DATSUN 310 4 & 5 SPEED (Cont.)

sion in stand (KV32100500), drain oil and remove bottom cover. Remove side flanges with side flange wrench (KV38103701), also using a puller if required. Remove bearing housing and primary drive gear as a unit.

2) Remove primary drive gear cover and discard seal bolt. Seal bolt is identified by white spot on the head. Retain bolts in order for reassembly reference. *See Fig. 4.* Mesh reverse gear with 1st or 2nd gear at same time to lock gears in position. Remove main drive input gear and bearing assembly.

3) Remove primary idle gear with slide hammer if necessary. Remove clutch housing bolts and clutch housing. Mark bolts for reassembly reference. *See Fig. 5.* Drive out primary drive and idler gear bearings with a press or puller. Press ball bearing out of main drive input gear, using bearing retainer as support.

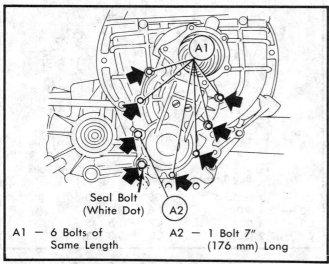

A1 — 6 Bolts of Same Length

A2 — 1 Bolt 7" (176 mm) Long

Fig. 4 Bolt Identification for Primary Gear Cover (4 and 5-Speed Transaxle Assemblies)

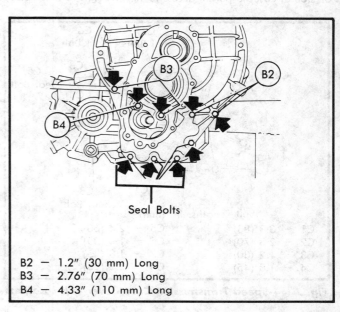

B2 — 1.2" (30 mm) Long
B3 — 2.76" (70 mm) Long
B4 — 4.33" (110 mm) Long

Fig. 5 Bolt Identification for Clutch Housing (4 and 5-Speed Transaxle Assemblies)

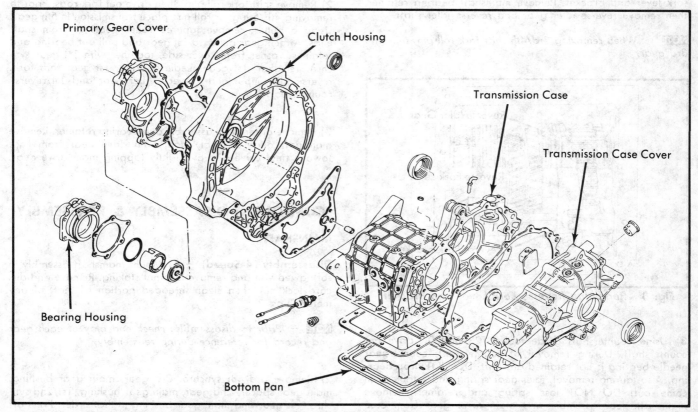

Fig. 6 Datsun Transmission/Transaxle Case Components (4-Speed Shown; 5-Speed Similar)

DATSUN 310 4 & 5 SPEED (Cont.)

TRANSMISSION CASE

4-Speed — 1) Remove transmission case cover and maintain bolts in order of removal for reference during reassembly. *See Fig. 7.* Remove check ball plugs, then take out locking springs and steel balls. Using a driver, knock out service plug (located on side of case) to permit access to 1st/2nd shift fork roll pin.

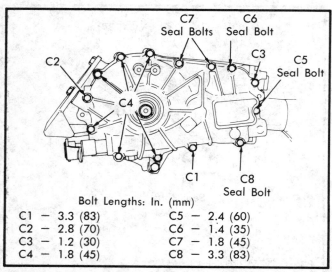

Bolt Lengths: In. (mm)

C1 — 3.3 (83)		C5 — 2.4 (60)	
C2 — 2.8 (70)		C6 — 1.4 (35)	
C3 — 1.2 (30)		C7 — 1.8 (45)	
C4 — 1.8 (45)		C8 — 3.3 (83)	

Fig. 7   4-Speed Transmission Case Cover Bolt Locations

2) Drive out each shift fork roll pin. Withdraw fork rods and remove shift forks, keeping interlock plungers with respective fork rod. Remove differential assembly, then remove reverse fork lever and bracket. Remove mainshaft bearing retainer, then remove reverse idler gear and reverse idler shaft.

NOTE — *When removing 3rd/4th shift fork roll pin, shift into 3rd gear.*

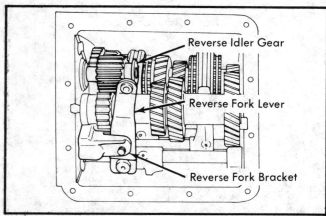

Fig. 8   Removing Reverse Fork Lever and Bracket

3) Using countershaft guide tool (ST23100000), drive out countershaft. During removal of countershaft, countergear needle bearing is not retained on shaft; DO NOT drop bearing. Also, during removal, idler gear spring and retainer will come out; DO NOT lose spring and retainer. Remove mainshaft gear assembly and main drive gear from case toward final drive side.

5-Speed — 1) Remove transmission case cover and maintain bolts in order of removal for reference during reassembly. See *Fig. 9.* Detach counter thrust bushing from 1st/reverse countergear. Remove check ball plugs, then take out locking springs and steel balls. Using a driver, knock out service plug (located on side of case) to permit access to 1st/2nd shift fork roll pin.

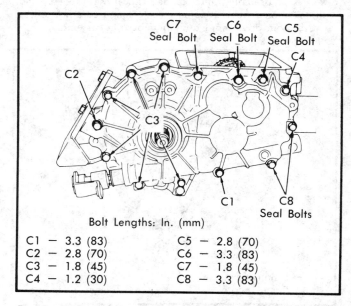

Bolt Lengths: In. (mm)

C1 — 3.3 (83)		C5 — 2.8 (70)	
C2 — 2.8 (70)		C6 — 3.3 (83)	
C3 — 1.8 (45)		C7 — 1.8 (45)	
C4 — 1.2 (30)		C8 — 3.3 (83)	

Fig. 9   5-Speed Transmission Case Cover Bolt Locations

2) Remove shift fork roll pins, then drive out fork rods. Prior to removing 4th/5th gear roll pin, place transmission in 5th gear. Using a puller, remove tapered roller bearings from shaft ends. Attach gear puller to 1st gear and pull out bearing and retainer washer from cover side, together with 1st gear synchro, 1st gear, 1st gear needle bearing, 1st gear shift fork, reverse idler input gear, reverse idler gear and 1st/reverse countergear.

3) Remove differential assembly and bearing retainer. Remove mainshaft gear assembly and main drive gear from case toward final drive side by slightly tapping main drive gear.

COMPONENT DISASSEMBLY & REASSEMBLY

MAINSHAFT

Disassembly (4-Speed) — 1) Mount mainshaft assembly in soft-jawed vise and remove lock nut staking. Remove and discard lock nut, then clean threaded portion of shaft of any metal chips.

NOTE — *Prior to disassembly, check end play of each gear and record for reference during reassembly.*

2) Remove 3rd/4th synchro, 3rd gear, main gear bushing, main gear spacer, 2nd gear, main gear bushing, 1st/2nd synchro, 1st gear and main gear bushing in that order. Press off main shaft bearing.

DATSUN 310 4 & 5 SPEED (Cont.)

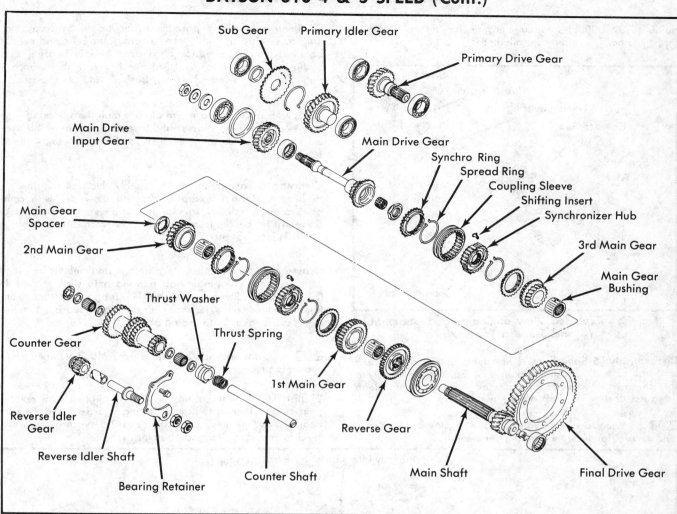

Fig. 10   Exploded View of 4-Speed Transmission Gear Assembly

3) To disassemble synchro assemblies, remove spread rings and shifting inserts. Remove coupling sleeve from synchro hub.

Cleaning & Inspection — Thoroughly clean all components in cleaning solvent, except seals, and blow dry with compressed air. Check all gears for excessive wear, chips or cracks and shaft for bending, cracking, wear or worn splines. Replace defective components.

Reassembly — 1) Insert synchro hub into coupling sleeve. Install shifting inserts into synchro hub grooves. Insert protrusion of 1 spread spring into groove so that insert is securely attached to inner side of coupling sleeve. Insert other spread spring in same manner on opposie side of hub. DO NOT hook front or rear ends of springs into same insert. Check operation by hand.

2) Apply gear oil to bushings. Press ball bearing onto mainshaft. Assemble main gear bushing and 1st gear. Assemble synchro ring, synchro assembly, main gear bushing, synchro ring, 2nd gear and main gear spacer in that order.

NOTE — *Be sure to align oil hole on bushing with main shaft when assembling 1st and 2nd main gear bushings.*

3) Insert 3rd main gear bushing. Assemble 3rd gear, synchro ring, synchro assembly and lock nut on main shaft in that order. When assembling 3rd/4th gear synchro assembly, ensure mounting direction is correct. See Fig. 11.

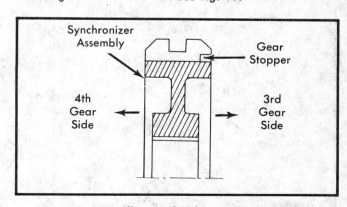

Fig. 11   Installing 3rd/4th Synchro Assembly

4) Place mainshaft in soft-jawed vise. Tighten mainshaft lock nut and stake it into groove of shaft to prevent loosening. Lubricate countershaft bearings with grease and insert needle bearings into both sides of countergear. Insert countershaft

DATSUN 310 4 & 5 SPEED (Cont.)

guide (ST32100000) into countergear. Ensure countergear thrust washer is properly installed. *See Fig. 12.*

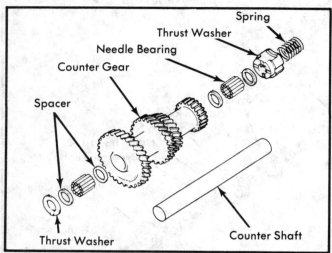

Fig. 12   *Exploded View of Countergear Assembly (4 and 5-Speed Transaxles)*

Disassembly (5-Speed) — 1) Remove countergear, 2nd/3rd shift fork and 4th/5th shift fork. Mount mainshaft assembly in soft-jawed vise. Remove and discard lock nut, then clean threaded portion of shaft of any metal chips.

NOTE — *Prior to disassembly, check end play of each gear and record for reference during reassembly.*

2) Remove following parts in order given: Synchro ring, 4th/5th synchro assembly, synchro ring, 4th gear and needle bearing, main gear spacer, 3rd gear, needle bearing and bushing, synchro ring, 2nd/3rd synchro assembly, synchro ring, 2nd gear, needle bearing, bushing and reverse gear.

3) Using a puller, remove and discard mainshaft bearing. Use new bearing during reassembly. If required, disassemble synchro assemblies in same manner as that given for 4-speed transmission.

Cleaning & Inspection — Thoroughly clean all components in cleaning solvent, except seals, and blow dry with compressed air. Check all gears for excessive wear, chips or cracks and shaft for bending, cracking, wear or worn splines. Replace defective components.

Reassembly — 1) Lubricate bushings and needle bearings with gear oil. Press mainshaft bearing onto shaft with drift (ST22350000). Remove mainshaft bearing outer race from housing. Place new outer race over mainshaft bearing, then install reverse gear onto mainshaft.

NOTE — *Cutout portion of reverse gear MUST be lined up to receive 2nd gear bushing.*

2) Install 2nd gear bushing with claw aligned with reverse gear cutout. Then install the following in order listed: Needle bearing, 2nd gear, synchro ring, 2nd/3rd synchro assembly, synchro ring and 3rd gear bushing.

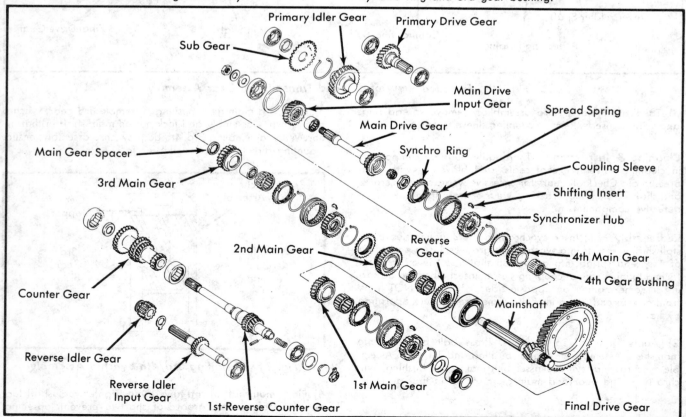

Fig. 13   *Exploded View of 5-Speed Transmission Gear Assembly*

DATSUN 310 4 & 5 SPEED (Cont.)

NOTE — *3rd gear bushing is same as 2nd gear bushing. When assembling 3rd gear bushing, be sure that claw is aligned with main gear spacer. When installing 2nd/3rd synchro hub, thinner spline tooth side must point toward 3rd gear.*

3) Install needle bearing, synchro ring, 3rd gear and main gear spacer. Uneven surface of main gear spacer must face 4th gear.

4) Install 4th gear bushing, synchro ring, 4th/5th synchro hub and mainshaft lock nut. Place mainshaft in vise, tighten lock nut and stake lock nut into groove of mainshaft to prevent loosening.

DIFFERENTIAL

Disassembly — Mount differential assembly in a soft-jawed vise. Using a puller (KV38103800), remove side bearings. Remove final drive gear attaching bolts and final drive gear. Separate differential case and remove pinion shaft. Remove side gears and pinion gears with thrust washers.

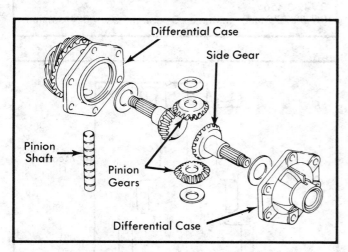

Fig. 14   Exploded View of Differential Assembly

Cleaning & Inspection — Clean all components in cleaning solvent and blow dry with compressed air. Check all parts for wear, chips, cracks or scoring. Replace defective parts.

Reassembly — **1)** Press differential side bearings onto case with drift (ST33200000). Install pinion gears, side gears, thrust washer and pinion shaft into differential case. Apply oil to side gear journals.

2) Mount a dial indicator and measure side gear end play. Measure each gear separately. Adjust side gear end play to less than .008" (.2 mm) by installing proper thrust washer. After adjustment ensure side gears rotate smoothly. Thrust washers are available in .008" (.2 mm) and .012" (.3 mm) thicknesses.

3) Apply thin coat of oil to pinion and side gear teeth and check operation. Install final drive gear on case. Apply locking compound to threaded portion of mounting bolts, install bolts and tighten. Using a dial gauge, check drive pinion-to-side gear backlash. Backlash reading should be .002-.006" (.06-.15 mm).

TRANSAXLE REASSEMBLY & ADJUSTMENTS

TRANSMISSION CASE

4-Speed — **1)** Using a press and drift (ST33400001), press in differential side flange oil seals. Lubricate seal lips with grease. Assemble main drive gear and mainshaft assembly in case.

2) Place 1st/2nd shift fork and 3rd/4th shift fork into respective coupling sleeve grooves. Slide 3rd/4th fork rod through transmission case and 3rd/4th fork. Secure rod to fork with new retaining pin.

3) Assemble check ball, check ball spring and ball plug. Apply locking compound to ball plug. Align notch in 3rd/4th fork rod with check ball and place in neutral position. Assemble 1st/2nd fork rod and reverse fork rod in similar manner.

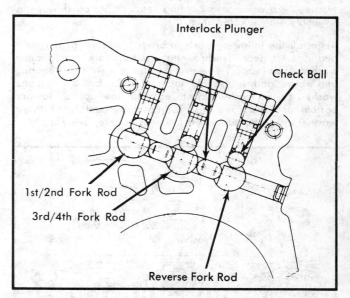

Fig. 15   Sectional View of 4-Speed Transmission Check Ball and Interlock Plunger Arrangement

4) Lubricate needle bearings with grease and install in both ends of countergear. Insert countershaft guide (ST23100000) into countergear, without forcing out bearings. Install countergear, thrust washers and thrust spring on transmission case at the same time. Insert countershaft into countergear, driving out guide tool.

NOTE — *Make sure thrust washers are properly installed and that cutout portion of countershaft is aligned with bearing retainer.*

5) Assemble reverse idle shaft, idler gear, bearing retainer, reverse fork and fork bracket. Be sure cutout portion of reverse idle shaft is aligned with bearing retainer. Tighten idle shaft mounting nut (double nut).

6) Insert differential case assembly. Set all fork rods to neutral position and assemble case cover to transmission case. Make sure bolts are installed in original location, replacing sealing bolts if resin coating of threads peels off. Ensure shifter (case cover side) engages with fork rod brackets correctly.

Manual Transaxles

DATSUN 310 4 & 5 SPEED (Cont.)

7) Install differential side flange. Apply locking compound to threads and tighten flange nuts with flange wrench (ST32400000). Always use NEW flange nuts.

5-Speed — 1) Install differential side flange oil seals. Insert main drive gear and mainshaft into transmission case. At the same time, insert 2nd/3rd shift fork, 4th/5th shift fork and countergear with thrust washer into transmission case.

2) Install countershaft bearing retaining plate. Insert countergear shaft. Slide 2nd/3rd fork rod through case and 2nd/3rd shift fork. Secure to fork with new retaining pin. Install 2nd/3rd check ball and spring, apply sealant to check plug and tighten plug. Align notch in 2nd/3rd fork rod with check ball and place in neutral position.

3) Insert interlock plunger between 2nd/3rd and 4th/5th fork rods. Assemble 4th/5th fork rod in same manner. Install counter needle bearing and bearing retainer. Install differential assembly with selected shim.

4) Install the following parts in order listed: 1st gear needle bearing, 1st gear, synchro ring, 1st shift fork and retainer washer. Then install 1st/reverse countergear with ball bearing and washer and reverse idler input gear with ball bearing and washer. Ensure washer is installed with claw pointed toward bottom of cover. *See Fig. 16.* Position countergear thrust washer with tabs positioned in notch in case. *See Fig. 17.*

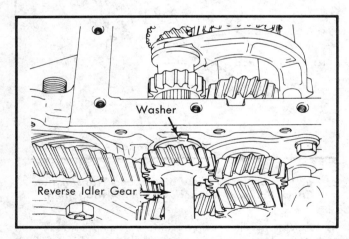

Fig. 16 *Installing Reverse Idler Input Gear Washer (5-Speed Transmission)*

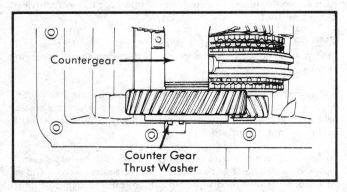

Fig. 17 *Countergear Thrust Washer Position (5-Speed Transmission)*

5) Then install reverse idler gear and reverse shift fork at the same time. Press bearing on with drift (ST22360002). Insert interlock plunger between 2nd/3rd and 1st/reverse fork rods and assemble 1st/reverse fork rod.

6) Measure 1st/reverse countergear bearing height. Select correct shims from table that correspond to measurement.

1st-Reverse Counter Gear Bearing Height Shims		
Bearing Height	**No. Shims**	**Thickness Needed**
3.472-3.480" (88.2-88.4 mm) 0		 0
3.465-3.471" (88.0-88.19 mm) 1		.... .008" (.2 mm)
3.457-3.464" (87.8-87.99 mm) 2		.... .016" (.4 mm)
3.449-3.456" (87.6-87.79 mm) 3		.... .024" (.6 mm)

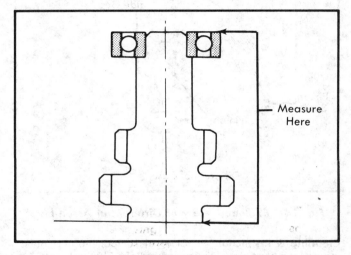

Fig. 18 *Measuring 1st/Reverse Countergear Bearing Height*

7) Determine main shaft bearing shim thickness. Place bearing outer race on main shaft bearing. Measure main shaft bearing height. *Fig. 19.*

8) Measure depth of main bearing outer race fitting portion of case cover. *Fig. 20.*

9) Subtract main shaft bearing height from case cover depth. Add .0197" (.5 mm). The result is the thickness of shim required.

NOTE — *Shims are available in the following thicknesses: .0012" (.03 mm), .0019" (.05 mm), .0028" (.07 mm), .0039" (.1 mm), .0178" (.3 mm), .0197" (.5 mm), .0276" (.7 mm) and .0354" (.9 mm).*

10) Install correct mainshaft bearing adjusting shim into case cover. Press mainshaft bearing outer race completely into case cover. Mount counter thrust bushing to 1st/reverse coun-

DATSUN 310 4 & 5 SPEED (Cont.)

tergear. Install thrust washer and selected shims to case cover with grease.

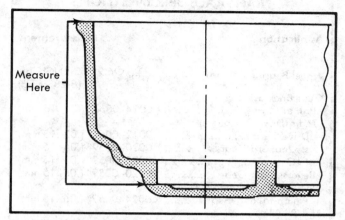

Fig. 19   Measuring Main Shaft Bearing Height

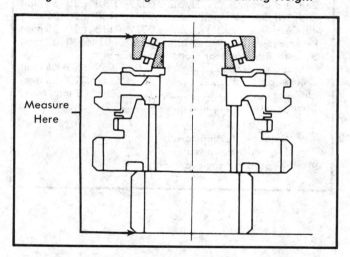

Fig. 20   Measuring Case Cover Depth

11) Insert 1st shift fork lock ball and place all forks in neutral position. Be sure shifter (case cover side) correctly engages with fork rod brackets. Assemble cover to transmission case and make sure all bolts are installed in original positions. Replace sealing bolts if resin coating of threads peels off. Install differential side flanges.

PRIMARY GEAR

1) Bolt clutch housing to transmission case. Install bolts into original positions and replace seal bolts if resin coating of threads peels off. Press bearings onto primary and main drive input gears with drift (ST37750000).

2) Measure sub-gear end play and select proper spacer so end play is less than .004" (.1 mm). Install both ends of ring spring into .197" (5.0 mm) holes of primary idler gear and sub-gear. Mount sub-gear on idler gear, then install spacer. Press bearing onto primary idler gear. Be sure sub-gear moves smoothly and end play is correct. See Fig. 22.

NOTE — *Spacers are available in thicknesses of .267" (6.80 mm), .270" (6.85 mm), .272" (6.90 mm), .274" (6.95 mm) and .276" (7.00 mm).*

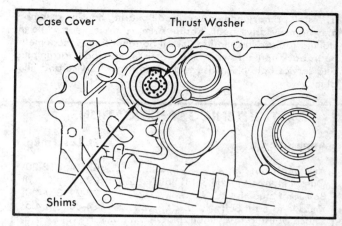

Fig. 21   Installing Thrust Washer and Shims

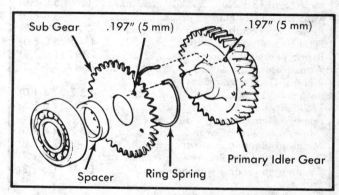

Fig. 22   Assembling 4 and 5-Speed Sub-Gear

3) Install primary idler gear into clutch housing. Install main drive input gear. Set primary idler sub-gear to proper position by inserting bar in hole of primary idler gear through hole in sub-gear.

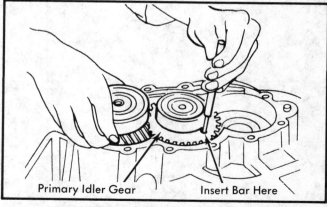

**Fig. 23   Assembling Primary Idler Gear
(4 and 5-Speed Transmissions)**

4) Install thrust washer and lock washer in that order, then install main drive gear mounting nut. Mounting nut must be installed with chamfered side facing lock washer. Tighten mounting nut, while 1st or 2nd and reverse gear are engaged, to prevent main drive gear from turning while tightening nut.

NOTE — *Ensure all bolts are installed in original positions and sealing bolts are replaced.*

DATSUN 310 4 & 5 SPEED (Cont.)

5) Install primary gear cover. Install bearing housing assembly and primary drive gear. Rotate primary drive gear while installing to ease installation. Install bottom cover, speedometer gear, back-up light switch, top switch (if equipped), drain plug and service hole plug. Use sealant on drain, service and filler plugs.

TIGHTENING SPECIFICATIONS

Application	Ft. Lbs. (mkg)
Axle Shaft Nut	87-145 (12-20)
Output Flange-to-Axle Shaft Bolts	29-36 (4.0-5.0)
Ball Joint Stud Nut	22-29 (3.0-4.0)
Knuckle-to-Strut Bolts	24-33 (3.3-4.5)
Clutch Housing-to-Cylinder Block	10-13 (1.4-1.8)
Transmission Case-to-Bracket	43-58 (6.0-8.0)
Main Shaft Lock Nut	36-43 (5.0-6.0)
Main Drive Gear Nut	43-58 (6.0-8.0)
Reverse Idler Shaft Mounting Nut	72-87 (10-12)
Final Gear Mounting Bolts	43-58 (6.0-8.0)
Bearing Retainer Bracket	12-17 (1.6-2.3)
Transmission Case Cover	12-17 (1.6-2.3)
Primary Gear Cover Bolts	
M6 Bolts	4.3-7.2 (.6-1.0)
M8 Bolts	12-17 (1.6-2.3)
Primary Gear Bearing Housing- -to-Primary Gear Cover	4.3-7.2 (.6-1.0)
Mainshaft Bearing Retainer①	12-16 (1.6-2.2)
Reverse Fork Lever Bracket①	12-16 (1.6-2.2)
Countergear Shaft Retaining Plate②	12-17 (1.6-2.3)

① — 4-speed transmissions only.
② — 5-speed transmissions only.

TRANSAXLE SPECIFICATIONS

Application	Measurement
Wheel Bearing Preload	①6.9-24.3 INCH lbs. (8-28 cmkg)
Gear Backlash	
Primary Drive Gear	.0024-.0063" (.06-.16 mm)
Main Drive & Counter	
Drive Gear	.0012-.0051" (.03-.13 mm)
1st, 2nd, 3rd Gears	.0020-.0059" (.05-.15 mm)
4th Gear②	.0020-.0059" (.05-.15 mm)
Reverse Idler Gear	.0020-.0059" (.05-.15 mm)
Differential Assembly Drive	
Pinion-to-Ring Gear	.0024-.0059" (.06-.15 mm)
End Play	
1st Gear	.0079-.0118" (.20-.30 mm)
2nd, 3rd Gears③	.0079-.0118" (.20-.30 mm)
2nd, 3rd Gears②	.0079-.0138" (.20-.35 mm)
4th Gear②	.0079-.0118" (.20-.30 mm)
Reverse Idler Gear②	0-.0146" (0-.37 mm)
Synchro Ring-to-Gear Cone	
Standard	.037-.059" (.95-1.5 mm)
Allowable Limit	.020" (.5 mm)
Side Gear	.008" (.2 mm) Max.
Countergear	"0"

① — Rotation starting torque.
② — 5-speed transmissions only.
③ — 4-speed transmissions only.

FIAT 5-SPEED

Strada
X1/9

DESCRIPTION

Transmission and final drive are incorporated in a single case. All forward gears are synchromesh type. High gear is indirect. Helical gears are used for all forward speeds. Access to transaxle internals is provided by a 2 piece case. Final drive is helical gear type and the only adjustment required is side bearing preload, which is accomplished through the use of shims.

LUBRICATION & ADJUSTMENT

See MANUAL TRANSMISSION SERVICING Section.

SERVICE (IN VEHICLE)

AXLE SHAFTS

Removal (Strada) — 1) Drain oil from transaxle. Remove left front wheel. With brakes applied, remove hub nut and washer. Remove 6 allen head bolts holding left axle shaft to drive shaft flange.

NOTE — *Discard allen head bolts and replace with new ones for installation.*

2) Pull axle shaft out of hub carrier. Remove clamp holding boot on CV joint at drive end. Using suitable pliers (A.81115), remove circlip from drive end of axle shaft and slide off CV joint.

3) Remove clamp holding boot on CV joint at hub carrier end. Remove CV joint from axle shaft making sure that circlip remains in place. Remove 3 bolts holding bearing retainer. Pull right axle shaft and bearing out of support and transaxle.

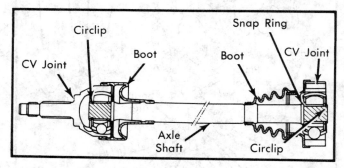

Fig. 1 Cutaway View of Axle Shaft Assembly

Removal (X1/9) — 1) Remove wheel and bolts and nuts holding shock absorber to support housing. Remove nut holding control arm ball joint to support housing and remove ball joint from housing.

2) Remove nut on strut rod ball joint and remove ball joint from housing. Drain oil from transaxle. Remove bolts and washers holding boot to transaxle housing and pull axle shaft and wheel hub out of housing.

3) Remove brake caliper and support bracket from support housing, then remove brake dust shield and rotor from housing. Remove clamp holding boot to CV joint and pull boot

back to uncover joint. Clean grease from joint and remove lock ring with joint. Remove axle shaft from joints.

Installation (All Models) — To install, reverse removal procedure, checking that snap ring is lying in axle shaft groove. Grease CV joint sockets and boots with FIAT MRM 2 grease or equivalent. Do not use more than 3.3 oz. (95 g) of grease.

WHEEL BEARINGS

Removal (Strada) — 1) With support housing removed from vehicle, place housing in press and using driver, press hub out of housing. Outer half of bearing will come out with hub. Use suitable extracting tool (A.47215) to remove inner race from hub shaft.

2) Remove outer cap and circlip with screwdriver. Using suitable bearing remover (A.74372), press out bearing from support housing. Remove seal.

Installation — To install, reverse removal procedure and install support housing in vehicle.

NOTE — *Bearings, ring nuts and seals must be replaced with new parts if removed from support housing.*

Removal (X1/9) — With support housing removed from vehicle, press hub out of support housing. Smooth out staking on hub bearing ring nut and unscrew nut with suitable octagonal wrench (A.57123). Remove bearing from support housing using suitable tool (8015).

Installation — Install new bearing in support housing using suitable tool (8015). Screw a NEW ring nut in housing and tighten using octagonal wrench. Stake hub nut. Press hub into support housing and install support housing in vehicle.

TRANSAXLE REMOVAL & INSTALLATION

Removal (Strada) — 1) Disconnect battery ground cable. Remove jack and spare wheel. Remove speedometer drive cable and gear. Remove air cleaner. Install an engine support crosspiece (A.70526) to engine.

2) Raise vehicle on lift. Remove front and left side shields. Disconnect ground cable, clutch operating cable and backup light switch connector from transmission. Remove starter motor.

3) Mark position of slots in relation to bolts on gear selector link for installation adjustment and remove gear selector link. Remove left and right axle shafts from flange. Remove 3 bolts and disengage differential output shaft, with bearing, from transaxle and support.

4) Place jack under transaxle. Remove center mounting bolt, support bracket and flywheel cover. Remove remaining transaxle-to-engine mounting bolts and lower transaxle out from under vehicle.

Removal (X1/9) — 1) Remove air cleaner and duct and disconnect positive battery cable. Loosen 2 bolts securing clutch slave cylinder and open bleed valve to allow push rod to retract. Disconnect return spring from clutch shaft. Disconnect push rod and move slave cylinder out of way.

FIAT 5-SPEED (Cont.)

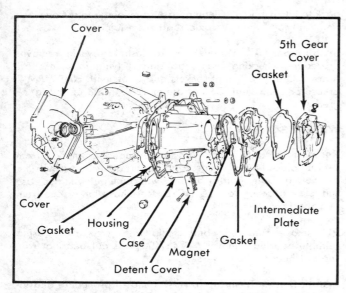

Fig. 2 Exploded View of Transaxle Housing Assembly

2) Install suitable support on engine and remove nuts and bolts securing transaxle to engine which are accessible from engine compartment. Raise vehicle and remove rear wheels. Remove 3 lower shields on left side.

3) Mark position of gearshift flexible link in relation to shift tube and remove bolts securing link to tube. Loosen bolt at transaxle end of link and swing link out of way. Disconnect all wiring to transaxle. Remove starter motor. Disconnect ground strap and remove exhaust pipe.

4) Remove CV joint-to-hub nuts. Remove bolts and nuts securing suspension control arm to supports. Pull hub off CV joints and tie differential output shafts to transaxle to prevent their falling out.

5) Remove flywheel cover and engine supporting crosspiece. Remove remaining nuts and bolts securing transaxle to engine. Using suitable support fixture (A.70575) installed on hydraulic jack, lower and remove transaxle from vehicle.

Installation (All Models) — To install, reverse removal procedure. Tighten suspension bolts with weight of vehicle on wheels.

TRANSAXLE DISASSEMBLY

1) Drain transaxle. Remove screws securing oil boots and remove differential output shafts. Remove reverse switch. Remove 5th gear cover.

2) Hold countershaft and mainshaft from turning, then remove countershaft and mainshaft nuts (do not reuse these nuts upon reassembly). Remove shift fork, synchro sleeve and synchro hub from mainshaft. Remove 5th gears from countershaft and mainshaft.

3) Remove 5th gear inner bearing race from mainshaft, then remove intermediate plate from transaxle case. Remove roller bearings from mainshaft and countershaft. Remove detent

cover, gasket, balls and springs. Remove nuts attaching housing to main case and lift case off studs.

4) Remove screws retaining shift forks and dogs to rails. Remove rails, forks and dogs from their seats in housing. Remove gear selector engagement lever support and remove gasket between transaxle main case and housing.

5) Remove reverse idler shaft retaining plate nut and remove plate and shaft. Remove countershaft, mainshaft and differential assemblies. Remove retaining lever, then remove gearshift control rod.

COMPONENT DISASSEMBLY & REASSEMBLY

DIFFERENTIAL ASSEMBLY

NOTE — *Disassembly and reassembly procedures for X1/9 model differentials were not available from manufacturer.*

Disassembly (Strada Only) — Remove 8 differential case bolts and pinion shaft lock plate. Using suitable puller (A.40005), remove differential bearings and speedometer drive gear. Drive pinion shaft from case. Remove side gear, pinion gears and thrust washers.

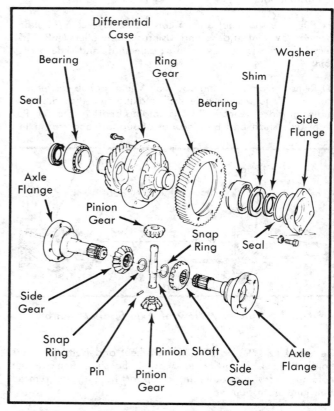

**Fig. 3 Exploded View of Differential Assembly
Strada Shown; X1/9 Similar**

Reassembly — **1)** Carefully inspect all parts for wear or damage. Install side gears in case directly opposite each other, seated in their counterbores. Install pinion gear in mesh with side gears.

FIAT 5-SPEED (Cont.)

2) Carefully rotate assembly so that pinion gear is directly opposite large opening in case and place 2nd pinion gear in mesh. Insert pinion shaft through pinion gears and line up hole in shaft with hole in case. Insert pinion shaft retaining pin.

3) Using a suitable driver, install differential bearings and speedometer drive gear. Install lock plate and pinion gear on case with 8 bolts.

TRANSAXLE REASSEMBLY & ADJUSTMENT

TRANSAXLE REASSEMBLY

1) Install mainshaft bearing and outer bearing ring for differential in housing. Install gearshift control rod in housing, complete with spring, gaskets, cover and boot. Install control lever on end of rod. Install differential case assembly in housing.

2) Check mainshaft run out using a dial indicator by placing shaft on centers and rotating by hand. Maximum run out is .001" (.03 mm). Check clearance between bushings and mainshaft gears, this clearance should be .001-.003" (.03-.08

mm). Install mainshaft and countershaft in housing. Check backlash between mainshaft and countershaft gears. Standard backlash is .004-.008" (.10-.20 mm).

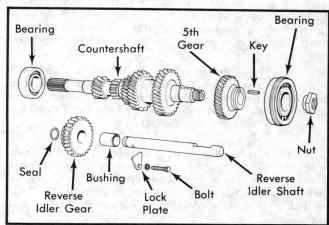

Fig. 4   Exploded View of Countershaft Assembly

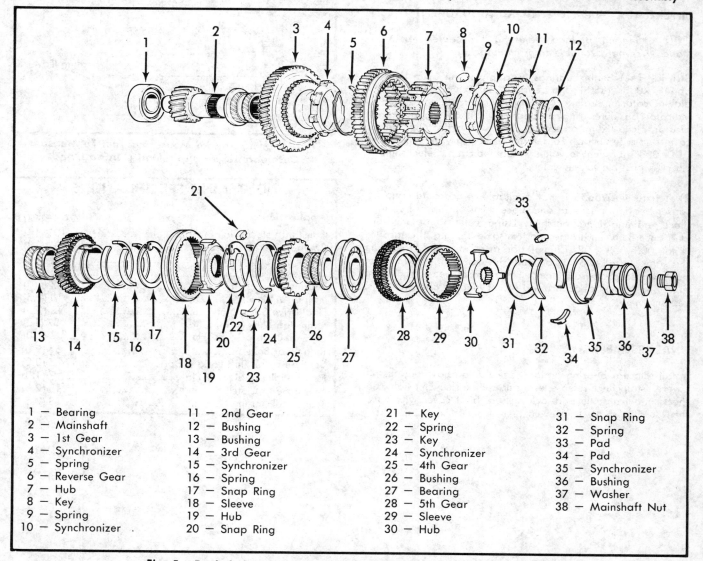

1 — Bearing	11 — 2nd Gear	21 — Key	31 — Snap Ring
2 — Mainshaft	12 — Bushing	22 — Spring	32 — Spring
3 — 1st Gear	13 — Bushing	23 — Key	33 — Pad
4 — Synchronizer	14 — 3rd Gear	24 — Synchronizer	34 — Pad
5 — Spring	15 — Synchronizer	25 — 4th Gear	35 — Synchronizer
6 — Reverse Gear	16 — Spring	26 — Bushing	36 — Bushing
7 — Hub	17 — Snap Ring	27 — Bearing	37 — Washer
8 — Key	18 — Sleeve	28 — 5th Gear	38 — Mainshaft Nut
9 — Spring	19 — Hub	29 — Sleeve	
10 — Synchronizer	20 — Snap Ring	30 — Hub	

Fig. 5   Exploded View of Fiat 5-Speed Transaxle Mainshaft Assembly

FIAT 5-SPEED (Cont.)

3) Check that clearance between reverse idler shaft and reverse idler gear bushing is .003-.006" (.08-.15 mm). Install reverse idler gear assembly with gasket in housing. Secure shaft with plate and bolt. Install main case-to-housing gasket. Make sure gear selector and engagement lever are seated on control lever; install on gear control rod. Install support for selector and engagement lever on housing and secure with nut.

4) Install shift rail detent rollers in their seats on support and install shift rails, forks and dogs. Install transmission maincase on housing. Insert three detent balls and springs in transmission case and install gasket and spring retainer cover. Install ball bearings on mainshaft and countershaft.

5) Install intermediate plate on transmission case. Install bushing, 5th gear and washer on mainshaft. Install synchronizer assembly to mainshaft. Install 5th gear, key and bearing on countershaft. Install mainshaft nut and countershaft nut and tighten. Install 5th gear cover on intermediate plate.

DIFFERENTIAL BEARING PRELOAD ADJUSTMENT

NOTE — *Bearing preload adjusting procedures for X1/9 model were not available from manufacturer.*

Strada — 1) Settle bearings by applying an axial load of about 770 lbs. (350 kg) to bearings. Set fixture A.95655 with dial indicator on sealing cover mounting surface and zero dial indicator on outer ring of bearing. Without changing indicator, place fixture on sealing cover with indicator feeler on cover and case surface. To determine necessary shim thickness, ADD .003" (.08 mm) to value on dial indicator. Select shim as close as possible to this value.

2) If fixture A.95655 is not available, place outer ring of carrier bearing in its seat and place shims on top of bearing. Place retaining flange on shims. Using feeler gauge, measure clearance between flange and transaxle housing. If clearance is not .003-.005" (.08-.13 mm), add or remove shims to obtain this value. Install two nuts on studs through flange and tighten nuts. Rotate gear train one full turn to set bearings, loosen nuts and check clearance again. If not to specifications, reshim.

FINAL ASSEMBLY

Install shim for bearing preload calculated above and install cover. Install clutch release lever and sliding sleeve. Install axle shafts into transaxle and lock oil seal boot cover with nuts, then tie axle shafts to prevent them from falling out.

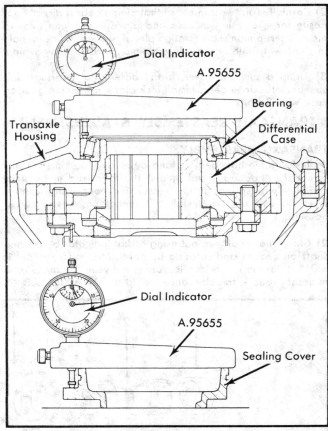

Fig. 6 Using Special Measuring Tool To Measure Differential Bearing Preload (Strada Only)

TIGHTENING SPECIFICATIONS

Application	Ft. Lbs. (mkg)
Constant Velocity Joint-to-Hub Nuts	101 (14)
Countershaft Nut	87 (12)
Clutch Housing-to-Engine	58 (8.0)
Differential Case Bolts	36 (5.0)
Bearing Cover Bolts	7 (1.0)
Fifth Gear Cover	18 (2.5)
Final Drive Cover Nuts	18 (2.5)
Mainshaft Nut	87 (12)
Oil Seal Boot-to-Transaxle	7 (1.0)
Ring Gear Bolts	65 (9.0)
Set Screws for Shift Forks & Dogs	14.5 (2.0)
Reverse Idler Shaft Lock Plate	7 (1.0)
Transaxle-to-Clutch Housing	18 (2.5)
Transaxle Housing Nuts	18 (2.5)

FIESTA 4-SPEED

Hatchback

DESCRIPTION

Transmission and final drive are mounted in a 2-piece transaxle case. Transmission is a 4-speed unit, fully synchronized in all forward gears. Forward gears are helically cut and in constant mesh. Reverse gears are spur cut and are engaged by a sliding reverse idler gear. Power is transfered to final drive assembly by direct mesh of differential ring gear to a gear on pinion shaft. Power is transmitted to wheels via equal-length axle drive shafts with constant velocity (CV) joints at both ends. Because of offset position of transaxle in vehicle, an additional shaft (primary shaft) is located between right axle drive shaft and transaxle.

LUBRICATION & ADJUSTMENT

See MANUAL TRANSMISSION SERVICING Section.

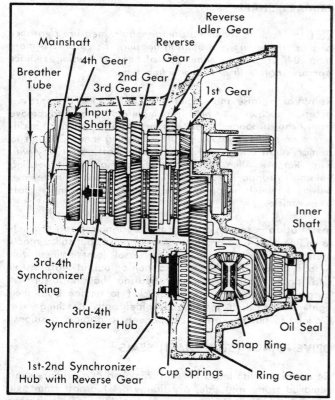

Fig. 1 Cutaway View of Fiesta Transaxle Assembly

SERVICE (IN VEHICLE)

WHEEL BEARINGS

Removal — 1) Remove wheel center cap, then remove hub nut and washer. Loosen wheel bolts. Raise and support front of vehicle. Remove wheel and reinstall 2 wheel bolts to reduce strain on disc retaining screw.

2) Remove brake caliper-to-knuckle bolts and hang caliper free of rotor. Remove hub and rotor assembly from axle shaft, using a puller if necessary. Remove cotter pin and nut from tie rod ball joint. Using a suitable remover, remove tie rod ball joint from knuckle.

3) Remove lower control arm-to-body mount bolt. Pull downward on inner end of control arm, remove ball joint-to-knuckle pinch bolt and separate ball joint from knuckle. Remove the 2 upper strut-to-fender bolts and withdraw strut and knuckle assembly.

Disassembly — Mount strut and knuckle assembly in a soft-jawed vise. Use pliers to pull out dust shield from groove on inner side of knuckle. Remove inner and outer grease seals, then lift out bearings. Using a hammer and blunt punch, drive out inner and outer bearing races.

Reassembly — Reverse disassembly procedure and note the following: Pack wheel bearings and cavity between seal lips with suitable wheel bearing grease. Install dust shield with cutout at bottom, next to ball joint hole in knuckle.

Installation — Reverse removal procedure and note the following: Install new hub nut, tighten to specification, and stake into slot in axle shaft.

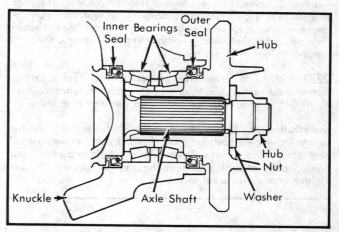

Fig. 2 Cutaway View of Hub and Knuckle Assembly

AXLE DRIVE SHAFTS

Removal (Left) — 1) Remove wheel center cap, then remove hub nut and washer. Loosen wheel bolts. Raise and support front of vehicle. Remove wheel.

2) Remove Allen bolts attaching inner CV joint to output shaft flange. Remove brake caliper-to-knuckle bolts and hang caliper free of rotor. Remove hub and rotor assembly from axle shaft, using puller if necessary. Remove cotter pin and nut from tie rod ball joint. Using a suitable remover, remove tie rod ball joint from knuckle.

3) Remove lower control arm-to-body mount bolt. Pull downward on inner end of control arm, remove ball joint-to-knuckle pinch bolt and separate ball joint from knuckle. Remove axle shaft from vehicle.

Installation — Clean inner CV joint and repack with approximately 1.5 oz. (40 grams) of suitable grease. Insert outer end of driveshaft through spindle carrier and continue assembly in reverse order of removal. If necessary, use hub installer to pull hub and disc assembly fully home on driveshaft. Install and tighten new hub nut. Stake nut into slot in drive shaft with pin punch.

NOTE — Do NOT attempt to drive hub onto driveshaft or CV joint will be damaged.

FIESTA 4-SPEED (Cont.)

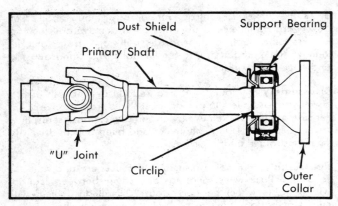

Fig. 3　Side View of Primary Shaft and Bearing

Removal (Right) — Remove wheel center cap, hub nut and washer. Disconnect inner CV joint from primary shaft flange. Remove wheel and reinstall 2 bolts to prevent strain on disc retaining screw. Remove bolts holding primary shaft bearing housing to bracket. Allow primary shaft to hang clear, then remove axle shaft from hub.

NOTE — *Prior to installation of right shaft, check clearance between dust shield and bearing outer race. If clearance is less than .04" (1 mm), replace shaft and bearing assembly.*

Installation — **1)** Loosen primary shaft bearing support bracket-to-engine bolts until bracket is free to move, but still contacts mating surface. Raise primary shaft and install and tighten bolts attaching bearing housing to support bracket. Tighten support bracket-to-engine bolts.

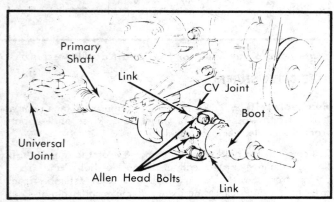

Fig. 4　Attachment of Right Axle Drive Shaft to Primary Shaft (Left Shaft Attaches to Stub Shaft Flange)

NOTE — *Tighten top support bracket-to-engine bolt first.*

2) Insert axle shaft splined end into hub. Install bolts attaching inner CV joint to primary shaft flange and tighten finger tight. Install washer and new hub nut. Then tighten bolts attaching inner CV joint to flange. Install wheel, lower vehicle to ground, and fully tighten wheel bolts. Tighten hub nut to specification and stake into slot in axle shaft. Install wheel center cap.

CV JOINT BELLOWS

Removal — With axle shaft removed from vehicle, remove large boot clamp from either CV joint and slide boot back on shaft. Pry open retaining clip and pull axle shaft out of CV joint. Repeat procedure for other CV joint.

Installation — Slide new bellows (boot) on shaft and install CV joint with retaining ring. Clean and lubricate CV joints and position bellows. Install new clamps and crimp to tighten.

PRIMARY SHAFT

NOTE — *Prior to removing primary shaft, measure clearance of support bearing and bearing housing. If clearance is more than .04" (1 mm) on either side of bearing housing, replace primary shaft with new production type.*

Removal — Raise and support front of vehicle. For improved access, detach exhaust pipe from manifold flange and remove front exhaust hanger. Then, support exhaust system at a different point. Remove Allen bolts attaching inner CV joint to primary shaft flange and support axle shaft out of way with wire. Remove Allen bolts attaching primary shaft bearing housing to support bracket. Pull outward on shaft to remove universal joint from output shaft and remove primary shaft from vehicle.

Installation — Loosen primary shaft bearing support bracket-to-engine bolts until bracket is free to move, but still contacts mating surface. Smear shaft universal joint splines with suitable grease and slide into position on output shaft. Install and tighten bolts attaching bearing housing-to-support bracket. Tighten top support bracket to engine bolt, then tighten bottom bolt. Install and tighten bolts attaching inner CV joint to flange. Restore components to original positions.

DRIVE FLANGE (STUB SHAFT) SEALS

Removal — With left drive shaft removed and primary shaft removed from right side, pry flange or stubshaft from axle with suitable tool. Using seal remover (T77F-6700-A), remove seals from transaxle housing.

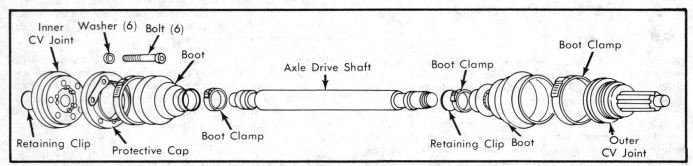

Fig. 5　Exploded View of Axle Shaft and CV Joints

FIESTA 4-SPEED (Cont.)

NOTE — *Position drain pan under transaxle to catch oil lost when stub shaft is removed.*

Installation — Install seals with suitable tool (T77F-3169-A for right seal; T77F-6700-A for left seal). Repack CV joints and use new snap rings on stub shafts. Drive stub shaft into position with soft-faced hammer until snap ring seats.

SPEEDOMETER DRIVEN GEAR & BEARING

Removal — Pry bearing locking pin out of housing with diagonal pliers. Pull bearing and driven gear from housing along with speedometer cable and housing. Separate pinion and bearing from cable.

Installation — Place pinion and bearing in housing and secure in place with locking pin. Connect speedometer drive shaft and housing.

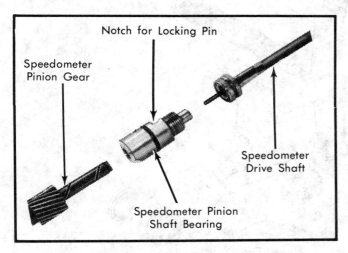

Fig. 6   Exploded View of Speedometer Driven Gear Assembly

TRANSAXLE REMOVAL & INSTALLATION

Removal — 1) Disconnect battery cables. Install engine support bracket as shown in *Fig. 7*.

CAUTION — *Transmission must be engaged in 4th gear to ensure correct adjustment of gear engagement upon installation.*

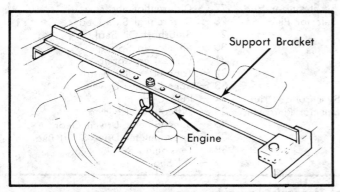

Fig. 7   Engine Support Bracket Installation

2) Remove speedometer driven gear. Push clutch cable between lever and support, release cable and unhook clutch cable from release lever.

3) Remove 4 upper transmission flange bolts. Raise vehicle and drain transmission oil through plunger-retainer hole. Care for plunger and spring during draining operation.

4) Remove selector rod spring from selector rod. Loosen selector rod locating bolt and withdraw selector rod from shift shaft.

5) Remove stabilizer shift bar from transmission. Unscrew and reposition 2 inner nuts toward outside of stud. Loosen lock nut and screw stud out of transmission housing with an Allen wrench. Suspend stabilizer and stud on engine support bar.

6) Disconnect axle drive shafts at inner CV joints. Disconnect and remove starter motor. Remove breather tube from side of transmission. Remove 2 lower flange bolts from transmission and 3 flange bolts from engine mounting. Lower and remove transmission.

Installation — 1) Lightly grease splines of input shaft and ensure that engine adapter plate is seated properly on engine guide bushings. Raise transmission into position and finger tighten 2 flange bolts. Align adapter plate using 2 drifts.

2) Install transmission and clutch adapter plate to engine mounting using 3 NEW self-locking bolts. Lower engine and tighten these 3 bolts and the 2 flange bolts to specifications.

3) Install the plunger retainer (removed for oil draining) with spring in plunger retainer hole. Install starter motor. Install axle shafts. Install stabilizer shift bar and tighten stud in transmission housing with Allen wrench. Lock in position with lock nut, then tighten inner nut on mounting until it contacts washer. Lock inner nut with outer nut.

NOTE — *Gear shift mechanism may be boot type (Fig. 8) or cranked rod type. Cranked rod type does not have a dust boot and is installed with a retract spring. Installation and adjustment of cranked rod type does not require 2¾" (70 mm) spacer.*

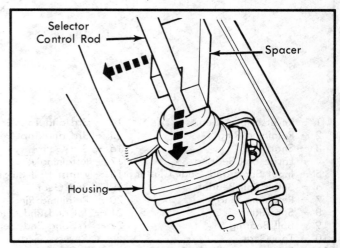

Fig. 8   Fitting Selector Rod on Boot Type Gearshift Shaft with Spacer Block in Position

4) Ensure that shift shaft and lever are in 4th gear position, then pull selector rod down onto shift shaft. Align hole in selector housing with shift lever and lock in position with .16" (4

Manual Transaxles

FIESTA 4-SPEED (Cont.)

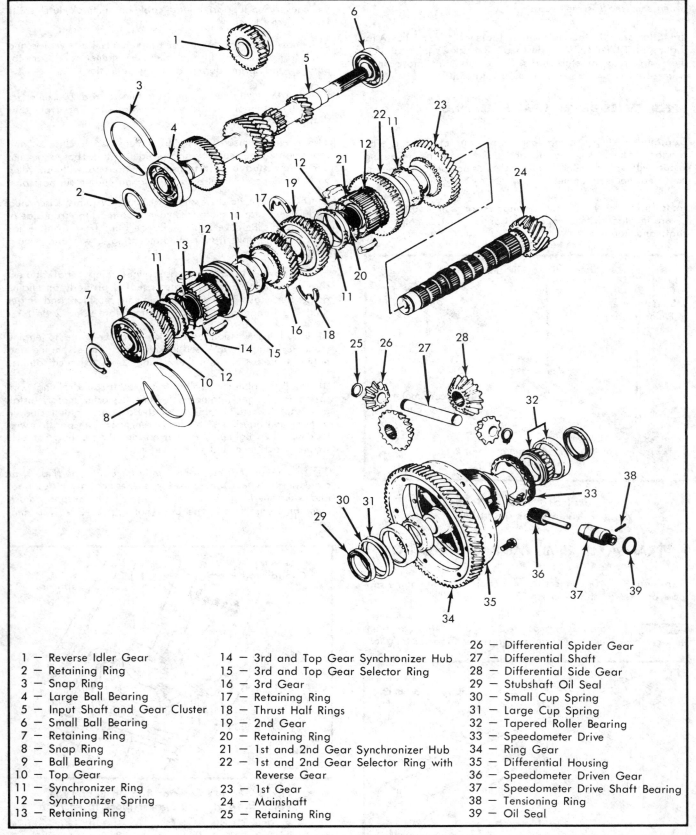

1 — Reverse Idler Gear
2 — Retaining Ring
3 — Snap Ring
4 — Large Ball Bearing
5 — Input Shaft and Gear Cluster
6 — Small Ball Bearing
7 — Retaining Ring
8 — Snap Ring
9 — Ball Bearing
10 — Top Gear
11 — Synchronizer Ring
12 — Synchronizer Spring
13 — Retaining Ring

14 — 3rd and Top Gear Synchronizer Hub
15 — 3rd and Top Gear Selector Ring
16 — 3rd Gear
17 — Retaining Ring
18 — Thrust Half Rings
19 — 2nd Gear
20 — Retaining Ring
21 — 1st and 2nd Gear Synchronizer Hub
22 — 1st and 2nd Gear Selector Ring with Reverse Gear
23 — 1st Gear
24 — Mainshaft
25 — Retaining Ring

26 — Differential Spider Gear
27 — Differential Shaft
28 — Differential Side Gear
29 — Stubshaft Oil Seal
30 — Small Cup Spring
31 — Large Cup Spring
32 — Tapered Roller Bearing
33 — Speedometer Drive
34 — Ring Gear
35 — Differential Housing
36 — Speedometer Driven Gear
37 — Speedometer Drive Shaft Bearing
38 — Tensioning Ring
39 — Oil Seal

Fig. 9 Exploded View of Transaxle Assembly

FIESTA 4-SPEED (Cont.)

mm) pin. Insert suitable 2¾" (70 mm) spacer between floor pan and selector rod. Rotate shift shaft clockwise to stop and tighten selector rod locating bolt. Install selector rod spring between rod and longitudinal member and check gear change operation.

5) Continue installation in reverse of removal procedure and refill with transmission oil. Release and remove engine support bracket.

TRANSAXLE DISASSEMBLY

1) Attach transmission to a suitable swivel type mount assembly stand. Allow oil to drain. Remove clutch release lever and thrust bearing with fork.

2) Remove selector shaft retaining nut with locking pin and spring. Remove 8 bolts in housing cover. Remove clips from main and input shaft bearings.

NOTE — *Revisions made to transaxles/differentials during 1979 require use of complete service kits. Component differential parts are not available separately. The transaxle build date code tag (lower right corner of tag) is located on upper bolt retaining two transaxle housings together. Differential service to transaxles built prior to 9 Sept. 1979 (code tag 9-J-9) require service kit D9RZ-4026-A (22 spline pinion gears and inner stub shafts). Transaxles built after that date require service kit EORZ-4026-B (23 spline pinion gears and inner stub shafts).*

Fig. 10   Removing Mainshaft and Input Shaft Clips

3) Remove 14 bolts in small housing section, then separate and remove housing. Remove selector lever retaining clip and selector lever. Remove selector fork guide shaft. Remove selector forks, shift locking plate and spring.

Fig. 11   Removing Shift Locking Plate and Springs

NOTE — *Remove magnetic disc at bottom of differential housing, using care not to drop it as it will shatter.*

4) Lift complete mainshaft assembly with input shaft assembly and reverse gear from housing as shown in *Fig. 12*. Remove differential assembly from case.

5) Remove mainshaft bearings and disassemble plastic cage. Remove oil slinger and discard. Remove bearing race. Drive out input shaft seal.

CAUTION — *Do not damage large transmission housing while driving out input shaft seal.*

Fig. 12   Removal of Mainshaft, Input Shaft and Reverse Gear from Housing

6) Drive out differential gear bearing race. Remove stub shaft seals (1 in each housing), and discard. Remove differential gear bearing cup and 2 cup springs using a suitable driver, from the small housing.

COMPONENT DISASSEMBLY & REASSEMBLY

MAINSHAFT

Disassembly — 1) Remove circlip. Using a suitable puller, remove bearing. Remove 4th gear and retaining ring in front of 3rd-4th gear synchromesh clutch assembly. Remove synchromesh clutch assembly complete with 3rd gear.

NOTE — *Synchromesh clutch assembly consists of 2 synchronizer rings and a synchromesh clutch.*

2) Remove retaining ring and locking plate halves, then remove 2nd gear. Remove retaining ring and remove 1st-2nd gear synchromesh clutch assembly complete with 1st gear.

3) To disassemble synchromesh clutch assembly, remove retaining springs with synchronizer bars and remove selector ring from synchronizer hub. See Fig. 13.

Inspection — Clean all parts thoroughly and air dry. Inspect for any damage. If there is no damage, apply a thin coat of transmission oil over all parts prior to reassembly.

FIESTA 4-SPEED (Cont.)

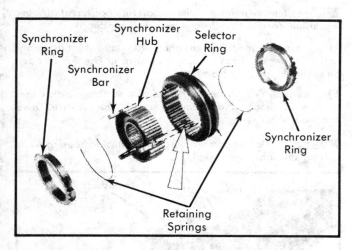

Fig. 13 *Disassembled View of Synchromesh Clutch*

Reassembly — 1) To reassemble, reverse disassembly procedure, using all new snap rings. Use caution not to over extend rings with pliers during installation.

2) Ensure selector groove on 1st-2nd gear synchromesh clutch assembly faces 1st gear. When pressing on mainshaft bearing, groove must face outward.

NOTE — *When installing new components (gears, hubs or selector rings) the running and end faces of gears and spline shaft sections, synchronizer cones and mainshaft running seats MUST be covered with general purpose grease.*

INPUT SHAFT

Disassembly — 1) Remove circlip from small housing end of input shaft. Replace large clip which was removed to allow small housing to separate.

2) Using suitable puller, remove bearing. Place input shaft in a suitable press and remove small input shaft bearing.

Reassembly — 1) Using suitable tool and press, press small input bearing on shaft against stop.

2) Remove large clip from groove. With groove outward, press large bearing on small housing end of input shaft and secure with clip.

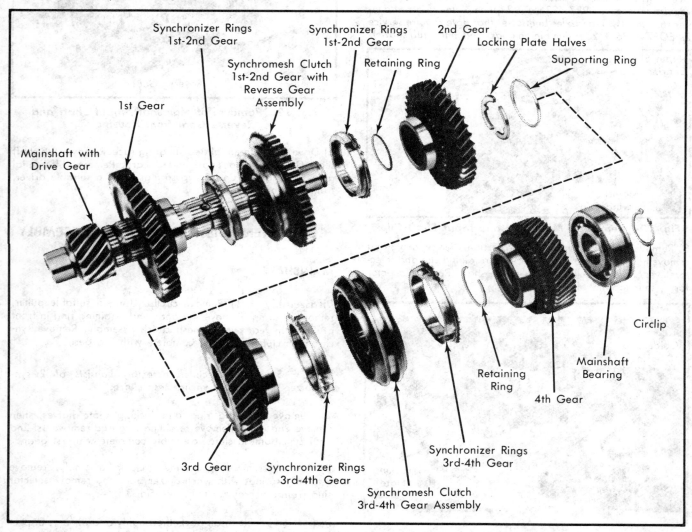

Fig. 14 *Exploded View of Transmission Mainshaft*

FIESTA 4-SPEED (Cont.)

DIFFERENTIAL ASSEMBLY

Disassembly — 1) Turn both differential side gears laterally and remove from housing. Remove differential spider gears by removing 1 clip from differential shaft and pushing shaft out of housing.

NOTE — *Discard clip. New clip MUST be used when spider gears are reassembled.*

2) Remove 2 differential gear tapered roller bearings, one from each end of housing, using a suitable puller. Remove speedometer drive gear.

3) Remove 6 bolts holding ring gear to differential housing. Remove gear from housing by tapping off with soft faced mallet.

Reassembly — 1) Align ring gear with threaded holes in housing and draw into position using new bolts. Tighten bolts evenly and alternately to ensure correct fit. Position speedometer drive gear on housing.

NOTE — *Deep chamfered edge of inner gear ring must point towards differential gear housing.*

2) Press tapered roller bearing on both ends of differential housing. Install differential spider gears by installing differential shaft together with differential spider gears into housing and replace clips.

3) Install differential side gears. Fit both side gears together snugly and with gears meshed, install in housing. Secure side gears by installing a constant velocity joint or plastic plug.

NOTE — *The constant velocity joint is used only to position the differential side gear and is removed after differential is positioned.*

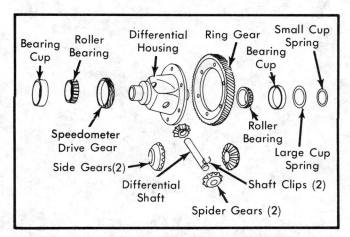

Fig. 15 Exploded View of Differential Assembly

SELECTOR ASSEMBLY

Removal — 1) Remove shift lever and reverse gear shift lever. Remove 2 bolts from guide lever retaining plate. Remove plate complete with 2 guide levers, then remove guide shaft.

2) Remove 2 clips and remove guide levers from guide lever retaining plate. Remove rubber collar from shift shaft and un-

screw selector block from shift shaft and press out shaft. Remove shaft seal and discard.

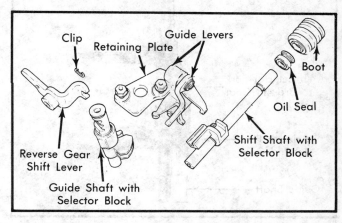

Fig. 16 Exploded View of Internal Selector Mechanism

Installation — 1) Replace shaft seal with suitable tool (T77F-7288-A) and slide hammer. Insert shaft and attach selector block. Install boot on control shaft.

2) Attach guide lever with clips to retainer plate. Insert guide shaft and fit retainer plate complete with guide lever. Ensure that guide lever is correctly seated. Place reverse gear selector lever on shaft and install clip.

TRANSAXLE REASSEMBLY

1) Drive differential roller bearing cup into large housing with suitable tool (T77F-4222-A) and insert bearing cup with 2 cup springs in small housing section. If there is no recess in transaxle housing, equal sized cup springs must be used. Bearing cup is a sliding fit and is secured in position by a single light blow of a punch.

2) Insert differential. Install new input shaft seal and mainshaft bearing race. Position new oil slinger and plastic mainshaft bearing cage.

3) Install new stubshaft seals and place ring gear/differential assembly in large housing. Both bearings on differential must be clean and lubricated with transmission oil when being reinstalled. New bearings do not need to be cleaned prior to lubricating.

4) Slide reverse gear idler onto shaft while at the same time inserting reverse gearshift lever into selector groove. Raise gearshift lever with idler gear and support on shaft detent, then install mainshaft and input shaft cluster. Lower selector lever and reverse idler gear.

5) Insert selector lock plate and fit selector forks. Insert springs in housing bore and insert selector fork guide shaft with the longer pin pointing downward. Position selector lever and retain in position with clip. Insert magnetic disc in recess at bottom of housing.

6) Use new gasket and install small housing section. Tighten to specifications. Insert main and input shaft bearings in small housing end and secure with large clips. (Clips are available in 3 different thicknesses. Use clip which just fits into groove of outer bearing race.) Rotate clips to accommodate cover seal.

7) Replace selector shaft locking pin with spring and retaining nut. Install clutch release shaft and link with thrust bearing.

Manual Transaxles

FIESTA 4-SPEED (Cont.)

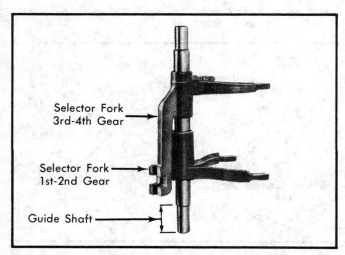

Selector Fork
3rd-4th Gear

Selector Fork
1st-2nd Gear

Guide Shaft

**Fig. 17 Installed Position of Guide
Shaft and Selector Rods**

TIGHTENING SPECIFICATIONS

Application	Ft. Lbs. (mkg)
Transmission-to-Engine Flange Bolts	30 (4.0)
Transmission-to-Engine Brace Bolts	65 (9.0)
Small Housing-to-Large Housing	18 (2.5)
Cover-to-Housing	7 (1.0)
Ring Gear-to-Housing	62 (8.0)
Shift Housing-to-Floor Pan	12 (1.6)
Selector Rod Assy.-to-Stabilizer Allen Screw	40 (5.5)
Guide Lever Retaining Plate-to-Large Housing Section	16 (2.2)
Selector Block-to-Shift Shaft	10 (1.4)
Plunger Retainer	22 (3.0)
Gear Shift Housing	4 (0.6)
Selector Rod-to-Shift Shaft	12 (1.6)

HONDA 4 & 5-SPEED

Accord
Civic
Prelude

TRANSAXLE IDENTIFICATION

Transaxle identification number is stamped into top of transaxle case near transaxle-to-engine union.

DESCRIPTION

Transmission and final drive are mounted in a common two piece case. Transmission is a four or five speed unit, fully synchronized in all forward gears. All forward gears are helically cut and are in constant mesh; reverse gears are spur cut and are engaged by a sliding reverse idler gear. On five speed transaxles, fifth gear is mounted on mainshaft on rear side of transaxle case (inside transaxle cover). Power transfer to the final drive assembly is by direct mesh of differential ring gear to a gear on transmission countershaft.

LUBRICATION & ADJUSTMENT

See *MANUAL TRANSMISSION SERVICING* Section.

TROUBLE SHOOTING

HARSH SHIFTS OR NOISY LOW GEAR OPERATION

Idle speed too high. Clutch not fully releasing.

SLIPS OUT OF GEAR

Synchronizer teeth worn. Interlock mechanism damaged. Weak interlock spring. Shift linkage out of adjustment.

TRANSMISSION NOISY

Worn or damaged gear teeth or bearings. Improperly adjusted clutch. Oil soaked or damaged clutch.

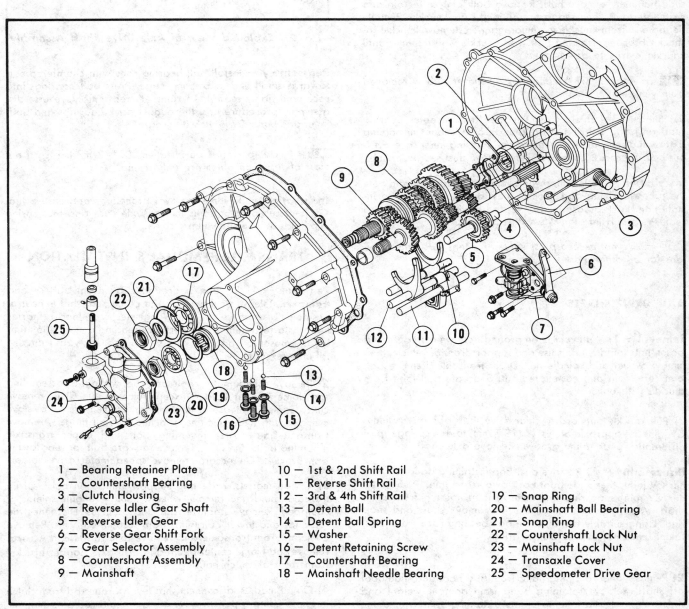

1 — Bearing Retainer Plate	10 — 1st & 2nd Shift Rail	
2 — Countershaft Bearing	11 — Reverse Shift Rail	
3 — Clutch Housing	12 — 3rd & 4th Shift Rail	19 — Snap Ring
4 — Reverse Idler Gear Shaft	13 — Detent Ball	20 — Mainshaft Ball Bearing
5 — Reverse Idler Gear	14 — Detent Ball Spring	21 — Snap Ring
6 — Reverse Gear Shift Fork	15 — Washer	22 — Countershaft Lock Nut
7 — Gear Selector Assembly	16 — Detent Retaining Screw	23 — Mainshaft Lock Nut
8 — Countershaft Assembly	17 — Countershaft Bearing	24 — Transaxle Cover
9 — Mainshaft	18 — Mainshaft Needle Bearing	25 — Speedometer Drive Gear

Fig. 1 Exploded View of Honda 4-Speed Manual Transmission Assembly

HONDA 4 & 5-SPEED (Cont.)

REVERSE GEAR ENGAGEMENT DURING FORWARD GEAR CHANGE

Weak or damaged reverse interlock mechanism.

SERVICE (IN VEHICLE)

WHEEL BEARINGS

Removal — **1)** With vehicle on ground, remove cotter pin and loosen hub spindle nut. Raise and support front of vehicle, then remove wheel and spindle nut. Remove caliper mounting bolts and support caliper out of way with wire. DO NOT disconnect hydraulic line.

2) Remove disc retaining screw, then install 2 bolts in disc. Turn each bolt 2 turns at a time to force disc from hub evenly. Using slide hammer, remove hub. Remove ball joint cotter pin and castellated nut, then separate ball joint from knuckle. Remove tie rod end from knuckle in similar manner. Remove knuckle-to-shock absorber retaining bolt. Tap knuckle with hammer until knuckle is free to be removed.

NOTE — *Replace wheel bearings whenever hub is removed from vehicle.*

3) Remove dust shield from knuckle. Remove outer bearing snap ring and bearing. Turn knuckle over, mount in holding fixture and remove seal, bearing and bearing inner race. Press out bearing races. Using a puller, remove dust seal from hub.

Installation — To install, reverse removal procedure and note the following: Hub and knuckle must be cleaned prior to installation. Pack grease in groove and sealing lip of hub dust seal. Press hub into knuckle with suitable press.

NOTE — *Do not exceed press value of 2 tons for Civic or 2.5 tons for all other models.*

AXLE DRIVE SHAFTS

Removal — **1)** With vehicle on ground, remove cotter pin and loosen hub spindle nut. Raise and support front of vehicle, then remove wheel and spindle nut. Drain transaxle. Remove ball joint cotter pin and castellated nut. Separate ball joint from knuckle with puller.

2) Pull knuckle outward to clear drive shaft of hub. Pry inner CV joint out approximately ½" (12.7 mm) to free spring clip of differential gear spline groove. Remove axle shaft.

Disassembly — **1)** Remove dust boot retaining band from inner CV joint, then slide boot back away from joint. Remove inner CV joint snap ring and remove joint housing from drive shaft. Wipe grease from joint, then remove shaft and snap ring. Using suitable driver, drive ball bearing race from joint, taking care not to lose ball bearings.

2) Remove inner retaining band from dust boot and slide boot off shaft. Remove retaining band from damper weight and slide weight off shaft. Remove outer retaining band from outer CV joint and clean joint of grease to check operation of joint.

NOTE — *Outer CV joint cannot be serviced. If joint is found to be worn or damaged, complete axle shaft assembly must be replaced.*

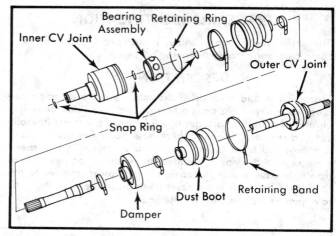

Fig. 2 **Exploded View of Axle Drive Shaft Assembly**

Reassembly — Install ball bearing race with chamfered end towards small end of bearing cage. Press ball bearings into race until firmly seated. To complete reassembly, reverse disassembly procedure and thoroughly pack bearings and both inner and outer CV joints with grease.

NOTE — *Damper must be installed .08" (2 mm) away from start of taper on outer drive shaft end.*

Installation — Reverse removal procedure and ensure that CV joint sub-axle bottoms in transaxle case and that spring clip holds axle securely in transaxle.

TRANSAXLE REMOVAL & INSTALLATION

Removal — **1)** Disconnect ground cable from battery and transaxle. Release steering lock and place gear shift in neutral position. Disconnect the following electrical leads: Starter motor, starter solenoid, temperature sending unit, ignition timing thermosensor, back-up light switch and coil wires from distributor (except Civic).

2) Remove speedometer cable and clip, without disassembling speedometer gear holder (except Accord). On Civic, remove clutch cable at release arm. On all others, remove clutch slave cylinder with hydraulic line attached. On all models, remove transaxle-side starter mounting bolt and upper transaxle mounting bolts. On Civic, remove forward bolt for rear torque arm bracket. On Accord, remove speedometer drive holder.

3) On all models, raise and support vehicle on hoist. Drain transaxle fluid and remove wheels. Remove engine shields, if equipped. Remove stabilizer bar and brackets. Disconnect tie rod ends and lower ball joints from suspension arms. Remove CV joints from transaxle and remove axle shafts. On Accord, remove sub-frame center beam and transaxle stopper bracket from front of clutch housing.

4) On all models, disconnect shift lever torque rod from clutch housing. Using a punch, drive out gear shift rod pin, then disconnect rod at transaxle case. Raise engine slightly (except Ac-

HONDA 4 & 5-SPEED (Cont.)

cord) and remove engine torque rods and brackets. On Civic, remove engine damper bracket from transaxle and rear engine mount and bracket from center beam. On Accord, remove clutch cover.

5) On all models, remove engine-side starter mounting bolt and starter. Place transmission jack under transaxle and remove remaining transaxle mounting bolts. On Prelude, remove upper bolt from engine damper bracket. On all models, pull transaxle away from engine block until mainshaft clears clutch pressure plate and dowels, then lower transaxle on jack. Remove both lower engine damper bracket bolts on Prelude while removing transaxle.

Installation — To install, reverse removal procedure and note the following: When connecting axle shafts to transaxle, ensure they are fully seated in transaxle case. After installation, refill transaxle with fluid and adjust shift linkage as needed.

TRANSAXLE DISASSEMBLY

1) On 5-speed transaxles, remove attaching bolts and lift off end cover. Remove mainshaft snap ring and thrust washer, then lift split collar from mainshaft groove. Remove attaching bolts and lift off 5th gear housing. Remove mainshaft bearing from housing, then remove spacer collar from mainshaft.

2) Insert mainshaft holder and lock gears in reverse position. Unstake lock nuts and remove lock nuts from mainshaft and countershaft (except Civic). Drive out pin securing 5th gear shift fork to shift rail, then slide shift fork, synchro sleeve and hub from mainshaft as a unit. Next, slide synchro ring, spring, 5th gear, needle bearing and thrust plate from mainshaft. Remove housing spacer (Civic).

NOTE — *Mainshaft lock nut of all transaxles has LEFT-HAND threads.*

3) On 4-speed transaxles, remove attaching bolts and remove end cover. Insert mainshaft holder and lock gears in reverse. Bend back locking tab of mainshaft lock nut and remove nut. Pull mainshaft bearing from shaft with puller. Remove countershaft bearing snap ring.

4) On all transaxles, remove 3 retaining screws from transaxle case bores, then remove detent balls and springs. Remove transaxle housing-to-clutch housing attaching bolts. Using a soft hammer, tap on transaxle housing bosses to loosen housing, then separate housings.

5) Lift reverse idler gear and shaft from clutch housing. On 4-speed transaxles, remove nut and washer, then lift off reverse shift fork. On 5-speed transaxles, remove 5th/reverse shift rail (with reverse shift fork attached) from housing. On Civic bend down lock plate tabs and remove screws from all shift rails, then lift off remaining shift rails, forks and guides. Before removing countershaft and mainshaft assemblies, record measurements listed in step 6).

6) Measure clearance between 5th/reverse shift shaft pin and reverse shift fork. Clearance should be .002-.014" (.05-.36 mm). If clearance is not as specified, measure width of reverse shift fork slot. Clearance should be .278-.285" (7.06-7.25 mm). Then measure reverse idle gear-to-shift fork clearance.

Clearance should be .02-.05" (.5-1.3 mm). If clearance exceeds specification, measure clearance between fingers of shift fork. Finger end gap clearance should be .47-.49" (12-12.5 mm). If any clearance exceeds specification, countershaft must be disassembled and clearances corrected. If clearances are within limits and no parts are defective, disassembly of countershaft is unnecessary.

7) On 4-speed, lock mainshaft in place, then shift transaxle into gear. Bend locking tab on lock nut out of countershaft slot. Loosen but do not remove lcok nut. On Civic, remove countershaft and mainshaft as an assembly. On Accord and Prelude, remove countershaft and mainshaft with 1st/2nd and 3rd/4th shift shafts from housing. On all models, remove gear selector attaching bolts and gear selector. Using a driver inserted through clutch housing, drive out differential assembly. Remove differential seals.

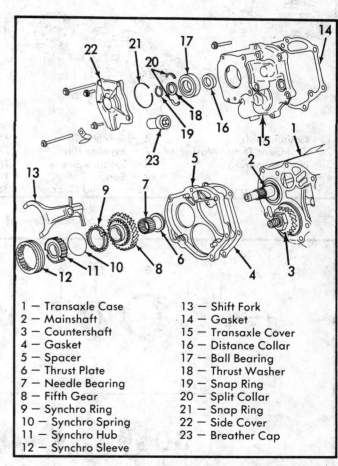

1 — Transaxle Case	13 — Shift Fork
2 — Mainshaft	14 — Gasket
3 — Countershaft	15 — Transaxle Cover
4 — Gasket	16 — Distance Collar
5 — Spacer	17 — Ball Bearing
6 — Thrust Plate	18 — Thrust Washer
7 — Needle Bearing	19 — Snap Ring
8 — Fifth Gear	20 — Split Collar
9 — Synchro Ring	21 — Snap Ring
10 — Synchro Spring	22 — Side Cover
11 — Synchro Hub	23 — Breather Cap
12 — Synchro Sleeve	

Fig. 3 Exploded View of Fifth Gear Components

COMPONENT DISASSEMBLY & REASSEMBLY

COUNTERSHAFT

NOTE — *Before disassembling countershaft, measure and record clearances listed in appropriate table. If clearances are within specifications and no parts are defective, disassembly of countershaft is unnecessary.*

HONDA 4 & 5-SPEED (Cont.)

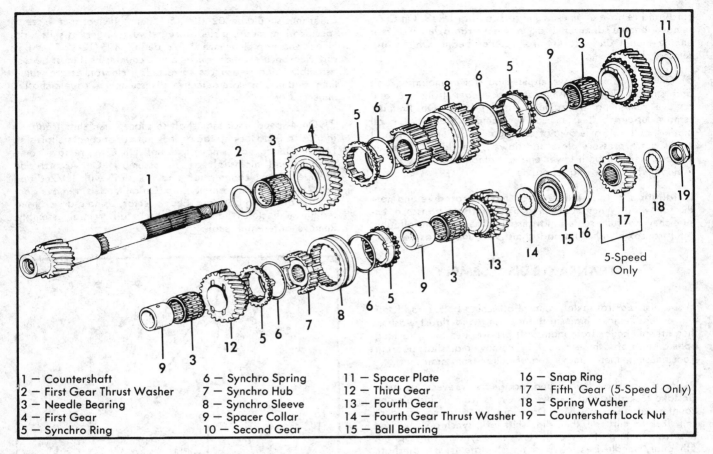

1 — Countershaft	6 — Synchro Spring	11 — Spacer Plate	16 — Snap Ring
2 — First Gear Thrust Washer	7 — Synchro Hub	12 — Third Gear	17 — Fifth Gear (5-Speed Only)
3 — Needle Bearing	8 — Synchro Sleeve	13 — Fourth Gear	18 — Spring Washer
4 — First Gear	9 — Spacer Collar	14 — Fourth Gear Thrust Washer	19 — Countershaft Lock Nut
5 — Synchro Ring	10 — Second Gear	15 — Ball Bearing	

Fig. 4   Exploded View of Civic Countershaft Assembly

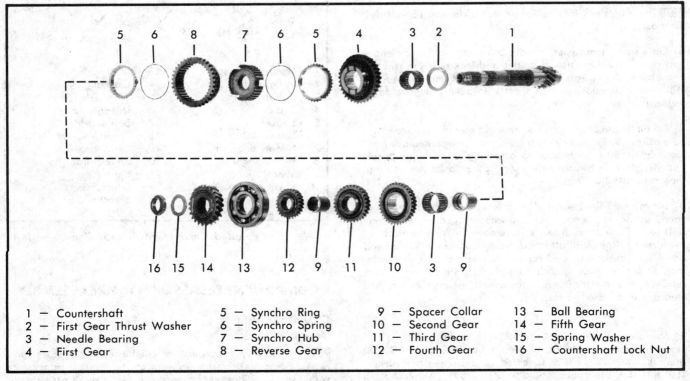

1 — Countershaft	5 — Synchro Ring	9 — Spacer Collar	13 — Ball Bearing
2 — First Gear Thrust Washer	6 — Synchro Spring	10 — Second Gear	14 — Fifth Gear
3 — Needle Bearing	7 — Synchro Hub	11 — Third Gear	15 — Spring Washer
4 — First Gear	8 — Reverse Gear	12 — Fourth Gear	16 — Countershaft Lock Nut

Fig. 5   Exploded View of Accord and Prelude Countershaft Assembly

HONDA 4 & 5-SPEED (Cont.)

Disassembly — If countershaft requires disassembly, remove lock nut and washer, then using a puller, remove ball bearing. Using appropriate illustration as a guide, remove remaining parts from countershaft.

Inspection — Inspect all parts for wear or damage and replace as necessary. Also, place synchro hubs on countershaft and slide them back and forth and ensure they slide freely. Using the appropriate table, measure clearances listed. If clearance is not within specifications, replace part showing greatest wear. With countershaft completely disassembled, measure runout through 2 revolutions. If specification is exceeded, replace shaft. If oil passages are damaged, replace shaft.

Countershaft/Mainshaft Clearance Table (Accord & Prelude)

Application	Specification In. (mm)
Countershaft/Mainshaft Runout①	.0016 (.04) Max.
Synchro Sleeve-to-Gear	
Standard	.033-.043 (.85-1.1)
Limit	.016 (.40)
Shift Fork-to-Sleeve (All)	
Standard	.02-.03 (.40-.47)
Limit	.039 (1.0)
Synchro Sleeve Gap	.268-.271 (6.8-6.9)
Third/Fourth Shift Shaft-to-Guide	.008-.02 (.20-.50)
Third/Fourth Shift Shaft Guide Tab	.469-.472 (11.9-12.0)
First Gear-to-Thrust Washer②	.001-.003 (.03-.08)
Second Gear-to-Third Gear②	
Standard	.0012-.004 (.03-.10)
Limit	.009 (.22)
Second Gear Thickness③	
Standard	1.198-1.2 (30.42-30.47)
Limit	1.192 (30.3)
Third Gear-to-Second Gear②	
Standard	.0012-.0071 (.03-.18)
Limit	.012 (.3)
Third Gear Thickness	
Standard	1.158-1.160 (29.42-29.47)
Limit	1.15 (29.3)
Fourth Gear-to-Spacer Collar②	
Standard	.0012-.0071 (.03-.18)
Limit	.012 (.3)
Fourth Gear Thickness④	
Standard	1.158-1.160 (29.42-29.47)
Limit	1.15 (29.3)
Fifth Gear-to-Spacer Collar	
Standard	.001-.005 (.03-.13)
Limit	.01 (.25)
Fifth Gear Thickness④	
Standard	1.06-1.062 (26.92-26.97)
Limit	1.055 (26.8)

① — Measured through two revolutions.
② — Measured from gear shoulder.
③ — Second gear spacer collar length:
Standard — 1.202-1.203" (30.53-30.55 mm)
Limit — 1.2016" (30.52 mm)
④ — Fourth and fifth gear spacer collar length:
Standard — 1.064-1.066" (27.03-27.08 mm).
Limit — 1.055 (26.8)

Countershaft/Mainshaft Clearance Table (Civic)

Application	Specification In. (mm)
Synchro Sleeve-to-Gear	.0016 (.04) Max.
Synchro Ring-to-Fork	
Standard	.02-.03 (.5-.8)
Limit	.04 (1.0)
Shift Fork End Thickness	
Standard	.25-.26 (6.4-6.6)
Limit	.23 (6.0)
First & Fourth Gear-to-Thrust Washer	
Standard	.0012-.0032 (.03-.08)
Limit	.0071 (.18)
Second & Third Gear-to-Spacer Collar	
Standard	.002-.0048 (.05-.12)
Limit	.0071 (.18)
Fifth Gear-to-Thrust Washer	.002-.016 (.05-.40)

NOTE — *Thrust washers for Accord and Prelude are available in 4 thicknesses: .116-.117" (2.96-2.98 mm), .117-.118" (2.98-3.00 mm), .118-.119" (3.00-3.02 mm) and .119-.120" (3.02-3.04 mm). Thrust washers for Civic are available in 3 thicknesses: .074-.078" (1.89-1.92 mm), .076-.077" (1.92-1.95 mm) and .077-.078" (1.95-1.98 mm). Spacer collars are available for Civic in 3 lengths: 1.104-1.105" (28.04-28.07 mm), 1.105-1.106" (28.07-28.10 mm) and 1.106-1.107" (28.10-28.13 mm).*

Reassembly — Reverse disassembly procedure, using illustrations as guides, and note the following: Coat all parts with oil before reassembling. Ensure correct thickness spacer collars and thrust washers are installed. When assembling synchro sleeve to its respective hub, ensure that the 3 sets of higher teeth (20° apart) on sleeve are aligned with deeper grooves on hub.

MAINSHAFT

Disassembly — If mainshaft requires disassembly, remove lock nut and washer (snap ring on Civic). Using a puller, remove bearing from mainshaft of Civic. Using appropriate illustration as a guide, remove remaining parts from mainshaft.

Inspection — Inspect mainshaft for wear or damage to teeth, splines and bearing journals, and replace complete mainshaft if necessary. Using appropriate table, measure clearances listed. If clearance is not within specifications, replace part showing greatest wear. With mainshaft completely disassembled (Accord and Prelude), measure runout through 2 revolutions. If specification is exceeded, replace shaft. If oil passages are damaged, replace shaft (Accord and Prelude).

Reassembly — Reverse disassembly procedure and note the following: Coat all parts with oil before reassembly and ensure correct thickness spacer collars and thrust washers are installed (if used).

Manual Transaxles

HONDA 4 & 5-SPEED (Cont.)

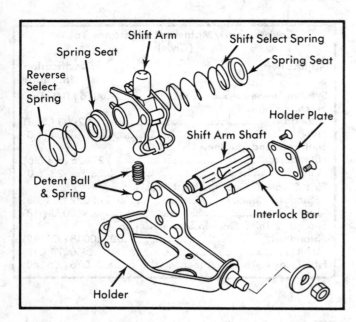

Fig. 6   Exploded View of Civic Gear Selector Assembly

GEAR SELECTOR

Disassembly (Civic) — Using an impact driver, remove holder plate attaching screws. Slide interlock bar from assembly. Pull shift arm shaft out and catch detent ball and spring when they drop from shift arm. Lift shift arm, spring seats and springs from holder.

Reassembly — Position shift arm, spring seats and springs into holder. Invert assembly and install detent ball and spring into bore in shift arm, then hold ball and spring in place and insert shift shaft through arm, seats, and springs. Install interlock bar. Install holder plate and tighten attaching screws, then stake screws in place with a center punch.

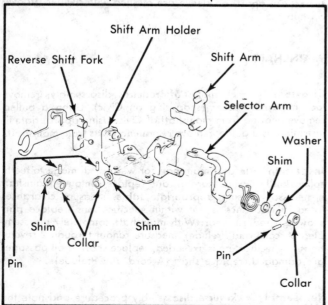

Fig. 7   Exploded View of Accord and Prelude Gear Selector Assembly

Disassembly (Accord & Prelude) — Using an impact driver, remove holder plate attaching screws. Drive out retaining pins, then remove reverse fork, shift arm and selector arm from holder. Measure clearances shown in chart. If any specification is exceeded, replace part showing greatest wear.

Reassembly — To reassemble, reverse disassembly procedure and note the following: If collar-to-shim clearances are not correct, select new shim for reassembly. Shims are available in 5 thicknesses in increments of .008" (.2 mm) ranging from .031" (.8 mm) to .063" (1.6 mm).

Gear Selector Specifications (Accord & Prelude)	
Application	**Specification In. (mm)**
Collar-to-Shim Clearance (All)	.0004-.008 (.01-.20)
Shift Arm-to-Shift Rod Guide	
Standard	.002-.01 (.05-.35)
Limit	.03 (.8)
Shift Rod Guide Slot Diameter	.46-.47 (11.8-12.0)
Selector Arm-to-Shift Rod Guide	
Standard	.002-.01 (.05-.25)
Limit	.02 (.5)
Selector Arm Tab Width	.469-.472 (11.9-12.0)
Shift Arm-to-Shift Guide	
Standard	.004-.012 (.1-.3)
Limit	.02 (.5)
Shift Guide Slot Width	.311-.315 (7.9-8.0)
Selector Arm-to-Interlock	
Standard	.002-.01 (.05-.25)
Limit	.03 (.7)
Selector Arm Finger End Gap	.396-.400 (10.05-10.15)

DIFFERENTIAL

Disassembly — Using a puller, pull bearings from differential housing. Remove attaching bolts (LEFT HAND thread) and lift ring gear from differential. Using a driver, remove pinion gear shaft retaining pin. Remove pinion shaft, pinion gears, side gears and thrust washers from housing.

Reassembly — Reverse disassembly procedure and note the following: Coat all parts with Molykote before reassembly. After reassembly, place differential assembly on blocks and install drive axle shafts. Using a dial indicator, check pinion gear-to-side gear backlash. Backlash should be .003-.006" (.08-.15 mm) for Civic and .002-.010" (.05-.25 mm) for Accord and Prelude. If backlash exceeds .008" (.2 mm) on Civic or .010" (.25 mm) on Accord and Prelude, disassemble differential and install new pinion gear thrust washers of different thickness.

NOTE — Thrust washers must be of an equal thickness. Washers are available in the following thicknesses: .028" (.7 mm), .032" (.8 mm), .035" (.9 mm) for all models and also .039" (1 mm) for Accord and Prelude.

HONDA 4 & 5-SPEED (Cont.)

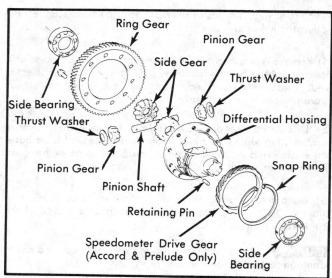

Fig. 8 Exploded View of Differential Assembly

TRANSAXLE REASSEMBLY & ADJUSTMENT

DIFFERENTIAL BEARING PRELOAD

1) Install differential bearing retaining snap ring into position in clutch housing, but do not install oil seals at this time. Place differential assembly into place in clutch housing. Install gasket and transaxle housing to clutch housing, then install all attaching bolts and tighten to specification. Using a hammer and driver, bottom differential assembly in housing.

2) Using a feeler gauge, measure clearance between snap ring and differential side bearing outer race. Clearance should not exceed .006" (.15 mm). If thickness is not within specification, select a new snap ring of appropriate thickness.

NOTE — *Snap rings are available in thicknesses ranging from .096" (2.44 mm) to .116" (2.95 mm) in .004" (0.1 mm) increments.*

TRANSAXLE REASSEMBLY

1) Install differential assembly into clutch housing. Install gear selector assembly onto clutch housing and tighten attaching bolts to specifications. Mesh mainshaft gears with countershaft gears, then install both assemblies into clutch housing. Install suitable holder tool to prevent gear from rotating, then shift transmission into gear and tighten countershaft lock nut to specifications. Stake countershaft lock nut into slot in countershaft, then remove holder tool.

NOTE — *It is extremely critical that countershaft lock nut be tightened to specifications. Overtightening may alter gear clearances, leading to premature wear.*

2) Raise 1st/2nd gear synchro sleeve to 2nd gear position, then install 1st/2nd shift fork. Turn shift fork clockwise and hook fork into gear selector assembly. Install 3rd/4th shift guide on 3rd/4th shift rail and retain with spring pin. Install 3rd/4th shift fork on shift rail, but do not install retaining bolt at this time. Install shift fork and rail into position on clutch housing, then hook shift guide into gear selector assembly. Install 1st/2nd shift rail.

CAUTION — *When installing shift guide shaft on Accord and Prelude, ensure guide shaft does not protrude more than .5" (12 mm) above interlock plate.*

3) On 5-speed transaxles, install 5th gear guide and reverse shift fork on reverse shift rail, then install assembly into position on clutch housing and ensure shift fork is hooked onto gear selector assembly. Install new lock plate on 5th/reverse shift fork, then install shoulder screw and tighten. Bend tab on lock plate against screw head. On 4-speed transaxles, install reverse gear shift guide and shift rail. Install reverse shift fork on stud on gear selector holder and attach special nut and washer.

4) On all transaxles, position reverse idler gear on reverse shift fork and align with idler shaft hole, then install reverse idler gear shaft. Attach 1st/2nd gear shift fork, 3rd/4th shift fork and reverse shift guide (4-speed) to shift rails using new lock plates and shoulder screws, then bend lock plate tabs against screw heads. Install a new gasket on clutch housing, then install 2 dowel pins into holes in clutch housing and tighten attaching bolts.

5) On 5-speed transaxles, install snap ring on countershaft bearing. Install housing spacer and gaskets. Then, with transaxle in reverse position, install thrust washer, needle bearing, 5th gear, synchro ring and spring on mainshaft. Assemble 5th gear synchro hub and sleeve on shift fork and install on transaxle. Attach 5th gear synchro hub and sleeve on shift fork and install on transaxle. Attach 5th gear shift fork to 5th/reverse shift rail by driving in spring pin. Install distance collar on mainshaft with shoulder against synchro hub.

6) On all transaxles, install 3 detent balls, washers, springs and retaining screws into bores in transaxle housing. On 4-speed transaxles, install mainshaft and countershaft bearing snap rings. Tighten mainshaft lock nut (LEFT-HAND threads). Stake shoulder of nut into slot in shaft. Install transaxle cover and tighten attaching bolts.

7) On 5-speed transaxles, install countershaft bearing and transaxle cover. Install split collar into place in groove of

NOTE — *When installing side cover, ensure cover is properly aligned on bearing before tightening bolts.*

8) On all transaxles, install pre-selected differential bearing snap ring into clutch housing. Install differential bearing oil seal into clutch housing with part number on oil seal facing away from snap ring. Install remaining differential bearing oil seal into transaxle housing in the same manner.

TIGHTENING SPECIFICATIONS

Application	Ft. Lbs. (mkg)
Hub Spindle Nut	87-130 (12-18)
Lower Ball Joint	25-33 (3.5-4.5)
Cover-to-Transaxle	7-10 (1.0-1.4)
Transaxle Hsg.-to-Clutch Hsg.	17-23 (2.4-3.2)
Mainshaft Lock Nut	
Accord & Prelude	58-72 (8.0-9.8)
Civic (4-Speed)	33 (4.6)
Countershaft Lock Nut	
Accord & Prelude	58-72 (8.0-9.8)
Civic	65 (9.0)
Ring Gear Attaching Bolts	
Accord & Prelude	67 (9.3)
Civic	72 (10)

PORSCHE 911SC 5-SPEED

DESCRIPTION

The 5-speed transaxle (code 915/63) combines both transmission and differential into a single assembly consisting of 3 sub-assemblies: Front cover, gear housing and transmission/clutch housing. In all gears, power flows from input shaft to pinion shaft through respective gear pairs. Torque is transferred to pinion gear, ring gear and drive axles. Reverse gear power flows from input shaft through reverse idler gear, sliding gear and then to pinion shaft.

LUBRICATION & ADJUSTMENT

See MANUAL TRANSMISSION SERVICING Section.

TRANSAXLE REMOVAL & INSTALLATION

Removal — 1) Transaxle and engine must be removed as a unit, then assemblies separated. Vehicle must be raised and supported with safety stands to remove assembly from below vehicle.

2) Disconnect battery ground cable. Remove engine block vent hose and plug vent hose hole. On A/C equipped vehicles, detach compressor at console but leave hoses connected.

NOTE — Air conditioning system is under pressure. DO NOT unhook hoses unless system is discharged first.

3) Remove relay plate cover and disconnect engine wires at relay plate, adapter plug, relay, socket and ignition control unit. Remove fuel hoses at filter and return line. Disconnect accelerator linkage.

4) Remove rear center tunnel cover in passenger compartment. Remove rubber boot in tunnel by pulling forward over selector rod. Loosen shift rod coupling and pull coupling off of transmission inner shift rod.

5) Disconnect speedometer sensor wires in tunnel. Remove rubber plug with wire plug. Drain crankcase and plug hoses on engine and oil tank. Remove heater hoses at exchangers. Remove rear stabilizer.

6) Disconnect ground strap at body and battery wires at starter. Disconnect accelerator linkage at pedal and clutch cable from transmission.

CAUTION — Be careful when jacking assembly upward not to damage secondary air injection pipes.

7) Place a suitable jack under engine/transmission assembly and apply a little upward pressure to relieve tension on motor mounts. Remove transmission and engine mount bolts. Lower engine/transmission assembly out of vehicle.

CAUTION — Do not move vehicle unless drive shafts are suspended horizontally, to prevent damage to dust covers.

Installation — To install, reverse removal procedure and note the following: Do not clamp heater hoses; slide them onto exchangers just before engine/transmission assembly is in final installation position.

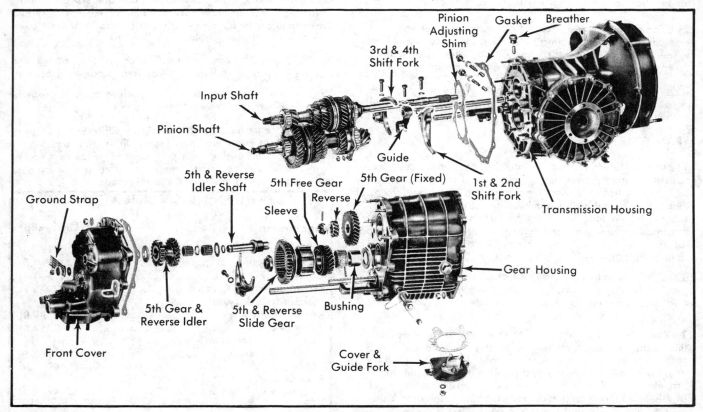

Fig. 1 Exploded View of 911SC 5-Speed Transaxle

PORSCHE 911SC 5-SPEED (Cont.)

TRANSAXLE DISASSEMBLY

GEAR HOUSING

1) Separate engine and transaxle assembly. Mount assembly on suitable stand and lock input shaft in place with special tool (P 37a). Engage 5th gear.

2) Drain lubricant. Remove transaxle front cover. Remove castle nut from input shaft. Remove flange nut from pinion shaft.

3) Identify needle bearing of 5th speed free gear to aid in reassembly. When assembling transmission, needle bearings, gears and other matched parts must be replaced in original positions. Remove guide fork cover and gasket.

4) Remove gear housing nuts (12). Remove housing and selector fork rod (5th and reverse) and fork rod and shaft. It may be necessary to tap gently with mallet to remove assembly from studs.

NOTE — *Shift fork rod for 5th and reverse must be in NEUTRAL position. If not, housing will jam.*

5) Remove 3rd/4th gear detent plug. Take out spring and detent. Remove bolt from 1st/2nd gear selector fork. Spread clamp with screwdriver. Remove input and pinion shaft retaining plates.

6) Remove input and pinion shaft assemblies from case. Shift fork rod for 3rd and 4th gear and shift fork for 1st and 2nd gear should come out with assembly. Remove detent.

7) Remove 1st/2nd shift detent plug and take out spring and detent. Pull out 1st/2nd shift fork rod.

NOTE — *Be sure to make note of number and thickness of shims between transmission housing and retaining plates for reassembly.*

8) To disassemble gear housing, drive shift detents securing roll pins out of respective seats. Drive out half-round dowel pin.

NOTE — *Be sure to remove pins and half-round dowel in order given. Detent parts are under spring tension.*

9) If bearing outer races are to be removed, special tool (US 8050 or equivalent) must be used. Gear housing must be heated to about 250° F (120° C) to drive out races.

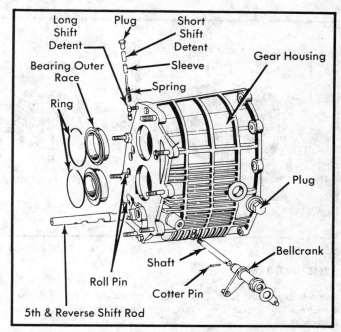

Fig. 2 Exploded View of Gear Housing

INPUT SHAFT

1) Place support plate (P 355a) in a vise and insert input shaft assembly. Remove flange nut with suitable tool (P 252a). Press roller bearing off shaft using thrust plates (VW 401 & 402) and thrust disc (VW 412).

2) Remove remaining parts in order shown in *Fig. 3*. Keep respective gear and needle bearing assemblies together for assembly in original locations.

3) Press roller bearing off input shaft with thrust tube (VW 415a) and press punch (VW 407).

PINION SHAFT

Carefully press roller bearing off pinion shaft using thrust plate (VW 401), disc (VW 412) and tube (P 255a). Remove pinion shaft components. Keep needle bearings and gear pairs together; these parts MUST be installed in original position. Remove speedometer drive gear.

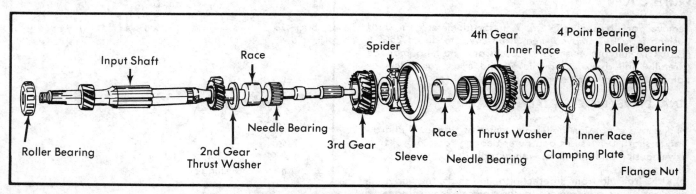

Fig. 3 Exploded View of Input Shaft Assembly

PORSCHE 911SC 5-SPEED (Cont.)

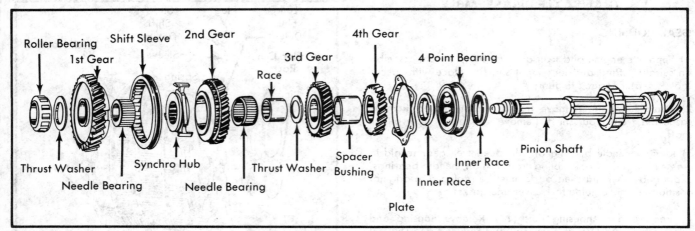

Fig. 4   Exploded View of Pinion Shaft Assembly

SYNCHRONIZERS

Remove clip from gear. Disassemble as shown in *Fig. 5 & Fig. 6*. Check all parts for wear or damage and replace as necessary.

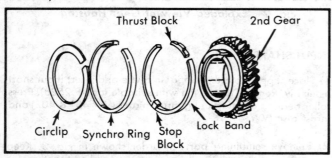

Fig. 5   Exploded View of 2nd Gear Synchronizer

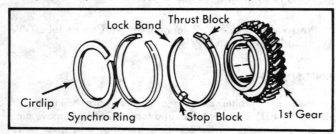

Fig. 6   Exploded View of 1st Gear Synchronizer

FRONT COVER

Remove parts as shown in *Fig. 7*. If speedometer gear shaft bushing is to be removed, heat front cover to about 250° F (120° C). Pull out bushing. If necessary, bushing may be carefully drilled out. Clean cover and check for cracks or damage. Replace parts as necessary.

FINAL DRIVE (DIFFERENTIAL)

1) Remove expansion bolt from center of flange. Withdraw flange shaft. Drive seals and outer bearing races out of final drive housing and side cover with suitable drift.

2) Drive roll pin from differential pinion shaft, then drive pinion shaft out and remove anchor piece. Remove tapered roller bearing with suitable puller and thrust piece (P 263).

Puller arms must fit through openings in magnetic carrier disc to remove bearing from side opposite ring gear.

3) Do not interchange spacer washers and shims. Right and left side must be kept separate and installed in original positions. Remove lock plates from ring gear retaining bolts. Remove bolts and ring gear.

FINAL DRIVE HOUSING

1) Remove adjusting lever spring and circlip. Pull adjusting lever off shaft and disengage auxiliary spring while pressing clutch release lever toward front transmission cover. Drive release lever shaft and bushings from housing.

2) Remove snap ring of input shaft bearing race. Bearing must first be driven slightly away from snap ring with soft punch.

3) Heat differential housing to about 250° F (120° C), and drive out both bearing races using suitable thrust blocks (US 8050 and P 254d).

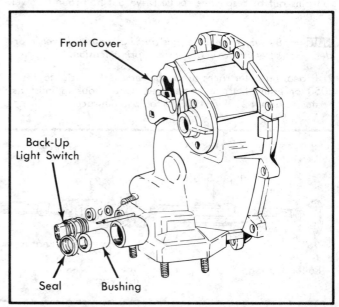

Fig. 7   Exploded View of Front Cover Assembly

PORSCHE 911SC 5-SPEED (Cont.)

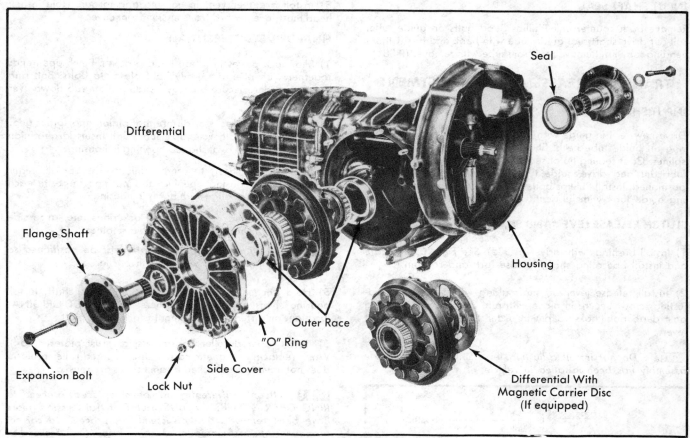

Fig. 8   Exploded View of Final Drive and Housing

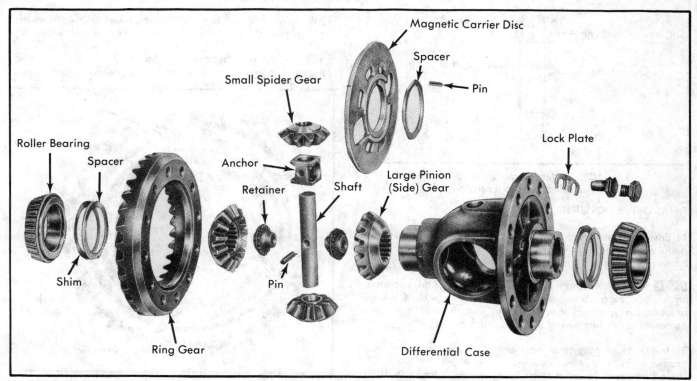

Fig. 9   Exploded View of Ring Gear and Carrier Assembly

PORSCHE 911SC 5-SPEED (Cont.)

INPUT SHAFT SEAL

Remove both countersunk Phillips head bolts on guide tube. Pull out drive shaft seal guide tube with hook and bar without bending tube lip. Remove seal from tube with remover (P 381).

TRANSAXLE REASSEMBLY & ADJUSTMENT

INPUT SHAFT SEAL

Drive new seal in guide with installer (P 381). Install new "O" ring on guide tube neck. Slide tube (P 382) over input shaft splines. Coat sealing lip of seal and "O" ring with light coat of lubricant and drive guide tube into housing until correctly positioned. Install Phillips bolts and tighten. Coat release bearing guide tube with lubricant for reassembly.

CLUTCH RELEASE LEVER AND SHAFT

1) Install bushings with driver (P 375). *See Fig. 10.* Lubricate and install operating shaft, release fork and roll pin.

2) Install release lever on shaft along with spring and adjusting screw. Secure in place with pin. Snap auxiliary spring past dead point to stop pin in order to pre-tension against lever.

NOTE — *Do not install adjusting lever until after transaxle assembly has been installed in vehicle.*

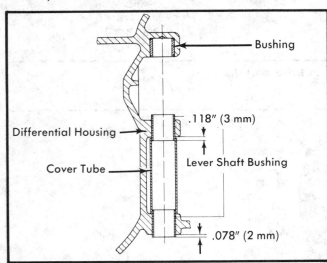

Fig. 10 Clutch Lever Shaft Bushing Installation and Location

FINAL DRIVE HOUSING

1) Ensure all parts are clean and dry. If pinion shaft or ring gear was damaged or broken, check center web bearing bores for cracks or damage. Replace housing if necessary.

NOTE — *Do not clean pressure-cast housings in corrosive liquids as magnesium alloy will be damaged. Cleaned pressure-cast housings must be treated with seasonal corrosion preservatives of bitumen or wax base such as TECTYL.*

2) Install snap ring securing input shaft bearing race into groove in housing. Heat housing to about 250° F (120° C). Drive both bearing outer races into place with tool (US 8050 or equivalent).

3) Install breather vent in housing and torque. Hole in hex head must face toward transmission front cover.

FINAL DRIVE (DIFFERENTIAL)

1) Slide lock plates into bolt head grooves. Pinch open ends together with pliers to firmly hold plates to bolts. Bolt ring gear to carrier. Secure bolts by bending plate tab down over corner of bolt head.

2) Coat thrust surfaces of differential pinion and spider gear with Molykote or other suitable lubricant. Insert large pinion side gears through oval shaped opening in housing.

3) Insert flange shafts to center pinions. Insert small spider gears through housing opening and position opposite each other so that bores align with bores in housing.

4) Install threaded retainers with lock rings into large side gears. Slide anchor between threaded retainers.

CAUTION — *Differential pinion shaft must be positioned so pinion shaft hole aligns with hole in anchor.*

5) Hold anchor in place and drive in pinion shaft. Install bearing shims and spacer washers in CORRECT ORIGINAL locations on differential housing. Install anchor pin.

6) Install tapered roller bearing using thrust plate (P 264). When replacing magnetic carrier disc, tapered roller preload does not have to be checked if same shims are reused.

NOTE — *If only differential has been replaced, proceed to RING GEAR & PINION ADJUSTMENT. If transmission gears have been removed and disassembled, proceed to correct assembly steps for remainder of transmission, then proceed to adjustment.*

SYNCHRONIZERS

1) Place synchro ring on clutch carrier; rough ring surfaces facing shift sleeve. Insert thrust block, stop block and lock band(s).

NOTE — *First gear synchro ring has only 1 lock band. Also, 1st gear synchro ring is identified by a groove on both sides.*

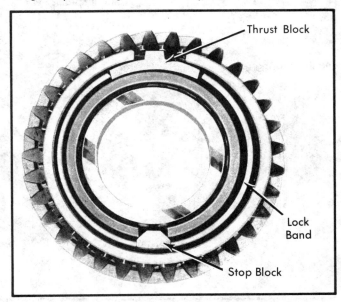

Fig. 11 Second Gear Synchronizer

PORSCHE 911SC 5-SPEED (Cont.)

2) Single lock band must be inserted with recess facing outward to accomodate small stop block. Stop block is directly opposite longer thrust block on 2nd gear synchro. Small stop block for 1st gear synchro is slightly offset and is bevelled on one side only. Install circlip after lock band, stop and thrust blocks are installed.

3) Maximum clearance between selector fork and shifting sleeve of 1st through 5th speed is .02" (.5 mm). Free diameter of synchro rings should be as follows:

1st gear .... 3.43" (87.1 mm)
2nd gear .... 3.47" (88.1 mm)
3rd, 4th & 5th gear .... 3.07" (78.0 mm)

INPUT SHAFT

1) Ensure all parts are dry and that there is no oil between contact surfaces. Press roller bearing on input shaft with thrust disc (VW 412) and thrust tube (VW 416b).

2) Install parts in order shown in *Fig. 3*. Be sure that needle bearings are installed with the same gears they were removed with.

3) Press roller bearing on end of input shaft with thrust plate (VW 401) and punch (VW 407). Torque flange nut to correct specification. Peen flange nut in place with punch.

4) Measure input shaft runout. Maximum allowable runout is .004" (.1 mm). If runout does not exceed .012" (.3 mm), it is possible to carefully straighten shaft with press and "V" blocks.

PINION SHAFT

1) All parts must be dry and free of oil. Pinion shaft and ring gear are marked with paired numbers. Check that these numbers match before assembly. Press roller bearing on pinion shaft with press punch (VW 407) and tube (VW 415a).

2) Bearing must be installed so ring of two-part bearing cage faces gears. Assemble parts on shaft as shown in *Fig. 4*. Press on final roller bearing with thrust disc (VW 412) and sleeve (VW 244b).

NOTE — *Asymmetrical pointed teeth of 1st/2nd synchro operating sleeve must face toward 1st gear wheel.*

3) Heat speedometer drive gear to about 250° F (120° C). Drive gear on.

GEAR HOUSING

1) Heat housing to about 250° F (120° C). Drive bearing outer races in position with tool (US 8050). Race with larger INSIDE diameter corresponds to pinion (lower) shaft. Race with smaller INSIDE diameter matches with input shaft.

2) Install 5th/reverse shift rod. Insert long shift detent. Drive in roll pin. Install spring and sleeve. Apply tension with special tool (P 366) and drive in roll pin. Release tension. Insert pin and short shift detent. Drive in plug.

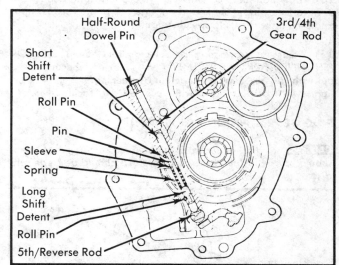

*Fig. 12   Cross-Sectional View
Showing Detent Positions*

INPUT & PINION ASSEMBLY-TO-HOUSING

1) Install same number and thickness of shims on transmission housing studs as noted during disassembly. Also determined by adjusting the pinion. Insert 1st/2nd gear selector fork rod.

2) If removed, insert 1st/2nd gear shift detent and spring. Torque bolt. Install pinion shaft with 1st/2nd gear selector fork so that pinion rests lightly in bearing race of transmission/differential housing. Slightly open selector fork clamping piece to prevent fork from binding on fork rod.

3) Insert input shaft and press into place with pinion shaft assembly. Torque clamping plate nuts to specification.

4) Lightly tighten 1st/2nd gear selector fork bolt. Insert detent from top. Unscrew 3rd/4th gear selector fork and clamping piece bolts. Push fork and clamping piece back. Install selector fork and rod.

5) Lightly tighten fork and clamp bolts. If not already done, insert detent and spring and torque plug. Adjust selector forks at this time. *See SELECTOR (SHIFTING) FORK ADJUSTMENT in this article.*

6) Install housing gasket on studs. Install gear housing with 5th/reverse gear selector fork rod and shaft. Torque correctly. Push fork rod in ball sleeve and selector shaft into shift pawl guides. Install guide fork cover, gasket and tighten.

7) Install idler gear shaft turning shaft until pin in housing stops rotation. Install reverse gear and start castle nut on threads. Install thrust washer for 5th (free) gear. Install 5th (free) gear needle bearing.

8) Install guide sleeve for 5th/reverse gear and start flange nut on threads. Install thrust needle bearing cage, idler gear with needle bearing cages, intermediate piece and thrust washer on idler shaft.

9) Slide 5th gear and reverse sliding gear with fork onto guide sleeve and selector fork rod. Open clamping piece on fork slightly for easier assembly. Lightly tighten selector fork bolt.

PORSCHE 911SC 5-SPEED (Cont.)

10) Apply light coat of oil to "O" ring and install. Use tool (P 37a) to block input shaft and engage 5th gear. Torque input and pinion shaft nuts to specification.

11) Adjust 5th/reverse gear selector fork. See *SELECTOR (SHIFTING) FORK ADJUSTMENT in this article.* Secure castle nut with roll pin. Secure flange nut by peening. Install back-up light switch actuating pin with recessed end facing switch.

RING GEAR & PINION ADJUSTMENT

CAUTION — *Unit must be assembled correctly. Front cover should not be installed at this time. Parts should be clean and dry.*

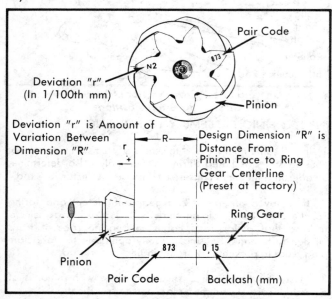

Fig. 13 Ring and Pinion Identification

1) Deviation "r" must be added to design dimension "R" to obtain adjusting dimension. Attach input and pinion shafts, without shims, to final drive housing with clamping plates.

2) Tighten flange nut on input shaft to proper torque before taking measurements. Install special plate (P 260a). Assemble 5th speed gears with synchro hub and shifting sleeve. Engage 5th gear. Block input shaft with special holder (P 37a). Torque flange nut to specification.

3) Move adjustable collar of universal setting gauge (VW-385) to 2.047" (52 mm) from center of contact plunger hole and tighten in position. Assemble gauge blocks (VW 385/4) on gauge shaft and screw contact plunger (VW 385/53) into place. Using knurled knob on opposite end of shaft from dial indicator, turn adjustable collar back to stop.

4) Adjust dial indicator to 0 with a .039" (1 mm) preload using master gauge (VW 385/52). This sets design dimension "R" of 2.61" (66.3 mm). Place magnetic setting pad (VW 385/17) on pinion face and insert setting gauge in gear housing with knurled adjusting knob on side toward housing cover. Dial indicator extension must be oriented toward setting pad.

5) Install side cover without "O" ring and tighten nuts evenly to specified torque. Turn knurled knob to adjust gauge block against bearing race until gauge shaft can just be turned by

hand. Note maximum clockwise deflection of dial indicator (when extension is perpendicular to pad on pinion shaft end). Use the following example to determine shim thickness:

EXAMPLE CALCULATION

Design value (R) set in indicator .... 2.610″(66.30 mm)
Minus indicated reading .... .011″ (.28 mm)
Equals distance to pinion shaft face .... 2.599″ (66.02 mm)

Adjustment value (R+r) .... 2.618″ (66.50 mm)
Minus distance to pinion shaft .... 2.599″ (66.01 mm)
Equals SHIM THICKNESS .... .019″ (.49 mm)

6) Shims are available in thicknesses of .004", .006" and .008" (.10, .15 & .20 mm). Any combination of shims up to .020" (.50 mm) may be used.

7) After installing correct shims, recheck adjustment value. Deviation of .001" (.03 mm) is allowable. No gear tooth contact pattern check is required.

8) To determine ring gear spacer thickness, proceed as follows: Side bearing outer races must be fully seated in housing and side cover. Install .138" (3.5 mm) spacer (S1) on ring gear side beneath side bearing. Install a .118" (3.0 mm) spacer (S2) on opposite side beneath other bearing.

9) Place differential with side bearings in housing. Install side cover with oil seal. DO NOT install side cover gasket at this time. Do not tighten.

10) Lightly tighten side cover with 2 nuts opposite each other to preload side bearings. Measure clearance between cover and housing with feeler gauge. Clearance should be about .006" (.15 mm) if bearings are correctly preloaded.

11) Replace spacer (S1) until correct clearance is obtained. Now tighten side cover to correct torque with all nuts (12). Install washer from tool (P 357) on U-axle flange. Slightly tighten expansion bolt.

12) Be sure pinion shaft is disengaged and side cover oil seal is removed to obtain accurate torque reading when rotating differential. Use an INCH lb. torque wrench and measure drag of assembled differential. Drag for SKF type bearings should be 22-30 INCH lbs. (25-35 cmkg). Drag for FAG type bearings should be 35-57 INCH lbs. (40-65 cmkg).

13) If differential drag is not within specifications, replace spacer washer and recheck. Remove differential and pull off both side bearings.

14) DO NOT interchange spacer washers after removal. Measure thickness of both spacers with micrometer. Add these measurements to obtain total spacer thickness for ring gear adjustment.

NOTE — *In order to check backlash correctly, spacer (S1) should be .004" (.1 mm) thinner than one half the sum of spacers (S1) and (S2). Spacer (S2) should be .004" (.1 mm) thicker than one half the total thickness of (S1) and (S2).*

RING GEAR BACKLASH

1) Install gear cluster with shims determined during pinion shaft adjustment. Be sure to tighten pinion shaft flange nut if not already done.

PORSCHE 911SC 5-SPEED (Cont.)

2) Install differential with side bearings and correct shims (S1) and (S2). Install side cover with oil seal. Lubricate oil seal lip.

CAUTION — *Be sure that some side clearance exists between housing and side cover, as cover nuts are being tightened. Do not allow pinion to jam.*

3) Tighten side cover nuts to specifications. Block pinion shaft with holder (P 259a).

4) Place washer from tool (P 357) onto axle flange. Mount dial indicator with sensor (P 259b). Attach dial indicator over axle flange. Be sure dial indicator has a slight preload.

5) Move dial indicator holder back and forth. Read backlash on dial. Rotate ring gear about 90° and measure backlash again. Readings must not vary by more than .002″ (.05 mm). Backlash tolerance is .0047″ (.12 mm) to .007″ (.18 mm). Compare reading with desired backlash recorded on ring gear.

6) Replace spacers (S1) and (S2) as necessary to obtain correct backlash. Use special tools (P 263 & 264b).

CAUTION — *Exchange spacers, but do not change TOTAL spacer thickness.*

7) When adjustment is completed, remove all special tools from housing. Install differential and gasket, and torque side cover to specifications.

SELECTOR (SHIFTING) FORK ADJUSTMENT

1) Input shaft flange nut must be correctly torqued. Install mounting plate (P 260a). Install 5th gear synchro hub and reverse sliding gear.

2) Block input shaft with tool (P 37a). Engage 5th gear. Torque input shaft flange nut. Turn 1st/2nd gear selector fork rod LEFT (in driving direction) to stop.

3) Turn fork rod slightly back until unmachined flat inner surface is nearly vertical. Do not turn past middle point or back to right stop.

4) Position 1st/2nd gear selector fork so that shift sleeve is exactly in middle between synchronizing rings. Tighten bolt to proper torque. Adjust 3rd/4th gear fork in same way.

5) Position 3rd/4th gear shift guide even with selector fork. Be sure there is .08-.12″ (2-3 mm) clearance between 3rd/4th shift guide and 1st/2nd shift guide. They must not touch. Check ease of shifting and readjust as necessary.

6) Adjust 5th/reverse gear fork as follows: Push idler gear on shaft against 5th (fixed) gear. Adjust idler gear and sliding gear to obtain a clearance of .040″ (1 mm) in NEUTRAL position.

7) Press idler gear gently in direction of travel. There should be no play between shift fork and sliding gear groove. Tighten selector fork bolt to proper torque.

FRONT COVER

Heat cover to about 250°F (120°C) and drive gear shift bushing in place. Drive shift rod seal on with suitable mandrel (P 369). Install new gasket and torque front cover nuts to specifications.

TIGHTENING SPECIFICATIONS

Application	Ft. Lbs. (mkg)
Side & Front Cover Nuts	16-18 (2.2-2.4)
Guide Fork Cover Nuts	16-18 (2.2-2.4)
Input Shaft Flange Nut	116-130 (16-18)
Input Shaft Castle Nut	87-101 (12-14)
Retaining Plate & Trans. Support Attachment	15-17 (2.1-2.4)
Pinion Shaft Flange Nut	174-188 (24-26)
Guide Fork Nut	6-7 (.8-.9)
Shift Detent Nut	11-13 (1.5-1.8)
Shift Fork Nuts	17-19 (2.4-2.6)
Ring Gear Bolts	83-87 (11.5-12.0)
Ring Gear Bolts (Self-Locking Differential)	
Grade 11.9	101-109 (14-15)
Grade 12.9	109-116 (15-16)
Expansion Bolt	19-22 (2.6-3.0)
Starter Nut	33-35 (4.6-4.8)
Front Relief Valve Plug	16-18 (2.2-2.4)

PORSCHE 924 5-SPEED

DESCRIPTION

The Porsche 924 is equipped with a manual transaxle (type 016/9) with a 5-speed transmission mounted in front of the final drive. Transaxle is a 3-piece case, consisting of rear cover, gear carrier and transmission case. Engine and transaxle are connected by a strong central tube which also houses the propeller shaft and supports the gearshift lever. Flanges at each end of central tube attach to clutch housing and transaxle. Propeller shaft is splined to clutch disc at the front and is connected to transmission mainshaft at the rear by a coupling. Access to this coupling is through an inspection hole in rear of central tube. A hypoid ring and pinion differential assembly drives double-jointed rear axle drive shafts. Complete drive train is mounted to unitized body by 2 front engine mounts and 2 rear transaxle mounts.

LUBRICATION & ADJUSTMENT

See *MANUAL TRANSMISSION SERVICING Section.*

SERVICE (IN VEHICLE)

FLANGED SHAFT SEAL

Removal — Disconnect inner CV joint from drive flange and support drive axle out of the way. Insert a long drift punch in 1 drive flange hole to prevent drive flange movement, then remove drive flange retaining bolt. Place a drip pan under transmission housing and pull out drive flange. Pry out oil seal.

Installation — Lightly lubricate seal lips and fully seat seal with driver (VW195). Install drive flange and tighten drive flange retaining bolt. Install drive axle and tighten bolts. Check and add lubricant to transaxle, if required.

REAR WHEEL BEARINGS

Removal — Remove brake drum and wheel. Disconnect drive shaft from axle flange. Press shaft from housing with double arm puller. Pry seal out of housing, remove circlip and drive grooved ball bearing and roller bearing out with soft drift.

Installation — Press grooved ball bearing in inner end of housing and replace circlip. Put spacer in housing and drive roller bearing in place (flanged side facing out). Install seal in inboard side of housing. Place outer spacer on shaft and press in along with bearing inner race, using castellated nut and suitable driver. See *Fig. 2.*

AXLE DRIVE SHAFTS

NOTE — *Axle drive shafts should be disassembled ONLY to replace defective rubber boots. If boots are replaced, check all components for wear or damage and replace as complete assembly.*

Disassembly — Assure boot and CV joint areas are clean. Remove clamp holding boot onto shaft and drive protective cap off CV joint. Remove circlip from end of axle. Press CV joint from shaft. Disassemble and inspect CV joint. See *Fig. 3.*

NOTE — *Ball hubs and joints are matched sets. DO NOT interchange any balls, hubs or joints between CV joints.*

Reassembly — Coat all parts with suitable lubricant and assemble joint. Check for smooth operation throughout entire range of travel. Press CV joint assembly onto axle splines with chamfered side facing bearing collar. Pack 1.6 oz. (45 grams) of molybdenum disulfide grease into each side of joint. Reinstall circlip, protective cap, boot and clamp.

REMOVAL & INSTALLATION

TRANSAXLE

Removal — 1) Detach exhaust pipe from catalytic converter and loosen exhaust holding brackets at central tube. Remove muffler clamp from transaxle end plate and remove entire converter and muffler assembly.

2) Push shift linkage dust boot back and remove lock wire from shift linkage connecting bolt. Remove connecting bolt.

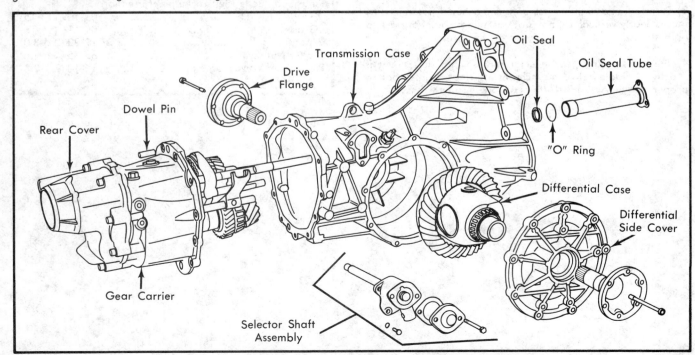

Fig. 1   Exploded View of Porsche 924 5-Speed Transaxle Assembly

PORSCHE 924 5-SPEED (Cont.)

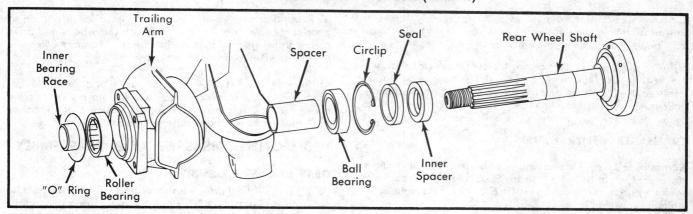

Fig. 2 Exploded View of Axle Drive Shaft and Wheel Bearing Assembly

From inside vehicle, fold back dust boot and inner cover on shift lever. Remove clamp from shift lever knob, then remove knob.

3) Remove circlip holding selector rod to shift lever. Pull shift rod and spring washer from shift lever pin. Turn shift lever 180° and tilt out to right. Press down on rubber seal between central tube and tunnel. Slide selector rod forward in tunnel about 12" (300 mm) to clear linkage at rear.

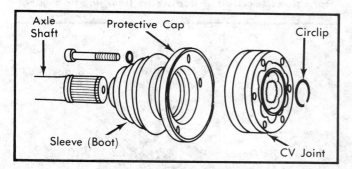

Fig. 3 Exploded View of Constant Velocity Joint

4) Remove plug from rear of central tube housing. Push shift rod protective tube back far enough so shift rod tube is outside central tube housing. Remove inspection plugs (1 located at bottom of central tube housing; the other on upper left side of transmission case). Remove propeller shaft-to-mainshaft coupling screws through inspection holes. Slide coupling back toward transmission case. See Fig. 4.

5) Detach axle shafts from transaxle and suspend from car in horizontal position. Disconnect wires from back-up light switch. Place a jack with transmission adapter (US 618 and 618/1) under transmission and raise slightly to release pressure from transmission suspension.

6) Remove transmission-to-central tube housing flange bolts. Remove transaxle mount bolts. Lower transaxle assembly and central tube until central tube rests on rear axle cross tube. Remove transaxle out rear.

Installation — 1) To install, reverse removal procedure and note the following: Before installing transaxle, check propeller shaft protrusion at rear flange. Shaft should extend .492-.531" (12.5-13.5 mm) beyond flange lips. Make small corrections by tapping end of shaft with soft-faced hammer.

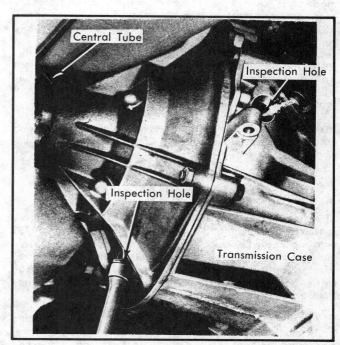

Fig. 4 Removing Propeller Shaft-to-Mainshaft Coupling Screws Through Inspection Holes

2) After installation, adjust shift linkage as follows: Place transmission in neutral and install intermediate shift lever with

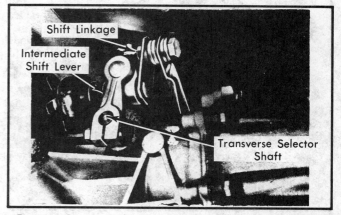

Fig. 5 Correct Adjustment Position of Shift Linkage

PORSCHE 924 5-SPEED (Cont.)

a 5° rearward offset from center of shaft. Ensure shift lever is in neutral, then move shift lever base to adjust shift lever to an 85° angle from rear of central tube.

3) With shift lever in neutral, the transverse selector shaft will be held in 3rd/4th gear (middle shift pattern) by spring pressure. With shift linkage connected and adjusted properly, shift lever will not lean to either side. If shift lever leans to either side, adjust at intermediate shift lever. See Fig. 5.

TRANSAXLE (CENTRAL) TUBE

Removal — 1) With transaxle assembly removed from vehicle, disconnect negative battery strap. Suspend engine from front eyelet with support fixture (VW10-222) and hold tight in installation position.

2) Support tube at front tunnel reinforcing brace with locally made block. Detach central tube from clutch housing. Remove rear reinforcement strut, then loosen rear axle mountings and lower torsion bar tube. Pull selector rod rearward. Remove central tube by lowering and pulling out to rear.

Inspection — Check for free rotation of central tube bearings by turning propeller shaft by hand. Shaft must turn easily without binding. If bearings or shaft are damaged, central tube with shaft and bearings must be replaced.

Installation — To install, reverse removal procedure and check propeller shaft protrusion. Check and adjust shift linkage.

TRANSAXLE DISASSEMBLY

1) Mount transaxle in holding fixture (VW540) and drain oil. Loosen bolts on mainshaft oil seal tube. Mount remover (9113) onto mainshaft keyway. Loosen tube with offset screwdriver and remove tube. Drive out seal with screwdriver. Remove selector shaft assembly. Remove transmission case-to-gear carrier bolts, drive out dowel pins and separate gear carrier from transmission case.

2) Mount gear carrier in soft-jawed vise with rear cover facing up. Remove cap from end of rear cover by driving a screwdriver into center of cap and prying up. Remove bolt from end of mainshaft.

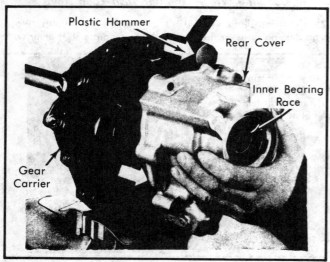

Fig. 6　Removing Rear Cover from Gear Carrier

3) Reposition gear carrier in vise, clamping lower portion of gear carrier housing. Remove cover attaching bolts and drive cover from gear carrier with plastic hammer. Remove mainshaft inner bearing race half.

4) Remove drive flange retaining bolt and drive flange. Remove final drive cover attaching bolts and pry cover from housing using 2 screwdrivers. DO NOT lose magnet on rear of final drive cover. Remove differential assembly.

COMPONENT DISASSEMBLY & REASSEMBLY

GEAR CARRIER ASSEMBLY

CAUTION — If final drive housing or pinion bearings are to be replaced and deviation "r" is not marked on ring gear, position of pinion shaft must be measured before removing gear assembly. See Drive Pinion Depth adjustment under Transaxle Reassembly & Adjustment in this article.

Disassembly — 1) Remove 5th gear clutch hub and 2nd half of mainshaft bearing inner race with puller and adapter (US 1078 & VW431). Remove 5th gear synchronizer ring. Support selector rod with a hammer to prevent damage to selector rod bore, then drive out 5th gear shift fork roll pin.

2) Remove snap ring from mainshaft, then remove 5th gear with synchro hub, needle bearing and 5th gear shift fork (5th gear/reverse selector rod remains in housing). Remove 5th gear/reverse selector rod stop screws from side of housing.

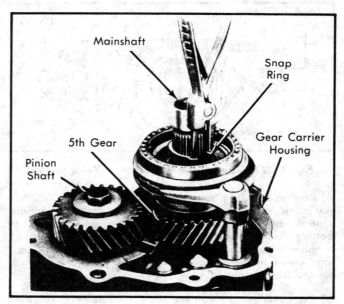

Fig. 7　Removing Snap Ring Retaining 5th Gear Components on Mainshaft

3) Clamp 4th gear/pinion shaft in soft-jawed vise and remove bolt from pinion shaft. Remove 5th gear from pinion shaft with puller. Remove adjusting shim.

4) Reposition gear carrier in vise by clamping carrier housing. Drive out 1st/2nd gear selector fork roll pin, while supporting with hammer. Turn selector fork up and drive out roll pin for 3rd/4th shift fork, while supporting with hammer. Pull out 3rd/4th selector rod (shift fork remains in synchro hub) without losing small interlock pin. Loosen reverse gear relay lever screw.

PORSCHE 924 5-SPEED (Cont.)

5) Partially pull out pinion shaft and mainshaft. Remove mainshaft assembly with 3rd/4th gear shift fork attached. Pull pinion shaft out far enough to remove 1st/2nd selector rod and shift fork. Swing out pinion shaft, clearing reverse gear.

Reassembly — 1) Insert interlock pins in correct position in carrier case bore. Insert springs and plungers for 1st through 4th gear detent. Insert reverse gear detent plunger and spring. Install 5th/reverse selector rod and relay lever. Press relay lever in direction of arrow shown in *Fig. 8* until lever rests on selector rod and in groove of gear.

2) Tighten adjusting screw against stop on threaded bushing. Press relay lever against screw and loosen screw until tip of threads can be heard to engage in threaded bushing. Tighten screw to 25 ft. lbs. (3.4 mkg). Select reverse gear several times and check that relay lever moves easily in all positions. Relay lever should be centered over reverse gear detent.

Fig. 8   Adjusting Reverse Relay Lever

3) Engage pinion shaft with reverse gear and partially insert pinion shaft into gear carrier. Install 1st/2nd gear shift fork and selector rod, then press pinion shaft into housing. Push 3rd/4th gear shift fork onto 5th/reverse gear selector rod.

4) Press off mainshaft inner bearing race, then partially install mainshaft into housing. Insert 3rd/4th gear shift fork into clutch sleeve and press mainshaft into housing until fully seated. Move selector rods into neutral position and check for proper position of interlock pins.

5) Install 3rd/4th gear shift rod and insert small interlock pin (coated with grease). Secure 3rd/4th and 1st/2nd gear shift forks and selector rods with roll pins. Install selector rod stop screws into carrier housing using new gaskets.

6) Position gear carrier assembly in soft-jawed vise, with jaws clamped on 4th gear of pinion shaft. Using a depth gauge, measure dimension "A" as shown in *Fig. 9* to determine correct 5th gear adjusting shim to install. Select correct 5th gear adjusting shim using the following table:

Pinion Shaft 5th Gear Adjusting Shim Chart	
If "A" Is **In. (mm)**	**Use This Shim** **In. (mm)**
.331-.339 (8.4-8.6)	.043 (1.1)
.343-.350 (8.7-8.9)	.055 (1.4)
.354-.362 (9.0-9.2)	.067 (1.7)
.366-.374 (9.3-9.5)	.079 (2.0)
.378-.386 (9.6-9.8)	.091 (2.3)

NOTE — *See Fig. 9 for Dimension "A" measurement.*

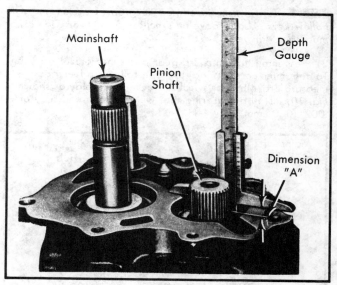

Fig. 9   Measuring Dimension for Selection of 5th Gear Pinion Shaft Adjusting Shim

7) Install selected 5th gear adjusting shim, then heat 5th gear to 250°F (120°C) and slide onto pinion shaft until seated. Install washer and bolt on end of pinion shaft and tighten bolt. Collar of washer must face pinion head.

8) Clamp mainshaft in soft-jawed vise so that mainshaft and pinion shaft are vertical. Heat mainshaft bearing inner race to 250°F (120°C) and slide it onto mainshaft until seated.

9) Install 5th gear with synchronizer hub, needle bearing and shift rod onto mainshaft. Install shift fork roll pin into fork and selector rod. Select a snap ring that will provide a maximum mainshaft end play of .002" (.05 mm), then install snap ring into mainshaft groove.

NOTE — *Mainshaft snap rings are available in following thicknesses: .050" (1.35 mm), .055" (1.40 mm) and .060" (1.45 mm).*

10) Install 5th gear synchronizer ring. Heat 5th gear clutch hub to 250°F (120°C) and install it on mainshaft until fully seated. Drive on mainshaft bearing inner race, then install guide sleeve and new gasket on gear carrier housing. Install rear cover on carrier housing.

11) Heat other half of mainshaft bearing inner race and drive onto mainshaft. Install washer and bolt on end of mainshaft and tighten bolt. Install and tighten rear cover mounting bolts. Install new rear cover cap.

PORSCHE 924 5-SPEED (Cont.)

MAINSHAFT ASSEMBLY

Disassembly — Remove snap ring from end of shaft. Remove 4th gear thrust washer, 4th gear, 4th gear needle bearings, synchronizer ring and snap ring. Using a press, press off 3rd gear, synchronizer ring, 3rd/4th gear synchro assembly and 3rd gear needle bearing.

Reassembly — 1) Inspect all components for wear or damage and replace as necessary. Install 3rd gear needle bearing onto mainshaft. Place synchro assembly, 3rd gear synchro ring and 3rd gear in correct relationship atop each other.

NOTE — *Turn synchronizer ring so grooves are in line with hollow keys. Also, groove on synchronizer hub or wide collar must face 4th gear.*

2) Press mainshaft into 3rd gear and synchronizer assembly. To determine correct snap ring to install, use a feeler gauge to measure 3rd/4th gear synchronizer hub end play as shown in Fig. 10. Install a snap ring that will allow an end play of 0-.002" (0-.05 mm).

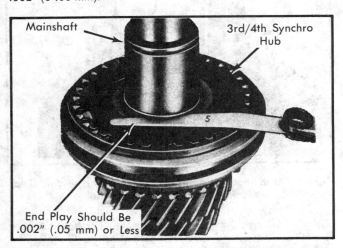

Fig. 10 *Checking 3rd/4th Gear Synchronizer Hub End Play*

NOTE — *Snap rings for 3rd/4th synchronizer hub end play adjustments are available in the following thicknesses: .059" (1.59 mm), .061" (1.56 mm) and .064" (1.62 mm).*

3) Install synchronizer ring on 4th gear side of synchronizer hub, then install 4th gear needle bearing, 4th gear, thrust washer and snap ring. Measure clearance between thrust washer and snap ring. Clearance should be .008-.013" (.20-.35 mm). If not, correct by installing a different thickness snap ring.

NOTE — *Snap rings for 4th gear end play adjustment are available in the following thicknesses: .065" (1.65 mm), .067" (1.70 mm) and .069" (1.75 mm).*

PINION SHAFT

Disassembly — 1) Mount pinion shaft assembly into a suitable holding fixture. Using a press, remove small inner bearing and 1st gear by pressing from shaft.

2) Remove 1st gear needle bearing and synchro ring. Remove snap ring, then press off 1st/2nd gear synchro hub assembly, 2nd gear synchro ring and 2nd gear.

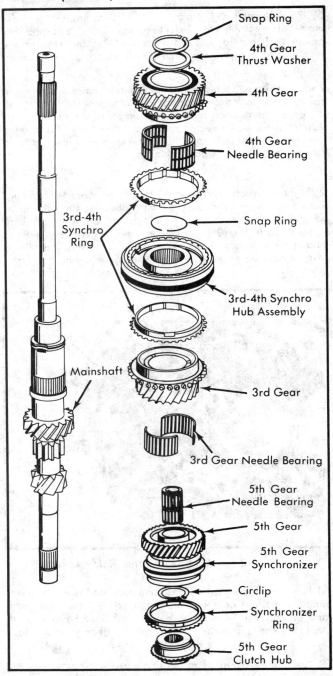

Fig. 11 *Exploded View of Mainshaft Assembly*

3) Remove 2nd gear needle bearing, snap ring, then press off 3rd gear. Remove circlip, then remove 4th gear snap ring and press off 4th gear and large bearing from shaft.

Reassembly — 1) Ensure all gears and shaft are oil-free and replace any damaged or defective parts. Press large bearing onto pinion shaft. Heat 4th gear to 250°F (120°C), slide gear onto pinion shaft (shoulder facing 3rd gear) and press until fully seated.

NOTE — *After approximately 3 minutes, press 4th gear onto shaft again to ensure correct adjustment of end play. After 4th gear has cooled, continue reassembly procedure.*

PORSCHE 924 5-SPEED (Cont.)

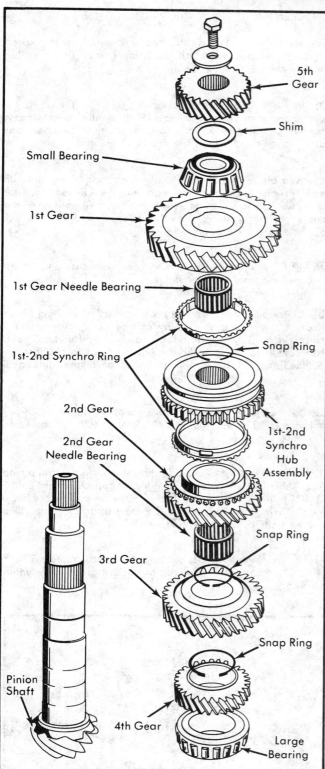

Fig. 12 Exploded View of Pinion Shaft Assembly

(Labels in figure, top to bottom: 5th Gear, Shim, Small Bearing, 1st Gear, 1st Gear Needle Bearing, 1st-2nd Synchro Ring, Snap Ring, 2nd Gear, 1st-2nd Synchro Hub Assembly, 2nd Gear Needle Bearing, Snap Ring, 3rd Gear, Snap Ring, Pinion Shaft, 4th Gear, Large Bearing)

2) Measure 4th gear end play with a feeler gauge and adjust end play to not more than .0008" (.02 mm) with correct snap ring. Snap rings are available in sizes ranging from .088" (2.24 mm) to .094" (2.40 mm) in .0008" (.02 mm) increments.

3) Install a .094" (2.4 mm) snap ring into second snap ring groove of pinion shaft. Heat 3rd gear to 250°F (120°C) and slide gear onto shaft with shoulder toward 2nd gear. Press gear onto shaft until seated against snap ring, then install retaining snap ring. Using a feeler gauge, measure 3rd gear end play as shown in *Fig. 13*. End play should be 0-.002" (0-.05 mm). If not, install a different thickness retaining snap ring.

NOTE — *Snap rings for 3rd gear end play adjustment are available in the following thicknesses: .065" (1.65 mm), .067" (1.70 mm) and .069" (1.75 mm).*

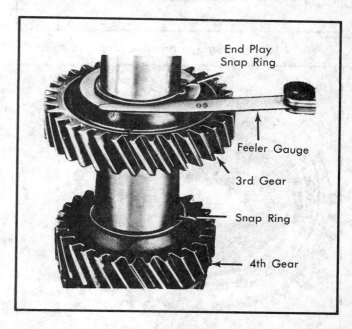

Fig. 13 Checking 3rd Gear End Play

(Labels in figure: End Play Snap Ring, Feeler Gauge, 3rd Gear, Snap Ring, 4th Gear)

4) Oil 2nd gear needle bearing and install on shaft. Place 2nd gear, 2nd gear synchro ring and synchro hub assembly atop one another. Press all components onto pinion shaft. Measure synchronizer hub assembly end play with a feeler gauge. End play should be 0-.0016" (0-.04 mm). Adjust end play with a suitable snap ring.

NOTE — *Snap rings for 1st/2nd synchronizer hub adjustment are available in the following thicknesses: .059" (1.50 mm), .061" (1.55 mm) and .063" (1.60 mm).*

5) Install remaining synchronizer ring onto hub. Oil and install 1st gear needle bearing, then slide 1st gear onto pinion shaft. Press pinion shaft small bearing onto shaft until fully seated.

SYNCHRONIZER ASSEMBLIES

Disassembly — Remove snap ring and separate synchronizer hub from sleeve. Use care not to lose or damage synchronizer keys and springs.

Inspection — Check all parts for wear or damage. Using a feeler gauge, check synchronizer rings for wear as shown in *Fig. 14*. Clearance "a" should be .039-.075" (1.0-1.9 mm) for 5th gear synchronizer or .039-.067" (1.0-1.7 mm) for all other synchronizers.

PORSCHE 924 5-SPEED (Cont.)

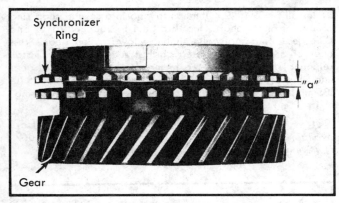

Fig. 14　*Checking Synchronizer Rings for Wear*

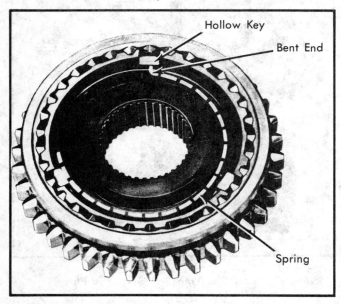

Fig. 15　*Assembled View of Synchronizer Assembly*

Reassembly — Reverse disassembly procedure and use *Fig. 15* as an assembly guide. Install springs offset 120°. Bent end of spring must engage in hollow key.

DIFFERENTIAL

Disassembly — 1) Place differential assembly in soft-jawed vise. Remove ring gear bolts and ring gear. Using a puller, remove differential side bearings.

2) Drive out pinion shaft lock pin with a punch. Then drive out pinion shaft with a punch. Rotate differential gear set and remove pinion gears, side gears, shims, thrust washers and drive flange nuts through opening in differential housing.

Reassembly — 1) Lubricate pinion gears and side gears with transmission oil. Position side gears with shims in housing. Stick thrust washers to pinion gears with grease, then position pinion gears in housing. Install pinion gear shaft, making sure lock pin hole in shaft and housing is aligned.

CAUTION — *Side gears, pinion gears, shims and thrust washers must not be interchanged.*

2) Check pinion and side gear adjustment by pushing pinion gears outward and check play of side gears. Adjustment is correct if no play can be felt by hand, but differential gears can be turned easily without binding. If not to specification outlined, correct by installing thicker or thinner side gear shims.

NOTE — *Side gear shims are available in the following thicknesses: .020" (.5 mm), .024" (.6 mm), .028" (.7 mm) and .032" (.8 mm).*

3) Install correct side gear adjusting shims, then install pinion gear shaft lock pin. Heat ring gear to approximately 250°F (120°C), then position ring gear in place on differential housing. Pull ring gear into place with new attaching bolts, then tighten bolts in crosswise manner.

4) Heat differential side bearings to approximately 212°F (100°C), then press them onto each end of differential housing.

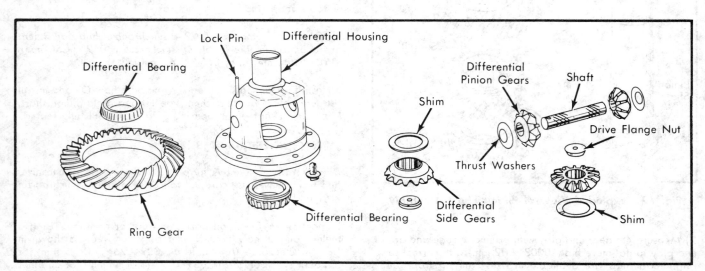

Fig. 16　*Exploded View of Differential Assembly*

PORSCHE 924 5-SPEED (Cont.)

TRANSAXLE REASSEMBLY & ADJUSTMENTS

PINION SHAFT ADJUSTMENTS

1) Install pinion shaft bearing outer races into final drive housing and gear carrier WITHOUT shims. Install assembled gear carrier to final drive housing and tighten attaching bolts.

2) Place magnetic measuring plate (VW385/17) onto rear end of pinion shaft, then mount a dial indicator to gear carrier as shown in *Fig. 17.* Zero dial indicator with .039" (1 mm) preload. Move pinion shaft up and down (without turning shaft) and record indicator reading.

CAUTION — *Turning pinion shaft during measurement will cause bearings to settle, giving an inaccurate reading.*

3) Remove gear carrier from final drive housing. To determine total thickness of shims necessary to obtain correct pinion depth and bearing preload, add constant preload value of .012" (.30 mm) to dial indicator reading just obtained. Resulting sum is total thickness of required shims.

4) Remove pinion shaft bearing outer race from gear carrier, then install a shim of total shim thickness determined in step **3)** behind outer race and reinstall race into gear carrier. Install gear carrier to final drive housing and tighten attaching bolts. Turn pinion shaft several times in each direction to settle bearings.

5) Adjust clamping ring on measuring bar (VW385/1) so dimension "a" in *Fig. 18* is 1.97" (50 mm). Next, assemble the following measuring tools onto measuring bar as shown in *Fig. 18:*

- Dial Indicator
- Centering Discs VW385/2 and 3
- Measuring Pin VW385/14
- Measuring Pin Extension VW385/15
- Setting Gauge VW385/27

With all tools asembled to bar, zero dial indicator with .039" (1 mm) preload and remove setting gauge (VW385/27).

NOTE — *Move clamping ring back to stop.*

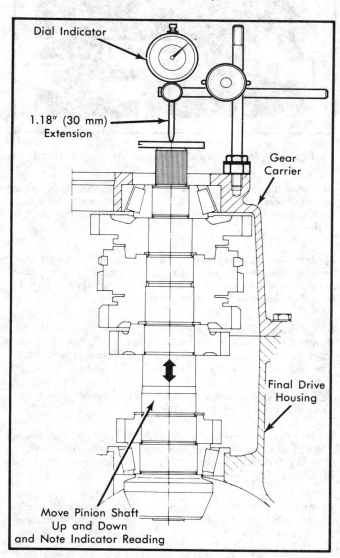

Fig. 17 *Measuring Pinion Shaft Play to Determine Total Pinion Adjusting Shim Thickness*

Labels in Fig. 17:
- Dial Indicator
- 1.18" (30 mm) Extension
- Gear Carrier
- Final Drive Housing
- Move Pinion Shaft Up and Down and Note Indicator Reading

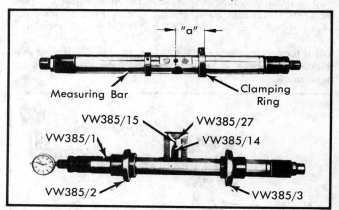

Fig. 18 *Assembling Measuring Tools for Pinion Depth Shim Selection*

Labels in Fig. 18:
- "a"
- Measuring Bar
- Clamping Ring
- VW385/15
- VW385/27
- VW385/1
- VW385/14
- VW385/2
- VW385/3

6) Place magnetic measuring plate (VW385/17) on end of pinion shaft. Install assembled measuring bar into final drive housing with centering disc (VW385/2) facing final drive cover. Install final drive cover and secure with 4 bolts.

7) Turn knob on end of measuring bar to move clamping ring and the other centering disc (VW385/3) outward, until bar can just barely be turned by hand.

8) Rotate measuring bar until measuring pin extension rests squarely against magnetic plate on pinion shaft. Then rotate bar back and forth over center. Read and record maximum dial indicator reading.

9) To determine correct pinion depth adjusting shim(s) to install behind bearing outer race in gear carrier, add the deviation number stamped on ring gear to the dial indicator reading obtained in step **8)**.

NOTE — *Deviation number stamped on ring gear is in hundredth millimeters. A marking of 25 would be .25 mm.*

10) To determine thickness of shim to install under pinion bearing outer race in final drive housing, subtract thickness of pinion depth shim determined in step **9)** from total pinion shim thickness obtained in step **3)**.

PORSCHE 924 5-SPEED (Cont.)

NOTE — *Shims for outer race installed in gear carrier are available in thicknesses of .008" (.20 mm) to .045" (1.15 mm) in various increments. Shims for outer bearing race in final drive housing are available in thicknesses of .009" (.24 mm) to .056" (1.41 mm) in various increments.*

11) Remove measuring bar assembly from final drive housing. Separate gear carrier from final drive housing. Remove pinion shaft bearing outer race from gear carrier and final drive housing, then install selected shims with outer race back into carrier and housing.

12) Install gear carrier to final drive and tighten attaching bolts. To check adjustment, reinstall measuring bar assembly and recheck measurements. If correct shims have been installed, dial indicator reading (counterclockwise) should be the ring gear deviation number with a tolerance of ±.0016" (.04 mm).

13) To check pinion bearing preload, lubricate pinion bearings with transmission oil, then check pinion shaft turning torque with an INCH lb. torque wrench as shown in *Fig. 19*. Pinion shaft turning torque with NEW bearings installed should be 17-34 INCH lbs. (20-40 cmkg). Turning torque with USED bearings installed should be 2.6-5.2 INCH lbs. (3-6 cmkg).

14) If turning torque is not within specifications, sufficient shim thickness for bearing preload and bearing settling has not been allowed.

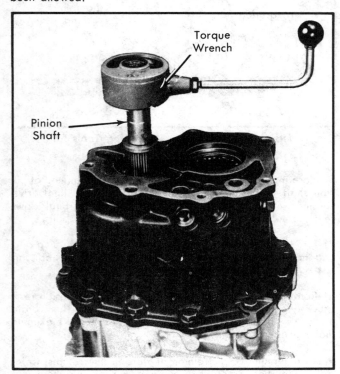

Fig. 19   Checking Pinion Shaft Turning Torque

RING GEAR ADJUSTMENTS

1) Remove gear carrier from final drive housing. Remove differential oil seals and side bearing outer races from final drive housing and take out shims. Reinstall side bearing outer races WITHOUT shims. Install differential assembly into final drive housing. Install final drive cover and tighten attaching bolts diagonally to 18 ft. lbs. (25 mkg).

NOTE — *Differential assembly is installed with ring gear side facing final drive cover.*

2) Position magnetic measuring plate (VW385/17) and dial indicator as shown in *Fig. 20*, then zero dial indicator with .039" (1 mm) preload. Move differential assembly up and down and note dial indicator reading.

CAUTION — *Do not rotate differential while taking measurement as bearings will settle and make measurement inaccurate.*

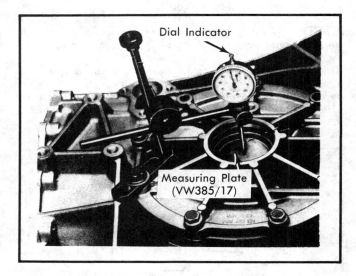

Fig. 20   Measuring Differential Bearing Preload

3) To the dial indicator reading obtained in step **2)**, add the constant preload value of .020" (.50 mm). Resulting sum is thickness of shims necessary for correct differential bearing preload.

4) Remove measuring tools and final drive housing cover. Remove differential side bearing outer race from cover, then reinstall race with a shim of the thickness obtained in step **3)** behind it. Reinstall final drive housing cover.

5) Lubricate differential side bearings with transmission oil, then connect an INCH lb. torque wrench to differential and check turning torque. Differential turning torque with NEW side bearings should be 22 INCH lbs. (25 cmkg).

NOTE — *It is not necessary to measure differential turning torque when used bearings are reinstalled.*

6) Insert clamping sleeve (VW521/4) with slotted sleeve (VW521/8) into differential and secure with nut. Adjust length of backlash measuring bar (VW388) until dimension "A" in *Fig. 21* is 3.11" (79 mm).

7) Attach measuring bar to clamping sleeve. Install dial indicator in holder (VW387) and bolt holder to final drive housing as shown in *Fig. 21*.

NOTE — *Dial indicator must be installed so foot will contact end of measuring bar at a 90° angle.*

PORSCHE 924 5-SPEED (Cont.)

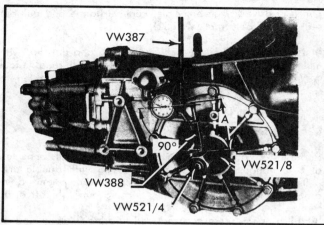

Fig. 21   Positioning of Ring Gear Backlash Measuring Tools

8) Turn ring gear to take up backlash. Zero dial indicator and clamp in holder. Turn ring gear in opposite direction until it is stopped and note indicator reading. This reading is ring gear backlash.

9) Check ring gear at 4 locations (90° apart) around circumference of ring gear. Add the 4 measurements together, then divide by 4 to find the average ring gear backlash. Ring gear backlash should be .004-.008" (.10-.20 mm).

NOTE — *Difference between the 4 ring gear backlash measurements must not exceed .002" (.06 mm). If measurements differ more than this, ring gear is incorrectly installed or final drive housing is damaged.*

10) To determine thickness of shim to install behind differential bearing outer race in final drive housing cover (opposite ring gear side), subtract the average ring gear backlash from the total shim thickness obtained in step **3)**. To this value add the constant preload value of .006" (.15 mm). Resulting sum is the thickness of ring gear adjusting shim to install in final drive housing cover.

NOTE — *Ring gear adjusting shims for final drive housing cover are available in thicknesses from .006" (.15 mm) to .047" (1.2 mm) in various increments.*

11) To determine thickness of ring gear adjusting shim to install behind differential side bearing outer race in final drive housing (ring gear side), subtract thickness of shim determined in step **10)** from the total ring gear adjusting shim thickness determined in step **3)**.

FINAL ASSEMBLY

1) Lightly coat joints of gear carrier and final drive housings with sealing compound. Mate units together and tighten bolts. Coat selector shaft with sealing compound and install into case. Tighten bolts.

2) Place differential assembly into final drive housing. Install differential cover magnet at the bottom. Install both drive axle flanges and tighten bolts.

3) Drive mainshaft seal into main oil tube stop with installer (9119). Install guide (9113) onto mainshaft. Slide oil seal tube with new "O" ring onto mainshaft, finger tighten bolts and remove guide. Tighten bolts. Install special shifter (9155/1) and check operation of transmission in all gear ranges.

TIGHTENING SPECIFICATIONS

Application	Ft. Lbs. (mkg)
Axle Shaft Nut	217-289 (30-40)
CV Joint Bolts	30 (4.2)
Gear Carrier-to-Transmission	17 (2.4)
Selector Shaft Cover	4-7 (.6-1.0)
Drive Flange Bolts	18 (2.5)
Final Drive Cover	18 (2.5)
Mainshaft End Bolt	36 (5.0)
5th Gear End Bolt	36 (5.0)
Reverse Relay Lever Bolt	25 (3.5)
Rear Cover-to-Gear Carrier	18 (2.5)
Ring Gear Bolts	61-72 (8.4-10.0)
Oil Seal Tube	7-12 (1.0-1.7)
Central Tube-to-Transaxle	
M10 Bolts	30 (4.2)
M12 Bolts	61 (8.4)
Central Tube-to-Clutch Housing	30 (4.2)

Manual Transaxles

PORSCHE 924 TURBO 5-SPEED

DESCRIPTION

The Porsche 924 Turbo is equipped with a manual transaxle (type 016/Y) with a five speed transmission mounted in front of the final drive. Engine and transaxle are connected by a strong central tube which also houses the propeller shaft and supports the gearshift lever. Flanges at each end of central tube attach to clutch housing and transaxle. Propeller shaft is splined to clutch disc at the front and is connected to transmission mainshaft at the rear by a coupling. Access to this coupling is through an inspection hole in rear of central tube. A hypoid ring and pinion differential assembly drives double-jointed rear axle drive shafts. Complete drive train is mounted to unitized body by 2 front engine mounts and 2 rear transaxle mounts.

NOTE — *The term "Transaxle" in this article refers to the rear axle transmission/differential assembly. The central tube and bell housings may be referred to as the "Transaxle tube". Axle drive shafts include the flexible couplings. Rear wheel axle shaft indicates the driven axle shaft mounted in the trailing arms of the rear wheel suspension.*

LUBRICATION & ADJUSTMENT

See MANUAL TRANSMISSION SERVICING Section.

SERVICE (IN VEHICLE)

FLANGED SHAFT SEAL

Removal — Remove socket head screws at inner end of shaft, then disconnect and support axle drive shaft. Remove inner flange bolt while holding flange from turning by inserting punch in drive flange bolt hole. Remove flange and pull out seal with suitable tool (VW681).

Installation — Fill cavity between sealing and dust lips with multi-purpose grease and drive seal in place with suitable tool (VW195). Replace flange and drive shaft and tighten to specifications.

REAR WHEEL BEARINGS

Removal — With brake drum off and drive shaft disconnected at axle flange, press shaft from housing with double arm puller. Pry seal out of housing, remove circlip and drive grooved ball bearing and roller bearing out with soft drift.

Installation — Press grooved ball bearing in inner end of housing and replace circlip. Put spacer in housing and drive roller bearing in place (flanged side facing out). Install seal in inboard side of housing. Put outer spacer on shaft and press in along with bearing inner race using castellated nut and suitable driver. See Fig. 2.

AXLE DRIVE SHAFT

Disassembly — Assure boot and CV joint areas are clean, then remove clamp holding boot on shaft. Drive protective cap off CV joint and remove circlip from end of axle. Press CV joint from shaft. Disassemble and inspect CV joint.

NOTE — *Ball hubs and joints are matched sets. DO NOT interchange any balls, hubs or joints between CV joints.*

Reassembly — Coat all parts with suitable lubricant and assemble joint. Check for smooth operation throughout entire range of travel. Press CV joint assembly on axle splines with

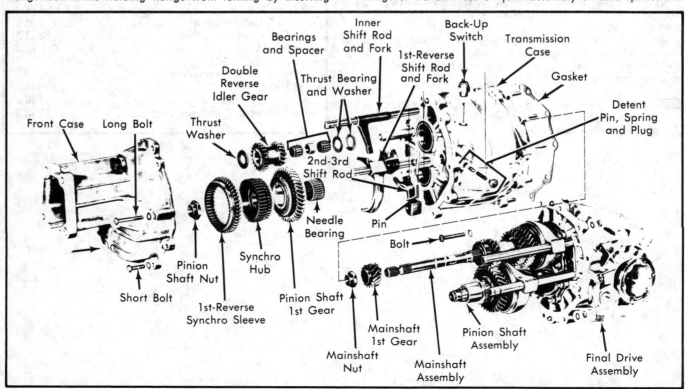

Fig. 1   Exploded View of Porsche 924 Turbo 5-Speed Transaxle Assembly

PORSCHE 924 TURBO 5-SPEED (Cont.)

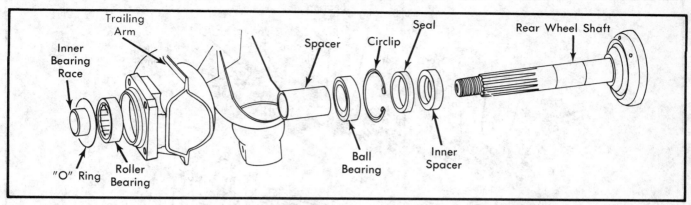

Fig. 2 Exploded View of Drive Axle Shaft and Wheel Bearing

chamfered side facing in towards the bearing collar. Pack about 1.6 oz. (45 grams) of suitable lubricant (molybdenum disulfide grease) into each side of joint. Reinstall circlip, protective cap, boot and clamp.

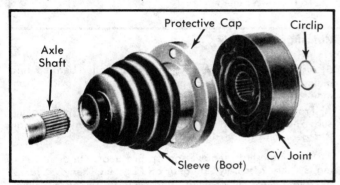

Fig. 3 Exploded View of Constant Velocity Joint

REMOVAL & INSTALLATION

TRANSAXLE

Removal — **1)** Loosen screw clamping selector rod to transmission linkage at rear of tunnel.

2) Lift shift lever dust cover and remove circlip holding selector rod to shift lever. Remove selector rod from shift lever pin.

3) Turn shift lever 180° and tilt out to right. Press down on rubber seal between central tube and tunnel. Slide selector rod forward in tunnel to clear linkage at rear.

4) Detach exhaust pipe at primary muffler and loosen exhaust holding brackets at central tube. Remove exhaust mounting bolts from transmission end plate and remove entire muffler assembly.

5) Disconnect back-up light switch wires and remove switch from transmission to prevent damage. Take wires out of clip on transmission.

6) Disconnect axle shafts from transaxle and suspend horizontally from car to prevent damage to boots. Remove socket head bolt at rear propeller shaft coupling through inspection hole in rear bell housing.

7) Place a jack (with support, US 618/1, attached) under transaxle and raise slightly. Remove transaxle bolts, then remove transaxle mounts.

8) Remove clutch housing-to-central tube bolts. Lower transaxle with central tube so that tube rests on rear axle cross tube. Move transaxle out to rear.

NOTE — *Do not raise too high. Left rear brake line is located above selector rod.*

Installation — To install, reverse removal procedure and note the following: Propeller shaft extends .748-.788" (19-20 mm) beyond rear flange surface. Improper position may cause clutch drag due to improper engagement of spline and clutch disc. Tighten all connecting bolts.

TRANSAXLE (CENTRAL) TUBE

Removal — **1)** Transaxle must be out of vehicle. Disconnect battery ground strap. Suspend engine from front eyelet with suitable fixture (VW10-222) and hold tight in installation position.

2) Support tube at front tunnel reinforcing brace with locally made block. Detach central tube from front bell housing and slide back about 4" (100 mm).

3) Remove rear reinforcement strut, then loosen rear axle mountings and lower torsion bar tube. Pull selector rod rearward. Remove central tube by lowering and pulling out to the rear.

Inspection — Propeller shaft must extend .748-.788" (19-20 mm) beyond face of bell housing flange in order to properly engage clutch disc splines. Correct shaft position by tapping end with soft faced hammer. Check free rotation of shaft.

NOTE — *Shaft must turn easily without noise or flat spots. If bearings or shaft are damaged the entire assembly must be replaced. Separate component replacement is not possible at this time.*

Installation — To install, reverse removal procedure.

TRANSAXLE DISASSEMBLY

TRANSMISSION DISASSEMBLY

1) Remove bolt attaching shifting rod to transaxle shift rod. From central tube access hole, remove bolt from sleeve connecting propeller shaft to mainshaft. Remove bolts attaching central tube to transaxle. Mount transaxle assembly in suitable holder. Drain oil.

PORSCHE 924 TURBO 5-SPEED (Cont.)

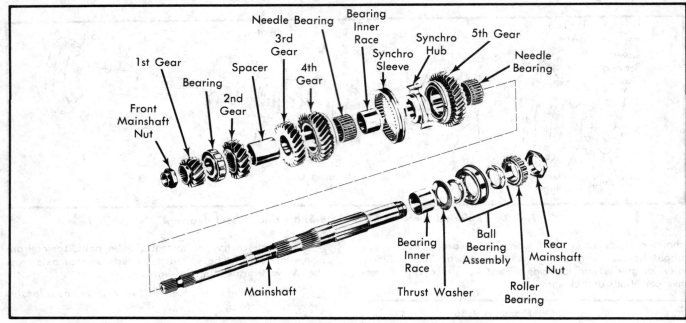

Fig. 4 Exploded View of Mainshaft Assembly

2) Remove bolts attaching front case to transmission case and remove front case. Engage 1st and 5th gears, then remove pinion shaft nut. Remove thrust washer, double reverse idler gear, bearings, spacer, thrust bearing and thrust washer from idler shaft.

3) Remove detent plug, spring and pin from case. Remove inner shift rod and fork. Remove back-up light switch and pin. With 1st and 5th gears still engaged, remove mainshaft nut.

4) Drive spring pins from 2nd-3rd operating lever and remove 2nd-3rd operating lever from rod. Remove 1st-reverse shift fork retaining pins and fork. Remove 1st-reverse synchro sleeve, synchro hub and pinion shaft 1st gear.

5) Using gear puller, remove 2nd gear, roller bearing and mainshaft 1st gear from mainshaft. Remove spacer from mainshaft.

6) From pinion shaft, remove bearings and 2nd gear making sure 2nd-3rd synchro parts are not loose. Remove 4th gear, 3rd gear and guide sleeve from pinion.

7) From mainshaft, remove spacer, 3rd gear, 4th gear, bearing, synchro assembly, 5th gear and bearing. Remove clamping plate nuts, pinion shaft and mainshaft. Remove shims, noting number and thickness for reassembly reference.

8) If mainshaft rear bearings require replacement, remove rear mainshaft nut and press needle bearing inner race off of shaft. Then, press ball and roller bearings off of mainshaft.

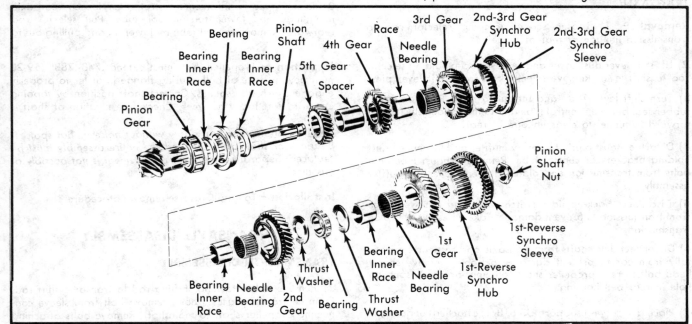

Fig. 5 Exploded View of Pinion Shaft Assembly

PORSCHE 924 TURBO 5-SPEED (Cont.)

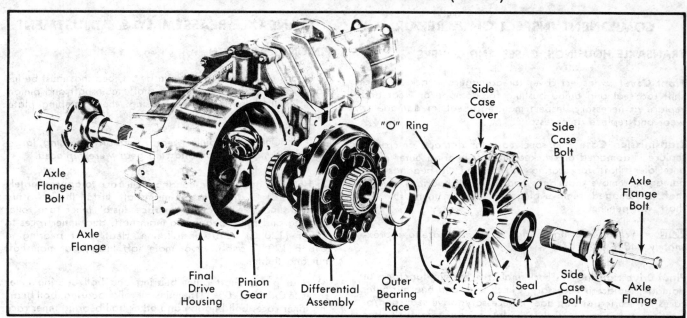

Fig. 6   Exploded View of Porsche 924 Turbo 5-Speed Final Drive Housing Assembly

FINAL DRIVE DISASSEMBLY

1) To remove axle flange bolt, install 2 bolts into flange adjacent to one another. Place a pry bar between bolts to keep flange from turning and remove axle flange bolt. Remove other axle flange bolt in same manner. *See Fig. 6.*

2) Remove side case cover bolts then side case cover. Remove "O" ring from side case cover. Remove differential assembly from final drive housing.

3) Pull bearings off differential assembly with bearing puller. Note thickness of shims when bearings are removed. Drive pinion shaft pin out of differential carrier. Remove pinion shaft. Rotate pinion gears until they can be removed from differential carrier. *See Fig. 7*

4) Remove axle flange nuts and side gears from differential carrier. Remove all ring gear bolts and drive ring gear from differential carrier with suitable punch.

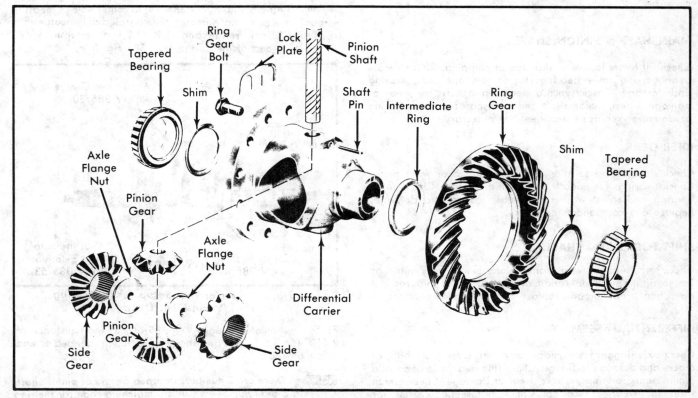

Fig. 7   Exploded View of Differential Assembly

PORSCHE 924 TURBO 5-SPEED (Cont.)

COMPONENT INSPECTION & REPAIR

TRANSAXLE HOUSINGS, CASES AND COVERS

Front Cover — Inspect cover for damage or cracks. Inspect shift rod seal and guide bushing for damage or wear and replace as necessary. Inspect mainshaft seal for damage or wear and replace as necessary.

Transmission Case — Inspect case for damage or cracks, replace if damaged or cracked. Inspect bearing outer races and idler shaft for scoring or damage. If bearings are damaged, remove snap rings and press out bearings. If idler shaft is damaged, remove plug and lock pin then drive out shaft with punch.

NOTE — *When replacing bearing races, heat case to approximately 248°F (120°C).*

Final Drive Housing — Check final drive housing for cracks or damage, replace if necessary. Check seals and bearing outer races for scoring or damage. If necessary, drive seals and/or bearings out of case. Check lock plate for damage. Lock plate must have free up and down movement when bolts are tightened. Replace bearing races in housing before replacing oil seals. Heat housing to approximately 248°F (120°C) before installing bearing races.

Side Case Cover — Inspect bearing outer race and seal for damage or scoring. Check cover for cracks or damage. Check large "O" ring for damage. If necessary, drive out bearing race and oil seal. Remove "O" ring. When replacing bearing outer races, heat side case cover to 248°F (120°C), then press bearing races into side case cover. Replace "O" ring if necessary.

MAINSHAFT & PINION SHAFT

Check all gears for wear, damage or chipping. Check needle bearings and roller bearings for smooth operation, scoring and damage. Check synchro sleeves and hubs for wear or damage. Check pinion shaft and mainshaft for wear, scoring or damage. Replace components as necessary.

IDLER GEAR

Check double reverse idler gear for chipped or worn teeth. Check bearings for smooth operation or scoring. Check thrust bearing and thrust washer for wear, scoring and damage. Replace any components necessary.

SHIFT FORKS AND SHAFTS

Check shift forks for wear, damage or cracks. Check shift rods for scoring. Check operation of shift forks on shift rods. If operation is not smooth, replace components as necessary.

DIFFERENTIAL ASSEMBLY

Check axle flanges for damage to splines, scoring on shaft, or cracks and damage to flange. Check ring gear, side gears and pinion gears for chips, cracks, wear or damage. Check pinion shaft for wear or scoring. Check differential carrier for cracks or damage. Replace any components necessary.

TRANSAXLE REASSEMBLY & ADJUSTMENT

PINION GEAR DEPTH

1) Before pinion gear depth can be set, bearings must be installed on mainshaft and pinion shaft, mainshaft and pinion shaft installed in final drive housing, then clamping plate installed.

NOTE — *Only adjust pinion gear if final drive housing, large pinion bearing or pinion and ring gear were replaced.*

2) Heat 5th gear needle bearing inner race to approximately 248°F (120°C) and press on mainshaft. Install thrust washer with ground side toward inner race. Install inner race roller bearing and roller bearing to mainshaft. Heat inner races to 248°F (120°C) before installation. Heat roller bearing to 248°F (120°C) and press on mainshaft. Install rear mainshaft nut and tighten.

3) Heat pinion shaft roller bearing and ball bearing inner races to 248°F (120°C). Then, install roller bearing, ball bearing inner race, ball bearing and other ball bearing inner race on pinion shaft.

4) Install both shafts to final drive housing. Install clamping plate (without any shims) and tighten nuts.

5) Slide special tube tool (9173) over pinion shaft, then install pinion shaft nut and tighten. On special measuring bar (VW 385/1) move adjusting ring so outside edge of ring is approximately 2.047" (52 mm) from center hole of machined flat surface.

6) Slide centering rings (VW 385/4) onto measuring bar. Install measuring plunger (VW 385/14) to center hole of measuring bar (machined flat surface), then install dial indicator with a .118" (3 mm) range and .55" (14 mm) extension (VW 385/53) on end of measuring bar. See Fig. 8.

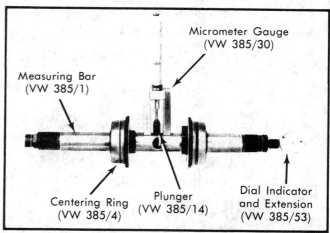

Micrometer Gauge (VW 385/30)

Measuring Bar (VW 385/1)

Centering Ring (VW 385/4)

Plunger (VW 385/14)

Dial Indicator and Extension (VW 385/53)

Fig. 8   Special Tool Setup for Measuring Pinion Gear Depth

7) Set micrometer gauge (VW 385/30) to read distance of 2.610" (66.3 mm) plus deviation measurement stamped on end of pinion shaft.

NOTE — *There are 2 numbers stamped on end of pinion shaft. One is a 3-digit number which is a matching code for the ring gear. The other number consists of a letter followed by 2 digits.*

PORSCHE 924 TURBO 5-SPEED (Cont.)

The digits represent the deviation measurement in hundredths of millimeters. For example, N 18 would represent a deviation of .18 mm (.007"). This deviation is added to the standard distance of 2.610" (66.3 mm).

8) With micrometer set to specifications, place over plunger on measuring bar. Adjust dial indicator to zero with a .040" (1 mm) preload. Place a magnetic disc (VW 385/17) onto end of pinion shaft.

9) Install measuring bar into final drive housing so that plunger on bar is in contact with the magnetic disc on end of pinion shaft. Install side case cover (without "O" ring) using only 4 bolts. Use bolts to pull cover into place (using a hammer may knock magnetic disc off pinion shaft).

10) Pull measuring bar until centering ring is engaged with side case cover. Rotate measuring bar slowly, watch dial indicator. When dial indicator reaches maximum deflection, note reading. This reading, added to the .040" (1 mm) preload is the shim thickness to be installed between pinion shaft bearing and clamping plate.

NOTE — *Dial indicator deflection must always be in a clockwise direction, with an indicator reading of between .040"-.080" (1-2 mm).*

11) Remove pinion shaft nut, special tube tool and clamping plate. Install determined shims then reinstall checking tools and recheck measurement. Measurement must be set distance 2.610" (66.3 mm) plus deviation marked on pinion shaft end. Maximum deviation of pinion depth is plus or minus .001" (.03 mm).

DIFFERENTIAL SIDE BEARING PRELOAD

NOTE — *Differential assembly must be assembled (without tapered bearings) before adjusting preload. Pinion shaft must be removed from final drive housing while adjusting preload.*

1) Install intermediate ring spacer and a .197" (5 mm) shim to differential carrier (opposite ring gear). Then press tapered bearing onto carrier. Press tapered bearing onto carrier ring gear side without shims.

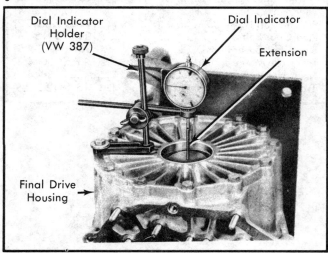

Fig. 9   Special Tool Setup for Measuring Differential Side Bearing Preload

2) Install differential assembly into final drive housing. Turn differential to seat tapered bearings. Install side case cover. In-

stall all side case cover bolts and tighten. Place magnetic disc (VW 385/17) on collar of differential.

3) Install dial indicator holder (VW 387) with dial indicator and extension rod to side case cover (use 1 case cover bolt). Zero dial indicator, then preload indicator to .080" (2 mm). See Fig. 9.

4) Move differential assembly up and down in final drive housing and note maximum dial indicator needle deflection. To this measured value (from dial indicator) add a constant value (preload) of .012" (.3 mm). Then add the already installed .197" (5 mm) shim to get total shim thickness.

NOTE — *When selecting shim thickness from measured values, always round measurements off to the nearest .05 mm (.002"). For example, if measured value is 1.17 mm (.046"), rounded off value is 1.15 mm (.045").*

5) Remove dial indicator and holder, side case cover and differential assembly. Remove both tapered bearings and install shims to both sides of differential assembly in the following manner:

- Divide total shim thickness value by 2.
- Add .004" (.1 mm) to one divided shim value.
- Subtract .004" (.1 mm) from other divided shim value.

Example: A total shim value of .258" (6.55 mm) would yield one shim pack of .133" (3.375 mm) and another shim pack of .125" (3.175 mm).

6) Install selected shim packs to differential assembly then press tapered bearings onto differential assembly.

DIFFERENTIAL RING GEAR BACKLASH

1) Install pinion shaft, mainshaft, shims and clamping plate to final drive housing. Install differential assembly into final drive housing.

NOTE — *When tightening bolts on side case cover and pinion shaft nut, check that ring gear has some backlash at all times. If ring gear binds up, remove differential assembly and move tapered bearing shims so some backlash will remain in ring gear.*

2) Install side case cover and tighten bolts.

NOTE — *Pinion gear must be held stationary while checking backlash. One way would be to install 1st-5th gears on pinion, 1st gear on mainshaft, idler double reverse gear on idler shaft, shift rods and forks, synchro sleeve and hub to final drive housing, then lock 1st and 5th gears together.*

3) Install pinion shaft nut and tighten. Install adjustable lever (VW 388) to clamping arbor (VW 521/4). Adjust lever length from large hexagon surface to upper surface of ball to 3.268" (83 mm).

4) Install clamping arbor with sleeve (9145) in differential assembly and clamp tight. Turn differential in both directions several times to seat tapered roller bearings.

5) Install dial indicator holder (VW 387), with dial indicator and extension so that dial indicator axis is perpendicular to lever. See Fig. 10. Turn differential against stop carefully with clamping arbor (VW 521/4) and set dial indicator to zero with a .080" (2 mm) preload.

PORSCHE 924 TURBO 5-SPEED (Cont.)

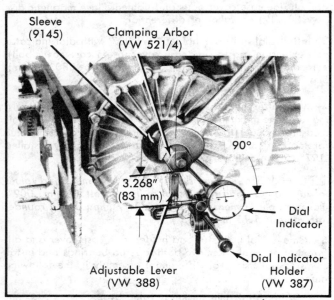

Fig. 10   Special Tool Setup for Measuring Ring Gear Backlash

6) Turn ring gear back and read amount of backlash. Note this value. Repeat this check every 90° ring gear rotation. Ring gear backlash specification is inscribed on ring gear.

7) If backlash is not to specifications, remove differential assembly, remove tapered bearings and move shim from one side to other until backlash is to specifications. Backlash specification is plus or minus .002" (.05 mm).

TRANSAXLE REASSEMBLY

NOTE — *Heat all parts which require press fit to 248° F (120° C) before installation.*

1) Install mainshaft and pinion shaft to final drive housing. Install same thickness shims that were removed or install shims determined in adjustment procedure. Install clamping plate and nuts and tighten.

2) On pinion shaft, install 5th gear and spacer. On mainshaft, install thrust washer, bearing inner race, needle bearing, 5th gear, synchro hub and sleeve with shift fork and rod, bearing inner race, needle bearing, 4th gear and 3rd gear. Install spacer, 2nd gear and bearing.

3) On pinion shaft, install 4th gear, bearing inner race, needle bearing, 3rd gear and 2nd-3rd synchro hub and sleeve with shift fork and rod. Then install bearing inner race, needle bearing, 2nd gear, thrust washer, bearing, thrust washer and bearing inner race.

4) Install transmission case and gasket to final drive housing. On idler shaft, install thrust washer, thrust bearing, needle bearing, spacer, needle bearing, double reverse gear and thrust washer.

5) On pinion shaft, install needle bearing, 1st gear, 1st-reverse synchro hub and sleeve with 1st-reverse shift fork and rod. Install 2nd-3rd operating lever onto 2nd-3rd shift rod and install spring pins in lever.

6) Install inner shift rod and fork to transmission case, fixed to 1st-reverse shift rod. On mainshaft, install 1st gear. Engage 1st and 5th gears, then install mainshaft nut and pinion shaft nut. Tighten pinion shaft nut, then mainshaft nut. Stake nuts to shafts.

7) Install detent pin, spring and plug to case. Install back-up switch pin and switch to transmission case. With all components installed, check operation of all components. Install front case to transmisssion case.

TIGHTENING SPECIFICATIONS

Application	Ft. Lbs. (mkg)
Axle Flange Bolt	34-36 (4.7-5.0)
Axle Flange-to-Axle Shaft	30 (4.2)
Back-Up Light Switch	18-23 (2.2-2.5)
Central Tube-to-Clutch Housing	30 (4.2)
Clamping Plate Nuts	16-18 (2.2-2.5)
Detent Plug	11-13 (1.5-1.8)
Front Case-to-Central Tube	61 (8.5)
Front Case-to-Transmission Case	16-18 (2.2-2.5)
Lock Plate on Final Drive Housing	6-7 (0.8-1.0)
Mainshaft Nut	
Front	116-130 (16-18)
Rear	159-174 (22-24)
Pinion Shaft Nut	145-159 (20-22)
Ring Gear Bolts	108-116 (15-16)
Side Case Cover Bolts	16-18 (2.2-2.5)
Transaxle Mount-to-Body	30 (4.2)
Transaxle-to-Transaxle Mount	30 (4.2)
Transmission Case-to-Final Drive	16-18 (2.2-2.5)

PORSCHE 928 5-SPEED

DESCRIPTION

The Porsche 928 is equipped with a manual transmission (type G28.03) which has 5-speeds and is mounted behind the rear transaxle. Engine and transaxle are connected by a rigid central tube which also houses the propeller shaft and supports the gear shift lever. Bell housings on each end of this tube attach to the engine and transaxle. The propeller shaft is splined to the clutch disc at the front and is connected to the transmission mainshaft at the rear by a coupling. Access to this coupling is through an inspection hole in the rear bell housing. A hypoid ring and pinion differential assembly drives joint rear axle drive shafts. The whole assembly is mounted to the unitized body by 2 front engine mounts and 2 rear transmission mounts.

NOTE — *The term "Transaxle" in this article refers to the rear axle transmission/differential assembly. The central tube and bell housings may be referred to as the "transaxle tube". Axle drive shafts include the flexible couplings. Rear wheel axle shaft indicates the driven axle shaft mounted in the trailing arms of the rear wheel suspension.*

LUBRICATION & ADJUSTMENT

See *MANUAL TRANSMISSION SERVICING* Section.

SERVICE (IN VEHICLE)

FLANGED SHAFT SEAL

Removal — Remove socket head screws at inner end of shaft, then disconnect and support axle drive shaft. Remove inner flange bolt while holding flange from turning by inserting punch in drive flange bolt hole. Remove flange and pull out seal with suitable tool (VW 681).

Installation — Fill cavity between sealing and dust lips with multi-purpose grease and drive seal in place with suitable tool (VW 195). Replace flange and drive shaft and tighten to specifications.

REAR WHEEL BEARINGS

Removal — With brake calipers off and drive shaft disconnected at axle flange, press shaft from housing, remove circlip and drive grooved ball bearing and roller bearing out with soft drift.

Installation — Press grooved ball bearing in inner end of housing and replace circlip. Put spacer in housing and drive roller bearing in place (flanged side facing out). Install seal in inboard side of housing. Put outer spacer in shaft and press in along with bearing inner race using castellated nut and suitable driver.

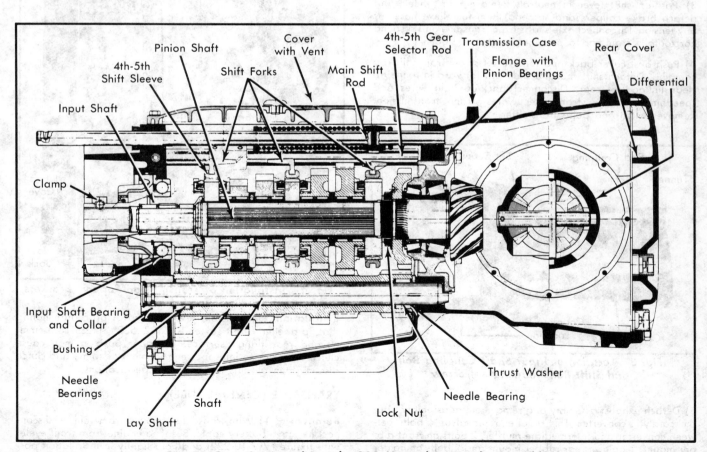

Fig. 1   Cross-Section of Porsche 928 Manual Transaxle Assembly

PORSCHE 928 5-SPEED (Cont.)

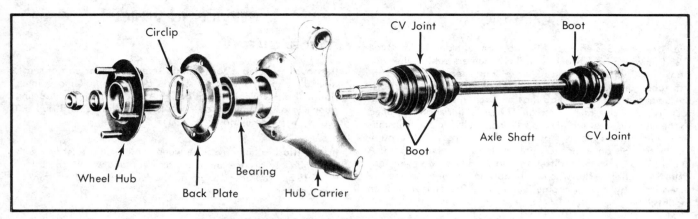

Fig. 2   Exploded View of Rear Axle Shaft Assembly

REMOVAL & INSTALLATION

TRANSAXLE ASSEMBLY

Removal — 1) Remove battery from case. Loosen rear wheels and position transmission in 5th gear. Loosen screw clamping selector rod to transmission linkage at rear of tunnel.

2) Open inspection cover (rubber cap) in transmission. Turn 1 wheel and hold opposite wheel to position coupling bolt between drive and input shafts for removal. Remove bolt.

3) Position shift lever in neutral. Remove rear wheels and detach brake calipers and suspend them to relieve hoses of any tension. Disconnect axle shafts from transaxle and suspend horizontally from car to prevent damage to boots.

4) Push dust cover back and remove set screw from shift rod coupling. Detach shift rod and slide rod forward in tunnel to clear linkage at rear. Disconnect back-up light wires and speedometer pulse transmitter wires from transmission. Remove switch and pulse transmitter.

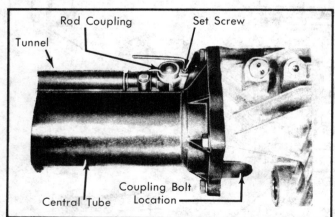

Fig. 3   Location of Input Shaft Coupling Bolt and Shift Rod Coupling Set Screw

5) Detach exhaust assembly and remove entire assembly after the catalytic converter. This requires removal of 4 bolts between converter and intermediate muffler, 2 bolts on front rubber mount, 1 bolt on rear rubber mount and 2 bolts on holder for main muffler. Remove battery box.

6) Remove 2 transmission mounting bolts on rear axle crossmember and 2 bolts between rear axle crossmember and frame. Place transmission jack beneath rear axle crossmember and mark position of crossmember. Remove remaining 4 bolts on crossmember. Tilt rear axle carefully and support in tilted position taking weight off the lower control arm link pins.

7) Mount transmission support bracket to transmission using fixtures (9148 and 9149). See *Fig. 4*. Remove 6 bolts between central tube and transmission. Pull transmission back to one side and lower from vehicle.

Fig. 4   Installation of Transmission Support Brackets

Installation — To install, reverse removal procedure noting that propeller shaft extends .492-.532" (12.5-13.5 mm) beyond rear flange surface. Improper position may cause clutch drag due to improper engagement of spline and clutch disc. Tighten all nuts and bolts to specifications.

TRANSAXLE (CENTRAL TUBE)

Removal — 1) With transaxle removed from vehicle, disconnect negative battery cable. Suspend engine from front eyelet with fixture (VW 10-222) and hold tightly in installation position.

PORSCHE 928 5-SPEED (Cont.)

2) Support tube at front tunnel reinforcing brace with a suitable front block. Detach central tube from front bell housing and slide back about 4" (100 mm).

3) Remove rear cross traverse in tunnel, then loosen rear axle mountings and lower torsion bar tube. Pull selector rod out to the rear. Remove central tube by lowering and pulling out to the rear.

Inspection — Propeller shaft must extend .492-.532" (12.5-13.5 mm) beyond face of bell housing flange in order to properly engage clutch disc splines. Correct shaft position by tapping end with soft faced hammer. Check free rotation of shaft turning by hand.

NOTE — *Shaft must turn easily without noise or flat spots. If bearings or shaft are damaged, entire assembly must be replaced. Separate component replacement is not possible as individual parts are not available.*

Installation — To install, reverse removal procedure.

TRANSAXLE DISASSEMBLY

1) Mount transaxle in suitable holding fixture and drain oil. Remove drive axle flanges. Remove selector shaft cap bolts, cap and spring.

2) Remove shift finger and shift fork pins. Slide selector shaft in as far as possible. Remove end plate mounting bolts and separate gear case from transaxle housing. Remove differential cover bolts and differential assembly.

COMPONENT DISASSEMBLY & REASSEMBLY

TRANSMISSION CASE

Disassembly — 1) Mount transmission in a suitable holding fixture and remove end cover and top cover. Remove mainshaft rod toward the rear.

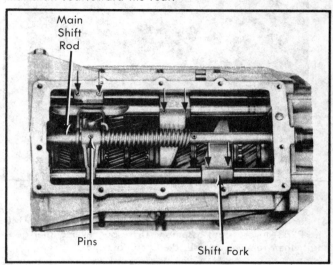

Fig. 5   Top View Showing Shift Rods and Forks

2) Remove remaining shift rods and forks toward rear of case insuring that reverse gear and 1st-2nd gears remain in neutral.

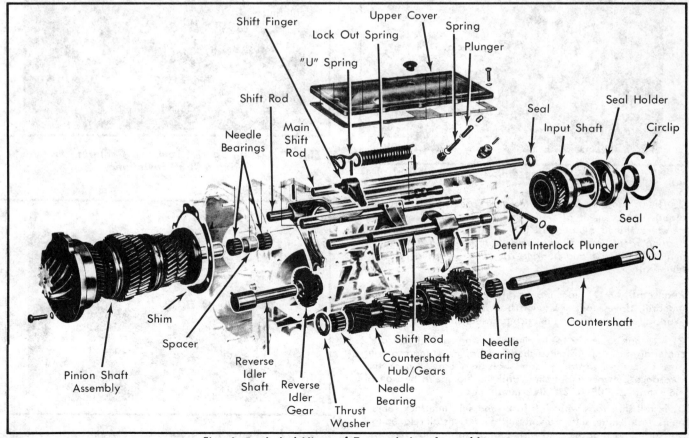

Fig. 6 Exploded View of Transmission Assembly

PORSCHE 928 5-SPEED (Cont.)

3) Remove the input shaft using special tools (9140 and 9148) and pulling shaft from the case.

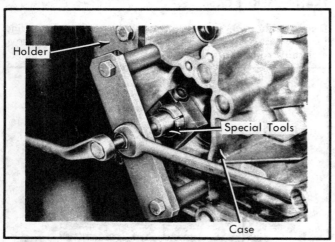

Fig. 7   View Showing Input Shaft Removal

4) Remove pinion shaft assembly using removal tools (9148 and P263) to press out assembly. Drive out reverse idler gear shaft, then remove reverse idler gear assembly.

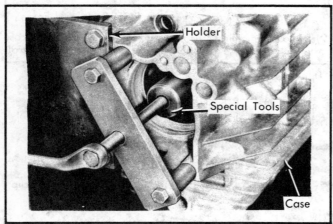

Fig. 8   View Showing Pinion Shaft Removal

NOTE — *Transmission and differential case (transaxle) repairs include replacement of seals and bearing races. Case temperature should be at least 300°F (150°C) when installing bearing races. Press load should be maintained for about 2 minutes until case and bearing race have reached the same temperature.*

Reassembly — 1) Place input shaft in case and using suitable mandrel, drive input shaft into ball bearing up to the stop. Work alternately over outer race to insure shaft is to the stop.

2) Attach installer (9144) to pinion bearing cover. Fabricate 2 centering pins and install as shown in *Fig. 10.* Using centering pins as guides, install pinion shaft into case. Check that clearance between input shaft and 4th-5th speed hub on pinion shaft is .008-.012" (.2-.3 mm).

3) Install shift rods with shift forks and shift interlock components. Install main shift rod with shift finger. Install relaxed lock out spring so that one end rests on "U" spring and the other end of roll pin faces up.

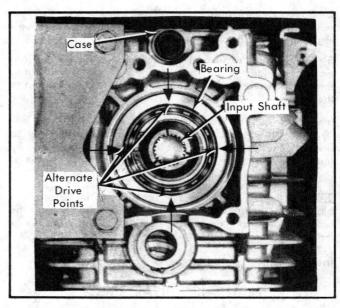

Fig. 9   Drive Points for Input Shaft Installation

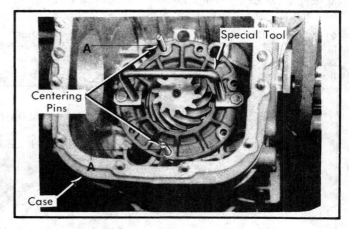

Fig. 10   Using Special Tool and Centering Pins for Pinion Shaft Installation

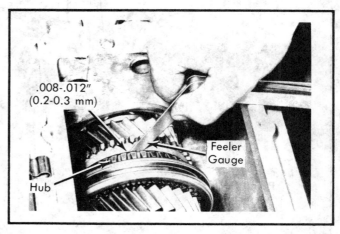

Fig. 11   Measuring Clearance Between Input Shaft and 4th-5th Speed Hub

PORSCHE 928 5-SPEED (Cont.)

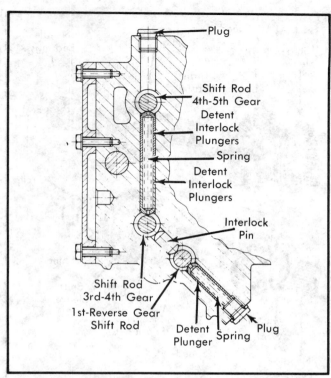

Fig. 12 Sectional View of Shift Rods and Interlock Components

4) Using special tool (9155), turn main shift rod until shift finger pin can be installed. In this position, the lock out spring will be under tension and depression for set screw in main shift rod faces left.

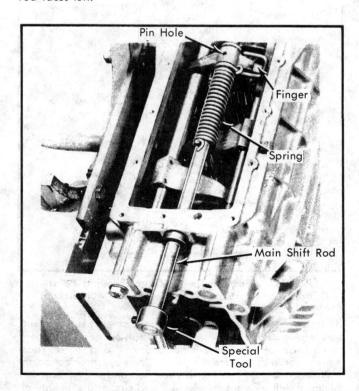

Fig. 13 View Showing Main Shift Rod Alignment

INPUT SHAFT

Disassembly — Place shaft assembly in press and using arbor (VW 457), press off ball bearing. Remove synchronizer ring, shift band and thrust block. Remove 2 needle bearings and spacer from inside shaft.

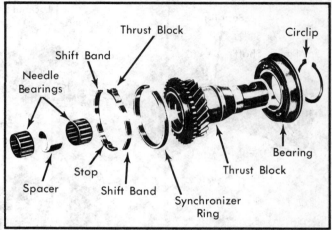

Fig. 14 Exploded View of Input Shaft Assembly

NOTE — All parts must be clean and free of grease before reassembly.

Reassembly — Install both needle bearings into shaft bore with spacer between bearings. Install shift band and thrust block. Install synchronizer ring. Heat ball bearing to 212° F (100° C) and press bearing onto shaft until tight. Hold pressure for 2 minutes until bearing cools. Install circlip.

PINION SHAFT

Disassembly — 1) Mount pinion shaft assembly in a suitable holding fixture and remove circlip and shim. Place shaft assembly in suitable press and press off shift sleeve and hub.

2) Remove needle bearing and inner race and mark for reassembly. Remove 4th gear, thrust washer, needle bearing and inner race and mark for reassembly.

3) Remove 3rd gear, shift sleeve and hub. Remove needle bearing and inner race and mark for reassembly. Remove 2nd gear, thrust washer, needle bearing and inner race and mark for reassembly.

4) Remove 1st gear, shift sleeve and hub, shim and lock nut, then remove reverse gear. Press off tapered roller bearing with bearing retaining plate as a unit. Using arbor (US 1103), press off tapered roller bearing.

NOTE — It is imperative that all parts are free of grease and finger prints during assembly unless otherwise specified. Large taper bearings and inner races must be heated to 212°F (100°C) prior to installation. Hold until temperature has balanced itself.

Reassembly — 1) Press end tapered roller bearing onto shaft. Press bearing retaining plate complete with tapered roller bearing and shim onto shaft. Install reverse gear with cavity facing lock nut. Install lock nut and tighten to 109-130 ft. lbs. (15-81 mkg), then stake lock nut. See Fig. 16.

PORSCHE 928 5-SPEED (Cont.)

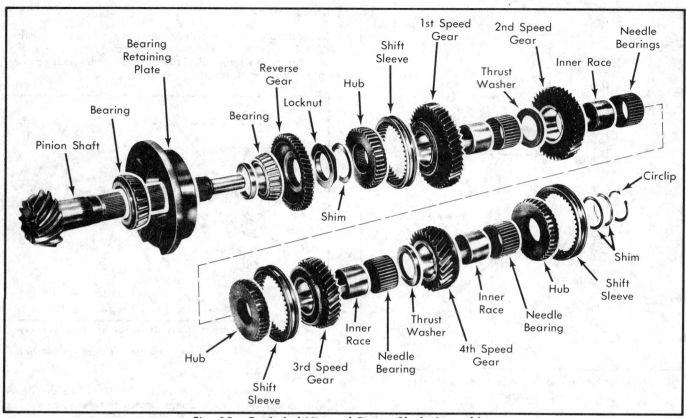

Fig. 15 Exploded View of Pinion Shaft Assembly

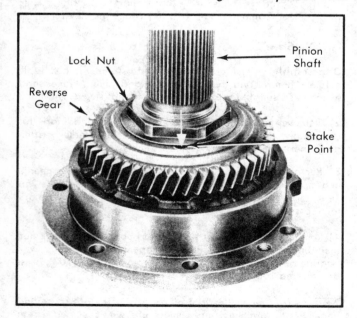

Fig. 16 Installation of Retainer Plate Assembly on Pinion Shaft With Lock Nut Staking Point Indicated

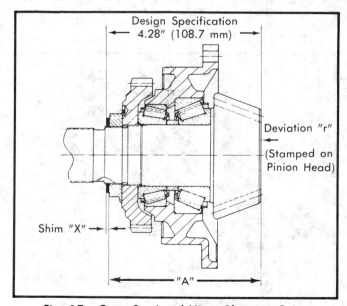

Fig. 17 Cross-Sectional View Showing Point Designations for Calculation of Shim "X" Thickness

2) To determine thickness of shim "X" in *Fig. 17*, measure and record distance from end of pinion shaft head to lock nut (dimension "A" in *Fig. 17*) with a caliper. Shim thickness is equal to dimension "A" plus deviation "r" (stamped on pinion head) subtracted from design specification of 4.28" (108.7 mm).

3) Install selected shim, hub and sleeve making sure flat surface on side flank faces 1st gear. Install 1st gear and check synchronization. Install needle bearings and inner races marked for 2nd, 3rd and 4th gears. Check synchronization. Install needle bearing and inner race, hub and sleeve, shim and circlip. Install a shim between hub and circlip to eliminate all end play. *See Fig. 19.*

PORSCHE 928 5-SPEED (Cont.)

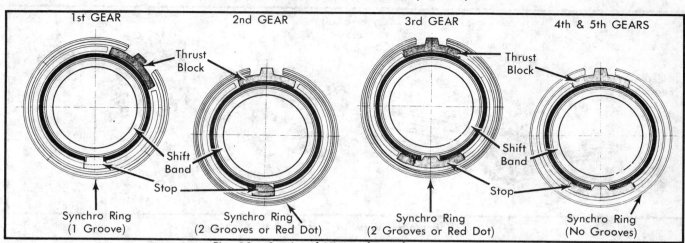

Fig. 18 Sectional View of Synchronizer Rings

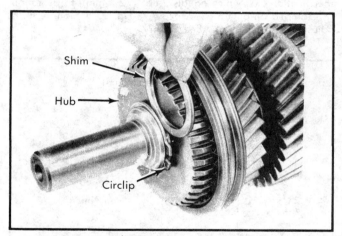

Fig. 19 Selecting Gear Set End Shim

SYNCHRONIZER ASSEMBLIES

NOTE — *Synchronizers MUST be replaced in pairs only.*

Disassembly — Transmission is equipped with modified synchronization for all forward speeds. Each synchronizer is different, therefore no parts are interchangeable between synchronizers. Mark synchronizers before disassembly to facilitate reassembly. Axial movement is eliminated by using a shift band with beveled flanks. See Fig. 18.

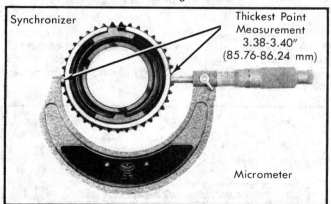

Fig. 20 Correct Position for Measuring Synchronizer Ring at Thickest Location

Inspection — Clean and dry all parts. Check for chipped teeth or any other irregularity. Using a micrometer, check all synchronizer rings at the thickest point. Measurement should read 3.38-3.40" (85.76-86.24 mm).

Reassembly — To reassemble, reverse disassembly procedure, insuring that correct parts for particular synchronizer are used.

NOTE — *When reassembling 1st gear, short side of shift band must be to right of thrust block. When reassembling 2nd gear, bevelled side of stop must face to right as seen from top view.*

COUNTERSHAFT

Disassembly — Remove circlip and needle bearing. Place countershaft assembly in a press. Using support rail (VW 457) and arbor (VW 407), press off countershaft drive gear and spacer. Remove countershaft 4th speed and 3rd speed gears. Remove end needle bearing.

Inspection — Clean and dry all parts. Check for chips, burrs or any irregularities.

NOTE — *When replacement of a gear is required, replace in pairs only.*

Reassembly — To reassemble, heat gears to 212° F (100° C) and reverse disassembly procedure with the following notes:

Place 3rd gear onto shaft so small shoulder faces stop. Place 4th gear onto shaft so large shoulder faces 3rd gear. Place countershaft gear onto shaft so large shoulder faces spacer. See Fig. 21.

DIFFERENTIAL

Disassembly — 1) Place differential assembly in vise fitted with jaw protectors. Remove ring gear bolts and drive ring gear off housing. Remove bearings (if required) using a double arm puller.

2) Remove pinion shaft lock pin, then remove pinion shaft, pinion gears, side gear drive flange nuts and side gears. Note location and thickness of any shims removed from side gears.

PORSCHE 928 5-SPEED (Cont.)

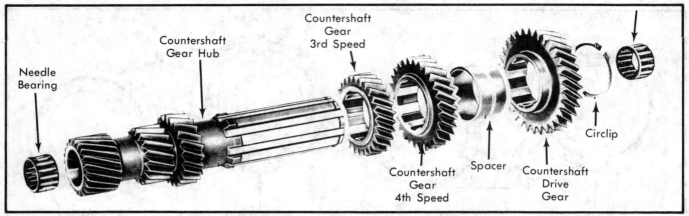

Fig. 21   Exploded View of Countershaft Assembly

Reassembly — 1) Heat ring gear to about 212°F (100°C) and place on case using centering pins to align bolt holes. Install new bolts and tighten crosswise to 109-130 ft. lbs. (15-18 mkg). Slide lock plate into bolt head groove, bend ends together, then bend lock plate ends down over side of bolt head.

2) Place correct shims under large gears and insert in case. Hold small gear thrust washers in place with grease and install small gears. Align gear and washer holes with bore and insert shaft. Position correctly and lock in position with lock pin.

3) If bearings were removed, heat inner bearing race to 212°F (100°C) and press on case.

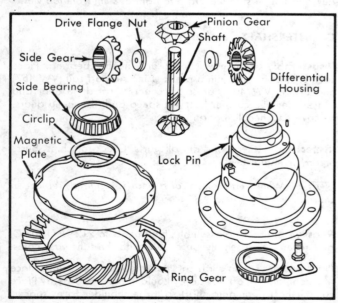

Fig. 22   Exploded View of Differential Assembly

TRANSAXLE REASSEMBLY & ADJUSTMENT

NOTE — *Differential assembly must be adjusted ONLY when repairs to assembly require replacement parts. Adjust ring gear if transmission case, side cover, pinion bearing and retaining plate, pinion and ring gear set, differential housing or differential bearings are replaced. Adjust pinion gear if transmission case, pinion bearing and retaining plate or pinion and ring gear set are replaced.*

1) Pinion depth adjustment is calculated by adding design specification "R", which equals 2.86" (72.7 mm), to deviation "r" stamped on pinion gear face. See *Fig. 23.* Pinion depth is adjusted by shims "S3". See *Fig. 27.*

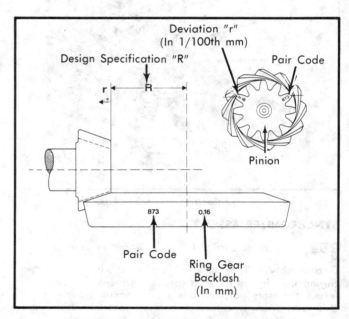

Fig. 23   Location of Stamped Codes and Specifications of Pinion and Ring Gears

2) Install input shaft. Install pinion without shim(s) and tighten bearing retaining plate bolts. Install 1 side cover without "O" ring and secure with 2 bolts. Set adjusting ring of universal master gauge (VW 385/1) at 2.36" (60 mm) from gauge center point. See *Fig. 24.*

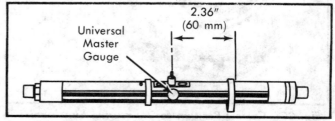

Fig. 24   Universal Master Measuring Gauge

PORSCHE 928 5-SPEED (Cont.)

3) Install centering discs (VW 385/4) onto master gauge and attach gauge plunger (VW 385/14) with dial indicator extension. See Fig. 25. Install opposite side cover without "O" ring and secure with 2 bolts.

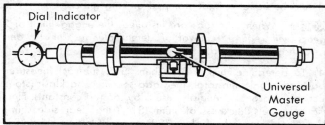

Fig. 25 Universal Master Measuring Gauge with Dial Indicator Attached

4) Install master gauge and set dial indicator at zero with .004" (1 mm) preload. Install gauge plate on pinion head. Carefully turn universal gauge until dial gauge extension is perpendicular to face of pinion head. At this time dial gauge needle will reach reversal point (highest point). Read and record dial gauge. See Fig. 26.

5) Remove master gauge and pinion shaft. Install calculated shim rounded off to nearest .002" (.05 mm) and pinion shaft. Recheck pinion depth adjustment. Adjustment should be 2.86" (72.7 mm) with variation of ±.001" (.03 mm).

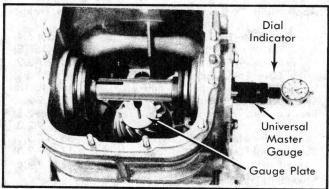

Fig. 26 Measuring Pinion Depth with Master Gauge

RING GEAR ADJUSTMENT

1) Remove pinion gear and preselected shim(s). Install differential assembly in case. Install ring gear end side cover without shims and tighten bolts. Carefully install opposite side cover.

2) Using a feeler gauge, measure clearance between transmission case and side cover. Total required shim thickness is equal to measured clearance, minus (−) .012" (.3 mm) for bearing preload.

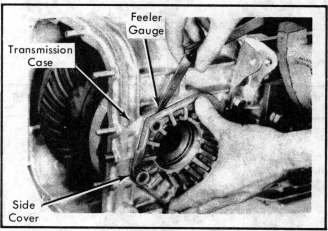

Fig. 28 Measuring Shim Thickness Between Side Cover and Transmission Case

RING GEAR BACKLASH ADJUSTMENT

1) Install countershaft assembly into transmission case. Install pinion shaft with preselected shim ("S3") and tighten bearing retainer bolts. Install differential assembly in case. Install ring gear end side cover with preselected shim pack and tighten bolts. Install opposite side cover and tighten bolts.

2) Turn differential in both directions several times to seat bearings. Mount dial indicator with support (VW 388) and set adjustable lever at 3.15" (80 mm). See Fig. 29.

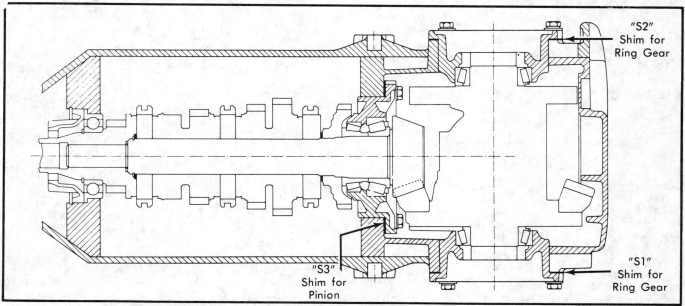

Fig. 27 Sectional View Showing Location of Pinion and Ring Gear Adjusting Shims

PORSCHE 928 5-SPEED (Cont.)

Fig. 29 Gauge Installation for Measuring Backlash

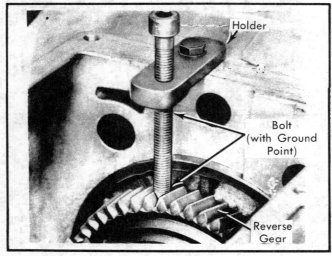

Fig. 30 Installation of Fabricated Tool on Reverse Gear to Hold Pinion Gear Assembly in Position

3) Engage 5th and reverse gears. Hold pinion gear assembly with a locally fabricated tool on reverse gear. *See Fig. 30.* Turn ring gear to stop by hand and set dial indicator at zero. Turn ring gear back and record amount of backlash. Backlash should be equal to that stamped on ring gear.

NOTE — *When shift rods are installed, the engagement of 2 gears will require removal of detent plunger for 1st and reverse gear shift rod.*

4) To determine thickness of shim "S1", subtract measured backlash from shim total, then add specified backlash (stamped on ring gear). Multiply results by .66 (lift constant). Final figure equals thickness of shim "S1" (ring gear side shim). Calculate thickness of shim "S2" by subtracting shim "S1" thickness from total shim thickness.

5) Remove side covers and divide shims to give correct shim "S1" and "S2" thicknesses. Install shift rods and forks into case. Install side covers and shims and tighten bolts.

6) Measure backlash again. If not within specifications, change shims "S1" and "S2" until specified backlash is obtained. Check backlash 4 times by turning ring gear 90° each time. The 4 measurements must not deviate from each other by more than .002" (.05 mm).

TIGHTENING SPECIFICATIONS

Application	Ft. Lbs. (mkg)
Central Tube-to-Transmission	39-46 (5.4-6.4)
Pinion Retaining Nut	109-130 (15-18)
Pinion Retaining Plate-to-Case	20-30 (2.7-3.2)
Upper Cover-to-Transmission Case	6-7 (.80-.95)
Ring Gear-to-Differential Housing	109-130 (15-18)
Side Cover-to-Transmission Case	14-17 (1.9-2.3)
Rear Cover-to-Transmission Case	14-17 (1.9-2.3)
Drain Plug	14-17 (1.9-2.3)
Drive Shaft-to-Input Shaft Coupling	33-36 (4.5-5.0)
Back-Up Light Switch	14-17 (1.9-2.3)
Axle Flange	28-33 (3.9-4.6)
Coupling-to-Main Shaft Rod	9-12 (1.3-1.7)

RENAULT LE CAR 4-SPEED

DESCRIPTION

Transaxle is equipped with a 4-speed transmission that is synchromeshed in all forward gears. Transaxle houses transmission and differential with a common oil supply used to lubricate both assemblies. Final drive is a hypoid type gear. Constant velocity joints are used at each end of axle drive shafts.

LUBRICATION & ADJUSTMENT

See MANUAL TRANSMISSION SERVICING Section

SERVICE (IN VEHICLE)

AXLE DRIVE SHAFTS

Removal — 1) Remove stub axle nut and washer using suitable hub locking tool (Rou. 436-01). Using suitable ball joint extender tool (T. Av. 476), disconnect upper and lower suspension and steering arm ball joints.

2) Mount drive shaft extracting tool (T Av. 235) on hub. Push out drive shaft far enough for lower ball joint to clear stub axle. Withdraw drive shaft. Repeat on other side.

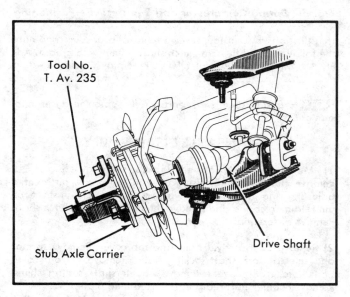

Fig. 1 Removing Axle Drive Shaft

NOTE — If components show excessive or abnormal wear, complete axle drive shaft must be replaced.

Installation — 1) Coat stub axle splines with grease. Insert drive shaft into side gear and hub, and at the same time connect lower ball joint into stub axle carrier.

2) Using installation tool (T Av. 409-01), draw drive shaft into hub splines. See Fig. 2. Using pliers, hold ball joint cone stationary and reconnect ball joints. Attach stub axle washer and nut. Tighten nut. Fill transaxle with oil.

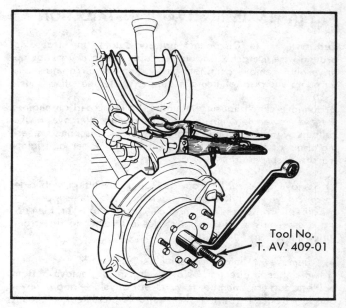

Fig. 2 Installing Axle Drive Shaft

WHEEL BEARINGS

Removal — Remove hub and disc assembly. Disconnect 3 ball joints using extractor (T Av. 476). Disconnect ball joints and withdraw stub axle carrier. Using puller (B. V. 28-01), remove outer bearing. Remove bearing cover plate. Press out inner bearing.

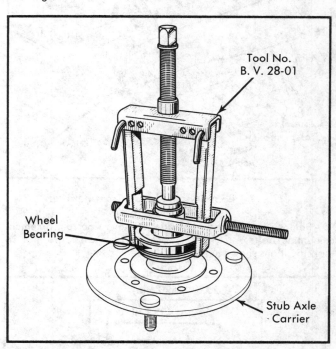

Fig. 3 Removing Wheel Bearing

Installation — Inspect condition of bearing carrier bore for damage or wear. Reverse removal procedure and note the following: Press inner bearing in. Place 1 oz. (25 g) of grease into stub axle carrier center section. Apply sealing compound and fit bearing cover plate.

RENAULT LE CAR 4-SPEED (Cont.)

TRANSAXLE REMOVAL & INSTALLATION

Removal — 1) Disconnect battery cables and transaxle ground wire. Detach speedometer cable. Remove water pump drive belt. Remove camshaft pulley. Remove air pump filter, air pump and bracket. Remove 2 upper starter mounting bolts.

2) Remove clutch housing mounting bolts located on engine. Remove lower left nut of clutch housing. Remove brake calipers without disconnecting brake hoses. Disconnect steering arms at steering rack end. Disconnect upper ball joints from front suspension.

3) Remove drive shafts from side gears by tilting stub axle carriers downward. Remove 2 mounting bolts from supporting bracket on transaxle. Disconnect clutch cable at lever, then using a screwdriver, push against sleeve retainer to free from supporting bracket.

4) Remove tubular crossmember top bolt, and tilt crossmember in direction of arrow in *Fig. 4*. Remove bottom bolt and tap crossmember toward rear of vehicle and remove. Support front of transaxle with suitable jack. Remove mounting pad and bracket.

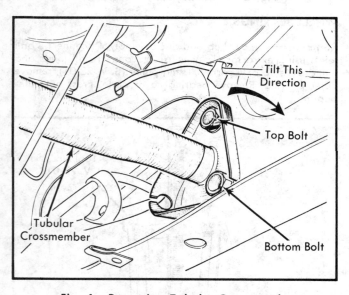

Fig. 4   Removing Tubular Crossmember

5) Remove starter and lay aside. Remove side reinforcement mounting bolts and clutch cover. Fabricate a square tube to specifications shown in *Fig. 5*.

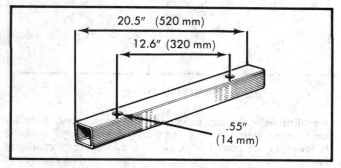

Fig. 5   Specifications of Square Tube Tool

6) Position spring compressor tool (Sus. 21) with hook end holding transaxle casing and threaded end bolted to square tube. See *Fig. 6*. Jack and tilt engine/transaxle assembly. Remove transaxle assembly so it does not catch on clutch mechanism.

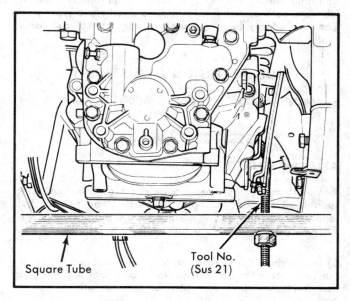

Fig. 6   Spring Compressor and Square Tube Positioning

Installation — To install, reverse removal procedure and note the following: Lightly coat clutch shaft splines with grease. Adjust free play at end of clutch lever. Free play should be within .125-.157" (3.2-4.0 mm).

NOTE — *Ensure drive shaft end is fully seated in differential side gears.*

TRANSAXLE DISASSEMBLY

1) Mount transaxle assembly onto suitable work stand. Remove clutch housing. Using a wrench, remove differential adjusting ring nuts and lock washers. Release clutch shaft roll pin retaining spring and remove the pin. Slide out clutch shaft. Remove differential.

2) Remove 12 top cover bolts and top cover. Remove springs and selector fork shaft locking balls. Remove 9 front cover bolts and front cover. Remove countershaft setting shims. Remove countershaft rear bearing retaining plate.

3) Using a punch, drive out 2 roll pins retaining reverse gear pinion shaft. Remove reverse gear selector shaft and locking disc between selector shafts. See *Fig. 7*.

4) Engage transmission gears. Unlock and remove speedometer end nut. Remove rubber washer and return transmission gears to neutral. Push final drive pinion in toward differential and remove taper roller bearing. Withdraw final drive pinion shaft.

5) Push countershaft toward differential, and remove rear bearing race. Remove front bearing, countershaft, reverse gear shaft and reverse gear. Using a punch, drive out 1st-2nd and 3rd-4th shift fork roll pins. Remove shafts and selector forks.

RENAULT LE CAR 4-SPEED (Cont.)

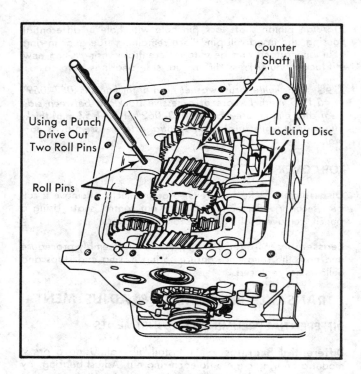

Fig. 7 *Removing Reverse Gear Selector Shaft*

6) Remove lock plate and mainshaft bearing adjusting nut. Remove 4th gear thrust washer. Push out countershaft front bearing race. Remove gear and synchro assembly from case.

COMPONENT DISASSEMBLY & REASSEMBLY

SYNCHRONIZER ASSEMBLIES

Disassembly — Mark the position of the sliding gear in relation to the hub before dismantling. Remove both synchro springs and slide assembly apart. Clean all parts thoroughly.

Reassembly — On 1st-2nd gear synchro, line up dismantling marks and place inner part of synchro below level of second speed sliding gear. On all synchros, install 2 springs into hub, covering all 3 slots. Ensure marks are aligned. Insert and position 3 shift keys.

INPUT SHAFT

Using a suitable press and holder tool (T. AR. 65), press bearing from shaft. To install, press bearing onto shaft using a press.

COUNTERSHAFT

Remove bearing at the clutch shaft end of countershaft, using extractor tool (B. Vi. 22-01) and shell tool (B. Vi. 41).

NOTE — *Installation of bearing will be completed during reassembly procedure.*

TRANSAXLE CASE

Using a press, push out the outer cage of the bearing which lies under the head of the final drive pinion. To install, press bearing onto shaft using a press.

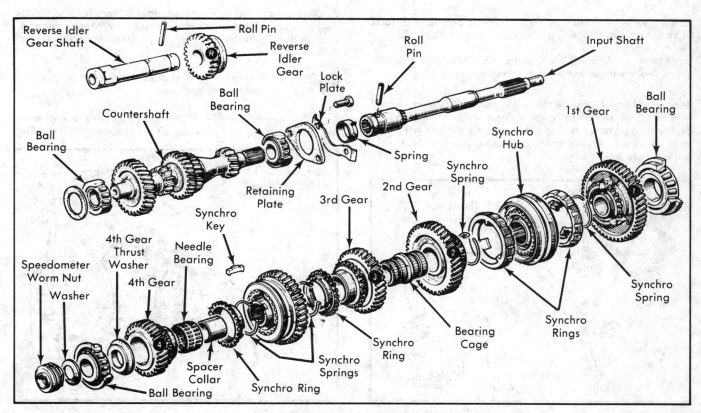

Fig. 8 *Exploded View of Transaxle Components*

Manual Transaxles

RENAULT LE CAR 4-SPEED (Cont.)

DIFFERENTIAL

Disassembly — 1) Place suitable thrust pad (Rou. 15-01) into side gear. Remove ring gear side bearing using suitable puller. Place thrust pad on other side and remove housing end side bearing with suitable puller.

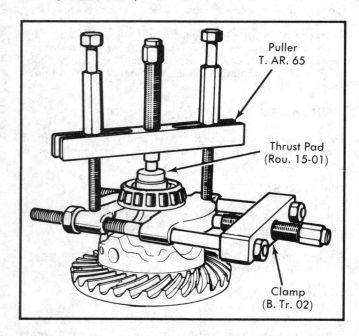

Fig. 9   Removing Differential Housing Side Bearing

2) Remove self-locking ring gear mounting bolts and discard. Drive out roll pin retaining pinion shaft using a punch.

Inspection — Check pinion gears, side bearings and side gears; replace those components found defective.

Reassembly — 1) Ensure that all components are lubricated with EP 80 oil and place Bakelite thrust washer in differential case with oil groove facing side gear. Fit pinions with their thrust washers into differential housing so that lock tabs engage hole in housing.

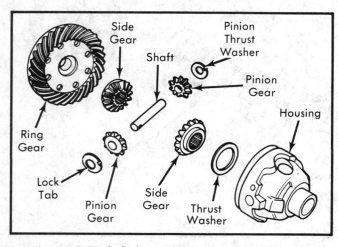

Fig. 10   Exploded View of Differential Assembly

2) Align pinion shaft lock pin hole with hole in differential housing and insert roll pin. Place remaining side gear in ring gear and attach ring gear to differential housing using new self-locking nuts. Press differential side bearings onto case.

NOTE — *Bakelite thrust washer normal thickness is .057-.059" (1.46-1.50 mm). In case of excessive backlash between side gear and pinion, use washer .060-.062" (1.53-1.57 mm) thick. Slight drag while turning differential after reassembly is normal.*

TOP COVER

Disassembly — Remove reverse gear selector. Remove 2 roll pins securing selector finger. Slide out control shaft. Using a punch, remove bushing and seal from cover.

Reassembly — To reassemble, reverse disassembly procedure and note the following: Ensure spring, spring end stops and bellows are replaced.

TRANSAXLE REASSEMBLY & ADJUSTMENT

DIFFERENTIAL PRELIMINARY ADJUSTMENTS

Differential Bearings — 1) Install oil seal. Using a press, mount a bearing cage onto each ring nut. Adjust bearings by turning ring nuts in or out. Attach transaxle housing to support (B. Vi 495).

2) Place differential into transaxle housing. Using a wrench, screw in adjusting ring nuts until bearing track races come in contact with taper rollers.

3) Differential must turn without play. If there is play, tighten ring nuts until differential turns without play. Mark position of ring nuts in relation with housing. Remove ring nuts and differential.

NOTE — *If tightening ring nuts does not remove play, install new bearings and fit with preload.*

Side Bearing Preload — 1) Rotate differential several turns to seat bearings. Wrap a piece of string around differential.

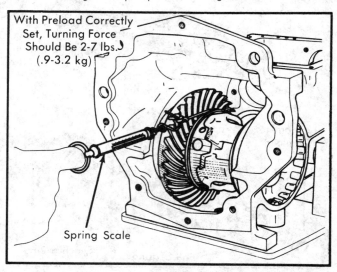

Fig. 11   Checking Differential Preload

RENAULT LE CAR 4-SPEED (Cont.)

Attach a spring scale to string and pull. Force required to rotate differential should be 2-7 lbs. (.9-3.2 kg). Force must be consistent during rotation of differential.

2) If more force is required, carefully loosen one of the adjusting ring nuts. If it turns too freely, carefully tighten the nut. Recheck preload again. When final adjustment is obtained, mark the position of ring nuts in relation to housing. Remove ring nuts and differential.

Transaxle Casing — Using a suitable press, install bearing outer race (under final drive pinion head) into the housing.

Mainshaft Bearing Adjusting Nut — Mount the tapered roller bearing outer cage into the adjusting nut using a press.

TRANSAXLE REASSEMBLY

1) Place transaxle casing vertically on flat surface. Place the stack of mainshaft gears inside the casing. Do not include 4th speed driven gear at this time.

2) Insert final drive pinion and begin mounting 2 hubs. Place a 2-part block under final drive pinion. Position a piece of tube to take load of 3rd-4th hub. Mount 2 synchros. Check position of synchro rings.

3) Attach transaxle casing to support (B. Vi 495). Ensure pinion splines mate with splines of 1st-2nd and 3rd-4th speed synchro hubs. Place 4th gear and gear ring into casing.

4) Install 2 needle roller cages and 4th gear sleeve. Position 4th gear thrust washer with large diameter facing toward gear. Screw bearing ring adjusting nut as far as possible.

5) Place tapered roller bearing onto final drive pinion hand tight. Hold sliding gear in place with wrench (B. Vi 499). Screw on speedometer drive pinion so tapered roller bearing is drawn into position. *See Fig. 12.*

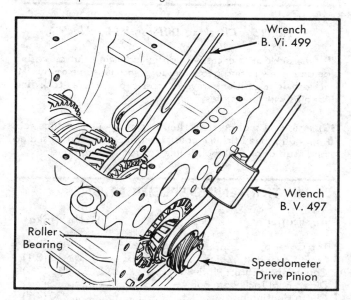

Fig. 12   Installing Tapered Roller Bearing

6) Remove speedometer drive pinion and insert spring washer. Replace drive pinion and tighten to 75-90 ft. lbs. (10-12 mkg)

using torque wrench fitted with suitable wrench (B. Vi. 497). Lock into position.

7) Adjust mainshaft bearing by turning ring nut. Unscrew ring nut until outer ring touches rollers using suitable wrench (B. Vi. 499). Bearings may be reused if there is no end play when mainshaft is turned.

8) If end play exists, continue to unscrew ring nut until end play has diminished. Lock ring nut with lock plate.

NOTE — *New bearings must be preloaded.*

9) If installing new bearings, unscrew ring nut while turning mainshaft by hand. When shaft becomes slightly hard to turn, stop unscrewing ring nut.

10) Rotate mainshaft several times to seat bearings. Tie a piece of string around 3rd-4th sliding gear groove. Attach a spring scale to string and pull. Gear should rotate under force of 1-3.5 lbs. (.5-1.6 kg). When correct adjustment is obtained, lock ring nut with lock plate. *See Fig. 13.*

11) Position 1st-2nd speed selector fork into casing. Slide selector shaft through casing bracket and into selector fork. Install roll pin with a punch.

NOTE — *Slot in roll pins must face toward differential.*

12) Position 3rd-4th speed selector fork into casing. Slide selector shaft through casing bracket and into selector fork. Install roll pin with a punch.

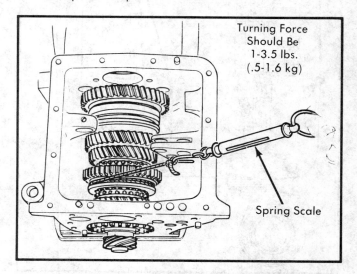

Turning Force Should Be 1-3.5 lbs. (.5-1.6 kg)

Spring Scale

Fig. 13   Checking Preload on New Bearings

13) Position transaxle casing so countershaft will stand vertically, with 4th gear resting on casing wall. Use a length of tube to mount bearing on clutch shaft side.

14) Position reverse gear in transaxle casing with groove facing toward differential. Install reverse gear shaft. Secure gear to shaft with a roll pin using a punch.

15) Install pinion stop roll pin with roll pin slit at right angle to shaft. Pinion stop roll pin should protrude out both ends of shaft equal amounts.

RENAULT LE CAR 4-SPEED (Cont.)

16) Place countershaft bearing race over rear of shaft and cover with retaining plate and lock plate. Tighten lock plate bolts and bend over tabs.

17) Install countershaft front bearing by sliding onto shaft. Using a piece of tubing, slide outer track race on until it is flush with case.

18) Adjust countershaft bearing end play using shims. End play must be between .001-.005" (.03-.13 mm). Attach a dial gauge on end of shaft, push bearing race in to obtain less play.

19) With proper amount of play obtained, place shims behind bearing track race. Last shim should extend beyond gasket face by .012" (.30 mm).

20) Install locking disc between selector shafts. Drop in lock balls and their springs. Longest spring is for 1st-2nd gear shaft.

21) Install speedometer gear sleeve in place with "O" ring seal. Position speedometer driven gear, countershaft adjusting shims and gasket. Install front cover.

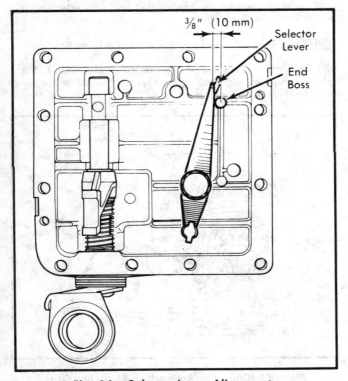

Fig. 14   Selector Lever Alignment

22) Line up top cover with cover ring and seal. Pull bellows over lever shaft and mount shaft on top cover along with spring, end stops and selector finger. Install roll pins.

23) Place reverse gear selector in position and tighten bolt. Line up selector lever with reverse gear shaft. Space end of selector lever 3/8" (10 mm) from center line of boss. See Fig. 14.

24) Position transaxle in neutral. Slide reverse gear so it rests on 4th gear of countershaft. Move cover and seal so end of gear lever engages in selector fork notches.

25) Reverse gear selector engages with notch on selector shaft and groove in gear. Secure the cover.

26) Place differential in housing. Insert clutch shaft and line up roll pin hole with hole in countershaft. Insert roll pin and retaining spring.

27) Coat threads on differential adjusting ring nuts with suitable sealant. Using suitable wrench (B. Vi. 494), turn ring nuts so that preload adjusting marks are opposite those on housing.

28) Adjust differential backlash as follows: Install a dial indicator on housing and check backlash. Measured value should be within .005-.010" (.13-.25 mm). See Fig. 15.

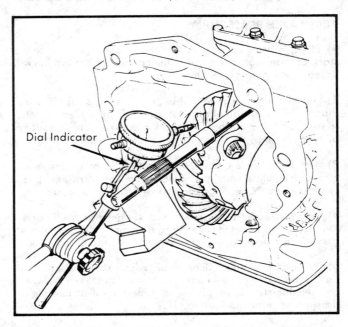

Fig. 15   Checking Differential Backlash

29) If backlash is excessive, loosen adjusting nut on casing side and screw in ring gear side adjusting nut same amount. If backlash is insufficient, reverse above procedure. Lock ring gear nuts with lock plates.

30) Install oil seal on clutch housing using suitable tube tool (B. Vi. 488), then fit clutch housing. Position housing by sliding along shaft of oil seal tool. Tighten clutch housing bolts.

TIGHTENING SPECIFICATIONS

Application	Ft. Lbs. (mkg)
Top Cover Bolt	10 (1.4)
Front Cover Bolt	15 (2.1)
Countershaft Thrust Plate Bolt	15 (2.1)
Differential Lock Plate Bolt	15 (2.1)
Clutch Housing Bolts	30 (4.2)
Speedometer Drive Pinion	75-90 (10.4-12.4)
Ring Gear Bolts	65-80 (9.0-11.1)
Reverse Gear Lever Bolt	20 (2.8)

SAAB 99 & 900 4 & 5-SPEED

DESCRIPTION

The transaxle assembly is a 2-piece unit containing both transmission and final drive. Transaxle assembly is located underneath the engine and part of transmission case serves as an engine oil sump. The transmission and final drive are assembled in rear section of the transaxle and primary gear unit is housed in the front section. All forward gears are in constant mesh while reverse gear is engaged by a sliding gear. The chain driven primary gear unit transmits engine power via the clutch to transmission. Final drive assembly consists of differential assembly, pinion shaft, and front drive axle shaft housings.

LUBRICATION & ADJUSTMENT

See MANUAL TRANSMISSION SERVICING Section.

SERVICE (IN VEHICLE)

AXLE DRIVE SHAFTS & WHEEL BEARINGS

NOTE — *Downward movement of 900 control arms is controlled by rubber buffer inside shock absorber. Therefore, remove shock absorber before raising vehicle or support control arm with a jack at outer end of lower control arm.*

Removal — 1) Remove hub cap, loosen hub nut and loosen wheel lugs. Raise and support vehicle. Remove wheels. Rotate brake disc to align recess in disc edge with brake pads. Disconnect parking brake cable. Remove caliper mounting bolts and hang caliper out of way with wire; DO NOT disconnect hydraulic line.

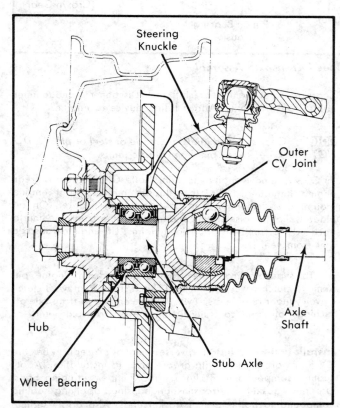

Hub

Wheel Bearing

Stub Axle

Steering Knuckle

Outer CV Joint

Axle Shaft

Fig. 1 Sectional View of Saab Steering Knuckle Assembly

2) Remove hub and disc assembly with extractor (8996084). Remove larger clamp on inner universal joint bellows. Remove steering arm and upper ball joint with remover (8995409). Disconnect screws on lower control arm bracket. Separate inner CV joint from drive flange. Cover end of rubber bellows to prevent needle bearings from falling onto floor.

3) Grasp wheel splash guard and pull axle assembly through wheel housing to remove. Thoroughly clean axle assembly. Place steering knuckle housing in a press and press out drive shaft. Remove snap ring from bearing housing. Press out and discard bearing.

NOTE — *Axle shafts cannot be disassembled. If damaged or defective, replace as complete assembly.*

Installation — 1) Press bearing into steering knuckle housing, then install snap ring. Mount axle shaft in a press and press on knuckle housing and bearing. Install inner oil seal. Press wheel hub and brake disc onto axle splines and install washer and new lock nut.

NOTE — *Do not tighten lock nut at this time.*

2) Install axle shaft through wheel housing. Mount any needle bearings which may have fallen out of inner CV joint on ends of "T" piece. Attach inner CV joint to drive flange. Install upper ball joint to steering knuckle and reinstall lower control arm bracket. Mount tie rod end to steering arm. Mount brake caliper.

3) Reinstall front wheel and lower vehicle. Tighten hub lock nut, then secure in place by peening into locking groove. Pump brake pedal several times to seat brake pads.

PRIMARY GEAR UNIT

Removal — 1) Remove hood, battery, radiator, grill and radiator/headlight assembly from vehicle. Disconnect exhaust pipe from manifold. Remove rubber bellows from throttle valve housing. Remove alternator. Remove engine mount nuts, then connect a suitable lifting device to engine so clutch end of engine will be lifted first. Remove front engine mount.

2) Raise engine until primary gear cover clears front engine beam. Remove cover. Remove chain tensioner. Remove upper and lower primary gear snap rings, and pull gears (with chains) off of housing simultaneously.

Installation — To install, reverse removal procedure and note the following: Install a new clutch shaft seal and cover gasket. Coat cover and housing mating surfaces with suitable sealing compound.

TRANSAXLE REMOVAL & INSTALLATION

Removal — 1) Remove hood, then disconnect battery cables and lift out battery. Drain coolant from radiator and engine. Disconnect power brake unit vacuum hose from intake manifold. Remove rubber bellows between air flow sensor and intake manifold. Disconnect and plug fuel line. Disconnect air flow sensor electrical leads. Remove air cleaner and mixture control unit.

2) On 900, remove air intake, preheater hose, crankcase ventilation hose and intake hose. Disconnect cable from oil

Manual Transaxles

SAAB 99 & 900 4 & 5-SPEED (Cont.)

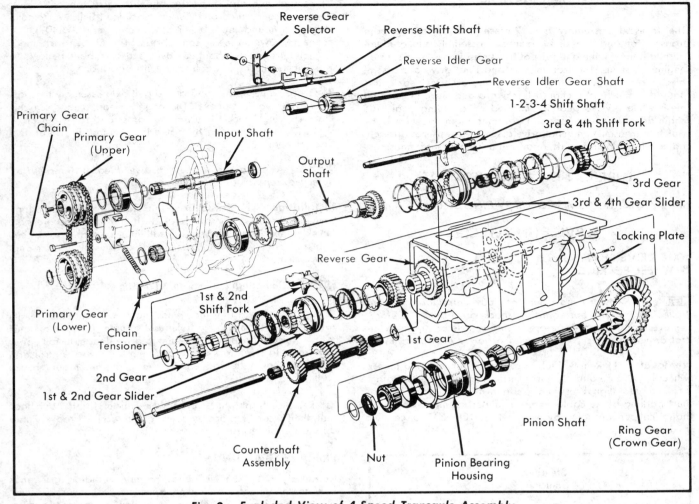

Fig. 2 Exploded View of 4-Speed Transaxle Assembly

pressure sender. On California vehicles, disconnect all EGR system hoses. If equipped with power steering, disconnect and plug hoses at steering pump.

3) Disconnect and remove ignition coil. Disconnect the following electrical connections: Temperature sending unit, radiator fan, thermostat contact, oil pressure sender, headlights and starter leads. Disconnect and plug all fuel injection lines (if equipped). Disconnect choke and throttle cables. Disconnect all water hoses. Disconnect hose to expansion tank.

4) Remove grille and hood locking cable. Remove radiator/headlight assembly. Disconnect hose from clutch slave cylinder and plug hose and hole in cylinder. Disconnect exhaust pipe from manifold and ground cable from transaxle. Remove bellows clamp and bellows from inner CV joints.

5) On 900, place spacer (8393209) between upper control arm underside and car body to unload suspension when car is raised. Insert spacer from engine compartment side. Raise and support front of car.

6) On all models, remove lower end piece from control arm. Pull out steering knuckle assembly and support end piece against control arm outer end. Put gear lever in neutral. Remove nut and knock out taper pin in gear shift rod joint.

Separate joint from gear shift rod. Disconnect speedometer cable from transaxle. Attach lifting device to engine.

NOTE — *Gear shift rod joints are made of steel or plastic. DO NOT knock out taper pin from plastic joints.*

7) On 99, remove engine mounting bolts. On 900, remove rear engine mounting bolts, then loosen nut on front engine mounting so mounting can be lifted from bracket. On all models, slightly raise engine and move engine/transaxle unit to each side to free constant velocity joints. Lift engine/transaxle unit from vehicle.

8) To separate transaxle from engine, drain engine oil. Remove clutch cover, starter and clutch shaft. Remove 3 clutch slave cylinder retaining screws. Remove engine-to-transaxle attaching bolts and carefully lift engine off transaxle unit.

Installation — To install, reverse removal procedure. Be sure CV joints are packed with grease prior to installation. Apply sealing compound to 3 clutch slave cylinder retaining bolts. Use new gasket on transmission housing, applying sealing compound to both sides of gasket ends. Also apply sealing compound to 6 bolts shown in *Fig. 3*.

SAAB 99 & 900 4 & 5-SPEED (Cont.)

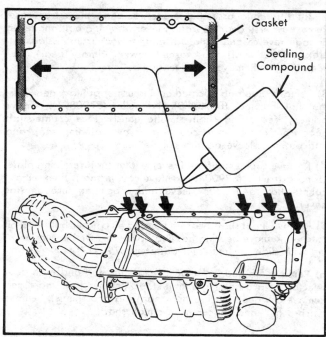

Fig. 3 Adding Sealing Compound to Gasket and Bolts

TRANSAXLE DISASSEMBLY

NOTE — *Prior to disassembling transmission gears, measure ring-to-pinion gear backlash and pinion depth. If ring and pinion gear set have less than 6000 miles (10,000 km), backlash and pinion depth can be adjusted to specifications. However, if mileage is exceeded, backlash and pinion depth must be set to that recorded prior to disassembly. See Pinion Depth Adjustment in this article.*

4-SPEED

1) Mount transaxle assembly on suitable work stand and drain transmission oil. Remove axle shaft housing attaching bolts and remove housings using a puller.

NOTE — *When removing axle housings, do not lose spring and plunger located in end of inner shaft. Also, note the number and thickness of adjusting shims installed with housings.*

2) Remove final drive cover. Measure ring-to-pinion gear backlash and pinion depth. Tilt differential assembly to one side and remove from case. Remove countershaft and reverse gear shaft locking plate. Remove countershaft with remover (8390049) so countershaft gear set drops down. Remove attaching bolts and separate primary gear housing from transaxle housing. Remove countershaft gear set.

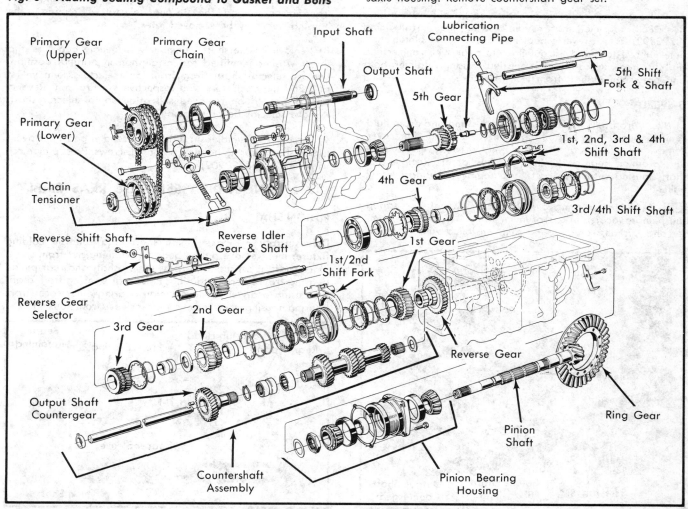

Fig. 4 Exploded View of 5-Speed Transaxle Assembly

SAAB 99 & 900 4 & 5-SPEED (Cont.)

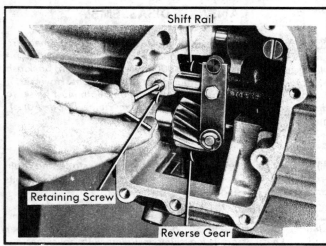

Fig. 5   Removing 4-Speed Reverse Gear Shift Rail Retaining Screw

3) Remove transaxle case side cover. Take out spring and ball catch for gear selector rod. Remove reverse gear shift rail retaining screw, then turn selector rod and pull out shift rail. Remove 1st/2nd and 3rd/4th gear shift rail, then lift out shift forks and 3rd gear sliding sleeve.

4) Pull out reverse idler gear shaft and lift out reverse idler gear. Pull out pinion shaft needle bearing, then install clamp (8790503) to lock reverse gear in place. Remove pinion shaft nut. Remove tool and lift out 3rd/4th gear synchronizer hub and 3rd gear. Remove pinion bearing housing retaining bolts and press pinion shaft from transaxle case.

5-SPEED

1) Mount transaxle assembly on a work stand and drain fluid. Remove primary gear housing front cover and side cover. Remove oil filler plug cover and final drive cover. Measure ring-to-pinion gear backlash and pinon depth. Remove axle shaft housing attaching bolts and remove housings with a puller.

NOTE — *When removing axle housings, do not lose spring and plunger located in end of inner shaft. Also, note the number and thickness of adjusting shims installed with housings.*

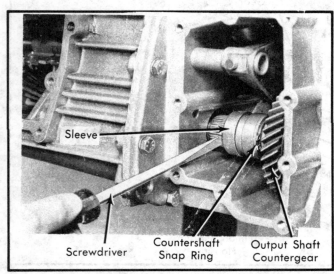

Fig. 6   Disconnecting 5-Speed Mainshaft Countergear

2) Tilt differential assembly to one side and remove from case. Remove reverse gear operating lever retaining bolt and lever. Engage reverse gear and 5th gear to lock transmission. Unstake output shaft tab washer (lower primary gear), then remove unit. Remove chain tensioner.

3) Remove snap ring (located behind upper primary gear). Using slide hammer (8390270) and puller (8790891), remove primary gears and chain simultaneously. Free countershaft gear from output shaft countergear by loosening snap ring and pushing sleeve against countershaft. See *Fig. 6.*

4) Remove countershaft and reverse idler shaft retaining plate. Using extractor (8390049), remove countershaft, then remove countershaft gear with sleeve and snap ring through side cover.

5) Remove input shaft bearing housing oil catcher bolts and oil catcher. Remove bearing housing bolts. Remove bearing housing with slide hammer and adapter (8790917).

6) Remove 5th gear selector fork locking stud and push gear selector toward housing until it stops. Remove fork and slider. Remove 5th gear synchro hub snap ring and shim(s). Remove synchro hub and spacer from pinion shaft.

7) Remove all primary gear housing retaining bolts. Drift dowels into case to separate primary gear housing from transmission housing. The 5th gear selector will remain in the housing and may be removed later.

8) Remove countershaft assembly with needle bearings and thrust washer identified for installation in original position. Remove selector shafts (from front) and selectors. Remove 1st and 2nd gear selectors with respective synchro unit. Reverse selector should be removed still attached to selector shaft. Remove selector ball and guide pin.

9) Remove reverse idler shaft and reverse idler gear. Remove 4 pinion shaft bearing housing retaining screws. Press pinion out with remover (8790909).

COMPONENT DISASSEMBLY & REASSEMBLY

PINION SHAFT

Disassembly — Place pinion shaft in a suitable holding fixture, then remove pinion bearing retaining nut from shaft. Place shaft in a press and press pinion shaft and rear pinion bearing from bearing housing. Press rear bearing from shaft, then using a driver, remove pinion bearing outer races from bearing housing, then remove spacer sleeve from housing.

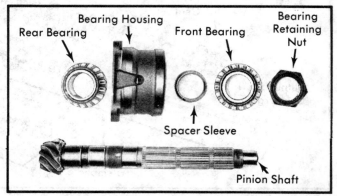

Fig. 7   Exploded View of Pinion Shaft Assembly

SAAB 99 & 900 4 & 5-SPEED (Cont.)

Reassembly — 1) Lubricate bearings with transmission oil, then press bearing outer races into bearing housing. Press rear pinion bearing onto pinion shaft until it butts against stop. Place spacer sleeve onto shaft, then install housing over sleeve. Place front bearing on shaft and position shaft in a press. Slowly press bearing into housing while turning housing by hand, until resistance is felt, then remove shaft from press. Coat bearing retaining nut threads with Loctite (or equivalent) and install, but do not tighten.

2) Install pinion shaft assembly in holding fixture and place in a vise. Attach spring pull gauge to housing as shown in *Fig. 8*. Tighten retaining nut until force required to rotate housing is 10-15 lbs. (4.5-6.8 kg) for new bearings or 4.2-9.2 lbs. (1.9-4.2 kg) for used bearings. Bearings are considered "used" when they have been in use for over 1200 miles (2000 km). When correct value is obtained, peen retaining nut with a drift to lock nut in position.

NOTE — *With the retaining nut correctly tightened, pinion bearing preload is set to correct specification.*

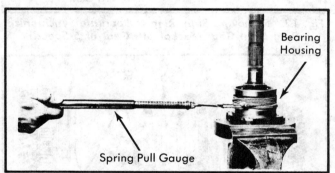

Fig. 8   Checking Pinion Bearing Preload

PRIMARY GEAR HOUSING

Disassembly (4-Speed) — 1) Remove primary gear cover attaching bolts and separate cover from housing. Remove chain tensioner. Remove lower primary gear snap ring. Remove upper primary gear snap ring (located behind primary gear). Using slide hammer (8390270) and puller (8790834), remove primary gears and chain simultaneously. Remove upper primary gear bearing snap ring. Using sleeve (8790842), press bearing out of upper primary gear.

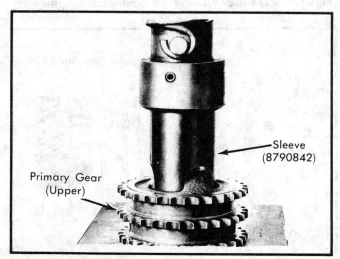

Fig. 9   Pressing Bearing Out of Upper Primary Gear

2) Remove 4 Allen screws from input shaft bearing retainer and remove retainer. Press input shaft out of housing. Remove input shaft bearing snap ring and press bearing off shaft. Remove needle bearing snap ring, then remove needle bearing from housing. Pry out input shaft oil seal.

Reassembly — 1) Inspect all parts for wear or damage; replace as necessary. Press in new input shaft oil seal and needle bearing (mark facing outward in housing). Install needle bearing snap ring. Press bearing onto input shaft and secure with snap ring. Press input shaft and bearings into housing. Install bearing retainer. Apply Loctite (or equivalent) to Allen screw threads. Install and tighten screws.

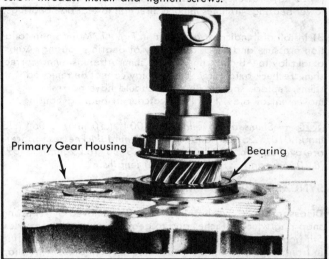

Fig. 10   Pressing Input Shaft and Bearing into Housing

2) Press bearing into upper primary gear. Install snap ring in outer groove with chamfer facing outward. Mount primary chain on both gears and install simultaneously. Install upper and lower primary gear snap rings. Apply Loctite (or equivalent) to chain tensioner mounting bolt threads. Install chain tensioner with oil passage at top and top edge of backing plate parallel with top edge of tensioner housing. Install primary gear cover and gasket.

Disassembly (5-Speed) — Remove 4 Allen screws from input shaft bearing retainer and remove retainer. Drive out bearing with drift (8390106) and sleeve (8390148). Remove needle bearing from primary gear case with a drift. Pry out input shaft oil seal. Remove upper primary gear snap ring. Using sleeve (8790842), press bearing out of upper primary gear.

NOTE — *DO NOT remove lever control ball valve. Check that ball moves easily and securely sets on seat. Ball acts at low speeds while going down hills to prevent oil from running out of gear case into primary gear housing.*

Reassembly — Inspect all parts for wear or damage; replace as necessary. Press in new input shaft oil seal and needle bearing (mark facing outward in housing). Press input shaft bearing into housing. Install bearing retainer. Apply Loctite (or equivalent) to Allen screw threads. Install and tighten screws.

OUTPUT SHAFT BEARING HOUSING (5-SPEED ONLY)

Disassembly — Remove oil catcher from bearing housing. Press output shaft out of bearing housing using support

SAAB 99 & 900 4 & 5-SPEED (Cont.)

(8390098), being careful not to damage lubrication connection pipe. Retain front bearing, spacer and shims. Using support (8790636) and ring (8790933), press rear bearing off output shaft. Drift bearing outer races out of bearing housing.

Reassembly — 1) Press rear bearing onto output shaft. Press outer races into bearing housing. Install output shaft, shims, spacer and bearing into bearing housing (shims must be installed between rear bearing and spacer).

2) Lubricate bearings and press together using support (8390098) and drift (7841075). While pressing with 3 tons (2722 kg) pressure, rotate bearing housing against upper and lower bearings 40 times in each direction to seat ball bearings.

3) Install dial indicator as shown in *Fig. 11*. Maintain installation pressure and check axial play of bearing housing. Adjust axial play to 0 by inserting correct shim. After installing correct shim, recheck axial play. If axial play cannot be removed with shims, replace spacer. Bearings should have no resistance to movement or play. Install oil catcher in bearing housing.

NOTE — *Shims are available in .004" (.10 mm), .006" (.15 mm), .010" (.25 mm) and .020" (.50 mm) thicknesses. Spacers are available in .3181" (8.08 mm), .3185" (8.09 mm), .3189" (8.10 mm) and .3192" (8.11 mm) lengths.*

SYNCHRONIZER ASSEMBLIES

Disassembly — Synchronizer rings are removed by removing snap ring which attaches ring to gear. On 5-speed transaxles, 5th gear synchronizer ring is removed by removing snap ring in front of guide ring. DO NOT remove synchronizer ring snap ring.

Reassembly — 1) Install guide ring for retaining ring, then, on 3rd and 4th gears only, lock guide rings in place on gears with snap rings. Install retaining spring on gear with long wire end nearest guide ring, then position other end on gear so there are 11 teeth between spring ends (5 teeth on 5th gear). Retaining spring for 1st gear is shorter and softer.

NOTE — *Guide rings for 3rd and 4th gears are assembled during production and are peened into position. DO NOT peen guide rings which are supplied as replacements.*

2) Install synchronizer ring onto gear so ends of spring fit into spaces between teeth. Install snap ring.

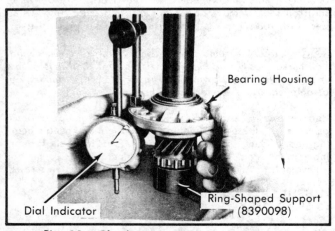

Fig. 11   Checking Axial Play of 5-Speed Output Shaft Bearing Housing

NOTE — *Synchronizer ring for 2nd gear has molybdenum-coated synchronizing surface for identification.*

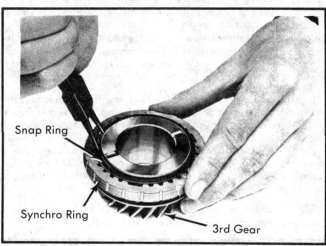

Fig. 12   Removing Snap Ring to Separate Synchronizer Ring From Gear (Except 5th Gear of 5-Speed)

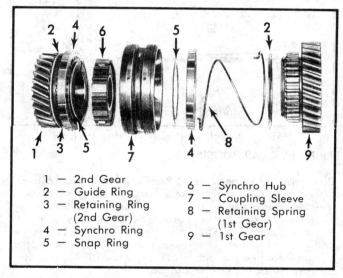

1 — 2nd Gear	6 — Synchro Hub
2 — Guide Ring	7 — Coupling Sleeve
3 — Retaining Ring (2nd Gear)	8 — Retaining Spring (1st Gear)
4 — Synchro Ring	9 — 1st Gear
5 — Snap Ring	

Fig. 13   Exploded View of 1st/2nd Gear Synchronizer

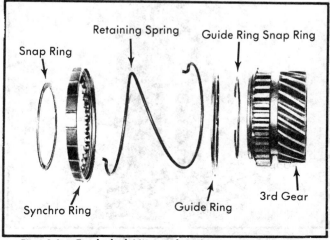

Fig. 14   Exploded View of 3rd Gear Synchronizer

SAAB 99 & 900 4 & 5-SPEED (Cont.)

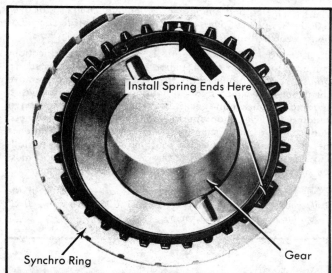

Fig. 15 Synchronizer Retaining Spring Installation

INNER AXLE SHAFT & BEARING HOUSING

Disassembly — Remove axle shaft snap ring and press axle shaft out of bearing housing. Using a screwdriver, remove oil seal from housing taking care not to damage housing. On left side bearing housing, remove shaft and lift out speedometer drive assembly. On both sides, press axle shaft roller bearings from housing. If new differential bearings are to be installed, remove bearing outer races from bearing housing using a drift.

NOTE — *A washer is located between race and housing on the right side to improve lubrication.*

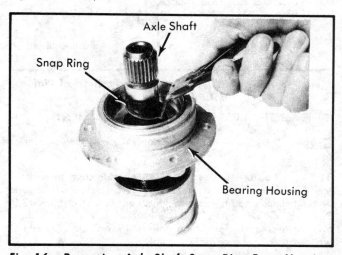

Fig. 16 Removing Axle Shaft Snap Ring From Housing

Reassembly — Press new axle shaft bearing into housing. Install lubrication washer on right side, then press new differential bearing outer races into bearing housing. Using a drift, press bearing housing oil seal into housing until it protrudes .08" (2 mm) above face of housing.

NOTE — *Axle shafts will be installed during Transaxle Reassembly.*

DIFFERENTIAL ASSEMBLY

Disassembly — If differential bearings require replacement, remove speedometer drive gear from left side and use puller to remove bearings from differential housing. Remove ring gear bolts and separate ring gear from differential. Remove snap ring, then press out pinion shaft. Remove pinion gears and side gears, thrust washers and gear springs from housing.

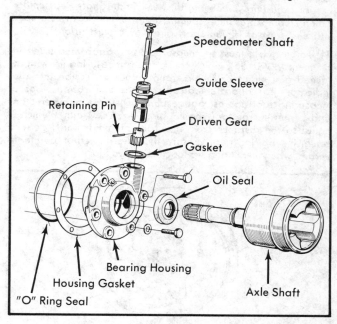

Fig. 17 Exploded View of Left Side Inner Axle Shaft and Differential Bearing Housing

Reassembly — Install pinion gears and side gears, thrust washers and springs into housing. Install pinion shaft and secure with snap ring. Mount ring gear on differential housing and install attaching bolts after applying Loctite (or equivalent) to threads. If removed, press new bearings onto housing, then install speedometer drive gear.

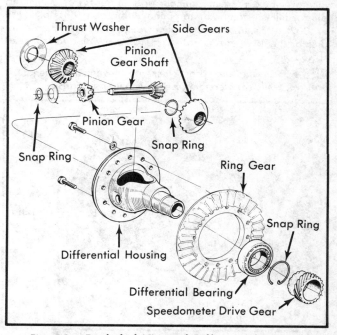

Fig. 18 Exploded View of Differential Assembly

SAAB 99 & 900 4 & 5-SPEED (Cont.)

TRANSAXLE REASSEMBLY & ADJUSTMENT

PINION DEPTH ADJUSTMENT

NOTE — *Pinion bearing preload must be correctly adjusted before adjusting pinion depth. See Pinion Shaft Reassembly. Pinion Depth Adjustment specifications (in metric) are stamped into end face of pinion shaft gear. (See Illustration).*

1) Pinion depth must be measured using Saab measuring instrument (8390155), which consists of a measuring jig with attached dial indicator and a gauge block for calibrating dial indicator. To calibrate indicator, place calibration stops of measuring tool against gauge block. Distance between stops and centerline of tool should be 2.362" (60 mm), which is equal to the distance from end face of pinion shaft gear to centerline of ring gear. Ensure that dial indicator pointer is zeroed when measuring tip touches gauge block.

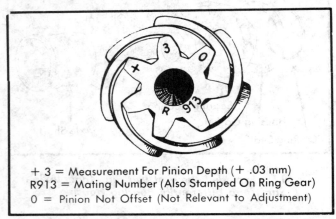

+ 3 = Measurement For Pinion Depth (+ .03 mm)
R913 = Mating Number (Also Stamped On Ring Gear)
0 = Pinion Not Offset (Not Relevant to Adjustment)

Fig. 19   End View of Pinion Shaft Gear Showing Pinion Depth Adjustment Specifications

2) Install pinion shaft into transaxle case and tighten bolts. Position measuring tool in transaxle case with measuring tip applied to flat end of pinion gear. See Fig. 20. Record reading. When pinion gear is correctly positioned, dial indicator should read the number (in hundredths of millimeter; plus or minus) stamped into pinion with a permitted tolerance of .002" (.05 mm). For example, if pinion is stamped — 7, indicator should read a negative (−) .07 mm with a tolerance of ± .05 mm.

NOTE — *On dial indicator, clockwise movement of needle is positive, while counterclockwise movement is negative.*

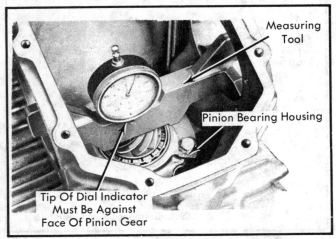

Measuring Tool

Pinion Bearing Housing

Tip Of Dial Indicator Must Be Against Face Of Pinion Gear

Fig. 20   Positioning Measuring Tool in Transaxle Case

NOTE — *If ring and pinion gear set have been in use for over 6,000 miles (10,000 km), reassemble pinion shaft to specifications recorded during disassembly.*

3) If measured pinion depth is not within specifications (stamped on pinion gear), pinion shaft must be adjusted. To adjust, remove pinion shaft from case and add or remove shims between pinion bearing housing and case as follows: If reading is higher than specifications, increase shim thickness; if reading is lower than specifications, reduce shim thickness. Reduce or increase shim thickness according to difference between measured value and specified value. Before reinstalling pinion shaft assembly, differential bearing preload must be adjusted. See *Differential Bearing Preload Adjustment.*

NOTE — *Pinion depth adjusting shims are available in the following thicknesses: .004" (.10 mm), .006" (.15 mm), .012" (.30 mm), and .020" (.50 mm).*

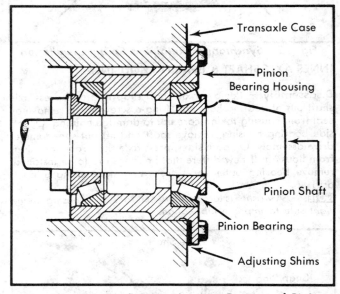

Transaxle Case

Pinion Bearing Housing

Pinion Shaft

Pinion Bearing

Adjusting Shims

Fig. 21   Sectional View Showing Position of Pinion Depth Adjusting Shims

DIFFERENTIAL BEARING PRELOAD ADJUSTMENT

NOTE — *Differential bearing preload must be adjusted prior to installation of pinion shaft.*

1) Position differential assembly in transaxle case, then install left side (side with speedometer drive gear) axle shaft housing without shims and tighten attaching bolts to 14-18 ft. lbs. (2.0-2.5 mkg). Oil differential bearings, install right side axle shaft housing and tighten attaching bolts to 19 INCH lbs. (22 cmkg) while rotating differential assembly.

NOTE — *If inner axle shaft is installed in right axle shaft housing, remove spring and plunger before mounting axle shaft housing.*

2) Using a feeler gauge, measure clearance between right axle housing and transaxle case at 2 points opposite each other. Compute the average of 2 measurements and select adjusting shims which equal the average. Then add an additional .008" (.2 mm) in shim thickness to obtain correct bearing preload.

3) Measure bearing preload with an INCH lb. torque wrench. Preload for new, slightly oiled bearings should be 16-24 INCH lbs. (18-28 cmkg). Preload for used bearings should be 7-11

SAAB 99 & 900 4 & 5-SPEED (Cont.)

INCH lbs. (8-13 cmkg). Bearings are considered "used" when they have been in service more than 1200 miles (2000 km).

NOTE — *Right-to-left distribution of shims will be determined during Ring Gear Backlash Adjustment. Up to 4 shims may be combined to obtain correct preload. Shims are available in the following thicknesses: .004" (.10 mm), .006" (.15 mm), .012" (.30 mm) and .020" (.50 mm).*

RING GEAR BACKLASH ADJUSTMENT

NOTE — *Ring gear adjustment specifications (in metric) are stamped into ring gear. See Fig. 22. If ring and pinion gear set have been in use for over 6,000 miles (10,000 km), reassemble differential according to specifications recorded during disassembly. Mount pinion shaft with shims in housing.*

1) Place differential assembly into transaxle case. Mount left side (speedometer drive gear side) axle shaft housing to transaxle case without adjusting shims and tighten attaching bolts to 14-18 ft. lbs. (2.0-2.5 mkg). Mount right side axle housing with the selected bearing preload adjusting shims and tighten attaching bolts to the same torque.

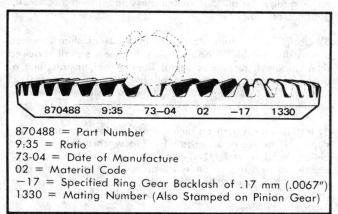

| 870488 | 9:35 | 73-04 | 02 | -17 | 1330 |

870488 = Part Number
9:35 = Ratio
73-04 = Date of Manufacture
02 = Material Code
-17 = Specified Ring Gear Backlash of .17 mm (.0067")
1330 = Mating Number (Also Stamped on Pinion Gear)

Fig. 22 Side View of Ring Gear Showing Differential Backlash Adjustment Specifications

2) Mount dial indicator on transaxle case so indicator tip is touching ring gear teeth. Move ring gear back and forth and measure backlash between ring gear and pinion gear in 4 different locations. After adjustment, remove differential.

NOTE — *Backlash measurements should not deviate from each other by more than .002" (.05 mm), if measurements deviate more than specified, ring gear is not properly installed. If backlash is not to specifications (stamped on ring gear), remove both axle shaft housings and move shims as necessary from right side housing to left side housing. Reinstall housings with shims and recheck backlash. If not to specifications, repeat adjustment procedure until correct backlash is obtained. DO NOT reduce total thickness of shim pack. Move shims from one side to the other.*

TRANSAXLE REASSEMBLY

4-Speed — **1)** Install 2 locating studs (8790438) into pinion shaft bearing housing mounting holes. Install preselected pinion depth adjusting shims on bearing housing, then position pinion shaft in transaxle case, using locating studs as guides. Gently tap pinion shaft until fully seated in case with plastic mallet and remove locating studs. Apply Loctite (or equivalent) to bearing housing mounting bolt threads. Install and tighten bolts.

2) Before installing reverse gear, measure distance from pinion bearing retaining nut to primary gear housing mounting sur-

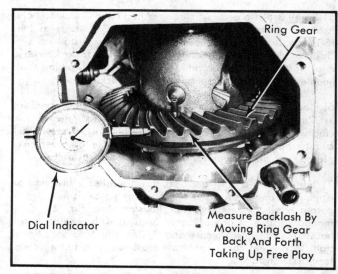

Fig. 23 Measuring Ring Gear Backlash

face on transaxle case. Distance should be 7.677-7.681" (195.0-195.1 mm). To accurately measure distance, set depth gauge to proper distance and mount on case. Measure distance between end of depth gauge and retaining nut with feeler gauge. Install shim of thickness equal to that of feeler gauge.

3) Using a micrometer, measure thickness of shim removed during disassembly. If original shim thickness equals required shim thickness, replace original shim. If not, install shim of proper thickness. Shims are available in thicknesses of .012" (.3 mm), .016" (.4 mm) and .02" (.05 mm). Install shim between retaining nut and reverse gear.

4) Install reverse gear onto pinion shaft. Fit 1st gear on reverse gear bearing sleeve. Install 1st/2nd synchronizer hub onto pinion shaft. Install 1st/2nd gear shift fork into coupling sleeve, then mount on synchronizer hub. Install 2nd gear sleeve, then mount 2nd gear on sleeve. Install 3rd gear spacer and sleeve on pinion shaft, then mount 3rd gear on sleeve.

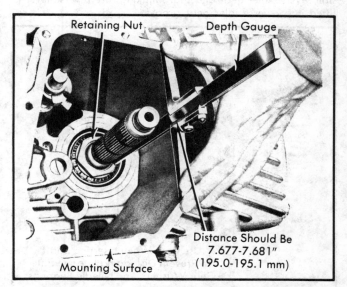

Fig. 24 Measuring Retaining Nut-to-Mounting Surface Distance

SAAB 99 & 900 4 & 5-SPEED (Cont.)

5) Install 3rd/4th gear synchronizer hub (with 3 locking holes facing outward) onto pinion shaft. Install 3rd/4th gear shift fork into 3rd/4th gear coupling sleeve, then install on synchronizer hub. Install locking tool (8790503) to lock reverse gear. Install and tighten pinion shaft nut. Install pinion shaft needle bearing and snap ring. Remove locking tool.

6) Place transmission gears in neutral, then install shift rail for 1st/2nd and 3rd/4th gear shift forks. Turn selector rod clockwise and install reverse shift rail. Tighten stop screw. Pack countershaft gear needle bearings with grease to hold them in place, then place gear set in bottom of transaxle case.

7) Ensure countershaft gear set thrust washer is installed on primary gear housing and oil connecting tube is installed in output shaft of primary gear housing. *See Fig. 25.* Coat mating surface of primary gear housing with sealant. Install housing onto transaxle case and tighten attaching bolts finger tight to prevent countergear set from jamming before countershaft is installed.

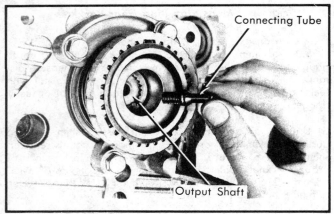

Connecting Tube

Output Shaft

Fig. 25   *Installing Oil Connecting Tube in Output Shaft*

8) Ease countershaft gear set into correct position. Install rear thrust washer onto gear. Insert countershaft gear shaft into gear set through bore in differential section of transaxle case. *See Fig. 26.* Tighten primary gear housing attaching bolts. Install reverse idler gear and shaft, making sure reverse lever is fitted into reverse idler gear groove.

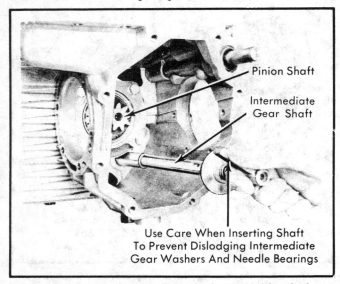

Pinion Shaft

Intermediate Gear Shaft

Use Care When Inserting Shaft To Prevent Dislodging Intermediate Gear Washers And Needle Bearings

Fig. 26   *Installing Countershaft Assembly Shaft*

9) Install locking plate over shaft ends. Apply Loctite (or equivalent) to attaching screw threads. Install and tighten screw. Insert spring and ball catch for gear selector rod and install transaxle case cover and gasket. Check ring gear backlash and adjust if necessary.

5-Speed — 1) Install 2 locating studs (8790438) into pinion shaft bearing housing mounting holes. Install preselected pinion depth adjusting shims on bearing housing, then position pinion shaft in transaxle case, using locating studs as guides. Gently tap pinion shaft with plastic mallet until fully seated in case, then remove locating studs. Apply Loctite (or equivalent) to bearing housing mounting bolt threads. Install and tighten bolts.

2) Before installing reverse gear, measure distance from pinion bearing retaining nut to primary gear housing mounting surface on transaxle case. Distance should be 7.677-7.681" (195.0-195.1 mm). To accurately measure distance, set depth gauge to proper distance and mount on case. Measure distance between end of depth gauge and retaining nut with feeler gauge. Install shim of thickness equal to that of feeler gauge. *See Fig. 24.*

3) Using a micrometer, measure thickness of shim removed during disassembly. If original shim thickness equals required shim thickness, reinstall original shim. If not, install shim of proper thickness. Shims are available in thicknesses of .012" (.3 mm), .016" (.4 mm) and .02" (.05 mm). Install shim between retaining nut and reverse gear.

4) Install reverse gear on pinion shaft. Fit 1st gear on bearing sleeve of reverse gear. Install 1st/2nd synchronizer hub onto pinion shaft. Insert 1st/2nd gear shift fork into 1st/2nd coupling sleeve and mount on synchronizer hub. Install 2nd gear sleeve with installer (8390148). Install 2nd gear onto sleeve. Install 3rd gear spacer and sleeve on pinion shaft, then install 3rd gear on sleeve.

5) Install 3rd/4th synchronizer hub onto pinion shaft. Install 3rd/4th gear shift fork into 3rd/4th gear coupling sleeve, then install on synchronizer hub. Install 4th gear bushing onto pinion shaft, then mount 4th gear onto bushing. Install selector shaft with double lockout guide pin.

6) Place transmission gears in neutral, then install gear shift shaft for 1st/2nd and 3rd/4th gear shift forks. Install reverse operating lever onto reverse selector shaft. Apply Loctite (or equivalent) to shaft stop bolt. Install and tighten stop bolt. Install 5th gear selector onto reverse selector shaft.

7) Install countershaft gear needle bearing into countershaft gear and install countershaft gear into housing. Install countershaft gear shaft, while aligning countershaft, just enough to hold gears in position. Thrust washer will be installed later.

8) Install 5th gear spacer, 5th gear synchronizer hub and snap ring onto pinion shaft. Measure distance between coupling sleeve and hub with feeler gauge so there is no play between parts on pinion shaft. Shims are available in .012" (.3 mm) and .016" (.4 mm) thicknesses. Remove snap ring, hub and spacer. Apply sealing compound to gasket surfaces of primary gear housing. Install gasket and housing to transmission housing.

9) Install spacer and 5th gear synchronizer hub on output shaft. Install shims selected to provide zero play between parts on shaft, then install snap ring. Install 5th gear operating sleeve and selector fork.

SAAB 99 & 900 4 & 5-SPEED (Cont.)

10) Install 3 output shaft guide pins (8790438) into lower primary gear bearing housing mounting bolt holes. Insert output shaft with bearing housing, oil catcher and oil connecting pipe installed on adapter (8790917). Mount the lower primary gear socket between the adapter and bearing housing. Insert bearing housing and output shaft assembly using slide hammer, so bearing housing is seated and output shaft meets operating sleeve.

11) Install output shaft countershaft thrust washer, coated with grease, so tab fits into recess of case. Slide output shaft countergear onto shaft and install sleeve, bearings and snap ring. Mount countershaft in case and slide gear toward thrust washer to allow alignment of gear for final installation.

12) Mount operating sleeve onto countershaft and insert snap ring into recess. Mount countergear thrust washer. Using installer (8390049), insert countergear shaft so it locks in position. Install reverse idler gear and spindle, then insert reverse idler gear shaft until it locks in position with installer (8390049).

13) Install locking plate into primary gear cover. Seal locking plate with Loctite (or equivalent), then coat threads with same sealant. Install and tighten bolts. Install upper primary gear and chain assembly. Ensure the hole for lower primary gear tab washer is facing outward. Mount chain tensioner. Coat threads of chain tensioner bolts with Loctite (or equivalent), then install and tighten bolts.

14) Lock pinion shaft by engaging reverse gear and 5th gear. Install pinion shaft nut and tighten. Bend 1 nut tab into hole provided in lower primary gear. Install reverse gear operating lever and tighten bolt. Seal bolt with Loctite (or equivalent). Install differential unit. Install selector ball and gearbox top cover gasket and cover. Install primary gear housing gasket and cover.

FINAL ASSEMBLY

1) Remove axle shaft housing from transaxle. Press axle housings onto axle shaft, then install snap rings to secure shafts in place. Install speedometer drive assembly into left axle shaft housing. Install "O" ring seals on both housings. Install spring and plunger in end of axle shaft. Install axle shaft housings onto transaxle case, making sure that correct adjusting shims are in place on each housing. Install and tighten bolts.

2) Recheck backlash adjustment and readjust if necessary. Install rear cover on transaxle case and tighten attaching bolts. Fill transaxle to correct fluid level with oil.

TIGHTENING SPECIFICATIONS

Application	Ft. Lbs. (mkg)
Hub-to-Rotor Bolts	22-36 (3-5)
Front Hub Nut	251-266 (35-37)
Input Shaft Nut (5-Speed)	67-81 (9-11)
Pinion Shaft Retaining Nut	30-45 (4-6)
All 8 mm Bolts	14-18 (2.0-2.5)
Transaxle Drain Plug	29-44 (4-6)
Speedometer Drive Shaft	21-36 (3-5)
Release Bearing Sleeve Screw	4-10 (.6-1.4)
Ring Gear Attaching Bolts	30-45 (4-6)
Axle Shaft Housing Bolts	14-18 (2.0-2.5)

SUBARU 4 & 5-SPEED

1600
1800

DESCRIPTION

Transmission has 4 or 5 speeds with synchromesh in all forward gears. Both transmission and differential are mounted in the same 2-piece aluminum housing. A hypoid-type gear is used for the final drive. Gear shift linkage is incorporated in transmission cover. Transmission and differential are lubricated from a common oil supply. Front axle drive shafts employ constant velocity joints at transaxle drive flange and axle shaft.

Four-wheel drive models have rear drive shaft which rotates with drive pinion at gear ratio of 1 to 1. Rear drive shaft is equipped with a claw clutch for 4-wheel drive shifting. Claw clutch has conventional type synchromesh system to ensure no damage to gears when shifting to 4-wheel drive while vehicle is in motion.

LUBRICATION & ADJUSTMENT

See *MANUAL TRANSMISSION SERVICING* Section.

TROUBLE SHOOTING

TRANSMISSION NOISE

Lubricant insufficient. Worn or chipped gears or bearings. If gear tooth surface is excessively worn, a growling sound should be apparent at high speed. When teeth are chipped, periodic knocking is audible at both high and low speeds.

DIFFERENTIAL NOISE

Lubricant insufficient. Tapered roller bearings out of adjustment. Ring and/or pinion gear out of adjustment, ring gear loose. Worn differential side gears, washers or pinion.

NOTE — *Noise from exhaust system, tires, wheel bearings etc. is easily mistaken for differential noise. Eliminate these noises prior to disassembling differential.*

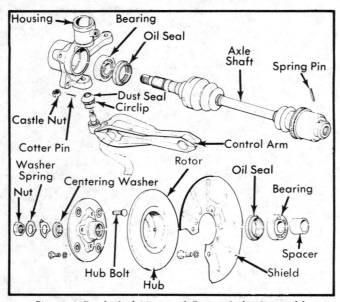

Fig. 1 Exploded View of Front Axle Assembly

HARD SHIFTING

Clutch not properly adjusted or hanging up when released. Worn, damaged or burred sleeve on gear spline or chamfered parts. Scratched bushings. Defective contact or worn synchro ring and gear cone.

SLIPS OUT OF GEAR

Loose engine mounts. Worn shifter fork or broken shifter fork rail spring. Damaged ball bearing. Excessive clearance between synchro hub and sleeve splines. Worn gears or bushings.

SERVICE (IN VEHICLE)

WHEEL BEARINGS

Removal — 1) Raise and support vehicle. Remove wheels. Disconnect parking brake linkage from caliper. Remove caliper mounting bolts and hang caliper from frame with wire; DO NOT remove hydraulic connection.

2) Remove bolts connecting shock absorber strut to housing. Remove parking brake hangar from tie rod, then remove cable bracket from housing.

3) Straighten staked portion of axle nut and remove nut. Remove tie rod ball joint and lower control arm ball joint from housing. Using a puller, remove hub and rotor assembly from axle shaft. Remove shield from housing and use a puller to remove housing from axle shaft.

Disassembly — Using brass drift and hammer, knock inner bearing from support housing. Pull out spacer and knock out outer bearing. Seals come out with bearings.

Reassembly — Use press and suitable adapter to reassemble. Set bearing into adapter and press into outer side of housing until race is totally seated. Place .5 oz. bearing grease inside support housing, then insert spacer. Repeat above procedure to install outer bearing. Lubricate lips of oil seals lightly and press into position.

Installation — To install, reverse removal procedure and tighten all bolts.

AXLE DRIVE SHAFTS

Removal — Drive out retaining pin which secures inner axle shaft to drive axle. Complete removal procedure by using procedure described for *Wheel Bearing Removal*. Remove axle shaft.

Installation — To install, reverse removal procedure and note the following: Use a new retaining pin to secure inner axle shaft to drive axle. Tighten all bolts.

CONSTANT VELOCITY (CV) JOINTS

NOTE — *Both ends of axle drive shaft have CV joints. Transaxle end can be disassembled, opposite end cannot.*

SUBARU 4 & 5-SPEED (Cont.)

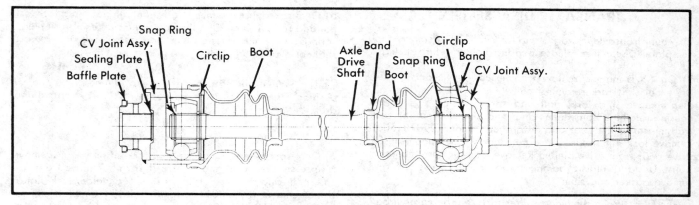

Fig. 2   Exploded View of Axle Drive Shaft Components

Disassembly — 1) Remove band retaining boot by bending back lock tab, then take off band. Remove circlip located at neck of outer race. Working from shaft assembly side, extract the outer race. Wipe grease off, then extract bearings. Remove cage from inner race by turning cage track groove and shifting cage.

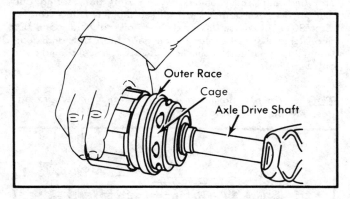

Fig. 3   Removing Outer Race and Ball Bearings

2) Using suitable pliers, remove snap ring fixing internal ring and shaft, then remove ring. Take off cage and boot being careful not to damage either component.

Inspection — Examine CV joint for corrosion, damage or wear. Ensure axle drive shaft does not have excessive deflection, twist or wear. Replace components as necessary.

Reassembly — To reassemble, reverse disassembly procedure.

TRANSAXLE REMOVAL & INSTALLATION

Removal — With battery disconnected and spare tire and air cleaner removed, proceed as follows:

1) Remove clutch cable return spring and clutch cable. Disconnect clip from speedometer cable and remove cable from transaxle housing. Disconnect back-up light switch, ground strap from vehicle body and starter harness. DO NOT remove battery cable from starter.

2) Remove starter with battery cable attached. Remove upper engine-to-transmission mounting bolts. Loosen lower mounting

bolts. Loosen transmission side stabilizer bar .39" (10 mm) and tighten engine side stabilizer bar the same amount. Slightly tilt engine backward to facilitate transaxle removal.

NOTE — *DO NOT tighten engine side stabilizer bar more than .39" (10 mm).*

3) On 4-WD vehicles, remove console and boots. Place drive selector in "4-WD" position, then remove nut connecting gear shift and drive selector rods. Remove 2 nuts securing drive selector rod and drive selector to plate. Remove gearshift lever boot installing screws. Remove nut connecting gearshift lever with operating lever. Pull up on gearshift lever and remove lever and boot.

4) On all models, raise front of car with a jack. Disconnect hot air intake hose and remove air stove from exhaust manifold. Loosen nuts securing exhaust pipe to engine manifold. Remove bolts securing front exhaust pipe to body bracket. Support front exhaust pipe while removing nuts securing pipe to exhaust manifold. Remove front exhaust pipe.

5) On 4-WD models, remove transmission skid plate. Disconnect rear propeller shaft from rear axle and transmission. Remove propeller shaft and plug open end of transmission assembly.

6) On all models except 4-WD, remove exhaust system shield. Remove gearshift retaining bolts from transmission. Free gearshift system from transmission.

7) On all models, remove stabilizer bar. Disconnect transverse links from front crossmember and lower transverse links. Drive out retaining pin which secures inner axle shaft to drive axle. Push wheel assembly toward outside of vehicle and separate axle shaft from drive axle. Remove clamp on left side of parking brake cable to facilitate removal of center crossmember.

8) Remove left and right transmission mounts. Support transaxle assembly with a jack. Remove center crossmember. Remove 2 nuts securing engine to transaxle. Move transaxle assembly rearward to clear mainshaft, then lower transaxle from vehicle.

Installation — To install, reverse removal procedure being sure to replace all locking nuts and tightening nut connecting control arm to crossmember only when vehicle has been lowered to floor.

SUBARU 4 & 5-SPEED (Cont.)

TRANSAXLE DISASSEMBLY

1) Mount transaxle in work stand (399935100). Remove stopper plate. Disconnect release bearing holder return springs.

2) On 4-WD models, remove transfer case cover and gasket. Drive out shift fork retaining pin. Remove transfer shift rail, then remove shift fork, ball and spring. Remove extension housing retaining bolts, then remove housing and gasket. Lock transmission in 1st gear and install gear holder (398781600). Remove lock nut staking, lock nut, lock washer and transfer drive gear from drive pinion. Remove transfer case mounting bolts. Using a plastic hammer, tap transfer case off and remove gasket and shim.

CAUTION — *When removing shifter fork rail, be carefull ball does not pop out of transmission case.*

3) On all models, remove clutch release fork and release bearing holder. Remove end cover, then remove gasket and mainshaft rear plate. Remove rear pinion shaft bearing retaining bolts from case.

Fig. 4 Removing Rear Cover on 5-Speed Transaxle

4) Clean splines of drive axle shafts, then wrap with tape. Remove 17 transaxle case retaining bolts, then separate case into 2 halves. Tap case as necessary to separate 2 halves and use care not to damage axle shaft oil seals. Using wooden hammer handle as pry bar, remove drive pinion shaft. Remove mainshaft and differential assembly.

NOTE — *Do not mix right and left roller bearing outer races.*

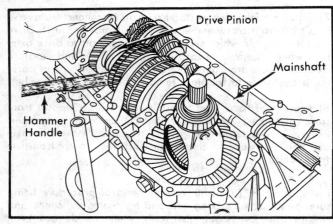

Fig. 5 Prying Pinion Shaft Out of Case

5) On 5-speed, use a punch to drive out 5th gear shift fork lock pin and remove fork. On all models, remove 3 shift rail plugs, springs and balls. Unscrew shift fork set screws and remove shift forks and fork rails.

NOTE — *When pulling out a rail, keep other rails in neutral position. To remove 3rd-4th rail, rotate it 90°. Take care not to drop shifter rail plungers.*

6) On 4-speed, remove reverse shift fork set screw and remove reverse shift rail arm and reverse shift rail. Remove transaxle case bolts and remove output shaft oil seal holder lock plates. Using remover (399780111), remove drive axle shaft oil seal holder and "O" ring. Remove speedometer driven gear snap ring and gear. Lightly tap speedometer shaft out of case. Oil seal should come out with shaft. Remove reverse idler gear shaft retaining pins. Remove reverse idler gear shaft, idler gear and shift lever.

7) On 5-speed, remove reverse idler gear shaft retaining pins. Remove reverse idler gear shaft, idler gear and shift lever. Remove reverse shift rail outer snap ring, then remove shift rail arm and shift rail. Remove reverse shift ball, spring and plunger. Remove output shaft oil seal holder. Using remover (399780111), remove drive axle shaft oil seal holder and "O" ring. Remove speedometer driven gear snap ring and gear. Lightly tap speedometer shaft out of case. Oil seal should come out with shaft.

NOTE — *When removing reverse shift rail arm, ensure ball does not pop out of case.*

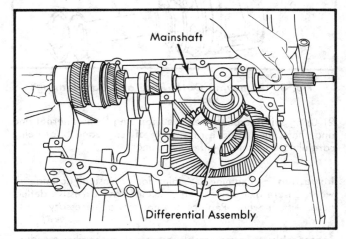

Fig. 6 Removing Mainshaft and Differential Assembly from Transaxle Case

COMPONENT DISASSEMBLY & REASSEMBLY

MAINSHAFT

Disassembly — **1)** On 5-speed models, remove lock nut staking, then remove lock nut. Using a press, remove 5th gear from shaft. Remove shaft key. On 4-speed models, remove snap ring from end of mainshaft.

NOTE — *Snap ring should not be reused.*

SUBARU 4 & 5-SPEED (Cont.)

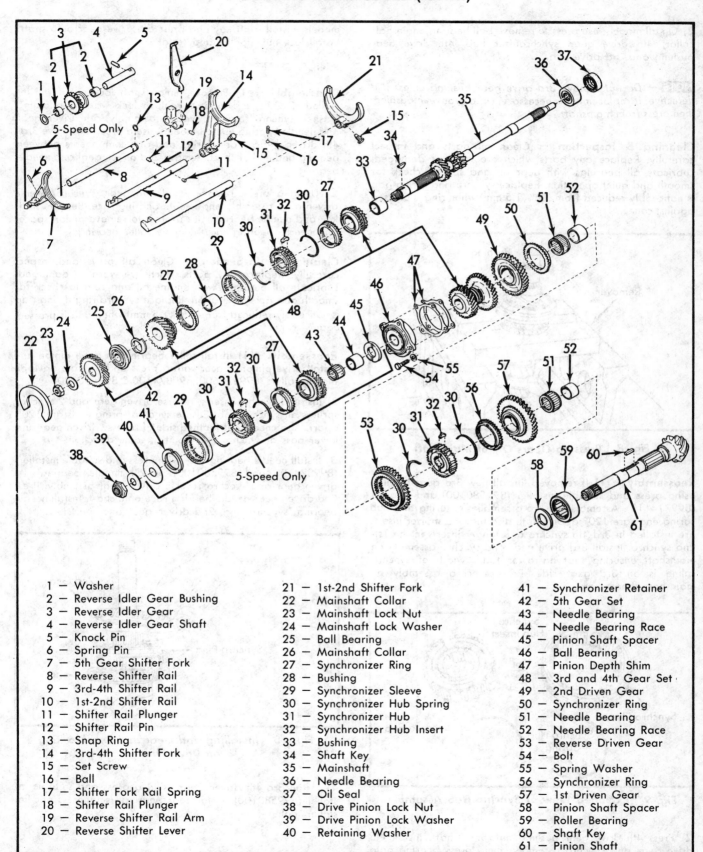

1 — Washer
2 — Reverse Idler Gear Bushing
3 — Reverse Idler Gear
4 — Reverse Idler Gear Shaft
5 — Knock Pin
6 — Spring Pin
7 — 5th Gear Shifter Fork
8 — Reverse Shifter Rail
9 — 3rd-4th Shifter Rail
10 — 1st-2nd Shifter Rail
11 — Shifter Rail Plunger
12 — Shifter Rail Pin
13 — Snap Ring
14 — 3rd-4th Shifter Fork
15 — Set Screw
16 — Ball
17 — Shifter Fork Rail Spring
18 — Shifter Rail Plunger
19 — Reverse Shifter Rail Arm
20 — Reverse Shifter Lever

21 — 1st-2nd Shifter Fork
22 — Mainshaft Collar
23 — Mainshaft Lock Nut
24 — Mainshaft Lock Washer
25 — Ball Bearing
26 — Mainshaft Collar
27 — Synchronizer Ring
28 — Bushing
29 — Synchronizer Sleeve
30 — Synchronizer Hub Spring
31 — Synchronizer Hub
32 — Synchronizer Hub Insert
33 — Bushing
34 — Shaft Key
35 — Mainshaft
36 — Needle Bearing
37 — Oil Seal
38 — Drive Pinion Lock Nut
39 — Drive Pinion Lock Washer
40 — Retaining Washer

41 — Synchronizer Retainer
42 — 5th Gear Set
43 — Needle Bearing
44 — Needle Bearing Race
45 — Pinion Shaft Spacer
46 — Ball Bearing
47 — Pinion Depth Shim
48 — 3rd and 4th Gear Set
49 — 2nd Driven Gear
50 — Synchronizer Ring
51 — Needle Bearing
52 — Needle Bearing Race
53 — Reverse Driven Gear
54 — Bolt
55 — Spring Washer
56 — Synchronizer Ring
57 — 1st Driven Gear
58 — Pinion Shaft Spacer
59 — Roller Bearing
60 — Shaft Key
61 — Pinion Shaft

Fig. 7 Exploded View of Transaxle Assembly Components

SUBARU 4 & 5-SPEED (Cont.)

2) On all models, use press to remove ball bearing, mainshaft collar, 4th drive gear, synchronizer hub, 4th drive gear bushing and 3rd drive gear.

NOTE – *Do not remove 3rd drive gear bushing unless it is defective. If replacement is necessary, cut a groove in bushing, then press from mainshaft.*

Cleaning & Inspection – Clean all parts and inspect carefully. Replace any parts which are worn or damaged. Lubricate all bearings with gear oil and spin to check for smooth and quiet operation. Replace synchro ring if ring gap is noticeably reduced from .06" (1.5 mm) when ring is pressed against cone.

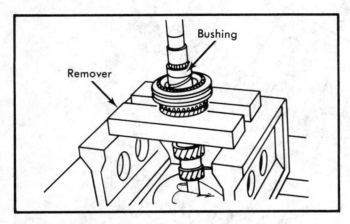

Fig. 8   Pressing Gears Off of Mainshaft

Reassembly – **1)** If removed, install new 3rd gear bushing using press and suitable installer (899580100) and retainer (899714110). Assemble synchro assemblies ensuring that hub spring ends are 120° apart. Note also that the shorter inserts are installed in 3rd-4th synchro and longer inserts in the 1st-2nd synchro. Install 3rd drive gear and synchro assembly on mainshaft ensuring that narrower tooth width of synchro spline is on 3rd gear side. Press synchro assembly on mainshaft, if necessary.

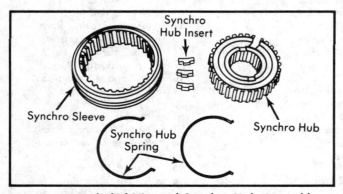

Fig. 9   Exploded View of Synchro Hub Assembly

2) Press 4th drive gear bushing onto mainshaft. Install 4th drive gear and synchro assembly; then, press bearing onto shaft. On 4-speed models, install 1 of 12 available snap rings on shaft to obtain 0-.002" (0-05 mm) end play. On 5-speed

models, install shaft key and press 5th drive gear onto shaft. Install lock nut, tighten and restake.

PINION SHAFT

Disassembly – **1)** Remove pinion shaft lock nut if still installed. On 5-speed models, remove lock washer, retaining washer, synchro retainer, synchro assembly, 5th driven gear and needle bearing. On all models, use a press to remove 3rd-4th driven gear, rear bearing and any components between bearing and end of shaft. Remove 2nd driven gear and needle bearing.

2) Using a press, remove 1st driven gear, synchro/reverse driven gear assembly and needle bearing race. Remove shaft key and needle bearing. Use a press to remove pinion spacer and needle bearing race. Remove roller bearing.

Cleaning & Inspection – Clean all parts and inspect carefully. Replace any parts which are worn or damaged. Lubricate all bearings with engine oil and spin to check for smooth and quiet operation. Replace synchro ring if ring gap is noticeably reduced from .06" (1.5 mm) when ring is pressed against cone.

Reassembly – **1)** Install roller bearing on drive pinion and install drive pinion spacer with a press and suitable drive pinion installers (899278600, 899874100 & 899580100).

2) Install 3 synchro inserts, reverse driven gear and 2 synchro springs on synchro hub. Ensure synchro spring ends are 120° apart. Also check that toothed side of reverse driven gear and lower boss of synchro hub point in same direction.

3) Install needle bearing race with press and suitable installers (899874100 and 899580100). Install needle bearing, 1st driven gear and synchro/reverse driven gear assembly. Press 2nd driven gear needle bearing race onto shaft. Install needle bearing, synchro ring, 2nd driven gear and shaft key.

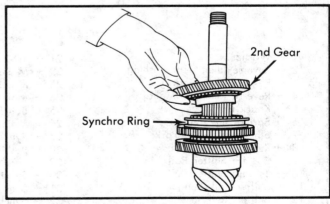

Fig. 10   Installing 2nd Gear and Synchro Ring on Drive Pinion

4) Install 3rd-4th driven gear using a press and suitable installer (899580100). Install rear bearing using press and installer tool.

NOTE – *If bearing slides onto shaft without being pressed on, no problem is indicated.*

SUBARU 4 & 5-SPEED (Cont.)

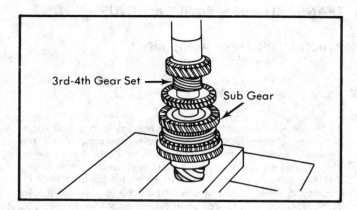

Fig. 11 Installing 3rd-4th Driven Gear on Drive Pinion

5) On 4-speed, install lock washer and tighten lock nut. On 5-speed, install grooved spacer, then press needle bearing race onto shaft. Install needle bearing, 5th driven gear, synchro assembly, synchro retainer, retainer washer, lock washer and lock nut. On 4-WD, install washer, pinion shaft collar, rear shaft drive gear, lock washer and lock nut.

NOTE — *On all models except 4-WD, stake pinion shaft lock nut at this time.*

DIFFERENTIAL ASSEMBLY

NOTE — *Rear differential of 4-WD vehicles is covered in DRIVE AXLE Section.*

Disassembly — Remove snap rings securing drive axle shafts to differential assembly and remove shafts. Right and left shafts are not interchangeable; mark for reassembly reference. Bend back ring gear bolt locking tabs. Remove ring gear bolts and lift off ring gear. Using a drift, remove pinion shaft retaining pin and pull out pinion shaft. Remove side gears, pinion gears and thrust washers. Remove side bearings with a puller.

Cleaning & Inspection — Wash and carefully inspect all parts. Replace all worn or damaged parts.

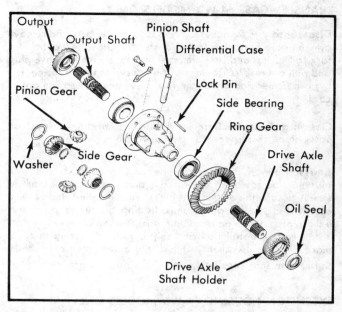

Fig. 13 Exploded View of Differential Assembly

Reassembly — **1)** Install differential side gears, pinions and washers in differential case and insert pinion shaft. Measure side gear and pinion backlash. The backlash should be .002-.006" (.05-.15 mm). If backlash is not correct, make adjustment by selecting a different thickness of washer.

2) Align pinion shaft with holes in case and drive lock pin from ring gear side until pin falls about .039" (1 mm) below surface. Lock pin in position by peening hole. Press side bearings onto case. Install ring gear. Install and tighten ring gear bolts, then bend locking tabs to hold bolts. Install drive axle shafts and secure with snap rings. Measure clearance between pinion shaft and tip of drive axle shaft. Adjust clearance to less than .008" (.2 mm) by using thicker snap ring.

NOTE — *Snap rings are available in 2 thicknesses: .039-.043" (1.0-1.1 mm) and .045-.049" (1.15-1.25 mm).*

Fig. 12 Removing or Installing Pinion Shaft in Differential Case

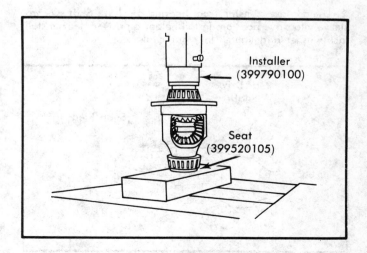

Fig. 14 Pressing Differential Bearings Onto Case

SUBARU 4 & 5-SPEED (Cont.)

TRANSFER CASE (4-WD MODELS ONLY)

Disassembly — Remove "O" ring from shifter arm and remove arm. Remove filler plug from transfer case, then pull out shifter fork rail spring and ball. Remove selector switch. Remove plug and pull out reverse accent shaft and reverse return spring. Using a hammer and aluminum rod, drive needle bearing out of case.

Cleaning & Inspection — Wash and carefully inspect all parts. Replace all worn or damaged parts.

Reassembly — Place needle bearing in bore of case with marked side toward front of case and press in until marked side is flush with case. Insert reverse return spring and reverse accent shaft, fit an aluminum adjusting gasket on plug and tighten plug. Place an aluminum gasket on selector switch and install switch. Install ball and shifter fork rail spring in case, place aluminum washer on filler plug and tighten plug. Slide shifter arm into case and install "O" ring on arm.

EXTENSION HOUSING (4-WD MODELS ONLY)

Disassembly — Remove snap ring from extension housing, then drive rear shaft from housing using a hammer and aluminum rod. Remove oil seal from rear of housing. Shift synchro into drive position. Install holder (899884100) on shaft and mount assembly in a vise. Unstake lock nut and remove lock nut and lock washer. Mount shaft assembly on retainer (899714110) and press out shaft. Remove bearing, spacer collar, rear driven gear, bushing, synchro hub and spacer.

Cleaning & Inspection — Wash and carefully inspect all parts. Replace all worn or damaged parts. Pay particular attention to extension housing rear bushing. If it is excessively worn or scratched, replace it.

Reassembly — **1)** Press rear bearing onto shaft. Install new oil seal in rear of extension housing. Using a plastic hammer, tap rear drive shaft into extension housing. Install snap ring in groove in extension housing. Install rear drive spacer, synchro hub, bushing, synchro ring, rear shaft driven gear and spacer collar.

2) Using a press, install front bearing on shaft. Shift synchro sleeve into drive position, install holder on driven gear, install lock washer and tighten lock nut. Stake nut.

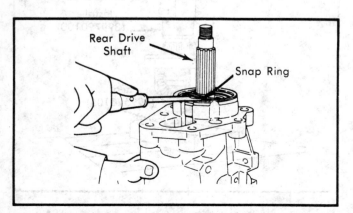

Fig. 15 Removing Snap Ring From Extension Housing

TRANSAXLE REASSEMBLY & ADJUSTMENT

PINION SHAFT DEPTH ADJUSTMENT

NOTE — *This adjustment must be performed using Subaru Pinion Gauge 899914100.*

1) Install pinion shaft assembly in transaxle case half (right half) with no shims between rear bearing and case. Install and tighten 2 pinion shaft retaining bolts to 22 ft. lbs. (3 mkg). Place pinion gauge on its edge on a level surface, then loosen 2 setting bolts on gauge plate. Adjust gauge plate so scale indicates 0.5 when edges of plate and scale are even. Tighten bolts. Place calibrated gauge into case as shown in *Fig. 16.*

NOTE — *Ensure dowel pins of gauge are installed in dowel holes of transaxle case.*

2) Slide gauge scale along plate until it comes in contact with drive pinion, then read and record value shown on scale. The thickness of shim(s) required to obtain correct drive pinion depth is determined by adding or subtracting value stamped on end of pinion to or from gauge scale value. Add if value stamped on pinion is prefixed by a "+"; subtract if value is prefixed by a "−". Select from 1 to 3 adjusting shims which will equal value just obtained. Remove gauge and pinion shaft from case.

NOTE — *If no value is stamped on pinion, value is zero. Adjusting shim(s) will be installed during Transaxle Reassembly.*

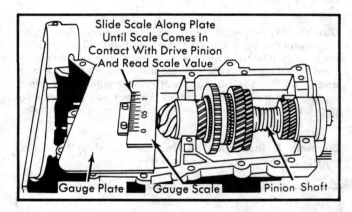

Fig. 16 Measuring Pinion Shaft Depth Using Special Gauge

TRANSAXLE REASSEMBLY

1) Press new oil seals into axle drive shaft holders. Place speedometer shaft side of transaxle case in a work stand, then screw axle shaft holder (without "O" ring) into case until threads are embedded completely in case. Install speedometer shaft outer snap ring and washer on shaft, then install assembly in case. Install speedometer driven gear on shaft and retain with outer snap ring. Press in new speedometer shaft oil seal.

NOTE — *Install speedometer driven gear snap ring from driven gear side to avoid damaging oil seal.*

SUBARU 4 & 5-SPEED (Cont.)

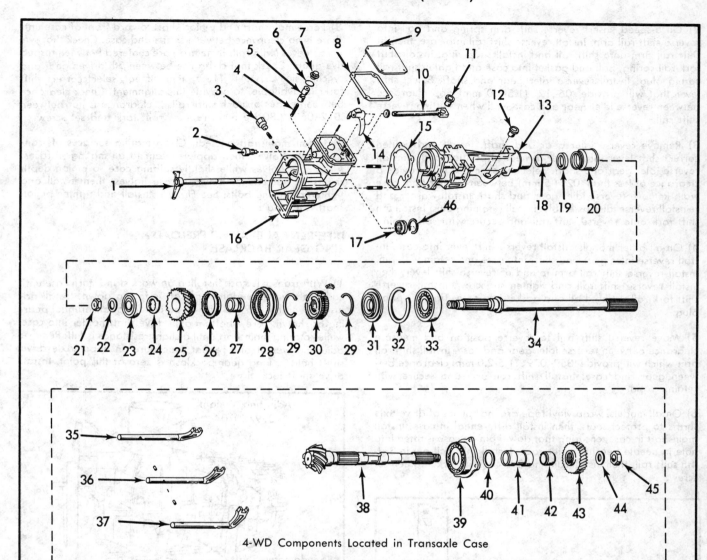

1 — Shifter Arm	16 — Transfer Case	31 — Rear Drive Spacer
2 — Selector Switch	17 — Needle Bearing	32 — Snap Ring
3 — Filler Plug	18 — Extension Bushing	33 — Bearing
4 — Reverse Return Spring	19 — Extension Oil Seal	34 — Rear Drive Shaft
5 — Reverse Accent Shaft	20 — Cover	35 — 1st-2nd Shifter Rail
6 — Gasket	21 — Rear Drive Shaft Lock Nut	36 — 3rd-4th Shifter Rail
7 — Plug	22 — Lock Washer	37 — Reverse Shifter Rail
8 — Cover Gasket	23 — Bearing	38 — Pinion Shaft
9 — Transfer Case Cover	24 — Spacer Collar	39 — Pinion Shaft Rear Bearing
10 — Rear Drive Shifter Rail	25 — Rear Shaft Driven Gear	40 — Washer
11 — Bushing	26 — Synchronizer Ring	41 — Pinion Shaft Collar
12 — Bushing	27 — Rear Shaft Driven Gear Bushing	42 — Needle Bearing Race
13 — Extension Housing	28 — Synchronizer Sleeve	43 — Rear Shaft Drive Gear
14 — Rear Drive Shifter Fork	29 — Synchronizer Hub Spring	44 — Lock Washer
15 — Case Gasket	30 — Synchronizer Hub	45 — Pinion Shaft Lock Nut
		46 — Snap Ring

Fig. 17 Exploded View of 4-WD Transfer Case, Extension Housing and Related Components

Manual Transaxles

SUBARU 4 & 5-SPEED (Cont.)

2) On 5-speed, insert reverse shift arm spring and ball into reverse shift rail arm. Install reverse shift rail into case, then fit shift rail arm onto shift rail and install snap ring. Install shift fork rail spring, ball and gasket into case and tighten shift rail spring plug. Install reverse idler gear and shaft. Select shift lever that will provide .06-.12" (1.5-3.0 mm) gap clearance between reverse idler gear and case wall when shifting reverse shift rail.

3) Remove reverse idler gear and shaft. Install and tighten correct shift lever. Shift lever to neutral position and reinstall reverse idler gear and shaft. Select washer that will provide a clearance of less than .02" (.5 mm) between washer and case wall. Remove reverse idler gear and shaft. Install washer and reinstall reverse idler assembly. Install retaining pins. Install 5th shift fork onto reverse shift rail and secure with spring pin.

4) On all other models, install reverse shift lever into case. Install reverse idler gear and shaft into case and retain with pin. Install reverse shift rail arm to end of reverse shift lever, then install reverse shift rail and tighten set screw. Install reverse shift fork rail spring, ball and gasket into case. Tighten spring plug.

5) Move reverse shift rail to reverse position and measure clearance between reverse idler gear and case. Install shift rail arm which will provide .059-.079" (1.5-2.0 mm) clearance between gear and case. Install shift rail arm and secure with retaining pin.

6) On all models, wrap vinyl tape around splines of drive axle shafts to protect seals, then install differential in case. Install mainshaft in case, ensuring that dowel pin on case is fitted into hole in needle bearing outer race. Install shift rail pin in 3rd-4th shift rail, then install rail and 3rd-4th shift fork. Tighten set screw.

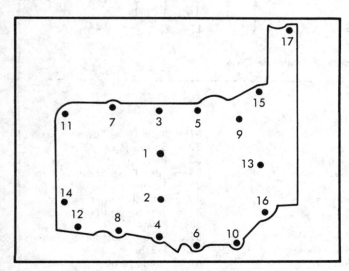

Fig. 18 Transaxle Case Tightening Sequence

7) Install previously selected pinion depth adjusting shim(s) on pinion shaft rear bearing. If more than 1 shim is used, do not place slit ends of shims on same side. Install pinion shaft in case, ensuring that dowel pin on case is fitted into hole in rear bearing outer race. Place shift rail plunger into hole in case. Install 1st-2nd shift rail and shift fork, then tighten set screw. Install shift rail balls, springs and plugs.

8) Force mainshaft and pinion shaft toward front of case until there is no clearance between shafts and case. Check that synchro sleeves (with rails in neutral) are centered between respective gears. Check that clearance between 5th driven gear and synchro sleeve is .41" (10.5 mm). If not, select correct shift forks (5 available) to provide this alignment. Check clearance between edges of each shift rail. If clearance is not between .012-.063" (.30-1.6 mm), replace rail, fork and set screw.

9) Install mainshaft oil seal. Clean mating surfaces of transaxle case halves, then apply sealant to all mating surfaces. Align case halves while slightly shifting case so pinion depth shim(s) is not caught between case halves, then install and tighten attaching bolts. See Fig. 18. Install and tighten pinion shaft retaining bolts.

DIFFERENTIAL BEARING PRELOAD & RING GEAR BACKLASH

1) With transaxle case installed on work stand, turn case until case half with speedometer shaft is facing down. Install adjusting weight (399780104) on outer race of differential bearing as shown. Screw bottom axle drive shaft holder into case while rotating mainshaft until a slight resistance is felt. Remove adjusting weight and repeat procedure on upper axle drive shaft holder. Ring gear backlash is zero at this point. Install drive shaft lock plate.

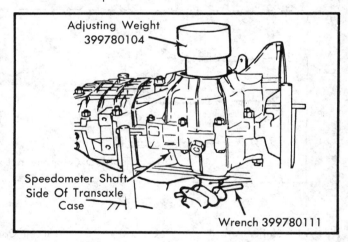

Fig. 19 View Showing Installation of Adjusting Weight

2) Loosen bottom drive shaft holder 1½ notches, then screw in upper holder by the same amount to obtain ring gear backlash. Turn upper holder in an additional ½ to 1 notch to obtain differential bearing preload. Tighten holder lock plates, then mark position of both holders for later readjustment. Install a dial indicator to transaxle case with tip of indicator inserted through transaxle drain hole and touching ring gear teeth. Measure ring gear backlash by rotating drive shafts back and forth taking up free play. Ring gear backlash should be .004-.007" (.10-.18 mm), if not, repeat adjustment procedure.

FINAL ASSEMBLY

1) With differential bearing preload and ring gear backlash correctly adjusted, remove both axle drive shaft holders.

SUBARU 4 & 5-SPEED (Cont.)

Install "O" ring seal on each holder than reinstall holders into transaxle case, making sure alignment marks on holders and case are aligned. Remove tape from around axle drive shaft splines.

2) On 4-WD models, remove pinion shaft lock nut, washer and rear shaft drive gear. Select a mainshaft collar which will provide 0-.012" (0-.30 mm) clearance between mainshaft bearing and transfer case. Install gasket and transfer case (with selected mainshaft collar) on transaxle and install, but do not tighten, transfer case-to-transaxle mounting nuts. Install rear shaft drive gear, washer and lock nut. Tighten lock nut and stake in 4 places. Tighten transfer case-to-transaxle mounting nuts. Install new "O" ring in shift arm groove.

3) Install gasket and extension housing on transfer case and tighten bolts. Install rear drive shift fork. Install shift rail spring and ball in transfer case, then install rear drive shift rail. Install roll pin to secure fork to rail. Install gasket and transfer case cover.

4) On all other models, select a mainshaft collar which will provide 0-.012" (0-.30 mm) clearance between mainshaft bearing and transaxle end cover for 4-speed, or 0-.008" (0-.20 mm) for 5-speed. Install transaxle end cover.

5) Adjust gear selector as follows: On all except 5-speed, insert a rod through hole in shift arm and shift into 4th gear. Move shift arm from 4th to 2nd gear, then to reverse position. Arm should move easily toward 2nd gear, but harder toward reverse because of return spring action. On 5-speed, insert rod and shift into 3rd gear. Arm should move easily toward 2nd gear, but harder toward reverse because of return spring action.

6) Next, make adjustment to equalize effort required to move lever to either position. Adjustment is performed by removing plug on cover and changing thickness of aluminum gasket. Install release bearing guide on case together with 2 release spring brackets. Install clutch release fork and release bearing holder. Secure with release bearing holder spring. Install clutch release fork seal ring and spring. Fill internal groove of release bearing holder with grease.

TIGHTENING SPECIFICATIONS

Application	Ft. Lbs. (mkg)
Lower Control Arm Ball Joint Nut	25 (3.5)
Tie Rod Ball Joint	22 (3.0)
Axle Shaft Nut	145 (20)
Drive Pinion-to-Case	22 (3.0)
Ring Gear-to-Differential	42-50 (5.8-6.8)
Transaxle Case Bolts	
8 mm Bolts	18 (2.5)
10 mm Bolts	29 (4.0)
Axle Shaft Holder Lock Plate	18 (2.5)
Drive Pinion Lock Nut	58 (8.0)
Transaxle Cover-to-Case	18 (2.5)
Shifter Rail Spring Plugs	15 (2.0)

TOYOTA TERCEL 4 & 5-SPEED

DESCRIPTION

Transaxle assembly consists of clutch/differential housing, intermediate plate and transmission case (4 or 5-speed) with common oil supply. The clutch/differential housing contains the clutch and differential assemblies in separate areas. The intermediate plate mounts to rear of clutch/differential housing and allows complete removal of transmission without engine removal. Transmission case is mounted to rear of intermediate plate. Transmission case is fully synchronized in all forward gears. Power is transmitted from input shaft, down through idler gear set to mainshaft and countershaft assemblies. Mainshaft is connected to pinion shaft by a splined sleeve connector. Pinion shaft transmits power to hypoid type differential which delivers power to axle drive shafts.

LUBRICATION & ADJUSTMENT

See *MANUAL TRANSMISSION SERVICING* Section.

SERVICE (IN VEHICLE)

AXLE DRIVE SHAFTS

Removal — 1) Raise and support vehicle; remove tire and wheel. Depress brake pedal and loosen axle shaft nut. Remove brake caliper and suspend caliper from frame; DO NOT remove hydraulic line. Remove upper steering knuckle-to-suspension strut bolts. Push down on steering knuckle to separate knuckle from strut. Remove stabilizer bar (if equipped).

2) Remove axle shaft nut. Press axle shaft out of hub with puller (SST09950-20013). Separate steering knuckle from strut and draw out axle drive shaft from rear of hub. Remove stiffener plate (right side only). Remove shaft from differential with remover (SST09648-16010). Install stopper (SST09563-16010) in differential case to prevent oil leakage.

NOTE — *Do not damage rubber boots of axle drive shaft. Always carry and store shaft in level position.*

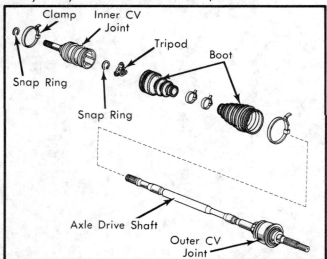

Clamp   Inner CV Joint

Tripod

Boot

Snap Ring

Snap Ring

Axle Drive Shaft

Outer CV Joint

Fig. 1   Exploded View of Axle Drive Shaft Assembly

NOTE — *Before disassembling axle drive shaft, check outer CV joint for any play. If play exists at outer CV joint, replace complete axle drive shaft assembly. Outer CV joint cannot be disassembled.*

Disassembly — Draw alignment marks on inner CV joint and shaft with chalk. Remove snap ring and boot clamps. Remove inner joint from shaft. Place index marks on tripod and axle shaft. Remove snap ring and tap body of tripod to drive tripod off shaft. Remove inner CV joint boot. Remove outer CV joint boot clamps and slide boot off axle shaft.

Reassembly — 1) Slide new boots onto drive axle shaft. Place clamping rings loosely over boots with open end of clamp away from direction of rotation. Do not tighten clamps at this time. Place beveled side of tripod onto shaft with beveled splines facing outer joint and align reference marks.

2) Before tapping tripod into final position, align centers of inner and outer joints. See *Fig. 2*. Tap tripod into position and install new snap ring. Pack outer CV joint with 7 ozs. (200 g) of grease (supplied with boot kit). Install outer boot and tighten clamps.

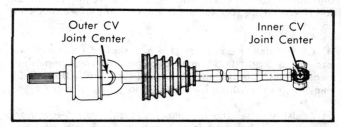

Outer CV Joint Center

Inner CV Joint Center

Fig. 2   Exploded View Showing Alignment of Inner and Outer CV Joint Centers

3) Pack inner CV joint with 5 ozs. (140 g) of grease (supplied with boot kit). Align reference marks made at disassembly and install inner CV joint. Install inner CV joint boot and tighten clamps. Install new snap ring on axle shaft.

NOTE — *Right axle shaft is 23.07" (586 mm) long. Left shaft is 27.09" (688 mm) long. If axle shaft does not meet length specification, replace axle shaft assembly.*

Installation — To install, reverse disassembly procedure and note the following: After installation of shafts, check front wheel alignment. Check boots for damage during installation. Measure the distance between drive shafts at transaxle. Distance should be less than 7.6" (194 mm).

WHEEL BEARINGS

Removal — 1) Raise and support vehicle; remove tire and wheel. Apply brakes and loosen axle shaft nut. Remove brake caliper and suspend from frame with wire; DO NOT remove hydraulic line. Disconnect and remove tie rod end with remover (SST09610-20011). Disconnect and remove stabilizer bar and strut bar.

2) Place a jack and block of wood under left lower control arm and slightly lift control arm. Right side does not require lifting. Remove lower control arm-to-crossmember attaching bolt. Disconnect control arm from crossmember. Remove axle shaft nut.

3) Press axle shaft out of hub assembly with puller (SST09950-20013). Remove steering knuckle-to-suspension strut retaining bolt and separate steering knuckle from strut. Remove lower control arm from steering knuckle. Mount steering knuckle in a vise and remove dust shield, then remove inner oil seal with puller.

TOYOTA TERCEL 4 & 5-SPEED (Cont.)

4) Press hub assembly out of steering knuckle with puller (SST09608-16031). Remove inner bearing and spacer from knuckle. Place reference marks on hub and disc assembly, then separate hub and disc. Place hub in vise and dislodge outer bearing from hub with hammer and chisel. Remove outer bearing with a puller. Remove scratches from hub bearing surface with oil stone.

NOTE — *Mark bearings for reassembly reference.*

Installation — 1) Place inner bearing, spacer and outer bearing onto bearing preload holder (SST09608-16040). Coat bearings and bearing housing of steering knuckle with oil. Place assembled bearings into bearing housing and tighten nut to 90 ft. lbs. (12.5 mkg). Rotate assembly back and forth to seat bearings. Install INCH lb. torque wrench and measure bearing preload while turning nut. Bearing preload should be 3.5-8.7 INCH lbs. (4-10 cmkg). See Fig. 3.

NOTE — *Spacers are available in 20 thicknesses ranging from .316" (8.03 mm) to .346" (8.79 mm) in .0016" (.04 mm) increments.*

2) If preload is not within specifications, select and install suitable spacer and repeat procedure. Mount hub to rotor, align marks made during removal and tighten hub-to-rotor bolts. Pack bearings and bearing housing with grease. Install outer bearing and oil seal in steering knuckle. Install preselected spacer and inner bearing in steering knuckle.

3) Place steering knuckle assembly in vise and press hub assembly into knuckle with press and arbor (SST09636-20010). Do not exceed 2,205 lbs. (1,000 kg) force. With pressure applied, rotate steering knuckle to seat bearings. Attach spring pull scale to steering knuckle stopper and measure frictional force. Frictional force should be .8-1.7 lbs. (.4-.8 kg).

4) Increase force to 7,716 lbs. (3,500 kg) and turn steering knuckle to seat bearings. Attach spring pull scale to steering knuckle stopper and measure bearing preload. Preload should be .8-2.5 lbs. (.4-1.1 kg). If below specification, install thinner spacer; if above specification, install thicker spacer. Install inner oil seal with installer (SST09554-22010) until seal is recessed .156" (4 mm) from end surface. Install dust shield.

5) Complete installation by reversing removal procedure and note the following: Install suspension components snugly. Lower vehicle to floor and bounce vehicle several times to settle suspension. Tighten suspension components with vehicle weight resting on suspension system.

TRANSAXLE REMOVAL & INSTALLATION

NOTE — *Transmission assembly may be removed without removing differential assembly. Procedure outlined covers removal of complete transaxle assembly.*

Removal — 1) Drain coolant from upper radiator tank. Disconnect negative battery cable, air cleaner inlet duct and upper radiator hose (from engine). Disconnect clutch cable. Remove starter motor. Disconnect and remove lower engine mount. Raise and support vehicle. Remove axle drive shafts as previously outlined. Remove 3 drain plugs and drain transaxle fluid.

2) Disconnect exhaust pipe at manifold and remove exhaust system. Remove transaxle stiffener plate on right side. Discon-

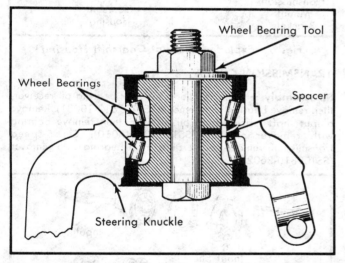

Fig. 3   Assembled View of Wheel Bearings and Bearing Preload Adjusting Tool in Wheel Hub Assembly

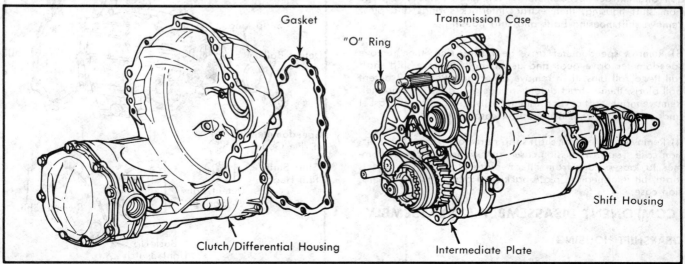

Fig. 4   Exploded View of Tercel Transaxle Assembly

TOYOTA TERCEL 4 & 5-SPEED (Cont.)

nect gear shift rod at housing rod yoke, then disconnect and remove shift lever housing rod retaining bolt. Disconnect and remove back-up light wiring connector. Disconnect speedometer cable at transaxle housing. Support transaxle on jack.

3) Remove 4 transaxle/clutch housing-to-engine mounting bolts. Remove engine rear support member and lower transaxle assembly out from under vehicle. Place a 1.2" (30 mm) block of wood between crossmember and oil pan to support engine for installation of transaxle assembly.

Installation — To install transaxle assembly, reverse removal procedure and note the following: Install 3 drain plugs and fill transaxle assembly with gear oil (SAE 90 GL-5 or SAE 80W-90).

TRANSAXLE DISASSEMBLY

1) Remove 9 transmission-to-clutch/differential housing bolts. Reinstall 4 bolts (8 mm) equal distance from differential side. Separate transmission from clutch/differential housing by inserting 4 bolts (10 mm) into same holes as previously installed bolts from transmission side. Tighten each 10 mm bolt a little at a time to force transmission from clutch/differential housing. Remove transmission from clutch/differential housing. See Fig. 5.

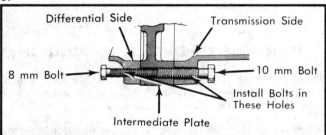

Fig. 5   Installation Position of Bolts to Separate Transmission from Clutch/Differential Housing

2) Remove reverse shift arm pivot from right side of transmission. Remove back-up light switch with slotted remover (SST09817-16010). Remove transmission mount brackets from shift lever housing. Remove speedometer driven gear retaining bolt and extract speedometer driven gear. Remove 2 plugs from shift housing, then extract interlock springs and pins. Remove shift housing bolts and shift housing.

3) Remove speedometer drive gear snap ring, then remove speedometer drive gear and detent ball. Remove shift shaft rail head roll pins, then remove rail heads. Remove 3 detent ball plugs, then extract detent springs and balls with magnet. Remove input shaft cover retaining bolts. Remove cover, gasket and input shaft from transmission case.

4) Remove countergear shaft snap ring from rear of transmission case. Tap transmission case protrusions with plastic hammer to loosen case from intermediate plate. When case is loose, tilt intermediate plate backward and remove transmission case.

COMPONENT DISASSEMBLY & REASSEMBLY

GEARSHIFT HOUSING

Disassembly — Tap lock pin from shift lever yoke with plastic hammer, then remove shift lever yoke. Extract shift lever from

rear of housing. Replace oil seal at collar with arbor (SST09304-12012).

Reassembly — To reassemble gearshift housing, reverse disassembly procedure and note the following: Ensure sliding action of shift lever is smooth and no binding is felt during shifting. Replace interlock springs and sleeves and speedometer driven gear, if defective.

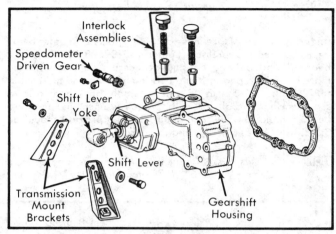

Fig. 6   Exploded View of Gearshift Housing

TRANSMISSION COVER

Disassembly — Remove idler gear rear bearing oil receiver, then remove bearing with remover (SST09612-10031). Remove output shaft rear bearing oil receiver, then remove bearing with remover/installer (SST09304-47010). On 5-speed transmission, remove countergear front bearing with remover (SST09310-36021).

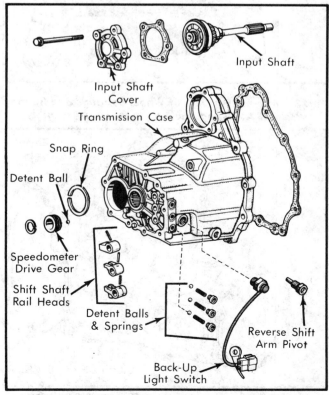

Fig. 7   Exploded View of Transmission Case

TOYOTA TERCEL 4 & 5-SPEED (Cont.)

Reassembly — On 5-speed transmission, press in countergear front bearing with installer (SST09304-47010) until bearing is flush with end surface. On all transmissions, install output shaft rear bearing with remover/installer (SST09304-47010) and install oil receiver. Install idler gear rear bearing with installer (SST09304-47010). Install oil receiver.

INTERMEDIATE PLATE

Disassembly — 1) Mount intermediate plate assembly in soft-jawed vise; secure plate at lower protrusion. Remove reverse shift arm circlip and shift arm. Drive out shift shaft fork roll pins with punch. Place all shift rails in neutral position; interlock notches must be aligned.

2) Remove reverse gearshift head from 5th/reverse shift rail (reverse shift rail of 4-speed). Remove 5th/reverse shift rail and shift fork. Remove 3rd/4th shift rail and shift fork. Remove 1st/2nd shift rail and shift forks. Remove interlock pins and springs.

NOTE — *Interlock pins are equal on 4 and 5-speed transmissions; however, 5-speed transmission has 4 slotted springs and 4-speed has 3 slotted springs.*

3) On 5-speed transmission, measure 5th gear thrust clearance with a feeler gauge. Clearance should be .006-.013" (.15-.33 mm) with maximum clearance of .016" (.4 mm). Remove snap ring retaining 5th gear assembly. Then using a puller, remove 5th gear and synchro assembly. Remove 5th gear needle bearing, spacer and steel ball. Assemble 5th gear and synchro assembly and set aside.

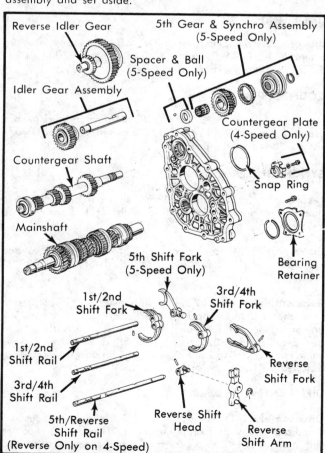

Reverse Idler Gear

5th Gear & Synchro Assembly (5-Speed Only)

Idler Gear Assembly

Spacer & Ball (5-Speed Only)

Countergear Shaft

Countergear Plate (4-Speed Only)

Mainshaft

Snap Ring

5th Shift Fork (5-Speed Only)

Bearing Retainer

1st/2nd Shift Fork

3rd/4th Shift Fork

1st/2nd Shift Rail

3rd/4th Shift Rail

5th/Reverse Shift Rail (Reverse Only on 4-Speed)

Reverse Shift Head

Reverse Shift Fork

Reverse Shift Arm

Fig. 8   Exploded View of Intermediate Plate Assembly

4) On 4-speed transmission, lock transmission, then remove countergear plate retaining bolt and countergear plate. On all transmissions, remove mainshaft bearing retainer. Remove mainshaft and idler gear snap rings. Pull reverse gear shaft, idler gear and mainshaft away from intermediate plate, then remove idler gear and reverse gear shaft together.

NOTE — *If mainshaft needs to be forced out of intermediate plate, use plastic hammer and support mainshaft during removal.*

5) Remove countergear shaft and output shaft together. Place input shaft bearing end on block of wood. Remove oil seal and bearing lock plate, then drive input bearing out of plate. Place countergear center bearing (front bearing on 4-speed) over blocks of wood and force bearing out of intermediate plate.

Reassembly — 1) Press in countergear center bearing (front bearing on 4-speed), then press in input bearing with groove (lip) upward. Secure input bearing with lock plate. Install input bearing oil seal so seal is even with surface of intermediate plate.

2) Mount intermediate plate lower protrusion in soft-jawed vise. Install mainshaft and countergear shaft together and insert halfway into plate. Align idler gear assembly with notched portion of reverse idler gear shaft. Tap idler gear assembly and reverse idler gear shaft halfway into plate and ensure idler gear does not contact mainshaft spacer.

3) Install idler gear and mainshaft snap rings. Install and tighten bearing retainer. On 4-speed, align countergear plate protrusion with cutout on countergear shaft. Install countergear plate, lock countergear shaft and tighten retaining bolt.

4) On 5-speed, align spacer groove with detent ball and install detent ball and spacer onto countershaft. Install 5th gear needle bearing, 5th gear and synchro ring. Align shifting keys with key slots in 5th gear synchro ring and press on synchro hub. Install snap ring which will provide .006-.013" (.15-.33 mm) clearance between 5th gear and intermediate plate.

NOTE — *Snap rings are available in 7 sizes. Select snap ring which will reduce clearance closest to zero.*

MAINSHAFT ASSEMBLY

NOTE — *Before disassembling mainshaft assembly, measure thrust clearance of 1st through 4th gears. Clearance for 1st gear should be .006-.0108" (.15-.275 mm); 2nd and 3rd gears should be .006-.0098" (.15-.25 mm) and 4th gear should be .0008-.0094" (.02-.24 mm). Maximum thrust clearance for all gears is .0118" (.30 mm).*

Disassembly — 1) Mount puller (SST09950-20012) in a vise and install mainshaft assembly. Remove mainshaft connecting sleeve with puller. Remove 5th gear snap ring, then pull off 5th gear with puller. Remove bearing snap ring, then pull off bearing and spacer with puller.

2) Slide off thrust bearing without dropping bearing. Slide 4th gear, synchro hub, synchro sleeve and needle bearing halves off shaft. After removing 4th gear, assemble it with synchro assembly and put aside. Remove snap ring, spacer and thrust bearing. Remove 3rd gear, synchro hub, and synchro sleeve from mainshaft with puller. Reassemble 3rd gear with synchro assembly and put aside.

TOYOTA TERCEL 4 & 5-SPEED (Cont.)

3) Remove snap ring, bushing, 1st gear bearing, 1st gear and synchro sleeve. Assemble 1st gear with synchro ring and put aside. Remove detent ball with magnet, then pull off 2nd gear synchro hub, synchro sleeve and 2nd gear. Reassemble 2nd gear to synchro sleeve and put aside.

Inspection — Measure flange thickness. If thickness is less than .118" (3.0 mm), replace mainshaft assembly. Check connecting sleeve and pinion splines for wear or damage; replace defective part. Check all gears, synchro assemblies, bearings and thrust bearings for wear or damage; replace defective parts.

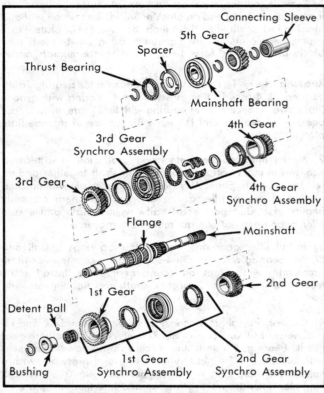

Fig. 9   Exploded View of Mainshaft Assembly

Reassembly — **1)** Coat mainshaft with grease. Align shifting keys of 2nd gear synchro hub with key slots in 2nd gear synchro ring and assemble synchro hub, ring and 2nd gear. Press assembly onto mainshaft. Insert detent ball. Slide 1st gear synchro ring, 1st gear, bearing and bushing onto mainshaft. Align key slots of 1st gear synchro ring with shifting keys in 2nd gear synchro hub. Groove of bushing must seat over detent ball.

2) Measure clearance for snap ring and choose a snap ring which will reduce 1st gear thrust clearance to zero. Snap rings are available in 9 thicknesses ranging from .0846-.0866" (2.15-2.20 mm) to .1004-.1024" (2.55-2.60 mm) in .002" (.05 mm) increments. Install snap ring and check thrust clearance of 1st and 2nd gear.

3) Assemble 3rd gear, synchro ring and synchro assembly with key slots of synchro ring aligned with synchro hub shifting keys. Press assembly onto mainshaft. Slide widest thrust bearing onto mainshaft. Install 4th gear needle bearing halves, synchro ring and 4th gear. Ensure key slots of 4th gear synchro ring align with shifting keys of synchro hub.

4) Install 4th gear spacer and snap ring. Coat 5th gear thrust bearing with grease and press into 5th gear spacer. Press

spacer onto mainshaft with bearing facing 4th gear. Press bearing onto mainshaft with groove at the top. Install a snap ring which will reduce bearing thrust clearance to zero. Measure thrust clearance of 3rd and 4th gears.

NOTE — *Snap rings are available in 9 thicknesses ranging from .0827-.0846" (2.10-2.15 mm) to .0984-.1004" (2.50-2.55 mm) in .002" (.05 mm) increments.*

5) Press 5th gear onto mainshaft and check thrust clearance. Select and install a snap ring which will reduce 5th gear thrust clearance to zero. Snap rings are available in 5 thicknesses: .0827-.0846" (2.10-2.15 mm) to .0906-.0926" (2.30-2.35 mm) in .002" (.05 mm) increments. Press mainshaft connecting sleeve onto mainshaft.

INPUT SHAFT

Disassembly — Remove input shaft bearing snap ring. Mount puller onto bearing, place puller in a vise and force input shaft out of bearing.

Reassembly — Mount input shaft bearing with snap ring groove facing rearward. Support bearing inner race with block (SST09515-20010), place a steel plate under the block and press bearing onto input shaft. Install a .0827-.0846" (2.10-2.15 mm) or .0886-.0906" (2.25-2.30 mm) thick snap ring to minimize thrust clearance.

IDLER SHAFT

Use procedure outlined for INPUT SHAFT. Snap rings are available in .0945-.0965" (2.40-2.45 mm) or .1004-.1024" (2.55-2.60 mm) thicknesses.

COUNTERSHAFT

Use procedure outlined for INPUT SHAFT. Snap rings are available in .0708-.0728" (1.80-1.85 mm) or .0768-.0787" (1.95-2.00 mm) thicknesses.

SYNCHRONIZER ASSEMBLIES

Disassembly — Mark the position of sliding gear in relation to hub before dismantling. Remove both synchro springs and slide assembly apart.

Inspection — Measure clearance between shift sleeve and corresponding shift fork. Clearance should not exceed .039" (1 mm).

Reassembly — On 1st/2nd synchro assembly, install 3 shift keys, then mount key springs 120° apart so spring ends will not be in line. Synchro hub for 3rd/4th gear has 3 shift keys and 3 coil springs. Synchro hub for 5th gear is assembled in same manner as 1st/2nd synchro hub with a shift key retainer installed on front side of hub.

DIFFERENTIAL ASSEMBLY

Disassembly — **1)** Mount transaxle/clutch housing on support stand and remove differential front cover. Measure and record ring gear backlash, ring gear runout and check tooth contact pattern. Remove and mark side bearing caps and side bearing washers. Lift out differential assembly.

TOYOTA TERCEL 4 & 5-SPEED (Cont.)

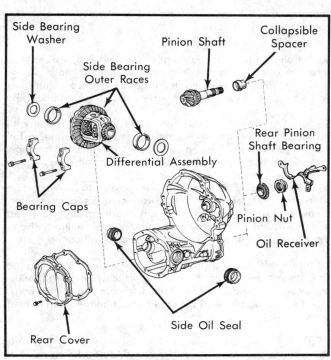

Fig. 10   View of Clutch/Differential Housing

2) Remove transaxle case oil seals. Install INCH lb. torque wrench and measure pinion shaft bearing preload for reassembly reference. Preload should be 5.2-8.7 INCH lbs. (6-10 cmkg). Remove bearing oil reservoir. Loosen staked portion of pinion shaft nut. Remove pinion shaft nut. While removing nut, turn pinion shaft clockwise with collar (SST09556-16010). Press out pinion shaft and collapsible spacer.

3) Remove pinion shaft front bearing with a puller. Remove shim and place aside for reassembly. Remove rear bearing and race. Remove differential side bearing races and mark for identification. Pull off side bearings and mark for identification.

NOTE — *Differential case has indentations for insertion of puller jaws to ease side bearing removal.*

4) Remove staking from ring gear bolt lock plates. Remove ring gear bolts and lock plate. Using chalk, draw alignment mark on ring gear and differential case. Tap ring gear off differential case. Tap out differential lock pin. Remove pinion shaft, pinion gears, side gears and thrust washers.

Reassembly — **1)** Install thrust washers, side gears, pinion gears and pinion shaft. Hold 1 side gear and measure backlash of opposite side gear. Backlash should be .0016-.0094" (.04-.24 mm). If backlash is not to specification, disassemble differential case and install proper side gear thrust washers. Recheck backlash and install lock pin. Stake differential case.

NOTE — *Side gear thrust washers are available in 6 thicknesses ranging from .059" (1.50 mm) to .069" (1.75 mm) in increments of .002" (.05 mm).*

2) Heat ring gear to 212° F (100° C). Install ring gear with marks aligned. Install new lock plates. Install and tighten nuts, then stake lock plates. Press on differential side bearings.

ADJUSTMENTS

PINION BEARING PRELOAD

1) Measure and record thickness of pinion shim with micrometer and install shim on pinion shaft. Press on new front bearing. Slide new collapsible spacer onto pinion shaft. Install pinion shaft and collapsible spacer into transaxle housing. Press in rear bearing (do not smash collapsible spacer) until threaded portion of pinion shaft extends .12" (3 mm) above rear bearing surface.

2) Coat threaded portion of pinion shaft with oil, then install pinion shaft nut. Tighten nut to 108 ft. lbs. (15 mkg).

3) Apply gear oil to bearings and rotate pinion shaft to seat bearings with socket (SST09556-16010). Attach INCH lb. torque wrench and measure bearing preload. Preload for new bearings should be 4.3-8.7 INCH lbs. (5-10 cmkg); used bearings should be 2.6-4.3 INCH lbs. (3-5 cmkg).

4) If preload is above specifications, replace collapsible spacer and test again. If preload is not to specification, gradually tighten pinion nut 5-10° at a time and measure preload after each tightening. If preload is insufficient after reaching maximum torque value of 267 ft. lbs. (37 mkg), loosen pinion nut and repeat procedure.

NOTE — *If preload is not within specifications after reaching maximum torque value, install new collapsible spacer and repeat procedure.*

RING GEAR BACKLASH

1) Mount clutch/differential housing so ring gear side of housing is down. Install outer side bearing races. Insert lower differential side bearing washer, then install differential case into housing. Tap differential into position with plastic hammer.

NOTE — *Do not interchange side bearings.*

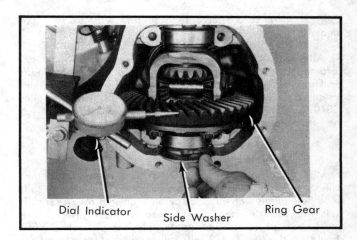

Fig. 11   Measuring Ring Gear Backlash

2) Mount dial indicator. Hold upper side bearing outer race against side bearing and measure ring gear backlash. Backlash should be .0039-.0059" (.10-.15 mm). Select and install a washer which will eliminate any clearance between outer race and housing. Recheck ring gear backlash.

TOYOTA TERCEL 4 & 5-SPEED (Cont.)

3) Remove differential, side bearing races and washer. Measure thickness of washers with micrometer, divide by 2 and select appropriate shims of equal thickness for each side of differential assembly. Reinstall differential assembly, side bearing outer races and washers. Measure ring gear runout. If not to specification, increase or decrease washer thickness until specification is obtained.

NOTE — *Side bearing washers are available in the following thicknesses: .103-.129" (2.62-3.28 mm) in .001" (.03 mm) increments. Backlash will change about .0008" (.02 mm) with .001" (.03 mm) alteration of side bearing washers.*

4) After adjusting ring gear backlash, install side bearing caps and tighten bolts. Do not interchange bearing caps. Mount dial indicator on pinion nut and measure total ring and pinion bearing preload. Preload should be 2.6-4.3 INCH lbs. (3-5 cmkg) PLUS amount of pinion bearing preload.

GEAR TOOTH CONTACT PATTERN

NOTE — *Final adjustments to differential are made with results from gear tooth contact pattern. See Gear Tooth Contact Pattern in DRIVE AXLES Section.*

1) If excessive heel or toe contact is evident, readjust pinion shaft depth. Pinion depth is adjusted by installing thinner shim (excessive toe contact) or thicker shim (excessive heel contact). Altering thickness of pinion washer .0039" (.10 mm) will change center of tooth contact ⅛ of total tooth contact.

NOTE — *Pinion washers are available in 16 thicknesses ranging from .0591" (1.50 mm) to .0768" (1.95 mm) in .0012" (.03 mm) increments.*

2) Too much flank or face contact reveals incorrect ring gear backlash. Too much flank contact can be eliminated by installing thicker side bearing washers (adjust backlash closer to high side of specification). Too much face contact can be eliminated by installing thinner side bearing washers (adjust backlash closer to low side of specification).

NOTE — *Increase or decrease both side washers in equal amounts.*

3) After adjusting pinion depth and ring gear backlash according to gear tooth contact pattern, check ring gear backlash. Stake pinion nut and reinstall rear cover and gasket. Install differential side bearing oil seals with installer (SST09223-46011) until seal protrudes .331-.354" (8.4-9.0 mm) from housing.

TRANSAXLE REASSEMBLY

1) Mount shift forks to respective synchro hubs and install shift rails. Slide reverse shift head onto rail and ensure reverse shift head hole aligns with interlock pin hole on shift rail. After shift rails have been inserted into intermediate plate, insert a wire into bottom of intermediate plate (interlock pin holes). Wire should go through first 2 shift rails and be stopped by final rail; 4.7" (120 mm) from outer circumference of intermediate plate.

2) Coat interlock pins with grease and push into position with wire. After insertion of interlock pins, reinsert wire and check

that it goes in 3.1" (80 mm) from end of intermediate plate. Insert 5th gear shift fork.

3) Set all shift forks in neutral position. Shift 2nd/3rd shift rail into 3rd gear position. Other rails should not move. Apply sealant to interlock pin plug and install plug. Secure shift arms to shift rails with roll pins. Install reverse shift arm and circlip.

4) Install gasket to intermediate plate and coat gasket with sealant. Mount transmission case to intermediate plate. Install countergear assembly snap ring. Insert detent balls and springs. Coat detent plug with sealant and install plug.

5) Insert reverse shift arm pivot and guide into lower portion of reverse shift arm with a screwdriver inserted from intermediate plate side. Install shift rail heads on shift rails and secure with roll pins. Install speedometer gear detent ball and drive gear. Install speedometer drive gear snap ring.

6) Install shift housing gasket and coat with sealant. Engage 3rd/4th shift head with the end of shift lever inside shift housing. Mount shift housing to transmission case and tighten bolts. Insert restricting pins and springs into shift housing and tighten screws.

NOTE — *Green restrict pin must be installed at 1st/2nd shift rail and red restrict pin must be installed at 5th/reverse shift rail.*

7) Install and tighten speedometer driven gear. Install transmission mounting brackets, back-up light switch and input shaft assembly. Install input shaft "O" ring on clutch housing. Mount transmission gasket and transmission case onto clutch/differential housing. Turn transaxle assembly so transmission case is up, turn input shaft and tighten attaching bolts. Check operation of transmission by shifting through all gear ranges.

TIGHTENING SPECIFICATIONS

Application	Ft. Lbs. (mkg)
Shift Hsg.-to-Transmission Case	8-11 (1.0-1.6)
Transmission-to-Intermediate Plate	11-15 (1.6-2.0)
Transaxle Hsg.-to-Intermediate Plate	8-11 (1.0-1.6)
Clutch/Differential Hsg.-to-Engine	37-57 (5.1-7.9)
Mainshaft Rear Bearing Retainer	8-11 (1.0-1.6)
Input Shaft Bearing Retainer	8-11 (1.0-1.6)
Countergear Plate (4-Speed)	8-11 (1.0-1.6)
Restrict Pin Plugs	27-32 (3.7-4.5)
Ring Gear Bolts	67-75 (9.3-10.4)
Pinion Nut	109-267 (15-37)
Side Bearing Caps	33-39 (4.6-5.4)
Differential Front Cover	8-11 (1.0-1.6)
Axle Shaft Nut	73-108 (10.0-15.0)
Hub-to-Rotor Bolts	29-36 (4.0-5.1)
Strut-to-Steering Knuckle	40-52 (5.5-7.2)
Lower Arm-to-Strut Bar	29-39 (4.0-5.4)
Ball Joint-to-Steering Knuckle	40-52 (5.5-7.2)
Lower Arm-to-Crossmember	51-65 (7.1-9.0)
Strut Bar-to-Strut Bracket	55-79 (7.6-10.9)
Stabilizer-to-Lower Arm	11-15 (1.6-2.0)
Stabilizer Bracket	22-32 (3.0-4.5)
Engine Front Mounting-to-Crossmember	26-39 (3.6-5.4)

VOLKSWAGEN JETTA, PICKUP, RABBIT & SCIROCCO 4 & 5-SPEED

DESCRIPTION

Transaxles are 4 or 5-speed, fully synchronized units, mounted transversely at the front of vehicle. Transmission gears are all helical cut and are in constant mesh with mating gears on countershaft. Forward gear engagement is accomplished through blocker ring type synchronizer assemblies. Reverse gears are spur type and are not in constant mesh, and are engaged by a sliding type reverse idler gear. Final drive portion of transaxle consists of a drive pinion shaft (which also carries some of the transmission gears), and a differential and ring gear assembly. The 4-speed transmission and final drive components are carried in a common 2-piece case. The 5-speed is almost identical to the 4-speed except the 5th gear assembly is located on the end of the pinion and mainshaft in a separate housing. Transaxle codes (020 for 4-speed, 020F for 5-speed) are stamped on lower side of transaxle case, adjacent to left axle drive flange.

LUBRICATION & ADJUSTMENT

See MANUAL TRANSMISSION SERVICING Section.

SERVICE (IN VEHICLE)

AXLE DRIVE SHAFTS

NOTE — *Vehicle weight must be resting on wheels to remove axle shaft nut.*

Removal — Remove axle shaft nut. Raise and support vehicle; remove tire and wheel. Remove Allen bolts connecting inner constant velocity (CV) joint to differential case drive flange. Press out drive shaft and guide shaft out of hub, past transaxle assembly.

NOTE — *Axle drive shafts should be disassembled ONLY to replace defective rubber boots. If boots are replaced, check all components for wear or damage and replace as complete assembly.*

Disassembly — 1) On inner CV joint, remove circlip from axle shaft and drive protective cap from CV joint. Place axle shaft in holder (VW 402) and press CV joint from shaft with adapter (VW 408a), supporting hub to prevent damage. Pivot hub and cage assembly out of inner joint, then push out and remove balls. Align ball hub grooves with cage and remove hub.

NOTE — *Inner CV joint and ball hub are matched sets. DO NOT interchange with outer joint. Also, balls of CV joints cannot be interchanged between CV joints.*

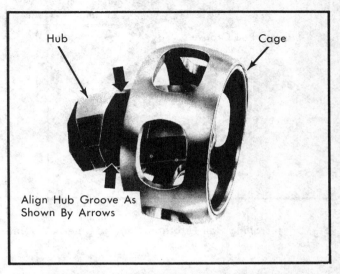

Fig. 2   Removing Inner CV Joint Ball Hub

2) Remove and discard inner boot clamp and boot. On outer CV joint, spread circlip inside ball hub and drive CV joint off axle shaft with brass drift; tap on hub. Mark position of ball hub and outer joint, then tilt cage and remove each ball. Align cage perpendicular to joint, align 2 large openings of cage with raised portions of joint and remove cage and hub. Position 1 retainer of hub in large opening and remove hub by tilting outward. Remove and discard outer boot and clamp.

Reassembly — 1) To reassemble CV joints, reverse disassembly procedure and note the following: Lubricate joints with 3 ozs. (90 g) of molybdenum disulphide grease. After inserting balls into inner CV joint hub and cage, insert hub and cage into joint perpendicularly. Chamfer of ball hub splines must face larger diameter of joint. Then rotate ball and cage into position and ensure CV joint wide ball groove and narrow hub groove are on same side of joint. See Fig. 3. Joint is correctly assembled if hub can move over shaft splines by hand.

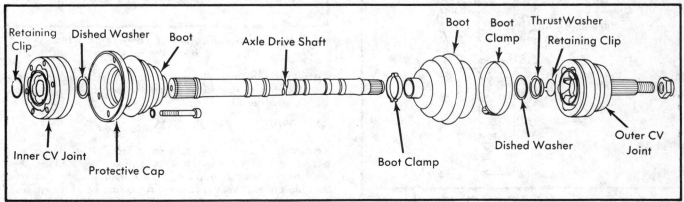

Fig. 1   Exploded View of Axle Drive Shafts

VOLKSWAGEN JETTA, PICKUP, RABBIT & SCIROCCO 4 & 5-SPEED (Cont.)

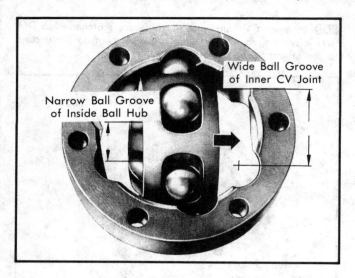

Fig. 3   Installing Ball Hub and Cage in Inner CV Joint

2) Outer CV joint alignment marks must match after reassembly. Replace dust boots and clamps. Install CV joints onto drive axle shaft with inside ball hub chamfer facing shaft. Outer CV joint must be assembled with dished washer concave side facing thrust washer and convex side of thrust washer facing CV joint. See Fig. 4.

NOTE — *The CV joint assembly shown in Fig. 4 is a new production assembly which may be installed on Jetta, Rabbit Convertible and Scirocco models. Former production assembly has snap ring installed closer to thrust washer. DO NOT interchange components between assemblies.*

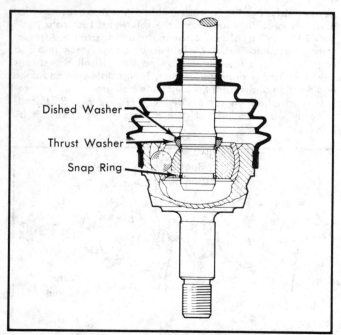

Fig 4   Cutaway View of Outer CV Joint Showing Installation of Dished and Thrust Washers

FRONT WHEEL BEARINGS

Removal — 1) With vehicle supported and drive axle shafts removed, remove caliper mounting bolts. Hang caliper from frame with wire; DO NOT disconnect hydraulic line. Remove brake disc. Remove lower steering knuckle housing-to-ball joint retaining bolt. Remove ball joint castellated nut and cotter pin, then separate ball joint from steering knuckle.

2) Separate tie rod end from steering knuckle. Mark position of camber adjustment bolt (upper bolt securing steering knuckle to strut assembly). Remove bolts securing steering knuckle to strut assembly and remove steering knuckle.

NOTE — *Camber adjustment must be checked after wheel bearing replacement. DO NOT lose camber adjustment bolt or eccentric washer.*

3) Mount steering knuckle in holding fixture and press out wheel hub. Remove dust shield. Remove circlips from both sides of bearing housing and press out bearing (toward outboard end of housing) with tools shown in Fig. 5. Remove inner wheel bearing race from hub.

NOTE — *Wheel bearing must be replaced. Removal procedure destroys wheel bearing for reinstallation.*

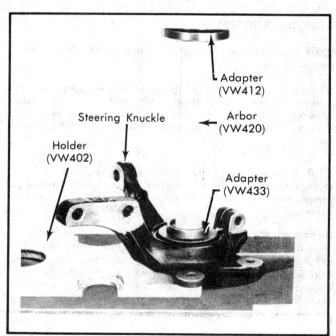

Fig. 5   Identification of Tools to Be Used to Replace Front Wheel Bearing

Installation — To install, reverse removal procedure and note the following: Ensure circlips are fully seated. Always replace ball joint cotter pin.

AXLE DRIVE FLANGE OIL SEALS

Removal — Disconnect axle shaft from drive flange and position out of the way. Remove cap from drive flange, then withdraw retaining snap ring and dished washer. Fasten a suitable puller (VW391) to drive flange and pull flange from transmission. Using a suitable seal puller (VW681), pry oil seal from housing.

VOLKSWAGEN JETTA, PICKUP, RABBIT & SCIROCCO 4 & 5-SPEED (Cont.)

Fig. 6   Using Puller to Remove Axle Drive Flange

Installation — Drive new seal into housing with suitable driver (US 4450). Install drive flange using puller used during removal (reverse puller for installation). Place dished washer on shaft with convex side away from flange, then drive circlip in place with driver (VW30-23). Replace dust cap and install drive shaft.

NOTE — *Pack open side of seals with multipurpose lubricant prior to installation. Check gear lube level and add as required.*

TRANSAXLE REMOVAL & INSTALLATION

Removal — **1)** Disconnect negative battery cable. Install engine support bar. Remove 3 transmission mount bolts located on left side of vehicle near battery. Disconnect speedometer cable from case and plug opening. Remove upper transaxle-to-engine bolts, electrical connection at back-up light switch and clutch cable. Remove shift linkage parts from relay lever on transaxle and rod lever.

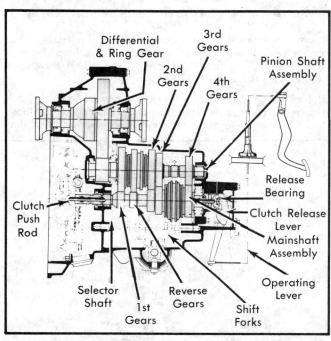

Fig. 7   View of 4-Speed Transaxle Assembly (5-Speed Similar)

2) Disconnect ground strap from transaxle. Remove starter and 2 engine-to-transaxle bolts on either side of starter opening. Remove exhaust pipe bracket from bottom of transaxle. Place floor jack with adapter under transaxle and raise until transaxle is supported. Remove rear transaxle mount and bracket.

3) Disconnect both axle drive shafts from drive flanges and wire up out of the way. Remove bolts attaching cover plates to transaxle. Remove small cover plate, then remove remaining transaxle-to-engine bolts and nuts. Lower transaxle and remove from under vehicle

Installation — To install, reverse removal procedure and note the following: Adjust shift linkage and check lubricant level. See *MANUAL TRANSMISSION SERVICING* Section.

TRANSAXLE DISASSEMBLY

NOTE — *Before disassembly, measure and record pinion depth and ring gear backlash.*

4-SPEED

1) Mount transaxle in holding fixture and drain fluid. Remove clutch release push rod from center of mainshaft and withdraw from bellhousing end. Install support bar (30-211) across mouth of bellhousing and install support block (VW 295a) between support bar and mainshaft. Tighten bolt of bar to take up clearance between bar and mainshaft. See *Fig. 8.*

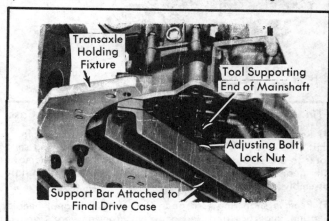

Fig. 8   Installation of Mainshaft Support Fixture

2) Remove cap, snap ring and spring washer from drive shaft flange. Remove both drive shaft flanges with remover (VW 391). Remove release bearing cover, pry circlips off release shaft. Remove release shaft, clutch lever and return spring. Remove release bearing and guide sleeve. Remove 2 mainshaft bearing retaining nut plugs. Remove 3 mainshaft bearing retaining nuts. Remove reverse idler shaft bolt and back-up light switch.

3) Remove selector shaft cover and lock bolt. Set shift forks in neutral position and remove selector shaft and spring with remover (US 4463). Remove 2 stud nuts and 12 bolts retaining transmission case to transaxle case. Install mounting plate on rear of transmission case and center remover (VW 391) on mainshaft. Separate transmission case from transaxle case. Remove mainshaft bearing retaining screws that fell into case. Remove magnet from transaxle case.

VOLKSWAGEN JETTA, PICKUP, RABBIT & SCIROCCO 4 & 5-SPEED (Cont.)

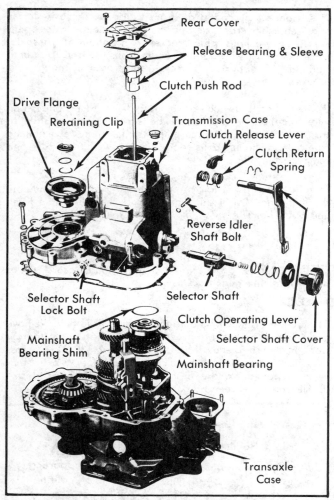

Fig. 9   Exploded View of 4-Speed Transmission Case

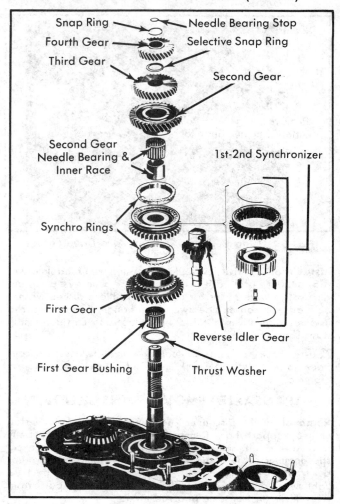

Fig. 10   View of 4-Speed Pinion Shaft Assembly

4) Remove mainshaft bearing shim. Remove 2 "E" clips from shift fork and pull shift fork shaft from housing. Swing shift forks to one side and remove reverse gear and shaft. Remove 4th gear snap ring from pinion shaft. Remove mainshaft assembly and 4th gear on pinion shaft as an assembly.

5) Remove snap ring, 3rd gear, 2nd gear, 2nd gear needle bearing and race and 2nd gear synchronizer ring. Using a puller, simultaneously remove 1st gear, 1st gear synchronizer ring, 1st-2nd gear synchronizer, 1st gear needle bearing and thrust washer. Remove pinion bearing cover bolts, remove cover and pull pinion shaft out of bore. Lift out differential unit.

NOTE — *All gears must be removed from pinion shaft before shaft and differential can be removed from case.*

5-SPEED

1) Mount transaxle in holding fixture and drain fluid. Remove clutch release push rod from center of mainshaft and withdraw from bellhousing end. Install support bar (30-211) across mouth of bellhousing and install support block (VW 295a) between support bar and mainshaft. Tighten bolt of bar to take up clearance between bar and mainshaft. See *Fig. 8*.

2) Remove rear housing bolts and rear housing. Remove backup light switch, 5th gear lockout and selector shaft detent.

Remove selector shaft cover. Set gears in neutral position and remove selector shaft and spring. Remove cap, snap ring and spring washer from drive shaft flange. Remove both drive shaft flanges with remover (VW 391).

3) Lock transmission in 5th and reverse gears and remove 5th gear synchronizer hub retaining bolt. Pry locking plate loose until tube can be turned and screw tube out of shift fork in a

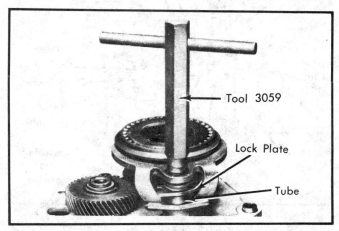

Fig. 11   Removing 5th Gear Synchronizer Assembly

VOLKSWAGEN JETTA, PICKUP, RABBIT & SCIROCCO 4 & 5-SPEED (Cont.)

counterclockwise rotation with remover (3059). Remove tube with remover (3038). Remove 5th gear synchronizer, 5th gear and shift fork from transmission case. Remove circlip and thrust washer from 5th gear and pull 5th gear off pinion shaft with a puller.

NOTE — *Do not pull selector rod out of tube.*

4) Remove recess bolts from mainshaft retainer plate. Remove transmission housing-to-transaxle housing bolts. Using remover (3042), remove transmission housing. Remove shift fork rod and forks. Remove 4th gear snap ring from pinion shaft. Remove mainshaft assembly and 4th gear on pinion shaft as an assembly.

5) Remove circlip from 3rd gear and remove 3rd gear, 2nd gear synchronizer, bearing and reverse gear. Use suitable puller and remove 1st gear synchronizer and 1st gear. Remove pinion bearing retainer plate and pinion shaft. Remove differential assembly from case.

COMPONENT DISASSEMBLY & REASSEMBLY

MAINSHAFT

Disassembly — Remove mainshaft bearing with puller on 5-speed (use a press and VW402 plate for 4-speed). On all transaxles, remove 4th gear, 4th gear needle bearing and 4th gear synchro ring. Remove 3rd-4th synchro assembly snap ring and simultaneously press 3rd gear and 3rd-4th synchro assembly off shaft. Remove 3rd gear needle bearing. Place reference marks on synchro hub and sleeve for reassembly reference, then push hub, shifting keys and spring out of sleeve.

Inspection — Check all shaft surfaces, splines, and gear teeth for wear, chipping, scoring, or other damage. Check clutch push rod bushing in mainshaft for wear or damage, and if replacement is necessary, drive out push rod bushing using a $3/8''$ (10 mm) rod inserted through rear of shaft. Position a new bushing and oil seal on front of mainshaft, and press into shaft until flush. Assemble synchro rings on gears and check ring-to-gear clearance. Clearance for new parts should be .044-.069" (1.12-1.75 mm) for 3rd gear, .051-.075" (1.3-1.9 mm) for 4th gear. Wear limit for used parts is .020" (.5 mm).

NOTE — *Replacement of any gear necessitates replacement of meshing gear, as gears are available as matched pairs only.*

Reassembly — 1) Position shifting keys in slots of synchronizer hub, then install hub into synchronizer sleeve, after aligning reference marks. Install key springs into assembly, making sure springs are positioned 120° offset of one another and that angled ends of springs engage hollowed-out portions of shifting keys.

2) Install 3rd gear needle bearing on shaft. Assemble 3rd gear, 3rd gear synchro ring and synchro assembly, ensuring notches in synchro ring engage 3 keys in synchro assembly and that splines in synchro hub face 3rd gear. Press mainshaft into assembled synchro assembly, 3rd gear and synchro ring. Install snap ring, 4th gear synchro ring, needle bearing and 4th gear. On 5-speed transmissions, press bearing on mainshaft with suitable press.

PINION SHAFT

NOTE — *Gears and synchronizer assembly were removed during Transmission Disassembly, and will be installed during Transmission Reassembly. Synchronizer overhaul and bearing replacement are covered below.*

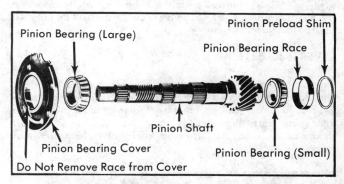

Fig. 13   Exploded View of 4-Speed Pinion Shaft

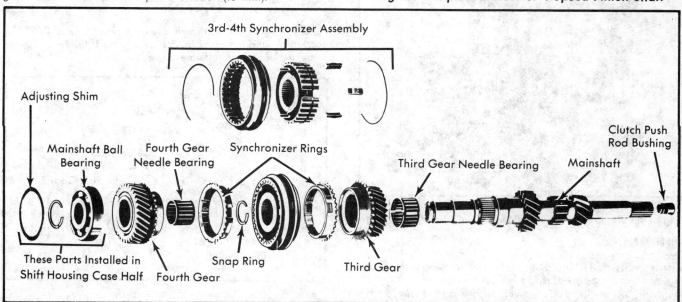

Fig. 12   Exploded View of 4-Speed Mainshaft Assembly

VOLKSWAGEN JETTA, PICKUP, RABBIT & SCIROCCO 4 & 5-SPEED (Cont.)

Disassembly — Bearings cannot be reused after removal from pinion shaft. If bearing replacement is required, use press to remove large and small bearings from shaft. Use puller to remove small bearing outer race from case. For reassembly reference, scribe reference marks on synchro hub and operating sleeve. Then, push hub, shifting keys and springs out of sleeve.

Inspection — Check all shaft surfaces, splines and gear teeth for wear, chipping, scoring or other damage. Assemble synchro rings on gears and check ring-to-gear clearance. Clearance for new parts should be .043-.067" (1.1-1.7 mm). Wear limit for used parts is .020" (.5 mm).

NOTE — *Replacement of any gear necessitates replacement of meshing gear, as gears are available as matched pairs only.*

Reassembly — If bearings were removed from pinion shaft, heat new bearings to approximately 212°F (100°C) and install on pinion shaft with press. Install shifting keys into synchronizer hub, then install hub into synchronizer sleeve, making sure reference marks are aligned. Install shifting key springs into assembly with springs offset 120° from each other. Angled ends of springs must engage hollowed out portions of shifting keys.

NOTE — *DO NOT install pinion bearing race into case half at this time; adjustment of pinion is required and will be covered in Transmission Reassembly.*

REVERSE IDLER GEAR & SHAFT

The stop sleeve is no longer installed on idler gear shaft. Gear end movement is limited by the stop on drive pinion shaft bearing retainer. To install, loosely install idler gear support bolt in idler gear shaft. Align shaft as shown in *Fig. 21*. Bolt in shaft should be an equal distance from each bolt hole in flange of case.

Fig. 14 Reverse Idler Gear Stop on Pinion Cover Plate

DIFFERENTIAL

Disassembly — 1) Ring gear is attached to differential housing by rivets on 5-speed. Drill out rivet heads with a ¹⁵⁄₃₂" (12 mm) drill bit, then knock out rivets with a drift. Remove ring gear bolt lock plate and remove bolts on 4-speed. Place assembly in a press and press off differential ring gear.

NOTE — *Ring gear is reinstalled with special bolts, washers and nuts. Serrations on shank of bolts lock bolt in housing.*

2) Remove snap rings from differential pinion shaft, and drive shaft out of housing. Remove snap rings securing side gears to axle drive flange shafts, and remove shafts from housing. Remove pinions and side gears. Rotate thrust cage and remove from housing.

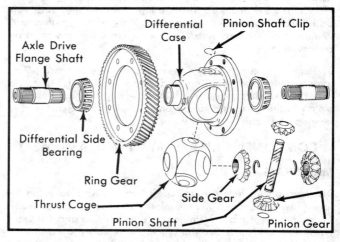

Fig. 15 Exploded View of Differential Assembly

Reassembly — 1) Insert thrust cage into differential housing. Insert pinion gears into housing and drive in pinion shaft. Install pinion shaft snap rings. Rotate thrust cage to align side gear shaft holes with side gear shaft holes of housing.

NOTE — *If bearings were removed from case, heat bearings to approximately 212° F (100° C) and use a press to drive bearings into place.*

2) Insert and position side gears so they mesh with pinion gears and are 180° apart. Rotate side gears into position inside housing. Install axle drive flange shafts, and push each shaft firmly against differential pinion shaft and install thickest snap ring possible. See Fig. 15.

NOTE — *There are two available snap rings. One is .079" (2.0 mm) thick, and the other is .091" (2.3 mm). If thicker snap ring jams sideways, install thinner snap ring.*

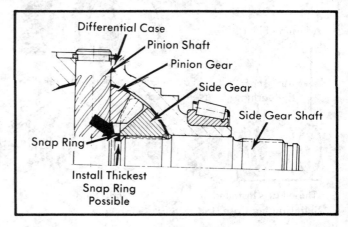

Fig. 16 Cutaway View of Differential Showing Flange Shaft Snap Ring Installation

VOLKSWAGEN JETTA, PICKUP, RABBIT & SCIROCCO 4 & 5-SPEED (Cont.)

3) Heat ring gear to approximately 212° F (100° C). Drive bolts into differential housing and place heated ring gear onto housing. Install washers and nuts onto ring gear bolts and torque to 50 ft. lbs. (7.0 mkg.)

TRANSAXLE REASSEMBLY & ADJUSTMENT

NOTE — *During reassembly of transaxle, it is not always necessary to perform all adjustments described in the following procedures. If transaxle case or mainshaft have been replaced, check mainshaft adjustment. If transaxle case, pinion bearings or ring and pinion set have been replaced, adjust drive pinion. If transaxle case, differential side bearings or differential have been replaced, adjust differential. If no components were replaced during reassembly, make corresponding adjustments to conform to specifications taken prior to disassembly.*

DIFFERENTIAL BEARING PRELOAD

1) If differential bearing race and shim were removed from final drive housing case half, position a .039" (1 mm) shim in bearing race bore and press in bearing race. Remove bearing race and shim from shift housing case half (if not already removed), and reinstall bearing race into housing **without shims**.

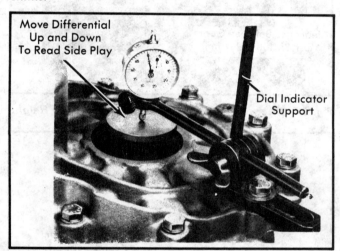

Fig. 17   Using a Dial Indicator to Measure Differential Side Play in Case

2) Install differential assembly into final drive housing case half. Position shift housing case half with gasket onto final drive housing case half and install and tighten attaching bolts. Place gauge block (VW385/17) onto axle drive flange shaft. Install dial indicator on shift housing case so button contacts gauge block. Zero dial indicator with .039" (1 mm) preload.

CAUTION — *Do not rotate differential when moving up and down as this will cause an incorrect reading.*

3) Move differential assembly up and down and note reading on dial indicator. Add constant preload figure of .016" (.4 mm) to dial indicator reading to obtain thickness of shim to install under shift housing case half differential bearing race.

4) Separate housings and remove differential. Press out shift housing case half differential bearing race, install shim just determined in bearing race bore, then reinstall bearing race with a press.

NOTE — *Adjusting shims are available in various thicknesses from .006" (.15 mm) to .039" (1 mm). Install a combination of shims as required to make up shim pack. Thickest shim should be inserted first, with thinnest against bearing race.*

5) Lubricate bearings with hypoid oil and reinstall in transaxle case. Install adapter and INCH lb. torque wrench to drive axle flange shaft and check rotating torque. Rotating torque for new bearings should be 11-31 INCH lbs. (13-36 cmkg); used bearings 2.7 INCH lbs. (3.1 cmkg). If not within specifications, recheck bearing condition and proper shim thickness.

PINION BEARING PRELOAD

1) If not already removed, use a puller to withdraw pinion bearing race from final drive housing case half. Temporarily install a .025" (.65 mm) shim into bearing race bore of case half, then reinstall race using a press. Install pinion shaft into bearing race, then install pinion bearing cover, tightening cover-to-case half bolts securely.

CAUTION — *Do not rotate pinion when moving up and down as this will cause an incorrect reading.*

2) Install surface plate on top of pinion shaft. Install dial indicator and support on case half so button of indicator contacts surface plate. *See Fig. 18.* Preload dial indicator with .039" (1 mm) and zero dial face. Move pinion up and down and note maximum dial indicator reading.

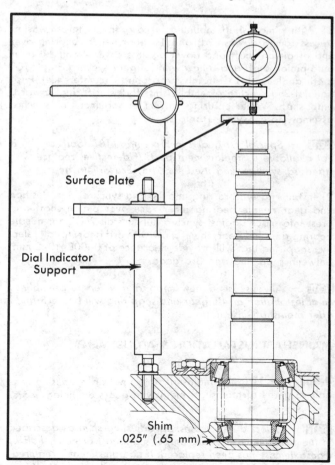

Fig. 18   Method Used to Measure Pinion Shaft End Play

VOLKSWAGEN JETTA, PICKUP, RABBIT & SCIROCCO 4 & 5-SPEED (Cont.)

3) To dial indicator reading, add thickness of shim temporarily installed under bearing race (.025" — .65 mm), plus a constant preload figure of .008" (.2 mm). Total of 3 figures equals thickness of shims to install under pinion bearing race in case half. Remove pinion and bearing race, replace .025" (.65 mm) shim with shim pack just determined, then reinstall bearing race.

NOTE — *Adjusting shims are available in thicknesses ranging from .026" (.65 mm) to .055" (1.4 mm) in increments of .002" (.5 mm). Install a combination of shims as required to make up shim pack.*

DIFFERENTIAL & PINION INSTALLATION

1) Place final drive housing on work bench and lubricate differential bearings with gear oil. Install differential assembly into transaxle case. Lubricate pinion bearings with gear oil and install pinion shaft. Install pinion bearing cover and tighten bearing retainer plate and transmission case-to-transaxle case attaching bolts.

2) Install adapter (VW548) to pinion shaft and measure rotating torque with INCH lb. torque wrench. Rotating torque for new bearings should be 4.5-13 INCH lbs. (5.2-15 cmkg); used bearings 2.7 INCH lbs. (3 cmkg) minimum.

PINION SHAFT REASSEMBLY

1) With pinion shaft mounted in case, install thrust washer (recess facing downward) and 1st gear needle bearing over end of pinion shaft and down against cover. Intall 1st gear onto pinion shaft and follow with 1st gear synchro ring (110° tooth angle and 3 teeth missing around circumference). Position 1st-2nd synchro assembly (shift fork slot facing upward) onto shaft. While ensuring correct engagement of synchro assembly, press synchro onto shaft.

NOTE — *Special 1st gear synchro ring (110° tooth angle) is not available as replacement part. If defective, replace with standard synchro ring used for 2nd, 3rd or 4th gear.*

2) Install 2nd synchro ring into 1st-2nd synchronizer. Position 2nd gear needle bearing inner race over pinion shaft and press into place against synchro hub. Install 2nd gear needle bearing and 2nd gear, then follow with 3rd gear. Install selective snap ring that will provide clearance of 0-.008" (0-.2 mm) between snap ring and 3rd gear.

NOTE — *Always use a new snap ring when reassembling. Final installation of 4th gear and snap ring will be performed after mainshaft installation.*

MAINSHAFT INSTALLATION & ADJUSTMENT

4-Speed — 1) Install mainshaft into final drive housing case half so gears of mainshaft mesh with gears of pinion gears.

NOTE — *Select a new mainshaft adjusting shim as described in the following procedure only if mainshaft or either half of transaxle case has been replaced. If no adjustment is required, install original shim in bore of shift housing case half and proceed to step 6).*

2) Install a suitable support bar (30-211) onto clutch housing side of final drive housing case half so adjusting bolt contacts front of mainshaft. Lift mainshaft up with adjusting bolt until a clearance of .039" (1 mm) exists between 2nd gear of pinion shaft and 3rd gear of mainshaft. Lock adjusting bolt, ensure clearance has not changed, and install dummy bearing measuring sleeve (VW 549) onto mainshaft.

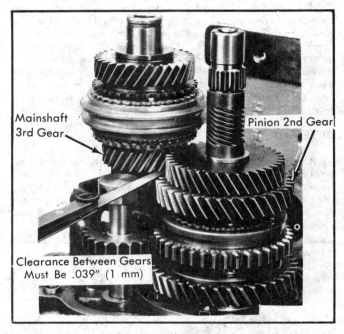

Mainshaft 3rd Gear

Pinion 2nd Gear

Clearance Between Gears Must Be .039" (1 mm)

Fig. 19   Measuring 4-Speed Mainshaft Installed Height

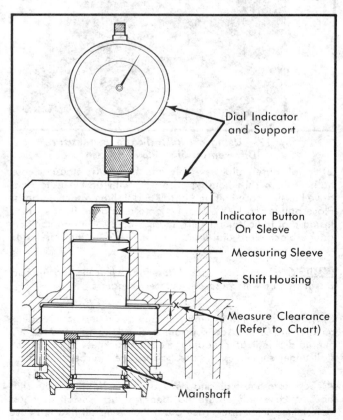

Dial Indicator and Support

Indicator Button On Sleeve

Measuring Sleeve

Shift Housing

Measure Clearance (Refer to Chart)

Mainshaft

Fig. 20   Measuring 4-Speed Mainshaft End Play

VOLKSWAGEN JETTA, PICKUP, RABBIT & SCIROCCO 4 & 5-SPEED (Cont.)

NOTE — *For measurement only, install a fourth gear thrust washer between measuring sleeve and shoulder of mainshaft. The thrust washer inside diameter can be enlarged with a file to ease installation and removal from mainshaft.*

Fig. 21   Centering 4-Speed Reverse Idler Shaft in Case

3) Install a new gasket onto final drive case half, then install shift housing case (without mainshaft ball bearing or clamping bolts installed) onto assembly. Install and tighten 5 bolts to 14 ft. lbs. (2.0 mkg) to secure case halves.

4) Install dial indicator assembly onto outside of shift housing case half. Position button of indicator against measuring sleeve tool. Zero dial indicator with .12" (.3 mm) preload. Grasp measuring sleeve and move up and down; read resulting play indicated on dial indicator. Select a shim (to be installed under bearing in shift housing case half) from table.

Mainshaft Bearing Shim Selection (4-Speed Only)	
End Play In. (mm)	**Shim Thickness In. (mm)**
0-.018 (0-.46) .... None	
.019-.029 (.47-.75) .... .012 (.30)	
.030-.041 (.76-1.04) .... .024 (.60)	
.042-.057 (1.05-1.45) .... ①.036 (.90)	
① — Use .012" (.30 mm) and .024" (.60 mm) shims.	

5) Remove dial indicator and separate case halves. Remove measuring sleeve and thrust washer. Install proper shim(s) just selected, into mainshaft ball bearing bore in shift housing case half.

NOTE — *Closed side of bearing cage MUST be installed toward shim(s) and housing, and press tool must contact bearing outer race only.*

6) Install mainshaft bearing on top of shim(s) and press into bore. Install clamping bolts and torque to 11 ft. lbs. (1.5 mkg). Install plastic caps on nuts of outside housing.

5-Speed — 1) Install mainshaft without shims into case. Hold mainshaft in place with special tool 30-211 and adapter VW 295A. Install 4th gear on pinion shaft and install circlip. Press mainshaft bearing with old shim into case. Install clamping plate and insert lower spring for selector rod into gear carrier housing.

2) Insert 1st-2nd gear shift fork into operating sleeve. Lift selector rod slightly and swing shift fork around pinion shaft, guiding 3rd-4th shift fork into synchronizer sleeve and reverse shift fork into relay lever. Push selector rod in and align shift forks.

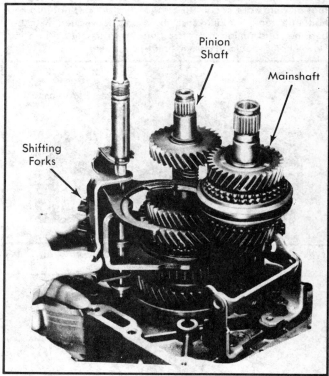

Fig. 22   Installing 5-Speed Shift Forks

REVERSE IDLER INSTALLATION

Temporarily install reverse idler shaft retaining bolt into idler shaft, then position shaft into case bore. Center reverse idler bolt so center of shaft is equal from each bolt hole of case. Remove bolt without disturbing shaft alignment.

SHIFT FORKS & SHIFT HOUSING INSTALLATION

4-Speed — 1) Install reverse shift fork and support onto case, and engage fork with reverse idler gear. Install 1st-2nd and 3rd-4th shift forks into sleeves of synchronizer assemblies, and reverse operating fork into engagement with all 3 shift forks.

VOLKSWAGEN JETTA, PICKUP, RABBIT & SCIROCCO 4 & 5-SPEED (Cont.)

With all parts in correct position, press fork shaft into housing and install 2 "E" clips to secure forks. Install 4th gear onto pinion shaft and secure with snap ring.

Fig. 23   Shift Fork Retaining Clip Locations

2) Make sure reverse idler shaft is still correctly positioned and that all gears are in neutral position. Install shift housing case half onto unit, making sure mainshaft is aligned with ball bearing, and pinion shaft is aligned with its needle bearing. Dowel holes should align one half of case with other.

Fig. 24   Installing 4-Speed Mainshaft Bearing Snap Ring

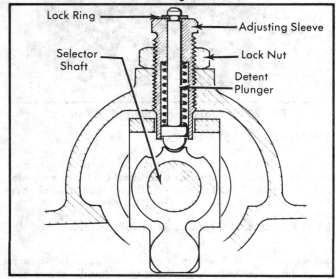

Fig. 25   Cutaway View of Case Showing Selector Shaft and Shaft Adjusting Components

3) Support mainshaft firmly with suitable support bar (30-211), and drive ball bearing onto mainshaft using suitable driver (30-23), to apply force to bearing's inner race only. Install reverse idler shaft bolt and torque to 14 ft. lbs. (2.0 mkg).

4) Install case bolts and torque diagonally to 18 ft. lbs. (2.5 mkg). Working through clutch release lever area of shift housing, install mainshaft-to-ball bearing snap ring. See Fig. 24.

5-Speed — 1) Install special tool VW 295A on mainshaft, install transmission case onto gear carrier. Install reverse gear shaft lock bolt and tighten. Install transmission case-to-gear case bolts and tighten. Install back-up light switch. Tighten mainshaft bearing clamping plate bolts. Install drive shaft flange, install spring washer and circlip, press circlip into place and check for proper setting.

2) Heat 5th gear to 212°F (100°C) and install. Install thrust washer and circlip. Install synchronizer with 5th gear onto mainshaft. Screw selector tube clockwise into shift fork, then screw tube out until it projects above shift fork by .19" (5 mm). See Fig. 26.

CAUTION — *Do not pull selector rod out of tube because shift forks in transmission will fall apart and transmission will have to be disassembled again.*

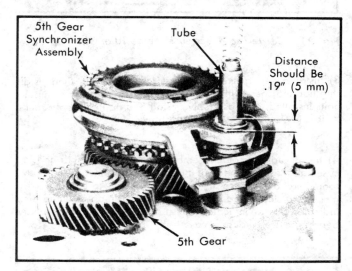

Fig. 26   View Showing Synchronizer with 5th Gear Installation and Tube Adjustment

3) Coat synchronizer hub bolt with locking compound and tighten. Place transmission in neutral and install selector shaft. Install spring and cover for selector shaft. Install lockout plunger for 5th gear and detent plunger for selector shaft. To adjust detent plunger, loosen lock nut and turn adjusting sleeve in until lock ring lifts off sleeve. Turn adjusting sleeve back until lock ring just contacts sleeve, tighten lock nut. Turn selector shaft slightly and check that lock ring lifts as soon as shaft is turned.

4) To adjust 5th gear lockout plunger, set transmission in neutral. Remove adjusting sleeve cap and loosen lock nut. Tighten adjusting sleeve until detent plunger just starts to move up. Loosen adjusting sleeve ⅓ turn and tighten lock nut. To

VOLKSWAGEN JETTA, PICKUP, RABBIT & SCIROCCO 4 & 5-SPEED (Cont.)

adjust 5th gear shift fork, shift selector lever in 5th gear position, lift 5th gear synchronizer sleeve slightly to eliminate play. Check engagement of sleeve coupling teeth on 5th gear for proper engagement. Overlap should be .039″ (1 mm). Adjust by turning selector tube. See *Fig. 27*.

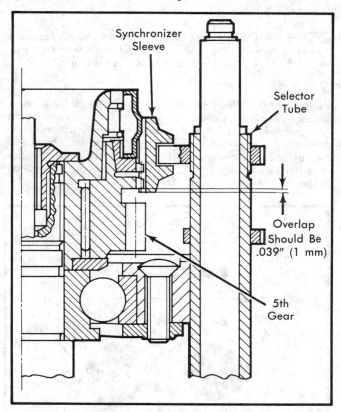

Fig. 27 Adjusting 5th Gear Shift Fork Position

FINAL ASSEMBLY

4-Speed — **1)** Install speedometer drive gear assembly, being careful to mesh drive gear with teeth on drive pinion shaft. Apply grease to clutch push rod and insert into mainshaft. Install release bearing and sleeve into rear end of shift housing.

Install Clips on Both Sides of Lever with a Screwdriver

Fig. 28 Installing Clutch Release Lever Clips (4-Speed)

2) Position clutch release lever and return spring in rear of shift housing, then install clutch operating lever through release lever and spring.

NOTE — *Bent ends of spring must contact housing, and center part of spring hooks over release lever. Install 2 snap rings to secure assembly.*

3) Apply grease to selector shaft and install into shift housing, engaging shift forks. Install 2 springs, spring seat and cover into case. Install selector shaft locking bolt into case and tighten. To adjust interlock plunger, loosen lock nut and turn adjusting sleeve until lock ring lifts off sleeve. Back off adjusting nut until lock ring lifts off sleeve. Back off adjusting nut until lock ring just touches sleeve and tighten lock nut. Turn selector shaft slightly and check that lock ring lifts as soon as shaft is turned.

NOTE — *Transmission must be in neutral with linkage disconnected when adjusting selector shaft.*

4) Install rear cover with a new gasket onto shift housing. If removed, install a new seal into selector shaft bore (shift lever end). Install new drive flange oil seals into housing, position drive flange onto shafts and retain with washers and snap rings. Install new plastic caps into flanges. If removed, install back-up light switch, drain and fill plugs into case.

5-Speed — Install new gasket and install transmission case cover with release bearing. Lubricate clutch push rod at ends and at bearing. Select all gears in sequence and check that they engage easily without jamming.

TIGHTENING SPECIFICATIONS

Application	Ft. Lbs. (mkg)
Axle Shaft Nut	173 (24)
Transaxle-to-Engine	40 (5.5)
Drive Shaft-to-Flange	32 (4.5)
Release Bearing Cover	11 (1.5)
Mainshaft Bearing Retaining Nuts	14 (2.0)
Reverse Idler Bolt	14 (2.0)
Case Half Bolts	18 (2.5)
Selector Shaft Cover	32 (4.5)
Selector Shaft Lock Nut	14 (2.0)
Filler Plug	14 (2.0)
Reverse Fork Support Bolts	11 (1.5)
Pinion Bearing Cover	29 (4.0)
Ring Cover Bolts	50 (7.0)
5th Gear Synchro Assembly	50 (7.0)
Reverse Shaft Bolt	22 (3.0)

VOLKSWAGEN VANAGON 4-SPEED

TRANSMISSION IDENTIFICATION

The Volkswagon Vanagon uses a Type 091 manual transmission. First 3 digits of transmission part number cast in right side of transmission case indicate transmission model. Transmission code letters (DK) and date of manufacture are stamped on bottom of transmission case.

DESCRIPTION

The transaxle assembly is a two piece unit containing both the transmission and the final drive. The transmission and the final drive are assembled in one section and the clutch is housed in the second section. The transaxle is mounted at rear of vehicle and engine is mounted to rear of transaxle. The transmission is a four-speed manual type. Gears are in constant mesh in all forward gears. The final drive, mounted between transmission and engine, uses a hypoid ring gear and pinion. The rear axle unit is a double joint type, using constant velocity (CV) joints on both ends of axle drive shafts. Outer wheel bearings are mounted in a housing connected to control arm.

LUBRICATION & ADJUSTMENT

See MANUAL TRANSMISSION SERVICING Section.

SERVICE (IN VEHICLE)

AXLE DRIVE SHAFTS

Removal & Installation — Remove socket head screws at each CV joint. Tilt shaft down and remove. To install, place shaft in position. Install and tighten socket head screws.

CONSTANT VELOCITY JOINTS

Disassembly — 1) Carefully drive protective cap off joint with small punch and pull cap back so that boot is turned inside out on driveshaft. Remove circlip from groove in shaft and slide outer ring towards end of shaft. Press shaft out of center ball hub. Remove cover and boot from shaft.

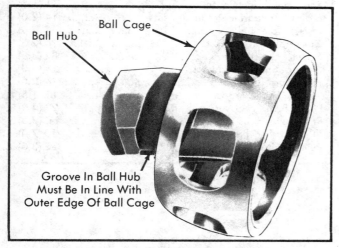

Fig. 1 Removing Ball Hub from Ball Cage

2) Push ball hub and cage from outer ring. Lift the 6 steel cage balls out of cage, taking care not to damage balls or cage. Rotate center ball hub to position in cage shown in Fig. 1. Hub groove must be in line with outer edge of ball cage. Tip hub out of ball cage.

NOTE — All CV joint components are machined for close tolerance fit with other components; do not intermix components of one CV joint with components of another.

Reassembly — Clean all components and check for wear or damage. Replace as necessary. Coat all CV joint components with molybdenum grease. Reverse disassembly procedure to assemble CV joint and install on axle. Make sure chamfered end of spline in center ball hub is on same side as large diameter side of outer ring. Check joint for smooth operation throughout entire range of travel.

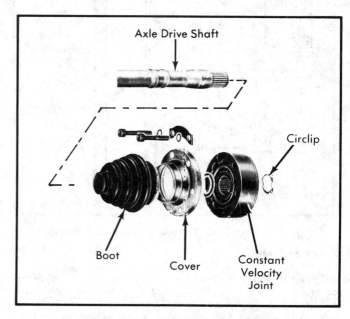

Fig. 2 Exploded View of Constant Velocity Joints

REAR WHEEL BEARING HOUSING

Removal — With vehicle on ground, remove cotter pin and loosen large nut at center of brake drum. Raise vehicle and position on safety stands. Disconnect axle drive shaft at wheel bearing flange. Wire axle up out of way. Remove brake drum and wheel hub. Remove brake backing plate bolts, and position brake backing plate out of way without disconnecting brake line or parking brake cable. Mark position of bearing housing, spring plate and control arm. Remove 4 bearing housing bolts and remove housing.

Disassembly — Place bearing housing in a vise and clamp against spring plate flange. Remove brake components if not previously removed. Using a puller, press axle shaft out of housing. Pry out oil seals, and remove circlip. Remove inner roller bearing race and spacer sleeve. Using a punch that contacts only bearing outer race, drive ball bearing out of housing. Remove roller bearing outer race if necessary.

VOLKSWAGEN VANAGON 4-SPEED (Cont.)

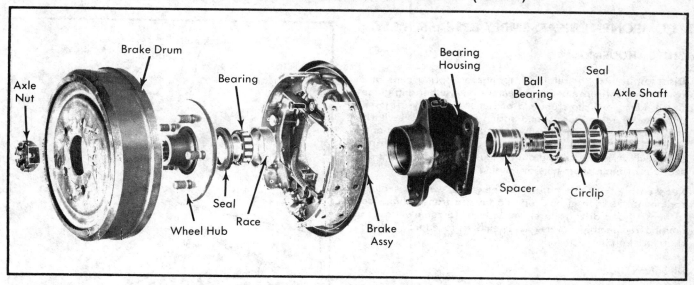

Fig. 3   Exploded View of Rear Wheel Bearing Housing and Related Parts

Reassembly — To reassemble, reverse disassembly procedure noting that if replacing spacer sleeve on one axle, the one on the opposite axle must also be replaced due to difference in diameter from original equipment. Fill housing with multi-purpose grease prior to inserting spacer sleeve, then drive wheel shaft in with soft punch or pull on with two arm puller. Apply sealer to sealing edge around bearing housing and brake backing plate if installing at this time.

Installation — Install bearing housing on spring plate and control arm, carefully aligning index marks made during removal. To complete installation, reverse removal procedure. Tighten axle nut to specification with vehicle on ground and install a new cotter pin.

TRANSAXLE REMOVAL & INSTALLATION

Removal — 1) Disconnect battery ground. Remove upper right transmission-to-engine bolt. Disconnect clutch hydraulic line from transmission case, then remove clutch slave cylinder from bracket and suspend from a wire, out of way.

NOTE — *Do not disconnect hydraulic line from slave cylinder.*

2) Remove upper left, then lower left transmission-to-engine bolts. Remove the bolts from left axle shaft, remove axle shaft from transmission and suspend with wire. Disconnect starter cables. Remove the bolts from right axle shaft, remove axle shaft from transmission and suspend with wire.

3) Remove lower right transmission-to-engine nut. Support engine. Disconnect back-up light wires, shift linkage and ground strap from transmission. Remove front transmission support-to-body bolts and support transmission. Separate transmission from engine and remove transmission.

Installation — To install transmission, reverse removal procedures and note the following: Clean and lubricate splines with grease; make sure air deflector plates are positioned correctly; make sure engine compartment seals are not damaged or missing.

TRANSAXLE DISASSEMBLY

1) Before attempting to remove clutch housing, loosen left differential adjusting ring to relieve tension in housing. Mark position of ring before loosening for ease of assembly. Remove (10) housing nuts from studs. Separate housing from transmission case. Remove circlip from input shaft. Pull reverse drive gear forward and unscrew input shaft from stud in end of mainshaft. Pry out drive flange center caps. Remove circlips and wavy spacers from center of flanges. Use 2 levers to pry drive flanges off of output shafts.

2) Remove screws from adjusting ring lock plates and remove lock plates. Measure depth of adjusting ring or mark position in case. Remove adjusting rings. Making sure ring gear teeth stay in mesh with pinion gear, rotate differential toward rear of transmission case and pull out through rear of case.

3) Remove attaching nuts and lift shift housing from gear carrier. Remove pinion bearing retaining ring from bearing race on differential end of case. Remove selector link, shaft and bracket from face of gear carrier. Remove (9) nuts from gear carrier mounting studs on transmission case. Apply leverage to end of pinion gear and press gear train and carrier out of case.

4) Loosen nut on reverse lever support clamp sleeve. Turn shaft far enough to remove reverse slider and shift fork. Slide shift forks off shift rods. Remove circlip from end of mainshaft. Press out mainshaft and drive pinion at the same time by applying pressure to end of mainshaft. Care must be taken not to damage any gear train components.

VOLKSWAGEN VANAGON 4-SPEED (Cont.)

COMPONENT DISASSEMBLY & REASSEMBLY

CLUTCH HOUSING

Disassembly — Pry retaining springs off spring clips and remove clutch release bearing. Remove release bearing guide sleeve. Remove circlip from end of clutch shaft. Pry off lever and remove return spring and spring collar. Remove clutch shaft lock bolt. Slide shaft outward, pressing out bushing and rubber seals. Remove bushing, seals and flat washer from shaft. Pull shaft inward and out of housing to remove. Pry oil seal out of input shaft hole in housing.

Reassembly — Coat outside of new seal with a sealing compound. Position in hole with lip toward transmission side of housing and drive squarely into place. To complete clutch housing reassembly, reverse disassembly procedure. Tighten shaft lock bolt to specifications.

DIFFERENTIAL

Disassembly — Remove ring gear bolts and drive ring gear off differential housing with a punch. Remove differential cover with a slide hammer. Remove side gears and thrust washers from housing and cover. If necessary, remove roller bearing using a press and suitable supports. Drive out pinion shaft lock pin. Drive pinion shaft out of differential housing. Remove pinion gears, spacer and thrust washer.

Reassembly — 1) Inspect all components for wear or damage and replace as necessary. If roller bearings were removed, heat to 212°F (100°C), and press into position using a press and suitable supports.

NOTE — *If unit is not equipped with spacer sleeve, or if components other than pinion shaft or roller bearings have been replaced, axial play must be checked and adjusted.*

2) To check axial play, install side gear with short shaft and both large thrust washers in differential cover. Place assembly in a vise and clamp gear tight against cover. Install side gear with long shaft in housing. Place sleeve on machined surface of side gear with short shaft. Position differential housing on cover. Install and tighten four bolts pulling housing into place on cover.

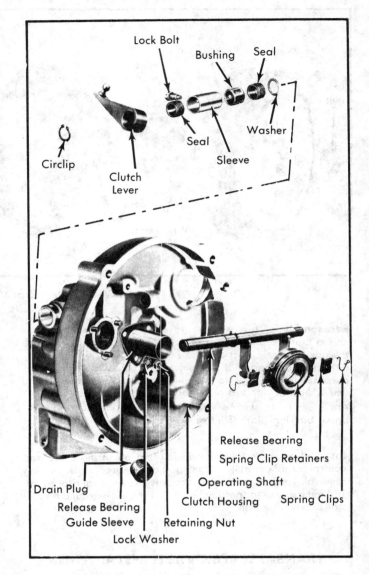

Fig. 4 Exploded View of Clutch Housing

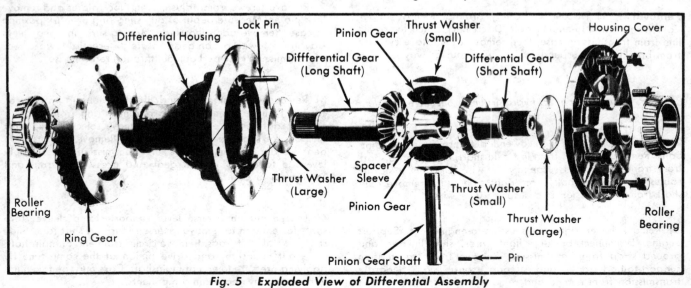

Fig. 5 Exploded View of Differential Assembly

VOLKSWAGEN VANAGON 4-SPEED (Cont.)

3) Install a suitable gauge bar with a dial indicator to end of drive gear shaft in housing. Dial indicator plunger must contact differential housing neck. Press down on side gear shaft and zero dial indicator with .080" (2 mm) preload.

4) Move side gear up and down to determine axial play. Play should be .001-.004" (.03-.11 mm). If not to specifications, install a spacer of correct size to obtain specified play. Recheck play after installing correct spacer. Spacers are available in the following lengths: 1.253" (31.84 mm), 1.257" (31.93 mm), 1.261" (32.02 mm), 1.264" (32.11 mm), and 1.268" (32.20 mm).

Dial Indicator

Fig. 6   Measuring Differential Gear Axial Play

MAINSHAFT

Disassembly — 1) With mainshaft removed from gear carrier, remove 4th gear, needle bearing and synchro ring.

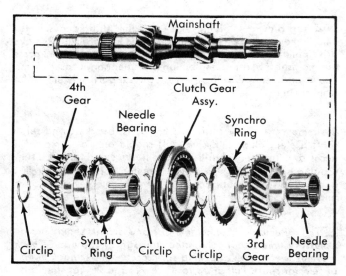

Mainshaft

4th Gear · Clutch Gear Assy. · Needle Bearing · Synchro Ring

Circlip · Synchro Ring · Circlip · Circlip · 3rd Gear · Needle Bearing

Fig. 7   Exploded View of Mainshaft Assembly

Remove circlip and slide off clutch gear assembly. Remove remaining circlip and slide off 3rd gear.

2) Open split in needle bearing cage just enough to slide over mainshaft splines and remove bearing. If necessary, remove spring rings from clutch gear assembly. Then separate synchronizer hub from sleeve.

Reassembly — 1) Inspect all parts for wear or damage and replace as necessary. Press synchro ring onto gear by hand and check clearance as shown in illustration. Specified clearance is .040-.075" (1.0-1.9 mm). If clearance is less than .023" (.6 mm), replace synchro ring or gear. If clutch gear assembly was disassembled, reassemble synchronizer hub to sleeve by meshing the teeth in various positions until a free sliding fit is obtained. Spring ring diameter for 3rd-4th gear clutch hub is 2.91" (74 mm) while larger ring for 1st-2nd clutch gear should be 3.07" (78 mm). Open ends of springs on opposite sides of assemby must be installed 120° apart with angled ends over the keys.

Clearance

Fig. 8   Measuring Synchro Ring-to-Gear Clearance

NOTE — *Synchronizer rings must be installed in exactly the same relationships that existed before removal. The 1st gear ring can be identified by having no notches in blank area on outer edge. Synchronizers for 2nd, 3rd and 4th gears each have 3 notches (depressions) in blank area on outer edge. Replacement synchronizers for 2nd, 3rd and 4th gears have teeth completely around the outer edge with no blanked off areas.*

2) To complete reassembly of mainshaft, reverse disassembly procedure, noting the following procedures: Install clutch gear assembly so that side with .040" (1 mm) deep groove is toward 4th gear, and the side of the clutch gear hub having the wide chamfer on teeth goes toward 3rd gear.

DRIVE PINION SHAFT

Disassembly — 1) Hold 4th gear down tight against spring on shaft. This will collapse spring and ease removal of circlip on end of shaft. With circlip removed, press shaft out of inner bearing race while supporting 4th gear. Remove spring and next circlip. Remove 3rd gear, 2nd gear, needle bearing, synchro rings, circlip, 1st/2nd synchro assembly, 1st gear and needle bearing.

VOLKSWAGEN VANAGON 4-SPEED (Cont.)

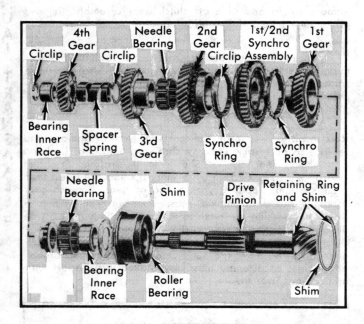

Fig. 9   *Exploded View of Pinion Shaft Assembly*

NOTE — *3rd gear circlips are available in thicknesses of .057" (1.45 mm) to .087" (2.2 mm) in increments of .006" (.15 mm).*

Fig. 10   *Checking Pinion Bearing Preload*

2) Note that inner needle bearing race is threaded and notched on end away from pinion. Place pinion in appliance (VW 293) to hold notched race, and place splined socket over pinion shaft. Turn shaft counterclockwise to remove inner race/nut. If necessary, disassemble synchro assembly hub. Press off tapered roller bearing with outer race. If required, use separating tool and press off inner race.

Reassembly — 1) Inspect all parts for wear or damage and replace as necessary. Press 1st and 2nd gear synchro rings onto gears and check clearance of 3rd and 4th gear. Specified clearance for new parts is .043-.071" (1.1-1.8 mm), with a minimum clearance of .023" (.6 mm) for used parts. If 1st/2nd synchro assembly was disassembled, reassemble in the same manner as for 3rd/4th synchro assembly.

2) Heat tapered roller bearing to about 212°F (100°C) and press into position. Allow to cool to room temperature, then heat inner race to about 140°F (60°C) and tighten on shaft by hand as far as possible. Place pinion in same appliance as for disassembly and tighten inner race to 144 ft. lbs. (20 mkg).

3) Check pinion bearing preload by installing shaft in transmission case and tightening retaining ring. Check for turning torque of 5.2-18.3 INCH lbs. (6-21 cmkg) for new bearing, 2.6-6.1 INCH lbs. (3-7 cmkg) for used bearing.

4) Install needle bearing, 1st gear, 1st/2nd synchro assembly with synchro rings, and install circlip. Synchro ring grooves must align with keys when pressing on. Assemble needle bearing, 2nd gear and 3rd gear on shaft, then fit circlip properly in groove.

5) Check axial play between circlip and 3rd gear. Correct play is .004-.010" (.10-.25 mm), with the lower limit preferred. Install proper circlip to obtain specified clearance.

6) Install spacer spring and 4th speed gear with shoulder toward spring. Press on 4th gear and install circlip.

TRANSMISSION CASE

Disassembly — Remove reverse gear shaft circlip from inside gearcase. Remove reverse drive gear, shaft and needle bearing as a unit with a plastic hammer. Remove lock rings from mainshaft needle bearing and drive bearing out.

Reassembly — Insert shaft, bearing and reverse drive gear as a unit. Drive mainshaft needle bearing in case with lettered side of bearing towards the driver. Install lock rings.

GEAR CARRIER

Disassembly — 1) Remove selector link shaft and selector link. Remove two bolts and then remove link bracket. Remove drive pinion bearing lock bolt. Using a suitable mandrel, press out mainshaft bearing and pinion shaft bearing. Loosen clamp sleeve and remove with reverse lever support and union nut from carrier.

2) Remove (4) relay shaft bracket bolts, brackets and relay shaft. Detent plugs and shift rails should only be removed if necessary. To remove, drill out detent plugs and thread a self-tapping bolt into plug until plug is pulled out. Remove circlips and pull shift rails out of carrier. Remove detent springs, balls and interlock, and intermediate pins.

NOTE — *Removal of selector shafts and detents should not be necessary unless shifting is either too stiff or too easy. Check movement effort by attaching spring scale under hook in end of selector shaft. Pull of 33 to 44 lbs. (15 to 20 kg) should be required to overcome detent springs.*

VOLKSWAGEN VANAGON 4-SPEED (Cont.)

Reassembly — Check all components for wear or damage and replace as necessary. Detent spring length should be $^{29}/_{32}$-$^{63}/_{64}$" (23-25 mm). Reverse disassembly procedure. Ensure that interlock and intermediate pins are properly installed so it is not possible to engage 2 gears at the same time.

SHIFT HOUSING

Disassembly — 1) Drill and tap plugs for rocker lever shaft. Remove rocker lever shaft, rocker lever and thrust washer.

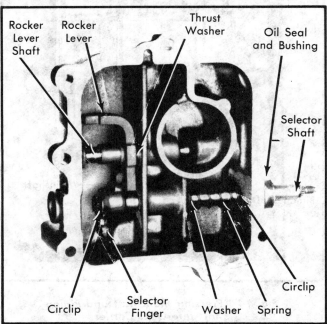

Rocker Lever Shaft
Rocker Lever
Thrust Washer
Oil Seal and Bushing
Selector Shaft
Circlip
Circlip
Selector Finger
Washer
Spring

Fig. 11 Vanagon Shift Housing Assembly

Remove back-up light switch plug and seal. Remove selector shaft oil seal and bushing.

2) Remove circlips from selector shaft. Push selector shaft out of shift housing. As selector shaft slides out, remove selector finger, washer and spring.

Reassembly — To reassemble shift housing, reverse disassembly procedures and install new seals.

TRANSAXLE REASSEMBLY & ADJUSTMENT

PINION DEPTH

NOTE — *Pinion bearing preload must be correctly adjusted before adjusting pinion depth; see Drive Pinion Shaft Reassembly.*

1) Pinion depth is checked using Universal Measuring Bar (VW 385/1). Screw in right adjusting ring until ring outer surface is flush with transaxle case. Install magnetic measuring plate (VW 385/17) on end of pinion gear.

2) Set dimension "A" (see *Fig. 13*) to 2.95" (75 mm) by sliding setting ring to correct distance from center of measuring bar. Slide 2 centering discs (VW 385/4) onto measuring bar until they contact setting rings. Attach measuring pin (VW 385/14) with extension (VW 385/16) to gauge pin hole in center of measuring bar. Attach a dial indicator to end of bar.

3) Position measuring bar in transaxle case. Install left adjusting ring in case until outer edge is flush with case. Loosen second setting ring and slide out with centering ring until measuring bar can just barely be turned by hand. Tighten screw in setting ring.

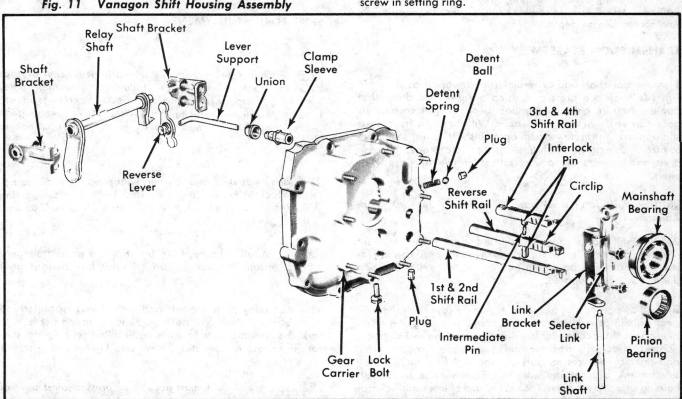

Shaft Bracket
Relay Shaft
Shaft Bracket
Lever Support
Union
Clamp Sleeve
Detent Ball
Detent Spring
Plug
3rd & 4th Shift Rail
Interlock Pin
Reverse Lever
Reverse Shift Rail
Circlip
Mainshaft Bearing
1st & 2nd Shift Rail
Link Bracket
Selector Link
Pinion Bearing
Gear Carrier
Lock Bolt
Plug
Intermediate Pin
Link Shaft

Fig. 12 Exploded View of Gear Carrier Assembly

VOLKSWAGEN VANAGON 4-SPEED (Cont.)

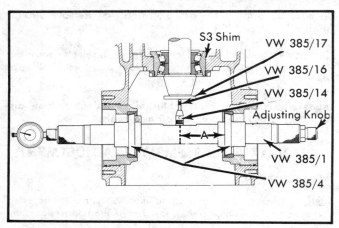

Fig. 13 Installation of Pinion Depth Checking Tools

4) Using setting block (VW 385/1), zero dial indicator. Turn measuring bar by hand until measuring pin extension is against measuring plate on pinion gear. Turn bar back and forth over center. Record maximum reading on dial indicator. Read deviation number stamped on ring gear.

NOTE — *Although production gears are no longer marked with deviation "r" in .01 mm readings, replacement gear sets will have this number. Shims (S3) must be installed between pinion bearing shoulder and gear case to correct axial placement of pinion gear for proper meshing with ring gear teeth.*

5) To find correct shim thickness (S3), add dial indicator deflection to "r" number stamped on gear. Shims are available in thicknesses of .006" (.15 mm), .008" (.20 mm), .012" (.30 mm), .016" (.40 mm), .020" (.50 mm), and .024" (.60 mm). Install shim or combination of shims required to obtain correct pinion depth.

TRANSMISSION REASSEMBLY

1) Mesh mainshaft and drive pinion and support as shown in *Fig. 14.* Place in a press and, using a sleeve type driver that applies pressure only to mainshaft bearing inner race, press gear carrier down onto gear train. With pressure from press still applied, install new circlip on mainshaft. Using same tool in press, push circlip down until it snaps into groove. Release press and squeeze circlip into bottom groove with a pair of pliers.

NOTE — *Shift forks must now be adjusted. See Shift Fork Adjustment.*

2) With shift forks correctly adjusted, tighten shift fork set screws and reverse lever support union nut to specifications. Install original shims on pinion bearing or new shims if pinion depth has been adjusted.

3) Position new carrier gasket on transaxle case studs. Position gear train in case. Install a new shim and retaining ring on pinion (large threaded roller bearing). Torque ring to 160 ft. lbs. (22 mkg), back off, then retorque to same specification. Install and tighten gear carrier nuts by working diagonally. Install selector link, bracket and link shaft. Tighten bolts. Install shift housing using new gasket. Make sure rocker lever and selector finger engages selector shafts correctly. Tighten shift housing bolts.

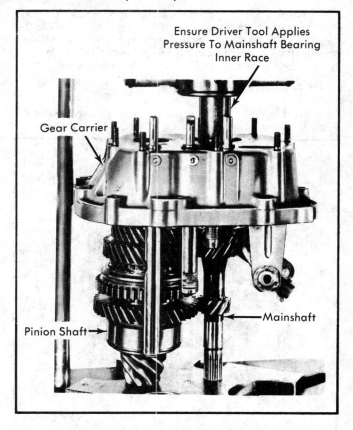

Fig. 14   Pressing Mainshaft and Pinion Shaft into Gear Carrier

SHIFT FORK ADJUSTMENT

NOTE — *Shift fork adjustment is made with special tool VW294b. Tool consists of the following: mounting plate, VW294b/2; mounting plate-to-gear carrier spacer, VW294b/4; pinion retaining ring, VW294b/7; reverse gear spacer, VW294b/10; and 2 bolts to hold gear carrier to mounting plate.*

1) Attach assembled gear carrier, with pinion shim S3, to adjusting tool VW294b (see *Fig. 15*). Tighten retaining ring (VW294b/7) by hand. Install shift forks for 1st/2nd and 3rd/4th gears.

NOTE — *Install flat side of 1st/2nd shift fork away from gear carrier. Install flat side of 3rd/4th shift fork toward gear carrier.*

2) Install relay lever support and relay lever. Place 1st/2nd gear selector in 2nd gear position. Slide operating sleeve, with fork, over synchro teeth until it is against 2nd gear. Center shift fork in groove of operating sleeve and tighten clamp screw.

CAUTION — *Shift fork must not rub or press against sides of groove in operating sleeve when in neutral position. Clearance must exist.*

VOLKSWAGEN VANAGON 4-SPEED (Cont.)

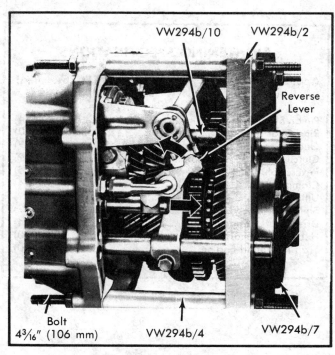

Fig. 15 Connecting Reverse Lever

VW294b/10   VW294b/2

Reverse Lever

Bolt 4³⁄₁₆" (106 mm)   VW294b/4   VW294b/7

3) Select 1st and 2nd gear position several times while turning mainshaft. Check clearance of shift fork in operating sleeve in each position. If necessary, reposition shift fork until there is same amount of clearance on selector shaft in both end positions then tighten clamp screw.

4) Place 3rd/4th gear selector shaft in 3rd gear position and adjust 3rd/4th gear shift fork in same manner as 1st/2nd.

CAUTION — *For correct adjustment of 3rd/4th gears, mainshaft bearing must be pressed fully into gear carrier housing.*

5) Place reverse gear selector shaft into reverse gear position. Adjust reverse gear so that sliding gear is fully in mesh with teeth on operating sleeve for 1st/2nd gear. Tighten union nut on relay lever support.

6) Shift out of reverse gear and press sliding gear lightly toward gear carrier. Clearance between reverse gear and 2nd gear on main shaft must be a minimum of .020" (.5 mm).

7) Engage 2nd gear and check clearance between operating sleeve and reverse sliding gear. Adjust if necessary. Check interlock mechanism. When gear is engaged, it must not be possible to engage any other gear.

SIDE BEARING PRELOAD & RING GEAR BACKLASH

1) Remove oil seals from side bearing adjusting rings. Install adjusting ring on ring gear side of case and screw in until ring

is approximately .004-.008" (.1-.2 mm) below measuring surface of case. Install differential in case, with ring gear on left side. Install opposite adjusting ring and tighten until differential is supported without preload.

2) Turn transmission so that differential is at top and install spacer bridge (VW381/8) on dowel pins to prevent case spreading. Install a torque gauge on ring gear side of differential. Spin differential 15 to 20 turns in each direction while at the same time lubricating side bearings with hypoid oil. While turning, screw in adjusting ring opposite ring gear until preload measured on torque gauge is 26-30 INCH Lbs. (30-35 cmkg) for new bearings and 2.6-6.1 INCH lbs. (3-7 cmkg) for used bearings. Measure and record depth to which adjusting rings are screwed in. Mark position of adjusting rings in case. Remove adjusting rings and differential. Rings must be installed on same side from which they are removed.

3) Install transmission gear train. *See Transmission Reassembly.* Install differential and adjusting rings. Turn adjusting rings until marks made during side bearing preload are aligned. Install a suitable measuring bracket (VW 381/7) on ring gear bolts. Mount a spacer bar and dial indicator across ring gear end of case. Turn mainshaft until dial indicator stem contacts measuring bracket on ring gear. Continue turning mainshaft until dial indicator shows .060" (1.5 mm) preload. Lock pinion shaft with a clamping bar bolted on gear carrier.

4) Turn ring gear by hand away from dial indicator until it is stopped by locked pinion. Now zero dial indicator. Again turn ring gear by hand toward dial indicator until it is stopped by locked pinion. The reading on dial indicator is ring gear backlash. Backlash should be .006-.010" (.15-.25 mm). If backlash not to specification, screw one adjusting ring inward and the other ring outward by exactly the same amount until backlash is within specification.

5) Recheck backlash measuring procedure at three other points on ring gear, 90° apart. All measurements must be within specification and not vary more than .002" (.06 mm). Install new oil seals and "O" rings in adjusting rings if not previously done. Coat outer surface of adjusting rings with an anti-rust preventative sealer. Install new adjusting ring lock plates and tighten screws evenly.

NOTE — *Do not tighten left hand adjusting ring until the clutch housing has been fitted and the nuts tightened.*

FINAL ASSEMBLY

Install clutch housing and tighten nuts to specification. Install thrust rings, axle drive shaft flanges and new circlips. It may be necessary to lift differential pinion gear shaft slightly to gain clearance for installation of circlips. Install new plastic caps in center of axle drive shaft flanges.

VOLKSWAGEN VANAGON 4-SPEED (Cont.)

TRANSAXLE SPECIFICATIONS

Application	Measurement
Synchro Ring-to-Gear Clearance (New Parts)	
1st and 2nd Gear	.040-.087" (1.0-2.2 mm)
3rd and 4th Gear	.040-.087" (1.0-2.2 mm)
Ring and Pinion Backlash	.006-.010" (.15-.25 mm)
Pinion Bearing Preload	
New Bearings	5.2-18.2 INCH lbs. (6.0-21 cmkg)
Used Bearings	2.6-6.1 INCH lbs. (3.0-7.0 cmkg)
Side Bearing Preload	
New Bearings	26-30 INCH lbs. (30.0-35.0 cmkg)
Used Bearings	2.6-6.1 INCH lbs. (3.0-7.0 cmkg)

TIGHTENING SPECIFICATIONS

Application	Ft. Lbs. (mkg)
Pinion Shaft Retainer Ring	162 (22.4)
Ring Gear Bolts	36 (5.0)
Gear Carrier	14 (1.9)
Clutch Housing	14 (1.9)
Reverse Shift Shaft Bracket	18 (2.5)
Clamp Sleeve	32 (4.4)
Union Nut	21 (2.9)
Shift Housing	14 (1.9)
Drive Shaft Flange Bolts	32 (4.4)
Hub-to-Axle Shaft Nut	253 (35.0)
Transmission-to-Engine	22 (3.0)

Section 7

OVERDRIVES & TRANSFER CASES

CONTENTS

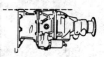

OVERDRIVES & TRANSFER CASES
Section 7

NOTE — ALSO SEE GENERAL INDEX.

LAYCOCK "L.H." TYPE

MGB

DESCRIPTION & OPERATION

Overdrive is a hydraulically operated unit, mounted to rear of transmission and splined directly to transmission mainshaft. Unit consists of a planet carrier assembly with three planet gears, a sliding clutch member actuated by hydraulic pressure, and an overrunning clutch. A single planetary gear train is used, consisting of a central sun gear in mesh with three planetary pinion gears, which in turn mesh with an internally toothed annulus (ring) gear. The annulus gear and overdrive mainshaft are an integral one-piece assembly. The hydraulic system consists of an electrically operated solenoid valve, mechanical pump, relief valve, and low pressure valve. Pump draws oil from sump, and oil from the pump discharge is directed to two operating pistons which move the sliding clutch.

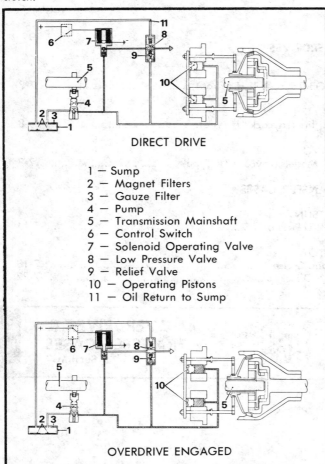

DIRECT DRIVE

1 — Sump
2 — Magnet Filters
3 — Gauze Filter
4 — Pump
5 — Transmission Mainshaft
6 — Control Switch
7 — Solenoid Operating Valve
8 — Low Pressure Valve
9 — Relief Valve
10 — Operating Pistons
11 — Oil Return to Sump

OVERDRIVE ENGAGED

Fig. 1   Schematics Showing Operation of Overdrive Control System

TROUBLE SHOOTING

OVERDRIVE DOES NOT ENGAGE

Low lubricant level. Solenoid is not energizing. Solenoid is energizing but not operating. Insufficient hydraulic pressure due to pump non-return valve not seating, solenoid ball valve not seating, or pump filter clogged. Internal damage to overdrive unit.

OVERDRIVE DOES NOT RELEASE

CAUTION — *Do not place vehicle in reverse, or extensive damage may occur.*

Electrical control circuit faulty. Clutch sliding member sticking. Internal damage to unit.

SLIPS WHEN ENGAGED

Low lubricant level. Worn or glazed clutch linings. Low hydraulic pressure caused by pump non-return valve not seating, relief valve not seating, solenoid valve not seating, or partially blocked pump or relief valve filter.

SLIPS IN REVERSE AND/OR FREEWHEELS ON OVERRUN

Worn or glazed clutch lining. Broken snap ring on sun gear.

TESTING

HYDRAULIC PRESSURE TEST

1) Check transmission fluid level and correct if necessary. Raise and support rear of vehicle so that wheels are free to turn.

2) Remove relief valve plug and sealing washer, then install a pressure gauge with suitable adapters. Start engine, engage 4th gear, and select overdrive.

3) Operate vehicle at 30 MPH and read pressure gauge. Pressure should be 400-420 psi (28.1-29.5 kg/cm^2). Remove pressure gauge and reinstall relief valve and sealing washer.

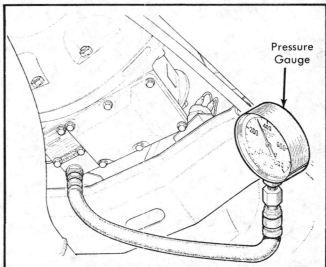

Pressure Gauge

Fig. 2   Bottom View of Vehicle Showing Pressure Gauge Installation

SERVICE (IN VEHICLE)

SOLENOID VALVE

Removal — **1)** Drain transmission and overdrive unit. Remove attaching screws and lift off solenoid cover and gasket. Remove solenoid by gently prying it out with a small screwdriver.

Overdrives

LAYCOCK "L.H." TYPE (Cont.)

NOTE — *Do not pull on electrical connector to remove solenoid valve.*

2) Remove valve assembly. Press solenoid coil and cap from housing. Remove plunger and ball from valve body. Remove "O" ring seals from valve body. If necessary for replacement, remove "O" ring seal from plunger.

Inspection — Check valve ball and seat for pitting and scoring. Reseat ball by lightly tapping onto seat using a suitable drift. Inspect "O" rings and replace as necessary.

Installation — Reverse removal procedure while noting the following: When installing solenoid and valve assembly to front housing the lead grommet must be pressed fully into its slot. Install a new gasket under solenoid cover.

SUMP FILTER

Removal — Drain transmission and overdrive unit. Clean sump cover. Remove cover attaching screws, cover and sump filter.

Cleaning & Inspection — Clean filter and two magnets attached to cover with gasoline and use reduced compressed air pressure to dry filter.

Installation — Install sump filter, cover and attaching screws. Fill transmission and overdrive unit using correct lubricant.

CAUTION — *Do not use any anti-friction type additives.*

RELIEF & LOW PRESSURE VALVE

Removal — Drain transmission and overdrive unit. Remove relief valve plug and washer, then remove the relief valve assembly. Remove filter, spacer tube, low pressure valve assembly, relief valve spring, and relief valve plunger.

Inspection — Inspect plunger and seat for pitting, scoring and wear. Check valve body "O" rings and replace as necessary. Check that spring is not broken, worn or distorted. Inspect all components for scratches, nicks, burrs, cracks, corrosion and excessive wear.

Installation — Reverse removal procedure while noting the following: Spacer tube must be fitted with slotted end farthest from filter and with slots lining up with oil outlet hole and locating stud.

PUMP & NON-RETURN VALVE

Removal — Drain transmission and overdrive unit. Remove sump cover and filter. Remove pump retaining plug. Remove non-return valve spring and ball, pump body, pump plunger spring and plunger. Separate non-return valve seat from pump body.

Inspection — Inspect all "O" rings and replace as necessary. Check valve seat and ball for pitting, corrosion, wear, nicks, burrs, and scratches. Inspect spring for distortion, loss of tension, or breakage.

Installation — Seat ball onto valve seat by lightly tapping with suitable drift. Install non-return valve seat to pump body, taking care not to damage pump body. Install pump plunger into case, ensuring that flat side of plunger is towards rear of overdrive unit. Install plunger spring, pump body assembly, non-return valve spring and ball. Install pump retaining plug,

sump filter and cover. Fill transmission and overdrive assembly with suitable lubricant.

CAUTION — *Do not use any anti-friction type additives.*

OVERDRIVE REMOVAL & INSTALLATION

REMOVAL

NOTE — *See appropriate article in MANUAL TRANSMISSION Section for transmission removal.*

Remove transmission with overdrive unit attached. Drain oil from transmission and overdrive unit. Remove shift assembly from transmission. Remove 8 nuts attaching overdrive unit to transmission adapter and slide overdrive from adapter.

INSTALLATION

Reverse removal procedures while noting the following: Do not force units together but turn output flange of overdrive unit to engage mainshaft splines.

OVERDRIVE DISASSEMBLY

NOTE — *Extreme cleanliness must be observed at all times in working on overdrive unit. Clean outside of overdrive thoroughly before proceeding with disassembly.*

1) Remove the following from overdrive unit using the procedures given under *SERVICE (IN VEHICLE)*: Relief and low pressure valve, solenoid valve, and oil pump and non-return valve.

2) Remove attaching screw, then withdraw retainer and speedometer bearing assembly. Remove speedometer driven gear. Remove "O" ring and oil seal from speedometer bearing.

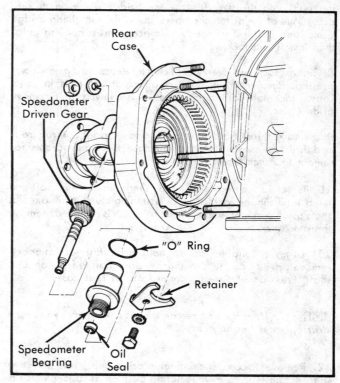

Fig. 3 Speedometer Driven Gear Removal

Overdrives

LAYCOCK "L.H." TYPE (Cont.)

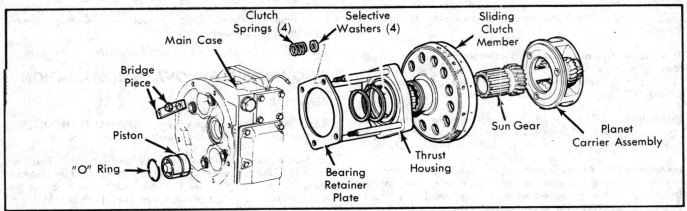

Fig. 4 *Disassembled View of Planet Carrier Assembly, Sliding Clutch, Sun Gear and Thrust Housing*

3) Remove lock nuts securing bridge pieces and remove bridge pieces. Remove rear case-to-main case attaching nuts and washers, then separate rear case from main case.

4) Remove planet carrier, sun gear, sliding clutch and thrust housing from main case as an assembly. Remove the 4 clutch springs and selective washers from thrust housing bolts.

5) Remove pistons from main case, then remove "O" ring seals from pistons. Pry snap ring from groove in sun gear, then withdraw sun gear from sliding clutch.

6) Remove bearing retainer plate from thrust housing. Note that ground face of retainer plate is installed toward bearing. Remove snap ring retaining thrust housing to sliding clutch and remove thrust housing. Press bearing from thrust housing.

7) Install thrust housing into rear of main case, inserting housing bolts into thrust rods. Lay one bridge piece on its side across one of the piston chambers. Invert the remaining bridge piece, and install it on the two adjacent thrust housing bolts, then install two lock nuts.

8) Tighten lock nuts evenly until clutch release springs are compressed. Remove snap rings retaining thrust rods in case. Loosen lock nuts until spring pressure is relieved, then remove bridge pieces.

9) Remove thrust housing, clutch release springs, thrust rods and thrust housing bolts from main case. Repeat procedure for remaining clutch thrust rods.

10) Remove snap ring retaining oil slinger in annulus shaft and remove oil slinger. Withdraw overrunning clutch from annulus shaft using care not to lose rollers as clutch is removed. Remove thrust washer.

11) Using a suitable tool to hold drive flange stationary, remove drive flange nut. Withdraw drive flange from annulus shaft. Press annulus shaft forward out of rear case.

NOTE — *If front bearing remains in rear case, remove using a drift on inner bearing race.*

12) Remove spacer, speedometer drive gear, and selective spacer from rear case while noting position of spacer which is identified by a groove cut on the outside.

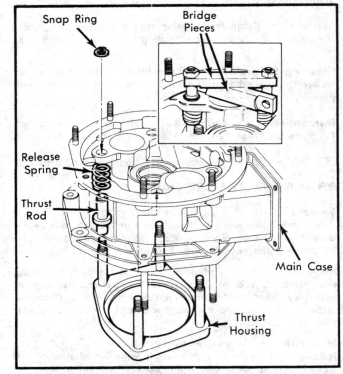

Fig. 5 *Removing Thrust Rods from Main Case*

13) Press rear bearing and oil seal from rear case. If not previously removed, press front bearing from annulus shaft.

CLEANING & INSPECTION

CLEANING

NOTE — *Do not clean sliding clutch in solvent. Wipe off with a clean lint-free cloth.*

Thoroughly wash all parts except sliding clutch in clean solvent. After cleaning, dry all parts except sliding clutch with dry filtered compressed air. Blow out all passages to remove any foreign material or cleaning solvent.

INSPECTION

1) Check all springs for weakness, collapse or distortion. Check bearings for pitting or scoring on races or balls. Inspect

LAYCOCK "L.H." TYPE (Cont.)

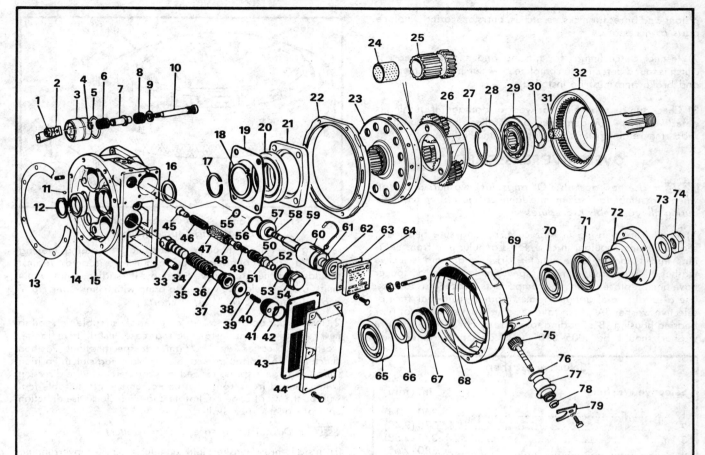

1 — Lock Nut	28 — Oil Slinger	54 — Plug
2 — Bridge Piece	29 — Overrunning Clutch	55 — "O" Ring
3 — Operating Piston	30 — Thrust Washer	56 — "O" Ring
4 — Snap Ring	31 — Bushing	57 — Valve Base
5 — "O" Ring	32 — Annulus Shaft	58 — Valve Ball
6 — Release Spring	33 — Pump Suction Tube	59 — Valve Plunger
7 — Thrust Rod	34 — Pump Plunger	60 — Solenoid Case
8 — Clutch Spring	35 — Pump Spring	61 — Solenoid Core
9 — Selective Washer	36 — "O" Ring	62 — Solenoid Cap
10 — Thrust Housing Bolt	37 — Pump Body	63 — Cover Gasket
11 — Pump Cam Ball	38 — Non-Return Valve Seat	64 — Solenoid Cover
12 — Snap Ring	39 — Valve Ball	65 — Front Bearing
13 — Gasket	40 — Non-Return Valve Spring	66 — Spacer
14 — Pump Cam	41 — Pump Plug	67 — Speedometer Drive Gear
15 — Main Case	42 — "O" Ring	68 — Selective Spacer
16 — Sun Gear Thrust Washer	43 — Sump Gasket & Filter	69 — Rear Case
17 — Split Ring	44 — Sump	70 — Rear Bearing
18 — Snap Ring	45 — Low Pressure Valve	71 — Oil Seal
19 — Bearing Retainer Plate	46 — Valve Spring	72 — Drive Flange
20 — Thrust Bearing	47 — Spacer Tube	73 — Washer
21 — Thrust Housing	48 — Setting Shim	74 — Lock Nut
22 — Brake Ring	49 — Relief Valve Plunger	75 — Speedometer Driven Gear
23 — Sliding Clutch Member	50 — Relief Valve Body	76 — "O" Ring
24 — Sun Gear Bushing	51 — "O" Ring	77 — Speedometer Bearing
25 — Sun Gear	52 — Filter	78 — Oil Seal
26 — Planet Carrier Assembly	53 — Sealing Washer	79 — Retainer
27 — Snap Ring		

Fig. 6 *Exploded View Showing Components of Laycock "L.H." Type Overdrive Assembly*

Overdrives

LAYCOCK "L.H." TYPE (Cont.)

pistons and bores for nicks, scratches, burrs or scoring. Replace parts as necessary.

2) Inspect clutch linings for glazing and excessive wear. If clutch is found defective, a complete new clutch sliding member and brake ring must be installed.

3) Check sun gear bushing for wear or damage. If bushing is defective, a new sun gear must be installed. Inspect sun gear snap ring retaining lugs for damage and tightness.

OVERDRIVE REASSEMBLY

NOTE — *Use new gaskets, "O" rings, lock washers and seals when reassembling. Maximum cleanliness must be maintained during all reassembly procedures.*

1) Press front bearing in rear case, making sure bearing is seated against shoulder in case. Press annulus into front bearing, install spacer, speedometer drive gear and selective washer. If rear case, annulus, speedometer gear, or spacer have been replaced with new components, proceed as follows: Use a suitable dial gauge to take reading from rear face of selective washer "A", then take reading from shoulder of rear bearing housing "B". Reading taken from rear face of selective washer should be .005-.010" (.13-.25 mm) greater than

Selective Washers	
Selective Washers	**In. (mm)**
1	.360 (9.14)
2	.370 (9.40)
3	.375 (9.53)
4	.380 (9.65)
5	.385 (9.78)

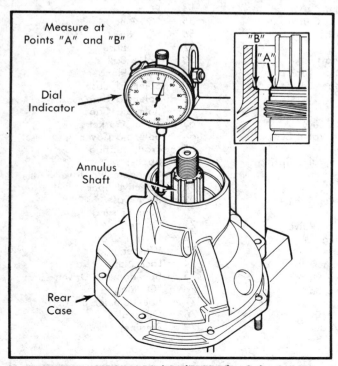

Fig. 7 Using a Dial Indicator for Selective Thrust Washer Selection

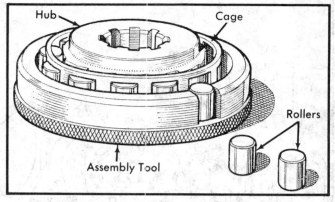

Fig. 8 Tool Set-Up for Installation of Overrunning Clutch Rollers

reading taken from shoulder of rear bearing housing, making sure that front bearing and annulus are seated against shoulders of their respective housings. If reading is not within limits, use new selective washer to bring within limits. See *Fig. 7* and refer to *Selective Washer chart.*

2) Install rear bearing to rear case. Apply suitable gear oil to new rear oil seal and install into rear case. Install drive flange, washer, nut, cotter key, and tighten to specifications. Position clutch hub and spring into cage of overrunning clutch. Position spring so cage is spring loaded in a counterclockwise direction (when viewed from front). Position assembly into suitable tool with open end of cage up. Rotate cage in a clockwise direction until all rollers are installed.

NOTE — *Do not use grease to retain rollers.*

3) Install thrust washer into annulus. Transfer overrunning clutch from assembly tool into its race in annulus. Install oil slinger and snap ring, making sure that overrunning clutch rotates in counterclockwise direction only. Align outer gears of planet carrier until punch marks on gears are toward outside of assembly and in line with locking pin. Install sun gear into planet carrier and recheck alignment of markings. Install planet carrier into annulus, then remove the sun gear. Use a suitable tool to align splines in planet carrier and overrunning clutch. See *Fig. 9.*

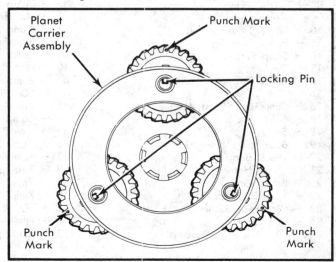

Fig. 9 Correct Alignment of Planet Carrier Gears for Sun Gear Installation

LAYCOCK "L.H." TYPE (Cont.)

4) Refit clutch release springs and thrust rods by reversing disassembly procedure. Press thrust bearing into thrust housing, then press housing assembly into sliding clutch member. Install bearing retaining snap ring.

5) Install thrust bearing retainer plate on thrust housing and ensure that ground face is positioned towards bearing. Install sun gear into sliding clutch, then install split ring.

6) Install "O" rings on operating pistons. Lubricate pistons with clean gear oil, then insert pistons into their bores.

7) Install selective washers, followed by clutch springs onto bolts of thrust housing. Coat mating faces of brake ring with a suitable sealer, then install brake ring into case.

NOTE — *Make sure that oil slot in brake ring is aligned with oil passage in main case and that cone of brake ring is towards front of unit.*

8) Install sliding clutch assembly into main case, then install bridge pieces and lock nuts to secure assembly in place. Position rear case on main case, then install and tighten attaching nuts.

9) Place spring in pump plunger, then insert pump plunger into its bore in main case, ensuring that flat side of plunger faces towards rear of unit. Push plunger against spring pressure until bottomed, then hold in place with a piece of wire.

10) Install "O" ring seals on pump body and retaining plug. Install the following into main case: Pump body, non-return valve seat, ball, spring and retaining plug. Tighten retaining plug.

11) Remove wire holding pump plunger in place. Install filter and sump cover. Install speedometer driven gear and bearing assembly. Install solenoid valve and relief and low pressure valve.

TIGHTENING SPECIFICATIONS

Application	Ft. Lbs. (mkg)
Overdrive Unit-to-Trans. Case	15-20 (2.1-2.8)
Drive Flange Lock Nut	110 (15.2)
Rear Case-to-Main Case	8 (1.1)

Overdrives

LAYCOCK "J" TYPE

Triumph	Volvo (Cont.)
Spitfire	GLE
Volvo	GT
DL	Coupe
GL	Diesel

DESCRIPTION & OPERATION

Overdrive is a hydraulically operated unit, mounted to rear of transmission and splined directly to transmission mainshaft. Unit consists of a single planetary assembly, a sliding clutch actuated by hydraulic pressure, and an overrunning clutch. A single planetary gear train is used, consisting of a central sun gear in mesh with three planetary pinion gears, which in turn mesh with an internally toothed annulus (ring) gear. The pinion carrier is connected to transmission mainshaft through the sun gear and an overrunning clutch. The annulus gear and overdrive mainshaft are an integral one-piece assembly. Hydraulic system pressure is developed by a plunger type pump driven by a cam keyed to transmission mainshaft. Pump draws oil from sump, through oil pan filter, and delivers it through a non-return valve and pressure filter to the clutch apply pistons, solenoid valve, and relief valve assembly.

TROUBLE SHOOTING

OVERDRIVE DOES NOT ENGAGE

Low lubricant level. Solenoid is not energizing. Solenoid is energizing but not operating. Insufficient hydraulic pressure. Damaged pump or internal damage to overdrive unit.

OVERDRIVE DOES NOT RELEASE

CAUTION — *Do not place vehicle in reverse or extensive damage may occur.*

Electrical control circuit faulty. Solenoid valve sticking. Relief valve sticking causing high residual pressure. Control orifice blocked. Clutch sliding member sticking. Internal damage to overdrive unit.

SLIPS WHEN ENGAGED

Low lubricant level. Solenoid valve sticking. Control orifice blocked. Worn or glazed clutch linings. Defective filter, non-return valve, or relief valve causing low operating pressure.

SLOW DISENGAGEMENT AND/OR FREEWHEELS ON OVERRUN

Relief valve sticking. Control valve sticking or blocked. Control orifice blocked. Internal damage to overdrive unit.

TESTING

HYDRAULIC PRESSURE TEST

Lift and support vehicle so rear wheels are free to turn. Remove plug adjacent to solenoid and install suitable pressure gauge using suitable adapters. With overdrive disengaged, start engine and shift transmission into high gear and operate at 25 MPH. Hydraulic pressure should read 20 psi (1.41 kg/cm²) on Triumph Spitfire, and 21 psi (1.5 kg/cm²) on Volvo. Engage overdrive and pressure should be approximately as shown in Hydraulic Pressure Specifications table. Disengage overdrive and pressure should return to normal in 3 seconds or less.

Hydraulic Pressure Specifications	
Application	**psi (kg/cm²)**
Triumph	
Spitfire	375-400 (26.4-28.1)
Volvo	
DL, GL, GT	380-425 (27-30)
GLE, Coupe, Diesel	455-500 (32-35)

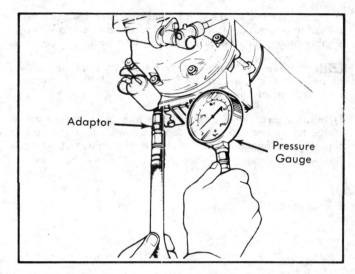

Fig. 1 Gauge Hook-Up for Hydraulic Pressure Test (Triumph Shown — Volvo Similar)

SOLENOID VALVE

Remove solenoid from overdrive unit. Test solenoid with 12 volt battery and an ammeter. When energized, solenoid draw should be approximately 2 amperes. Check that valve plunger moves fully forward when solenoid is energized, and returns under spring pressure when de-energized. Replace unit if defective.

SERVICE (IN VEHICLE)

NOTE — *Upon completion of all in-vehicle service, fill transmission and overdrive unit and check operation. Recheck fluid level. Do NOT use any type of anti-friction additives.*

SOLENOID VALVE

Removal — Raise vehicle on a hoist and disconnect wires from solenoid valve. Remove valve from overdrive unit using a 1" (25 mm) open end wrench.

CAUTION — *Do not attempt to remove valve using pliers or similar tools as valve is easily damaged.*

Installation — Install new "O" ring seal on valve end of solenoid, install into overdrive unit, and tighten with 1" (25 mm) open end wrench. Connect wires to solenoid valve.

SUMP FILTER & PRESSURE FILTER

Removal — Remove sump cover attaching bolts and sump cover. Remove gasket and pull sump filter out. Remove

LAYCOCK "J" TYPE (Cont.)

pressure filter base plug (largest plug under sump cover). Aluminum gasket and pressure filter will come out with plug.

Cleaning & Inspection — Clean pressure filter and sump filter in solvent or kerosene. Use reduced compressed air pressure to dry filters, or place on a lint-free cloth to air dry. If either filter is damaged or plugged so it cannot be cleaned, replace filter.

Installation — Install new aluminum washer on plug, then install pressure filter and plug into overdrive unit. Install sump filter, gasket and sump cover.

RELIEF VALVE ASSEMBLY

Removal — Remove sump cover, filter and gasket. Remove relief valve piston plug (bore farthest from pressure filter bore). Remove dashpot piston assembly, relief valve and spring assembly. Remove relief valve body and valve sleeve by using pliers with narrow jaws and pulling from case with firm pressure. Use suitable wire loop to remove cylinder and washer.

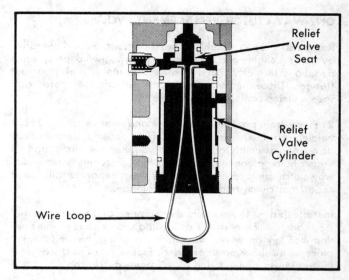

Fig. 3 Relief Valve Removal

2) Position relief valve and spring assembly into dashpot cup while ensuring that both ends of residual pressure spring are correctly positioned. Position components in relief valve outer sleeve while engaging relief valve piston in housing. Install base plug and tighten until flush with casing. Install sump filter, gasket, and sump cover.

PUMP NON-RETURN VALVE

Removal — Remove sump cover, filter and gasket. Remove pump plug (center bore), then remove valve seat spring and check ball, making sure not to lose spring and ball when plug is removed. Remove non-return valve seat using a magnet or suitable wire loop.

Cleaning & Inspection — Clean all parts in solvent and blow dry with filtered compressed air. Check valve seat and ball for pitting, corrosion, wear, nicks, burrs, and scratches. Inspect spring for distortion, loss of tension, or breakage. Discard "O" ring.

Installation — Install new "O" ring on pump plug, place spring in plug, position check ball on top of spring and valve seat on check ball. Carefully thread assembly into case and tighten until flush with casing. Install sump filter, gasket, and sump cover.

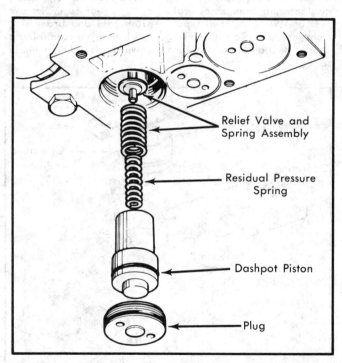

Fig. 2 Disassembled View of Relief Valve Assembly (Triumph Shown—Volvo Similar)

Cleaning & Inspection — Wash all parts in solvent and blow dry with filtered compressed air. Inspect piston, sleeve, and valve body for scratches, nicks, burrs, cracks, corrosion and excessive wear. Make sure piston moves freely in sleeve. Check for broken, worn or distorted springs. Discard old "O" rings.

NOTE — *Do not clean orifice with wire.*

Installation — 1) Clean control orifice, located in relief valve bore in case, with compressed air. Install new "O" rings, lightly oil all components with transmission oil. Install relief body in bore and use relief valve outer sleeve to seat body, making sure end of body with "O" ring is nearest to outside of case.

REAR OIL SEAL

Removal — Raise vehicle on hoist. Mark rear universal joint and pinion yoke for reassembly reference and remove propeller shaft. Remove drive flange nut, washer, and drive flange. Use a suitable tool to remove rear oil seal.

Installation — Lubricate new seal with transmission oil and install in rear case, making sure seal is fully seated. Install drive flange, washer and a new self-locking nut. Install propeller shaft, aligning marks made during removal. Check and correct lubricant level in transmission and overdrive, then lower vehicle.

LAYCOCK "J" TYPE (Cont.)

ONE-WAY CLUTCH REPLACEMENT (VOLVO)

Removal — 1) With vehicle raised on hoist, unload overdrive by starting engine and engaging overdrive, then depress clutch pedal and turn off engine. Disconnect propeller shaft at output flange. Disconnect ground cable from solenoid and speedometer cable from overdrive.

2) Place drain pan under overdrive and remove nuts and bolts holding rear overdrive housing to front housing. Remove overdrive rear assembly and place in vise. Remove circlip and oil slinger holding one-way clutch in place. Carefully remove one-way clutch using care not to drop rollers. Separate rollers and cage from clutch and check for damage.

Installation — 1) Assemble clutch, spring and roller cage and turn cage clockwise as far as it will go. Lock cage in this position with key on closed side and insert rollers, holding them in place with rubber band or string. Ensure that thrust washer is in position in annulus and install one-way clutch.

NOTE — *Thickness of new thrust washer should be .150" (3.8 mm).*

2) Install oil slinger and circlip. Ensure that gasket in front of brake has not been damaged. Fit new gasket to mounting face and install overdrive rear assembly. Connect ground cable, speedometer cable and drive shaft.

OVERDRIVE REMOVAL & INSTALLATION

REMOVAL

NOTE — *Before removing transmission and overdrive unit from vehicle, operate vehicle, engage overdrive, then disengage overdrive with clutch pedal depressed. This procedure will relieve torque loading on overrunning clutch and pinion carrier, thereby easing removal.*

1) Remove transmission with overdrive unit attached. *See appropriate article in MANUAL TRANSMISSION Section for transmission removal.*

2) Remove 8 nuts securing overdrive main case to adapter. Separate overdrive from transmission while leaving adaptor plate in position on transmission. Slide overdrive over mainshaft and off transmission. If difficulty is encountered in separating the overdrive from transmission, proceed as follows: Remove plug adjacent to solenoid, then screw in and tighten suitable adapter to allow oil to be pumped into unit using lubrication gun. This will pressurize unit and release spline loading on mainshaft and allow easy removal. De-energize solenoid when overdrive has separated from adapter ¾" (19.05 mm).

INSTALLATION

1) Clean gasket surfaces of overdrive case and transmission adapter. Apply a light coat of sealer to case-to-adapter gasket and position on overdrive front case, taking care not to tear gasket on studs. Using a long screwdriver, rotate overrunning clutch splines (innermost set of splines) in a counterclockwise direction until splines are in line with splines in planet carrier. Ensure that pump cam and sun gear snap ring are correctly positioned on mainshaft.

2) Rotate transmission mainshaft so peak of pump cam is at bottom. Position transmission in low gear. Install overdrive to transmission while rotating output shaft of overdrive in a clockwise direction and applying slight pressure until splines are engaged. Pump strap assembly should ride smoothly onto cam and overdrive should butt up to adapter plate without undue force. If overdrive unit will not come within ⅝" (15.88 mm) of adapter, then planet carrier and overrunning clutch splines are not properly aligned and overdrive must be removed and splines aligned. Install and tighten 8 nuts attaching overdrive to adapter. Install transmission and overdrive into vehicle and fill with suitable lubricant.

OVERDRIVE DISASSEMBLY

NOTE — *Extreme cleanliness must be observed at all times in working on overdrive unit. Clean outside of overdrive thoroughly before proceeding with disassembly.*

1) Remove solenoid valve with a 1" (25 mm) open end wrench. Remove operating piston bridge pieces. Progressively loosen nuts securing front case, brake ring and rear case. Remove nuts and washers, then separate front case and brake ring from rear case. Tap brake ring loose from front case using a copper drift and hammer. Then remove clutch sliding member springs from rear case.

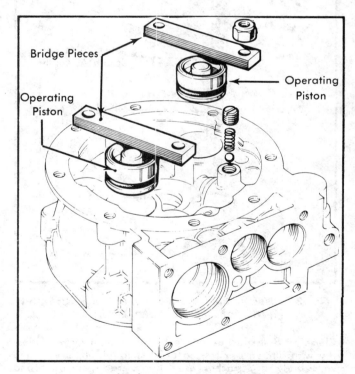

Fig. 4   Clutch Operating Piston Removal

2) Using a pair of pliers, carefully remove operating pistons from front case and identify them with their respective bores. Remove sump cover, gasket and sump filter. Remove pressure filter base plug (largest plug under sump cover), aluminum gasket and pressure filter. Remove relief valve piston plug (bore farthest from pressure filter bore), dashpot piston assembly, relief valve residual pressure spring, and relief valve and spring assembly. Remove relief valve body and valve

LAYCOCK "J" TYPE (Cont.)

sleeve by using pliers with narrow jaws and pulling from case with firm pressure. Remove pump non-return valve plug (center bore), then remove valve seat spring and check ball. Remove non-return valve seat using a magnet or wire loop with hooked end. Remove pump body and pump plunger.

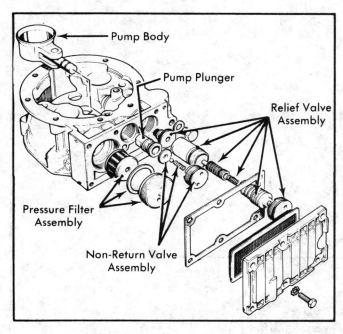

Fig. 5 Exploded View of Front Case Valves and Filters

3) Remove sliding clutch, sun gear and thrust bearing cover assembly from annulus in rear case. Remove planet carrier assembly taking care not to damage oil catcher attached to underside of carrier assembly. Remove sun gear snap ring and sliding clutch snap ring, then push sun gear out of sliding clutch hub. Insert a suitable remover tool into sliding clutch hub, support thrust bearing cover, and tap on end of tool to drive clutch hub from thrust bearing. Remove thrust bearing snap ring, then press bearing from cover using an arbor press.

4) Remove snap ring and oil thrower. Insert a suitable tool over the overrunning clutch, reach through tool with finger and pull overrunning clutch into tool, and remove tool and overrunning clutch as an assembly. Remove mainshaft thrust washer from recess in annulus. Separate overrunning clutch from removal tool and disassemble.

5) Remove speedometer driven gear attaching bolt, housing and driven gear from rear housing. Remove drive flange attaching nut and washer. Remove drive flange using a suitable tool. Drive annulus from rear case using a soft mallet and striking on end of tail shaft. Remove front bearing, speedometer drive gear and spacer from annulus. Remove oil seal from rear case and drive out rear bearing.

CLEANING & INSPECTION

CLEANING

NOTE — *Do not clean sliding clutch or solenoid valve in solvent. Wipe off with a clean lint-free cloth.*

Thoroughly wash all parts in clean solvent. After cleaning, dry all parts with dry filtered compressed air. Blow out all passages to remove any foreign material or cleaning solvent. To clean valve portion of solenoid valve, immerse valve portion (up to threads) in clean solvent, allow to soak until clean, then air dry on a clean shop cloth.

INSPECTION

Front Case — Cracks in case or in valve or piston bores. Nicks, scratches, grooves or warpage on mating surfaces or in valve or piston bores. Worn or stripped threads on plugs, studs, or in valve bores. Blocked oil passages or control orifice.

Rear Case — Cracks in case or in mainshaft bearing snap ring groove. Nick, scratches, or warpage on mating surfaces. Worn, stripped, or galled threads in stud holes. Worn or loose rear bushing.

Pump, Valves & Pistons — Scratches, nicks, burrs, excessive wear, pitting, or corrosion of any pump or valve component. Weak, broken or distorted relief valve springs. Torn, distorted or plugged sump filter or pressure filter. Cracked or warped sump cover. Nicks, scratches or wear on operating pistons. Wear, grooves, burrs and cracks in piston bores.

Brake Ring — Worn, grooved, distorted, or burned clutch surfaces. Cracks in brake ring or at stud holes.

Sliding Clutch, Thrust Bearing & Cover — Worn, burned, loose or peeling friction material. Cracks in clutch hub or friction surface. Worn, rough, galled bearings and races in thrust bearing. Weak, broken or distorted clutch return springs.

Annulus, Planet Carrier & Sun Gear — Loose or worn bushing in annulus gear bore. Chipped, worn or broken teeth in annulus gear. Worn, broken or chipped splines on sun gear and mainshaft. Bent or distorted mainshaft. Plugged lubrication holes. Worn, burned, or rough clutch surface on annulus gear. Cracks in mainshaft or sun gear. Loose or worn pins in planet carrier. Cracked, worn or chipped teeth on planet carrier gears. Rough, galled or worn bearings.

Overrunning Clutch — Cracked or worn hub and rollers. Broken or distorted spring, or cracked, bent, or broken cage. Worn thrust washer. Worn clutch race in annulus gear bore. Cracked clutch hub. Worn splines.

OVERDRIVE REASSEMBLY

NOTE — *Use new gaskets, "O" rings, lock washers and seals when reassembling. Maximum cleanliness must be maintained during all reassembly procedures.*

1) Position speedometer drive gear into rear case with plain boss facing front bearing. Press front bearing into rear case until seated against shoulder in case. Press front bearing along with rear casing and speedometer driving gear onto annulus until front bearing seats on shoulder of annulus. Install spacer onto annulus mainshaft. Press rear bearing into rear case and onto annulus mainshaft. Install new oil seal and press on drive flange. Install washer, new self-locking nut, and tighten to specifications.

Overdrives

LAYCOCK "J" TYPE (Cont.)

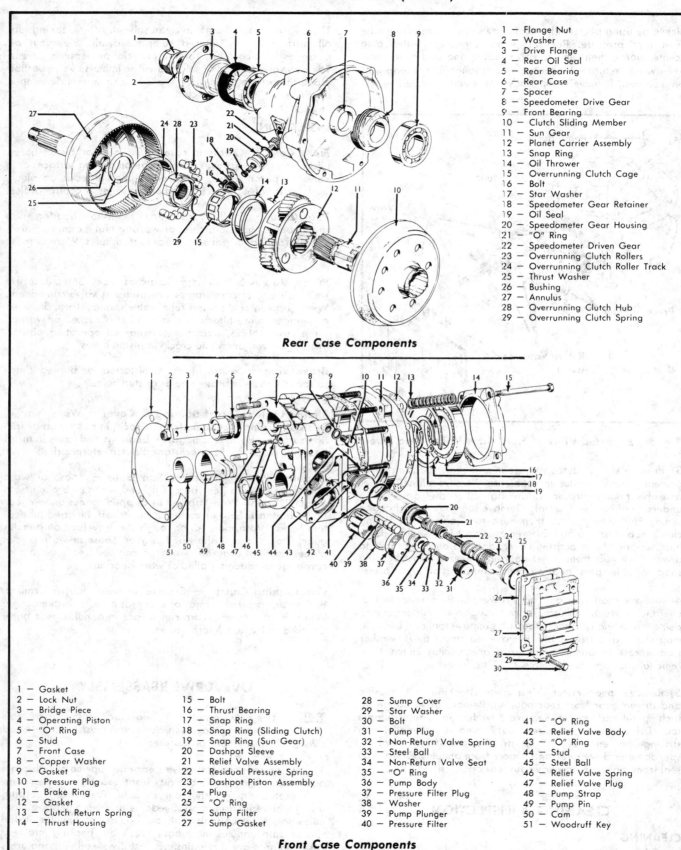

1 — Flange Nut
2 — Washer
3 — Drive Flange
4 — Rear Oil Seal
5 — Rear Bearing
6 — Rear Case
7 — Spacer
8 — Speedometer Drive Gear
9 — Front Bearing
10 — Clutch Sliding Member
11 — Sun Gear
12 — Planet Carrier Assembly
13 — Snap Ring
14 — Oil Thrower
15 — Overrunning Clutch Cage
16 — Bolt
17 — Star Washer
18 — Speedometer Gear Retainer
19 — Oil Seal
20 — Speedometer Gear Housing
21 — "O" Ring
22 — Speedometer Driven Gear
23 — Overrunning Clutch Rollers
24 — Overrunning Clutch Roller Track
25 — Thrust Washer
26 — Bushing
27 — Annulus
28 — Overrunning Clutch Hub
29 — Overrunning Clutch Spring

Rear Case Components

1 — Gasket
2 — Lock Nut
3 — Bridge Piece
4 — Operating Piston
5 — "O" Ring
6 — Stud
7 — Front Case
8 — Copper Washer
9 — Gasket
10 — Pressure Plug
11 — Brake Ring
12 — Gasket
13 — Clutch Return Spring
14 — Thrust Housing
15 — Bolt
16 — Thrust Bearing
17 — Snap Ring
18 — Snap Ring (Sliding Clutch)
19 — Snap Ring (Sun Gear)
20 — Dashpot Sleeve
21 — Relief Valve Assembly
22 — Residual Pressure Spring
23 — Dashpot Piston Assembly
24 — Plug
25 — "O" Ring
26 — Sump Filter
27 — Sump Gasket
28 — Sump Cover
29 — Star Washer
30 — Bolt
31 — Pump Plug
32 — Non-Return Valve Spring
33 — Steel Ball
34 — Non-Return Valve Seat
35 — "O" Ring
36 — Pump Body
37 — Pressure Filter Plug
38 — Washer
39 — Pump Plunger
40 — Pressure Filter
41 — "O" Ring
42 — Relief Valve Body
43 — "O" Ring
44 — Stud
45 — Steel Ball
46 — Relief Valve Spring
47 — Relief Valve Plug
48 — Pump Strap
49 — Pump Pin
50 — Cam
51 — Woodruff Key

Front Case Components

Fig. 6   Disassembled View of Overdrive Components

LAYCOCK "J" TYPE (Cont.)

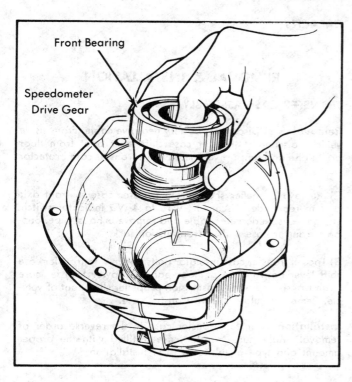

Fig. 7 Speedometer Drive Gear and Front Bearing Positions in Rear Case

2) Position clutch hub and spring into cage of overrunning clutch. Position spring so cage is spring loaded in a counterclockwise direction (when viewed from front). Position assembly into assembling tool (L178 or equivalent), with open end of cage up. Rotate cage in a clockwise direction until all rollers are installed. Install thrust washer into annulus. Transfer overrunning clutch from assembly tool into its race in annulus. Install oil thrower and snap ring.

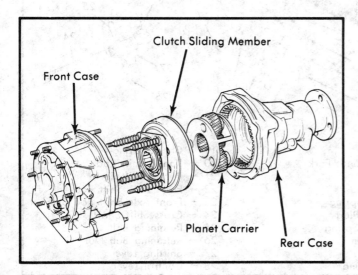

Fig. 8 Exploded View of Main Components of Laycock "J" Type Overdrive Unit

NOTE — *Check that overrunning clutch rotates in counterclockwise direction only.*

3) Press thrust bearing into housing and install snap ring. Install thrust bearing housing onto hub of clutch sliding member and install snap ring securing bearing to hub. Install sun gear into hub and install snap ring on sun gear extension.

4) Lubricate operating pistons with transmission oil, install new "O" rings, then install pistons (counterbored end out) in their respective bores. Install solenoid valve with new "O" ring, making sure not to overtighten. Install new aluminum washer on pressure filter plug, then install pressure filter and plug into front case. Install pump body and pump plunger. Install new "O" ring on pump plug, place spring in plug, position check ball on top of spring and valve seat on check ball. Carefully thread assembly into case and tighten.

5) Install relief body in bore and use relief valve outer sleeve to seat body, making sure that end of body with "O" ring is nearest to outside of case. Position relief valve and spring assembly into dashpot cup while ensuring that both ends of residual pressure spring is correctly positioned. Position components in relief valve outer sleeve while engaging relief valve piston in housing. Install base plug and tighten. Install sump filter, gasket and sump cover.

6) Mount rear case assembly upright in a soft-jawed vise, then install planet carrier assembly. Install sliding clutch assembly including return springs onto cone of annulus. Engage sun gear with planet carrier gears. Apply light coat of sealer to new gaskets and install on both sides of brake ring. Install brake ring to rear case and align stud holes.

NOTE — *Gears can be meshed in any position.*

7) Position front case over thrust housing pins while aligning with studs in brake ring. Install and tighten nuts evenly, securing front and rear case assemblies, while making sure copper washers are installed to 2 top studs. Install 2 bridge pieces and install new self-locking nuts.

NOTE — *Clutch return spring pressure should be felt as cases draw together.*

TIGHTENING SPECIFICATIONS

Application	Ft. Lbs. (mkg)
Sump Cover	6 (.83)
Pressure Filter Cover	16 (2.2)
Relief Valve Plug	16 (2.2)
Operation Piston Bridge	6-8 (.83-1.1)
Front-to-Rear Cover	13-15 (1.8-2.1)
Drive Flange Nut	
Triumph	80-130 (11.1-18.0)
Volvo	80-100 (11.1-13.8)

Transfer Cases

DATSUN 4-WD PICKUP

DESCRIPTION

The transfer case used on Datsun 4-WD Pickup is bolted to frame and connected to transmission, rear axle and front axle by propeller shafts. Transfer case has 2 ranges, High and Low. Transfer case can be shifted into 4-WD High range at any speed, providing locking hubs are in the lock position. Vehicle must be stopped before shifting transfer case into 4-WD Low range. Transfer case is provided with an indicator switch and light. Indicator light will come on when transfer lever is in any position except 2-WD High range (light is on in 4-WD High, Neutral or 4-WD Low).

LUBRICATION

SERVICE INTERVAL

Check fluid level every 15,000 miles or 12 months (whichever comes first). When towing trailer, change fluid every 30,000 miles or 24 months (whichever comes first).

FLUID TYPE

Use SAE 90 gear oil (API-GL-4).

CAPACITY

3.0 pts.

REMOVAL & INSTALLATION

TRANSFER CASE ASSEMBLY

Removal — 1) Disconnect battery negative cable. From inside vehicle, disconnect transfer case shift lever boot from floor pan. Raise and support vehicle. Remove transfer case protector pan.

2) Remove propeller shafts from transfer case to front axle and to rear axle. Disconnect wire to 4-WD indicator switch. Disconnect speedometer cable and remove exhaust pipe. Support transfer case with a transmission jack.

3) Loosen transfer case insulator bolts. Make sure transfer case shift lever boot is free of floor pan and lower transfer case (with transfer case-to-transmission propeller shaft) out of vehicle. Remove insulators from transfer case.

Installation — Install transfer case in the reverse order of removal. Make sure transfer case if filled with the proper amount and type of lubricant after installation.

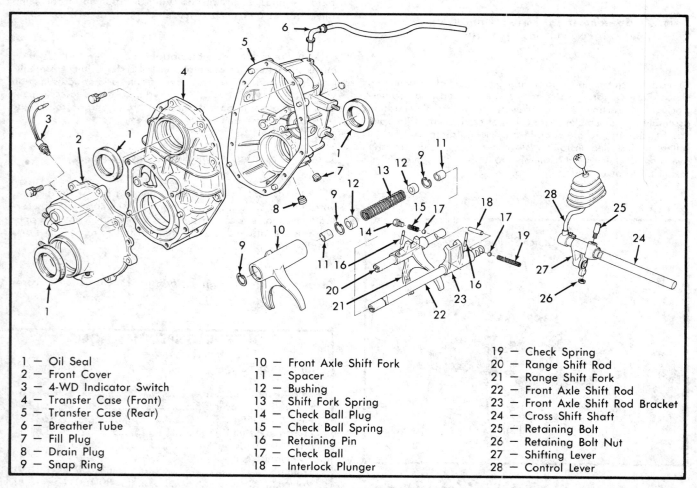

1 — Oil Seal	10 — Front Axle Shift Fork	19 — Check Spring
2 — Front Cover	11 — Spacer	20 — Range Shift Rod
3 — 4-WD Indicator Switch	12 — Bushing	21 — Range Shift Fork
4 — Transfer Case (Front)	13 — Shift Fork Spring	22 — Front Axle Shift Rod
5 — Transfer Case (Rear)	14 — Check Ball Plug	23 — Front Axle Shift Rod Bracket
6 — Breather Tube	15 — Check Ball Spring	24 — Cross Shift Shaft
7 — Fill Plug	16 — Retaining Pin	25 — Retaining Bolt
8 — Drain Plug	17 — Check Ball	26 — Retaining Bolt Nut
9 — Snap Ring	18 — Interlock Plunger	27 — Shifting Lever
		28 — Control Lever

Fig. 1 Exploded View of Datsun 4-WD Pickup Transfer Case and Shifting Assembly

DATSUN 4-WD PICKUP (Cont.)

TRANSFER CASE DISASSEMBLY

1) Make sure transfer case is clean of dirt and grease. Drain gear oil. Place control lever in 4-WD Low range or 2-WD High range to aid in removing companion flange lock nuts.

2) Place companion flange holding tool (ST31530000) on companion flange, then remove companion flanges and nuts. Remove 4-WD indicator switch. Remove transfer case front cover, tapping cover with a mallet will aid in removal.

3) Remove front axle output shaft and needle bearing. Remove snap ring retaining front axle shift fork, then remove shift fork assembly with spacer and synchro sleeve. *Refer to Fig. 1.*

4) Remove synchro hub snap ring, then remove synchro hub. Remove front transfer case bolts then front case (tapping with mallet to aid removal).

NOTE — *Do not pry case halves apart with screwdriver.*

5) Remove retaining bolt nut then drive retaining bolt out with a punch. Remove cross shift shaft. Remove control lever retaining nut then remove control lever. Remove shifting lever with differential lever. Remove check ball plug, check spring and check ball.

6) Drive range shift fork retaining pin out. Tap rear axle output shaft assembly with mallet and remove it with range shift fork and countergear assembly. Then remove transfer case input shaft assembly from transfer case.

NOTE — *When removing countergear assembly, be careful not to drop needle bearings.*

7) Remove transfer case front shim. Remove range fork rods, interlock plunger, steel ball and check spring. Insert an M8 bolt into front axle shift fork, install nut on bolt then tighten to relieve spring tension. *See Fig. 2.* Remove snap ring then slowly remove nut from M8 bolt. Remove spring retainer bushings and shift fork spring. Separate components.

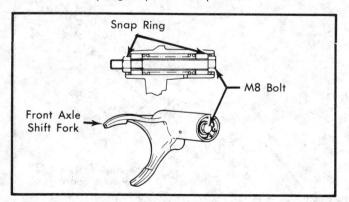

Fig. 2   Compressing Front Axle Shift Fork Spring with M8 Bolt to Remove Snap Rings

8) Press front and rear bearings off transfer case input shaft. Remove end spacers, needle bearings and center spacer from countergear. Check gear end play before disassembling rear axle output shaft. *Refer to Gear End Play chart and Fig. 3.* Press bearing off front of rear axle output shaft. Remove thrust washer and ball, then low range gear and needle bearings.

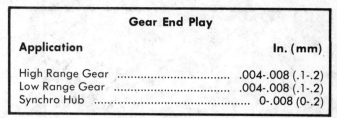

Gear End Play	
Application	**In. (mm)**
High Range Gear	.004-.008 (.1-.2)
Low Range Gear	.004-.008 (.1-.2)
Synchro Hub	0-.008 (0-.2)

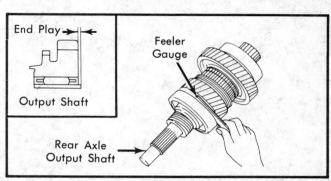

Fig. 3   Checking Gear End Play of Rear Axle Output Shaft

9) From rear of rear axle output shaft, press speedometer drive gear off. Remove spacer and ball, then press bearing off rear axle output shaft. Remove thrust washer and steel ball, then remove high range gear, needle bearings and synchro sleeve.

10) If transfer case, bearings or oil seals are damaged in transfer case assembly, remove damaged components as follows. On front cover, pry oil seal out, remove snap ring then press bearing out. On transfer front and rear cases, pry out damaged oil seals.

TRANSFER CASE INSPECTION

1) Check transfer cases for cracks, damage or warpage. Check shift rods and forks for warpage, scoring or other damage. Inspect shift springs, check springs and interlock plunger for damage. Replace components as necessary.

2) Check all gears, input and output shafts for excessive wear, chips, cracks or other damage. Replace components as necessary.

TRANSFER CASE REASSEMBLY

NOTE — *Lubricate all bearings with gear oil, apply grease to steel balls and to thrust washers.*

1) Install needle bearings and high range gear to the rear of rear axle output shaft. Install steel ball and thrust washer against high range gear (on rear axle output shaft). Press ball bearing onto rear axle output shaft. Install spacer, steel ball with speedometer drive gear to rear axle output shaft.

2) Install needle bearings, synchro sleeve and low range gear to front of rear axle output shaft. Install steel ball and thrust washer to low range gear. Press ball bearing to front of rear axle output shaft.

Transfer Cases

DATSUN 4-WD PICKUP (Cont.)

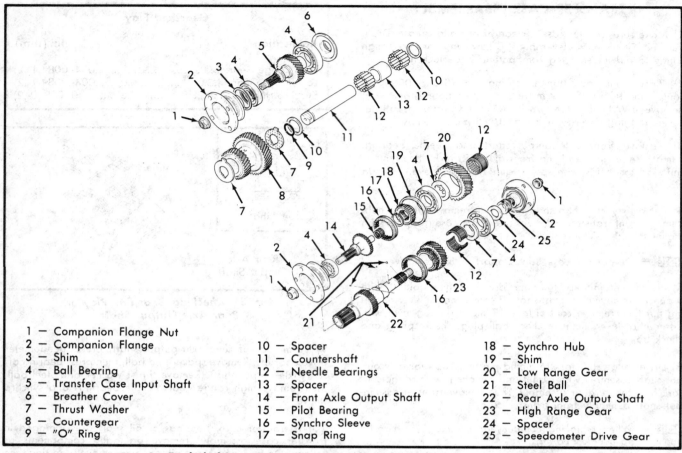

1 — Companion Flange Nut
2 — Companion Flange
3 — Shim
4 — Ball Bearing
5 — Transfer Case Input Shaft
6 — Breather Cover
7 — Thrust Washer
8 — Countergear
9 — "O" Ring

10 — Spacer
11 — Countershaft
12 — Needle Bearings
13 — Spacer
14 — Front Axle Output Shaft
15 — Pilot Bearing
16 — Synchro Sleeve
17 — Snap Ring

18 — Synchro Hub
19 — Shim
20 — Low Range Gear
21 — Steel Ball
22 — Rear Axle Output Shaft
23 — High Range Gear
24 — Spacer
25 — Speedometer Drive Gear

Fig. 4 *Exploded View of Datsun 4-WD Pickup Transfer Case Gear Assembly*

3) If ball bearings, rear axle output shaft, transfer case input shaft or transfer front and rear cases are replaced, new shims need to be selected. To select shims, perform the following measuring procedures.

4) Measure bearing seating depths on both transfer cases ("A", "B", "C" and "D"). *Refer to Fig. 5.* When measuring bearing seating depth "C", be sure breather cover is installed. With new ball bearings installed on transfer case input shaft,

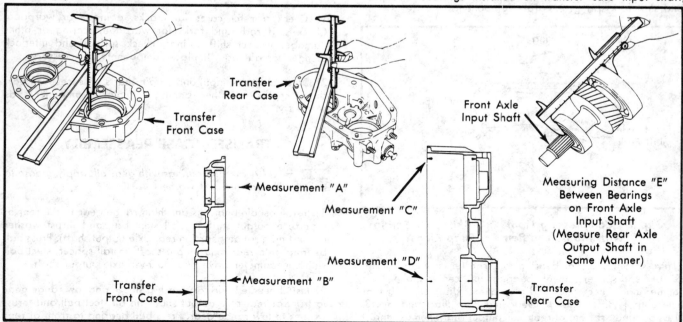

Fig. 5 *Measuring Transfer Cases and Gear Assemblies to Determine Shim Thickness*

DATSUN 4-WD PICKUP (Cont.)

measure distance ("E") between outer edge of bearings. Then measure distance ("F") between outer edge of bearings on rear axle output shaft.

5) To select transfer case input shaft shim, add measurement "A" to "C" then subtract distance "E". To select rear axle output shaft shim, add measurement "B" to "D" then subtract distance "F". See *Fig. 5*. Select shims so shaft end play will be .002-.006" (.06-.15 mm) on transfer case input shaft or .0-.005" (.0-.13 mm) on rear axle output shaft. Shims are available from .004" (.1 mm) up to .016" (.4 mm) for transfer case input shaft or from .004" (.1 mm) up to .020" (.5 mm) for rear axle output shaft.

6) If transfer case input shaft bearings are not already pressed on shaft (from shim selection), press bearings onto transfer case input shaft. Install breather cover to transfer case input shaft. Install center spacer, needle bearings and spacers to countergear.

7) Install transfer case input shaft to transfer front case. Drive front axle shift fork plug out of transfer front case (this is necessary to install front axle shift fork). Install check spring and ball into hole in transfer rear case and retain with special retaining tool (ST23620000). See *Fig. 6*.

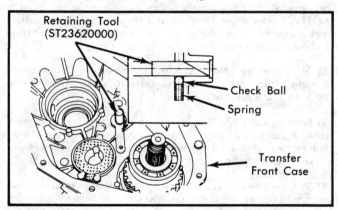

Fig. 6   Using Retaining Tool (ST23620000) to Retain Check Ball and Spring in Transfer Front Case

8) Install range shift fork to its synchro sleeve. Attach front axle shift rod bracket to front axle shift rod and secure it with a retaining pin. Install front axle shift rod to transfer rear case, pushing special tool (ST23620000) out of way. Install interlock plunger. Reassemble front axle shift fork in reverse order of disassembly (using an M8 bolt to compress spring to install snap rings).

9) Install new "O" ring (lubricated) to countershaft. Install countershaft to countergear, make sure thrust washer is already installed to countergear. Install countergear assembly to transfer rear case. Lift countergear assembly slightly and install rear axle output shaft assembly to transfer rear case. When installing rear axle output shaft gear assembly, make sure gears mesh together.

10) Install companion flange and nut to rear axle output shaft. Tighten nut finger tight. Tap on front end of rear axle output shaft to make sure it is seated properly. Install range shift rod to case and secure with retaining pin. Apply sealant to front axle shift fork plug hole, then drive plug into case. Install check ball and spring, apply sealant to plug and install plug.

11) Install synchro hub to front of rear axle output shaft. Select snap ring thickness so that synchro hub end play will be .0-.008" (.0-.2 mm). See *Fig. 7*. Snap rings are available from .051" (1.3 mm) to .067" (1.7 mm) in .004" (.1 mm) increments. Install snap rings selected.

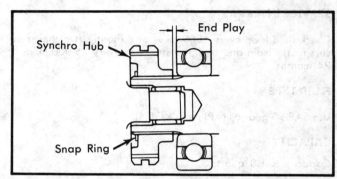

Fig. 7   Measuring Synchro Hub to Bearing Clearance for Snap Ring Selection

12) Install shift lever with differential lever, then install cross shift shaft. Apply grease to thrust washer and shims selected in steps **4)** and **5)**, then install them in transfer front case. Clean mating surfaces of transfer cases, apply sealant to mating surfaces and install transfer front case to transfer rear case. Make sure gear assemblies, shift forks, shift rods, shims and thrust washer remain in position. Tapping case with mallet will aid in installation.

13) Install spacer, front axle shift fork assembly and spacer, then secure with snap ring. Install greased pilot bearing to rear axle output shaft, then install front axle output shaft to rear axle output shaft. Clean mating surfaces of transfer case and front cover, apply sealant to mating surfaces and install front cover. Install other 2 companion flanges.

14) Remove previously installed companion flange nut (it was tightened finger tight), then install all new companion flange nuts and tighten. Install 4-WD indicator switch.

TIGHTENING SPECIFICATIONS

Application	Ft. Lbs. (mkg)
Check Ball Plug	14-18 (1.9-2.5)
Companion Flange Nuts	87-101 (12.0-14.0)

TOYOTA LAND CRUISER

DESCRIPTION

The transfer case used on Toyota Land Cruiser models is installed behind the transmission, and the transfer gear can be shifted into high and low speeds as an auxiliary unit of the transmission. The front drive mechanism is mounted at front of the transfer case, and the transfer case front drive control mechanism is available with a vacuum control shifting mechanism or a mechanical (direct drive) shifting mechanism.

LUBRICATION

SERVICE INTERVAL

Check fluid level every 6000 miles or 6 months (whichever occurs first). Drain and refill transfer case every 25,000 miles or 24 months.

FLUID TYPE

Use SAE-90 gear oil (API service GL-4).

CAPACITY

Capacity is 1.8 quarts.

REMOVAL & INSTALLATION

TRANSFER CASE ASSEMBLY

Removal — 1) Remove transmission and transfer case assembly from vehicles. See *appropriate article in MANUAL TRANSMISSIONS Section.*

2) Remove shift lever guide (direct drive only), then remove transfer case shift lever and rod as an assembly. Remove back-up light switch from transmission case.

CAUTION — *Back-up light switch must always be removed before separating transfer case from transmission case.*

3) Remove transfer case cover and gasket and power take-off cover and gasket. Remove stake marks from transmission output shaft nut, then hold power take-off companion flange stationary and remove output shaft nut.

NOTE — *When removing transmission output shaft nut, have front drive engaged.*

4) Remove the five transfer case-to-transmission case attaching bolts. Using a suitable puller, separate transfer case from transmission case.

CAUTION — *When separating transfer case from transmission case, hold power take-off gear to prevent it from falling out of case.*

Installation — To install, reverse removal procedure and note the following: After transfer case is attached to transmission case, stake transmission output shaft nut in place. With transmission and transfer case assembly installed in vehicle, fill both cases with gear oil.

TRANSFER CASE DISASSEMBLY

1) Remove diaphragm cylinder or shift fork guide assembly and gasket from extension housing. Remove stake marks from parking brake drum retaining nut. Engage front drive, then lock companion flange in place and remove retaining nut from parking brake drum.

2) Slide parking brake drum off transfer case output shaft. Remove attaching bolts, then pull parking brake assembly and backing plate off transfer case.

3) Remove lock plate, then slide speedometer driven gear from case. Remove attaching bolts and pull output shaft rear bearing retainer and shim from output shaft. Slide speedometer drive gear and spacer from shaft.

4) Remove stake marks from companion flange retaining nut, then hold flange stationary and remove nut. Remove extension housing and gasket together with internal parts from transfer case.

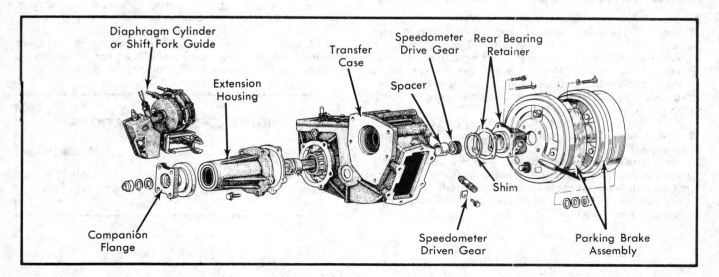

Fig. 1 Exploded View of Toyota Land Cruiser Transfer Case Assembly

TOYOTA LAND CRUISER (Cont.)

5) Remove companion flange from front output shaft, then drive front shaft from extension housing. If necessary, pry oil seal from extension housing, then remove snap ring and press out front shaft bearing.

6) Remove transfer case cover assembly and gasket. Remove plug, then invert transfer case and remove gear shift fork lock ball and spring from shift fork.

7) Remove lock plate, and drive shift fork shaft out rear of transfer case using a brass rod. Remove shift fork from case.

8) Install holding tool (SST 09318-60011) between low speed gear and transfer case to prevent gear from moving forward. Using a press, remove outlet shaft and high speed gear assembly from case. Remove low speed gear from case. Remove clutch sleeve from output shaft. See *Fig. 2*.

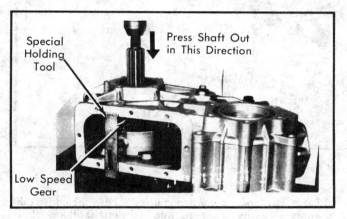

Fig. 2   Pressing Output Shaft and High Speed Gear from Transfer Case

9) Place output shaft assembly in a press with plates supporting high speed gear. Press output shaft from high speed gear and bearing.

10) Using a feeler gauge, measure idler gear thrust clearance between idler gear thrust washer and case. Thrust clearance should be less than .016" (.4 mm). If clearance is not within specified limits, new idler gear thrust washers of a different thickness will have to be installed. See *Fig. 3*.

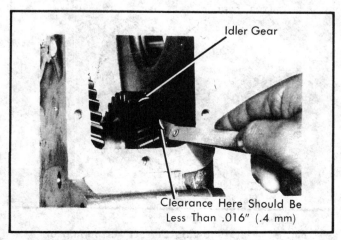

Fig. 3   Measuring Idler Gear Thrust Clearance

11) Remove idler gear shaft lock plate. Using a suitable tool, press idler gear shaft from case. Take out idler gear with bearings, spacer and thrust washers.

NOTE — *Prior to removal, note the installed position of idler gear thrust washers.*

CLEANING & INSPECTION

NOTE — *After disassembly, wash all parts thoroughly, and inspect them as follows:*

TRANSFER CASE & COVER

Inspect transfer case and cover assembly for cracks and damage. Inspect the oil seals and bushings for wear and damage.

OUTPUT SHAFT

Inspect output shaft splines, gear contact surfaces and bearing contact surfaces for wear and damage. Also, check oil clearance between gears and output shaft. Clearance should be .0014-.0032" (.035-.081 mm).

GEARS

Inspect gear teeth, thrust faces, inside diameter surfaces, and coned parts for wear and damage. Also, check oil clearance between gears and output shaft. Clearance should be .0014-.0032" (.035-.081 mm).

BEARINGS

Inspect all bearings for wear and damage and smooth rotation. If bearings require replacement, also replace outer races.

SLEEVES & SHIFT FORKS

Insert shift forks in sleeve grooves, and measure clearance between sleeve and fork. Clearance should be .04" (1 mm) or less.

IDLER GEAR ASSEMBLY

Inspect idler gear and shaft for wear and damage. Check idler gear bearings for wear, damage and smooth rotation.

EXTENSION HOUSING

Inspect front shaft, bearing, oil seal and extension housing for wear and damage.

DIAPHRAGM CYLINDER

Inspect all parts for wear and damage. Inspect diaphragm for deterioration and cracks.

TRANSFER CASE REASSEMBLY

1) Assemble bearings, spacer and thrust washers to idler gear, then place gear in position in transfer case. Install a new "O" ring on idler gear shaft, then drive shaft into case from rear. Install idler gear shaft lock plate.

TOYOTA LAND CRUISER (Cont.)

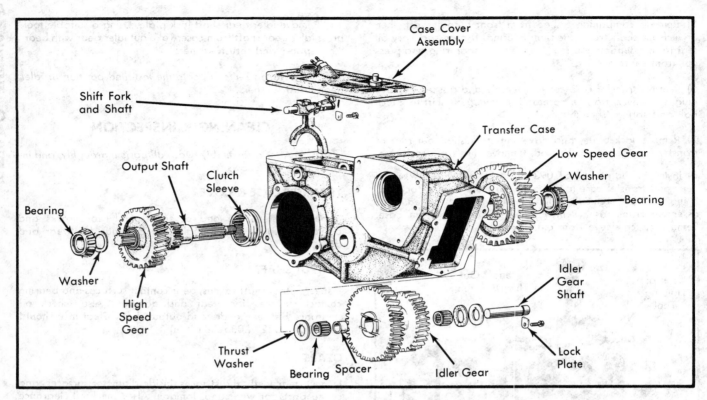

Fig. 4   Exploded View Showing Toyota Land Cruiser Transfer Case Gear Assemblies

2) Recheck idler gear thrust clearance. Thrust clearance should be .016" (.4 mm). If clearance is not within specified limits, replace thrust washer with one of correct thickness. *See Fig. 3.*

NOTE — *Idler gear thrust washers are available in the following thicknesses: .047-.051" (1.2-1.3 mm), .051-.055" (1.3-1.4 mm), and .055-.059" (1.4-1.5 mm).*

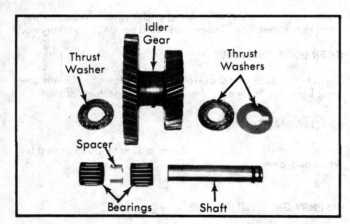

Fig. 5   Disassembled View of Idler Gear Assembly

3) Slide high speed gear onto output shaft. Place washer on top of high speed gear, then press front bearing onto output shaft. Next, place low speed gear, washer and output shaft rear bearing in position in transfer case.

4) Install clutch sleeve on output shaft. Insert shaft into case and through low speed gear, washer and bearing. Press rear bearing fully onto output shaft.

5) Place shift fork into position in transfer case, then drive shift fork shaft into case from rear. Install shift fork shaft lock plate. Insert lock ball and spring into shift fork, then install and tighten retaining plug.

6) Install case cover and gasket on transfer case and ensure inner lever on cover engages shift fork groove. Install and tighten cover attaching screws.

7) Install clutch sleeve on front end of output shaft and ensure that it is positioned as shown in *Fig. 6.*

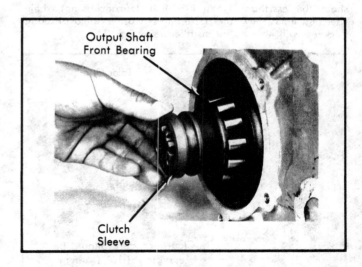

Fig. 6   View Showing Correct Positioning of Clutch Sleeve on Output Shaft

TOYOTA LAND CRUISER (Cont.)

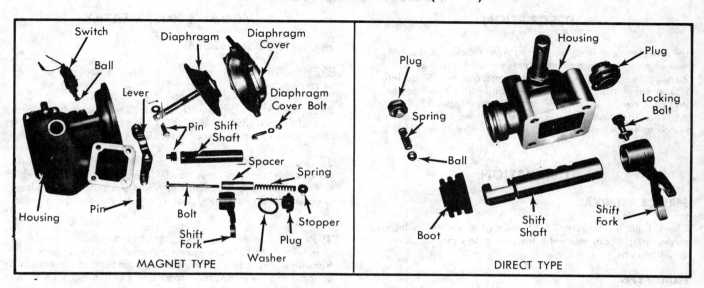

Fig. 7 Diaphragm Cylinder or Shift Fork Guide

8) If removed, press front shaft bearing into extension housing, then install retaining snap ring. Install oil seal into extension housing. Install front shaft into extension housing, then install companion flange on end of shaft.

9) Coat extension housing gasket with sealer, then install extension housing on transfer case. Install washers and companion flange retaining nut on end of front shaft. Hold companion flange stationary and tighten retaining nut. Stake nut in place.

10) Slide spacer and speedometer drive gear onto rear of output shaft. Place rear output shaft bearing adjusting shim (same size as was removed) against rear bearing outer race, then install rear bearing retainer and gasket.

Bearing Preload Should Be
2.6-9.0 lbs. (1.2-4.2 kg) for New Bearings
or More Than 1.04 lbs. (.47 kg) for Used Bearings

Fig. 8 Checking Output Shaft Bearing Preload

11) Position parking brake assembly and backing plate against rear bearing retainer, then install backing plate attaching bolts with short bolt installed at upper left. Install parking brake drum. Engage front drive and lock companion flange in place, then install drum retaining nut and washers.

12) Disengage front drive. Attach a spring pull gauge to parking brake drum and measure output shaft bearing preload. See Fig. 8.

NOTE — *Ensure that transfer case is in neutral when checking output shaft bearing preload.*

13) Output shaft bearing preload should be 2.6-9.0 lbs. (1.2-4.1 kg) on new bearings or more than 1.04 lbs. (.47 kg) on used bearings.

14) If preload is within specifications, stake parking brake drum retaining nut in place. If not within specifications, correct by changing thickness of output shaft rear bearing adjusting shim.

NOTE — *Output shaft rear bearing adjusting shims are available in the following thicknesses: .004" (.10 mm), .006" (.15 mm), .008" (.20 mm), and .010" (.25 mm).*

15) Install speedometer driven gear and lock plate. Install diaphragm cylinder or shift fork guide assembly with gasket onto extension housing.

TIGHTENING SPECIFICATIONS

Application	Ft. Lbs. (mkg)
Transfer Case-to-Transmission Bolts	36-58 (5.0-8.0)
Companion Flange Nut	80-101 (11.0-14.0)
Parking Brake Assy. Bolts	14-22 (2.0-3.0)
Parking Brake Drum Nut	80-101 (11.0-14.0)

Transfer Cases

TOYOTA 4-WD PICKUP

DESCRIPTION

The transfer case used on Toyota 4-WD Pickup is mounted to rear of transmission by an adapter housing. Transfer case has 2 ranges, High and Low. Transfer case can be shifted into 4-WD in either range (High or Low) and can be shifted into 4-WD High range at any time, providing the locking hubs are in the "Lock" position. Transfer case is provided with an indicator switch to tell what position transfer selector lever is in.

LUBRICATION

SERVICE INTERVAL

Check fluid level every 7,500 miles or 6 months (whichever comes first). Drain and refill transfer case every 30,000 miles or 24 months.

FLUID TYPE

Use SAE 90 gear oil (API-GL-4).

CAPACITY

3.4 pts. (1.6 liters).

REMOVAL & INSTALLATION

TRANSFER CASE ASSEMBLY

NOTE — *Transmission and transfer case are removed together as an assembly.*

Removal — 1) Disconnect battery negative cable. Using special wrench (SST 09305-20011), remove transmission shift lever. Remove transfer shift lever. Raise and support vehicle.

2) Drain transfer case. Mark propeller shaft "U" joints to flanges on transfer case and differential for reassembly reference. Remove propeller shaft. Remove clutch flexible hose bracket. Disconnect electrical connectors from transfer indicator switch.

3) Remove engine rear mounting bolts. Support transmission case with a jack and remove crossmember. Lower jack until transmission and transfer case are low enough to be removed. Support engine with safety stand and wooden block under oil pan. Remove bolts attaching transmission to engine and remove transmission and tansfer case as an assembly.

4) Separate transfer case from transmission by removing bolts attaching adapter housing to transmission. Do not pry on transmission or adapter housing when separating.

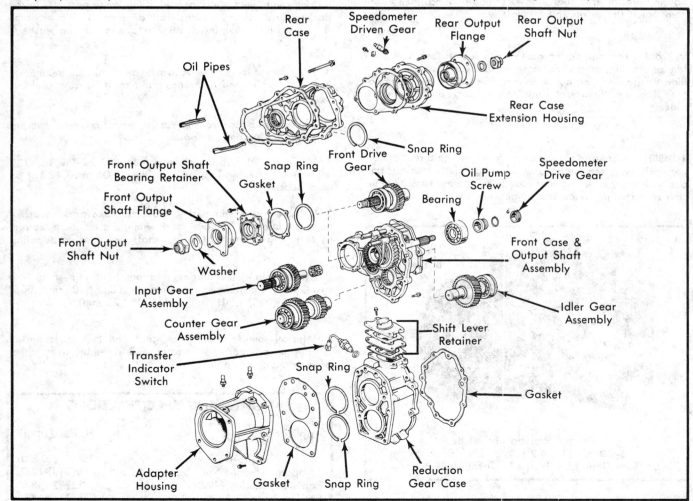

Fig. 1 Exploded View of Toyota 4-WD Pickup Transfer Case Assembly

TOYOTA 4-WD PICKUP (Cont.)

Installation — Install transmission and transfer case in the reverse order of removal. Make sure marks on propeller shaft are aligned correctly and all electrical connectors are connected. Fill transfer case with correct type and amount of gear oil.

TRANSFER CASE DISASSEMBLY

Disassembly — **1)** Remove front output shaft nut. Remove flange and front drive gear bearing retainer. Remove adapter housing bolts and adapter housing. Remove reduction gear case together with input gear and countergear by tapping with a mallet.

2) Remove snap rings from input gear bearing and from countergear bearing. Then remove input gear and countergear by tapping with a mallet.

3) Remove output shaft nut, flange, and bearing retainer housing. Then remove rear case, with idler gear, by tapping with a mallet. Remove snap ring from idler gear bearing and remove idler gear by tapping with a mallet.

4) Hold front case upright so clutch hub and ball will not fall out. Remove snap ring from front drive gear bearing. Tap front drive gear out of front case.

NOTE — *When removing front drive gear, hold front case upright or clutch hub and ball will fall out.*

5) Move the shift forks to 2-WD High range. Drive out spring pins from both shift forks. Remove shift forks with synchro sleeves.

6) Remove detent plugs, springs, balls and then remove interlock pin. Remove snap ring from output shaft bearing. Place front case on wooden blocks and drive output shaft out of case with a mallet.

7) Remove snap ring on input gear shaft, then remove bearing with bearing puller. On output shaft, check oil gear clearance. Standard clearance is .0004-.0022" (.010-.055 mm) with a maximum limit of .003" (.075 mm).

8) Check low gear thrust clearance by placing output shaft in a vise and attaching a dial indicator so that indicator button is against low gear. Push gear toward bearing and then pull away from bearing. Dial indicator should indicate a thrust clearance of .004-.010" (.10-.25 mm) with a maximum clearance of .012" (.30 mm).

9) If clearance is not to specifications, select thickness snap ring so that clearance will be to specifications. Remove output shaft bearing snap ring then press low gear and bearing off shaft. With gear and bearing removed from shaft, place shaft in "V" blocks and measure shaft runout. Runout should be less than .001" (.03 mm).

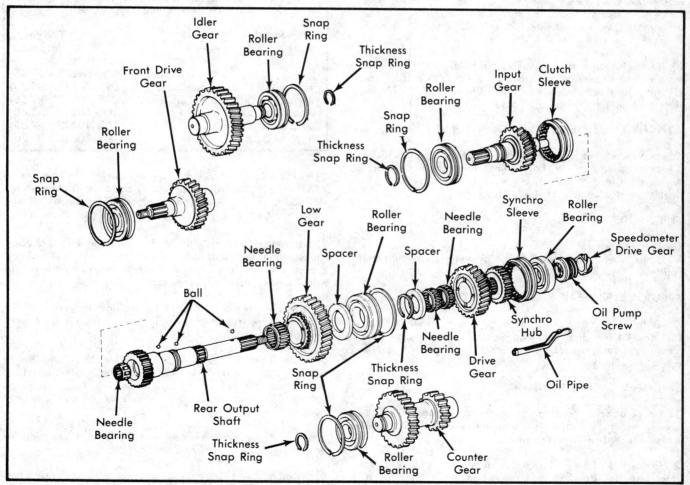

Fig. 2 Exploded View of Toyota 4-WD Pickup Transfer Case Gears

Transfer Cases

TOYOTA 4-WD PICKUP (Cont.)

10) Remove snap ring on countergear, then remove bearing with puller. Remove idler gear snap ring and then remove bearing with puller. On front drive gear, press bearing off front drive gear shaft using bench press.

11) If necessary, remove bearings from transfer cases with bench press and adapter (SST 09310-35010) or special bearing puller (SST 09612-30012). If necessary, remove oil seals with oil seal puller (SST 09308-00010).

12) Remove speedometer drive gear and ball then driven gear. Remove oil screw and ball. Remove transfer shift lever indicator.

CLEANING & INSPECTION

BEARINGS

Inspect bearings for wear and damage. Also check bearings for smooth rotation. Replace bearings as necessary.

GEARS

1) Check gear teeth, thrust faces, inside diameter surfaces, and toothed (for synchro sleeve) portion for wear or damage.

2) Check oil clearances between gears and shafts. Low gear oil clearance should be .004-.002" (.10-.25 mm) with a maximum clearance of .012" (.30 mm). Oil clearance on transfer drive gear should be .0004-.002" (.01-.05 mm) with a maximum clearance of .0028" (.071 mm).

3) Thrust clearance of low gear should be .004-.010" (.10-.25 mm) with a maximum clearance of .012" (.30 mm). Thrust clearance of transfer gear should be .004-.011" (.10-.27 mm) with a maximum clearance of .013" (.32 mm)

SYNCHRO HUBS, SLEEVES & SHIFT FORKS

Check synchro hub and sleeve for smooth sliding operation. Check synchro hub on shaft splines for smooth operation. Check clearance of shift forks to synchro sleeves. Clearance should be a maximum of .040" (1.0 mm).

SHIFT RODS

Check shift rods for wear or damage. Check plugs, springs, balls and interlock pin for damage or wear. Make sure shift rods slide smoothly in transfer case.

SPEEDOMETER GEAR & OIL PUMP SCREW

Check the oil pump screw for damage, scoring or wear. Check "O" ring for damage. Check oil pipes for crimps or bending. Check speedometer gear for scoring, damage and smooth operation. Check "O" ring for damage.

TRANSFER CASE & HOUSINGS

1) Check adapter housing for cracks or damage. Check oil seal for damage, replace if necessary (when installing seal, make sure flat surface is upward).

2) Check reduction gear case for damage or cracks. Check front case for damage or cracks, and check bearings for damage, scoring and smoothness of operation. Replace bearings as necessary.

3) Check rear case for damage or cracks. Check bearing for damage, scoring and smoothness of operation. Replace as necessary.

4) Check extension housing and bearing retainer for damage or cracks. Check oil seals for damage, replace as necessary. Check flanges, shift lever and shift lever retainer for damage, scoring or wear.

5) Check transfer indicator for proper operation. Connect ohmmeter leads to switch connector. With switch plunger extended there should be no continuity (infinity reading). With switch plunger pushed in, there should be full continuity (zero reading). Replace switch if necessary.

TRANSFER CASE REASSEMBLY

NOTE — Apply gear lubricant to all gears, bearings, shafts and seals during assembly.

1) Install low gear, spacer, roller bearing and thickness snap ring to rear output shaft. Select thickness snap ring that allows minimum axial play of bearing. See Rear Output Shaft Thickness Snap Ring chart. Install rear output shaft into front case then install snap ring to roller bearing. Install bearing retainer to front case and tighten bolts.

Rear Output Shaft Snap Rings	
Snap Ring Mark	Thickness In. (mm)
0	.094-.096 (2.40-2.45)
1	.096-.098 (2.45-2.50)
2	.098-.100 (2.50-2.55)
3	.100-.102 (2.55-2.60)
4	.102-.104 (2.60-2.65)
5	.104-.106 (2.65-2.70)

2) Install range shift rod and interlock pin in front case. Install 4-WD shift rod in front case. Install clip on rod. Move range shift rod to the high 2-WD position, then install detent ball and spring (to both rods). Apply sealant to plugs and install.

3) Install synchro sleeve and shift fork to range shift rod. Install spring pin through shift fork and into rod. Install steel ball and spacer to output shaft. Install 2 sets of needle bearings and transfer drive gear to output shaft.

4) Install synchro hub to output shaft. Install synchro sleeve and shift fork (together) to output shaft. Install spring pin through shift fork into shift rod.

5) Place front case (with output shaft installed) into upright position. Install front drive gear (with roller bearing installed) to front case. Install snap ring onto bearing. Apply grease to oil seal in bearing retainer and install bearing retainer to front case.

NOTE — Bearing retainer has an oil groove. Make sure this groove is aligned to oil hole in front case.

6) Install oil pipes to front case with cut out sides of oil pipes towards top of front case (as case would be installed in vehicle).

TOYOTA 4-WD PICKUP (Cont.)

7) Install bearing on idler gear then select thickness snap ring that allows minimum axial play and install. *See Idler Gear Snap Ring chart for snap rings available.* Install idler gear into rear case. Install snap ring on bearing. Install rear case with idler gear, to front case. Install 6 1.9" (47 mm) bolts to rear case as shown in *Fig. 3.*

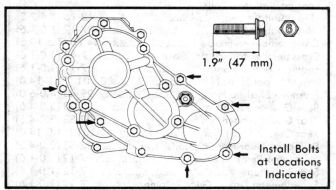

Fig. 3   Installation Bolts Needed when Installing Rear Case to Front Case

Idler Gear Snap Rings	
Snap Ring Mark	**Thickness In. (mm)**
A	.059-.061 (1.50-1.55)
B	.063-.065 (1.60-1.65)

8) Install roller bearing and oil pump screw to output shaft. Install steel ball and speedometer drive gear to output shaft. Apply grease to oil seal of front case extension housing. Then install extension housing using 7 1.5" (37 mm) bolts installed as shown in *Fig. 4.*

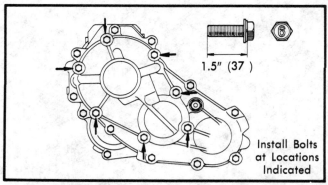

Fig. 4   Installation Bolts Needed when Installing Extension Housing to Rear Case

9) Install output flange then output shaft nut. After tightening nut, stake nut to output shaft. Installl needle bearing to front of output shaft (inside end of shaft).

10) Install roller bearing and thickness snap ring to input gear. *See Input Gear Snap Ring chart for snap rings available.* Install roller bearing and thickness snap ring to countergear. *See Countergear Snap Ring chart for snap rings available.* In-

stall input gear to reduction gear case, then install snap ring on roller bearing.

Input Gear Snap Rings	
Snap Ring Mark	**Thickness In. (mm)**
1	.081-.083 (2.05-2.10)
3	.085-.087 (2.15-2.20)
5	.089-.091 (2.25-2.30)

Countergear Snap Rings	
Snap Ring Mark	**Thickness In. (mm)**
1	.083-.085 (2.10-2.15)
3	.087-.089 (2.20-2.25)

11) Install reduction gear case to front case and install 4 4.4" (112 mm) bolts and 2 1.9" (47 mm) bolts to case as shown in *Fig. 5.* Apply grease to oil seal in adapter housing and install housing to reduction gear case using 6 1.5" (37 mm) bolts as shown in *Fig. 6.*

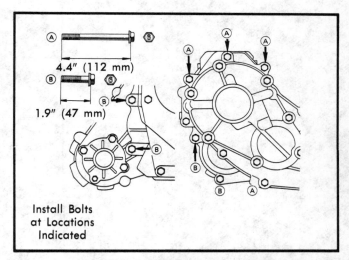

Fig. 5   Installation Bolts Needed when Installing Reduction Gear Case to Front Case

12) Install flange to front output shaft then install front output shaft nut. After tightening, stake nut to shaft. Install transfer indicator switch. Connect ohmmeter leads to switch connector and move shift forks to make sure switch operates.

13) Install shift lever retainer and speedometer driven gear and sleeve. Attach transfer case to transmission. Apply sealant to bolts. Install transmission shift lever retainer to adapter housing. Attach engine rear mount to transfer case.

TOYOTA 4-WD PICKUP (Cont.)

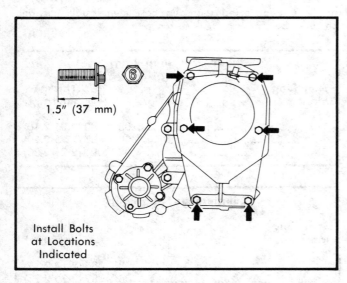

1.5" (37 mm)

Install Bolts
at Locations
Indicated

Fig. 6   Installation Bolts Needed when Installing Adapter Housing to Reduction Gear Case

TIGHTENING SPECIFICATIONS

Application	Ft. Lbs. (mkg)
Adapter Housing Bolts	22-33 (3.0-4.5)
Bearing Retainer Bolts	
Front Output Shaft	12-16 (1.6-2.2)
Rear Output Shaft	7-12 (1.0-1.6)
Crossmember-to-Frame	54-76 (7.5-10.5)
Crossmember-to-Transfer Case	7-12 (1.0-1.6)
Engine Mounting Bolts	7-12 (1.0-1.6)
Front Output Shaft Nut	80-101 (11.0-14.0)
Propeller Shaft to Flange	29-43 (4.0-6.0)
Rear Case-to-Front Case	22-33 (3.0-4.5)
Rear Case-to-Extension Housing	22-33 (3.0-4.5)
Rear Output Shaft Nut	80-101 (11.0-14.0)
Reduction Gear Housing Bolts	22-33 (3.0-4.5)
Shift Lever Retainer	7-12 (1.0-1.6)
Shift Rod Plugs	7-12 (1.0-1.6)
Speedometer Driven Gear Retainer	7-12 (1.0-1.6)
Transfer Indicator Switch	22-36 (3.0-5.0)
Transmission-to-Engine Bolts	36-58 (5.0-8.0)

CONTENTS

Section 8
CLUTCHES

CLUTCHES
Section 8

NOTE – ALSO SEE GENERAL INDEX

Clutches

CLUTCH TROUBLE SHOOTING

CONDITION	POSSIBLE CAUSE	CORRECTION
► Chattering or Grabbing	1) Incorrect Lever Adjustment	1) Adjust Clutch
	2) Oil or Grease on Facings	2) Check for Oil Leaks
	3) Loose "U" Joint Flange	3) Check "U" Joint Flange and Tighten
	4) Worn Input Shaft Spline	4) Replace Shaft
	5) Binding Pressure Plate	5) Check for Binding, Replace as Necessary
	6) Binding Release Lever	6) Free Binding Levers or Replace
	7) Binding Disc Hub	7) Replace Disc and Adjust Clutch
	8) Glazed Facings	8) Replace Disc After Checking Pressure Plate and Flywheel for Scoring. Replace as Necessary
	9) Unequal Pressure Plate Contact	9) Check Release Lever Clearance, Disc Thickness, and Pressure Plate for Paralleism with Flywheel
	10) Bent Clutch Disc	10) Replace Clutch Disc
	11) Uneven Spring Pressure	11) Adjust Spring Tension
	12) Incorrect Transmission Alignment.	12) Check Clutch Housing Alignment
	13) Loose Facings	13) Replace Clutch Disc
	14) Scored Pressure Plate	14) Replace Pressure Plate if Warped More Than .015"
	15) Worn Pressure Plate, Disc or Flywheel	15) Replace When There are Signs of Excessive Wear, Heat Checking or Scoring
	16) Clutch Disc Hub Sticking on Shaft	16) Check Shaft for Excessive Wear or Burrs, Check Shaft for Distortion and Replace as Necessary
	17) Worn or Binding Release Levers	17) Replace Levers and Release Bearing
	18) Broken or Weak Pressure Springs	18) Replace Springs
	19) Sticking Clutch Pedal	19) Check for Worn or Misaligned Components
	20) Incorrect Disc Facing	20) Replace Clutch Disc
	21) Engine Loose in Chassis	21) Check Motor Mounts and Replace or Tighten
► Spinning	1) Dry or Worn Bushings	1) Replace Bushings
	2) Misaligned Clutch Housing	2) Check Clutch Housing Alignment
	3) Bent or Distorted Clutch Disc.	3) Replace Clutch Disc
	4) Warped Pressure Plate	4) Replace Pressure Plate
	5) Excessive Pedal Free Play	5) Readjust Pedal Free Play

Clutches

CLUTCH TROUBLE SHOOTING

CONDITION	POSSIBLE CAUSE	CORRECTION
► Dragging	1) Oil or Grease on Facings	1) Free Release Levers
	2) Incorrect Lever Adjustment	2) Check for Damage and Readjust Lever
	3) Incorrect Pedal Adjustment	3) Adjust Pedal
	4) Dust or Dirt on Clutch	4) Disassemble Clutch and Clean Throughly
	5) Worn or Broken Facings	5) Replace Clutch Disc
	6) Bent Clutch Disc	6) Replace Clutch Disc, Check for Cause
	7) Clutch Disc Hub Binding on Shaft	7) Check Shaft for Burrs or Gummed Splines
	8) Binding Pilot Bushing	8) Replace Pilot Bushing
	9) Sticking Release Bearing Sleeve	9) Free Sleeve, Check for Scoring or Rough Spots
	10) Warped Pressure Plate	10) Replace Pressure Plate if Worn More Than .015"
► Rattling	1) Weak or Broken Release Lever Spring	1) Replace Spring
	2) Damaged Pressure Plate	2) Replace Pressure Plate and Adjust Clutch
	3) Broken Clutch Return Spring	3) Replace Return Spring
	4) Worn Splines in Clutch Disc Hub or Transmission Input Shaft	4) Replace Clutch Disc or Transmission Input Shaft
	5) Worn Clutch Release Bearings	5) Replace Release Bearing, Check Tips of Release Levers for Wear, Replace as Necessary
	6) Dry or Worn Pilot Bushing	6) Lubricate or Replace Pilot Bushing
	7) Unequal Release Lever Contact	7) Readjust Release Levers
	8) Incorrect Pedal Freeplay	8) Adjust Pedal Free Play
	9) Warped Clutch Disc	9) Replace Clutch Disc, Check Pressure Plate for Wear and Replace as Necessary
► Slipping	1) Pressure Springs Worn or Broken	1) Replace Springs
	2) Worn Facing	2) Replace Clutch Disc
	3) Incorrect Clutch Alignment	3) Adjust Clutch
	4) Oil or Grease on Facings	4) Replace Clutch Disc, Fix Oil Leaks
	5) Warped Clutch Disc	5) Replace Clutch Disc
	6) Warped or Scored Pressure Plate	6) Replace Pressure Plate if Scored, Heat Checked, or Warped More Than .015", Test Spring Tension and Replace Clutch Disc
	7) Binding Release Levers	7) Free Release Lever
	8) Binding Clutch Pedal	8) Check for Worn or Misaligned Parts

Clutches

CLUTCH TROUBLE SHOOTING

CONDITION	POSSIBLE CAUSE	CORRECTION
▶ Squeaking	1) No Lubrication in Release Bearing	1) Lubricate
	2) Worn Release Bearing	2) Replace Release Bearing
	3) Dry or Worn Pilot Bushing	3) Lubricate or Replace Pilot Bushing
	4) Pilot Bearing Turning in Crankshaft	4) Replace Pilot Bearing
	5) Worn Input Shaft Bearing	5) Replace Input Shaft Bearing
	6) Incorrect Transmission Alignment	6) Check Clutch Housing Alignment
	7) No Lubrication Between Clutch Fork and Pivot	7) Lubricate
	8) No Lubrication in Torque Shaft	8) Lubricate
▶ Heavy, Stiff Pedal	1) Dry or Binding Linkage Components	1) Lubricate Linkage Components
	2) Sticking Release Bearing Sleeve	2) Check Release Bearing Sleeve for Wear, Burrs or Roughness on Mating Surface
	3) Dry or Binding Pedal Hub	3) Replace Bushing or Bearings in Pedal Hub and Lubricate
	4) Pedal Interference With Floorboard or Mat	4) Check for Pedal Interference
	5) Rough, Dry or Binding Pivot Ball, or Fork Pivots	5) Lubricate All Moving Points
▶ Grinding	1) Dry Release Bearing	1) Replace Release Bearing
	2) Worn or Dry Pilot Bearing	2) Lubricate or Replace Pilot Bearing
	3) Worn Input Shaft Bearing	3) Replace Input Shaft Bearing
▶ Whirring	1) Incorrect Pedal Free Play	1) Adjust Pedal Free Play
	2) Incorrect Transmission Alignment	2) Check Clutch Housing Alignment

AUDI 4000

DESCRIPTION

Clutch is single plate dry disc type, using a diaphragm type pressure plate and a pre-lubricated clutch release bearing. Clutch is cable actuated.

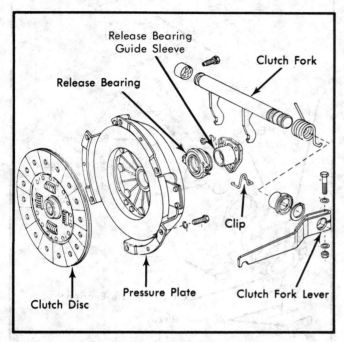

Fig. 1 Exploded View of Clutch Assembly

REMOVAL & INSTALLATION

CLUTCH ASSEMBLY

Removal — 1) Disconnect negative battery cable. Disconnect exhaust header pipe at manifold and bracket on transmission.

2) Remove bolt mounting shift assembly coupling to rear of transmission shifting shaft and separate assemblies. Unhook clutch cable at release lever. Disconnect speedometer.

3) Disconnect axle drive shafts at inner drive flanges. Remove starter. Take out front clutch housing cover plate. Remove transmission-to-engine mounting bolts.

4) Suitably support transmission with jack. Remove transmission rear mounts and brackets. Pry transmission away from engine and slide it out of vehicle.

5) Install holding tool (10-201) to flywheel and index (mark) pressure plate and flywheel. Loosen pressure plate bolts ¼ turn at a time in a diagonal pattern. Slide pressure plate off flywheel dowels and separate clutch disc.

Installation — To install, reverse removal procedure and note: Use clutch alignment tool to fit pressure plate and clutch. Make sure alignment marks are observed.

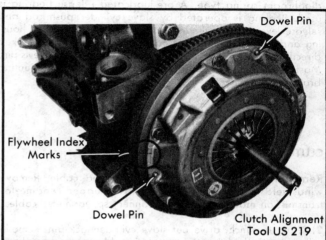

Fig. 2 Aligning Clutch Assembly Reference Marks for Reinstallation

CLUTCH RELEASE BEARING

1) With transmission separated from engine, remove spring clips securing release bearing to clutch fork. Bearing is pre-lubricated; do not wash in any cleaning solution.

2) Rotate bearing and check for roughness or noise, replace as necessary. Apply Molykote paste to bearing contact points on clutch fork. To install, reverse removal procedure.

PILOT BEARING

Lock flywheel to prevent rotation. Install suitable remover (10-202) and remove pilot bearing. Install bearing with suitable installer (VW207C) and seat bearing until distance from flywheel recess to bushing edge is 1/16" (1.5 mm). Lubricate bearing.

ADJUSTMENT

CLUTCH PEDAL FREE PLAY

Adjust clutch pedal free play by loosening and adjusting both counternuts at clutch cable. Pedal will have .59" (15 mm) free play when properly adjusted.

TIGHTENING SPECIFICATIONS

Application	Ft. Lbs. (mkg)
Clutch Assembly-to-Flywheel	18 (2.5)
Transmission-to-Engine	40 (5.5)

Clutches

AUDI 5000

DESCRIPTION

Clutch is a single plate, dry disc type. Pressure plate is a diaphragm spring type. A pre-lubricated release bearing is used. Bearing is operated by slave cylinder push rod and release lever. Slave cylinder is mounted to top of clutch housing and extends to inside of housing. Clutch pedal is hooked directly to clutch master cylinder push rod fork via a clevis pin. Master cylinder is secured to clutch/brake pedal mounting brace.

REMOVAL & INSTALLATION

CLUTCH ASSEMBLY

Removal — 1) Disconnect battery ground cable. Remove windshield washer bottle. Remove upper engine-to-transmission mounting bolts. Disconnect speedometer cable.

2) Using a punch, drive out slave cylinder lock pin. Remove cylinder with fluid line connected. Suitably support weight of engine. Remove exhaust heat shield. Disconnect exhaust pipe at manifold.

3) Disconnect axle drive shafts at transaxle and hang out of way. Disconnect back-up light wire. Pry off both shifting and adjusting rods. Remove lower engine-to-transmission mounting bolts.

4) Take out starter. Remove subframe cover shield. Slightly raise transmission. Remove transmission support bolts and bushings from both sides of subframe, then loosen both rear subframe mounting bolts. Remove right side transmission bracket. Remove transmission off dowels and take out of vehicle.

5) Index mark position of pressure plate in relation to flywheel. Insert flywheel retainer tool. Loosen pressure plate mounting bolt evenly in a diagonal pattern until pressure is relieved. Remove pressure plate and clutch disc.

Installation — To install, reverse removal procedure and note following: Clutch disc spring cage must face pressure plate. Clutch disc must slide freely with no radial play on input shaft. Lubricate input shaft splines with appropriate grease. Align pressure plate index marks. Use clutch disc alignment tool to center disc.

RELEASE BEARING & LEVER

Removal — Remove transmission. Remove cap bolt (attaching 2 retainer pieces) at lower edge of release lever. Slide release lever and bearing out of slave cylinder push rod and off guide sleeve. Disengage circlip and retainer clips keeping release bearing to lever. Separate bearing from lever. If necessary, guide sleeve can also be removed.

Inspection — Check clutch release bearing for wear or unusual noise. Do not wash bearing in solvent. If bearing is excessively noisy, replace.

Installation — To install, reverse removal procedure and note: Lubricate ball cap located in clutch housing with appropriate grease. Make sure clutch release lever locates directly into slave cylinder push rod tip. Push rod tip should be lubricated.

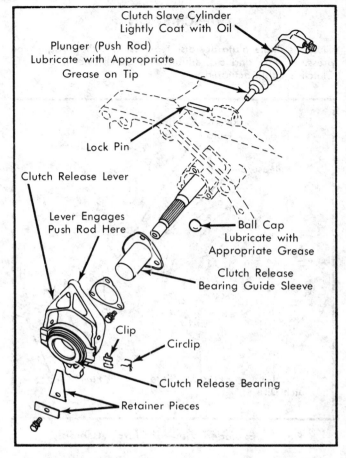

Fig. 1   Clutch Release Bearing with Related Components

MASTER CYLINDER

Removal — Disconnect and plug fluid lines. Separate cylinder from clutch pedal by removing clevis pin. Remove 2 bolts mounting master cylinder to pedal bracket and take out cylinder.

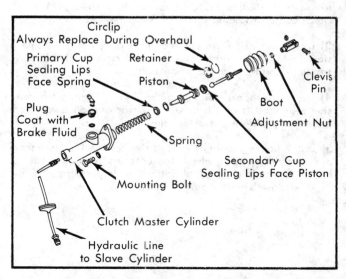

Fig. 2   Exploded View of Master Cylinder

Clutches

AUDI 5000 (Cont.)

Installation — Reverse removal procedure and bleed air from fluid line.

SLAVE CYLINDER

Removal — Working from under vehicle, drive out slave cylinder lock pin located on top of transmission. Slide cylinder back until push rod clears, then maneuver cylinder until fluid line can be disconnected and plugged.

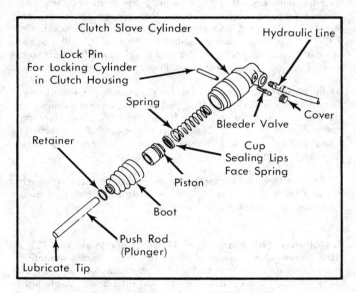

Fig. 3   Exploded View of Slave Cylinder

Installation — To install, reverse removal procedure. Coat outer surface of cylinder with oil before inserting into place. Bleed air from fluid line.

ADJUSTMENTS

CLUTCH PEDAL

Adjust master cylinder push rod so that in the rest position clutch pedal stands ⅜″ (10 mm) above brake pedal.

NOTE — *If clutch pedal is correctly adjusted but fails to properly return, check hydraulic system for air, a tight pedal bushing or jammed return spring.*

HYDRAULIC SYSTEM BLEEDING

Use only pressure bleeding equipment to bleed system. Follow manufacturer's instructions.

TIGHTENING SPECIFICATIONS	
Application	**Ft. Lbs. (mkg)**
Pressure Plate Bolts	18 (2.5)
Drive Flange Bolt	18 (2.5)
Drive Shaft-to-Transaxle Bolts	32 (4.5)

BMW

320i
528i
633CSi
733i

DESCRIPTION

Clutch is dry single disc type using a diaphragm spring pressure plate. System is hydraulically operated by a clutch housing mounted slave cylinder and a firewall mounted master cylinder. Slave cylinder automatically adjusts for disc wear.

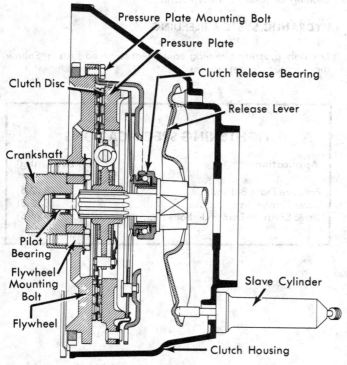

Fig. 1 Typical BMW Clutch Assembly

Pressure Plate Mounting Bolt
Pressure Plate
Clutch Release Bearing
Clutch Disc
Release Lever
Crankshaft
Pilot Bearing
Flywheel Mounting Bolt
Flywheel
Slave Cylinder
Clutch Housing

REMOVAL & INSTALLATION

CLUTCH ASSEMBLY

Removal (320i) — 1) Remove console and lift off circlip and washer from selector with transmission in reverse gear. Lift off selector rod, leaving gearshift lever attached to vehicle. Disconnect speedometer cable and housing from rear of transmission. Disconnect back-up light switch wires.

2) Remove exhaust pipe support bracket and disconnect exhaust pipe from manifold. Fit clamp tool (26 1 012) to propeller shaft coupling and remove bolts mounting propeller shaft to transmission. Remove heat shield and detach center support bearing. Bend propeller shaft down and pull it from centering journal. Place shaft out of way.

3) Detach clutch slave cylinder and hydraulic line bracket from clutch housing. Remove flywheel inspection cover and bolts securing transmission to engine. Support transmission with jack and remove crossmember-to-body bolts. Slide transmission

rearward and lower clear of engine. Loosen pressure plate bolts one turn at a time and remove clutch assembly.

Removal (Except 320i) — 1) Detach selector rod from gearshift lever. From inside vehicle, lift shift lever dust boot and remove circlip holding lever in position. Remove shift lever. Detach any exhaust system components which may interfere with transmission removal.

2) Fit clamp tool (26 1 011) to propeller shaft coupling and remove bolts holding coupling to transmission shaft coupler. Remove heat shield and detach bearing center bracket. On 733i, remove web under propeller shaft tunnel. On all models, remove center support bearing and bend propeller shaft so it can be removed from front coupling and placed out of way.

3) Support transmission and detach crossmember from body. Disconnect speedometer cable and housing from transmission. Detach clutch slave cylinder from clutch housing, leaving hydraulic line attached. Disconnect any electrical connections from transmission and remove transmission mounting nuts. Remove transmission.

4) Remove flywheel inspection cover and bolts securing clutch housing to engine. Loosen pressure plate bolts one turn at a time and remove clutch assembly.

Installation (All Models) — 1) Using alignment tool (21 2 100), install clutch disc and pressure plate. Tighten mounting bolts one turn at at time to 16-17 ft. lbs. (2.2-2.4 mkg). On all except 320i, install clutch housing. On all models, apply light film of grease to all friction surfaces and install transmission.

2) Install slave cylinder so that bleeder screw is at bottom. Install propeller shaft and preload center bearing by moving bracket .078″ (2.0 mm) forward in slots provided. Install and tighten NEW nuts to 72 ft. lbs. (10.3 mkg) while holding bolts in front propeller shaft coupling.

RELEASE BEARING & LEVER

Removal & Installation — With transmission and clutch housing removed from engine, remove spring from pivot end of release arm and slide off arm and bearing assembly. Separate release bearing from arm and measure for overall length of 1.95±.02″ (49.5±.4 mm). Replace as required. To install, pack lubricating groove with suitable lubricant and reverse removal procedure.

CLUTCH MASTER CYLINDER

Removal — Remove trim under left side of instrument panel and remove bolt attaching master cylinder push rod to clutch pedal. Siphon off most of fluid from master cylinder reservoir and detach hydraulic lines from cylinder. On 733i only, remove windshield washer tank. On all models, remove mounting bolts at firewall and remove cylinder from vehicle.

Installation — To install, reverse removal procedures and bleed hydraulic system. On 633CSi and 733i, ensure that pedal over center spring is engaged in pedal guide before attaching push rod.

Clutches

BMW (Cont.)

CLUTCH SLAVE CYLINDER

Removal & Installation — Siphon fluid from reservoir and detach slave cylinder from housing. Disconnect hydraulic line and remove cylinder. To install, reverse removal procedure ensuring that cylinder is mounted with bleeder screw at bottom. Fill reservoir and bleed system.

OVERHAUL

CLUTCH MASTER CYLINDER

Slide dust boot off and remove circlip holding push rod. Remove piston assembly and clean master cylinder and parts with alcohol. Inspect cylinder bore for corrosion or scoring; replace if required. Lubricate internal parts with brake fluid and reassemble. Adjust push rod length to approximately 5.5" (140 mm). See Fig. 2.

NOTE — *Coat friction surfaces of external controls lightly with Molykote 2 (or equivalent) prior to assembly.*

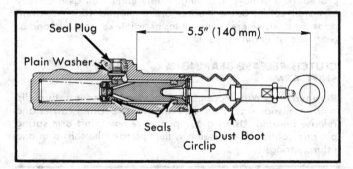

Fig. 2 Sectional View of Clutch Master Cylinder

CLUTCH SLAVE CYLINDER

Remove retaining ring and take out push rod and boot. Remove piston and clean all internal parts with alcohol. Inspect bore for scoring and corrosion; replace if necessary. Lubricate all internal parts with brake fluid and reassemble.

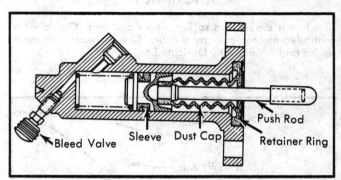

Fig. 3 Sectional View of Clutch Slave Cylinder

ADJUSTMENT

NOTE — *Clutch free play is automatically adjusted for disc wear.*

HYDRAULIC BLEEDING

Ensure that fluid reservoir is full and attach bleeder hose to bleed screw on slave cylinder. Submerge end of hose in partly filled container of brake fluid and pump clutch pedal about 10 times. Hold pedal down on last stroke and loosen bleeder screw to allow air to escape. Close bleeder screw and repeat until air is bled from system.

NOTE — *Coat friction surfaces of bearing points lightly with Molykote 2 (or equivalent) prior to assembly.*

CHRYSLER CORP. IMPORTS – EXC. FRONT-WHEEL-DRIVE MODELS

Arrow	Colt Wagon
Arrow Pickup	D50 Pickup
Challenger	Sapporo

DESCRIPTION

Clutch is a diaphragm spring, single disc type. Operation is controlled mechanically by a cable. Clutch release bearing is sealed and permanently lubricated.

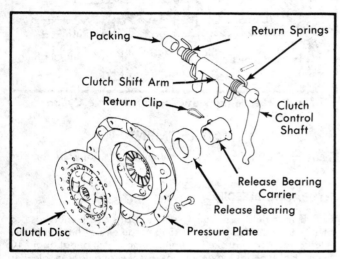

Fig. 1   Exploded View of Clutch Assembly

REMOVAL & INSTALLATION

CLUTCH ASSEMBLY

1) Disconnect battery ground cable. Remove air cleaner and starter. Remove bell housing-to-transmission mounting bolts.

2) From inside vehicle, remove console box (if equipped); remove back bone carpet. Remove dust cover retaining plate. Remove extension housing attaching bolts and control lever assembly.

NOTE – *Lever should be in 2nd gear on 4-speed transmissions and in 1st gear on 5-speed transmissions.*

3) Raise and support vehicle on jack stands; drain transmission fluid. Disconnect propeller shaft-to-differential pinion flange bolts and remove propeller shaft from transmission. Disconnect speedometer and backup light connector from transmission. Disconnect exhaust pipe and clutch cable from transmission and exhaust manifold. Support rear of engine on safety stands. With a service jack placed under transmission, remove rear engine support bracket.

NOTE – *Place jack under transmission oil pan, with the support area as wide as possible.*

4) Remove bell housing cover and remaining transmission-to-bell housing mounting bolts. Pull transmission assembly rearward from engine and remove from vehicle.

NOTE – *Use care not to twist front end of main drive gear.*

5) Insert clutch centering tool (MD998017) into clutch center hole to prevent dropping clutch disc. Alternately loosen clutch attaching bolts diagonally and evenly and remove clutch cover assembly. Separate pressure plate and clutch disc.

6) To install, reverse removal procedure and note the following: Use clutch centering tool (MD998017) to center clutch disc on flywheel. Adjust clutch cable and clutch pedal.

NOTE – *Clutch disc must be installed with stamped manufacturer's mark on pressure plate side.*

CLUTCH CABLE

Removal – Loosen cable adjusting wheel inside engine compartment, then loosen clutch pedal lock nut. Remove clutch cable from pedal lever, then remove cable from clutch shift lever and remove.

Installation – To install clutch cable, reverse the removal procedure and note following: Apply engine oil as necessary to install cable. Some models are equipped with insulating pads. Fit pads where cable routes near intake manifold and at rear side of engine mount.

CLUTCH RELEASE BEARING & SHIFT ARM

Removal – With transmission removed, remove return clip on transmission side, then slide off release bearing carrier and release bearing. Using a 3/16" punch, remove shift arm spring pin and control lever assembly, then remove the shift arm and return springs.

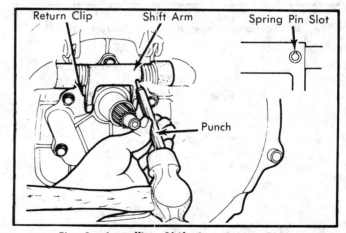

Fig. 2   Installing Shift Arm Spring Pins

Installation – 1) Insert lever and shaft into transmission case from left side. Place shift arm, felt packings and return springs on shaft assembly.

2) Apply grease to inside of bushing and oil seal lips. Apply engine oil to felt packings. Align shift arm pin holes and control shaft pin holes. Drive spring pins into position. See *Fig. 2*.

NOTE – *Spring pin slot direction must be at right angle to control shaft centerline.*

CHRYSLER CORP. IMPORTS — EXC. FRONT-WHEEL-DRIVE MODELS (Cont.)

ADJUSTMENTS

PEDAL HEIGHT ADJUSTMENT

Rotate clutch pedal adjusting bolt (at top of clutch pedal) so that height is as indicated in table. Height is measured between toe board and top of clutch pedal pad.

Clutch Pedal Height and Travel		
Application	Height In. (mm)	Travel In. (mm)
Pickup Trucks		
2000 cc Engine	6.5 (166)	5.5 (140)
2600 cc Engine	6.9 (176)	5.9 (150)
All Others		
1600 cc	6.8 (175)	5.5 (140)
2600 cc	7.2 (185)	5.9 (150)

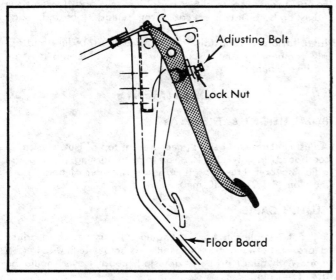

Fig. 3   Clutch Pedal Adjustment Procedure

CLUTCH CABLE

Pull clutch outer cable toward engine compartment. Rotate cable adjusting nut until .12-.16" (3-4 mm) clearance is obtained between adjusting nut and holder. Clutch pedal free play should be .8-1.2" (20-30 mm) for Arrow passenger cars, .8-1.4" (20-35 mm) for Arrow and D50 Pickups, and .6-.8" (15-20 mm) for all other models.

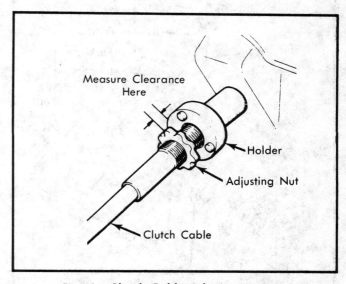

Fig. 4   Clutch Cable Adjustment Point

TIGHTENING SPECIFICATIONS	
Application	Ft. Lbs. (mkg)
Transmission-to-Engine Bolts	22-30 (3.0-4.2)
Transmission-to-Engine Flange Bolts	32-39 (4.4-5.4)
Starter Bolts	16-23 (2.2-3.2)

CHRYSLER CORP. IMPORTS — FRONT-WHEEL-DRIVE MODELS

Champ
Colt Hatchback

DESCRIPTION

Clutch is a diaphragm spring, single disc type. Operation is controlled mechanically by a cable. Clutch release bearing is sealed and permanently lubricated.

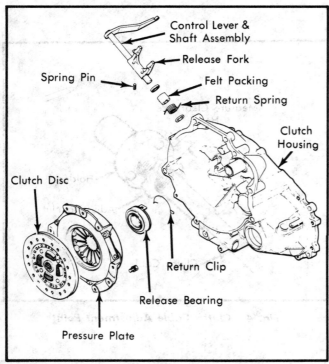

Fig. 1   Exploded View of Champ & Colt Clutch Assembly

REMOVAL & INSTALLATION

CLUTCH ASSEMBLY

Removal — 1) From inside engine compartment, disconnect negative cable from battery. Remove the following from transaxle:

- Clutch cable
- Speedometer cable
- Backup light switch harness
- Starter motor
- Front roll rod
- Four top engine-to-transaxle bolts

2) Raise vehicle and remove front tires. Remove under cover and remove shift rod from extension. Drain transaxle fluid. Disconnect drive shafts from transaxle.

CAUTION — *Drive shaft retaining rings should be replaced with new ones on reassembly. Also, use care not to damage drive shaft boots.*

3) Disconnect range selector cable. Remove engine rear cover. Remove coupling bolt at each end of front roll bar, and at the same time, loosen engine side roll rod bracket.

4) Support engine with a suitable lifting device, then remove engine-to-transaxle mounting bolts. Remove transaxle mount insulator-to-transaxle mount bracket nuts, and at the same time, loosen transaxle mount bracket. Remove and lower transaxle assembly from vehicle.

5) Insert clutch disc guide tool (MD998017) in clutch center hole, loosen pressure plate attaching bolts diagonally one by one and remove pressure plate assembly. Remove clutch disc.

Installation — To install, reverse removal procedure and note the following: Use clutch disc guide tool (MD998017) to center clutch disc on flywheel. Adjust clutch cable and clutch pedal.

NOTE — *Clutch disc must be installed with stamped manufacturer's mark on pressure plate side.*

CLUTCH CABLE

Removal — Loosen the cable adjusting wheel inside engine compartment. Loosen clutch pedal lock nut and back off the adjusting bolt. Disconnect cable from release lever and pedal.

Installation — To install, reverse removal procedure and apply engine oil as necessary. Split pin at cable end must be positively bent.

ADJUSTMENTS

PEDAL HEIGHT & FREE PLAY

Adjust clutch pedal height (measured at top of clutch pedal to toe board) to 7.1-7.3" (180-185 mm) by turning clutch pedal adjusting bolt. Free play (measured at center of pedal pad) must be .8-1.2" (20-30 mm).

CLUTCH CABLE

Pull outer cable out toward engine compartment and adjust clearance between adjusting nut and holder to .20-.24" (5-6 mm). With pedal properly adjusted, pedal travel should be 5.7" (145 mm).

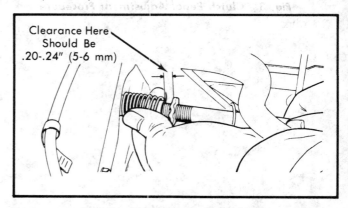

Fig. 2   Clutch Cable Adjustment

COURIER

Pickup

DESCRIPTION

Clutch is of single dry disc type. Clutch assembly consists of clutch disc, clutch cover and pressure plate assembly, and clutch release mechanism. Clutch housing also acts as the transmission input shaft bearing retainer, and contains the input shaft bearing oil seal and a selective fit thrust washer for controlling input shaft end play. Clutch release mechanism is hydraulic, consisting of a firewall mounted master cylinder and a slave cylinder mounted on flywheel housing. To control clutch engagement, a one-way valve is mounted on clutch master cylinder to control the flow of return fluid when pressure on clutch pedal is released (2300 cc engine).

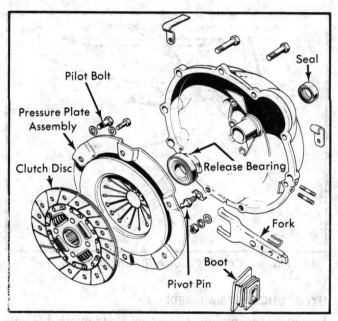

Fig. 1   Exploded View of Clutch Assembly with Detail of Internal Components

REMOVAL & INSTALLATION

CLUTCH ASSEMBLY

Removal — 1) Disconnect negative battery cable. Place transmission in neutral and remove shift lever, tower and boots as an assembly; cover hole. Raise vehicle. Disconnect drive shaft and remove from transmission.

2) Disconnect exhaust pipe brackets from transmission case and clutch housing. Remove exhaust pipe and catalytic assembly. Disconnect clutch release lever return spring. Remove clutch slave cylinder and secure to one side.

3) Remove speedometer cable from extension housing and disconnect wiring from starter and transmission. Using a suitable jack, support engine and remove starter. Support transmission and remove transmission-to-engine rear plate attaching bolts.

4) Remove crossmember attaching bolts at transmission and frame side rails, and remove crossmember. Lower jack supporting engine and remove transmission by sliding rearward and downward. Mark location of two pilot bolt holes on flywheel and pressure plate and remove clutch attaching bolts and clutch assembly.

NOTE — *Transmissions have aluminum cases. Install flat washer between case and attaching bolt or nut.*

Installation — To install, reverse removal procedure and note: Align clutch disc and flywheel with centering tool. Install pressure plate and bolts finger tight, then tighten bolts a few turns at a time in a criss-cross pattern. Bleed hydraulic system and adjust clutch pedal free play.

RELEASE LEVER & BEARING

Removal — With transmission removed, disconnect release collar spring and slide out release lever, boot and bearing. Inspect all parts for wear or damage.

Installation — To install, apply lubricant to input shaft bearing retainer of clutch housing and pivot bolt. Seat release lever on pivot. Apply lubricant to bearing contact surface of lever. Install release bearing and hook release collar spring. Lubricate face of release bearing. Lever and bearing must operate freely.

CLUTCH MASTER CYLINDER

Removal — Disconnect and plug hydraulic lines. Remove master cylinder attaching nuts. Remove master cylinder.

Installation — To install, start pedal push rod into cylinder, then position cylinder against firewall. Install and tighten attaching nuts. Connect hydraulic line. Bleed hydraulic system and check pedal free play.

CLUTCH SLAVE CYLINDER

Removal — 1) Disconnect brake fluid inlet hose at slave cylinder.

2) Unhook release lever from push rod.

3) Remove nuts attaching slave cylinder to clutch housing. Remove cylinder.

Installation — 1) Locate cylinder on studs in housing. Tighten nuts.

2) Connect fluid inlet hose.

3) Fill master cylinder. Bleed hydraulic system.

4) Hook clutch release lever into slave cylinder push rod.

OVERHAUL

CLUTCH MASTER CYLINDER

1) Clean outside of cylinder, drain fluid and remove dust boot. Using a screwdriver, remove piston stop ring and washer. Remove piston, piston cup and return spring from cylinder.

2) Wash all parts in clean alcohol or brake fluid. Check all rubber components and replace if damaged, worn, softened or swollen. Check cylinder bore for wear or damage, and check clearance between cylinder bore and piston. Replace cylinder or piston if clearance is more than .004" (.102 mm).

3) To assemble, dip all parts in clean brake fluid and reverse disassembly procedure. When assembled, fill reservoir with fluid and operate piston with a screwdriver until fluid is ejected at outlet fitting.

COURIER (Cont.)

CLUTCH MASTER CYLINDER ONE-WAY VALVE

Disassembly — Remove cap from side of clutch master cylinder. *See Fig. 2.* Slide out washer, one-way valve and spring.

Reassembly — Position spring along with one-way valve into cylinder housing. Fit cap and washer.

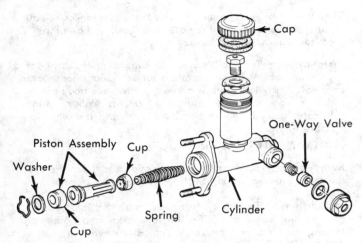

Fig. 2 Exploded View of Clutch Master Cylinder Assembly with Detail of One-Way Valve Used on Models Equipped with 2300 cc Engine

SLAVE CYLINDER

Disassembly — 1) Clean outside of housing. Remove dust boot and clutch release rod.

2) Remove piston assembly and return spring. Remove bleeder screw cap, bleeder screw and steel ball.

Inspection — Check cylinder bore and piston for roughness, wear or scoring. Clearance between cylinder bore and piston should be .004" (.102 mm). Replace piston or cylinder if specification is exceeded.

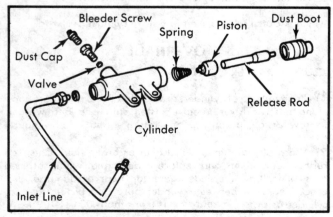

Fig. 3 Exploded View of Courier Slave Cylinder

Reassembly — 1) Lightly coat piston and cups with brake fluid. Fit cups to piston. Install piston into cylinder.

2) Install release rod and boot. Place steel ball into cylinder. Screw in bleeder and fit dust cap.

ADJUSTMENTS

CLUTCH PEDAL

Pedal free play is adjusted by loosening lock nut on push rod and rotating rod until .025-.121" (.64-3.07 mm) free travel is obtained at pedal pad. *See Fig. 4.* Tighten lock nut when adjustment is completed.

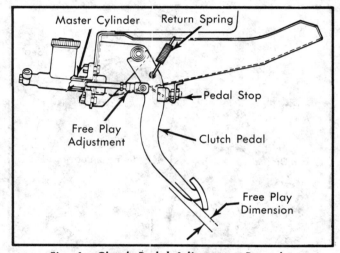

Fig. 4 Clutch Pedal Adjustment Procedure

HYDRAULIC SYSTEM BLEEDING

Remove rubber cap from bleeder valve and attach a bleeder tube and fixture to bleeder screw. Place other end of tube in a glass jar of brake fluid and open bleeder screw. Depress clutch pedal and allow to return slowly. Continue pumping action until air bubbles cease to appear in glass jar, then close bleeder screw. Install rubber cap on bleeder screw and fill master cylinder.

NOTE — *During bleeding, master cylinder must be kept ¾ full of brake fluid.*

TIGHTENING SPECIFICATIONS

Application	Ft. Lbs. (mkg)
Clutch Housing-to-Engine	
2000 cc Engine	34-45 (4.7-6.2)
2300 cc Engine	28-40 (3.9-5.5)
Pressure Plate-to-Flywheel	13-20 (1.8-2.8)
Slave Cylinder-to-Clutch Housing	12-17 (1.7-2.4)
Pivot Pin	23-34 (3.2-4.7)
Master Cylinder Attaching Bolts	13-18 (1.8-2.4)

Clutches

DATSUN — EXCEPT 310

DESCRIPTION

Clutch is dry, single disc type. All models use a diaphragm spring type pressure plate and pre-lubricated clutch release bearing. Clutch is operated by a firewall mounted master cylinder and a clutch housing mounted slave cylinder. All models except 210 with 5-speed transmissions have non-adjustable slave cylinder assembly.

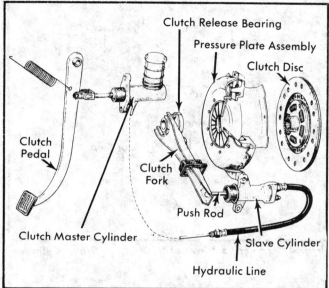

Fig. 1 Typical Datsun Hydraulically Operated Clutch System

REMOVAL & INSTALLATION

CLUTCH ASSEMBLY

NOTE — *Removal procedure is general. Not all steps apply to each model.*

Removal — 1) Disconnect negative battery cable and accelerator linkage. Remove console box and place transmission shift lever in neutral. Remove control lever boots, snap ring (nut, if required), and shift lever pin. Remove shift control lever.

2) Raise and support vehicle on safety stands and disconnect exhaust pipe from manifold. If required, remove bolts mounting exhaust pipe bracket to extension housing or rear engine crossmember. Remove exhaust pipe insulator (if equipped) and lay over exhaust pipe.

3) Disconnect back-up light, neutral, overdrive and transmission controlled spark connectors (if equipped). Disconnect speedometer cable on all except 4-WD models. On 4-WD models, remove primary and front propeller shafts, and front differential carrier crossmember.

NOTE — *Index mark propeller shafts and companion flanges prior to removal.*

4) Remove slave cylinder. On all except 4-WD, separate center support bearing (if equipped) from crossmember and remove

propeller shaft. On all models, plug rear extension of transmission after removing propeller shaft to prevent loss of transmission fluid.

5) Support engine on suitable jack. Support transmission with transmission jack, then loosen rear engine mount attaching bolt and remove rear engine mounting bracket. Remove starter. Remove engine-to-transmission bolts. With engine supported and transmission mounted on transmission jack, slide transmission rearward and remove from vehicle.

6) Install clutch aligning tool and loosen pressure plate mounting bolts one turn at a time. Use a criss-cross pattern to loosen bolts until spring pressure is relieved. Remove clutch disc and pressure plate assembly.

Installation — To install, reverse removal procedure and note the following:

- Lubricate clutch disc splines with small amount of multipurpose grease.
- Slip clutch assembly over guide dowels.
- Use clutch aligning tool to center disc and pressure plate.
- Tighten bolts one turn at a time in a criss-cross pattern.
- Adjust linkage and pedal.
- Check and refill transmission lubricant.
- Bleed clutch hydraulic system and replenish fluid.

CLUTCH MASTER CYLINDER

Removal & Installation — Disconnect master cylinder push rod at clevis. Disconnect hydraulic line to slave cylinder. Remove cylinder attaching bolts and remove cylinder. Remove master cylinder dust cover if equipped. On 280ZX models only, remove windshield washer tank and clear fuel injection resistor before removing master cylinder. To install, reverse removal procedure and bleed hydraulic system.

CLUTCH SLAVE CYLINDER

Removal & Installation — Remove clutch fork return spring (if equipped). Disconnect hydraulic line from cylinder, remove bolts attaching cylinder to clutch housing, and remove slave cylinder. To install, reverse removal procedure and bleed hydraulic system.

CLUTCH RELEASE BEARING & LEVER

Removal — With transmission removed from vehicle, remove dust boot from clutch housing. Disconnect release lever retaining spring or return spring, as required, and retaining clips holding release bearing to lever. Remove bearing and lever through front of clutch housing. Remove bearing from collar using a puller.

Installation — To install, reverse removal procedure and note the following: Apply multi-purpose grease to inside surface of bearing collar, release bearing contact points, release bearing, ball pin in clutch housing, and ball contact points on release lever.

DATSUN — EXCEPT 310 (Cont.)

OVERHAUL

NOTE — *Master cylinders and slave cylinders may be supplied by more than one manufacturer. Parts are not interchangeable. Ensure that overhaul kit matches cylinder.*

CLUTCH MASTER CYLINDER

1) With master cylinder removed, remove filler cap and drain fluid. Remove dust cover and snap ring. Remove push rod and stopper. Remove supply valve stopper, then take out piston, spring seat and return spring.

2) Clean all parts in clean brake fluid and inspect for wear or damage. If cylinder-to-piston clearance exceeds .006" (.15 mm) replace defective part. Replace piston cup and dust cover during overhaul. To assemble, coat all parts with brake fluid and reverse disassembly procedure. Bleed hydraulic system and adjust pedal height.

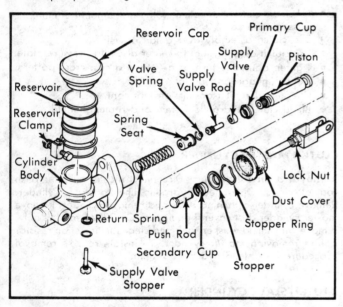

Fig. 2   Exploded View of Clutch Master Cylinder

CLUTCH SLAVE CYLINDER

1) With slave cylinder removed, remove push rod and dust cover. Remove piston and piston cup as an assembly. Remove bleeder screw.

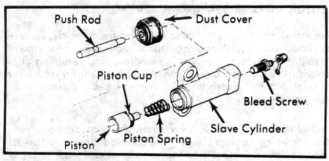

Fig. 3   Exploded View of Clutch Slave Cylinder Assembly (Except 210)

2) Clean all parts in clean brake fluid and inspect for wear or damage. If cylinder-to-piston clearance exceeds .006" (.15 mm), replace defective part. Replace piston cup and dust cover during overhaul. To assemble, coat all parts with brake fluid and reverse disassembly procedure. Ensure piston cup is installed properly and bleed hydraulic system.

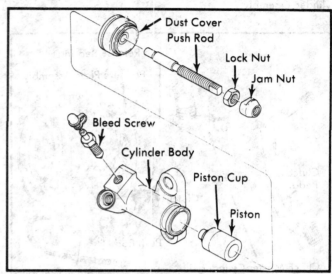

Fig. 4   Exploded View of 210 Clutch Slave Cylinder

ADJUSTMENT

PEDAL HEIGHT & FREE PLAY

Adjust clutch pedal height to specification with adjusting rod on 280ZX or by turning pedal stopper adjusting nut on other models. Adjust pedal free play to .04-.20" (1-5 mm) by turning clutch master cylinder push rod in or out.

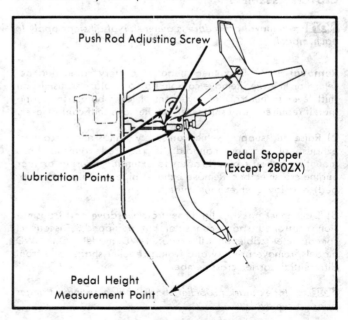

Fig. 5   Clutch Pedal Height Measurement and Free Play Adjustment Locations

DATSUN — EXCEPT 310 (Cont.)

Pedal Height Specifications	
Application	**In. (mm)**
200SX	6.61-6.85 (168-174)
210	5.63-5.87 (143-149)
280ZX	7.99 (203)
510	6.34-6.57 (161-167)
810	6.91 (176)
Pickup	6.73-6.97 (171-177)

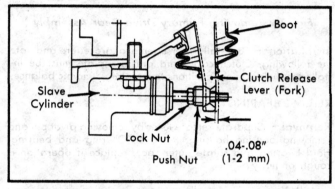

Fig. 6 Clutch Fork Free Play Adjustment Location for Datsun 210

CLUTCH FORK FREE PLAY (310)

Loosen lock nut and push rod nut and turn push rod until release bearing lightly touches clutch diaphragm spring. Turn rod back (in opposite direction) about 1¼ turn and tighten lock nut. This provides about .04-.08" (1-2 mm) clearance between push nut and lever. Work clutch pedal several times and recheck pedal play.

HYDRAULIC SYSTEM BLEEDING

1) Remove dust cap from slave cylinder bleed plug. Check fluid level in master cylinder, fill as necessary. Open bleed plug approximately ¾ turn.

2) Attach a tube to slave cylinder bleed plug, and place opposite end of tube in a container half-full of brake fluid. Push clutch pedal to bottom of travel.

3) With pedal down, tighten bleed plug. Continue operation until air bubbles are no longer seen in container. Close bleed plug on a downward stroke of pedal. Install dust cap and adjust fluid level in master cylinder.

TIGHTENING SPECIFICATIONS	
Application	**Ft. Lbs. (mkg)**
Clutch-to-Flywheel	12-15 (1.6-2.1)
Engine-to-Transmission	
210	12-16 (1.6-2.2)
All Others	32-43 (4.4-5.9)

DATSUN 310

DESCRIPTION

Clutch is a single, dry disc, diaphragm spring type. Main components consist of: clutch cover, pressure plate, and diaphragm spring. Clutch plates are riveted together. A release bearing and fork control clutch engagement and disengagement. Clutch is hydraulic type with a firewall mounted master cylinder and clutch housing mounted slave cylinder.

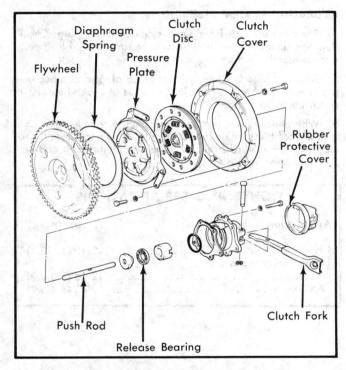

Fig. 1   Exploded View of Clutch Components

REMOVAL & INSTALLATION

CLUTCH ASSEMBLY

NOTE — *Clutch assembly can be serviced, removed, or overhauled while transmission and engine remain in vehicle. Also, transmission cannot be removed without removing engine.*

Removal — 1) Disconnect battery ground cable, fresh air duct and high tension cable between coil and distributor. Remove fuel filter from bracket. Remove clutch slave cylinder. Remove access hole cover from right wheel well and detach dust cover. Remove clutch release fork retaining clip and pin and remove release fork through access hole.

2) Remove bearing housing attaching bolts and remove primary drive gear assembly through access hole. See *Fig.* 2. Remove upper clutch housing inspection cover. Rotate ring gear with suitable tool and loosen clutch cover attaching bolts evenly. Lift out clutch cover and disc through inspection cover opening. Remove strap securing pressure plate to clutch cover and remove disc.

NOTE — *Keep strap in relative position. It is part of clutch cover dynamic balance.*

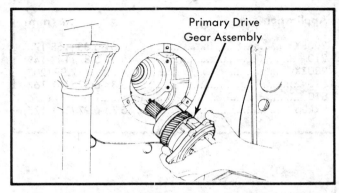

Fig. 2   Removing Primary Drive Gear Assembly

Installation — To install, reverse removal procedure and note the following: Clutch cover and pressure plate must be installed in their original positions to maintain dynamic balance.

RELEASE BEARING

Removal — Separate release lever by removing pivot pin and removing bearing housing. Remove "O" ring and bearing. Hold bearing and rotate outer race, replace if operation is rough or noisy.

Installation — To install, reverse removal procedure and apply multi-purpose grease to sliding parts of release lever.

CLUTCH MASTER CYLINDER

Removal & Installation — Disconnect master cylinder push rod at clevis. Disconnect hydraulic line to slave cylinder. Remove cylinder attaching bolts and remove cylinder. To install, reverse removal procedure and bleed hydraulic system.

SLAVE CYLINDER

Removal & Installation — Disconnect clutch hose from slave cylinder. Remove slave cylinder attaching bolts and remove cylinder. To install, reverse removal procedure and bleed hydraulic system.

OVERHAUL

MASTER CYLINDER

Disassembly — Remove filler cap and drain fluid. Remove dust cover and snap ring. Remove push rod and stopper. Remove supply valve stopper, then take out piston, spring seat and return spring.

Cleaning & Inspection — Clean all parts in clean brake fluid and inspect for wear or damage. If cylinder-to-piston clearance exceeds .006" (.15 mm), replace defective part. Replace piston cup and dust cover during overhaul.

Reassembly — To assemble, coat all parts with brake fluid and reverse disassembly procedure. Bleed system and adjust pedal height.

Clutches

DATSUN 310 (Cont.)

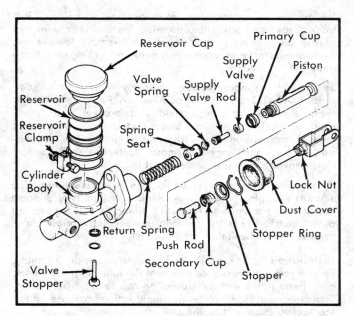

Fig. 3   Exploded View of Master Cylinder

SLAVE CYLINDER

Disassembly — Remove push rod and dust cover. Remove piston and piston cup as an assembly. Remove bleeder screw.

Cleaning & Inspection — Clean all parts in clean brake fluid and inspect for wear or damage. If cylinder-to-piston clearance exceeds .006" (.15 mm), replace defective part. Replace piston cup and dust cover during overhaul.

Reassembly — To assemble, coat all parts with brake fluid and reverse disassembly procedure. Ensure piston cup is properly installed and bleed system.

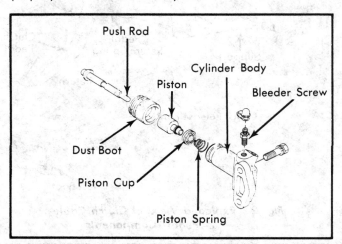

Fig. 4   Exploded View of Clutch Slave Cylinder

NOTE — *When pressure plate and clutch disc are replaced, or if any components of release mechanism is replaced, a new push rod may have to be installed.*

ADJUSTMENTS

CLUTCH PEDAL HEIGHT & FREE PLAY

Adjust clutch pedal height by turning master cylinder push rod. Correct height is 7.05-7.28" (179-185 mm). Tighten lock nut. Adjust stopper nut so pedal free play is .04-.20" (1-5 mm). Tighten lock nut. See *Fig. 5.*

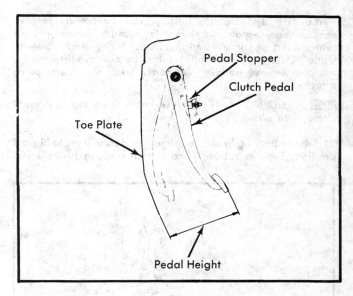

Fig. 5   Pedal Height and Free Play Adjustment

HYDRAULIC SYSTEM BLEEDING

Fit bleeder hose to bleeder valve. Place opposite end into a clear container partially filled with brake fluid. Pump clutch pedal two or three times and hold to floor. Break bleeder valve loose and allow air to vent. Close bleeder screw and allow pedal to return. Repeat procedure until no air bubbles are present in discharged fluid.

TIGHTENING SPECIFICATIONS	
Application	**Ft. Lbs. (mkg)**
Clutch Cover Assy.-to-Flywheel Bolt	5-7 (.7-1.0)
Pressure Plate Strap Bolt	7-9 (1.0-1.3)

FIAT BRAVA

DESCRIPTION

Clutch is a dry, single disc type using a diaphragm spring pressure plate. Clutch disc is a conventional friction lining kind. Clutch operation is accomplished by a control cable attached at upper end directly to clutch pedal and lower end to clutch release fork.

REMOVAL & INSTALLATION

CLUTCH ASSEMBLY

Removal — 1) Disconnect battery ground cable and remove exhaust pipe-to-manifold clamp. From inside vehicle, pry up center insert of console and disconnect wiring from cigarette lighter. Disengage gear shift retainer by pulling shift lever up sharply. Remove handle with upper boot and center piece attached.

NOTE — *DO NOT twist shift lever while removing to prevent damage to plastic retainer.*

2) Release parking brake adjustment and raise lever to highest position. Remove rubber handle from parking brake lever.

Remove center console and lower boot retaining ring. Pull back carpet and insulation material. Remove rear screws in plastic tunnel cover and lift to free and remove lower boot. Remove selector lever locking ring bolts and locking ring. Place gear shift in Neutral.

3) Raise and support vehicle on safety stands. Install compressor (A70025) on flexible coupling and disconnect propeller shaft. Remove protection shield and bracket and secure propeller shaft out of way. Disconnect electrical wires from rear of transmission. Place transmission jack under transmission and support engine. Remove starter bolts. Disconnect clutch linkage and speedometer cable.

4) Remove flywheel cover bolts, then remove exhaust pipe support and place out of way. Remove transmission support mount. Pull transmission rearward, tilting to slide input shaft out of clutch. Lower transmission to floor. Index mark clutch position on flywheel, then remove clutch.

Installation — To install clutch and transmission assembly, reverse removal procedure and note the following: Clutch disc must be installed with protrusion on hub facing transmission. Lubricate input shaft splines sparingly with oil and use centering tool to align clutch disc.

ADJUSTMENT

CLUTCH PEDAL HEIGHT

Clutch pedal height is adjusted by loosening lock nut (near firewall) and rotating adjustment nut until pedal height is adjusted.

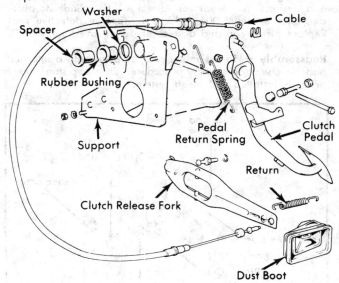

Fig. 2   Exploded View of Clutch Cable & Pedal Components

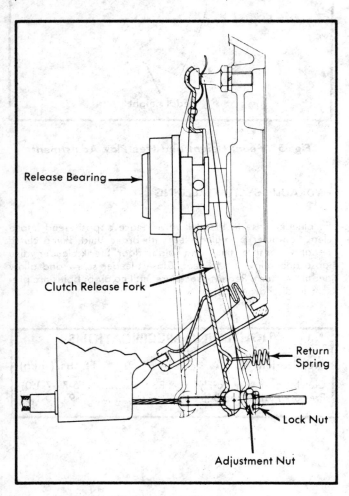

Fig. 1   Clutch Actuating Components

TIGHTENING SPECIFICATIONS

Application	Ft. Lbs. (mkg)
Clutch-to-Flywheel	22 (3.0)

Clutches

FIAT SPIDER 2000

DESCRIPTION

Clutch is a dry, single-disc, diaphragm spring type. Clutch is engaged or disengaged through a cable which is actuated by the clutch pedal. Mechanism is self-adjusting to compensate for wear and there is no pedal free play.

REMOVAL & INSTALLATION

CLUTCH ASSEMBLY

Removal — 1) Raise and support vehicle. From inside driver's compartment, press down on gearshift lever and pry out retaining ring with screwdriver. Remove transmission cover.

2) From under vehicle, disconnect propeller shaft from transmission and remove safety cross strap. Remove propeller shaft center pillow block. Disconnect speedometer drive from transmission. Disconnect all electrical leads from transmission case. Disconnect clutch fork return spring and remove adjusting rod.

3) Remove inspection cover from bottom of clutch housing. Disconnect exhaust pipe support bracket from rear of transmission and remove starter from clutch housing. Position a suitable transmission holding fixture (A. 70509) to a floor jack and position under transmission.

4) Remove bolts securing transmission to engine and remove rear crossmember. With transmission supported by jack, pull to rear until input shaft clears release bearing. Lower jack when transmission is clear and remove from under vehicle. Remove clutch assembly from flywheel after marking their relationship for reinstallation.

Installation — To install transmission and clutch assembly, reverse removal procedure and note the following: Use centering tool to align clutch and flywheel. Lubricate transmission input shaft splines sparingly.

ADJUSTMENT

CLUTCH PEDAL HEIGHT

Loosen lock nut and rotate adjustment nut until clutch pedal height reaches desired level.

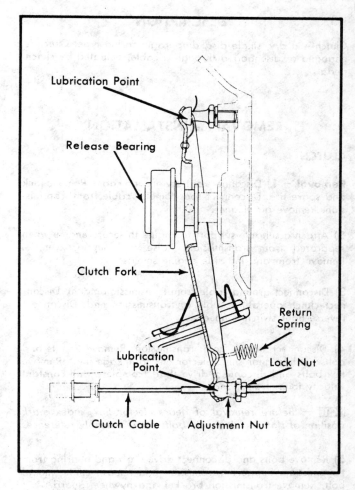

Fig. 1   Clutch Actuating Components Showing Cable Adjustment Point

TIGHTENING SPECIFICATIONS

Application	Ft. Lbs. (mkg)
Clutch-to-Flywheel	22 (3.0)
Transmission Case-to-Bell Housing Bolts	36 (5.0)
Transmission Case-to-Bell Housing Nut	18 (2.5)
Bell Housing-to-Engine Mounts	61 (8.4)

Clutches

FIAT STRADA

DESCRIPTION

Clutch is a dry, single disc, diaphragm spring type. Clutch is engaged or disengaged through a cable, actuated by clutch pedal.

REMOVAL & INSTALLATION

CLUTCH

Removal — **1)** Disconnect battery ground cable. Remove jack and spare tire. Disconnect speedometer cable from transmission. Remove air cleaner.

2) Attach a suitable support to engine to secure engine when separated from transmission. Raise and support vehicle. Remove front and left side engine shields.

3) Disconnect ground cable from transmission mount. Disconnect clutch operating cable at transmission end. Disconnect reverse light switch connector.

4) Disconnect starter from transmission. Remove 2 nuts and bolts holding gear shift selector link to linkage joint. Remove hex bolts and disconnect drive shaft (complete with constant velocity joint) from flange.

NOTE — *Before removal of gear selector link, index mark position of slots in relation to bolts for reassembly reference.*

5) Remove bolts and disconnect drive shaft and bearing from transmission. Support transmission and remove center mount bolt. Remove transmission bracket and flywheel guard.

6) Remove remaining nuts and bolts attaching transmission to engine. Disconnect left side rubber mount and bracket, and lower transmission out of vehicle. Index mark clutch cover and flywheel, and loosen attaching bolts alternately and evenly. Remove clutch assembly.

Installation — With protruding portion of clutch assembly facing away from flywheel, loosely assemble clutch assembly to flywheel. Use clutch aligning tool (70210) to center clutch disc. Tighten clutch cover bolts alternately and evenly. To complete installation, reverse removal procedure.

CLUTCH CABLE

Removal — Remove spring clip from pin on clutch pedal. Remove cable eyelet from pin. At transmission end of cable, remove lock nut, adjusting nut and block. Remove threaded cable end from lever and remove bushing. Remove bolts at cable housing flange and remove cable.

Installation — Grease inside diameter of cable eyelet. Install in reverse order of removal. Adjust pedal height if necessary.

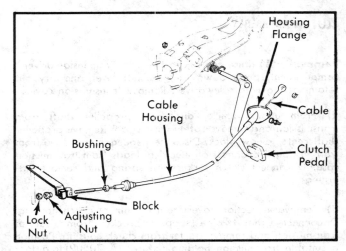

Fig. 1 Clutch Cable Components

ADJUSTMENT

CLUTCH PEDAL HEIGHT (STRADA)

Clutch pedal height should be 1.18" (30 mm) lower than brake pedal. If height is not to specification, loosen adjustment lock nut and rotate adjusting nut until pedal height is as specified.

TIGHTENING SPECIFICATIONS

Application	Ft. Lbs. (mkg)
Clutch Cover-to-Flywheel	28 (3.9)
Transmission-to-Clutch Housing	18 (2.5)
Clutch Housing-to-Engine	58 (8.0)
Axle Shaft-to-Hub	159 (22)
Starter-to-Clutch Housing	18 (2.5)

FIAT X1/9

DESCRIPTION

Clutch is a dry, single plate, diaphragm spring type. Clutch actuation is hydraulic, using a firewall mounted master cylinder and a clutch housing mounted slave cylinder. A prelubricated clutch release bearing is also used.

REMOVAL & INSTALLATION

CLUTCH ASSEMBLY

Removal — 1) Disconnect positive battery cable. Remove air cleaner and carburetor duct cooling. From inside engine compartment, separate slave cylinder from transmission case. Install engine support. Remove upper transmission-to-cranckcase mounting bolts.

2) Working from under the vehicle, disconnect and swing out-of-way shifting flexible link. Disconnect back-up lights and seat belt warning system wire. Remove starter. Disconnect and remove exhaust pipe.

3) Remove nuts from the hub end of half shaft. Remove attaching hardware mounting suspension control arm to supports. Free half shaft from hub end and fix other end to transmission to prevent premature disconnection.

4) Remove the following items: Flywheel cover, engine crossmember support, and lower engine-to-transmission bolts. Remove transmission/differential from below vehicle. Mark clutch position on flywheel and remove clutch.

Installation — To install, reverse removal procedure using suitable tool (A. 70210) to center clutch assembly.

CLUTCH MASTER CYLINDER

Removal — Steering column must be removed to gain access to clutch master cylinder. Disconnect and cap master cylinder hydraulic line. Remove two bolts attaching cylinder to support plate. Withdraw cylinder from actuating rod and remove from vehicle.

Installation — To install, reverse removal procedure and bleed hydraulic system.

CLUTCH SLAVE CYLINDER

Removal — Remove slave cylinder hydraulic hose and union. Disconnect cylinder push rod from clutch release bearing fork. Slightly compress return spring and remove two mounting bolts; slowly withdraw cylinder from support plate.

Installation — To install, reverse removal procedure ensuring slave cylinder snugly fits against support and that hydraulic system is bled.

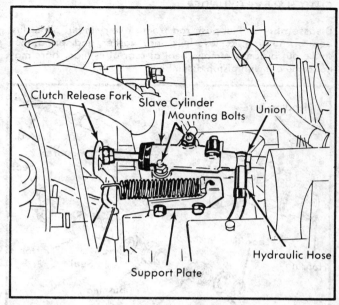

Fig. 1 Clutch Slave Cylinder Location

ADJUSTMENT

NOTE — Clutch mechanism automatically adjusts to compensate for wear and there is no pedal free play.

OVERHAUL

CLUTCH MASTER CYLINDER

Disassembly — Ease rubber dust boot back and remove snap ring, using long nosed pliers. Remove seal and complete plunger assembly. Pull out remaining gasket, seal and spring.

Reassembly — Lightly coat all components with brake fluid. Insert spring and seal into position. Fit piston assembly and seal, then install snap ring. Slip boot over cylinder housing.

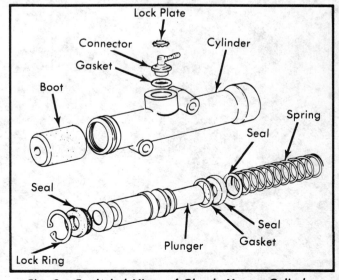

Fig. 2 Exploded View of Clutch Master Cylinder

FIAT X1/9 (Cont.)

CLUTCH SLAVE CYLINDER

Disassembly — Pull push rod from slave cylinder. Slide dust boot off housing. Remove lock ring, washer, and spring, then shake out piston assembly. Seal at rear of cylinder bore may not come out with piston assembly.

Reassembly — Lightly coat all components with brake fluid before reassembly. Insert rear seal, and piston assembly. Refit spring, washer, and lock ring. Install dust boot and push rod.

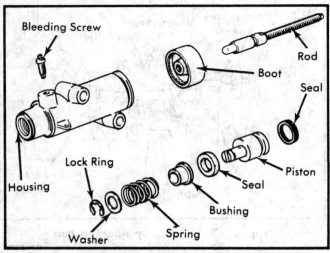

Fig. 3   Exploded View of Clutch Slave Cylinder

TIGHTENING SPECIFICATIONS

Application	Ft. Lbs. (mkg)
Clutch Flywheel Bolts	11 (1.5)
Clutch Release Fork Bolt	18 (2.5)
Slave Cylinder Piston Adjusting Nut	18 (2.5)
Slave Cylinder Support Plate-to-Transmission Case	18 (2.5)
Support Plate-to-Transmission Case Stud Nut	18 (2.5)

FIESTA

Hatchback

DESCRIPTION

The Fiesta clutch consists of a single dry plate clutch disc and a diaphragm spring pressure plate. The disc has 4 torsion springs. The clutch assembly is operated by an automatic self-adjusting device with a release shaft and thrust bearing inside the clutch housing. Fiesta uses two types of gearshift mechanisms, one with a boot on the selector rod, and one with a cranked shifter rod.

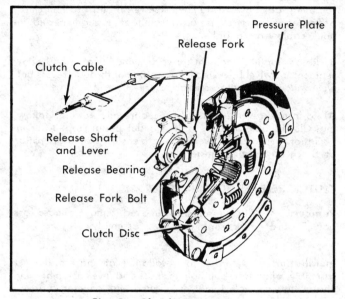

Fig. 1   Clutch Components

REMOVAL & INSTALLATION

CLUTCH ASSEMBLY

Removal — 1) Engage transmission in 4th gear position to ensure correct adjustment after installation. Disconnect battery ground cable. Install suitable engine support bar and clamp. Engine must be supported when transmission is removed.

2) Unscrew speedometer driven gear. Unhook clutch cable from release lever by pulling cable through between lever and support. Remove 4 upper transmission flange bolts. Raise vehicle and drain transmission fluid.

NOTE — *Remove plunger retainer and drain fluid out through plunger retainer hole.*

3) Remove selector rod spring from selector rod. Loosen selector rod locating bolt. Withdraw selector rod from shift shaft. Remove stabilizer shift assembly from transmission.

4) Unscrew and reposition 2 inner nuts on rubber coupling and engine support. Loosen lock nut on stud and remove stud from transmission housing with Allen wrench.

NOTE — *Allow stabilizer and screw to hang on engine support bar.*

5) Remove left drive shaft by removing 6 Allen bolts at coupling of inner constant velocity joint and stub shaft. Remove starter and transmission breather tube. Remove 2 lower flange bolts from transmission.

6) Remove 3 bolts from engine mounting. Withdraw transmission to free input shaft from clutch spline. Lower transmission on suitable jack and remove. Remove screws from pressure plate evenly (one turn at a time) and remove clutch assembly from flywheel.

Installation — 1) Apply light coating of grease to splines of drive shaft and differential gear, input shaft splines and thrust bearing carrier bore.

2) Ensure engine adapter plate is properly seated on engine guide bushings. Install transmission. Insert 2 flange bolts and snug. Align engine adapter plate and secure with 2 pins.

3) Mount transmission and clutch adapter plate to engine mounting using 3 new self-locking bolts. Lower engine and tighten bolts. Tighten 2 flange bolts at this time. Install control shaft plunger with spring and retainer.

NOTE — *Lightly coat retainer threads with "Omnifit" type lubricant.*

4) Install starter and connect cable. Install breather tube so it is suspended freely through hole in side member. Install stabilizer gear to transmission, gently turning Allen screw in as far as stop in transmission housing.

5) Lock screw with nut on rubber coupling of stabilizer. Bring inner nuts on engine mount into contact, and torque outer engine mount nuts.

6) On models with selector rod with boot, place shift shaft and lever in 4th gear position. Pull selector rod down onto shaft and align hole in selector housing with shift lever. Lock in place with a .16" (4 mm) pin.

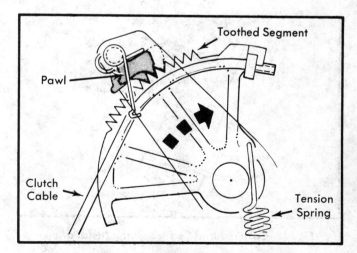

Fig. 2   Automatic Clutch Cable Adjuster

7) Insert suitable spacer between floor pan and selector rod. *See Fig. 4 for spacer dimensions.* Using a suitable arbor, turn shift shaft clockwise to stop. Tighten selector rod locating bolt.

8) Fit selector rod spring into position on selector rod and frame member. Check operation of shift lever.

FIESTA (Cont.)

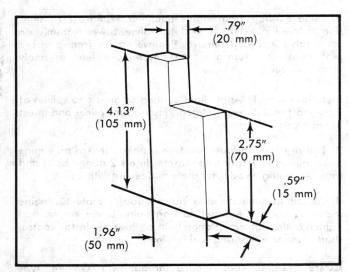

Fig. 3   Selector Rod Spacer Dimensions

9) On models with cranked rod gear shift mechanism place shift shaft and lever in 4th gear position. Loosen selector rod locating bolt and pull shift lever down. Align lever with hole in selector housing and lock with a .16" (4 mm) pin.

10) Using a suitable arbor, rotate shaft clockwise to stop. Tighten selector rod locating bolt. Remove arbor and check shift operation.

NOTE — *After installation of the new cranked rod gear shift mechanism, and before any adjustment is made, the retract spring must be installed.*

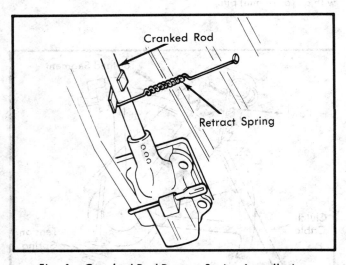

Fig. 4   Cranked Rod Retract Spring Installation

AUTOMATIC CLUTCH CABLE ADJUSTER

Fiesta is equipped with an automatic clutch cable adjuster, and no manual adjustment is required. Automatic adjuster is located at upper end of clutch pedal. Cable tension is set whenever clutch pedal is depressed as pawl engages with nearest adjusting segment.

CLUTCH CABLE

Removal & Installation — 1) Push cable between lever and support; release and unhook cable from release lever with suitable pliers.

2) Remove lower insulating panel on left side of dash. Bend retaining tabs upward; remove screws and lift off. Pull clutch pedal rearward to release pawl from toothed segment and unhook cable from pedal.

3) Rotate toothed segment forward, unhook cable and allow segment to swivel backward. Pull cable out through recess between pedal and automatic adjuster.

4) To install, reverse removal procedure and note the following: Clutch cable must be routed under pedal stop. After installation, press pedal several times to ensure proper operation of clutch automatic adjuster.

CLUTCH RELEASE FORK & LEVER

Removal — With transmission removed, remove release fork bolt. Separate fork, shaft and lever assembly.

Installation — 1) Prior to installation of shaft and lever assembly, align fork bolt hole in shaft and lever assembly and ensure that the hole is not misaligned with counterbore.

2) Thread fork bolt into position until bolt shank is fully seated in counterbore. If bolt fails to seat in counterbore by hand, replace shaft and lever assembly. Reverse removal procedure and tighten release fork bolt.

TIGHTENING SPECIFICATIONS	
Application	**Ft. Lbs. (mkg)**
Gearbox-to-Engine Flange Bolts	30 (4.1)
Gearbox-to-Engine Brace	
Self-Locking Bolts	65 (9.0)
Small Housing-to-Large Housing	18 (2.5)
Gearshift Lock Cap Nut-to-Housing	22 (3.0)
Gear/Differential Housing	
10.9 Grade Bolt	59 (8.1)
12.9 Grade Bolt	70 (9.6)
Shift Housing-to-Floor Pan	12 (1.7)
Cover-to-Housing	
Sheet Metal Bolt	7.5 (1.0)
Die Cast Bolt	9 (1.2)
Pressure Plate-to-Flywheel	13 (1.8)
Selector Rod Mechanism-to-	
Stabilizer Allen Screw	40 (5.5)

Clutches

HONDA ACCORD & PRELUDE

DESCRIPTION

Clutch is a single plate, dry disc type. Clutch assembly consists of clutch disc, clutch cover and pressure plate assembly, and clutch release mechanism. Clutch release mechanism is hydraulic, consisting of a firewall mounted master cylinder and a slave cylinder mounted to clutch housing. Clutch release fork free play is adjustable.

REMOVAL & INSTALLATION

CLUTCH

Removal — 1) Disconnect battery ground at transmission. Put gear shift in Neutral. Disconnect following electrical wiring.

- Positive battery cable at starter.
- Black/White wire from starter solenoid.
- Yellow/Green wire from water temperature sending unit.
- Black/Yellow and yellow wires from ignition timing thermosensor.
- Green/Black and yellow wires from back-up light switch.
- Red/Blue wires (Accord) or Pink/Blue wires (Prelude) from distributor.

2) On Prelude, remove speedometer cable clip and cable without disassembling gear holder. On all models, remove clutch slave cylinder with hydraulic line attached. Remove transmission side starter mount bolt and upper transmission mounting bolts.

3) Raise and suitably support vehicle; drain transmission fluid. Remove front wheels and engine shields. Support transmission with transmission jack. Remove stabilizer bar retaining nuts. On Prelude, remove both mounting brackets and then stabilizer bar.

4) On Accord, remove bolt securing speedometer drive holder and pull assembly out of transmission. Remove subframe center beam and transmission stopper bracket from front of clutch housing. Disconnect lower torque rod at transmission and remove shift rod yoke attaching bolt.

5) On all models, disconnect both lower arm ball joints and tie rod end ball joints with suitable remover. Turn right steering knuckle to outer most position with screwdriver against inboard constant velocity (CV) joint. Pry right axle out of transmission housing $\frac{1}{4}$" (forcing axle spring clip out of groove inside differential gear splines). Pull axle out of housing. Repeat operation on left axle.

6) On Prelude, disconnect shift lever torque rod from clutch housing; remove shift rod clevis bolt and engine torque rods and brackets. On Accord, remove clutch cover.

7) On all models, remove remaining starter mounting bolt and remove starter. Remove remaining transmission mounting bolts. On Accord, remove engine-to-transmission mounting bolts.

8) On Prelude, remove upper engine damper bracket bolt. On all models, pull transmission away from engine to clear dowel pins (remove both lower damper bracket bolts at same time on Prelude). Lower transmission and remove from vehicle.

9) Check diaphragm for wear at release bearing contact area by inserting alignment tool (07974-6890100). Measure clearance between tool and fingers of spring with feeler gauge. Maximum limit is .04" (1.0 mm). Install holding device on ring gear and loosen pressure plate bolts 2 turns at a time in a criss-cross pattern. Remove pressure plate and separate clutch disc.

Installation — To install, reverse removal procedure and note: Make sure flywheel dowels align with pressure plate dowel holes. Use suitable clutch disc alignment tool and torque pressure plate bolts in criss-cross pattern. Refill transmission with SAE 10W-40 oil.

CLUTCH MASTER CYLINDER

Removal — Separate clutch pedal operating rod from master cylinder push rod by removing through pin at clevis. Disconnect and plug hydraulic lines. Remove nuts mounting master cylinder to firewall. Make sure brake fluid does not spill on painted surfaces.

Installation — To install, reverse removal procedure and bleed hydraulic system.

CLUTCH SLAVE CYLINDER

Removal — Disconnect hydraulic line from slave cylinder. Unhook return spring. Separate threaded rod from end of slave cylinder. Remove slave cylinder mounting bolts and take cylinder off clutch housing.

Installation — To install, reverse removal procedure and bleed hydraulic system.

CLUTCH RELEASE FORK AND BEARING

Removal — With transmission removed, separate slave cylinder push rod from release fork. Remove boot and carefully remove fork retainer clip. Pull fork through clutch housing from inside. Remove bearing retainer clip and pull bearing assembly from sleeve. If worn, bearing may be driven from holder and a new bearing installed. Radius side of bearing must go on holder first.

Installation — Coat all contact areas lightly with grease. Attach bearing and holder to fork with retainer clips. Install fork and sliding bearing assembly onto sleeve. Ensure that fork snaps onto pivot bolt and install boot. Move release fork back and forth to check for freedom of movement.

OVERHAUL

MASTER CYLINDER

NOTE — *The master cylinders used on Accord and Prelude differ in external appearance. Overhaul procedures are similar.*

Disassembly & Reassembly — 1) Remove boot and take off snap ring. Cover open end of cylinder with a shop rag and force piston out with compressed air. Bend spring retainer tabs and separate piston, cups, retainer, return spring and valve assembly.

2) Clean all parts with brake fluid and check for wear or damage. If cylinder bore-to-piston clearance exceeds .006" (.15 mm), replace defective part. Replace all rubber parts during overhaul. Reassemble by reversing disassembly procedure: Rotate piston during installation.

HONDA ACCORD & PRELUDE (Cont.)

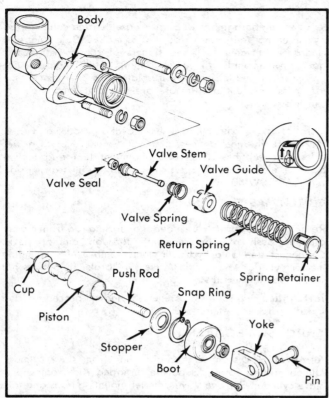

Fig. 1 Exploded View of Accord Master Cylinder. Prelude Cylinder is Similar Except Fluid Reservoir Is Separate From Cylinder Body

CLUTCH SLAVE CYLINDER

Disassembly & Reassembly — 1) Remove push rod and dust boot. Cover open end of cylinder with a shop rag and force piston out with compressed air. Remove piston cup and bleed screw.

2) Clean all parts in brake fluid and check for wear or damage. If cylinder bore-to-piston clearance exceeds .006" (.15 mm), replace defective part. Replace all rubber parts dur-

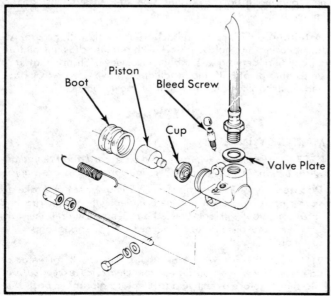

Fig. 2 Exploded View of Slave Cylinder

ing overhaul and coat all parts with brake fluid prior to reassembly. To reassemble, reverse disassembly procedure and insert piston with rotating motion.

ADJUSTMENT

CLUTCH PEDAL HEIGHT AND FREE PLAY

Adjust clutch pedal height to 7.24" (184 mm) by rotating pedal stop bolt in direction necessary to achieve specified height. Adjust pedal free play clearance (between clutch pedal push rod and master cylinder) to .05-.13" (1-3 mm) by loosening lock nut on push rod and rotating push rod.

CLUTCH RELEASE FORK FREE PLAY

Release fork free play should be .08-.10" (2.0-2.6 mm). To adjust, loosen lock nut and hold push rod end nut stationary while rotating push rod with screwdriver. Turn clockwise to decrease free play; counterclockwise to increase free play.

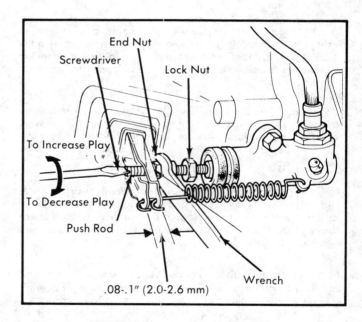

Fig. 3 Clutch Release Fork Adjustment Locations

TIGHTENING SPECIFICATIONS

Application	Ft. Lbs. (mkg)
Flywheel-to-Crankshaft Bolts	
Accord	49-53 (6.8-7.3)
Prelude	51 (7.1)
Pressure Plate-to-Flywheel	
Accord	7-10 (1.0-1.4)
Prelude	19 (2.6)
Front and Rear Torque Rod Bolts	54 (7.5)

Clutches

HONDA CIVIC

DESCRIPTION

Clutch is single plate dry disc type, using a diaphragm spring to engage pressure plate. Clutch has a mechanical release system consisting of clutch pedal, cable, clutch release lever, and release bearing.

REMOVAL & INSTALLATION

CLUTCH

Removal — 1) Disconnect battery ground at transmission. Release steering lock and put gear shift lever in neutral. Disconnect following engine compartment wiring:

- Positive battery cable at starter.
- Black/White wire from starter solenoid.
- Yellow/Green wire from water temperature sending unit.
- Black/Yellow and yellow wires from ignition timing thermosensor.
- Green/Black and yellow wires from back-up light switch.

2) Remove speedometer cable clip and cable but do not disassemble speedometer gear holder. Disconnect clutch cable at release arm and remove transmission side starter mounting bolt. Remove top transmission mounting bolt and forward bolt for rear torque arm bracket.

3) Raise and support vehicle and drain transmission oil. Remove front wheels and stabilizer bar mounting brackets. Disconnect lower support arms at ball joints OR at pivot bolts. Disconnect tie rod end ball joints.

4) Turn right side steering knuckle outward as far as it will go and pry inboard constant velocity (CV) joint out of transmission housing approximately ½" to force spring clip out of differential gear splines. Pull axle out the rest of the way and repeat for left side. Disconnect shift lever torque rod from clutch housing. Slide pin retainer back and drive spring pin out with punch, then disconnect shift rod.

5) Place a jack under engine with a wooden block between jack pad and engine, then raise engine enough to take weight off mounts. Remove both front and rear torque rods and rear torque rod brackets. Remove engine damper bracket from transmission and remove rear engine mount with its bracket.

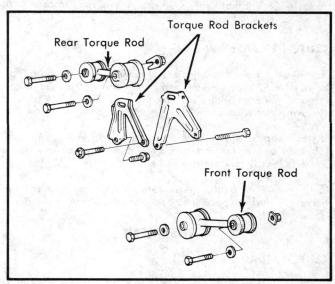

Fig. 2   Torque Rod and Bracket Components

6) Place a 1" x 2" x 4" block of wood between center beam and oil pan, then lower jack so that engine rests on center beam. Remove engine side starter mounting bolt, then remove starter and lower through chassis. Remove 2 remaining transmission mounting bolts. Raise transmission enough with transmission jack to take weight off engine and pull away from engine. Lower transmission clear of engine.

7) Install ring gear holder to keep flywheel from turning. Loosen pressure plate mounting bolts 2-turns at a time in a criss-cross pattern to prevent warping. Remove pressure plate and clutch disc.

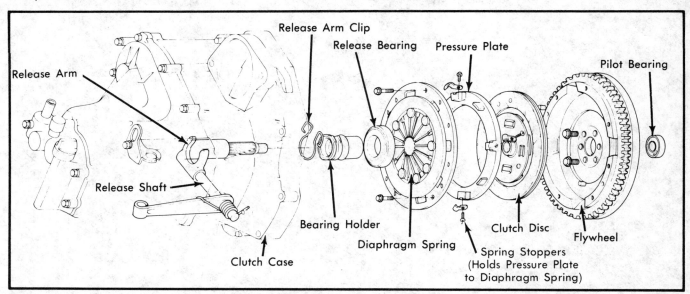

Fig. 1   Exploded View of Clutch Assembly with Bell Housing

Clutches

HONDA CIVIC (Cont.)

Installation — Use a suitable alignment tool and install disc and pressure plate. Tighten bolts 2-turns at a time in a criss-cross pattern. Ensure that the 2 dowel pins are installed in clutch housing and complete installation in reverse order of removal. Ensure that drain plug is tight and refill transmission with SAE 10W-40 oil.

CLUTCH RELEASE BEARING

Removal — Carefully pry ends of release bearing clip out of holes in fork. Slide bearing and holder off shaft sleeve. Bearing and holder may also be removed with release fork by first removing clutch fork shaft.

Installation — Lightly coat all contact surfaces with suitable lubricant and reverse removal procedure. Replace lock plate on shift fork if fork shaft was removed.

NOTE — *Do not bend release bearing clips any further than necessary during removal or installation of bearing holder.*

ADJUSTMENT

CLUTCH PEDAL

Ensure that pedal return spring holds clutch pedal against stop-pad. Turn adjusting nut in or out to give ⅛ - 5⁄32" (3-4 mm) free play at release arm. Free play at pedal should be ⅜ - 1³⁄16" (10-30 mm) and disengagement height should be at least 1³⁄16" (30 mm) from floor. If free play and/or pedal disengagement height exceed these specifications, clutch components may require replacement.

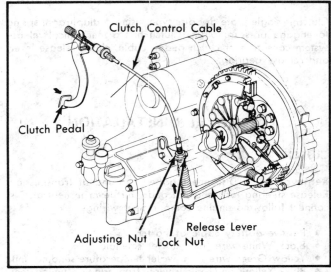

Fig. 3   Clutch Adjustment Point for Civic

TIGHTENING SPECIFICATIONS

Application	Ft. Lbs (mkg)
Clutch-to-Flywheel	9 (1.2)
Flywheel-to-Crankshaft	50 (7.0)
Front and Rear Torque Rod Bolts	54 (7.5)

LUV

Pickup

DESCRIPTION

Clutch assembly is a single dry disc type using a diaphragm spring pressure plate with a pre-lubricated release bearing. Clutch release lever is cable actuated. Cable is hooked to release lever and clutch pedal.

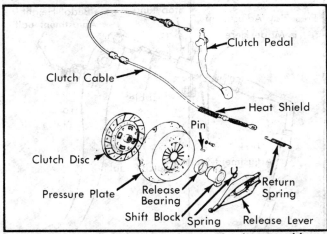

Fig. 1 Exploded View of LUV Clutch Assembly

REMOVAL & INSTALLATION

CLUTCH ASSEMBLY

NOTE — *Transfer case is removed with transmission on 4-WD models. Disconnect additional components as required during transmission removal.*

Removal — **1)** Disconnect negative battery cable. Slide gearshift lever boot upward on lever, remove gearshift lever attaching bolts and remove lever assembly. Remove starter attaching bolts and lay starter aside.

2) Raise vehicle on hoist and disconnect exhaust pipe hanger at transmission. Disconnect speedometer cable at transmission. Remove propeller shaft.

3) Remove clutch release lever return spring. Remove flywheel inspection cover. Remove 3 bolts mounting frame bracket to rear mount. Using a jack slightly raise transmission and remove 4 crossmember-to-frame bracket bolts. Remove 2 bolts mounting transmission extension housing. Lower engine/transmission assembly and support rear of engine.

4) Disconnect electrical leads at transmission. Remove transmission to engine attaching bolts and remove transmission.

5) Mark pressure plate and flywheel for reassembly reference. Loosen clutch to flywheel attaching bolts one turn at a time until spring pressure is released. Support clutch assembly with a suitable clutch aligning tool, remove bolts, and remove clutch.

Installation — Apply a thin coat of Lubriplate or equivalent to clutch disc splines. Install clutch assembly to flywheel, matching alignment marks made at disassembly. Use a suitable clutch alignment tool to center assembly on flywheel, then install and tighten attaching nuts. To complete installation, reverse removal procedures.

RELEASE BEARING, SHIFT BLOCK & RELEASE LEVER

Removal — Remove release lever from transmission case. Disengage release bearing to lever retaining springs. Slide out release bearing with shift block. Remove release lever from transmission ball stud.

Inspection — **1)** Check release bearing for noise or lubricant loss by spinning bearing. Replace bearing if either condition exists.

2) Inspect release lever ball socket and lever contact surface for signs of excessive wear. Also, check retaining spring for signs of weakening. Make sure spring will hold lever tightly to ball stud.

Installation — Install release lever ball stud in cover. Lube shift block inner groove, ball seat and release bearing contact surface. Install release lever and bearing assembly. Attach release bearing spring to lever and spring clip to ball stud.

PILOT BEARING

Check pilot bearing for seizing, sticking, abnormal noise or wear. If replacement is required, use a suitable tool (J-23907) to remove bearing.

CLUTCH CABLE

Removal — **1)** Loosen clutch cable lock nut and adjusting nut. Free cable from various routing clips in engine compartment. Working under vehicle, disengage return spring from release lever.

2) Disconnect cable from release lever and pull cable forward through bracket. Separate cable from clutch pedal and pull cable into engine compartment. Remove cable out of engine compartment. Make sure boots are not damaged.

Installation — To install, reverse removal procedure and note: Make sure cable is not kinked or bent sharply.

ADJUSTMENT

CLUTCH CABLE

Pull cable into engine compartment. Rotate adjuster nut until washer damper assembly is brought back into contact with firewall. Work clutch pedal several times. Pull cable out again and fully tighten nut. Back adjusting nut off until there is about .196" (5 mm) between adjusting nut and boot. See Fig. 2. Tighten lock nut.

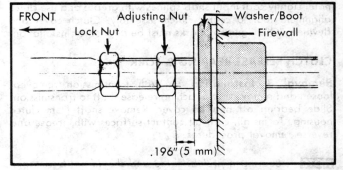

Fig. 2 Clutch Cable Adjustment Gap

MAZDA GLC

DESCRIPTION

Clutch is a dry, single disc, diaphragm type, and cable actuated. A prelubricated clutch release bearing is used and is located in the transmission housing.

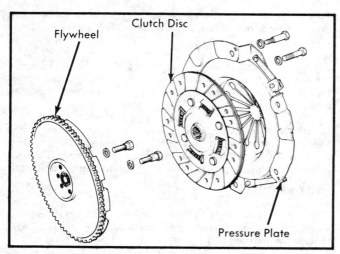

Fig. 1 Exploded View of Clutch Assembly

REMOVAL & INSTALLATION

CLUTCH ASSEMBLY

Removal — 1) Disconnect battery ground cable. Place gear shift lever in neutral; remove lever and hardware. Raise and support vehicle; drain transmission. Disconnect and remove propeller shaft. Disconnect speedometer cable, back-up light switch and exhaust pipe hanger on clutch housing.

2) Remove exhaust pipe support bracket from clutch housing and disconnect clutch cable from release lever. Remove clutch housing splash guard. Remove starter. Disconnect exhaust pipe hanger from extension housing. Place jack under rear of engine, protecting oil pan with a block of wood.

3) Disconnect transmission support member. Remove engine-to-transmission attaching bolts and carefully slide transmission back until it can be lowered from the vehicle. Install flywheel holding tool and loosen pressure plate mounting bolts evenly until assembly can be removed. Separate clutch disc and pressure plate.

Installation — To Install, reverse removal procedures and note: Lightly coat input shaft splines with grease and use clutch alignment tool to center clutch assembly. Clutch cover and flywheel "O" alignment marks must be aligned at installation.

CLUTCH RELEASE BEARING & FORK

Removal & Installation — With transmission removed, loosen and remove bolt attaching release shaft to transmission. Slide bearing off bearing cover. Remove shaft from clutch housing. To install, coat all contact surfaces with grease and reverse removal procedures.

NOTE — *Bearing is prelubricated and should not be washed in any solvent or cleaning solution.*

CLUTCH CABLE

Removal & Installation — Loosen cable lock nut and adjustment nut. Pull cable toward clutch pedal and disconnect from pedal. Push cable through stop ring into engine compartment and disconnect cable at clutch lever. Remove retainer ring at bracket, separate cable housing at bracket and remove cable. See Fig. 2. To install, reverse removal procedure.

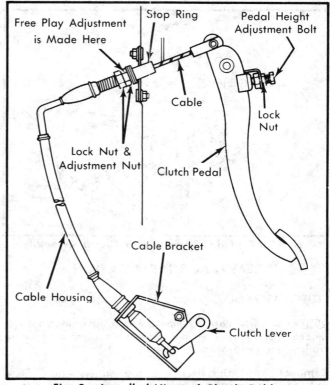

Fig. 2 Installed View of Clutch Cable with Detail of Items to Disconnect for Cable Removal. Illustration Also Shows Pedal Height Location.

PILOT BEARING

Removal & Installation — Pilot bearing is pressed into flywheel. Remove by using suitable puller. To install, lubricate bearing and install using suitable driver.

ADJUSTMENTS

CLUTCH PEDAL HEIGHT & FREE PLAY

Pedal Height — Adjust pedal height to 7.5-7.7" (190-195 mm) by loosening lock nut and rotating adjusting bolt until correct height is obtained. Tighten lock nut. See Fig. 2.

Free Play — Clutch pedal free play should be .39-.59" (10-15 mm) and is adjusted by setting release cable clearance at engine compartment side of firewall. Loosen lock nut, pull outer cable and turn adjusting nut until clearance is .06-.09" (1.5-2.3 mm). Tighten lock nut and check pedal free play. See Fig. 2.

TIGHTENING SPECIFICATIONS

Application	Ft. Lbs. (mkg)
Flywheel-to-Crankshaft	60-65 (8.3-8.9)
Pressure Plate Assembly-to-Flywheel	13-20 (1.8-2.7)

MAZDA 626, RX7 & B2000 PICKUP

DESCRIPTION

Clutch is a dry, single disc, diaphragm spring type. Clutch system is hydraulic using a firewall mounted master cylinder and a slave cylinder attached to clutch housing. Release bearing is pre-lubricated and sealed.

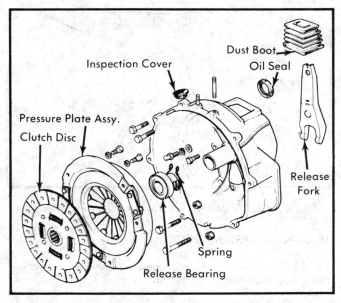

Fig. 1   Exploded View of Mazda Clutch Assembly

REMOVAL & INSTALLATION

CLUTCH ASSEMBLY

Removal — **1)** Disconnect negative battery cable. Place gearshift lever in neutral and remove gear shift knob. Remove console box or insert (if equipped). Remove gearshift lever dust boot, retainer (if equipped) and gearshift lever. B2000 gearshift lever components include wave washer, shim and bushing.

2) Raise and support vehicle; drain transmission. Disconnect and remove propeller shaft. Disconnect and/or remove exhaust and emission control components as required. Remove clutch release cylinder and place out of way without disconnecting fluid line. Disconnect and remove starter, speedometer cable, back-up lights and other electrical connections.

3) Place jack under rear end of engine, protecting oil pan with wooden block. Position transmission jack under transmission and remove transmission-to-engine mounting bolts. If equipped, remove transmission-to-crossmember bolts, crossmember-to-frame bolts and crossmember.

4) Slide transmission back until input shaft is cleared and remove from vehicle. Install flywheel holding tool and loosen pressure plate mounting bolts evenly until assembly can be removed. Separate clutch disc and pressure plate. Remove release bearing and fork.

Installation — To install, reverse removal procedure and note: Lightly coat input shaft splines with grease and use clutch alignment tool to center clutch assembly. Clutch cover and flywheel "O" alignment marks must be aligned at installation.

CLUTCH MASTER CYLINDER

Removal & Installation — Disconnect hydraulic line from master cylinder. Remove nuts mounting cylinder to firewall. Unhook clutch pedal from cylinder push rod. Remove cylinder. To install, reverse removal procedure and bleed hydraulic system.

CLUTCH SLAVE CYLINDER

Removal & Installation — Raise vehicle and support. Disconnect fluid hose. Remove nuts mounting slave cylinder to clutch housing and slide off cylinder. To install, reverse removal procedure and bleed clutch.

PILOT BEARING

Rotary Engine Models — Remove nut mounting flywheel to eccentric shaft. Free flywheel from shaft. It may be necessary to use puller to remove flywheel. Use a slide hammer (49 1285 071) to remove bearing and seals. Use installer tool 49 0823 72A (or equivalent) to seat new bearing into place. Install seal.

Piston Engine Models — Pilot bearing is pressed into flywheel. If replacement is required, remove using a suitable puller. To install lubricate bearing with grease and install into flywheel using a driver.

OVERHAUL

CLUTCH MASTER CYLINDER

NOTE — *Master cylinder used on B2000 has different external appearance. Disassembly procedure is identical.*

Disassembly — **1)** Clean outer portion of cylinder. Remove reservoir cap assembly and drain brake fluid. Remove reservoir connector link and reservoir. Remove piston stop ring, washer and piston assembly. Separate piston, cups and return spring.

2) Clean all parts in alcohol or brake fluid and blow dry with compressed air. Check all parts for wear, damage or deforma-

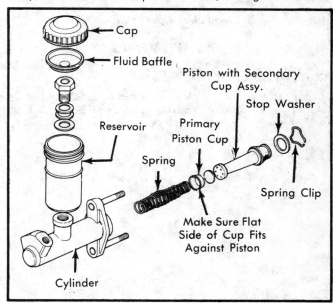

Fig. 2   Exploded View of Clutch Master Cylinder

MAZDA 626, RX7 & B2000 PICKUP (Cont.)

tion. If cylinder bore-to-piston clearance exceeds .006" (.15 mm), replace defective part. Replace parts as required and coat all components with brake fluid before assembly.

Reassembly — Reverse disassembly procedure and note: Install primary cup with flat side of cup against piston and ensure compensating port is open. After assembly, fill reservoir with clean brake fluid and operate piston with screwdriver until fluid is ejected at outlet port.

CLUTCH SLAVE CYLINDER

1) Clean outside of cylinder. Remove dust boot and release rod. Remove piston and cup assembly from cylinder, using compressed air if required. Remove spring, bleeder screw and valve. Clean all parts in brake fluid or alcohol and dry with compressed air.

2) Check all parts for wear or damage. If cylinder bore-to-piston clearance exceeds .006" (.15 mm), replace piston or cylinder. To reassemble, reverse disassembly procedure.

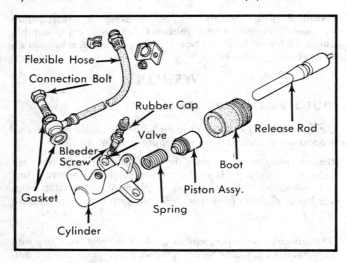

Fig. 3   Exploded View of Slave Cylinder

ADJUSTMENTS

CLUTCH PEDAL FREE PLAY

Adjust clutch pedal free play (measured at pedal pad) to .04-.12" (1-3 mm) on 626 and B2000 models, or .02-.12" (.5-3 mm) on RX7 models, by loosening lock nut and turning pedal stop-

per bolt to correct specifications. Tighten lock nut. When free play is correct, pedal height should be 7.5-7.7" (190-195 mm) on RX7; 7.6-7.8" (193-198 mm) on 626 and 8.5-8.7" (215-220 mm) on B2000 models.

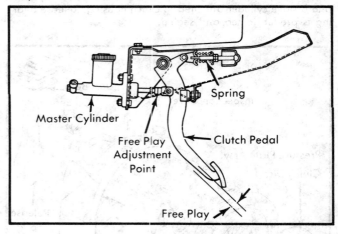

Fig. 4   Clutch Pedal Free Play Adjustment Location

HYDRAULIC SYSTEM BLEEDING

1) Clutch hydraulic system must be bled whenever a fluid line has been disconnected or air has entered system. To bleed system, remove bleed screw cap at slave cylinder and attach a hose. Place opposite end in a jar partially filled with brake fluid. Check master cylinder fluid reservoir often during bleeding process and maintain level at ¾ full.

2) Open bleed screw, depress clutch pedal and allow pedal to return slowly. Continue operation until no air bubbles are seen in discharged fluid. Close bleeder screw, remove hose and attach dust cap to bleed screw.

TIGHTENING SPECIFICATIONS

Application	Ft. Lbs. (mkg)
Flywheel-to-Crankshaft (Piston Engines)	112-118 (15.5-16.3)
Flywheel-to-Eccentric Shaft (Rotary Engines)	289-362 (40-50)
Clutch-to-Flywheel	13-20 (1.8-2.7)

MERCEDES-BENZ

240D

DESCRIPTION

Dry single disc type clutch uses a diaphragm spring type pressure plate. Clutch actuation is hydraulic, using a clutch pedal mounted master cylinder and a clutch housing mounted slave cylinder. A pedal mounted over-center spring assists in clutch pedal actuation. A sealed prelubricated clutch release bearing is also used.

REMOVAL & INSTALLATION

Removal — 1) Disconnect battery ground cable, support transmission with suitable jack, then remove rear crossmember, exhaust support bracket, exhaust pipe and clamp. Loosen, DO NOT remove, propeller shaft center bearing, remove propeller shaft-to-transmission bolts, and ensuring that companion plate remains attached to propeller shaft, push propeller shaft towards rear.

2) Remove tachometer drive from rear of transmission. Remove clutch slave cylinder and pull towards the rear with lines connected, until rod is released from clutch housing. Remove shift linkage from transmission shift levers. Remove starter.

3) Remove transmission-to-intermediate flange attaching bolts (removing two upper bolts last). Pull transmission out horizontally, until input shaft is clear of clutch. Then remove in a downward direction.

4) Loosen pressure plate attaching bolts 1 to 1½ turns at a time until tension is released, then remove all bolts, pressure plate and clutch disc.

Installation — 1) To install, place slave cylinder and line above transmission, then, using an aligning tool, center clutch disc on flywheel and install pressure plate. Tighten bolts 1 to 1½ turns at a time until tight.

NOTE — When installing propeller shaft to transmission, raise engine and transmission with suitable jack. Tighten propeller shaft center bearing clamp nut to 22-29 ft. lbs. (3-4 mkg).

CAUTION — During installation, make sure that clutch is fully pulled into recess in flywheel.

2) To complete installation, reverse removal procedure. Bleed slave cylinder and check hydraulic fluid level. Check clutch adjustment and shift linkage adjustment.

RELEASE BEARING & LEVER

Removal — Remove release bearing from bearing tube on front transmission cover. Move release lever down and to the left, then pull from ball pin on clutch housing.

Installation — To install, apply suitable lubricant to all bearing and lever contact surfaces, and reverse removal procedure.

CLUTCH MASTER CYLINDER

Removal — 1) Remove floor mats and lining from driver compartment, then remove cover under instrument panel. Siphon fluid from reservoir to below minimum mark and loosen input line by pulling elbow out of rubber clamping ring on master cylinder.

2) Disconnect pressure line from master cylinder and unscrew master cylinder from pedal assembly. Remove master cylinder and connecting hose, leaving push rod on clutch pedal.

Installation — To install, reverse removal procedure, adjust fluid level in reservoir, adjust master cylinder push rod length to a clearance of .008" (.2 mm) by loosening hex nut of eccentric adjusting screw and turning screw. Bleed hydraulic system.

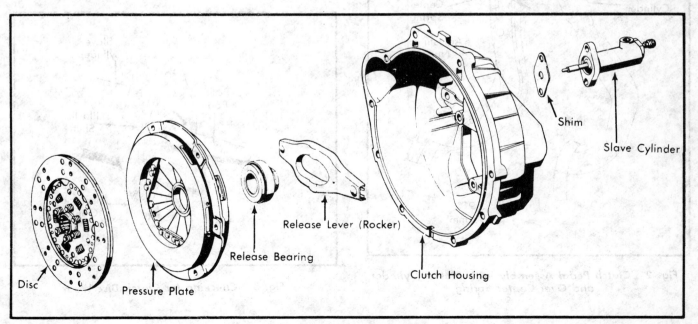

Disc   Pressure Plate   Release Bearing   Release Lever (Rocker)   Clutch Housing   Shim   Slave Cylinder

Fig. 1 Mercedes 240D Clutch Components

MERCEDES-BENZ (Cont.)

CLUTCH SLAVE CYLINDER

Removal — Disconnect hydraulic line from slave cylinder, then plug line with a rubber cap to prevent loss of fluid. Remove bolts attaching cylinder to clutch housing, then remove slave cylinder and push rod from housing as an assembly.

NOTE — *Take care not to lose plastic shim installed between cylinder and housing. Shim is recessed to accommodate inspection gauge.*

Installation — To install, place shim with grooved end against clutch housing and hold in position. Insert slave cylinder with push rod into clutch housing, and install and tighten mounting bolts. Connect hydraulic line to cylinder and bleed hydraulic system.

NOTE — *Wear on clutch disc may only be checked using special inspection gauge inserted in groove of plastic shim. Disc is serviceable if notches on gauge disappear in flange. If notches remain visible, wear limit is exceeded and disc must be replaced. See illustration.*

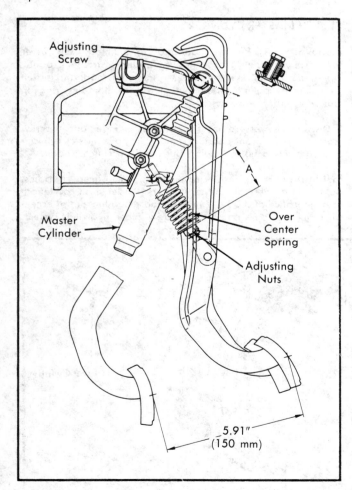

Fig. 2 Clutch Pedal Assembly with Master Cylinder and Over Center Spring

ADJUSTMENT

OVER CENTER SPRING

Adjust nuts at bottom of over center spring so that spring length measured across retainers is 2.05" (52.5 mm). Improper adjustment will result in failure of pedal to return when released or excessive pressure required to depress pedal.

HYDRAULIC SYSTEM BLEEDING

With Pressure Bleeder — 1) Connect pressure line of bleeder to opened bleeder screw of slave cylinder. Fluid reservoir of vehicle should be almost empty so brake fluid can flow from bottom upward through system, allowing air to escape in upward direction.

2) Make sure bleeder is set at lowest possible pressure, and watch reservoir to prevent overflow of fluid. When fluid approaches maximum level in reservoir, remove bleeder and close bleeder screw. Adjust fluid level in reservoir, if necessary, to maximum level in reservoir.

With Assistance of Brake System — 1) Check fluid level in reservoir and make sure it is at maximum level. Place a hose on bleeder screw of right front brake caliper and open screw. Press down on brake pedal until hose is filled with brake fluid and no more air bubbles are showing.

2) Place opposite end of hose on clutch slave cylinder bleeder screw, and open screw. Keep pressure on brake pedal. Close bleeder screw on caliper and release brake pedal. Repeat operation until no more air bubbles appear at fluid reservoir.

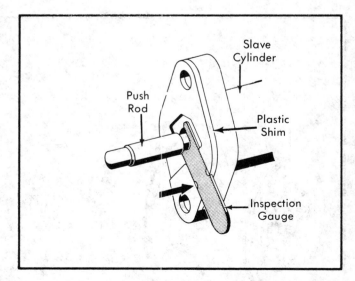

Fig. 3 Checking for Clutch Disc Wear

Clutches

MGB

DESCRIPTION

Clutch is single dry disc type, using a diaphragm spring type pressure plate. Clutch actuation is hydraulic, using a firewall mounted master cylinder and a bell housing mounted slave cylinder. Release bearing is graphite type, and is mounted in a cup which fits into fork of clutch release lever.

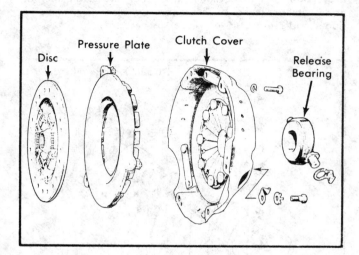

Fig. 1   Exploded View of Clutch Assembly

REMOVAL & INSTALLATION

CLUTCH ASSEMBLY

Removal — 1) Disconnect battery, remove hood, and drain oil and coolant. Disconnect oil cooler lines at filter and oil pressure line at block. Remove all coolant hoses and radiator.

2) Remove air cleaner, heater valve, and distributor cap. Disconnect all electrical wiring, vacuum hoses and throttle linkage. Remove shift lever. Disconnect wires from transmission and remove from retaining clips. Separate clutch slave cylinder from housing and wire out of way.

3) Disconnect speedometer cable, exhaust pipe at manifold, and drive shaft. Remove engine restraint rod. Remove 4 bolts holding rear mounting crossmember to chassis, and lower transmission to fixed crossmember.

4) Remove bolts holding bracket to crossmember, then remove nuts holding rear mounts to crossmember. Remove crossmember. Attach hoist and lift engine slightly, free front engine mounts, and lift out engine/transmission assembly.

5) Remove bolts securing transmission to engine. Separate engine from transmission, then loosen the clutch bolts evenly to remove plate from flywheel. Flywheel side of clutch disc is marked.

Installation — Use aligning tool to center clutch disc and install disc with "Flywheel Side" marking toward flywheel. Place pressure plate in position with marks on flywheel and pressure plate aligned. Tighten mounting bolts gradually to 25-30 ft. lbs. (3.5-4.1 mkg). To complete installation, reverse removal procedure.

CLUTCH MASTER CYLINDER

Removal — 1) Drain fluid from master cylinder through slave cylinder bleeder. Remove facia panel below left side of steering wheel, then remove rubber plug in bulkhead. See Fig. 2.

2) Remove 8 screws holding cover plate and seal to pedal box. Separate push rod from clutch pedal at clevis pin. Disconnect hydraulic outlet line and remove master cylinder.

NOTE — *Access to lower bolt is achieved inside car through hole in bulkhead.*

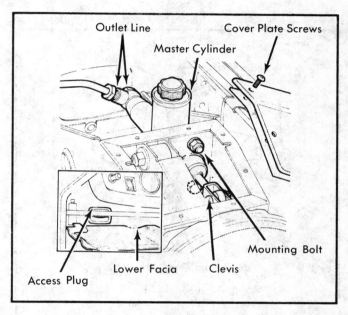

Fig. 2   Items to Take Off in Order to Free Master Cylinder for Removal

Installation — Reverse removal procedure and bleed hydraulic system.

CLUTCH SLAVE CYLINDER

Removal — Remove bolts and washers holding slave cylinder. Slide cylinder from push rod. Remove fluid hose from cylinder being careful not to lose copper sealing washer. Plug open end of hose.

Installation — Reverse removal procedure and bleed hydraulic system.

CLUTCH RELEASE BEARING

Removal & Installation — With transmission separated from engine, release clips holding release bearing to fork by rotating clips forward. Slide bearing from fork. To install, reverse removal procedure, ensuring that spring arms on clips are on transmission side of clutch fork.

MGB (Cont.)

OVERHAUL

CLUTCH MASTER CYLINDER

Disassembly — 1) Drain fluid and pull dust boot back. Remove circlip from push rod, then withdraw rod, washer, clip, and boot.

2) Remove piston with secondary cup seal. Remove piston washer, main cup, seal spring retainer, and spring. Remove secondary cup seal from piston by stretching over end of piston.

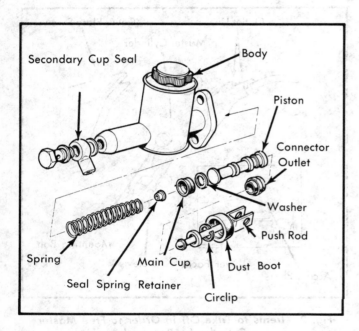

Fig. 3   Exploded View of MGB Clutch Master Cylinder

Inspection — Wash cylinder body in alcohol and clean internal parts with brake fluid. If bore is free of ridges, scores or grooves, new seals may be used. If not, replace master cylinder body.

Reassembly — Coat all components with brake fluid. reverse removal procedure and note the following: Be sure secondary cup seal lip faces toward rear of piston. Insert spring into cylinder bore, large end first. Install circlip, then dust boot.

CLUTCH SLAVE CYLINDER

Disassembly — Remove retaining ring, pull back dust cover and remove small internal retaining ring. Apply air pressure to fluid port and remove piston, cup, spring retainer, and spring. Remove bleeder screw.

Inspection — Wash cylinder in alcohol and clean internal parts with brake fluid. Check bore for scoring, grooves or ridges and replace slave cylinder as necessary.

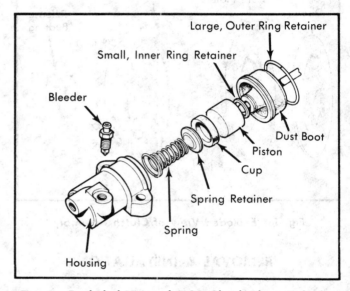

Fig. 4   Exploded View of MGB Clutch Slave Cylinder

Reassembly — Reverse removal procedure, noting the following: Install bleeder screw last, after checking that orifice is not blocked. Use a new cup seal.

ADJUSTMENT

HYDRAULIC BLEEDING

1) Fill master cylinder. Attach bleed tube to bleed valve on slave cylinder. Submerge free end of tube in container of brake fluid.

2) Slowly depress pedal to force air out. Close bleed valve and let pedal rise unassisted. Check that fluid level does not drop too low, and repeat until no more bubbles of air are visible.

PEUGEOT

504
505
604

DESCRIPTION

Clutch is a dry, single disc, diaphragm spring type. Clutch actuation is hydraulic, using a firewall mounted master cylinder and a bell housing mounted slave cylinder. A pre-lubricated clutch release bearing is also used. Due to hydraulic system design, no adjustments, with the exception of bleeding hydraulic system, is necessary.

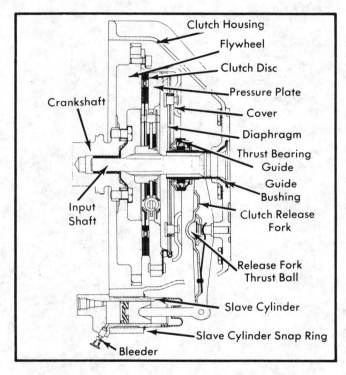

Fig. 1 Sectional View of Clutch Assembly

Clutch Housing
Flywheel
Clutch Disc
Pressure Plate
Cover
Diaphragm
Thrust Bearing Guide
Guide Bushing
Clutch Release Fork
Release Fork Thrust Ball
Slave Cylinder
Slave Cylinder Snap Ring
Crankshaft
Input Shaft
Bleeder

REMOVAL & INSTALLATION

CLUTCH ASSEMBLY

NOTE — *Engine and transmission must be removed as an assembly.*

Removal — 1) Remove hood, battery with tray, ignition coil, starter, radiator, expansion tank, and windshield washer bottle. Disconnect heater hoses, fuel lines, throttle controls, vacuum lines, and all chassis-to-engine electrical wires. Remove air cleaner and ducting to fuel injection or carburetion system.

2) On models equipped with air conditioning, it will be necessary to remove and set aside under hood components of the air conditioning system. DO NOT disconnect hoses or pressure connections. Disconnect electrical leads to compressor, pressure switch, thermostat, and electric cooling fan. Free receiver-drier, condenser and compressor from their mountings and move to right side of vehicle.

3) If equipped with power steering, remove power steering pump and set aside without disconnecting hoses. On all models, remove upper clutch housing-to-engine mounting bolts and inspection plates. Disconnect exhaust pipe from manifold and remove muffler and exhaust pipe supporting brackets with heat deflector.

4) Attach suitable hoisting sling and raise engine until transmission contacts tunnel. On 604 models, fit propeller shaft tube support between muffler and body and tighten to support tube slightly. Remove steering coupling clamp bolts and replace with slightly longer bolts. Lower front cross member about 1.2″ (30 mm) with steering rack attached.

5) On 504 and 505, attach transmission support tool (8.0125) and tighten to support transmission. On all models, remove lower clutch housing-to-engine bolts. Pull engine slightly forward and carefully lift from vehicle. Attach engine to suitable workstand and mark pressure plate and flywheel for reassembly reference. Remove pressure plate mounting bolts evenly and remove clutch assembly.

NOTE — *Clutch slave cylinder and release assembly remains with housing.*

Installation — Lubricate transmission input splines and clutch release bearing guide with Molykote (or equivalent). Use centering tool to align clutch assembly on flywheel and tighten pressure plate bolts evenly to 11 ft. lbs. (1.5 mkg). To complete installation, reverse removal procedure, ensuring that all reference marks are aligned.

NOTE — *Clutch disc must be installed with flexible hub toward transmission. Replace pressure plate mounting bolt washers during installation.*

CLUTCH RELEASE BEARING & FORK

Removal — Remove slave cylinder from clutch housing. Remove release bearing from fork by turning it counterclockwise. Remove clutch fork by pulling it outward until backing spring is disengaged from ball stud.

Installation — Pack rubber cup on ball stud with grease. To install clutch fork, slide fork from inside toward outside of clutch housing. Lift fork backing spring with a screwdriver and engage fork on ball stud with spring seated against rubber cup. Install release bearing by sliding onto shaft and engaging fork with clockwise rotation.

NOTE — *Bushing is self-lubricated. DO NOT wash in any cleaning solution. Lubricate with motor oil when installing.*

PILOT BUSHING

Bushing is press fit in rear of crankshaft. Bushing must be replaced if excessive clearance with transmission input shaft is evident. Remove and install bushing using suitable pullers and drivers.

CLUTCH MASTER CYLINDER

Removal & Installation — Disconnect and plug master cylinder hydraulic lines from fluid reservoir and to slave cylinder. Remove bolts securing master cylinder to pedal assembly and

Clutches

PEUGEOT (Cont.)

remove master cylinder. To install, reverse removal procedure and bleed hydraulic system.

CLUTCH SLAVE CYLINDER

Removal & Installation — Disconnect hydraulic line at slave cylinder. Remove snap ring securing cylinder in clutch housing, then slide slave cylinder from clutch housing mounting. To install, reverse removal procedure and bleed hydraulic system.

NOTE — *Overhaul procedures for clutch slave cylinder and master cylinder not provided by manufacturer.*

ADJUSTMENT

HYDRAULIC SYSTEM BLEEDING

Fabricate bleed tube using suitable rubber hose, clamps and adaptor from suitable bleeder kit (ARC 50). Attach hose to slave cylinder bleeder and pressure bleeder (ARC 50 or equivalent) to bleed tube. Adjust bleed pressure to 25.6 psi (1.8 kg/cm^2). Open bleed screw and observe fluid level in master cylinder. Close bleed screw when fluid reaches specified level.

PORSCHE

911SC
924
928

DESCRIPTION

The 928 model uses a dual disc dry clutch and a diaphragm spring type pressure plate. All other models use a single disc dry clutch with the diaphragm spring type pressure plate. The 924 Turbo and 928 clutches are hydraulically operated and self adjusting, while the 911SC and 924 models are mechanically operated through an adjustable cable.

REMOVAL & INSTALLATION

CLUTCH ASSEMBLY

Removal (911SC) — 1) Raise and support vehicle. Disconnect negative battery cable and remove air cleaner. Loosen engine block vent hose at engine and plug vent cover hole. If equipped with air conditioning, detach compressor and place out of way but DO NOT disconnect hoses.

2) Remove relay plate cover and disconnect the engine wires at relay plate, adapter plug, relay plate socket, and ignition control unit. Remove fuel hoses at filter and return line. Disconnect accelerator linkage.

3) Remove rear center tunnel cover in passenger compartment. Slide boot forward over shift selector rod and disconnect coupling from inner shift rod. Disconnect speedometer sensor wires in tunnel. Drain engine oil and plug hoses on engine and oil tank.

4) Remove heater hoses at exchangers. Remove rear stabilizer. Disconnect ground strap at body and battery wires at starter. Disconnect accelerator linkage from pedal and clutch cable at transmission. Remove axle shafts from flanges at transmission.

5) Place suitable jack under engine/transmission assembly and lift slightly, using caution to prevent damage to secondary air injection pipes. Loosen transmission and engine mounting bolts and carefully lower assembly from vehicle.

6) Remove circlip from clutch release lever shaft and pull off lever and rubber ring. Remove mounting bolts and pull transmission from engine. Mark pressure plate and flywheel for reassembly and insert alignment tool. Loosen bolts 1 or 2 turns at a time in a diagonal pattern and separate clutch assembly from engine.

Removal (924 and 924 Turbo) — 1) Support front of engine and disconnect battery ground cable. Loosen and remove clutch cable at holder, then remove holder nut. Remove bottom engine cover and clutch bell housing inspection cover. Disconnect oil temperature sensor wire at rear of oil pan.

2) Loosen clutch pressure plate mounting bolts evenly, about 2 turns at a time until all are removed. Turn engine with crankshaft pulley bolt. Place a block of wood between drive shaft tube and crossmember, then remove engine to bell housing bolts.

3) Remove exhaust system from primary muffler to rear of vehicle. Disconnect plug for backup light switch and remove

wires from clip on transmission. Remove back-up light switch. Working inside vehicle, pull up shift lever boot and remove circlip, selector rod and wave washer from shift lever pin.

4) Remove axle shafts from transmission. Suspend with wire in a horizontal position to prevent damage to axle shaft boots. Carefully lift transmission slightly, and remove mounts. Move transmission and central tube back about 3.35" (85 mm). Remove clutch disc, pressure plate and release bearing.

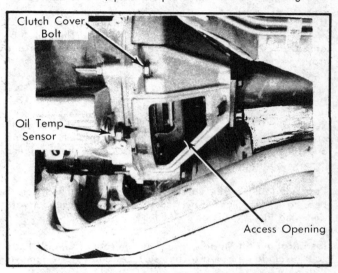

Fig. 1 924 Clutch Housing Access

Removal (928) — 1) Remove lower body brace. Remove slave cylinder, leaving line connected. Remove lower clutch housing with starter attached and suspend from stabilizer bar. Remove coupling screws and push coupling back onto drive shaft.

2) Remove release bearing sleeve mounting bolts and push sleeve toward flywheel. Mark pressure plate, intermediate ring and flywheel for reassembly alignment since they are a balanced unit. Loosen pressure plate mounting bolts evenly 1 or 2 turns at a time until free. Disconnect release lever at ball stud and remove pressure plate, intermediate plate, clutch discs, release bearing, release bearing sleeve, and short drive shaft as an assembly.

Inspection — 1) Check pressure plate and disc for wear, cracks, burning or loose rivets. Replace any part found defective. Check ends of diaphragm spring for wear marks from release bearing.

2) Lay a straightedge across pressure plate face and check for distortion; up to .011" (.3 mm) is permissible. Place clutch disc on input shaft and see that it moves freely on splines. Check disc for maximum allowable runout of .24" (.6 mm).

3) Check clutch release bearing for noise or rough operation. Do not wash bearing in any cleaning solution; clean with a lint free cloth only. Replace bearing if contaminated or loud. Check pilot bearing in crankshaft for rough operation, replace as necessary.

Installation (All Models) — 1) On 928, assemble and install clutch as a unit, noting that rigid disc is against flywheel and

PORSCHE (Cont.)

spring center disc is between pressure plate and intermediate plate. Use short drive shaft to ensure alignment. On 911SC and 924 models, use alignment tool and install clutch assembly.

2) On all models, ensure that marks on flywheel and clutch assembly are aligned and tighten pressure plate bolts one turn at a time in a diagonal pattern. If installing new clutch, balancing marks on clutch and flywheel should be offset 180°.

3) On 911SC models, pull release lever in opposite direction of engine when transmission is installed on engine. There must be at least .78" (20.0 mm) clearance between release lever and transmission housing. On all models, complete installation in reverse order of removal.

CLUTCH RELEASE BEARING

Removal (911SC & 928) — Bearing is removed with pressure plate. Remove by laying pressure plate on bearing and removing snap ring on flywheel side of clutch fingers. Remove bearing along with washers.

Removal (924 & 924 Turbo) — With clutch removed, detach bearing spring clips from release lever. Move lever forward and take bearing off of guide tube.

Installation (All Models) — Apply thin coat of suitable lubricant to guide tube and friction surfaces and reverse removal procedures.

ADJUSTMENT

CLUTCH ADJUSTMENT

911SC — Clutch free play must be checked at transmission adjusting lever due to auxiliary clutch spring. With cable snug, adjust play at lever to .040" (1.0 mm). Clutch pedal travel may be adjusted at stop on floor plate. Release travel should be .965-1.004" (24.5-25.5 mm) when measured at cable end.

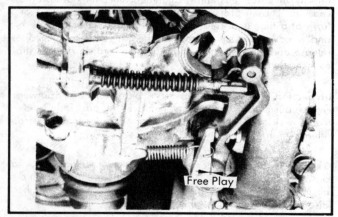

Fig. 2 View of 911SC Clutch Adjusting Mechanism

924 — With release bearing against diaphragm spring, lower end of cable should be 5.36-5.52" (136.0-140.0 mm) when measured from lower edge of cable holder to pin at release lever. To adjust, turn outboard release lever on shaft and tighten in position. Adjust cable with counternuts on holder to give .8-1.0" (20.0-25.0 mm) free play at clutch pedal.

924 Turbo & 928 — No adjustment is necessary due to automatic adjustment by slave cylinder. There must be .02" (.5 mm) play between end of push rod and master cylinder piston. This gives approximately .12" (3.0 mm) free play at pedal pad. If necessary, correct play by adjusting push rod.

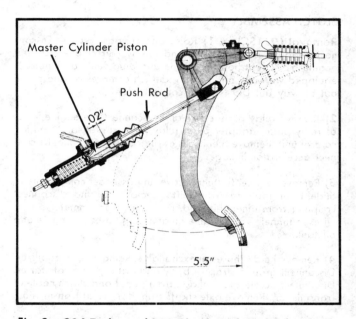

Fig. 3 924 Turbo and 928 Clutch Push Rod Adjustment

PEDAL ADJUSTMENT

911SC & 924 — **1)** With engine running and warm, reverse gear must be able to be engaged silently when clutch pedal is fully depressed. Release lever should move .6" (15.0 mm) to completely disengage clutch. If cable housing rests on bottom of guide clamp when clutch pedal is fully depressed, inner cable must be adjusted at yoke end.

2) Measure from threaded cable end of yoke to outer edge of lock nut. Adjust if not within .7-.9 (17.0-22.0 mm). If arc of cable is too large and allows cable to come out of guide clamp when pedal is released, inner cable must be shortened at yoke end.

Clutches

RENAULT

Le Car

DESCRIPTION

Clutch system is single disc dry plate type. Main components are: Disc, diaphragm spring operated pressure plate, ball bearing type clutch release bearing, release fork, and pilot bearing. Clutch operation is mechanical through cable actuation.

REMOVAL & INSTALLATION

CLUTCH ASSEMBLY

Removal — 1) Disconnnect battery. Separate speedometer. Remove water pump belt, camshaft belt, and air injection components. Remove both upper starter bolts (it may be necessary to use special wrench Ele. 565).

2) Remove clutch housing mounting bolts. Take off calipers and support out of way. Disconnect tie rods at steering rack end. Disconnect upper ball joints. Separate axle drive shafts by pulling stub axle out and down.

NOTE — *Be careful not to damage oil seal lips on differential adjusting ring nuts.*

3) Remove bolts from support tab on underside of transaxle. Disconnect and free clutch cable lever. Remove tubular crossmember bolts and slide crossmember out rearward. Use a jack and support front of transaxle. Remove front mount. Remove lower starter bolt. Remove clutch cover and any side reinforcement bolts. Remove transaxle from vehicle. Mark pressure plate assembly for installation reference and remove entire clutch assembly.

Installation — To install, reverse removal procedure and note following: Larger end of clutch disc hub should face engine. Use centering tool to align pressure plate and disc. Lightly grease input shaft and axle drive shaft splines. Make sure axle drive shafts fully seat into side gears.

CLUTCH CABLE

Removal — Disconnect cable from lever on transaxle. Free transaxle end of cable from sleeve stop. From inside vehicle, remove clutch pedal retaining clip and cable-to-pedal clevis pin. Slide pedal off of pivot rod, free cable from sleeve stop on pedal bracket, and remove cable.

Installation — To install, reverse removal procedure and note the following: Lubricate pedal bores and retaining pins with Molykote BR 2 lubricant. Adjust clutch free play.

CLUTCH RELEASE BEARING & FORK

Removal — With transaxle removed, disconnect the return spring from release bearing and fork, and slide bearing off transmission input shaft. Using a suitable tool (Emb. 384), extract fork retaining roll pins. Remove fork shaft, fork, and return spring.

Installation — 1) Lubricate fork shaft with Molykote BR 2 grease. Slide shaft into transaxle housing (fitted with rubber seal) and through release fork and return spring.

2) Align holes in shaft with those in fork and install roll pins, making sure that pins protrude $\frac{1}{32}$" on forward side of fork. Lubricate bearing sleeve and fork fingers with Molykote BR 2 grease, and slide bearing onto transmission input shaft.

3) Install return spring, placing ends in holes of release bearing support and in fork. Lubricate bearing face and portion of clutch diaphragm spring which bearing contacts with Molykote BR 2 grease. Install transmission and adjust clutch free play.

PILOT BEARING

Removal — Remove transaxle, clutch assembly and flywheel. Using a suitable tool (Mot. 11), extract bearing from crankshaft.

Installation — Using a suitable driver, install pilot bearing into crankshaft. Install flywheel, clutch assembly and transaxle. Adjust clutch free play.

OIL SEAL

Removal — Remove transaxle from vehicle. Remove the clutch housing attaching bolts and separate clutch housing from transmission. Using a suitable tool, remove oil seal from clutch housing.

Installation — Fit oil seal into place over special tool B. Vi. 526 or 488. Coat paper gasket with sealer. Place tool inside clutch release bearing guide to spread seal lip. Refit clutch housing on transaxle and slide tool along clutch shaft, then remove tool. Tighten clutch housing nuts.

ADJUSTMENT

CLUTCH FREE PLAY

Loosen lock nut. Turn adjusting nut to obtain free travel at end of release lever of $\frac{1}{8}$ -$\frac{5}{32}$" (3-4 mm).

TIGHTENING SPECIFICATIONS	
Application	**Ft. Lbs. (mkg)**
Flywheel-to-Crankshaft	35 (4.8)
Clutch Housing-to-Transmission	
8 mm Bolts	15 (2.0)
10 mm Bolts	30 (4.1)

SAAB

99
900

DESCRIPTION

Clutch is dry, single plate, diaphragm spring type. Primary components are: Disc, pressure plate assembly, and release bearing. Release bearing is a special design ball bearing with elongated outer ring which presses directly against diaphragm when clutch pedal is let out. Clutch operation is hydraulic. Clutch pedal operates on a master cylinder which is connected to slave cylinder. Slave cylinder is located inside clutch cover around input shaft. Slave cylinder acts directly on release bearing. Clutch adjustment is automatic.

REMOVAL & INSTALLATION

CLUTCH ASSEMBLY

Removal — 1) On 99 models, drain coolant, remove hood and disconnect negative battery cable. Disconnect wiring harness from fan housing and the following electrical leads: ignition coil, oil pressure switch, temperature switch, headlight wiper motor and thermal fan switch on radiator.

2) Disconnect radiator hoses. Remove grille and radiator. On all models, remove clutch housing cover, and install suitable spacer (8390023) between cover and diaphragm spring.

NOTE — Clutch pedal must be depressed to fit spacer.

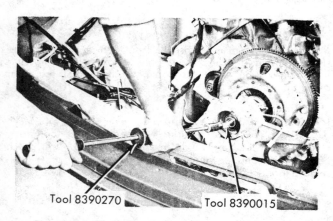

Tool 8390270   Tool 8390015

Fig. 1   Pulling Input Shaft Using Special Tools

3) Remove retaining ring and seal cap from input shaft. Remove plastic propeller from input shaft. On 99 models, pull out input shaft using slide hammer (8390270) and universal adapter (8390015). On 900 models, insert an M8 bolt into clutch shaft and install tool 8393175. Withdraw the shaft as far as possible.

4) Remove slave cylinder retaining bolts. Remove pressure plate mounting bolts and remove pressure plate, clutch disc, slave cylinder (hydraulic line attached) and release bearing as an assembly.

NOTE — Make sure diaphragm spring does not damage slave cylinder sleeve.

Fig. 2   Lifting Out Clutch Assembly — Illustration Shows Relationship of Clutch Assembly to Surrounding Engine Components

NOTE — Before beginning clutch installation make sure input shaft seal is in good condition. Seal is located inside slave cylinder in primary gear case. Seal forms a direct bond with sealing surface of input shaft.

CAUTION — Make sure diaphragm spring does not damage slave cylinder sleeve during installation.

Installation — 1) Reassemble clutch assembly and loosely install two pressure plate retaining bolts.

NOTE — Hardened side of release bearing faces diaphragm spring.

2) Bolt slave cylinder guide sleeve to primary gear casing. Install input shaft and make sure it engages clutch disc splines and bearing. Install plastic propeller, seal cap and retaining ring to input shaft.

3) Tighten clutch assembly (pressure plate) to flywheel. Depress clutch pedal and remove spacer. With pedal depressed, install sliding lock ring toward slave cylinder. Complete installation by reversing removal procedure.

NOTE — DO NOT depress clutch pedal farther than necessary. Seal lip may be pressed too far, causing a hydraulic leak and seal damage.

CLUTCH MASTER CYLINDER

Removal & Installation -- Remove hydraulic line at rear of cylinder. From under instrument panel in vehicle, remove access cover on left side. Remove push rod pin at clutch pedal. Remove master cylinder retaining nuts from firewall. From engine compartment, remove fluid supply line from top of cylinder and position so fluid does not leak. Remove master cylinder. To install, reverse removal procedure and bleed system.

CLUTCH SLAVE CYLINDER

NOTE — Slave cylinder removal is accomplished during clutch assembly removal. See Clutch Assembly Removal in this article.

SAAB (Cont.)

OVERHAUL

CLUTCH MASTER CYLINDER

Disassembly — Pull back sealing bellows and remove retaining ring. Remove push rod and washer. Remove piston, convex washer, piston seal, and spring. Inspect cylinder bore for wear or damage. Replace complete assembly if cylinder is worn or damaged. Replace seal if worn or swollen.

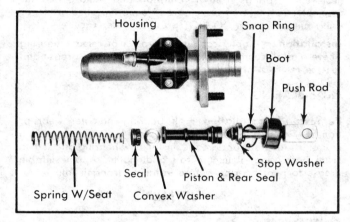

Fig. 3   Exploded View of Clutch Master Cylinder

Reassembly — Install return spring and spring retainer. Lubricate piston and seals with Girling Rubber Grease No. 3 . Install seals, convex washer and piston. Install push rod followed by washer and retaining ring. Install sealing bellows.

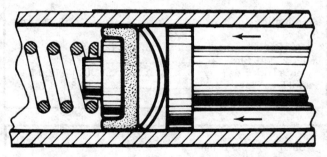

Fig. 4   Cut-Away View of Clutch Master Cylinder Bore Showing Convex Washer Correctly Installed. Convex Side MUST Face Master Cylinder Piston

CLUTCH SLAVE CYLINDER

Disassembly — 1) Remove clutch release bearing from slave cylinder.

2) Set slave cylinder with release bearing end facing up. Press cylinder sleeve out.

3) Remove "O" ring from sleeve.

4) Remove piston and lip seal.

NOTE — *Before beginning reassembly, lightly coat lip seal and piston (not "O" ring) with Caster Rubber Grease (or equivalent).*

Reassembly — 1) Fit "O" ring to sleeve flange.

2) Slide seal lip on sleeve.

3) Coat sleeve flange with brake fluid. Insert sleeve into cylinder. Push seal lip part way into cylinder.

4) Guide sleeve and cylinder together by pushing on piston until lock rings and "O" ring are fitted.

5) Place slave cylinder on support and seat sleeve into cylinder.

6) Fit release bearing to piston.

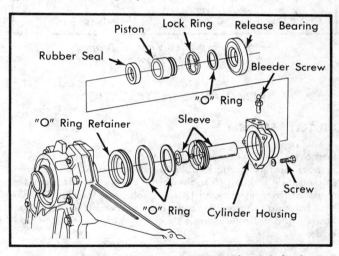

Fig. 5   Exploded View of Clutch Slave Cylinder

ADJUSTMENT

HYDRAULIC SYSTEM BLEEDING

1) Connect a ¼ " hose to slave cylinder bleeder screw, and place opposite end in a container partially filled with hydraulic fluid. Fill master cylinder reservoir with hydraulic fluid. Open bleeder screw on slave cylinder ½ turn.

2) Place a coolant system tester over filler opening of master cylinder. Pump tester until all air has been removed from system. Close slave cylinder bleeder screw and check to see that all air has been expelled by depressing clutch pedal.

SUBARU

1600

DESCRIPTION

Clutch is a single dry disc type with a diaphragm spring pressure plate. Actuation is mechanical through a cable. Sealed release bearing requires no lubrication.

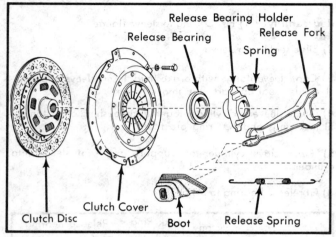

Fig. 1   Exploded View of Subaru Clutch Assembly

REMOVAL & INSTALLATION

CLUTCH ASSEMBLY

Removal — 1) Remove spare tire and support bracket. Remove battery ground cable. Disconnect clutch cable from release fork and detach rubber boot. Disconnect speedometer cable at transmission and loosen cable retainer clip. Disconnect back-up lamp switch connector, black and white starter harness (NOT battery cable), and ground cable on vehicle body.

2) Remove starter with battery cable attached. Remove upper engine-to-transmission bolts and loosen lower nuts. Loosen transmission side torque rod stopper nut by about .4" (10 mm) and tighten engine side nut by the same amount. On 4-WD models, separate both the gear selector and 4-WD selector system from the transmission.

3) On all models, raise and support front end of vehicle and remove front exhaust pipe assembly. On 4-WD models, remove transmission cover and rear drive shaft. Plug rear of transmission to prevent oil from running out. Remove exhaust cover and gearshift system from all except 4-WD models.

4) On all models, remove stabilizer, then lower both left and right transverse links. Drive spring pins from inner ends of axle shafts and push wheels out until axles separate from driving splines. Remove clamp on left side of hand brake cable. Remove nuts from transmission mounting pads.

5) Support transmission with a jack and remove crossmember. Remove nuts securing transmission to engine and move transmission away from engine. Ensure that mainshaft clears engine and lower transmission from vehicle. Remove pressure plate mounting bolts and take off clutch assembly.

Installation — Using alignment tool, place clutch disc and pressure plate in position on flywheel. Ensure that there is a gap of 120° between "O" marks on flywheel and pressure plate. Tighten bolts to 12 ft. lbs. (1.6 mkg) gradually in a criss-cross pattern. Reverse removal procedure to complete installation.

CLUTCH RELEASE BEARING

Removal — With transmission separated from engine, disconnect return springs from transmission and remove bearing assembly. Bearing may be removed from or installed on sleeve using suitable press. DO NOT press on outer race.

Installation — Lightly coat inner groove of release bearing sleeve and all contact surfaces with multi-purpose grease and reverse removal procedures.

PILOT BEARING

Removal & Installation — If bearing indicates wear or damage, extract bearing and oil seal. Inspect transmission mainshaft for wear or damage. Install new bearing and seal in crankshaft using aluminum rod and mallet. Apply suitable grease to pilot bearing before installing transmission.

ADJUSTMENT

CLUTCH FREE PLAY

Remove fork return and adjust spherical nut so that there is .08-.12" (2.0-3.0 mm) play at fork end. Use care not to twist cable during adjustment. Attach return spring and ensure that cable is routed without kinks or sharp bends.

Clutch Adjustment Specifications	
Application	**In. (mm)**
Clutch Pedal Stroke	5.1-5.4 (129-137)
Release Fork Stroke	.67-.71 (17-18)
Release Fork Free Play	.08-.12 (2.0-3.0)
Pedal Free Play	.50-.80 (1.3-2.0)

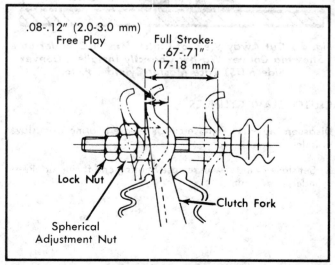

Fig. 2   Clutch Cable Adjustment Locations and Specifications

TOYOTA CELICA, COROLLA, CORONA, PICKUP & SUPRA

DESCRIPTION

Clutch is a dry, single plate, diaphragm spring type which is hydraulically operated by a firewall mounted master cylinder and clutch housing mounted slave cylinder. The slave cylinder used on 4-WD Pickup is adjustable; all others are non-adjustable and clearance is automatically compensated for by internal design of cylinder.

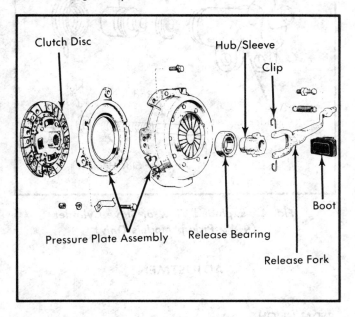

Fig. 1 Exploded View of Typical Clutch Arrangement. Pressure Plate Assembly and Hub/Sleeve Retainer Springs May Vary Between Models.

REMOVAL & INSTALLATION

CLUTCH ASSEMBLY

NOTE — *Clutch removal procedures are of a general nature written to cover all Toyota models.*

Removal — 1) Disconnect battery cable. Remove air cleaner and drain cooling system, then disconnect top radiator hose. Disconnect accelerator control rod linkage. Remove shift lever boot and shifter assembly. Remove starter.

2) Raise vehicle and support at front and rear with jack stands. If equipped, remove protective cover from under engine.

3) Remove clutch slave cylinder, but only disconnect hydraulic line if necessary. Disconnect exhaust pipe support bracket from mounting and separate exhaust pipe from manifold. Disconnect speedometer cable and electrical leads from transmission.

4) Scribe index marks on drive shaft and coupling for reinstallation reference, then remove drive shaft. Insert suitable plug into extension housing to prevent oil spillage.

5) Support engine with suitable jack, using a wooden block to protect oil pan. Support transmission with transmission jack and remove rear support crossmember. Lower transmission jack slightly and remove transmission-to-engine bolts. Pull transmission to rear; lower and remove from vehicle.

6) Index mark clutch assembly and flywheel for reassembly reference. Loosen bolts securing clutch assembly, alternately and evenly until pressure plate is released. Separate clutch disc and pressure plate.

Installation — To install, reverse removal procedure and note the following: Use a suitable aligning tool to center clutch disc on flywheel. Tighten clutch pressure plate attaching bolts alternately and evenly in a diagonal progression. With transmission installed, adjust clutch.

CLUTCH MASTER CYLINDER

Removal & Installation — Disconnect master cylinder push rod at clutch pedal by removing cotter pin and clevis. Disconnect hydraulic line at cylinder. Remove cylinder attaching nuts and remove cylinder from firewall. To install, reverse removal procedure and adjust pedal height, free play and bleed hydraulic system.

CLUTCH SLAVE CYLINDER

Removal & Installation — Raise and support vehicle on safety stands. Disconnect hydraulic line and clip. Remove slave cylinder attaching nuts and remove slave cylinder. To install, reverse removal procedure and bleed hydraulic system.

CLUTCH RELEASE BEARING

Removal — With transmission removed, check release bearing for freedom of rotation with bearing still installed on hub. To remove, disconnect spring clips from bearing collar and slide bearing off transmission input shaft. Use a press to remove and install bearing on sleeve.

Installation — Slide bearing and collar over transmission input shaft and secure to release lever with new retaining clips. Apply grease to diaphragm spring contact points before installing transmission.

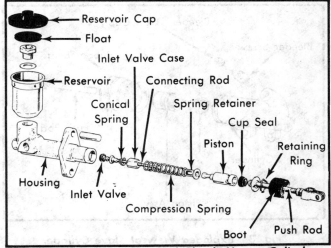

Fig. 2 Exploded View of Clutch Master Cylinder

TOYOTA CELICA, COROLLA, CORONA, PICKUP & SUPRA (Cont.)

OVERHAUL

CLUTCH MASTER CYLINDER

Disassembly — 1) With cylinder removed from vehicle, clamp it into a soft jawed vise. Remove reservoir, snap ring, and push rod. Pull out piston, cup, and remaining internal components. Further disassemble piston by prying up spring retainer and separating retainer from piston.

Cleaning & Inspection — Wash all parts in clean brake fluid and dry with compressed air. Master cylinder bore-to-piston clearance should not exceed .006" (.15 mm). Check compression spring for distortion or weakening and reservoir for damage. Ensure reservoir vent hole is open. Replace defective parts as required.

Reassembly — Dip cylinder cups into clean brake fluid or coat with rubber grease before assembly. Assemble piston components in reverse order of disassembly. Install piston assembly, push rod and reservoir into master cylinder.

CLUTCH SLAVE CYLINDER

Disassembly — Remove rubber boot and push rod. Remove piston assembly and spring from bore. If necessary, remove bleeder screw.

Cleaning & Inspection — Wash all parts in clean brake fluid and dry with compressed air. Slave cylinder bore-to-piston clearance should not exceed .006" (.15 mm). Replace defective parts. Replace piston cups during overhaul.

Reassembly — Install piston cups on piston and coat with brake grease. Install spring and piston assembly into cylinder bore and install rubber boot (protruded part down). Install push rod and bleeder screw.

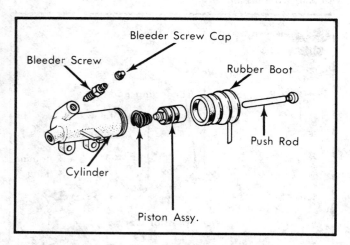

*Fig. 3 Exploded View of Slave Cylinder
(External Design Differs Among Models)*

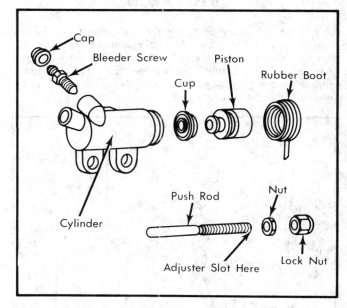

*Fig. 4 Exploded View of Slave Cylinder
(4-WD Pickup Models Only)*

ADJUSTMENT

PEDAL HEIGHT

Adjust pedal stop bolt at top of pedal assembly until specified pedal height is obtained. Height is measured from floor mat to top of pedal pad.

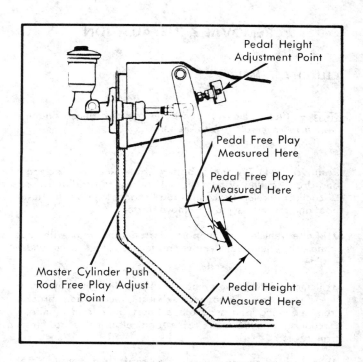

Fig. 5 Pedal Height and Free Play Measuring Points

TOYOTA CELICA, COROLLA, CORONA, PICKUP & SUPRA (Cont.)

Pedal Height Specifications

Application	Height In. (mm)
Celica & Supra	6.3-6.7 (159.5-169.5)
Corolla	6.9-7.3 (175-185)
Corona	6.5-6.9 (166-176)
Pickup	6.0-6.4 (152-162)

Pedal Free Play

Application	In. (mm)
Celica, Corolla & Corona	.5-.9 (13-23)
2-WD Pickup & Supra	.2-.6 (5-15)
4-WD Pickup	1.0-1.8 (25-45)

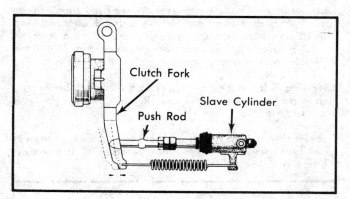

**Fig. 6 Clutch Fork Free Play Adjustment
(4-WD Pickup Models Only)**

PEDAL FREE PLAY

Except 4-WD Pickup — To adjust free play (measured at pedal pad), loosen lock nut on master cylinder push rod and turn push rod in or out until free play is within specifications. Tighten lock nut.

4-WD Pickup — Prior to adjusting pedal free play as described for other models, adjust clutch fork free play. To adjust fork free play, loosen lock nut on slave cylinder push rod and screw push rod in or out to obtain .08-.12" (2-3 mm) free play at clutch fork. Tighten lock nut and adjust pedal free play to 1.0-1.8" (25-45 mm).

HYDRAULIC SYSTEM BLEEDING

1) Raise and support vehicle on safety stands. Check master cylinder reservoir often during bleeding operation; add fluid as required. Remove slave cylinder bleeder screw cap and connect flexible hose to bleeder and immerse opposite end of tube in jar partially filled with brake fluid.

2) Pump clutch pedal several times. With pedal depressed, loosen screw ½ turn, exhaust air and close before pressure is depleted. Repeat operation until no air bubbles are seen in discharged fluid. Close bleeder screw on down stroke of pedal. Check system for leaks and fill master cylinder reservoir.

TIGHTENING SPECIFICATIONS

Application	Ft. Lbs. (mkg)
Pressure Plate-to-Flywheel	11-15 (1.5-2.0)
Clutch Housing-to-Engine	
Supra	22-23 (3.0-4.5)
All Others	36-58 (5.0-8.0)

Clutches

TOYOTA LAND CRUISER

DESCRIPTION

Clutch is a dry single disc type using a diaphragm type pressure plate. Clutch is hydraulically operated by a firewall mounted master cylinder and a clutch housing mounted slave cylinder. A prelubricated sealed release bearing is used.

REMOVAL & INSTALLATION

CLUTCH ASSEMBLY

Removal — 1) Drain transmission oil, transfer case oil, and fuel tank. Remove transmission undercover and disconnect front and rear driveshafts, power take-off shaft, speedometer cable and parking brake cable. Remove front seat with frames and console box. Remove rear heater tube clamp and shift lever knobs.

2) Remove fuel tank cover and fuel tank. Remove shift lever dust boots and transmission cover. Disconnect front drive indicator wire harness, transfer switch wire harness, and vacuum hoses (if equipped). Disconnect back-up light switch harness.

3) Using suitable tool (09305-60010), remove shift lever hold down nut and lift out shift lever. Support transmission assembly with rope and floor jack. Remove bolts attaching transmission to engine and lower assembly from vehicle.

4) Disconnect clutch fork return spring and remove slave cylinder, but do not disconnect hydraulic line unless necessary. Remove release bearing retaining clips, and release bearing with collar. Remove clutch lever assembly.

5) Mark pressure plate and flywheel for reassembly reference. Loosen clutch attaching bolts one turn at a time until spring pressure is released, then remove bolts and clutch assembly

Installation — To install, reverse removal procedure and note the following: Use suitable aligning tool to center disc on flywheel. Tighten clutch attaching bolts alternately and evenly. After reinstallation, adjust clutch fork free play and bleed hydraulic system if necessary.

CLUTCH MASTER CYLINDER

Removal — Remove clevis pin connecting master cylinder push rod to clutch pedal. Disconnect hydraulic line from cylinder body and plug opening. Remove cylinder attaching bolts at firewall and remove master cylinder. **CAUTION** — *Do not allow fluid to spill on painted surfaces.*

Installation — To install, reverse removal procedure, adjust pedal height and clutch pedal free play, and bleed hydraulic system. Check hydraulic system for leaks.

CLUTCH SLAVE CYLINDER

Removal — Plug master cylinder reservoir cap. Disconnect clutch return spring from hanger. Disconnect flexible hose from metal line and remove clip. Remove slave cylinder retaining bolts and remove slave cylinder.

Installation — To install, reverse removal procedure, adjust clutch fork free play and bleed hydraulic system.

CLUTCH RELEASE BEARING

Removal & Installation -- With clutch assembly removed, remove release bearing from hub with suitable bearing remover/installer (0931500021). To install bearing, lubricate with multi-purpose grease and seat bearing with the remover/installer.

PILOT BEARING

Removal & Installation — With clutch assembly removed, check pilot bearing in end of crankshaft for roughness or noise during rotation. If defective, remove using a suitable puller (09303-55010). To install, lubricate bearing with multi-purpose grease and insert into crankshaft using driver (09304-47010).

OVERHAUL

CLUTCH MASTER CYLINDER

Disassembly — With master cylinder removed from vehicle, drain fluid from reservoir and remove push rod, boot and snap ring as an assembly. Using a deep socket, remove reservoir retaining nut and lift reservoir from master cylinder. Pull piston assembly from master cylinder.

Cleaning & Inspection — Wash all parts in clean brake fluid and inspect for wear or damage. Replace master cylinder if scored or worn excessively.

Reassembly — Use cylinder overhaul kit and soak all parts in clean brake fluid. Assemble in reverse order of disassembly. Fill reservoir with fluid and bleed cylinder.

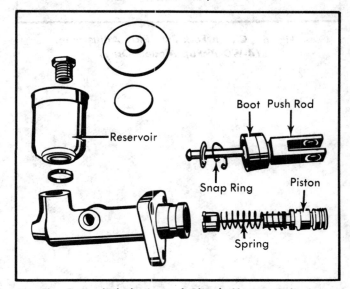

Fig. 1 Exploded View of Clutch Master Cylinder

CLUTCH SLAVE CYLINDER

Disassembly — Remove push rod assembly and rubber boot from cylinder body. Withdraw cylinder piston and cup seal. Loosen and remove bleeder screw.

TOYOTA LAND CRUISER (Cont.)

Cleaning & Inspection — Wash all parts in clean brake fluid and inspect for wear or damage. If slave cylinder bore-to-piston clearance exceeds .006" (.15 mm), replace defective part. Replace piston cups during overhaul.

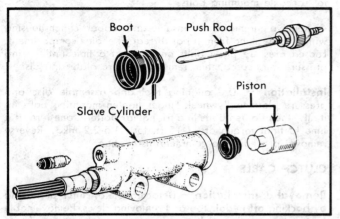

Fig. 2 Exploded View of Clutch Slave Cylinder

Reassembly — Soak all parts in clean brake fluid before reassembly. Reverse disassembly procedure and install boot with protruded part down.

ADJUSTMENTS

PEDAL HEIGHT

Pedal height is measured from floor to top of pedal pad. To adjust, loosen lock nut and turn stop bolt to give pedal height of 8.5" (215 mm) on vehicles equipped with power brake unit, or 7.8" (198 mm) on vehicles without power brakes.

PEDAL FREE PLAY

Clutch pedal free play is that distance of free movement before master cylinder push rod contacts piston. To adjust, loosen lock nut and turn push rod to obtain .02-.12" (.5-3.0 mm) free play. Tighten lock nut.

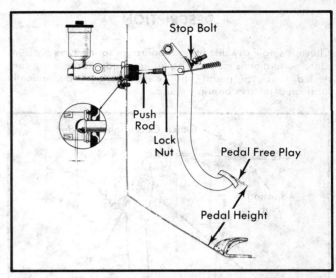

Fig. 3 Pedal Height Measuring and Adjustment Points

CLUTCH FORK FREE PLAY

To adjust clutch fork free play, loosen lock nut at slave cylinder and turn push rod tip while holding push rod nut with suitable wrench. Free play should be .12-.16" (3-4 mm). Tighten lock nut and check clutch pedal free play.

HYDRAULIC SYSTEM BLEEDING

1) Connect a flexible tube to slave cylinder bleeder screw, and place opposite end in a container partially filled with brake fluid.

2) Pump clutch pedal several times. With pedal depressed, loosen bleeder screw one-third to one-half turn and allow air to bleed out. Tighten bleeder screw.

3) Continue operation until air bubbles are no longer seen in fluid being discharged into container. Tighten bleeder screw securely and install cap. Check fluid level in master cylinder reservoir, and check system for leaks.

TOYOTA TERCEL

DESCRIPTION

Clutch is single dry disc using diaphragm spring type pressure plate. Actuation is mechanical, using an adjustable cable connected to clutch pedal and release fork. A permanently lubricated release bearing is used.

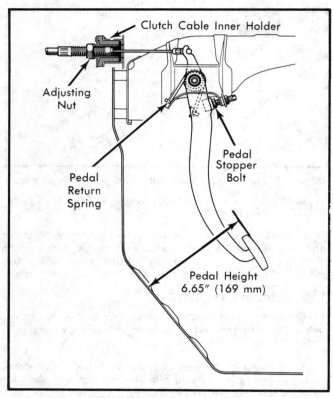

Fig. 1 Pedal Height and Free Play Adjustment

REMOVAL & INSTALLATION

CLUTCH ASSEMBLY

NOTE — *Engine must be removed to replace clutch assembly.*

Removal — 1) Remove engine hood, air cleaner case and battery negative terminal. Drain cooling system and wrap drive shaft boots with shop towels. Disconnect solenoid valve, water temperature switch and electric cooling fan connectors. Remove differential side plate stiffener bolts and exhaust pipe.

2) Remove radiator and windshield washer tank. Disconnect heater, fuel and brake booster hoses. Disconnect accelerator, choke and clutch release cables. Disconnect high tension wire from coil, alternator "B" terminal and connector from alternator and starter cable at starter.

3) Ensure that no bonding wires are connected from engine to chassis and disconnect engine mounts and engine shock absorber at lower right front of engine. Attach engine hoisting sling to engine and support differential with a jack. Remove engine to transaxle mounting bolts.

4) Remove engine from transaxle and support clutch housing with a cable slung from a bar at rear of engine compartment. Loosen pressure plate bolts one turn at a time until spring pressure is released, then remove pressure plate and disc.

Installation — Use aligning tool and assemble disc and pressure plate to flywheel. Finger tighten mounting bolts initially, then tighten bolts in a triangular pattern, one turn at a time to final torque of 11-15 ft. lbs. (1.5-2.2 mkg). Reverse removal procedure to complete installation.

CLUTCH CABLE

Removal & Installation -- Detach cable at clutch pedal end by backing off pedal stop and removing clevis. Remove cable from release fork and free from engine compartment. To install, lubricate clevis attachment points with multipurpose grease and reverse removal procedure. Adjust pedal stop.

CLUTCH RELEASE BEARING

Removal & Installation — With engine removed from vehicle, remove retaining clips from bearing collar and clutch fork. Slide assembly from transmission. If bearing does not rotate smoothly, press off collar with driver (09315-00010). Use press and driver (09315-00021) to install new bearing on sleeve. Lightly grease inner groove of bearing collar and all contact surfaces and reverse removal procedures.

PILOT BEARING

Removal & Installation — If pilot bearing is worn or damaged, pull from crankshaft with puller (09303-35010). Coat new bearing with multipurpose grease and drive into crankshaft with installer (090304-12012).

ADJUSTMENTS

PEDAL HEIGHT

Measure distance from floor panel to upper surface of clutch pedal. Adjust pedal stopper bolt to give 6.65" (169 mm) pedal height.

CLUTCH PEDAL FREE PLAY

With release bearing contacting pressure plate, pedal play should be .8-1.4" (20-35 mm). To adjust, pull slightly on release cable and turn adjusting nut. Ensure that adjusting nut protrusion and cable holder inner notch are aligned, then depress pedal several times and recheck pedal play.

Clutches

TRIUMPH

Spitfire
TR7
TR8

DESCRIPTION

Clutch is dry, single plate, diaphragm spring type. Clutch actuation is hydraulic, using a firewall mounted master cylinder and a clutch housing-mounted slave cylinder. Due to self-adjusting feature of clutch assembly, no adjustment, with the exception of bleeding hydraulic system, is necessary.

REMOVAL & INSTALLATION

CLUTCH ASSEMBLY

Removal (Spitfire) — 1) Disconnect battery. Remove gear shift lever. On models equipped with overdrive, pry off knob cap and disconnect wires. Remove knob.

2) Remove transmission tunnel cover and propeller shaft cover. Disconnect propeller shaft and speedometer cable. Remove clutch slave cylinder, raise vehicle, and drain transmission.

3) Support engine. Disconnect exhaust pipe bracket and remove rear mounting nuts from transmission. Remove cable from clutch housing, remove lower housing bolts, and lower vehicle.

4) Remove starter bolts. Disconnect wires from transmission. Remove upper clutch housing bolts and remove transmission. Separate transmission and clutch housing.

Removal (TR7) — 1) Raise and support vehicle. Disconnect battery ground cable. Remove gear shift lever assembly. Index mark and separate propeller shaft from transmission. Disconnect exhaust pipe at intake manifold (pipe may have to be completely removed).

2) Disconnect speedometer cable and all electrical wires attached to transmission. Remove starter heat shroud. Place a jack (with wood block) under oil pan. Remove slave cylinder without disconnecting fluid line. Hang cylinder out of way.

3) Remove 2 bolts holding oil pan plate to clutch housing. Remove 4 nuts keeping transmission rear crossmember to body. Slightly lower engine. Remove starter.

4) Remove nuts and bolts mounting clutch housing to engine. Support transmission with appropriate jack. Slide back transmission/clutch housing assembly and remove from vehicle.

5) Index mark pressure plate with flywheel. Loosen 6 pressure plate mounting bolts evenly (a few turns at a time). Slide out pressure plate with clutch disc.

Removal (TR8) — 1) Disconnect battery. Remove gear shift lever assembly. Raise and support vehicle. Remove exhaust system, leaving tail pipes loosely in place. Disconnect oxygen sensors (if so equipped). Index mark and separate propeller shaft from transmission. Place a jack (with wood block) under oil pan. Raise engine.

2) Remove 2 bolts holding oil pan plate to clutch housing and bolt holding clutch pipe to rear engine plate. Remove heat shield and slave cylinder without disconnecting fluid line. Sup-

port cylinder out of way. Remove nuts attaching transmission rear crossmember to body. Lower engine.

3) Disconnect and remove speedometer cable. Disconnect wiring harness plug. Remove all but 3 clutch housing bolts. Remove 4 bolts holding flywheel cover to clutch housing. Support transmission with appropriate jack and remove 3 remaining clutch housing bolts. Slide back transmission/clutch housing assembly and remove from vehicle.

4) Index mark pressure plate with flywheel. Loosen 6 pressure plate mounting bolts evenly (a few turns at a time). Slide out pressure plate with clutch disc.

Installation (All Models) — Reverse removal procedure and note the following: Ensure index marks on pressure plate align with those on flywheel. Use clutch aligning tool to center clutch disc. Tighten clutch bolts evenly and gradually.

CLUTCH MASTER CYLINDER

Removal — 1) Disconnect hydraulic line and drain fluid. Plug open port and line.

2) Disconnect clevis mounting push rod to clutch pedal.

3) Remove 2 bolts (Spitfire) or 2 nuts (TR7 and TR8) mounting master cylinder to bracket (Spitfire) or bulkhead (TR7 and TR8).

Installation — Reverse removal procedure and bleed hydraulic system.

CLUTCH SLAVE CYLINDER

Removal — Raise and support vehicle. Disconnect and plug hydraulic line and remove slave cylinder.

NOTE — *On TR7 and TR8 models, do not move operating rod in a forward direction. Forward movement may cause release lever to dislodge. Transmission removal would then become necessary for installation of release lever.*

Installation — Reverse removal procedure and note:
- On Spitfire models, centralize push rod in housing before sliding slave cylinder in position.
- On TR7 and TR8 models, slave cylinder must be mounted with bleed screw ABOVE fluid pipe.
- Bleed hydraulic line.

CLUTCH RELEASE BEARING

Removal (Spitfire) — With transmission assembly removed, remove clutch fork pivot pin and remove fork and bearing assembly. Drive pins from fork and remove bearing and sleeve. Using a suitable press, remove bearing from sleeve.

Installation — Reverse removal procedure. Lubricate all bearing contact points with multi-purpose grease.

Removal (TR7 and TR8) — With transmission assembly removed, use crow's foot wrench (ST 1136) and unscrew clutch release lever pivot bolt from clutch housing. Remove release lever, complete with pivot bolt and release bearing.

Clutches

TRIUMPH (Cont.)

Installation — Reverse removal procedure, making sure fork and collar engage evenly.

OVERHAUL

CLUTCH MASTER CYLINDER

Disassembly (Spitfire) — 1) Drain fluid and remove master cylinder. Pull back rubber boot and release circlip, then pull out push rod and washer.

2) Apply compressed air to fluid inlet to remove piston and spring assembly. Remove thimble and spring from piston assembly, then disengage valve stem from slot in thimble. Remove seal spacer from valve stem and seals from valve and piston.

Reassembly — Reverse removal procedure, using new rubber seals and lubricating parts with brake fluid.

Disassembly (TR7 & TR8) — 1) Remove master cylinder. Pull up rubber boot and remove snap ring. Slide out push rod and washer.

2) Pull out piston, spring, and seal as an assembly. It may be necessary to use air pressure to force out assembly.

3) Straighten spring thimble prong, then remove thimble and spring from piston. Disengage valve stem from slot in thimble. Slip spacer off valve stem. Remove valve seal.

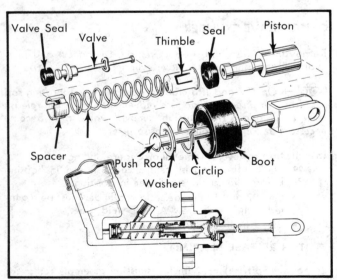

Fig. 1   Exploded View of Master Cylinder (TR7 and TR8 Shown; Spitfire Similar)

Reassembly — 1) Fit spacer, spring and thimble to valve stem. Fit new seal to piston with lip facing spring. Put spring thimble on piston and depress thimble prong.

2) Lubricate master cylinder bore with brake fluid and slide seal assembly, spring and piston into place. Reverse disassembly procedure to assemble remaining components.

CLUTCH SLAVE CYLINDER

Disassembly — Remove slave cylinder and pull off dust cover. Remove circlip, then take out piston, seal and spring.

Inspection — Look at cylinder bore and piston for signs of damage. Replace either or both parts if wear is excessive.

Reassembly — Reverse removal procedure, lubricating parts with brake fluid and fitting small end of spring to piston.

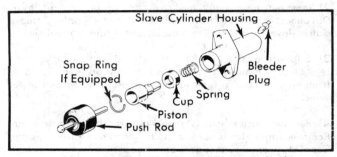

Fig. 2   Exploded View of Slave Cylinder (TR7 and TR8 Shown; Spitfire Similar)

ADJUSTMENT

HYDRAULIC SYSTEM BLEEDING

1) Fill master cylinder. Attach bleed tube to bleed valve on slave cylinder. Submerge free end of tube in container of brake fluid.

2) Slowly depress pedal to force air out. Close bleed valve and let pedal rise unassisted. Check that fluid level does not drop too low, and repeat until no more air bubbles are visible.

TIGHTENING SPECIFICATIONS

Application	Ft. Lbs. (mkg)
Clutch Assembly-to-Flywheel	22 (3.0)
Clutch Housing-to-Transmission	32 (4.4)
Slave Cylinder-to-Clutch Housing	21 (2.9)

Clutches

VOLKSWAGEN DASHER

DESCRIPTION

Clutch is single plate dry disc type, using a diaphragm type pressure plate and a pre-lubricated clutch release bearing. Clutch is cable actuated.

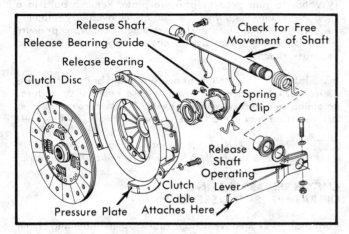

Fig. 1 Exploded View of Clutch Assembly

REMOVAL & INSTALLATION

TRANSAXLE & CLUTCH ASSEMBLIES

Removal — 1) Disconnect battery ground cable from battery. Disconnect exhaust pipe at manifold. Disconnect exhaust pipe bracket from rear of transaxle.

2) Disconnect gear shift lever and shift linkage. Disconnect back-up light wires. On some models there is a bolt mounting gear shift linkage to transaxle that must be removed.

3) Loosen clutch cable adjustment nut and disengage clutch housing from left side engine mount. Separate clutch cable from operating lever. Disconnect speedometer cable.

4) Disconnect front wheel axle drive shafts at transaxle. Suspend drive shafts with wire out of way. Remove starter.

5) Remove clutch housing front cover plate. Remove bolts mounting transaxle-to-engine. Place a jack under transaxle for support. Unbolt transaxle carrier from body. Slide transaxle to rear until input shaft is clear of clutch assembly. Lower out transaxle.

6) Lock flywheel to prevent rotation and index mark pressure plate and flywheel. Loosen pressure plate bolts 1/4 turn at a time, working in a diagonal pattern. Slide pressure plate off dowels on flywheel.

Installation — 1) Using a clutch alignment tool, fit pressure plate with clutch. Make sure alignment marks are observed. Loosely attach assembly with 6 bolts.

NOTE — If replacement pressure plate has white paint spot, it is a balance mark and should be 180° from countersunk hole or 180° from white paint mark on flywheel.

2) Tighten pressure plate bolts in criss-cross pattern about 2 turns at a time.

3) Position transaxle to engine. Loosely fit bolts holding transaxle carrier to body. Reverse removal procedure to install remaining components.

Fig. 2 View Showing Clutch Assembly Alignment on Flywheel

CLUTCH RELEASE BEARING

Removal & Installation — With transaxle removed, remove spring clips without removing bearing from release shaft. Slide bearing off bearing guide. To install, roughen plastic guide sleeve with emery cloth, but do not lubricate. Lubricate metal guide sleeve with molybdenum disulphide paste. Coat pivoting points between bearing and operating shaft with multi-purpose grease. Position bearing to shaft and install spring clips.

NOTE — Bearing is pre-lubricated, DO NOT wash in solvent.

CLUTCH CABLE

Removal & Installation — Loosen cable adjusting nuts and free clutch cable housing from support bracket. Separate cable from clutch operating lever (mounted on side of clutch housing). Disconnect cable at pedal and force cable and housing into passenger compartment and remove. To install new cable, reverse removal procedure and adjust pedal free play.

NOTE — If new clutch cable has been installed, make sure to recheck clutch pedal free play after 300 miles.

PILOT BEARING

Removal & Installation — Lock flywheel to prevent rotation. Install suitable remover (10-202) and remove pilot bearing. Install bearing with suitable installer (VW207C) and seat bearing until distance from flywheel recess to bushing edge is 1/16" (1.5 mm). Lubricate bearing.

ADJUSTMENT

CLUTCH PEDAL FREE PLAY

Clutch pedal free play (measured at pedal pad) should be 5/8" (16 mm). To increase measurement, loosen top adjusting nut until specification is obtained. Tighten bottom nut until locked against bracket. To decrease measurement, loosen bottom adjusting nut until specification is obtained. Tighten top nut until locked against bracket.

TIGHTENING SPECIFICATIONS

Application	Ft. Lbs. (mkg)
Clutch Assembly-to-Flywheel	18 (2.5)
Transmission-to-Engine	40 (5.5)
Clutch Lever-to-Transmission	18 (2.5)
Drive Shaft-to-Transmission	33 (4.5)

VOLKSWAGEN JETTA, RABBIT, RABBIT PICKUP & SCIROCCO

DESCRIPTION

Clutch is a single plate dry disc type, using a diaphragm type pressure plate and a transmission mounted clutch release bearing. Clutch is cable operated.

REMOVAL & INSTALLATION

TRANSAXLE & CLUTCH ASSEMBLY

Removal — 1) Disconnect battery ground strap and attach an engine support assembly. Remove left transaxle mount bolts and mount. Disconnect back-up light wires, speedometer drive cable (plug hole) and clutch cable.

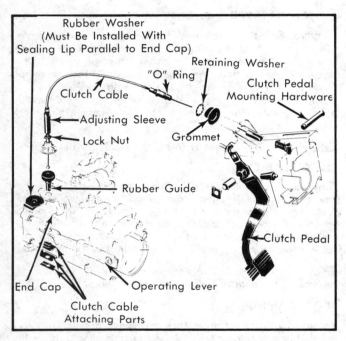

Fig. 1 *Clutch Cable Routing & Adjusting Location*

2) Remove upper clutch housing-to-transaxle bolts. Remove starter. Align flywheel lug with boss on bell housing (models equipped with flywheel which has cutouts). Disconnect shift linkage at rod lever and relay lever and remove front selector rod.

NOTE — *Vehicles with cutouts in flywheel can be identified by a stud/nut at right engine-to-transaxle mounting position. Flywheel on this type vehicle MUST be aligned before separating engine/transaxle.*

3) Remove exhaust pipe bracket. Remove transaxle rear mount and support transaxle on suitable jack. Disconnect left and right drive shafts at transaxle and wire up out of way. Remove large plate cover bolts (plate remains on engine). Remove small cover bolts and cover.

4) Remove right engine-to-transaxle bolt (stud/nut). Vehicles with cutouts in flywheel, pull transaxle away from engine to clear dowels and lower and remove transaxle. On all other vehicles, pull transaxle away from engine; cocking engine so right side drive flange clears flywheel. Lower and remove transaxle.

5) With transaxle removed from engine, install holding tool (VW558) to ring gear or pressure plate. Remove bolts in a diagonal manner until flywheel can be removed. Pry retaining ring from release plate and lift release plate from pressure plate. Remove pressure plate bolts in diagonal manner and separate clutch disc.

Installation — To install, coat pressure plate bolts with Loctite 270 or 271 (or equivalent) and reverse removal procedure. Retaining ring ends must be between 2 slots in release plate. Use centering tool (VW547) to center clutch disc on flywheel.

NOTE — *If new flywheel is to be installed, a new timing mark must be cut into flywheel ¼" (6 mm) to right of TDC mark.*

CLUTCH RELEASE BEARING & OPERATING LEVER ASSEMBLY

Removal — 1) Remove 4 bolts and washers mounting clutch release cover to the far left end of transaxle case. Cover is waffle patterned. Remove 2 circlips located at each side of clutch lever.

2) Pull operating lever and release shaft assembly out of case. Lift return spring along with clutch lever out of transaxle case. Take out release bearing, guide sleeve and push rod. Check all seals and bearing; replace defective parts.

Installation — 1) Coat ends of push rod with multi-purpose grease and insert back into position. Grease sliding surface of bearing and guide sleeve.

2) Position return spring and clutch lever inside transaxle case. Return spring center hook should fit on top of clutch lever lug. Spring end hooks must point down to hold clutch lever away from release bearing.

3) Lightly coat release shaft with multipurpose grease. Fit shaft. Work operating lever until splines on release shaft mesh with those in clutch lever.

4) Install circlips. Make sure when operating lever is in normal position that return spring has tension. Fit gasket and cover.

ADJUSTMENT

CLUTCH PEDAL FREE PLAY

Clutch pedal free play should be ⁹⁄₁₆-1" (15-25 mm) at clutch pedal and ¼" (6 mm) at operating lever. To adjust, loosen clutch cable lock nut in engine compartment. Turn adjusting sleeve until correct measurement is obtained and tighten lock nut. Operate clutch pedal several times and check free play.

TIGHTENING SPECIFICATIONS	
Application	**Ft. Lbs. (mkg)**
Transmission-to-Engine	47 (5.5)
Drive Shaft-to-Transmission	32 (4.5)
Pressure Plate Bolts	54 (7.5)
Flywheel Bolts	14 (2.0)
Cover Plate	11 (1.5)

Clutches

VOLKSWAGEN VANAGON

DESCRIPTION

Clutch is dry, single disc, diaphragm spring type which is hydraulically operated by a firewall mounted master cylinder and a clutch housing mounted slave cylinder. Slave cylinder is non-adjustable and clearance is automatically compensated for by internal design of cylinder.

REMOVAL & INSTALLATION

CLUTCH ASSEMBLY

Removal — 1) Disconnect battery ground strap. Remove right upper engine/transmission bolt.

2) Remove hydraulic clutch line bracket from transmission but do not disconnect line. Remove slave cylinder from mounting bracket and suspend with wire.

3) Remove left upper engine/transmission bolt. Remove left lower engine/transmission nut. Remove left drive shaft hex bolts and remove drive shaft from transmission and suspend with wire.

4) Disconnect starter cables, remove right drive shaft hex bolts and suspend drive shaft with wire. Remove right side lower engine/transmission nut.

5) Support engine with chain or engine support (VW 785/1). Disconnect ground strap from near transmission mount. Remove front transmission mount from body.

6) Support transmission using jack (US 618 & US 618/5) and lower front of transmission by loosening engine support (loosen spindle on VW 785/1) until there is enough room to remove transmission. Separate transmission from engine and remove from vehicle.

7) Lock flywheel with VW 215C (or equivalent). Index mark pressure plate and flywheel for reassembly reference. Loosen pressure plate-to-flywheel bolts evenly in a diagonal fashion and remove clutch assembly.

Installation — Apply molybdenum disulphide grease to release bearing. Lubricate transmission input shaft with molybdenum disulphide powder. Position clutch disc against flywheel and align using a centering tool. Install pressure plate and tighten bolts evenly in a diagonal fashion. Replace transmission, reversing removal procedure and noting the following:

- Insert rear bolt for slave cylinder before installing.
- Position air deflector plates correctly.

CLUTCH RELEASE BEARING

Removal — Remove transmission as outlined in Clutch Assembly in this article. Pry off clip retainers from bearing and disengage spring clips. Remove release bearing by sliding off guide tube.

NOTE — *Do not wash bearing in solvent or cleaning solution. Wipe with dry cloth to clean.*

Installation — Lubricate release shaft and release bearing pivot points with molybdenum disulphide grease. Position bearing to shaft and install spring clips and retainers. Make sure clips are correctly positioned.

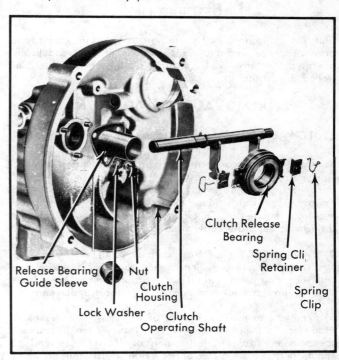

Clutch Release Bearing

Spring Clip Retainer

Spring Clip

Release Bearing Guide Sleeve

Nut

Clutch Housing

Lock Washer

Clutch Operating Shaft

Fig. 1   Clutch Release Bearing Assembly

CLUTCH MASTER CYLINDER

Removal & Installation — Disconnect master cylinder push rod at clutch pedal by removing cotter pin and clevis. Disconnect hydraulic line at cylinder. Remove cylinder attaching bolts and remove cylinder from firewall. To install, reverse removal procedure and pressure bleed the system following bleeder manufacturer's instructions.

CLUTCH SLAVE CYLINDER

Removal — Disconnect hydraulic line from slave cylinder. Disconnect slave cylinder push rod from clutch lever ball. Remove mounting bolts and remove cylinder.

Installation — Grease clutch lever ball lightly. Insert rear bolt to slave cylinder and install on vehicle. Install front bolt, attach hydraulic line and clutch lever. Pressure bleed system following bleeder manufacturer's instructions.

TIGHTENING SPECIFICATIONS

Application	Ft. Lbs. (mkg)
Engine-to-Transmission Nuts & Bolts	22 (3.0)
Drive Shaft-to-Transmission Bolts	33 (4.5)
Pressure Plate-to-Flywheel Bolts	18 (2.5)

VOLVO

DL	GLE
GL	Coupe
GT	Diesel

DESCRIPTION

Clutch is single dry disc type using a diaphragm spring type pressure plate. GLE and Coupe models use a hydraulically operated 9" clutch, while all other models use a cable controlled 8¼" clutch.

REMOVAL & INSTALLATION

CLUTCH ASSEMBLY

Removal — 1) Disconnect battery ground cable and back-up light wiring harness connector. Working from under vehicle, disconnect gear shift lever from gear shift rod. On GLE and Coupe, unbolt clutch slave cylinder from housing and disconnect from release arm. On all other models, unhook clutch fork spring and separate cable from housing.

2) Separate shift boot from carpet. Using a 4 mm Allen wrench, remove reverse gear detent fork. Remove lock ring with snap ring pliers and lift out gearshift lever. Remove front exhaust pipe bracket and position a support under engine.

3) Remove crossmember at rear of transmission. Index mark propeller shaft and disconnect from transmission. Disconnect speedometer cable from transmission. Lower rear end of engine and remove all except top right clutch housing bolts. Remove front starter bracket and free starter from clutch housing.

4) Install transmission jack and remove last clutch housing bolt. Pull transmission to rear and turn to clear propeller shaft tunnel. Lower transmission clear of vehicle. Loosen pressure plate bolts gradually in a diagonal pattern and remove clutch assembly.

Installation — To install transmission and clutch assembly, reverse removal procedure and note the following: Install clutch disc with long side of hub to rear using alignment tool 999 5111 (or equivalent). Install pressure plate and tighten bolts gradually in a criss-cross pattern. Adjust clutch pedal play on all except GLE and Coupe.

NOTE — GLE and Coupe pressure plates have raised fingers and use a 1⁷⁄₁₆" (36.5 mm) long release bearing. Remaining model pressure plate fingers are straight and require the use of a 1¹¹⁄₁₆" (43.0 mm) long release bearing. Pressure plates and bearings must never be mixed.

CLUTCH CABLE

Removal — Remove return spring and disconnect clutch cable at clutch fork; extract cable. Remove cover panel under instrument cluster. Remove clevis pin at upper end of cable. Separate clutch fork adjustment mechanism from clutch housing, if necessary. Force cable out of rubber grommet located in firewall.

Installation — Insert new cable into rubber grommet, feed it through cable guide and attach at upper end with clevis pin. Position adjustment mechanism into clutch housing. Attach cable to clutch fork, then refit return spring.

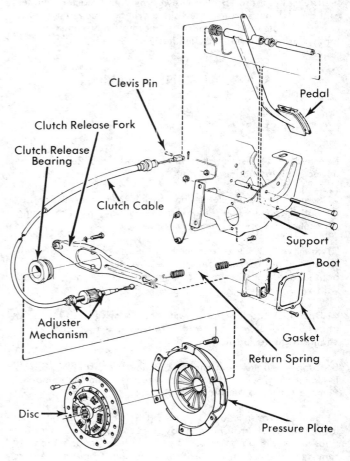

Fig. 1 Volvo Mechanical Linkage Clutch System

HYDRAULIC CLUTCH ACTUATION

Manufacturer does not provide maintenance instructions for hydraulically operated clutch linkage. There should be no free play in this type linkage.

PILOT BEARING

Remove retaining clip and remove bearing using puller (SVO 4090). Pack bearing with heat resistant grease and install into crankshaft using a driver. Install retaining clip.

ADJUSTMENT

CLUTCH FREE PLAY (EXCEPT GLE & COUPE)

Using adjustment mechanism attached to clutch housing, set free play. Adjustment is correct when approximately ⅛" (3-5 mm) clutch fork free play is obtained.

Section 9

DRIVE AXLES

CONTENTS

DRIVE AXLES
Section 9

Drive Axles

DRIVE AXLE TROUBLE SHOOTING

NOTE — *This is a general trouble shooting guide. When using this guide, locate the condition in column 1 that corresponds to your problem and determine the possible causes in column two. Match the number of the possible cause with the same number in column three, and you will have the suggested correction.*

CONDITION	POSSIBLE CAUSE	CORRECTION
▶ Wheel Noise	1) Wheel loose 2) Faulty, worn wheel bearings	1) Tighten lug nuts 2) Replace bearings
▶ Axle shaft noise	1) Misaligned axle housing 2) Bent or sprung axle 3) Pinion bearing end play 4) Excessive ring gear backlash 5) Incorrect pinion bearing adjustment 6) Loose companion flange nut 7) Incorrect wheel bearing adjustment 8) Scuffed tooth contact surfaces	1) Check alignment and correct 2) Replace axle shaft 3) Check pinion bearing preload 4) Check backlash and adjust 5) Adjust pinion bearings 6) Tighten nut to specification 7) Adjust wheel bearings 8) Adjust or replace gears
▶ Axle Breakage	1) Incorrect wheel bearing adjustment 2) Misaligned axle housing 3) Vehicle overloaded 4) Clutch grabs	1) Replace axle, adjust bearing 2) Replace shaft and correct alignment 3) Replace axle, reduce vehicle load 4) Replace axle, repair clutch
▶ Differential case breakage	1) Incorrect differential bearing adjustment 2) Excessive ring gear clearance 3) Vehicle overloaded 4) Erratic clutch operation	1) Check gears and bearings for damage, reassemble and adjust bearings 2) Check gears and bearings for damage, reassemble and adjust bearings 3) Check gears and bearings for damage, reduce vehicle load 4) Check gears and bearings for damage, avoid erratic clutch use
▶ Broken differential side gear	1) Excessive housing deflection 2) Worn thrust washers 3) Misaligned axle housing	1) Replace damaged gears, check other gears for damage and check axle housing alignment 2) Replace damaged gears, check other gears for damage and replace worn thrust washers 3) Replace damaged gears, check other gears for damage and check axle housing alignment
▶ Differential gears scored	1) Insufficient lubricant 2) Incorrect lubricant 3) One wheel spins excessively	1) Replace scored gears and fill rear axle to capacity with correct lubricant 2) Replace scored gears, clean housing and fill axle to capacity with correct lubricant 3) Replace scored gears and service as necessary
▶ Ring gear and pinion tooth breakage	1) Vehicle overloaded 2) Erratic clutch operation 3) Ice spotted pavement 4) Normal fatigue 5) Incorrect adjustment	1) Replace gears, reduce vehicle load 2) Replace gears and avoid erratic clutch operation 3) Replace gears 4) Replace gears and examine other components for fatigue 5) Replace gears and examine other components for wear. Make sure ring gear backlash is correct

Drive Axles

DRIVE AXLE TROUBLE SHOOTING (Cont.)

CONDITION	POSSIBLE CAUSE	CORRECTION
► Axle Noise	1) Insufficient lubricant	1) Fill axle to capacity with correct lubricant
	2) Incorrect ring gear and pinion adjustment	2) Check tooth contact pattern
	3) Worn ring gear or pinion teeth	3) Check tooth contact pattern and replace ring gear and pinion if necessary
	4) Loose pinion bearings	4) Adjust pinion bearings
	5) Loose differential gear bearings	5) Adjust differential gear bearings
	6) Misaligned ring gear	6) Check ring gear runout
	7) Loose carrier bolts	7) Tighten to specification
► Loss of lubricant	1) Lubricant level to high	1) Drain to correct level
	2) Worn axle shaft seals	2) Replace seals
	3) Cracked housing	3) Replace or repair housing
	4) Worn drive pinion seal	4) Replace seal
	5) Scored or worn companion flange	5) Replace flange and seal
► Unit overheats	1) Lubricant level low	1) Fill axle to capacity with correct lubricant
	2) Incorrect lubricant	2) Drain axle and refill to capacity with correct lubricant
	3) Bearings adjusted too tight	3) Readjust bearings
	4) Insufficient ring gear to pinion clearance	4) Readjust ring gear and pinion backlash and check ring and pinion for wear or scoring

Drive Axles

GEAR TOOTH PATTERNS

PRELIMINARY INSPECTION

Wipe lubricant from internal parts, then rotate gears and inspect for wear or damage. Mount a dial indicator to housing and check backlash at several points around ring gear. Backlash must be within specifications at all points. If no defects are found, check gear tooth pattern.

GEAR TOOTH CONTACT PATTERN

NOTE — *Drive pattern should be well centered on ring gear teeth. Coast pattern should be centered but may be slightly toward toe of ring gear teeth.*

Paint ring gear teeth with a suitable marking compound, then wrap a cloth or rope around drive pinion flange to act as a brake. Rotate ring gear until a clear tooth pattern is obtained. Gear tooth contact pattern will disclose whether correct pinion bearing mounting shim has been installed and drive gear backlash set properly. Backlash between drive gear and pinion must be maintained within specified limits until correct tooth pattern is obtained.

GEAR BACKLASH & PINION SHIM CHANGES

NOTE — *Change in tooth pattern is directly related to change in shim and backlash.*

1) With no change in backlash, moving pinion further from ring gear moves drive pattern toward heel and top of tooth, and moves coast pattern toward toe and top of tooth.

2) With no change in backlash, moving pinion closer to ring gear moves drive pattern toward toe and bottom of tooth, and moves coast pattern toward heel and bottom of tooth.

3) With no change in pinion shim thickness, an increase in backlash moves ring gear further from pinion. Drive pattern moves toward heel and top of tooth, and coast pattern moves toward heel and top of tooth.

4) With no change in pinion shim thickness, a decrease in backlash moves ring gear closer to pinion gear. Drive pattern moves toward toe and bottom of tooth, and coast pattern moves toward toe and bottom of tooth.

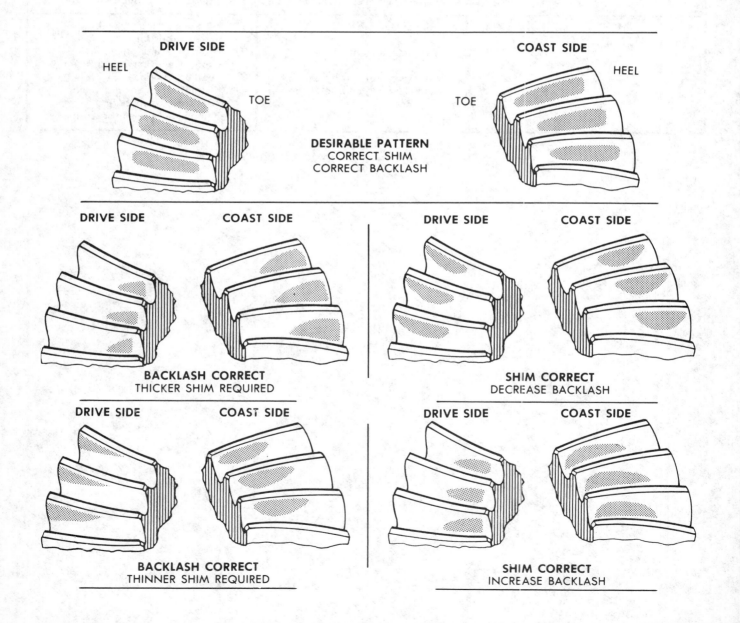

DRIVE SIDE   **COAST SIDE**

HEEL   TOE   TOE   HEEL

DESIRABLE PATTERN
CORRECT SHIM
CORRECT BACKLASH

DRIVE SIDE   **COAST SIDE**   **DRIVE SIDE**   **COAST SIDE**

BACKLASH CORRECT
THICKER SHIM REQUIRED

SHIM CORRECT
DECREASE BACKLASH

DRIVE SIDE   **COAST SIDE**   **DRIVE SIDE**   **COAST SIDE**

BACKLASH CORRECT
THINNER SHIM REQUIRED

SHIM CORRECT
INCREASE BACKLASH

Drive Axles

BMW INTEGRAL CARRIER

320i

DESCRIPTION

Final drive assembly has hypoid type ring and pinion gear and may have a multi-disc, self-locking differential (ZF DL-175). Housing has a removable rear cover. Differential carrier is retained in the sides of the housing by retaining plates and is supported by tapered roller bearings. Shims under the retaining plates maintain proper carrier bearing preload. Drive pinion gear is supported by roller bearings and preload is maintained by a collapsible spacer between the bearings.

AXLE RATIO & IDENTIFICATION

The ring and pinion gear set with Klingelnberg tooth design can be identified by the letter "K" stamped on the drive pinion gear head; Gleason teeth are noted by an "H" stamping. Letter "S" indicates a self-locking differential. To determine axle ratio, divide number of ring gear teeth by number of drive pinion gear teeth. The number of teeth on ring and drive pinion gears is stamped on forward left side of differential housing.

REMOVAL & INSTALLATION

CONSTANT VELOCITY JOINT

Removal — Remove cover from joint housing, then remove snap ring from end of drive shaft. Remove clamps from boot, then press drive shaft from joint. Remove dust boot.

Installation — To install, reverse removal procedure.

DRIVE SHAFT

Removal — Rear drive shaft flange access is through a hole in the rear axle support. Detach from final drive by removing flange bolts.

Installation — To install, reverse removal procedure using sealer on boot-to-joint surfaces and install seal cover after packing joint with suitable grease.

AXLE SHAFTS & BEARINGS

Removal — Raise and support vehicle. Remove wheel, loosen castellated nut securing flange to axle shaft, then using a suitable puller, remove flange. Remove drive shaft, then using a soft headed mallet, drive axle shaft inward and out of housing. Drive out bearings and seals, then remove spacer sleeve and shim.

Installation — 1) To install, reverse removal procedure noting the following: Install inner bearing, then determine distance between outer races of inner and outer bearings.

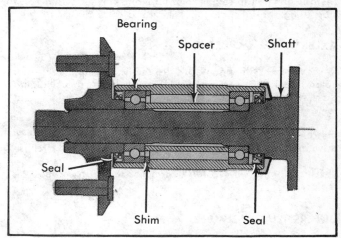

Fig. 2 Sectional View of Axle Shaft Assembly

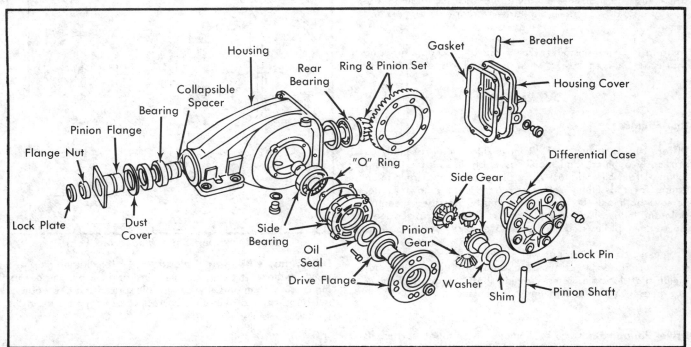

Fig. 1 Exploded View of BMW 320i Final Drive Assembly

BMW INTEGRAL CARRIER (Cont.)

2) Measure spacer and shim, then install spacer and a suitable shim that will obtain a wheel bearing play of .002-.004" (.05-.10 mm).

3) Pack bearings and hub with suitable grease, then using new seals, complete installation procedure.

DRIVE PINION COMPANION FLANGE OIL SEAL

Removal — Pull out shaft seal using special tool (00 5 000) used in conjunction with new special tools (00 5 006 and 33 1 309).

NOTE — *Using the above tools eliminates complete disassembly of differential to replace seal.*

Installation — Dip seal in gear lube and drive in seal against stop using special tools (33 1 170 and 00 5 500).

AXLE FLANGE & OIL SEAL

Removal — With final drive assembly mounted in special holder (33 1 040), remove cover. Remove bent circlips holding drive flange at pinion side gear. Pull out drive flange and remove shaft seal.

Installation — Fill groove between seal lips with grease and drive axle seal into position. Replace drive flange and circlips.

NOTE — *Flanges with scored bearing or seal surfaces must be replaced.*

DIFFERENTIAL ASSEMBLY

Removal — Detach propeller shaft and drive shafts from final drive. Suspend shafts out of way and detach self aligning support at final drive. Detach final drive at rear axle support and remove.

Installation — To install, reverse removal procedure ensuring that assembly is stress-free when tightened to specific torque.

OVERHAUL

DISASSEMBLY

Differential Housing — **1)** Remove differential assembly as previously outlined, and mount assembly in suitable holding fixture. Drain oil and mark drive pinion shaft and companion flange for reassembly reference. Remove rear cover plate. Remove both axle flanges, as previously described, keeping right and left parts separated. Mark and remove carrier bearing retainer plates and shims. Remove carrier from housing.

2) Remove carrier bearings with suitable puller. Remove bolts securing ring gear to carrier then remove ring gear. Drive out pinion shaft lock pin. Remove pinion shaft and gears. Remove side gears with shims and thrust washers.

Drive Pinion Gear — **1)** Remove differential carrier as previously outlined, then using an inch pound torque wrench, check preload on drive pinion gear. Hold companion flange

and remove retaining nut. Press drive pinion from flange and housing, then remove bearings.

2) Remove drive pinion shaft oil seal then extract pinion inner bearing race from case with special tool (33 1 350) and adapters. Note shim thickness under bearing race. Pull out front bearing race.

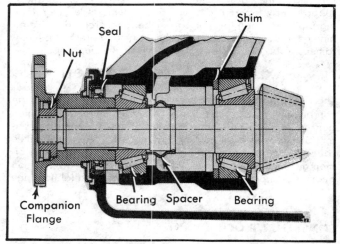

Fig. 3   Sectional View of Drive Pinion Gear Assembly

REASSEMBLY & ADJUSTMENT

Differential Assembly -- Reverse disassembly procedure noting the following checks and adjustments.

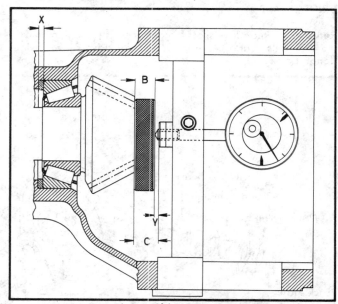

Fig. 4   Pinion Shim Measuring Points

Drive Pinion Bearing Preload — **1)** If original ring and pinion gear set is being installed, install drive pinion gear using original shim and new collapsible spacer. If a new gear set is being installed determine correct size of shim to use in the following manner:

- Use special tool (33 1 381 with 33 1 382) and a dial indicator set at "0" with a preload of 0.157" (4 mm).

BMW INTEGRAL CARRIER (Cont.)

- Position tool (33 1 382) on drive pinion. Install tool (33 1 381) in case and note value of "Y".
- Basic adjustment "C" is 0.434" (11.02 mm). Master gauge "B" is 0.354" (9.00 mm).
- Place shims on "X" that correspond to the difference. Shims are available in 0.0004-0.0012" (0.01-0.03 mm).

2) Remove, then reinstall drive pinion, bearings and cones as required, so new shim(s), collapsible spacer and seal can be installed. Install companion flange and collared nut. Tighten nut to obtain specified pinion shaft bearing preload.

NOTE — *If preload is exceeded, new collapsible spacer must be installed and procedure repeated.*

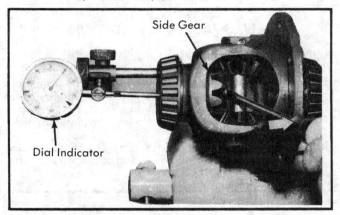

Fig. 5   Checking Side Gear-to-Pinion Gear Backlash

Side Gear-to-Pinion Gear Backlash — With pinion gears and one side gear installed, mount dial indicator to carrier. Force side gear against case and zero the indicator, then force side gear against pinion gears. Value indicated is .002" greater than desired thickness of shim and cup spring. Repeat procedure on opposite side gear.

Differential Bearing Preload — With differential carrier installed in housing without ring gear, and with carrier bear-

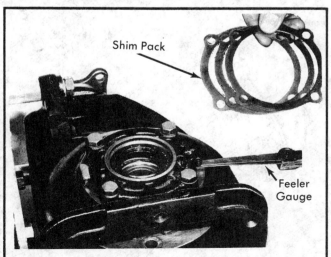

Fig. 6   Measuring for Differential Shim Pack Preload Requirements

ing retainer plates installed without shims, thread a bolt in against differential pinion gear shaft. Equally tighten retainer plate bolts until specified bearing preload is obtained. Using feeler gauge, check clearance between retainer plate and housing to determine required shim thickness. Take required shims and install them equally under both retainer plates.

Ring-to-Drive Pinion Gear Backlash — After establishing differential bearing preload, check ring-to-pinion gear tooth contact pattern. While maintaining established shim thickness, move shims from one retainer plate to the other, as necessary, to obtain proper contact pattern. After setting backlash, complete differential reassembly procedure.

Fig. 7   Checking Ring Gear Backlash

AXLE ASSEMBLY SPECIFICATIONS

Application	Specification
Axle Shaft End Play	.002-.004" (.05-.10 mm)
Axle Drive Flange Runout (Max.)	.006" (.15 mm)
Ring-to-Pinion Gear Backlash	.002-.004" (.06-.11 mm)
Drive Pinion Gear Bearing Preload	
W/Oil Seal	15-29 INCH lbs. (17-33 cmkg)
W/O Oil Seal	13-28 INCH lbs. (15-32 cmkg)
Differential Bearing Preload	
W/Oil Seal	21-34 INCH lbs. (24-39 cmkg)

TIGHTENING SPECIFICATIONS

Application	Ft. Lbs. (mkg)
Rear Housing Cover Bolts	32-35 (4.3-4.8)
Companion Flange Nut (Min.)	108 (15)
Carrier Bearing Retainer Plate Bolts	16-17 (2.2-2.4)
Drive Flange Nuts	24-27 (3.3-3.7)
Ring Gear-to-Carrier Bolts①②	63-74 (8.7-10.2)

① — Using Loctite.
② — Tighten evenly in criss-cross pattern.

Drive Axles

BMW SPLIT HOUSING

528i
633CSi
733i

DESCRIPTION

Differential has hypoid type ring and pinion gear set, and may have one of two clutch pack type limited slip units. Left side of housing is the housing cover and must be removed to expose carrier assembly. Cover incorporates a ball bearing and oil seal for left axle flange, and a bearing cone for the left differential carrier bearing. Right carrier bearing and seal are incorporated in housing. The pinion gear is supported by roller bearings and preload is maintained by a collapsible spacer.

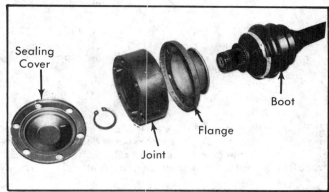

Fig. 2 Exploded View of Half Shaft Constant Velocity Joint

AXLE RATIO & IDENTIFICATION

Ring and pinion gear set with Klingelnberg tooth design can be identified by the letter "K" stamped on the head of the pinion gear; Gleason teeth are noted by an "H" stamping. To determine axle ratio, divide number of ring gear teeth by number of pinion gear teeth. The number of teeth on ring and pinion, and the code for limited slip differential (S), is stamped on right side of differential housing after ratio indication.

REMOVAL & INSTALLATION

DRIVE SHAFTS & UNIVERSAL JOINTS

Removal — Remove drive shaft after removing retaining bolts from axle and half shaft flanges. Remove cover from joint housing and snap ring from end of drive shaft. Remove clamps from boot then press drive shaft from joint. Remove dust boot.

Installation — To install, reverse removal procedure using sealer on boot-to-joint surfaces, and install seal cover after packing joint with suitable grease.

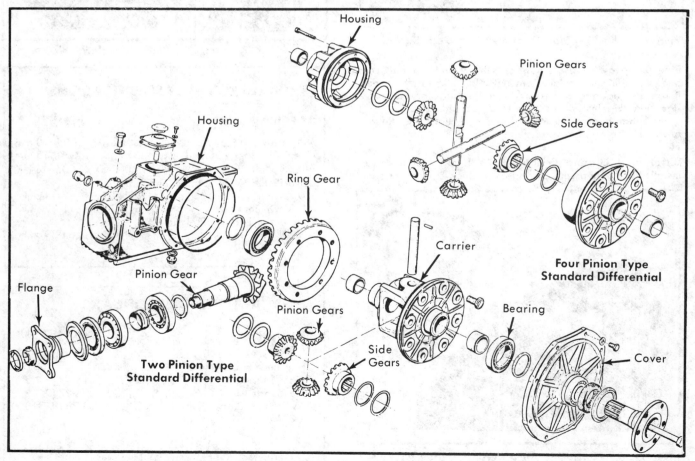

Fig. 1 Exploded View of BMW Split Housing Differential

BMW SPLIT HOUSING (Cont.)

AXLE SHAFTS & BEARINGS

Removal — Raise and support vehicle. Remove wheel, drive shaft, axle flange retaining nut, and using a puller, (if required), remove axle flange. Using soft headed mallet, drive axle shaft out of housing. Drive out bearings and seals, then remove spacer sleeve and shim.

Installation — 1) To install, reverse removal procedure noting the following: Install outer bearing then determine distance between outer race of outer bearing and shoulder in hub for inner bearing (dimension "B"). Subtract from spacer length (dimension "A") and use shim ("C") to give .004" (0.1 mm) end play. See Fig. 3.

2) Pack bearing with 1.2 oz. (35 g) of suitable lubricant and lubricate sealing lips. Complete installation procedure.

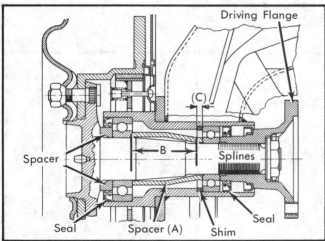

Fig. 3   Wheel Bearings and Axle Shaft

AXLE FLANGE, SEAL & BEARING

Removal — Hold axle flange and remove retaining bolt. Use puller to remove axle flange. Pry out oil seal. Ball bearing may be removed from cover with puller if required.

Installation — To install, reverse removal procedure after packing bearing and seal cavity with suitable lubricant.

Fig. 4   Removing Drive Flange Ball Bearing

NOTE — On models with circlips and grooves in drive flange shafts, insert circlip in case, and press drive flange in by hand until snap ring engages. Replace loose driving flanges.

DIFFERENTIAL CARRIER ASSEMBLY

NOTE — Differential carrier can be removed from housing with differential assembly installed in vehicle. After removing axle flanges, follow Differential Carrier, Disassembly and Overhaul procedures, in this story.

DIFFERENTIAL ASSEMBLY

Removal — Remove propeller shaft and drive shafts, tie drive shafts up out of way. Support differential and remove bolts securing it to front brackets and rear support. Remove differential assembly.

Installation — To install, reverse removal procedure, insuring rear support is stress free when installed.

OVERHAUL

DISASSEMBLY

Differential Assembly — 1) Remove differential assembly as previously outlined and mount assembly in suitable holding fixture. Drain oil and mark pinion shaft and companion flange for reassembly reference. Remove inspection hole cover, mount dial indicator in one cover bolt hole and check ring gear backface runout and ring-to-pinion gear backlash. Check gear tooth contact pattern.

NOTE — Refer to Rear Axle Gear Tooth Patterns in this Section.

2) Remove axle flanges and side cover, then remove differential carrier assembly. Proceed as follows for standard or limited slip differential carrier disassembly.

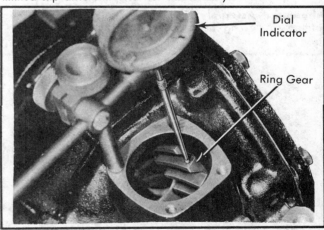

Fig. 5   Checking Ring Gear Backlash

Standard Two Pinion Differential Carrier — Remove carrier bearings with puller and separate ring gear from carrier. Drive out pinion shaft lock pin and differential shaft. Remove pinion gears, side gears with shims, and thrust washers.

Standard Four Pinion Differential Carrier — Remove carrier bearings with puller and separate carrier halves. Lift out pinion gears and shafts, then remove side gears with shims and thrust washers. Unbolt and remove ring gear from carrier.

BMW SPLIT HOUSING (Cont.)

Limited Slip Differential Carrier — Remove carrier bearings with puller. Unscrew case cover bolts and remove case cover. Invert case and lift off of clutch and gear assembly. Remove ring gear.

Drive Pinion Gear — 1) Remove differential carrier as previously described, then check pinion bearing preload using an inch pound torque wrench. Remove pinion flange nut lock ring, hold flange and remove nut. Press drive pinion out through flange and housing.

Fig. 6   Checking Pinion Bearing Preload

2) Remove oil seal and lift out front bearing. Remove front and rear bearing races with special extractor tool (33 1 350).

REASSEMBLY & ADJUSTMENT

Differential Assembly — Reverse disassembly procedure noting the following checks and adjustments.

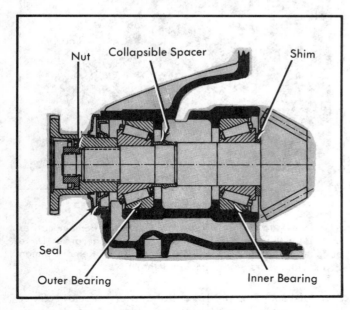

Fig. 7   Sectional View of Drive Pinion Gear and Bearing Assembly

Drive Pinion Bearing Preload — 1) If original ring and pinion gear set is being installed, and gear tooth pattern and pinion bearing preload were satisfactory at time of disassembly, install drive pinion gear using original shim and a new collapsible spacer.

2) If a new gear set is being installed, it will be necessary to determine correct pinion depth shim using special gauge block and gauge tool (33 1 400). Place .159" (4.05 mm) thick gauge disc ("A") on pinion and press bearing into position with beveled side of disc toward drive pinion.

3) Install front bearing and drive pinion flange without shaft seal. Tighten pinion shaft nut to give 18-20 INCH lbs. (21-23 cmkg) rotating torque. Zero dial indicator on gauge tool with .16" (4 mm) preload. Insert gauge assembly in housing.

4) Measured pinion depth (E) is figured by adding gauge block dimension (C) to ½ gauge tool diameter (D) and distance from tool to block (Y). Specified basic pinion depth (E) of Klingelnberg teeth is 2.32" (59.00 mm) and depth of Gleason teeth is 2.43" (61.85 mm).

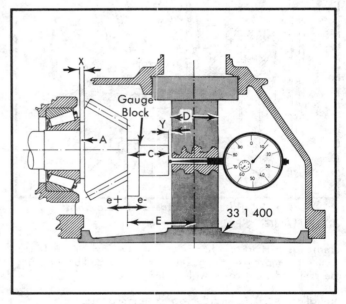

Fig. 8   Measuring Pinion Depth

NOTE — *Klingelnberg teeth have a constant depth and flank dimension and are identified by the letter "K" stamped on the ring and pinion gears. Gleason teeth are higher and wider on the outside than on the inside and are marked with the letter "H" or "F" on ring and pinion gears. Individual differences in manufacture of pinions will be stamped or etched on the end of the pinion gear in .01 mm such as −15, indicating that the pinion face is .15 mm closer to the gauge than basic E dimension. This number (e) must be added to (E) if (+) or subtracted if (−) to determine "E" specified.*

5) Thickness of shim "X" to be used in final assembly may be determined by comparing "E" measured with "E" specified and adding or subtracting difference (a) to gauge disc thickness. *See illustration and sample calculation.*

BMW SPLIT HOUSING (Cont.)

Sample Calculation for Pinion Depth Shim

(E) Klingelnberg	2.323″ (59 mm)
Plus	.006″ (.15 mm)
Equals (E) Specified	2.329″ (59.15 mm)
Difference (a)	.011″ (.27 mm)
Gauge Disc (A)	− .011″ (.27 mm)
Equals Shim (X) Requirement	.148″ (3.78 mm)

NOTE — *If (E) specified is larger than (E) measured, subtract difference (a) from disc (A) thickness; if (E) specified is smaller, add difference (a) to gauge disc thickness to determine shim (X) thickness.*

6) Remove drive pinion and pull off taper bearing. Replace gauge disc (A) with shim (X) of proper thickness, assuring that bevelled inside diameter faces drive pinion. Install collapsible spacer, seal, companion flange and collared nut to obtain specified drive pinion preload.

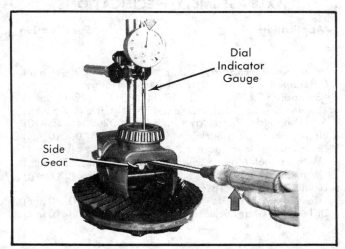

Fig. 9 *Checking Side-to-Pinion Gear Backlash*

NOTE — *If preload is exceeded, new collapsible spacer must be installed and the procedure repeated. Seal should be lubricated with gear lube prior to installation.*

Side-to-Pinion Gear Backlash (Standard Differentials) — Install two pinion gears with shaft and one side gear. Mount dial indicator to carrier so plunger contacts side gear. Force side gear hard against pinion gears, zero indicator, then force side gear hard against case. With proper shim and thrust washer, backlash should be as specified, and preload of all three gears should not exceed specified value. Repeat procedure on opposite side (with second set of pinions on four pinion type), then retain side gears pressed outward against carrier so axle flange retaining bolts can later be installed.

Limited Slip Differential Clutch Assembly — 1) Install in order: outer plates, inner plates, pressure rings, rear axle shaft gears, differential shaft gears and differential shafts. Measure installed height (A) from case edge to outer plate.

2) Measure distance (B) from inner face of side cover to flange surface. Place diaphragm springs together and measure thickness (C). Cover and spring thickness (B+C) must be from .004″ to .016″ (0.1 to 0.4 mm) less than installed height (A). If not within these specifications, correct with outer plates of proper thickness.

3) Remove parts from case and install stepped disc with smooth side facing case, diaphragm spring with concave side facing differential shaft, and thrust washer with oil pockets facing inboard. Complete assembly and tighten to specification.

4) Install axle flanges in carrier and clamp one flange in a vise. Use torque wrench to check breakaway torque of assembly. If not within specifications, install thicker or thinner outer plates.

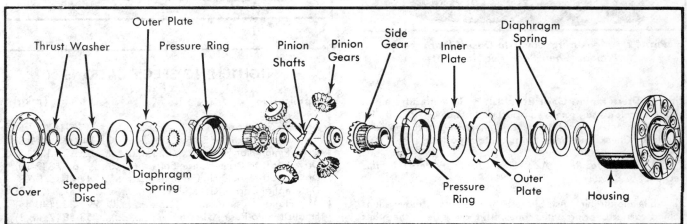

Fig. 10 *Exploded View of Limited Slip Differential*

Drive Axles

BMW SPLIT HOUSING (Cont.)

Fig. 11   Checking Torque on Limited Slip Differential

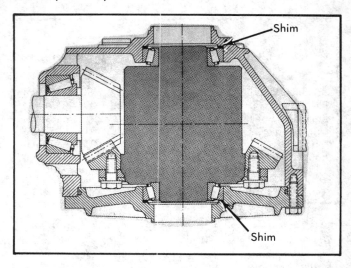

Fig. 13   Sectional View Showing Ring Gear Backlash Shim Locations

Differential Bearing Preload — Install one shim behind carrier bearing outer cone in side cover. Install bearing cone using suitable installer (33 1 350). Install drive flange bolt without flange so it contacts pinion gear shaft. Install carrier in housing without ring gear and tighten cover mounting screws evenly to 15-18 ft. lbs. (2-2.5 mkg). Check minimum rotating torque of 19 INCH lbs. (22 cmkg). If torque is less than specified, install thicker shim under bearing race in cover. Use feeler gauge to determine gap between cover and case. Subtract this thickness from shim used under bearing race to determine actual shim pack to be used in final assembly. Install ring gear warm (176-212°F) using locking compound on bolts.

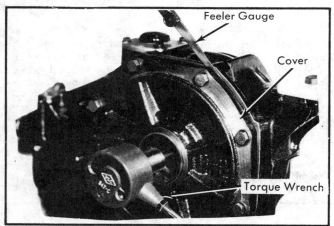

Fig. 12   Measuring Cover-to-Case Clearance for Preload Shim Pack Requirements

Ring-to-Drive Pinion Gear Backlash — **1)** With differential bearing preload set, remove inspection hole cover, mount dial indicator in one cover bolt hole, and check ring-to-pinion gear backlash. Check ring gear tooth contact pattern.

NOTE — *Refer to Rear Axle Gear Tooth Patterns in this Section.*

2) While maintaining established shim thickness, move shims behind carrier bearing outer cones, from one side to the other as necessary to obtain proper contact pattern. After setting backlash, complete differential reassembly procedure.

AXLE ASSEMBLY SPECIFICATIONS

Application	Specification
Wheel Bearing End Play	.002-.004" (.05-.10 mm)
Differential Gear Rotating Torque (At Flange)	
Standard	19-34 INCH lbs. (22-39 cmkg)
Limited Slip	36-54 ft. lbs. (5-7.5 mkg)
Axle Drive Flange End Play	.002-.004" (.05-.10)
Ring-to-Pinion Gear Backlash	.002-.004" (.05-.10 mm)
Drive Pinion Gear Bearing Preload	
Without Seal (Max.)	28 INCH lbs. (30 cmkg)
With Oil Seal (Max.)	29 INCH lbs. (33 cmkg)
Limited Slip Clutch Assembly	
Case-to-Plate End Play	.004-.016" (.10-.40 mm)
Differential Gear Backlash ..	①.0012-.004" (.03-.10 mm)

① — 528i — 0-.0027" (0-.07 mm).

TIGHTENING SPECIFICATIONS

Application	Ft. Lbs. (mkg)
Housing Cover Bolts	15-18 (2-2.5)
Ring Gear-to-Carrier Bolts	121-143 (16.8-19.8)
Drive Pinion Flange Nut	111 (15)
Drive Shaft-to-Drive Flange Bolts	65-72 (9-10)
Drive Shaft-to-Axle Flange Bolts	44-48 (6.1-6.8)
Differential Carrier Cover Bolts	15-18 (2-2.5)
Axle Flange Nut	295-332 (40-45)
Final Drive-to-Rear Axle Carrier	53-58 (7.3-8.1)
Final Drive-to-Rubber Mount	53-58 (7.3-8.1)

CHRYSLER CORP. IMPORTS

Arrow	Colt Wagon
Arrow Pickup	D50 Pickup
Challenger	Sapporo

DESCRIPTION

Rear axle is of the banjo type, utilizing the removable carrier style differential. Light weight construction joins split tubular housings for each side with center covers welded to axle housing. Final drive is of the hypoid style. Axle shafts are semi-floating type supported with bearings at their respective ends in axle housing. Bearings are fitted to axles with pressure type bearing retainers.

AXLE RATIO & IDENTIFICATION

Two different differentials are used on passenger vehicles and only one differential is used on pickups. Type "A" differential is used on Arrow with 1600 cc engine (gear ratio 3.909:1 on manual transmission, 3.545:1 on automatic transmission). Type "B" differential is used on Arrow with 2600 cc engine, Challenger, Colt Wagon and Sapporo (gear ratio 3.545:1). Pickups use a modified version of type "B" differential (gear ratio 3.909:1). Side bearing preload is adjusted by shims on type "A" differentials and by side bearing nuts on all other differentials. Pinion bearing preload and pinion depth adjustments are made with shims, while differential side gears are adjusted with spacers on all models.

REMOVAL & INSTALLATION

AXLE SHAFTS & BEARINGS

Removal (Pickups) — 1) Raise and support rear axle housing so rear wheels clear ground. Remove rear wheel and brake drum. Disconnect hydraulic line from wheel cylinder. Disconnect bearing case from axle housing. Remove back plate, bearing case and axle shaft as an assembly. Use suitable puller set (CT-1003 & C-637) if required, and remove axle shaft.

2) Remove "O" ring and shims, retain shims for reassembly. Using suitable tool (C-637 with hook), remove and discard inner axle shaft oil seal. Mount back plate, bearing case and axle shaft assembly in a vise. Loosen axle shaft bearing lock washer, then using suitable wrench (MB990785), remove lock nut on rear of back plate. Remove washers and reinstall lock nut on axle shaft approximately 3 turns.

3) Install suitable puller (MB990787A) to bearing case on rear of back plate. Remove bearing case, then using a hammer and drift, remove bearing outer race. Remove outer bearing oil seal.

4) Using a dial indicator, inspect axle shaft deflection at points shown in illustration. Replace axle shaft if specifications are exceeded. Inspect wheel hub bolts for tightness and bearing outer retainer for deformation, replace defective parts as necessary.

Installation — 1) Apply lubricant to outer bearing race and lip of outer oil seal and seat each in bearing case. Slide bearing case and bearing over axle shaft and install inner bearing race and bearing.

2) Install washer, lock washer and lock nut in that order and tighten lock nut with suitable tool (MB990785). Bend tab on

lock washer into lock nut groove. Install inner oil seal with suitable driver (C-4572).

NOTE — *If lock washer does not engage lock nut groove, retighten lock nut, without damaging lock washer.*

3) Starting on left side, install .039" (1 mm) shim between axle shaft assembly and axle housing. Tighten all bolts. Insert right axle shaft assembly into axle housing. Using shims of proper size, set clearance between bearing case and axle housing to .002-.008" (.05-.20 mm). Complete installation by reversing removal procedure.

NOTE — *Clearance must be measured with bearing case seated against axle housing.*

Axle Shaft Deflection Table	
Application	**Service Limit In. (mm)**
Point "A"	
Pickups	0-.0024 (0-.06)
All Others	0-.0015 (0-.04)
Point "B"	
Pickups	0-.039 (0-1)
All Others	0-.001 (0-.025)
Point "C" (Passenger Only)	0-.039 (0-1)

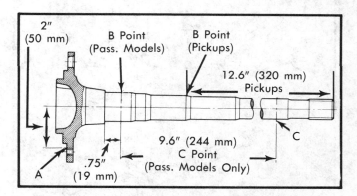

Fig. 1 Measuring Axle Shaft Deflection

Removal (All Others) — 1) Raise and support rear axle housing so rear wheels clear ground. Remove rear wheel and brake back plate nuts, then disconnect wheel cylinder brake line. Fix suitable puller set (CT-1003 & C-637) to lug studs and work slide hammer until axle shaft is free to be withdrawn. Set brake back plate with parking brake attached out of way. Using suitable tool (C-637 with hook) remove axle shaft oil seal.

NOTE — *To remove axle shaft on rear disc brake models, disconnect and plug hydraulic line, disconnect parking brake cable at caliper and remove caliper and rotor. Then continue with procedure described for drum brake models.*

2) To remove axle bearing proceed as follows: Grind down bearing retainer at one point until retainer thickness is .04-.06" (1.0-1.5 mm), then chisel ground portion and remove retainer. Using suitable bearing puller or press (CT-1120) remove bearing from axle.

CHRYSLER CORP. IMPORTS (Cont.)

3) Using a dial indicator, inspect axle shaft deflection at 3 points. See *Fig. 1*. Replace axle shaft if specifications listed in table are exceeded.

4) Rear axle bearing should be replaced when bearing noise is detected. Inspect wheel hub bolts for tightness and bearing outer retainer for deformation, replace defective parts as necessary.

Installation – 1) Fit outer bearing retainer flat side against shaft splined end, then install bearing and inner bearing retainer. Seat bearing retainer with smaller chamfered side directed to the bearing.

NOTE – *Ensure bearing is completely seated.*

2) Lightly coat lips of oil seal with grease and using oil seal installer (DT1007D & C4171), fit axle shaft oil seal in rear axle housing. Using packing and shims in proper sequence, set clearance between bearing and outer bearing retainer to 0-.01" (0-.25 mm).

3) Carefully insert axle shaft assembly into axle housing using care not to damage seal. Slightly turn axle shaft until splines line up with differential side gears. Align packing oil holes with outer bearing retainer and tighten bearing retainer to axle housing flange. Complete installation by reversing removal procedure. Bleed hydraulic system.

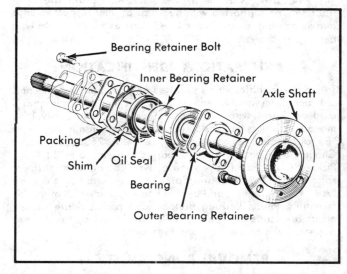

Fig. 3   Exploded View of Axle Shaft Assembly (Passenger Car Models)

DIFFERENTIAL CARRIER

Removal – Drain oil from rear axle differential housing, then disconnect propeller shaft. Pull out both rear axle shafts approximately 2½". Remove differential gear housing mounting nuts and withdraw the differential gear carrier. It may be necessary to tap outside of housing to break gear carrier loose.

Installation – Lightly coat each bearing and gear with oil. Apply sealing compound on packing and axle housing seat, then assemble gear carrier to axle housing with nuts and tighten. Fill differential gear housing with 1.2 quart of suitable multi-purpose gear oil (API GL-5).

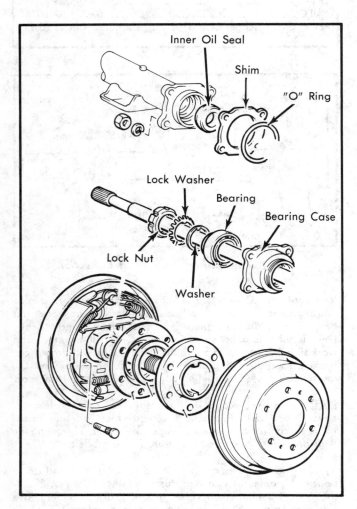

Fig. 2   Exploded View of Pickup Axle Assembly

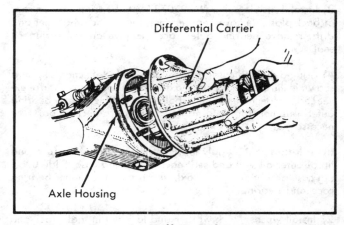

Fig. 4   Removing Differential Gear Housing

CHRYSLER CORP. IMPORTS (Cont.)

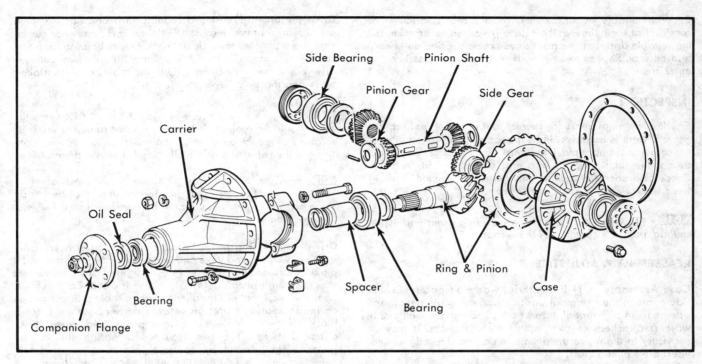

Fig. 5   *Exploded View of Chrysler Corp. Import Type "B" Differential Assembly*

OVERHAUL

DISASSEMBLY

NOTE – *Remove side bearing lock nuts on Type "B" and pickup differentials with appropriate spanner before beginning disassembly of differential gear assembly.*

Differential Gear Assembly – 1) Remove bearing carrier cap and lever gear case assembly from housing. Using suitable bearing puller tool, pull differential side bearing. Keep right and left bearings and shims in sequence for reassembly.

2) Remove ring gear lock plate tabs and loosen bolts in diagonal sequence, then remove ring gear. Drive out pinion shaft lock pin from ring gear back side using a punch; pull out pinion shaft and pinion. Pinion side gears and spacers are now accessible. Note placement of pinion side gear and spacers and ensure they are reassembled in same position.

Drive Pinion – 1) Hold end yoke with suitable tool (C-3281) and remove lock nut, then remove end yoke. Using a wheel puller, force out drive pinion with adjusting shim, rear inner bearing race, spacer and preload adjusting shim.

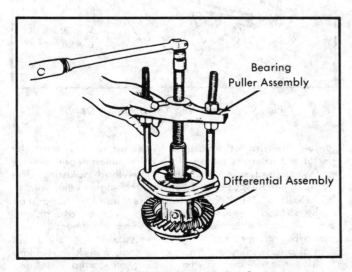

Fig. 6   *Removing Differential Side Bearings*

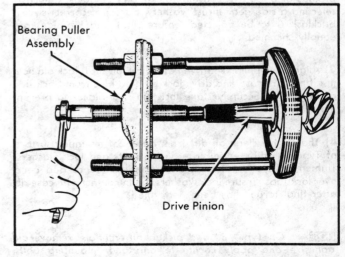

Fig. 7   *Removing Rear Drive Pinion Bearing*

CHRYSLER CORP. IMPORTS (Cont.)

2) With suitable bearing puller, remove rear bearing inner race and at same time, pull off drive pinion adjusting shim. Using suitable drift, remove front drive pinion bearing outer race and oil seal. Repeat same procedure to remove rear bearing outer race.

INSPECTION

Check differential gears for correct tooth contact and replace gears if wear is excessive. Inspect bearing faces for roughness or score marks and replace bearing assembly, if necessary. Ensure splines of side gears and rear axle shafts fit correctly. Check clearance between pinion gears and pinion shaft, if wear is excessive, replace components.

NOTE — *To check gear tooth contact using paint impression method, refer to beginning of this section.*

REASSEMBLY & ADJUSTMENT

Case Assembly — 1) Install thrust washers (spacers) behind side gears in their original position and assemble pinion and side gears in differential. Insert both pinion gears, with pinion washers attached, so they mesh with side gears. It may be necessary to slightly rotate pinions to achieve desired meshing. Insert drive pinion shaft.

Fig. 8   Checking Differential and Side Gear Backlash

2) Check pinion and side gear backlash as shown in illustration. If backlash is beyond .002-.005" (.05-.127 mm) on pickups or 0-.003" (0-.08 mm) on all other models, adjust by selecting a side gear thrust washer (spacer) of correct size. If backlash is to be adjusted, ensure right and left sides are equally shimmed.

3) Align drive pinion shaft with drive pinion shaft lock pin hole in differential case and drive lock pin into hole from back side of ring gear. Securely stake lock pin in 2 places to prevent movement.

4) Thoroughly clean all dirt from ring gear mounting surface of Type "A" differential case. Install bolts and lock washers. Tighten bolts alternately in a diagonal sequence and bend over lock tabs. Ensure lock washers are in contact with case rib after final torque has been performed.

NOTE — *On Type "B" and pickup differentials, remove old adhesive and apply Loctite to ring gear mounting bolts. Tighten bolts and do not move vehicle for 1 hour.*

Drive Pinion — 1) Using a suitable drift and hammer or a press, seat front and rear bearing outer races into gear carrier ensuring that outer races do not cock. Ensure bearing races are completely seated before proceeding. Install shim between drive pinion and rear bearing. Using suitable bearing installer, press bearing onto drive pinion shaft.

2) If drive pinion and bearings are scheduled to be reused, shims should be replaced with new shims of same thickness. In instances where the gear set is to be replaced, install new shims that are the same thickness as the used shims on drive pinion.

NOTE — *When determining the desired thickness of shim pack, amount of compression (sinkage) of shim pack and wear of the bearing (where old bearing is reused) must be taken into consideration.*

Drive Pinion Depth — Install drive pinion spacer, front bearing, washer, end yoke and washer in order of removal. Fit pinion shaft retaining nut and slowly tighten nut, continuously checking, until pinion bearing preload is 6-9 INCH lbs. (7-10 cmkg) with oil seal not installed. Place suitable cylinder gauge on inside bearing pedestals of gear carrier housing. Place a block gauge on top end of drive pinion and slip a feeler gauge between the two gauges to obtain the correct pinion height. Select appropriate shim(s) to adjust pinion height to within ±.0012" (.03 mm) of measurement taken with block gauge and feeler gauge.

NOTE — *If pinion depth has to be adjusted by more than .065" (1.65 mm), use two shims. One MUST be .0118" (.30 mm).*

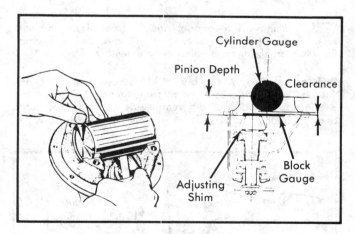

Fig. 9   Measuring Drive Pinion Depth

Pinion Bearing Preload — This adjustment must be performed after the setting of the drive pinion depth. Remove end yoke and insert the bearing preload adjusting shim between pinion spacer and bearing, then tighten end yoke to 9-11 INCH lbs. (10-13 cmkg) with oil seal installed. In addition to the preload adjusting shims, there are spacers available to provide proper adjustment. After finishing adjustment of drive pinion bearing preload, remove end yoke and apply a thin coat of grease to outer surface of oil seal, then drive seal into position in gear carrier. After greasing oil seal lip, insert end yoke and tighten nut.

CHRYSLER CORP. IMPORTS (Cont.)

NOTE — *Side bearing preload on Type "B" and pickup differentials is adjusted by proper tightening of side bearing nut.*

Side Bearing Preload (Type "A") — Fit each side bearing into differential case, leaving shims out; use suitable tool (CT-1102) for this procedure. Ensure side bearings are completely seated before proceeding. Install differential case assembly on gear carrier, then calculate clearance between side bearing outer race and gear carrier as shown in illustration. After obtaining clearance add .002" (.05 mm) preload figure to each side. Insert shims equally on both sides. Align gear carrier and bearing cap index marks, then tighten cap retaining bolts.

Side Bearing (Pickup & Type "B") — After adjusting pinion bearing preload, install side bearing inner races with suitable installer. Install differential carrier in housing and install outer races. Align bearing cap index marks and tighten cap bolts to 7-11 ft. lbs. (1-1.5 mkg). Install bearing nuts. Tighten bearing nuts in clockwise rotation until bearing outer surface is flush with bearing cap outer surface. Back bearing nut out counterclockwise and retighten nut to completely seat bearing. After bearing is completely seated, tighten bearing cap bolts. After tightening bearing caps, turn bearing nuts $\frac{1}{30}$ turn clockwise ($\frac{1}{2}$ pitch of 15 bearing nut holes). Check ring gear deflection.

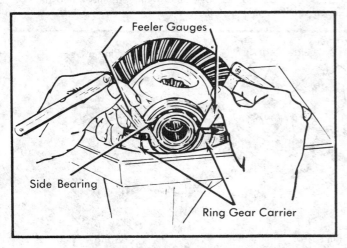

Fig. 10 Measuring Clearance Between Side Bearing and Gear Carrier (Type "A" Differentials)

Ring Gear Deflection (Backside) — Attach a dial indicator to back side of ring gear and measure deflection. If ring gear has excessive deflection, correct position of the assembly in relation to differential case by shifting position of shims (Type "A") or by tightening/loosening bearing nuts (all others). Recheck measurement. Install lock plate on Type "B" and pickup differentials. Replace ring gear or differential case if runout exceeds .003" (.075 mm) on Type "B" or .002" (.05 mm) on all others.

Drive Pinion Backlash — Measure backlash of drive pinion in at least four different spots on ring gear face with drive pinion securely fixed in final position. Set up a dial indicator on ring

gear teeth edges. If measured backlash exceeds .005-.007", correct position of assembly as described for *Ring Gear Deflection*.

NOTE — *Check gear tooth contact using paint impression method described at beginning of this section.*

Final Inspection & Assembly — Lightly coat each gear and bearing before and during reassembly with gear oil. After installing each component, ensure all rotating parts are free to move smoothly. Install differential gear assembly to axle housing after applying sealing agent and tighten gear carrier mounting nuts in diagonal sequence.

AXLE ASSEMBLY SPECIFICATIONS

Application	Specifications In. (mm)
Bearing-to-Bearing Retainer	
Pickup	.002-.008 (.05-.20)
All Others	0-.01 (0-.30)
Differential Pinion-to-Pinion Shaft	
Pickup	0-.0025 (0-.07)
All Others	.001-.003 (.02-.08)
Differential Pinion and Side Gear Backlash	
Pickup	.002-.005 (.05-.13)
All Others	0-.003 (0-.08)
Drive Pinion and Ring Gear Backlash	.005-.007 (.13-.18)
Ring Gear Runout (Backside)	
Type "B"	0-.003 (0-.08)
All Others	0-.002 (0-.05)
Drive Pinion Preload	
With Seal	9-11 INCH lbs. (10-13 cmkg)
Without Seal	6-9 INCH lbs. (7-10 cmkg)

TIGHTENING SPECIFICATIONS

Application	Ft. Lbs. (mkg)
Outer Bearing Retainer	
Pickup	36-43 (5-6)
All Others	25-36 (3.5-5)
Ring Gear-to-Differential Case	
Type "A"	47-54 (6.5-7.5)
All Others	58-65 (8-9)
Final Drive End Yoke (Final Torque)	120-160 (16.5-22)
Differential Carrier Cap	
Pickup	40-47 (5.5-6.5)
All Others	25-29 (3.5-4)
Differential Gear Carrier	
Assembly-to-Axle Housing	18-22 (2.5-3)
Lock Plate (Except Type "A")	11-16 (1.5-2)

COURIER

Pickup

DESCRIPTION

This axle assembly incorporates a removable carrier differential, having a hypoid type ring and pinion gear set, with the pinion being retained in the carrier by a companion flange and nut. Semi-floating axles are secured in the housing by the axle shaft bearing retainers.

AXLE RATIO & IDENTIFICATION

Only one type of axle assembly is used. Axle ratio can be determined by dividing the number of ring gear teeth by the number of pinion gear teeth.

REMOVAL & INSTALLATION

AXLE SHAFTS & BEARINGS

Removal — After removing complete brake assembly, including nuts securing backing plate and bearing housing-to-axle housing, slide axle shaft out of housing. Remove inner oil seal from axle shaft, spread locking tabs on lock washer, then using a suitable spanner (T72J-4252) remove lock nut and

washer. Using a suitable puller (T72J-1225), remove bearing with housing from shaft. Remove bearing cup and outer seal from bearing housing.

Installation — 1) Using suitable tool (T72J-1177), install new outer seal in bearing housing. Press or drive new bearing cup into retainer using tool (T72J-4252-B). Install brake backing plate and bearing housing on axle shaft, then position bearing on axle shaft.

NOTE — *Ensure bearing taper points in right direction.*

2) Slide tool (T72J-4252-A) over shaft. Place axle shaft on end in press. Press bearing in place. Install lock washer and nut, using spanner to tighten nut.

3) Install axle shaft and loosely assemble 2 bolts through bearing housing and axle housing flange. Mount dial indicator to backing plate so axle end play can be measured.

4) If end play is not to specification, adjustment is made by using appropriate shims between axle housing flange and bearing housing. After correct end play is obtained, install and tighten as necessary, all remaining components.

NOTE — *If both axles have been removed, check end play of each shaft as it is installed.*

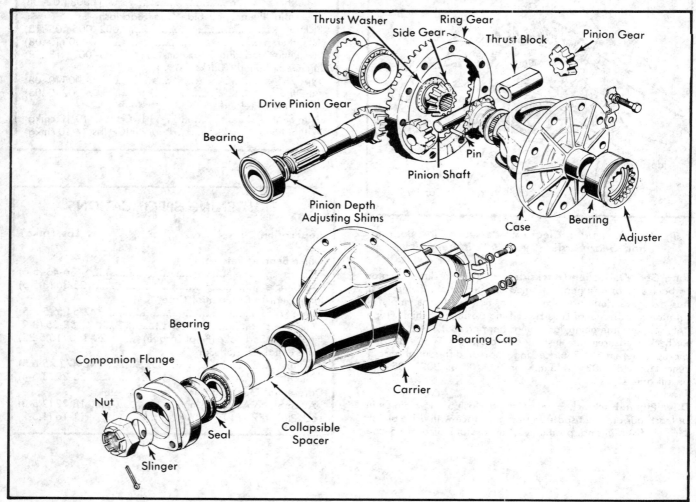

*Fig. 1 **Exploded View of Courier Differential Assembly***

COURIER (Cont.)

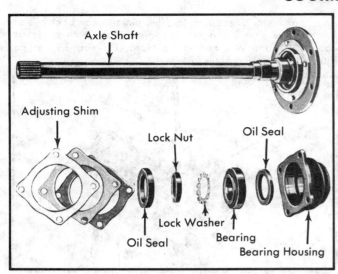

Fig. 2   Exploded View of Axle Assembly

DIFFERENTIAL CARRIER

Removal — Raise and support vehicle. Drain lubricant from differential, replace drain plug, then remove axle shafts as previously outlined. Mark drive shaft and companion flange at differential for reference at time of reassembly, then remove drive shaft. Remove carrier-to-housing retaining nuts, then remove carrier from housing.

Installation — Reverse removal procedure using a suitable sealer between the carrier and axle housing, and insure the drive shaft-to-companion flange reference marks are aligned.

OVERHAUL

DISASSEMBLY

1) Remove differential carrier as previously outlined, then mount carrier assembly in a suitable holding fixture with ring gear facing upward. Mount a dial indicator to carrier housing and check ring gear runout for reference at time of reassembly. Also make a gear tooth contact pattern check. *Refer to Rear Axle Gear Tooth Patterns in this section.*

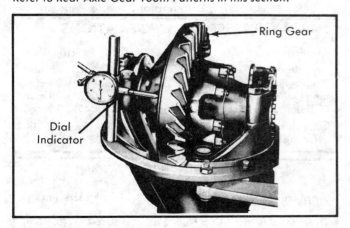

Fig. 3   Checking Ring Gear Backface Runout

2) Punch mark differential bearing caps and adjusters for reference at time of reassembly. Remove adjuster lock plates.

Loosen bearing cap nuts and back off adjusters using suitable spanner (T72J-4067). Remove nuts, bearing caps and adjusters, keeping each bearing cap with its own adjuster.

NOTE — *Left adjuster has left hand threads.*

3) Lift out differential assembly keeping each bearing outer race with its own bearing. To remove differential bearings, use a suitable puller (T70P-4221). Remove bolts and locks retaining ring gear to case, then remove ring gear. Drive out differential pinion shaft lock pin and remove pinion shaft and thrust block. Rotate pinion gears 90° and remove them. Lift out differential side gears along with their thrust washers.

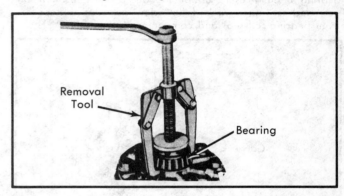

Fig. 4   Removing Differential Bearings

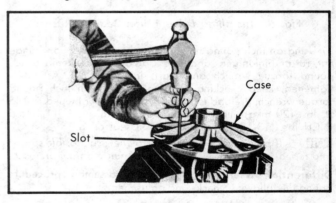

Fig. 5   Removing Pinion Shaft Lock Pin

CAUTION — *If required, use soft headed mallet to tap pinion gear from case and guide pinion out to avoid damage to gear teeth.*

4) Hold pinion gear companion flange and remove nut, then flange. Remove drive pinion and rear bearing. Remove collapsible spacer, oil seal and front bearing. Remove pinion bearing races from carrier using a drift in the slots provided. Remove bearing from pinion gear using suitable tool (T72J-4630) and remove pinion gear shim.

REASSEMBLY & ADJUSTMENT

Case Assembly — **1)** If original ring and pinion gear set is being installed, use original shim between bearing and pinion head. If a new gear set is being installed, determine the size of shim to use in the following manner: Drive pinions may be stamped either "A1, A2, A3" (positive amount) or "A-1, A-2, A-3" (negative amount). Compare marks on tapered ends of old and new gears. Subtract the two numbers. A "+" number requires installation of THINNER shim than original. A "—" num-

COURIER (Cont.)

ber requires installation of THICKER shim than original. If gear is not marked, gear set is nominal size and NEW shim of original thickness in carrier should be used.

NOTE — *Gear sets are stamped in increments of .0004" (.01 mm). To determine amount of variation, multiply stamped number times .0004" (.01 mm) and use the correct plus ("+") or minus ("−") sign. DO NOT use more than 4 shims.*

2) Using suitable driver (T72J-4616-A) install pinion gear bearing races. Install selected shim on pinion gear then install bearing on pinion using suitable tool and a press. Install pinion gear and bearing in carrier followed by the collapsible spacer, front bearing, oil seal and companion flange nut.

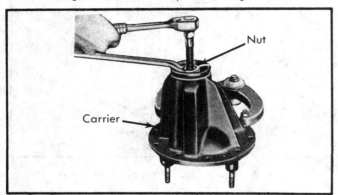

Fig. 6   Installing Drive Pinion Bearing Races

3) Using an inch pound torque wrench on companion flange nut, rotate pinion gear and note drag of oil seal. Remove inch pound torque wrench and start tightening nut. As nut is tightened, keep checking rotating torque with inch pound torque wrench. Preload is correct when nut is tightened to 145 ft. lbs. (20 mkg) minimum, and rotating torque is 11.3-15.6 INCH lbs. (13-18 cmkg) plus the oil seal drag.

NOTE — *If preload is exceeded, install new collapsible spacer and repeat procedure. Do not back-off nut to obtain preload.*

Differential Assembly — Reverse disassembly procedure noting the following checks and adjustments.

Side-to-Pinion Gear Backlash — After installing side and pinion gears, insert pinion shaft, without thrust block, into its proper position. Check side-to-pinion gear backlash. If backlash exceeds .008" (.20 mm), refer to table and install appropriate side gear thrust washers to obtain the correct backlash. Remove pinion shaft, then reinstall it with the thrust block.

Side Gear Thrust Washers	
I.D. Mark	Thickness
0	.079" (2.0 mm)
1	.083" (2.1 mm)
2	.087" (2.2 mm)

Ring-to-Drive Pinion Gear Backlash — After differential is completely assembled and installed in carrier, snug bearing cap nuts. Turn adjusters, using spanner, until bearings are properly seated and end play is eliminated with a slight amount of ring-to-drive pinion gear backlash. Slightly tighten one bearing cap nut on each side. Mount dial indicator to carrier flange with indicator plunger set at a right angle to

ring gear teeth. Check ring-to-drive pinion gear backlash at four or five points around ring gear. Turn both adjusters equally to obtain specified backlash. Proceed by setting differential bearing preload.

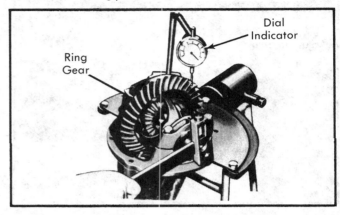

Fig. 7   Checking Ring-to-Pinion Gear Backlash

Differential Bearing Preload — Taking care not to disturb ring-to-pinion gear backlash, set preload using a dial indicator. *See Fig. 8.* After setting preload, tighten bearing cap nuts and complete assembly procedure.

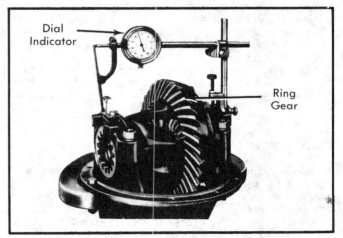

Fig. 8   Checking Differential Bearing Preload

AXLE ASSEMBLY SPECIFICATIONS

Application	Specification
Axle Shaft End Play①	.002-.006" (.05-.15 mm)
Ring-to-Pinion Gear Backlash..	.0075-.0083" (.19-.21 mm)
Ring Gear Backface Runout (Max.)	.003" (.08 mm)
Differential Bearing Preload	.0045" (.11 mm)

① — If both shafts were removed, end play of first shaft installed should be .026-.033" (.65-.82 mm).

TIGHTENING SPECIFICATIONS

Application	Ft. Lbs. (mkg)
Differential Bearing Cap Nuts	40.5-49.5 (5.6-6.8)
Carrier-to-Axle Housing Nuts	11.5-17.0 (1.6-2.35)
Axle Shaft Bearing Retainer Bolts	12-16 (1.7-2.2)
Ring Gear-to-Case Bolts	39.5-47.0 (5.4-6.5)
Companion Flange Nut	145-250 (20-34.5)

DATSUN INTEGRAL HOUSING

280ZX
810 Sedan
4-WD Pickup (Front Axle)

DESCRIPTION

The axle assembly is the hypoid gear type with integral carrier housing. The pinion bearing preload adjustment is made with a spacer and washer between the front and rear bearing cones. The differential side bearing preload and the pinion depth adjustment are made by shims. Driving power is transmitted to the rear axle by ball spline type driveshaft with universal joints at both ends.

AXLE RATIO & IDENTIFICATION

One basic type of axle assembly is used in these Datsun models. Differences exist in ring gear diameter used between model application. The R180 (180 mm ring gear) is used as rear axle assembly in all 810 sedans, all automatic transmission 280ZX and 2-seater 280ZX with manual transmission. The R180 is also used as the front axle in all 4-WD pickups. The R200 (200 mm ring gear) is used in all 280ZX Grand Luxury and 2+2 models with manual transmission. To determine axle ratio, divide number of ring gear teeth by number of drive pinion gear teeth.

REMOVAL & INSTALLATION

FRONT AXLE DRIVE SHAFTS & BEARINGS (4-WD PICKUP)

NOTE — *To remove locking hub, refer to Locking Hubs article in this Section, then proceed with removal procedure. Ensure locking knob is set to "Lock" before removal.*

Removal — 1) Raise and support vehicle; remove tire and wheel. Disconnect hydraulic line at brake caliper and remove caliper assembly. Remove locking hub cover retaining screws and remove cover. Remove drive clutch snap ring and drive clutch. Remove rebound bumper and stabilizer bar-to-lower link bolt. Remove axle shaft-to-differential carrier bolts and remove axle shaft. (To ease removal, turn steering wheel in opposite direction).

2) Remove knuckle arm-to-knuckle bolt. Loosen (DO NOT remove) upper and lower ball joint castellated nuts to within 3 threads of stud end. Separate ball joints from spindle using remover (ST29020001). Jack up lower link, then remove ball joint castellated nut. Separate knuckle from upper and lower links.

3) Using a screwdriver, pry up lock washer tab. Remove wheel lock nut with remover (KV40102500). Remove and discard lock washer, then remove special washer. Push wheel bearing support out of wheel hub, then separate hub from knuckle using a puller. Remove bearing collar from spindle.

4) Drive out inner wheel bearing and grease seal by tapping outer race with brass drift and hammer. Separate hub and rotor. Remove outer wheel bearing by tapping hub assembly against block of wood to shift bearing position, then remove bearing with bearing removal tool. Remove grease seal. Remove drive shaft bearing from bearing support with a drift.

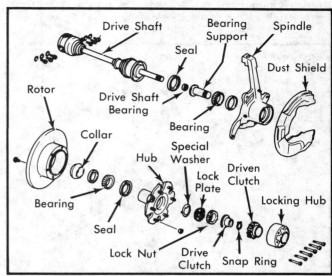

Fig. 1   Exploded View of 4-WD Pickup Front Axle

Installation — 1) To install, reverse removal procedure and note the following: Coat bearings and seals with suitable grease and ensure seals are installed properly. Install same bearing collar that was removed, or use new bearing collar of same number. Always use new lock washer.

2) Tighten lock nut to 108-145 ft. lbs. (15-20 mkg) and turn hub several times in both directions to seat bearings. Attach a spring gauge to wheel stud and check that wheel bearing preload is 2.2-9.5 lbs. (1.0-4.3 kg). If preload is higher than specified, replace bearing collar with a thicker collar (increase stamped number by 1). If preload is lower than specified, replace bearing collar with a thinner collar (decrease stamped number by 1). Repeat procedure until correct preload is obtained.

3) When bearing preload is correct, bend lock washer tab up into lock nut groove and install hub and knuckle assembly. Before installing locking hub cover, adjust axle shaft end play to .004-.012″ (.1-.3 mm) by using a snap ring of proper thickness. Snap rings are available in 5 thicknesses from .043-.075″ (1.1-1.9 mm) in .008″ (.2 mm) increments.

REAR AXLE DRIVE SHAFTS & BEARINGS (EXCEPT 4-WD PICKUP)

Removal — 1) Raise and support vehicle; remove tire and wheel. On 810 models, remove brake drum; on 280ZX models, disconnect hydraulic line at caliper and remove caliper and disc. Disconnect drive shaft from axle shaft outer flange. Remove differential side yoke attaching bolt. Remove wheel bearing lock nut while holding drive axle shaft outer flange stationary.

NOTE — *280ZX models with R200 differential use flanges on both ends instead of a removable yoke with single retaining bolt on inner end.*

NOTE — *Do not reuse bearings or grease seal after removal.*

Installation — To install, reverse removal procedure and note the following: Clean and inspect all parts for wear or damage and replace as necessary. Grease wheel bearings and housing before installation. When installing bearings, ensure outer

DATSUN INTEGRAL HOUSING (Cont.)

bearing is installed with seal facing wheel and that inner bearing is installed with seal facing differential.

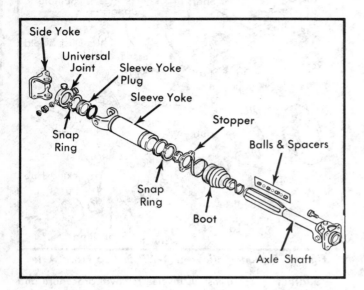

Fig. 2 Exploded View of Rear Axle Drive Shaft Assembly (R200 Differential Shown — R180 Similar)

2) Axle housings are stamped with letter "A", "B" or "C" (280ZX) or "M", "N" or "P" (810). Ensure bearing spacer of same stamping is installed. Tighten lock nut to 181-239 ft. lbs. (25-33 mkg) and check that axle shaft end play is 0-.012" (0-.3 mm) on 810 or .008-.020" (.2-.5 mm) on 280ZX and that turning torque of axle shaft is less than 2.6 INCH lbs. (1.2 cmkg) at hub bolt. If either adjustment is not correct, replace bearing spacer and repeat procedure. Bleed and adjust brakes.

PINION FLANGE & OIL SEAL

Removal — Drain differential, then raise and support vehicle. Disconnect propeller shaft from pinion flange. On 280ZX only, remove muffler, insulator and exhaust tube mounting bolts to free them from body. On all models, hold pinion flange and remove pinion nut, then remove flange with puller. Remove oil seal.

Installation — To install, reverse removal procedure and note the following: Apply suitable grease between seal lips before installation. Tighten pinion nut to specifications and ensure pinion bearing preload is correctly adjusted. Fill differential to proper level with gear oil.

AXLE ASSEMBLY

NOTE — Drive shafts of 280ZX models are connected to R180 differential with yokes and to R200 with companion flanges.

Removal — Raise and support rear of vehicle. Drain differential gear oil. Disconnect propeller shaft at companion flange.

Disconnect drive shafts at each wheel and remove side yoke fixing bolts at differential. Remove side yokes and drive shafts as assemblies. On 280ZX, remove front shield. On all models, support differential on suitable jack and remove mounting bolts at suspension members. On 810 models, remove nut on end of differential bracket. On all models, lower assembly on jack and remove from vehicle.

NOTE — Support suspension member on a stand to prevent damage to insulators.

Installation — To install, reverse removal procedure and tighten all nuts and bolts to specifications. Fill assembly to correct level with gear oil.

OVERHAUL

FRONT AXLE DRIVE SHAFT (4-WD PICKUP)

Manufacturer does not recommend disassembly of front drive shaft on 4-WD pickup. Replace as complete assembly only.

REAR AXLE DRIVE SHAFT (EXCEPT 4-WD PICKUP)

Disassembly — Remove universal joint from differential end of drive shaft. Remove snap ring from sleeve yoke plug and remove plug. Compress drive shaft and remove snap ring from stopper, then remove stopper. Disconnect boot and separate drive shaft carefully so as not to lose balls and spacers.

Cleaning & Inspection — Check rubber boot and oil seals for damage and replace as necessary. Inspect drive shaft for straightness, cracks, damage and distortion; replace drive shaft if necessary. Check all other components for wear, damage and distortion; replace complete drive shaft assembly if any faulty part is found. Check drive shaft play as shown in Fig. 3. Replace complete assembly if play exceeds .04" (1 mm) on 810 or .008" (.2 mm) on 280ZX.

NOTE — Measurement should be taken with drive shaft fully compressed.

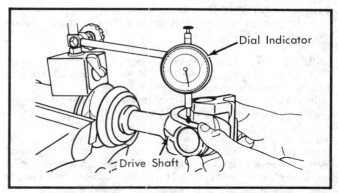

Fig. 3 Measuring Play in Rear Drive Shaft

DATSUN INTEGRAL HOUSING (Cont.)

Reassembly — 1) To reassemble, reverse disassembly procedure and note the following: Align yokes and ensure steel balls and spacers are installed in correct order. Adjust distance between spider journals (measured from center to center) to length of 13.54" (344 mm). Cover sleeve yoke with boot and secure with boot band.

2) Adjust axial play of universal joint to within .0008" (.2 mm) by use of snap rings. Snap rings of equal thickness must be installed on each end of yoke sleeves. Apply grease to ball grooves and oil grooves with about 1¼ ozs. (35 g) of oil in bottom end of sleeve yoke.

DIFFERENTIAL

NOTE — *Front axle assembly of 4-WD pickup is overhauled in same manner as that for 810 models (R180 differential).*

Disassembly — 1) Mount differential carrier assembly in holding fixture and remove rear mounting member and cover plate. Record backlash readings at several points around ring gear for use during reassembly assembly. On R180 differential, remove retainer bolts and pull side retainers from case with puller.

NOTE — *Retainers and shims of R180 differential must be marked for reassembly. Retainers and shims are not interchangeable.*

2) On R200 differential, pry side flange out while holding with hand to prevent them from jumping out of carrier. Remove bearing cap bolts and bearing caps. Mark carrier, caps and bearing outer races so they may be reinstalled in original position. On all models, extract differential case from carrier. On R180 differentials, remove side bearing outer races from retainers using puller (ST33290001).

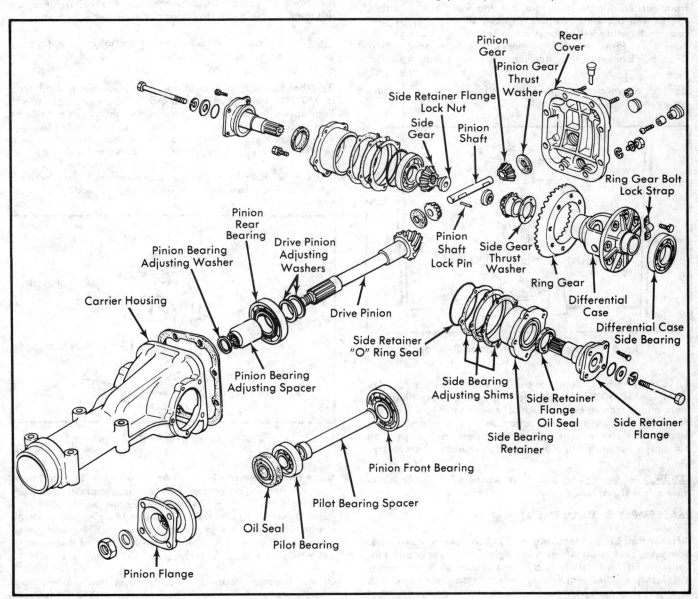

Fig. 4 Exploded View of Datsun Integral Carrier Differential Assembly

Drive Axles

DATSUN INTEGRAL HOUSING (Cont.)

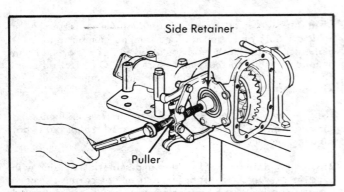

Fig. 5 Removing R180 Differential Side Retainer

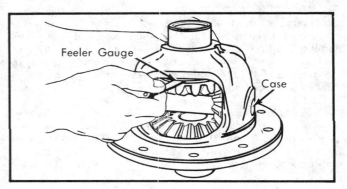

Fig. 7 Measuring Side Gear-to-Thrust Washer Clearance

3) Hold pinion flange stationary and remove pinion nut, then remove pinion flange with suitable puller. Press drive pinion from carrier and remove rear bearing inner race, bearing spacer and adjusting washers. Remove oil seal. Remove pilot bearing together with pilot bearing spacer and front bearing inner race. Press rear bearing inner race from drive pinion. Drive out front and rear bearing outer races with a drift.

NOTE — *Keep left and right side bearings separate, they are not interchangeable.*

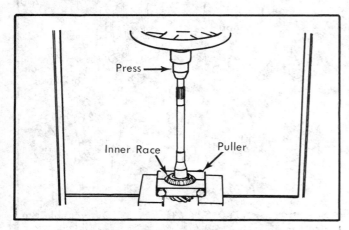

Fig. 6 Removing Pinion Gear Bearing

4) To disassemble differential case, remove side bearings with puller set (ST3306S001). Remove ring gear by unfolding lock strap and loosening bolts. Punch off pinion shaft lock pin from ring gear side, then remove pinion shaft, pinion gears, side gears and thrust washers. Thoroughly clean and inspect all parts for wear or damage and repair or replace as necessary.

CAUTION — *Mark gears and thrust washers for installation in their original position.*

REASSEMBLY & ADJUSTMENT

Differential Case Assembly — 1) Assemble pinion gears, side gears and thrust washers in original positions in differential case. Fit pinion shaft to differential case so that it aligns with lock pin holes. Adjust side gear-to-pinion gear backlash or adjust clearance between rear face of side gear and thrust washer. Install pinion shaft lock pin and lock in place with punch.

2) Apply gear oil to gear tooth surface and thrust surfaces and ensure gears rotate smoothly. Install ring gear on differential case and install bolts and new lock washers.

NOTE — *Tighten ring gear bolts diagonally while tapping around bolt heads with hammer.*

3) When replacing side bearings, measure bearing width with a .787" (20 mm) gauge and a 5.5 lb. (2.5 kg) weight block. Bearing width should be slightly smaller than gauge. Press fit side bearing inner race on differential case and side bearing outer race into side retainers. Install new oil seal on side retainer and apply grease to cavity between seal lips.

NOTE — *R200 differential has non-removable side bearing retainers. R200 bearings are .827" (21 mm) wide.*

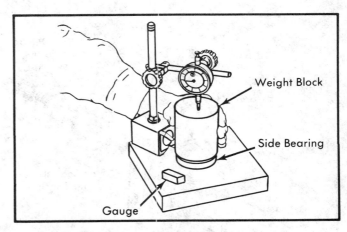

Fig. 8 Measuring Side Bearing Width

Drive Pinion Bearing Preload Adjustment — 1) Install front and rear bearing outer races into carrier. Install dummy pinion shaft (ST31212000 — R180 differentials; KV38100110 — R200 differentials) with rear bearing and original pinion depth washer between bearing and pinion head. If ring and pinion gear contact pattern was NOT correct at time of disassembly, use new pinion depth washer .122" (3.09 mm) thick.

2) Install pinion bearing preload spacer and washer, front bearing cone, drive pinion dummy collar (ST31214000 — R180 differentials; KV38100130 — R200 differential), companion flange and nut onto dummy shaft. Do not install oil seal at

DATSUN INTEGRAL HOUSING (Cont.)

this time. Tighten nut to specified torque. If pinion shaft can not be turned by hand during entire process of tightening nut, replace preload spacer and washer with thicker ones.

3) Using an inch pound torque wrench, check rotating torque of pinion shaft. If preload is not within specification, install thicker adjusting washer to decrease preload torque or thinner washer to increase preload torque.

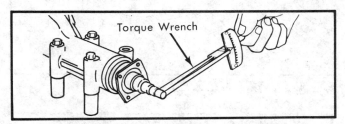

Fig. 9 Checking Drive Pinion Bearing Preload

Drive Pinion Gear Installed Height — 1) Leave dummy drive shaft installed (as described under Preload Adjustment) and install height gauge (ST31211000 — R180 differentials; KV38100120 — R200 differential) in bearing bores of carrier. Measure clearance between end of pinion gearhead and height gauge using feeler gauge. Thickness of drive pinion height adjusting washer can be determined by one of the following formulas:

R180 Differential $\quad T = W + N - [(H - D' - S) \times .01] - .2$

R200 Differential $\quad T = N - [(H - D') \times .01] + 3.0$

NOTE — *Formula values are given in Millimeters.*

T = Thickness of adjusting washer needed.
W = Thickness of washer temporarily installed.
N = Clearance between gauge and dummy shaft.
H = Figure marked on drive pinion head.
D' = Figure marked on dummy shaft.
S = Figure marked on height gauge.

NOTE — *If values signifying H, D, and S are not given, regard them as zero.*

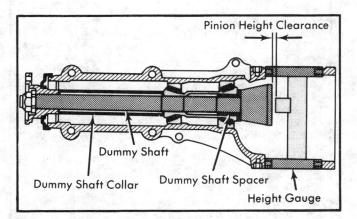

Fig. 10 Measuring Drive Pinion Gear Installed Height

2) After determining correct thickness of required pinion height adjusting washer, remove dummy shaft and height gauge. Fit correct pinion height adjusting washer on drive pinion gear and press fit rear bearing inner race. Lubricate pinion bearings then install drive pinion gear, pinion bearing spacer and washer, pilot bearing race, pilot bearing spacer, pilot bearing and oil seal. Install pinion flange and tighten pinion nut to specified torque.

Side Bearing Preload — 1) Required thickness of left and right side retainer shims can be obtained by the following formulas:

R180 Differential $\quad T_1 = (A + C + G_1 - D) \times .01 + .76 - E$
$\quad\quad\quad\quad\quad\quad\quad\quad T_2 = (B + D + G_2) \times .01 + .76 - F$

R200 Differential $\quad T_1 = (A - C + D - H') \times .01 + E + 2.05$
$\quad\quad\quad\quad\quad\quad\quad\quad T_2 = (B - D + H') \times .01 + F + G + 1.95$

NOTE — *Formula values are given in Millimeters.*

T_1 = Required thickness of left side retainer shim.
T_2 = Required thickness of right side retainer shim.
$A \,\&\, B$ = Figure marked on gear carrier.
$C \,\&\, D$ = Figure marked on differential case.
$E \,\&\, F$ = Difference in width of left or right bearing.
$G_1 \,\&\, G_2$ = Figure marked on left or right retainers.
G = Thickness difference from standard (8.10 mm) spacer.
H' = Variation figure marked on ring gear.

NOTE — *If values signifying A, B, C, D, G_1, and G_2 are not given, regard them as zero.*

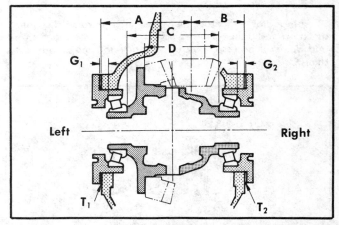

Fig. 11 Side Bearing Preload Formula Values

2) On R180 differentials, install differential case assembly in gear carrier in reverse order of disassembly. Fit correct shims and "O" ring seal in both side retainers in carrier. Arrow should point as shown in *Fig. 13*.

3) On R200 differentials, install differential case assembly with side bearing outer races into gear carrier. Insert side bearing washers and drive in spacer between right side washer and housing. Align marks on bearing cap and carrier and install bolts. Tighten to specifications.

NOTE — *Use care in installing spacer to avoid tilting side bearing outer race.*

DATSUN INTEGRAL HOUSING (Cont.)

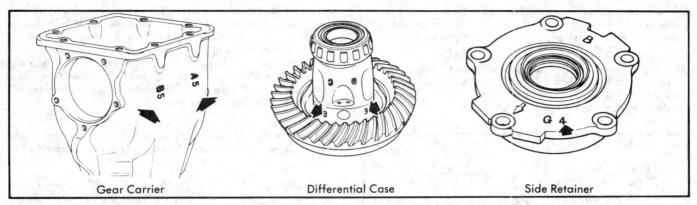

Gear Carrier   Differential Case   Side Retainer

Fig. 12 Side Bearing Preload Identification Marks (R180 Differential Shown)

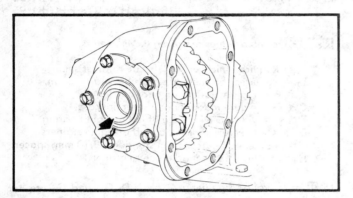

Fig. 13 Aligning Side Retainer During Installation

4) Using dial indicator, measure ring gear-to-drive pinion backlash and adjust if necessary. Check side bearing preload, and adjust if necessary by adding or removing side retainer shims.

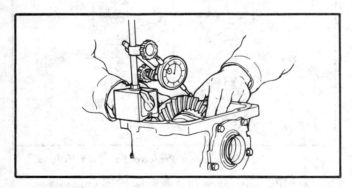

Fig. 14 Measuring Ring Gear Backlash

NOTE — *If side bearing preload is readjusted, ring gear-to-drive pinion backlash must be checked and adjusted if necessary.*

Final Inspection & Assembly — After all adjustments are to specifications, make tooth contact pattern test and make any necessary corrections. *See Gear Tooth Contact Pattern at beginning of this section.* Install rear cover and tighten nuts to specifications. Refill axle assembly to correct level with gear oil.

AXLE ASSEMBLY SPECIFICATIONS

Application	Specification INCH Lbs. (cmkg)
Pinion Bearing Preload	
Without Oil Seal	
All Models	9-11 (10.3-12.6)
With Oil Seal	
Pickup	8-15 (9.2-17.3)
All Others	9.5-12 (10.9-13.8)
	In. (mm)
Ring Gear-to-Pinion Backlash	
280ZX (R180 Differential)	.004-.008 (.10-.20)
All Others	.005-.007 (.13-.18)
Side Gear Backlash	.004-.008 (.10-.20)

TIGHTENING SPECIFICATIONS

Application	Ft. Lbs. (mkg)
Wheel Bearing Lock Nut	
Pickup (Front)	108-145 (15.0-20.0)
All Others (Rear)	181-239 (25.0-33.0)
Drive Shaft Flange Bolts	
R180 Differential	23-31 (3.2-4.3)
R200 Differential	36-43 (5.0-6.0)
Pinion Flange-to-Propeller Shaft Flange	
810	17-24 (2.4-3.3)
All Others	25-33 (3.5-4.5)
Rear Cover Bolts	
280ZX (R200 Differential)	12-17 (1.7-2.4)
810	14-19 (1.9-2.6)
All Others	29-30 (4.0-4.2)
Rear Cover-to-Mount	
R180 Differential	43-51 (6-7)
R200 Differential	54-69 (7.5-9.5)
Drive Pinion Nut	
R180 Differential	123-145 (17-20)
R200 Differential	137-159 (19-22)
Ring Gear Bolts	
R180 Differential	65-72 (9-10)
R200 Differential	43-51 (6-7)
Side Bearing Retainer Bolts	
R180 Differential	6.5-8.7 (.9-1.2)
Side Bearing Cap Bolts	
R200	65-72 (9-10)

Drive Axles

DATSUN SEPARATE CARRIER

200SX
210
510
810 Wagon
Pickup (Rear Axle)

DESCRIPTION

Differential gear carrier assembly has a hypoid type ring and pinion gear set. The gear carrier is constructed of cast iron. The drive pinion is mounted in two tapered roller bearings that are preloaded by a collapsible spacer. Drive pinion is aligned into position with a shim located between shoulder on drive pinion and rear bearing. Differential case is supported in carrier by two tapered roller side bearings. The side bearings are preloaded by inserting shims between bearings and differential. Case houses two side gears that mesh with two pinion gears mounted on a pinion shaft. The pinion shaft is held in the case with a lock pin. Pinion and side gears are set in front of thrust washers.

AXLE RATIO & IDENTIFICATION

Datsun does not identify rear axle with a particular outside identification marking, however all models use same basic type of removable carrier rear axle. It should be noted that part or model numbers may vary between vehicle models, but the internal design is similar. Various axle ratios are available depending on model and whether manual or automatic transmission equipped. Ratio may be determined by dividing number of ring gear teeth by number of pinion gear teeth.

REMOVAL & INSTALLATION

AXLE SHAFTS & BEARINGS

Removal — Raise and support vehicle; remove tire and wheel. Disconnect parking brake linkage and hydraulic line. On 200SX, remove brake caliper. On all other models, remove brake drum. Remove brake back plate (dust shield on 200SX) retaining nuts and pull assembly from housing with suitable slide hammer.

Disassembly — Mount axle shaft assembly in a vise or mounting fixture and cut bearing collar with a chisel. On pickups, bend lock tabs away and remove wheel bearing lock nut. On all models, remove wheel bearing with brake back plate (dust shield) using suitable puller.

NOTE — *Axle bearings on pickups are tapered roller type. Outer race may be removed from back plate after removing oil seal by tapping out with a brass drift.*

Reassembly — On pickups only, fit bearing outer race into position in back plate using brass drift and install oil seal. Pack seal lips with grease and install bearing and nut lock washers, then tighten lock nut to 108-145 ft. lbs. (15-20 mkg). Bend up lock tabs on washer. On all models except pickups, install bearing spacer, bearing and new collar using suitable press.

Installation — To install, reverse removal procedure and note the following: On all models except pickup, insert axle shaft and adjust gap between wheel bearing and axle tube end to 0-.004" (.1 mm) by installing appropriate shim. See *Fig. 2.* On pickup models, insert shims between back plate and axle tube end so that measured axle shaft end play is .0008-.006" (.02-.15 mm). On all other models, mount dial gauge and check axle shaft end play. End play should be .002-.016" (.05-.41 mm) on 200SX; .008-.020" (.20-.50 mm) on 810 and .004-.018" (.10-.46 mm) on 210 and 510.

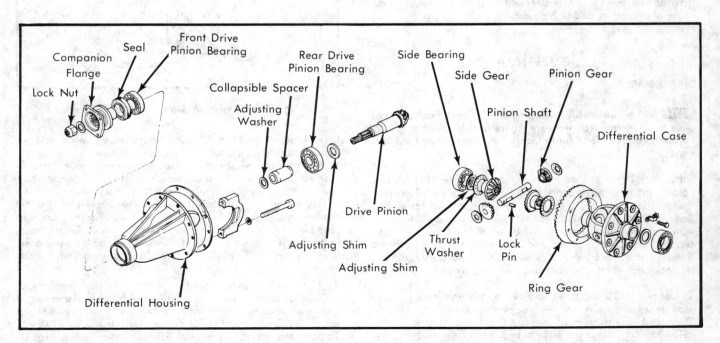

Fig. 1 Exploded View of Datsun Separate Carrier Differential Assembly

DATSUN SEPARATE CARRIER (Cont.)

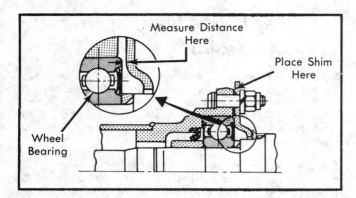

Fig. 2 Location for Checking Clearance Between Wheel Bearing and Axle Tube End on All Models Except Pickup

PINION FLANGE SEAL

Removal — Raise and support rear end of vehicle, then drain gear oil. Index mark propeller shaft and companion flange, then detach shaft and wire out-of-way. Remove drive pinion nut and companion flange. Remove oil seal.

Installation — Set new oil seal into position and pack grease between seal lips. Position companion flange and flat washer on drive pinion, then tighten nut and check bearing preload.

DIFFERENTIAL CARRIER

Removal — Raise and support vehicle on safety stands placed under rear axle housing. Drain gear lubricant. Index mark propeller shaft and remove. Withdraw rear axle shafts as previously described. Remove nuts mounting differential gear carrier to rear axle housing and lift out gear carrier.

Installation — To install differential gear carrier, reverse removal procedure and tighten nuts.

OVERHAUL

DISASSEMBLY

NOTE — *Predisassembly inspection of ring gear backlash and gear tooth contact can indicate where possible problems may be oriented. See Gear Tooth Contact at beginning of this section.*

Differential — 1) Mount differential carrier in suitable holding fixture, index mark side bearing caps and carrier. Remove bearing caps and lift out differential assembly. Remove drive pinion lock nut and pull companion flange off with a gear puller. Remove drive pinion together with rear bearing inner race, spacer and washer. Drive pinion can be freed by tapping front end of assembly. If necessary, extract oil seal and withdraw front bearing inner race.

2) Use puller (ST30031000) and extract bearing from drive pinion gear. Remove front and rear bearing races using a drift. Disassemble differential case as follows: Using puller (ST33051001), remove side bearings. Keep right and left side components separate for reassembly reference.

3) Bend back ring gear retaining bolt lock tabs and remove bolts by loosening in a diagonal sequence. Drive out pinion shaft lock pin and remove pinion gears, side gears and thrust washers. Identify gears and thrust washers for installation in original positions.

CLEANING & INSPECTION

Clean all disassembled parts and visually inspect for excessive wear. Check all gears for wear and replace if necessary. Inspect thrust washer surfaces and be sure they are free from surface scratches.

NOTE *Drive pinion and ring gear are replaced only as a set.*

REASSEMBLY & ADJUSTMENT

Case Assembly — 1) Fit pinion, side gears and thrust washers in differential case. Assemble pinion shaft to differential case so lock pin holes align with shaft. Insert side gear thrust washers of proper thickness to obtain specified clearance between rear face of side gear and thrust washer. Insert pinion shaft lock pin and secure by peening with a punch.

2) Lightly oil gear tooth areas and all thrust surfaces, then check that gears turn freely and smoothly. Fit ring gear on differential case, tighten bolts in diagonal manner and bend over lock tabs. If side bearing is to be replaced, measure thickness of new ones using suitable tool set as shown in *Fig. 3*. Normal bearing thickness should be as specified. Using a press, seat side bearing cone into differential case.

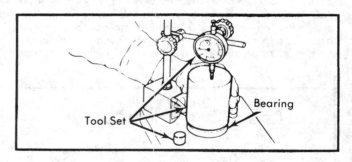

Fig. 3 Measuring Side Bearing Thickness

Drive Pinion Height — 1) Pinion height is adjusted with drive pinion adjusting washer placed behind drive pinion gear. Variation from the standard size to the drive gear center is marked on drive pinion gear head. If tolerance is greater than standard size, number is marked in "+", if less than standard size, marking is "-". Install front and rear drive pinion outer races in gear carrier. Fit drive pinion adjusting washers and rear bearing on suitable dummy shaft. Position dummy shaft in final drive housing without drive pinion adjusting spacer, then put on front pinion bearing and companion flange.

2) Tighten drive pinion nut to specified preload setting. DO NOT overtighten pinion nut. Install suitable drive pinion height gauge on final drive housing and measure clearance between end of gauge and surface of dummy shaft as shown in *Fig. 5*. To calculate thickness of needed drive pinion adjusting washer, use one of the following formulas:

DATSUN SEPARATE CARRIER (Cont.)

210	$T = W + N - .01H - .18$
200SX & 510	$T = N - .01(H - D - S) + 2.98$
810 & Pickup	$T = N - .01(H - D - S) + 2.18$

T = Thickness of needed shim.
W = Thickness of temporary shim.
N = Clearance between depth gauge and dummy shaft.
H = Figure stamped on drive pinion head.
D = Figure stamped on dummy shaft.
S = Figure marked on height gauge.

NOTE — *Formula values are expressed in millimeters.*

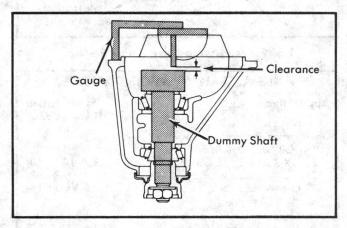

Fig. 4   Checking Drive Pinion Height Adjustment

3) Remove dummy shaft from gear carrier, take out pinion rear bearing from dummy shaft, select correct shims based upon calculations and refit pinion rear bearing and drive pinion. Ensure face side of shims are toward back of pinion gear.

NOTE — *Pinion nut, oil seal and collapsible spacer must NEVER be reused. Always use new parts during overhaul.*

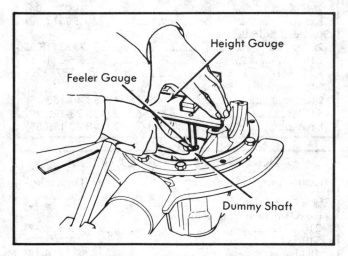

Fig. 5   Measuring Clearance Between Height Gauge and Dummy Shaft

Drive Pinion Preload — **1)** After obtaining final pinion bearing height, lubricate front bearing and place into carrier. Fit new oil seal in carrier and fill space between seal lips with grease. Slip new collapsible spacer on drive pinion, then lubricate pinion rear bearing. Insert companion flange in oil seal while holding flange tightly against pinion front bearing cone.

2) Working from rear of carrier, insert drive pinion into companion flange. Ensure drive pinion threads and mounting nut are dirt free, then holding companion flange, tighten nut. This will pull drive pinion into front bearing cone and flange. When drive pinion is pulled into front bearing cone, bearing end play will be reduced.

3) With end play still in evidence, companion flange will be felt bottoming on collapsible spacer. Slowly turn nut and continuously check end play to ensure bearing preload does not exceed specifications. When end play is eliminated, final preload is being approached. Turn pinion in both directions to seat bearing. Adjust bearing preload to specifications using an INCH lb. torque wrench.

NOTE — *Never try to decrease bearing preload by backing off pinion nut; always replace collapsible spacer.*

Backlash & Side Bearing Preload — **1)** Preload is adjusted with shims. Procedure is done after overhaul work has been completed on differential assembly. When assembling without changing side bearings, install shims of original thickness. If bearings are being replaced, use the following formula to determine the required thickness of adjusting shims:

210	$T1 = (A - C + D - H')x.01 + .20 + E$
	$T2 = (B - D + H')x.01 + .20 + F$
200SX & 510	$T1 = (A - C + D - H')x.01 + .20 + E$
	$T2 = (B - D + H')x.01 + .09 + F$
810 & Pickup	$T1 = (A - C + D - H')x.01 + .175 + E$
	$T2 = (B - D + H')x.01 + .150 + F$

T1 = Left shim thickness.
T2 = Right shim thickness.
A = Figure marked on left bearing carrier.
B = Figure marked on right bearing carrier.
C & D = Figure stamped on differential case (+ or - number).
E & F = Deviation from standard bearing thickness.
H' = Figure stamped on ring gear.

NOTE — *Formula values are expressed in millimeters.*

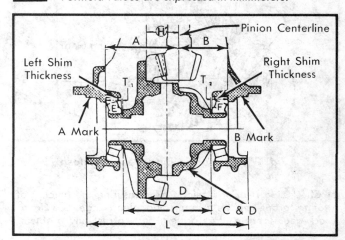

Fig. 6   Calculating Side Bearing Shim Thickness

DATSUN SEPARATE CARRIER (Cont.)

2) Side bearing thickness is measured using a suitable press (ST3250S0000) and applying approximately 5.5 lbs. (2.5 kg). Measure thickness in at least three locations.

3) Fit side bearing shim of differential case and press in both side bearing inner races. Place differential case assembly into gear carrier using a rubber mallet. Align index marks on bearing cap and gear carrier, then install bearing cap on carrier.

4) As a second check, measure distance between bearing caps using a micrometer. *See Fig. 7.* Specification obtained should be as indicated in table. Correct any deviation with shim of proper thickness.

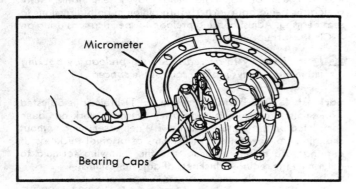

Fig. 7 Measuring Distance Between Bearing Caps

5) Using suitable dial indicator, measure ring gear-to-drive pinion backlash. Measurement should be as indicated in specifications. If backlash is less than specified, decrease thickness of left shim and increase right shim by same amount. If backlash is more than specified, reverse placement of shims in procedure above. Using same dial indicator, check ring gear deflection. Runout should be as specified.

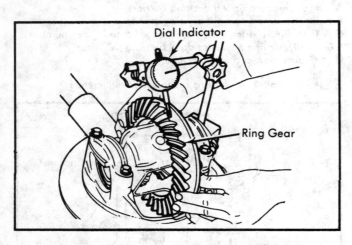

Fig. 8 Measuring Ring Gear Backlash

6) Check side bearing preload by measuring the amount of rotating torque needed to turn companion flange. *See Fig. 9.* Check gear tooth contact pattern and correct any problem.

NOTE — *See Gear Tooth Pattern at beginning of this Section.*

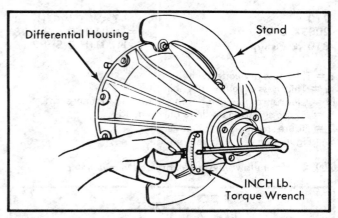

Fig. 9 Measuring Drive Pinion Preload

AXLE ASSEMBLY SPECIFICATIONS

Application	Specification INCH Lbs. (cmkg)
Drive Pinion Preload	
With Oil Seal Installed	
200SX & 510	6.0-8.7 (7-10)
210	5-7 (6-9)
All Others	9.5-14 (11-16)
Side Bearing Preload	
Measured at Ring Gear Bolt	
All Models Except 210	3.7-6.2 (1.7-2.8)

	In. (mm)
Ring Gear-to-Pinion Backlash	
210	.004-.006 (.10-.15)
200SX & 510	.005-.007 (.13-.18)
All Others	.006-.008 (.15-.20)
Pinion Gear-to-Side Gear Backlash	
All Models	.004-.008 (.10-.20)
Ring Gear Backface Runout	
200SX	.0016 (.04)
Pickup	.0031 (.08)
Standard Side Bearing Thickness	
200SX & 510	.7283 (18.5)
210	.6890 (17.5)
All Others	.7874 (20)
Distance Between Bearing Cap Edges	
210	6.039-6.041 (153.40-153.45)
510	6.820-6.822 (173.23-173.29)
810	7.811-7.817 (198.40-198.55)

TIGHTENING SPECIFICATIONS

Application	Ft. Lbs. (mkg)
Drive Pinion Nut	101-217 (14-30)
Ring Gear Retaining Bolts	
210	43-51 (6-7)
510	51-58 (7-8)
All Others	58-72 (8-10)
Side Bearing Cap Bolts	36-43 (5-6)
Differential Carrier-to-Axle Housing	
200SX	18-25 (2.5-3.5)
810	14-18 (2.0-2.5)
All Others	12-18 (1.7-2.5)
Companion Flange-to-Propeller Shaft	17-24 (2.4-3.3)

FIAT BRAVA & SPIDER 2000

DESCRIPTION

Rear axle assembly uses an integral carrier type differential having a hypoid type ring and drive pinion gear set. Drive pinion bearing preload is maintained by a collapsible spacer and differential bearing preload is obtained through the use of shims between the bearings and rear axle housing. Semi-floating axles use ball bearings retained on the axle by a press fit retaining ring and the axle is secured in the housing with a retaining flange. A removable rear cover permits inspection and service of differential assembly.

AXLE RATIO & IDENTIFICATION

Fiat uses only one rear axle assembly in both models. The axle ratio is 3.58:1; a twelve tooth drive pinion with a forty-three tooth ring gear.

REMOVAL & INSTALLATION

NOTE — *Removal and Installation procedures are not available for Spider 2000 model.*

AXLE SHAFTS & BEARINGS

Removal — 1) Raise and support vehicle. Remove rear wheels and brake drums. Remove bolts retaining axle shaft retaining flange to brake backing plate.

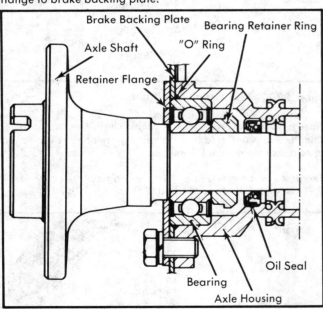

Brake Backing Plate
Bearing Retainer Ring
Axle Shaft
"O" Ring
Retainer Flange
Oil Seal
Bearing
Axle Housing

Fig. 1   Sectional View of Brava Axle Shaft and Bearing Assembly

2) Attach slide hammer to axle flange and pull axle from housing using care to guide the brake backing plate off the axle as it is extracted.

3) Remove axle bearing from shaft using an arbor press and suitable support tools. Discard axle shaft bearing retainer. Inspect retainer seat on axle shaft and if seat is scored or damaged, replace axle shaft.

Installation — 1) Place retainer flange and bearing on axle shaft. Heat bearing retaining ring to about 600°F (300°C) and place heated retainer on axle shaft.

2) Using an arbor press and appropriate support tools, press bearing retainer onto shaft until bearing is locked between retainer and shoulder on axle shaft.

NOTE — *Do not exceed 13,000 lbs. (5910 kg) force with press, as damage to axle shaft assembly may occur.*

3) If axle is to be installed at this time, replace oil seal inside axle housing (if required), and install axle in reverse order of removal.

REAR AXLE ASSEMBLY

Removal — Raise and support vehicle. Release parking brake and remove spring from parking brake bracket and support. Pull cable housings away from bracket and remove cables from bracket and support. Remove propeller shaft from drive pinion flange and stabilizer bars from rear axle housing. Remove brake hose from "T" connector and slip link out of slot in bracket on axle housing. Support rear axle assembly with floor jack(s), remove shock absorber-to-axle housing bolts and lower and remove axle assembly.

Installation — Reverse removal procedure then bleed the brake system and check for proper operation of parking brake.

OVERHAUL

DISASSEMBLY

NOTE — *Overhaul of differential assembly can be accomplished with rear axle assembly installed in vehicle.*

Differential Case Assembly — 1) Raise and support vehicle, remove axle shafts as previously described and separate propeller shaft from drive pinion flange. Drain lubricant from housing and remove rear housing cover.

2) Install spreader (8064) on housing, mark differential bearing caps for reference at time of reassembly, then remove bearing caps. Spread housing and remove differential case along with bearings and shims, noting position of bearing outer race and shims and keeping all left and right side components separated.

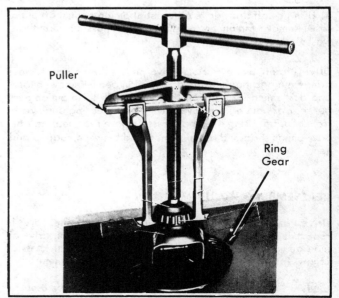

Puller
Ring Gear

Fig. 2   Removing Differential Bearings from Case

FIAT BRAVA & SPIDER 2000 (Cont.)

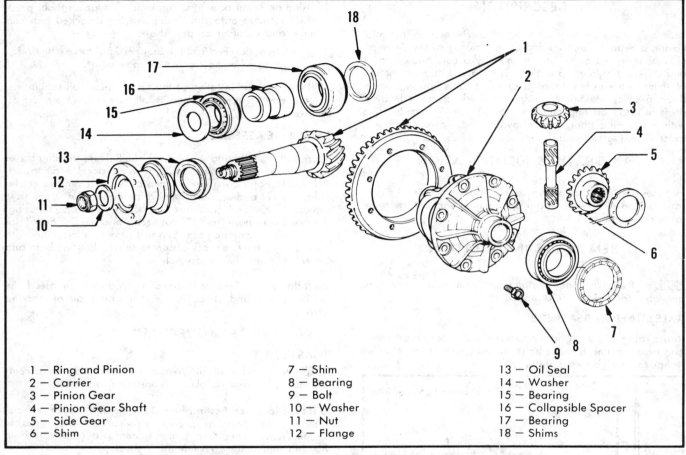

1 — Ring and Pinion	7 — Shim	13 — Oil Seal
2 — Carrier	8 — Bearing	14 — Washer
3 — Pinion Gear	9 — Bolt	15 — Bearing
4 — Pinion Gear Shaft	10 — Washer	16 — Collapsible Spacer
5 — Side Gear	11 — Nut	17 — Bearing
6 — Shim	12 — Flange	18 — Shims

Fig. 3   Exploded View of Brava & Spider 2000 Differential Assembly

3) Using a puller, remove differential bearings from case. Keep bearings separated with other components. Put locating reference marks on ring gear and case, then remove eight ring gear-to-case retaining bolts and remove ring gear.

4) Using a soft drift, drive differential pinion gear shaft out of case. Remove pinion gears, side gears, and side gear thrust washers.

Drive Pinion Gear — Hold drive pinion flange and remove flange nut and flange from drive pinion gear. Remove oil seal and dust shield from pinion shaft then push drive pinion gear out rear of housing. Remove drive pinion bearing outer races from housing. Using an arbor press, remove rear bearing from drive pinion shaft and retain shims found between bearing and gear.

REASSEMBLY & ADJUSTMENT

Drive Pinion Gear — 1) Install pinion bearing outer races in rear axle housing. Before installing rear bearing on drive pinion gear, establish pinion depth adjusting shim thickness as follows (all values given are in hundredths of a millimeter):

NOTE — If the original ring and pinion gears will be used for reassembly, and ring-to-drive pinion gear tooth contact pattern is satisfactory, use original shim(s).

Note marking on original drive pinion shaft. Measure original shim thickness and add it to the value given on the pinion shaft to establish the nominal dimension.

Example: Pinion marking is +10 and original shim thickness is 2.90. Nominal dimension is 3.00 (2.90 plus +10).

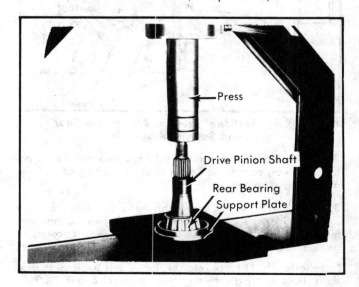

Fig. 4   Removing Rear Bearing from Drive Pinion Gear

FIAT BRAVA & SPIDER 2000 (Cont.)

Note marking on new pinion gear and subtract this value from the established nominal dimension and this will give you the new required shim thickness.

EXAMPLE: Nominal dimension is 3.00 and marking on new drive pinion is +20, then new shim thickness is 2.80 (3.00 minus +20).

2) Place new (or original) pinion depth adjusting shim on drive pinion gear. Press rear bearing on drive pinion gear. Lubricate bearing and install drive pinion and bearing in housing. Install new collapsible spacer, front pinion bearing, dust shield, new oil seal and pinion flange in housing.

3) Start pinion flange nut on shaft and as nut is tightened, keep checking rotating torque of pinion shaft (pinion bearing preload) using an inch pound torque wrench. Tighten nut until pinion bearing preload is within specifications.

NOTE — *If pinion bearing preload torque is exceeded, do not back off nut to obtain preload. Install new collapsible spacer and repeat procedure.*

Differential Case Assembly — **1)** Place thrust washers on side gears and install side gears in case. Install pinion gears by rolling them into position and install pinion shaft. Check rotating torque of one side gear while holding the other. If torque is not to specification, install new thrust washers on side gears.

NOTE — *Thrust washers are available in thicknesses from .0709" (1.80 mm) to .0817" (2.10 mm) in increments of .002" (.05 mm).*

2) Install ring gear on case and tighten bolts to specified torque. Press differential bearings onto case, and if using original bearings, spread housing and install case using original shims. If using new bearings or case, install case in housing and insert enough shims equally on both sides to eliminate any end play.

3) Install bearing caps and bolts and tighten bolts. Measure ring gear backlash using a dial indicator mounted to housing with plunger contacting ring gear at a right angle to the ring gear teeth. Block drive pinion flange from turning. Zero dial indicator. Rotate ring gear back as far as possible and note

backlash reading on indicator. If backlash is not within specification, adjust backlash by changing size of shims. To increase backlash, increase size of shim on pinion side of carrier, and to decrease backlash, increase size of shim on ring gear side of carrier. When changing shims, be sure to install shims of equal size to opposite side of carrier.

4) After determining correct shims to be used, add .002" (.05 mm) more shim thickness to each side. Install spreader on housing, spread housing and install bearing outer races and shims. Remove spreader and install bearing caps and tighten bolts. With differential completely assembled, check ring-to-pinion gear tooth contact pattern to ensure all adjustments are correct.

AXLE ASSEMBLY SPECIFICATIONS

Application	Specification
Pinion Bearing	
Preload	12-14 INCH Lbs. (14-16 cmkg)
Ring-to-Pinion Gear Backlash......	.003-.005" (.08-.13 mm)
Side Gear Rotating Torque	22-36 ft. lbs. (3-5 mkg)
Differential Bearing	
Preload	①Slip Fit Plus .004" (.10 mm)

① — .002" (.05 mm) on each side of differential case.

TIGHTENING SPECIFICATIONS

Application	Ft. Lbs. (mkg)
Axle Shaft Retaining Flange Bolts	36 (5)
Cover-to-Housing Bolts	18 (2.5)
Differential Bearing Cap Bolts	36 (5)
Ring Gear-to-Case Bolts..............................	72 (10)

JAGUAR

XJ6

DESCRIPTION

The differential assembly is of hypoid design with center line of drive pinion gear set below centerline of ring gear. A collapsible spacer is used to set drive pinion bearing preload and all other differential adjustments are accomplished using shims. Stub axles transmit power out of the differential, through independent rear suspension, to drive wheels. A clutch pack limited slip unit, "Powr-Lok", is used on some models.

AXLE RATIO & IDENTIFICATION

Jaguar uses only one basic rear axle design, however, unit may or may not be fitted with a traction lock device. Also, several different axle ratios are used. To determine axle ratio, divide number of ring gear teeth by number of pinion gear teeth. Whether or not axle is fitted with traction lock should be determined by owner inquiry or test.

REMOVAL & INSTALLATION

REAR SUSPENSION ASSEMBLY

NOTE – *This procedure is provided since many operations on the final drive require removal of rear suspension assembly before starting work on final drive.*

Removal – **1)** Raise and support vehicle. Place stands forward of radius arms on body with wood blocks between body and stands. Remove wheels. Remove mufflers from tail pipes. Remove safety wire and bolts securing safety strap to body. Remove radius arm securing bolt, safety strap and radius arm from body mounting post. Disconnect and plug brake lines at body.

2) Remove clevis pin securing hand brake cable to actuating levers on crossmember. Loosen lock nut and remove outer hand brake cable screw from adjuster block. Detach drive shaft from differential. Place jack under rear suspension. Remove bolts and lock nuts securing crossmember mounts to frame. Lower and remove rear suspension from vehicle.

Installation – To install, reverse removal procedure and note the following: Bleed brakes. Tighten radius arm nuts on lower control arm when weight of vehicle is on wheels.

HALF SHAFT

Removal – **1)** Remove rear suspension assembly. Remove rear hub as follows: Remove fulcrum shaft grease fitting. Withdraw cotter pin and remove nut and washers from splined end of half shaft. Using suitable puller, pull hub and carrier from half shaft.

2) Remove spacer from half shaft and examine inner oil seal track. Replace track if necessary. Remove 1 nut from outer suspension arm fulcrum shaft and using soft hammer, drift out shaft. Remove hub and carrier assembly from car.

3) Support suspension arm with jack and remove nut and bolt securing top of forward shock absorber. Remove nuts and washer securing shock absorber to suspension arm and remove shock. Remove 4 nuts securing half shaft flange to stub axle flange and brake rotor.

4) Pull half shaft from suspension unit noting number of camber shims installed between half shaft flange and brake rotor. If necessary, remove joint shields by drilling out rivets.

Installation – **1)** To install, reverse removal procedure, noting the following: If necessary, replace joint shield, positioning grease nipple access hole correctly. Cover joint lines in shield with non-hardening waterproof sealing compound. Be sure to replace camber shims.

2) To reinstall rear hub, proceed as follows: Install suitable dummy shaft (JD. 14) in hub carrier fulcrum. Install carrier on suspension arm, installing shims removed from between carrier and suspension arm. Replace outer suspension arm fulcrum shaft, displacing dummy shaft. Secure shaft with nut and reinstall grease nipple.

3) If necessary, install oil seal track to half shaft splined flange, replace spacer. Thoroughly clean and de-grease splines of half shaft and bore of hub. Using a small brush, sparingly apply Loctite "Stud Lock" to outer two thirds of half shaft splines. Assemble hub carrier to half shaft. Install washer and tighten hub carrier assembly nut. Install new cotter pin.

4) Install dial indicator so it bears against hub and zero indicator. Using 2 levers, pry out on hub and measure hub bearing endfloat. If endfloat exceeds specifications, overhaul rear hub and carrier assembly. After installation of rear suspension in vehicle, check rear wheel camber.

STUB AXLE OIL SEAL

Removal – **1)** Remove half shaft. Remove locking wire and withdraw bolts securing brake caliper to final drive unit. Remove brake rotor, noting number of shims removed between rotor and stub axle flange. Remove lock wire and 5 bolts securing caliper mounting bracket.

2) Withdraw drive shaft, together with caliper mounting shims, ball bearing and oil seal. Turn down tab washer and remove nut from stub axle. Remove ball bearing and caliper mounting bracket from stub axle.

Installation – **1)** Lightly oil new seal and position carefully in final drive case. Press seal squarely and fully seat in case groove. Do NOT remove protruding portion of seal. Coat seal with hypoid oil and place caliper mounting bracket and seal assembly over stub axle. Slide ball bearing on drive shaft followed by new tab washer and nut. Ensure bearing seats square to stub axle shoulder and tighten nut. Turn tab up on washer.

2) Lightly oil stub axle splines and install shaft in final drive housing. Install bolts securing mounting bracket finger tight. Using feeler gauge, measure dimension between inside face of mounting bracket and final drive housing. The measurement obtained determines shim thickness required. Remove stub axle and select shims of required thickness, and thinly coat mating faces and shims with suitable sealant. Tighten bolts in a diagonal sequence.

3) Wire lock securing bolts to tension in clockwise direction. Install brake rotors and half shaft flange, using shims removed from between rotor and flange. Install caliper on mounting bracket. Install suitable distance spacers (oversize nuts) to rotor studs and tighten nuts. Use feeler gauges to ensure that rotor is centrally located between jaws of caliper. If necessary

JAGUAR (Cont.)

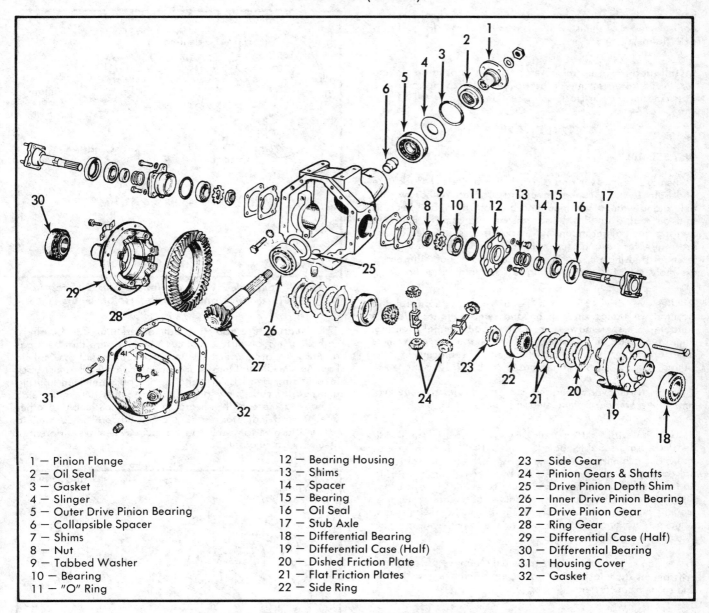

Fig. 1 *Exploded View of Jaguar "Power-Lok" Differential Assembly*

1 — Pinion Flange	12 — Bearing Housing	23 — Side Gear
2 — Oil Seal	13 — Shims	24 — Pinion Gears & Shafts
3 — Gasket	14 — Spacer	25 — Drive Pinion Depth Shim
4 — Slinger	15 — Bearing	26 — Inner Drive Pinion Bearing
5 — Outer Drive Pinion Bearing	16 — Oil Seal	27 — Drive Pinion Gear
6 — Collapsible Spacer	17 — Stub Axle	28 — Ring Gear
7 — Shims	18 — Differential Bearing	29 — Differential Case (Half)
8 — Nut	19 — Differential Case (Half)	30 — Differential Bearing
9 — Tabbed Washer	20 — Dished Friction Plate	31 — Housing Cover
10 — Bearing	21 — Flat Friction Plates	32 — Gasket
11 — "O" Ring	22 — Side Ring	

add to or remove from shim pack between flange and disc to center rotor. Continue assembly in reverse of disassembly procedure.

PINION FLANGE & SEAL

Removal — Disconnect propeller shaft. Check and record torque required to turn drive shaft flange clockwise (viewed from front) through backlash movement. Block rear wheels and remove flange securing nut and washer. Remove flange. Pry oil seal out of final drive case. Lightly score oil seal recess with tang of file.

Installation — 1) Ensure oil seal recess is clean and free of oil. Lightly tap new oil seal into recess ensuring seal is square with case. Reinstall flange, washer and nut. Tighten nut to 120 ft. lbs. (16.5 mkg) while rotating flange to ensure bearing seats correctly. Again check pinion preload.

2) If preload is below specifications, continue tightening flange nut until specified preload is obtained. However, if preload exceeds maximum specified value, new collapsible spacer must be installed (see differential overhaul). Reconnect propeller shaft and remove wheel chocks.

FINAL DRIVE UNIT

Removal — 1) Remove rear suspension assembly and drain final drive unit. Remove final drive mounting plate and shock absorber/spring units. Remove nuts securing half shaft inner universal joint to brake rotor and disconnect half shaft, noting shims removed. Remove nut from inner suspension arm fulcrum shaft and drive out shaft. Repeat for other side of unit. Disconnect hand brake levers from compensator.

2) Remove locking wire from final drive mounting bolts, remove bolts and crossmember by tilting forward over pinion.

JAGUAR (Cont.)

Remove calipers from final drive unit. Remove brake rotors, noting number of shims removed from between rotor and stub axle flange.

Installation — To install, reverse removal procedure making sure brake rotor is centered between jaws of caliper and wire lock tension bolts in clockwise direction.

OVERHAUL

DISASSEMBLY

1) Remove rear cover and discard gasket. Remove lock wire and bolts securing caliper mounting bracket. Withdraw stub axle along with caliper mounting bracket shims, ball bearing and oil seal. Turn down tab washer and remove nut, ball bearing and caliper mounting bracket from stub axle. Repeat procedure for second stub axle. Remove bolts securing differential bearing caps and lift off caps. Pry out differential assembly using two levers, taking care not to damage housing.

2) Remove drive pinion nut and washer. Mark relative positions of flange and pinion and remove flange. Using a suitable press, remove pinion from differential housing. Remove oil seal, oil thrower and outer bearing cone. Examine inner and outer bearing cups for wear. If replacement is required, extract cups using suitable tools (SL.14 & SL.14/1).

NOTE — *If removal of bearing cups is difficult, carefully heat final drive housing behind bearing cups.*

3) On "Powr-Lok" differentials only, remove differential side bearings using suitable tools (SL. 14 & 14/3). If no reference marks are present, scribe a line across both halves of differential case to ensure correct reassembly. Remove bolts securing both halves of differential case. Split case and remove clutch discs and plates from one side. Remove differential side ring, pinion side gear and pinion cross shafts complete with gears. Remove remaining side gear and ring and extract remaining clutch discs and plates.

4) On non "Powr-Lok" differentials only, remove peening and drift pinion shaft lock pin out of carrier. Remove gears, shaft and shims from carrier.

REASSEMBLY & ADJUSTMENT

Case Assembly — 1) On "Powr-Lok" differentials, install clutch plates and discs alternately into flange half of case. Install two belleville clutch plates so that convex sides are against case. Install side ring and position one side gear into ring recess. Install cross shafts. Install pinion cross shafts complete with pinion gears, ensuring that ramps on shafts coincide with mating ramps in case.

2) Assemble differential case halves ensuring that reference marks are lined up and clutch friction plate tongues are aligned with grooves in differential case. Install bolts but do not tighten yet. Check alignment of splines by inserting both stub axles. Tighten differential case bolts with stub axles in position. With one stub axle locked, other axle must not turn more than .75" (19 mm) measured on a 6" (152 mm) radius.

3) On non "Powr-Lok" differentials, install pinion shaft, shims and gears into differential carrier. Secure lock pin by peening.

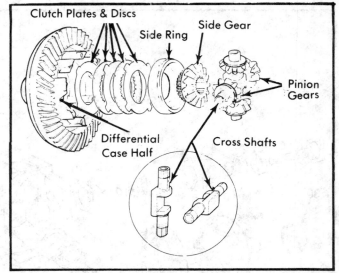

Fig. 2   Exploded View of Limited Slip Differential Clutch Pack and Side and Pinion Gears

Side Bearing Preload -- Install differential side bearings, without shims, on differential case, making sure that bearings and housing are perfectly clean. Place differential assembly in housing. Install dial indicator with indicator leg against back face of ring gear. Using suitable pry bars between housing and bearing cups, move differential assembly fully to one side of housing. Zero dial indicator and move assembly to other side. Record indicator reading and add .009" (.20 mm) to reading to give total shim pack required. Remove differential assembly from housing.

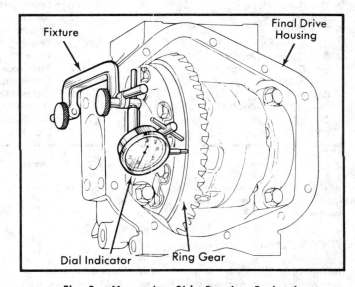

Fig. 3   Measuring Side Bearing Preload

Drive Pinion Depth — 1) Place pinion, together with inner bearing cone, into housing. Turn housing over and support pinion. Install pinion outer bearing cone, flange, washer and nut, omitting collapsible spacer, oil slinger and oil seal, tighten nut. Using suitable dial indicator support fixture (SL.3), zero dial indicator on setting block (4 H.A.). Place dial indicator fixture firmly on face of pinion and note indicator reading to bottom of housing bearing bore (see illustration).

JAGUAR (Cont.)

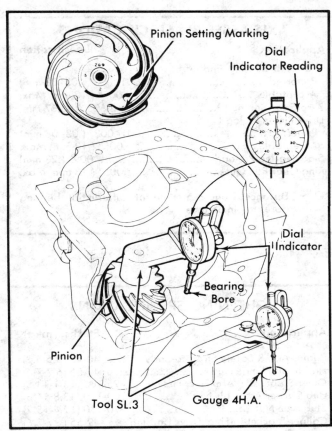

Fig. 4 Measuring Drive Pinion Gear Installed Depth

2) The indicator reading shows deviation of pinion setting from zero cone setting. This value should agree with value etched on face of pinion at bottom. For example, if value etched on pinion is −2, dial indicator should read −.002". If setting is incorrect, dismantle pinion and remove pinion inner bearing cup. Add or remove shims as required, reassemble and recheck pinion depth.

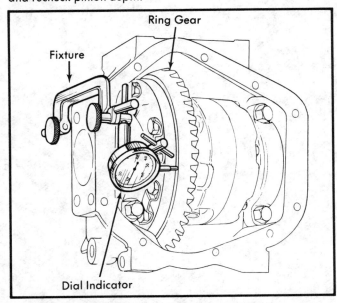

Fig. 5 Measuring to Determine Ring Gear Side Shim Thickness

3) When setting is correct, extract pinion from housing sufficiently far to remove outer bearing cone. Install collapsible spacer to pinion ensuring that it seats firmly on machined shoulder of pinion. Insert pinion into housing, install outer bearing cone, oil slinger and oil seal. Lightly grease splines of pinion shaft and install flange. Install new washer on end of pinion with convex side facing end of shaft. Install but DO NOT tighten nut.

Backlash Adjustment — **1)** Place differential assembly, complete with side bearings but less shims, in housing. Ensure that bearings and housing are perfectly clean. Install dial indicator on housing with feeler on back face of ring gear. Pry differential case and ring gear assembly away from pinion until opposite side bearing is seated against housing. Zero dial indicator at this point.

2) Move differential assembly towards pinion until ring gear is deeply meshed with pinion. Note indicator reading and from this value, subtract the backlash allowance etched on drive gear (eg. B/L.007 denotes .007"). This result will yield the thickness of shims (in inches) to be placed between differential case and side bearing on ring gear side of differential. Install this thickness of shims, taking shims from pack determined previously under "Side Bearing Preload". Install balance of total shims required on opposite side of case. An example of calculations required follows:

EXAMPLE:

Side Bearing Preload Reading	.080"
PLUS Preload Value	.009"
Total Shim Pack	.089"
Pinion-to-Ring Gear Clearance	.042"
MINUS Etched Backlash Value	.007"
Total Ring Gear Side Shims	.035"
Total Shim Pack	.089"
MINUS Ring Gear Side Shims	.035"
Opposite Ring Gear Shim Pack	.054"

3) With shims calculated installed, lower differential assembly into position, lightly tapping bearings home with soft hammer. Make sure ring and pinion gears mesh as installation proceeds. Install side bearing caps, ensuring proper cap is placed on proper bearing. Tighten cap bolts. Mount dial indicator on housing with feeler against back face of ring gear. Turn pinion by hand and check ring gear run out. If run out exceeds specifications, disassemble differential, clean all mounting surfaces and check for burrs.

4) Now place dial indicator to measure ring gear backlash. Move ring gear and check that backlash is to the specification etched on ring gear. If backlash is not to specifications, transfer necessary shims from side of differential case to the other.

NOTE — *To increase backlash, remove shims from ring gear side and install on opposite side and visa versa. Finally, run a gear tooth contact pattern and adjust shims as necessary.*

JAGUAR Cont.)

Pinion Bearing Preload — Install pinion and stub axle oil seals. Install stub axles following procedure given under stub axle removal and installation. Tighten flange nut to specified torque. During tightening process, rotate flange to ensure correct seating of taper roller bearings. Use care not to overtighten nut. If nut is overtightened, install a new collapsible spacer as pinion bearing preload will otherwise be incorrect. Install final drive rear cover using new gasket and suitable sealer (Hylomar).

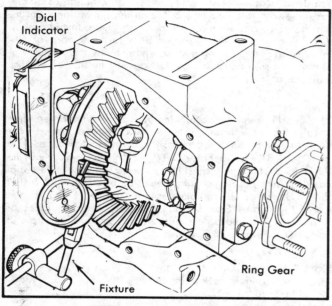

Fig. 6 Measuring Ring Gear-to-Drive Pinion Gear Backlash

AXLE ASSEMBLY SPECIFICATIONS

Application	Specification
Rear Hub Bearing Endfloat	
Preferred	.001-.003″ (.03-.08 mm)
Acceptable	.005″ (.13 mm) Max.
Zero Cone Setting ①	2.625″ (66.67 mm)
Drive Pinion Preload	
Preferred	.001-.003″ (.03-.08 mm)
Acceptable	.005″ (.13 mm) Max.
Side Bearing Preload	.009″ (.23 mm)
Ring Gear Run Out	.005″ (.13 mm) Max.

① — Distance from centerline of differential bearing bores to pinion face.

TIGHTENING SPECIFICATIONS

Application	Ft. Lbs. (mkg)
Radius Arm & Safety Strap-to-Body	40-45 (5.5-6.2)
Half Shaft Flange Nuts	49-55 (6.7-7.6)
Outer Suspension Arm Fulcrum Nut	95-105 (13.1-14.5)
Hub Carrier Assembly Nut	100-120 (13.8-16.6)
Stub Axle Nut	90-110 (12.4-15.2)
Caliper Bracket-to-Final Drive Housing	49-55 (6.7-7.6)
Pinion Flange Nut	120-130 (16.6-18)
Differential Case Bolts	43-50 (5.9-6.9)
Bearing Cap Bolts	63-70 (8.7-9.6)

LUV

Pickup

DESCRIPTION

Rear axle housing is banjo type with removable differential carrier and semi-floating axle shafts. Front axle has removable differential carrier and full-floating axle shafts. Both differentials are hypoid type ring and pinion gears. The axle shafts are retained in housing by cone-type roller bearings and bearing retainers at axle housing outer ends.

AXLE RATIO & IDENTIFICATION

All LUV models are equipped with one type of rear axle. The front axle on 4-wheel drive models is similar to rear axle. The gear ratio of both differentials is 4.10:1 and is determined by dividing the number of ring gear teeth by the number of drive pinion gear teeth.

REMOVAL & INSTALLATION

AXLE SHAFTS & BEARINGS

NOTE — *Front axle assembly must be removed prior to removal of axle shafts and bearings.*

Removal (Front) — **1)** Disconnect propeller shaft at front differential. Raise front of vehicle on hoist until weight is removed from springs. Suitably support frame on jack stands. Remove wheels and skid plate. Completely loosen torsion bar by turning height control arm adjusting bolts. Remove strut bars. Remove stabilizer bar-to-lower control arm bolts and disconnect stabilizer.

2) Remove brake calipers from supports and hang on frame with suitable wire. Disconnect ball joints at outer tie rods. Remove upper control arms from frame brackets by removing upper pivot shaft bolts. Tape shim packs together and mark for reinstallation for proper camber and caster adjustments. Remove lower control arm link ends, shock absorber-to-lower control arm bolts and lower control arms.

3) Shift transfer shift lever into "2H" position and set locking hub knob to "FREE" position. Remove locking hub assembly, then remove snap ring and shims from end of spindle. Remove hub and rotor assembly along with upper link and front axle (both sides). Disconnect pitman arm and idler arm, then remove steering linkage assembly.

NOTE — *See Locking Hub article in this section for complete removal and installation procedures of locking hubs.*

4) Support front axle assembly on suitable jack and remove 4 axle case mounting bolts. Lower and remove front axle assembly. DO NOT damage Birfield or double off-set joints. Drain differential housing, remove 4 axle mounting bracket-to-axle housing bolts. Pull axle shafts from both sides of housing.

5) Remove axle shaft bearing from steering knuckle using suitable tool (J23907). Drive out bearing races with brass drift and replace races with suitable press. Install new bearings with suitable tools (J8092 & J29019).

Installation — **1)** Install axle shafts in housing and tighten 4 axle mounting bracket-to-axle housing bolts. Place front axle assembly on hoist jack and position under vehicle frame. Install axle assembly and tighten case mounting bracket bolts. Install pitman arm to steering sector shaft and idler arm to pivot shaft. Tighten bolts.

2) Install hub and rotor assemblies with upper control arms to axle shaft ends, then install pivot shaft to frame bracket. Install camber and caster adjusting shims in original positions. Refit shock absorbers, then connect lower control arms to frame brackets. Connect ball joints to knuckle arms and tighten castellated nuts.

3) Install strut bars, stabilizer bar ends, then tighten control arm adjusting bolts. Install disc brake caliper assemblies. Thoroughly lubricate locking hub body and lock washer, then install snap ring. Push axle shaft with hand pressure and set clearance between locking hub body and snap ring to 0-.01" (0-.3 mm) using required shims. Install gasket and locking hub cover, aligning stopper rails during installation.

4) Install wheels and skid plate. Align propeller shaft index marks and install propeller shaft. Tighten all nuts and bolts, then lower vehicle. Fill front differential with suitable lubricant and bleed hydraulic brake system if required.

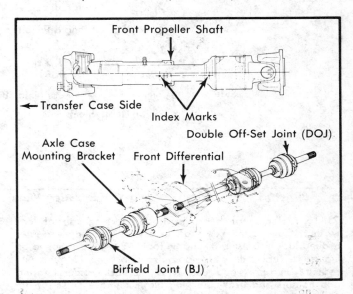

Fig. 1 *Exploded View of LUV 4-WD Front Axle Assembly*

Removal (Rear) — **1)** Raise vehicle. Remove wheel and tire assembly. Remove brake drum, brake shoes, and disconnect parking brake inner cable. Disconnect brake line from wheel cylinder and cover end to prevent loss of fluid and entry of dirt. From inboard side of brake backing plate, remove four nuts from the bearing holder through bolts. Pull axle shaft from housing.

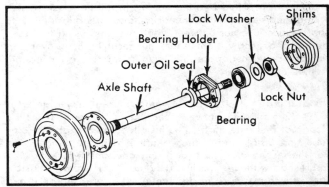

Fig. 2 *Exploded View of Rear Axle Shaft Assembly*

LUV (Cont.)

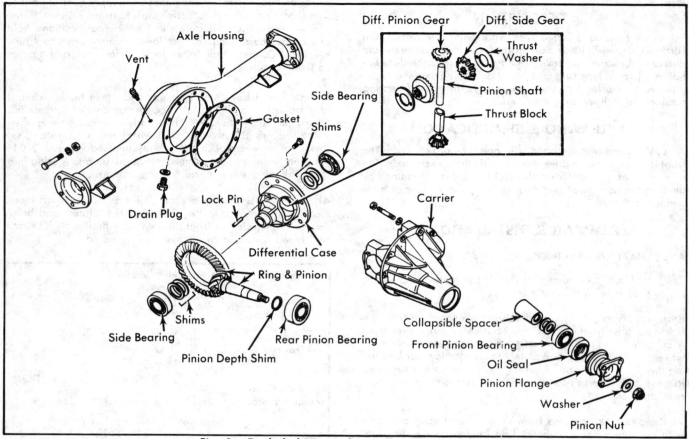

Fig. 3   Exploded View of LUV Rear Axle Assembly

2) To replace rear bearings, flatten locking tab of lock washer, then mount axle shaft in a vise, clamping vise jaws around lock nut. Using a suitable tool (J-24246) positioned on lug bolts, turn axle shaft loose from lock nut. Mount axle assembly in a press and remove lock nut, lock washer, bearing and holder, and brake backing plate. Remove oil seal from outboard side of bearing holder, then drive off bearing outer race with a drift.

3) To reassemble, install bearing outer race and grease seal into bearing holder using suitable drivers. Apply wheel bearing grease to bearing holder, rear axle tube, and bearing inner race. Insert the four through bolts into backing plate, then install bearing holder to backing plate, making sure oil seal side of bearing holder is against backing plate. Place backing plate assembly over axle shaft, position bearing over axle shaft and press into bearing holder. Install new lock washer with dished side away from bearing, and thread lock nut onto shaft. Place lock nut between vise jaws, and using tool used during disassembly, tighten lock nut securely. Bend over portion of lock washer opposite to locating tab to prevent lock nut from turning.

Installation — 1) If both axle shafts were removed, insert a .079" (2 mm) shim between bearing holder and axle tube flange of first axle shaft to be installed. Insert shaft into axle tube and install and tighten bearing holder-to-flange bolts. For the second axle shaft (or if only one shaft was removed), insert shaft without shims into axle tube until it comes into contact with thrust block in differential. Measure clearance between bearing holder and axle tube flange. See Fig. 4.

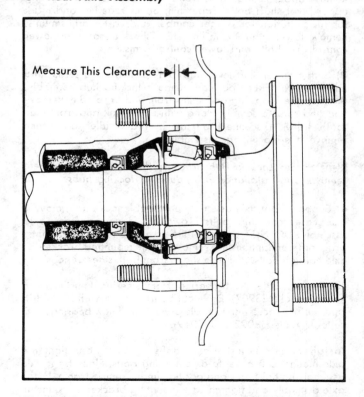

Fig. 4   Sectional View of Axle Shaft Bearing Assembly Measurement for Rear Axle Shaft Shim Requirements

LUV (Cont.)

2) Proper size shim for this location may be determined by adding .012" (.3 mm) to measurement just obtained. Select a shim or combination of shims, withdraw axle shaft, and install shims between bearing holder and flange face. Reinstall axle shaft and tighten 4 through bolts. Connect brake line to wheel cylinder, then install brake shoes, parking brake cable, and brake drum. Install wheel and tire assembly, adjust brakes and bleed system.

DIFFERENTIAL CARRIER

NOTE — *Front differential carrier is removed from front axle after axle has been removed from vehicle.*

Removal (Rear) — 1) Raise rear of vehicle, remove wheels and brake drums. Disconnect brake lines at wheel cylinders. Disconnect parking brake cable brackets at rear spring location, remove 4 through bolts from each end flange and partially withdraw axle shafts from axle tubes.

2) Disconnect propeller shaft from pinion flange and place out of way. Remove nuts attaching carrier to axle housing and remove carrier assembly.

Installation — To install, reverse removal procedure, making sure to refill axle with lubricant.

OVERHAUL

FRONT AXLE SHAFTS

NOTE — *Axle shaft assembly is an integral unit and should be disassembled only to replace defective parts.*

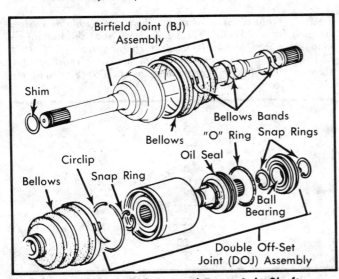

Fig. 5   Exploded View of Front Axle Shafts

Disassembly — 1) Remove front axle assembly and axle shafts as previously described. Using a screwdriver or equivalent, lift hooked end of bellows band on larger diameter end of double off-set joint (DOJ), then carefully remove bellows. Repeat procedure to remove band on smaller end. Discard bellows bands.

2) Slide bellows toward Birfield joint (BJ) side and pry off circlip. Hold DOJ case with hand and withdraw shaft. Remove grease, then remove 6 balls by prying out with screwdriver inserted against shaft. Rotate bearing cage ½ pitch to align

cage ball guide with ball retainer projection, then slide bearing cage toward bellows. Remove ball retainer snap ring and remove ball retainer. Remove bearing cage and bellows. See Fig. 6.

NOTE — *Bearing cage can NOT be removed in reverse direction.*

Fig. 6   Removing Bearing Cage and Retainer

NOTE — *BJ assembly is secured in position with axle shaft and can NOT be disassembled. BJ assembly should be removed from DOJ assembly ONLY to replace bellows.*

Inspection — Wipe all parts clean with a rag. Inspect the BJ and DOJ assemblies for play in normal direction of rotation. If variance exceeds $2\frac{1}{2}°$, replace entire axle shaft. If axle shaft-to-case contact is found, check steering angle. If axle shaft-to-circlip or bottom case contact is found, check for transverse misalignment of front axle assembly.

Reassembly — 1) Carefully install bellows to BJ assembly and fill half of the cavity with specified grease. Fill bearing cage with specified grease and seat bellows. Install new bellows band. During installation of bellows, equalize air pressure on both sides to prevent premature wear due to collapse of bellows.

2) Working from DOJ assembly side, push bellows band and bellows onto shaft. Slide bearing cage onto shaft (smaller diameter side toward BJ end), then slide ball retainer onto shaft. Secure ball retainer with snap ring. Align ball guide of bearing cage with ball retainer projection, then turn cage ½ pitch. Press ball bearings into postion with fingers.

3) Fill half the clearance of DOJ case with suitable grease and position case over DOJ bearing assembly. Install circlip in groove with ends positioned at inner circumference, away from ball bearing groove. Pack DOJ assembly with suitable grease and install bellows as previously described for BJ assembly.

DIFFERENTIAL ASSEMBLIES

NOTE — *Overhaul procedures of front and rear differentials are similar.*

Disassembly — 1) Mark side bearing caps for reassembly reference, remove nuts and bearing caps, then remove differential case assembly. Remove differential side bearings from case using suitable puller and adapter. Record thickness of each side bearing and shim pack, then place with appropriate bearing race.

Drive Axles

LUV (Cont.)

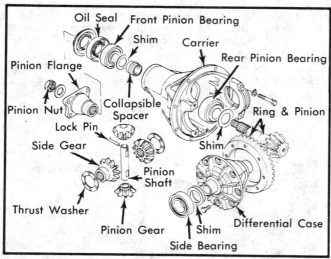

Fig. 7 Exploded View of Front Differential Assembly

NOTE — *Keep right and left side bearing races with respective bearings.*

2) Remove ring gear bolts and separate ring gear from case. Drive out pinion shaft lock pin using a long drift. Remove pinion shaft using a drift, then withdraw thrust block (rear differential), pinion gears, side gears and thrust washers.

NOTE — *It may be necessary to remove caulking in lock pin using a 5 mm drill.*

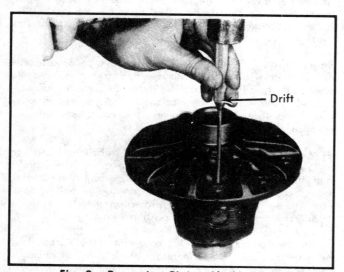

Fig. 8 Removing Pinion Shaft Lock Pin

3) Remove pinion nut and pinion flange. Drive the pinion gear from carrier using a soft hammer or drift. Withdraw front pinion bearing and oil seal. Using a drift, remove pinion bearing races from carrier. Mount pinion gear in a press and remove rear pinion bearing and depth shim from pinion gear.

REASSEMBLY & ADJUSTMENT

Drive Pinion Depth — 1) Install front and rear pinion bearing races into carrier bores, lubricate pinion bearings, then position in respective races. Install suitable gauging plate, preload stud and pilot through pinion bearings and tighten snugly.

Rotate bearings to insure proper seating, then tighten lock nut until 20 INCH lbs. (25 cmkg) of torque are required to rotate new bearings, or 8-10 INCH lbs. (9.2-11.5 cmkg) are required to rotate used bearings.

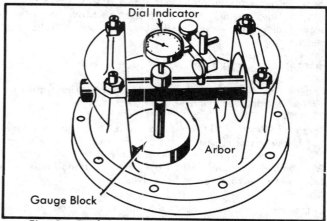

Fig. 9 Tool Arrangement for Measuring Drive Pinion Installed Height

2) Place mounting discs on arbor tool and place assembly in position in side bearing bores. Install bearing caps snugly. Mount a dial indicator on arbor post and preload dial ½ revolution, then tighten indicator in this position. Position indicator plunger on gauge plate, slowly swing across until highest reading is obtained, then "zero" indicator on highest reading of gauge plate. Swing plunger off gauge plate and note indicator reading. Reading is the correct thickness of rear pinion bearing depth shim for a nominal drive pinion.

NOTE — *Front differential pinion shims are available in sizes ranging from .059-.077" (1.5-1.95 mm). Rear differential pinion shims are available in sizes ranging from .086-.101" (2.18-2.56 mm). A rear differential indicator reading of 0 (zero) or .001" (.03 mm) requires shims of .100" (2.54 mm) and .101" (2.56 mm) respectively.*

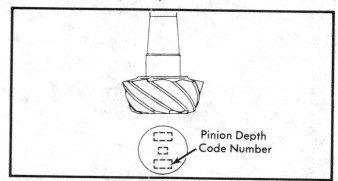

Fig. 10 Pinion Depth Code Location on Pinion Head

3) Examine head of drive pinion; pinion depth code is stamped by chemical ink and is the lower of three numbers. A "+" (plus) number indicates need for greater mounting distance (decreased shim thickness), while a "−" (minus) number indicates need for smaller mounting distance (increased shim thickness). See appropriate chart to determine proper shim variation to compensate for plus or minus markings.

NOTE — *If no pinion depth code is present, pinion is "nominal" and no correction to dial indicator reading is required.*

LUV (Cont.)

Pinion Depth Shim Chart (Front Differential)

Pinion Code	Correction Required
+6	Subtract .0024" (.06 mm)
+4	Subtract .0016" (.04 mm)
+2	Subtract .0008" (.02 mm)
0	No Correction Required
—2	Add .0008" (.02 mm)
—4	Add .0016" (.04 mm)
—6	Add .0024" (.04 mm)

Pinion Depth Shim Chart (Rear Differential)

Pinion Code	Correction Required
+10	Subtract .005" (.13 mm)
+8	Subtract .004" (.10 mm)
+6	Subtract .003" (.08 mm)
+4	Subtract .002" (.05 mm)
+2	Subtract .001" (.03 mm)
0	No Correction Required
—2	Add .001" (.03 mm)
—4	Add .002" (.05 mm)
—6	Add .003" (.08 mm)
—8	Add .004" (.10 mm)
—10	Add .005" (.13 mm)

4) Place selected shim on drive pinion and press rear bearing onto pinion. Remove gauging tools from carrier.

NOTE — *DO NOT press on roller cage; press only on bearing inner race.*

Pinion Bearing Preload — 1) Place drive pinion and collapsible spacer into carrier, then install front pinion bearing and oil seal. Mount pinion flange on drive pinion, apply lubricant to pinion threads and install pinion nut. Tighten rear differential nut to 85 ft. lbs. (11.3 mkg) and front differential nut to 108-145 ft. lbs. (15-20 mkg). Rotate pinion to insure bearings are seated, then wind a small amount of string (approximately 4-6 windings) around pinion flange. Using a pull scale, note reading required to rotate flange.

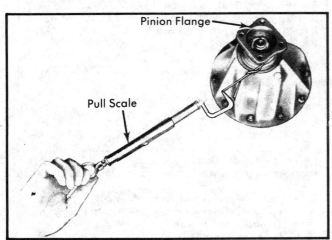

Fig. 11   Using Pull Scale to Measure Drive Pinion Bearing Preload

2) Continue tightening nut in small increments until pull required to rotate flange is 17 lbs. (7.7 kg) for new bearings or 7-9 lbs. (3.2-4.1 kg) for reused bearings.

CAUTION — *Preload builds quickly. Nut should be tightened only in small increments and pull scale used after each small amount of tightening. If preload is exceeded, a new collapsible bearing spacer must be installed.*

Case Assembly — 1) Install side gears and thrust washers in case. Position thrust washers 180° apart, then roll gears into position making sure they are in alignment to allow installation of pinion shaft.

2) Place thrust block between pinion gears (rear differential only). Drive pinion shaft into position, making sure lock pin hole aligns with hole in case. Measure backlash between side gears and pinion gears; if greater than .003" (.08 mm), install selective thrust washers to bring backlash within specifications.

3) Washers are available in thicknesses of .041" (1.04 mm), .045" (1.14 mm), .049" (1.24 mm) and .053" (1.35 mm).

NOTE — *Increasing washer thickness decreases backlash; decreasing washer thickness increases backlash.*

4) Install lock pin in pinion shaft and caulk end to prevent loosening. Install ring gear in position on case, apply Loctite (or equivalent) to threads and tighten bolts in diagonal sequence to 80-87 ft. lbs. (11-12 mkg) on rear differential or to 44-58 ft. lbs. (6-8 mkg) on front differential.

Backlash & Side Bearing Preload — 1) If original side bearings, differential case, ring and pinion, and differential carrier are being reused, the original shims may be reinstalled in their respective positions. If only new side bearings are being installed, measure new bearings with a micrometer and compare thickness with original bearings. If new bearing is thicker, SUBTRACT difference from shim pack. If new bearing is thinner, ADD difference to shim pack.

2) If new bearings, and/or differential case, ring and pinion, or differential carrier are being installed, new shims must be selected as follows: Install side bearings onto differential case, but do not install shims at this time. Mount case into carrier bores. Move ring gear tightly against carrier on ring gear side (away from pinion), and hold in this position. Using a feeler gauge, measure clearance between bearing and differential carrier on side opposite ring gear. Record clearance.

3) Proper preload is established using the predetermined dimension of .002" (.05 mm). Therefore, ADD this dimension to clearance obtained in step **2)** for proper preload. This will give required total thickness of both shim packs. Equally divide the total dimension for required shim pack thickness for each side.

4) Remove case from carrier, remove side bearings and install shim packs, then reinstall bearings. Install differential case into carrier, tapping carefully into place. Install side bearing caps in original positions, install and tighten attaching bolts. Measure runout of ring gear. If runout exceeds .002" (.05 mm), correct by cleaning or replacing parts. See *Fig. 12.*

LUV (Cont.)

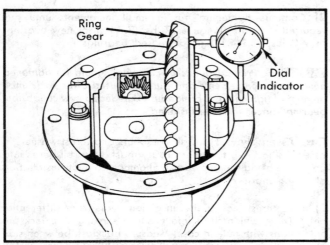

Fig. 12 Checking Ring Gear Backface Runout

NOTE — *Backlash changes approximately .002" (.05 mm) for each .003" (.08 mm) shim change.*

5) Mount a dial indicator against ring gear teeth and measure backlash in three locations. Backlash should be .005-.007" (.13-.18 mm) on rear differential and .004-.006" (.10-.15 mm) on front differential. If not within specifications, shims behind side bearings must be adjusted. To increase backlash, right side bearing shim must be increased and left side bearing decreased. To decrease backlash, right side bearing shim must be decreased and left side bearing increased.

NOTE — *To maintain preload when backlash is adjusted, the total thickness of both shim packs must not be altered. Therefore, if it is necessary to increase one shim pack, the opposite shim pack must be decreased by the same amount.*

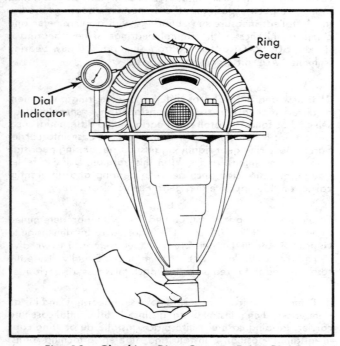

Fig. 13 Checking Ring Gear-to-Drive Pinion Gear Backlash

AXLE ASSEMBLY SPECIFICATIONS

Application	Specification
Pinion Bearing Preload①	
New Bearings	17 Lbs. (7.7 kg)
Used Bearings	7-9 Lbs. (3.2-4.1 kg)
Side & Pinion Gear Backlash	.003" (.08 mm) Max.
Side Bearing Preload②	.002" (.05 mm)
Ring Gear Backface Runout	.002" (.05 mm) Max.
Ring Gear Backlash	
Front	.004-.006" (.10-.15 mm)
Rear	.005-.007" (.13-.18 mm)

① — Measured with pull scale.
② — Add to side bearing "zero clearance" shim pack.

TIGHTENING SPECIFICATIONS

Application	Ft. Lbs. (mkg)
Ball Joint Stud Nuts①	75 (10)
Ball Joint-to-Lower Arm	45 (6)
Control Arm Pivot-to-Frame	
Upper	50 (7)
Lower	130 (18)
Upper Control Arm Pivot Shaft Bushing	220 (30)
Lower Control Arm-to-Crossmember	94 (13)
Rotor-to-Hub	36 (5)
Strut Bar-to-Lower Arm	45 (6)
Strut Bar-to-Frame	
Lock Nut	50 (7)
Nut	15 (2)
Pitman Arm-to-Steering Shaft	160 (22)
Idler Arm-to-Pivot Shaft	87 (12)
Front Axle Mounting Bolts	14.5 (2)
Rear Propeller Shaft-to-Pinion Flange	18 (2.5)
Rear Axle Shaft Lock Nut	190 (26.3)
Rear Axle Bearing Through Bolt	52 (7.2)
Ring Gear-to-Case Bolts②	
Front	44-58 (6-8)
Rear	85 (11.8)
Bearing Cap Nuts	
Front	50 (7)
Rear	75 (10)
Pinion Flange Nut③	
Front	108-145 (15-20)
Rear	85 (11.8)
Carrier-to-Housing Bolts	18 (2.5)
Front Axle Shaft-to-Axle Case	44 (6)

① — Plus additional torque to align cotter pin hole. NEVER back off to align cotter pin.
② — Threads coated with Loctite.
③ — Initial torque only.

MAZDA

GLC
626
RX7
B2000 Pickup

DESCRIPTION

Axle housing is banjo type with removable differential carrier and semi-floating axle shafts. Ring and pinion are hypoid type, in which centerline of pinion is set below centerline of ring gear. Differential case may be either two pinion or four pinion design. The axle shafts are retained in housing by ball bearings and bearing retainers at axle housing outer ends.

AXLE RATIO & IDENTIFICATION

All Mazda models use one basic type of rear axle assembly. Any differences in Removal & Installation or Overhaul procedures will be noted where they occur. To determine axle ratio, divide number of ring gear teeth by number of pinion teeth.

REMOVAL & INSTALLATION

AXLE SHAFTS & BEARINGS

Removal — 1) Raise and support vehicle; remove tire and wheel. Remove brake drum and brake shoes. Disconnect and plug hydraulic line from wheel cylinder. Disconnect parking brake cable. From inboard side of backing plate, remove 4 nuts from axle housing through bolts. Pull axle shaft, backing plate, bearing housing (pickup) and shims (if equipped) from axle housing with suitable puller. Remove oil seal from axle housing.

2) To replace rear bearings on pickup, flatten locking tabs of lock washer, then loosen lock nut with spanner wrench (490603622A). Remove lock nut and washer. Using a puller, remove bearing and housing assembly from axle shaft, then remove backing plate. Remove bearing and oil seal from housing. To reassemble, reverse disassembly.

3) To replace rear bearings on all models except pickup, mount axle shaft assembly in vise or mounting fixture. Carefully grind down bearing collar, then chisel collar off without damaging axle shaft. Remove bearing and backing plate, using puller if required. Install backing plate and spacer on shaft (chamfered edge of spacer must face axle shaft flange). Press bearing onto shaft until seated, then press new bearing collar onto shaft without any lubricant.

CAUTION — *Do not press bearing and collar onto shaft at the same time. If bearing collar is installed with less than 2.7 tons pressure, replace bearing collar.*

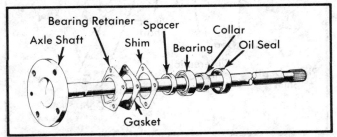

Fig. 1   Exploded View of Axle Shaft Assembly (Except Pickup)

Installation — 1) Apply a light coat of grease to oil seal and install oil seal in housing. Temporarily mount axle shaft and backing plate on axle housing with mounting nuts. Install dial indicator on backing plate and check axle shaft end play. End play should be .002-.006" (.05-.15 mm) on pickup and 0-.004" (0-.1 mm) on all other models.

2) On pickup only, if both axle shafts were removed, the end play of each shaft must be measured separately. The end play for first axle shaft installed should be .026-.033" (.65-.85 mm). The end play for the second axle shaft installed should be set to normal end play clearance of .002-.006" (.05-.15 mm).

3) After installing correct shim pack, install and tighten all attaching bolts and nuts. Install brake shoes and drum. Connect hydraulic lines to wheel cylinders, adjust brakes and bleed hydraulic system.

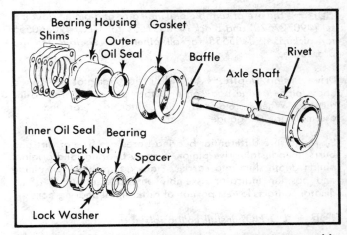

Fig. 2   Exploded View of Pickup Axle Shaft Assembly

DIFFERENTIAL CARRIER

Removal — Raise vehicle until rear wheels are clear of ground. Remove drain plug and drain rear axle lubricant, reinstall plug and tighten. Remove axle shafts. Mark propeller shaft and pinion flange for reassembly reference, then disconnect propeller shaft. Remove carrier attaching nuts and withdraw carrier from axle housing.

Installation — To install, reverse removal procedure, making sure to refill axle with lubricant.

OVERHAUL

DISASSEMBLY

1) Mount carrier in a suitable repair stand. Punch identification marks on side bearing supports of carrier, differential bearing caps and side bearing adjusters. Remove adjuster lock plates, loosen bearing cap attaching nuts or bolts, and slightly back off adjusters to relieve preload.

2) Remove bearing caps and adjusters, then withdraw differential assembly from carrier, making sure side bearing races remain with their respective bearings. If necessary for replacement, use a suitable puller and remove side bearings from gear case. Straighten lock tabs, remove ring gear attaching bolts, and separate ring gear from gear case.

MAZDA (Cont.)

3) Drive out differential pinion shaft lock pin with a punch and remove pinion shaft. Rotate pinion gears 90° and remove gears, thrust washer, thrust block (if equipped) and differential side gears.

4) Remove pinion nut and pinion flange. Remove drive pinion and rear bearing assembly, adjusting shims (if equipped), spacer and bearing collar (if used). Remove front oil seal and withdraw front pinion bearing. Using a press, remove rear bearing from drive pinion, then lift off pinion adjusting shim. If necessary for replacement, use a drift punch and remove pinion bearing races from carrier.

NOTE — *It may be necessary to tap end of pinion with a soft hammer to remove from carrier.*

REASSEMBLY & ADJUSTMENT

NOTE — *The use of suitable dial indicator and pinion gauging set (490727570) and block (498531555 for GLC, 490660555 for pickup, 490305555 for all others) is required for this procedure.*

Drive Pinion Depth — **1)** Install dial indicator on gauge body, place gauge body on a surface plate and preload indicator. When preloaded, turn outer ring of indicator assembly to "O" gauge.

2) Make sure differential bearing bores are free of dirt and burrs, then install drive pinion, dummy bearing, and original pinion depth shim into carrier. Place gauge block on pinion and position indicator assembly on block so button of indicator contacts lowest portion of differential bearing bore.

NOTE — *DO NOT install collapsible spacer.*

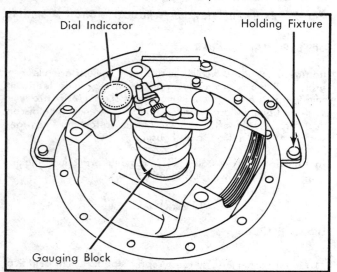

Fig. 3 Measuring Drive Pinion Installed Height

3) Record the amount indicator moves in a "+" (plus) or "−" (minus) direction from zero. Remove gauging assembly and pinion from carrier. Check rear face of pinion for the machining correction figure. If pinion is marked "+" (plus), SUBTRACT amount specified on pinion from dial indicator reading; if marked "−" (minus), ADD amount to indicator reading.

NOTE — *Figures on pinion are hundredth millimeters.*

4) Select correct pinion depth adjusting shim to be used for reassembly by adding or subtracting the amount determined in steps **2)** and **3)** from the thickness of the original pinion depth shim used during gauging process. Position correct shim (from chart) on pinion and install pinion bearing.

Pinion Depth Adjusting Shims	
Identification Mark	**Thickness In. (mm)**
08	.121 (3.08)
11	.122 (3.11)
14	.124 (3.14)
17	.125 (3.17)
20	.126 (3.20)
23	.127 (3.23)
26	.128 (3.26)
29	.130 (3.29)
32	.131 (3.32)
35	.132 (3.35)
38	.133 (3.38)
41	.134 (3.41)
44	.135 (3.44)
47	.137 (3.47)

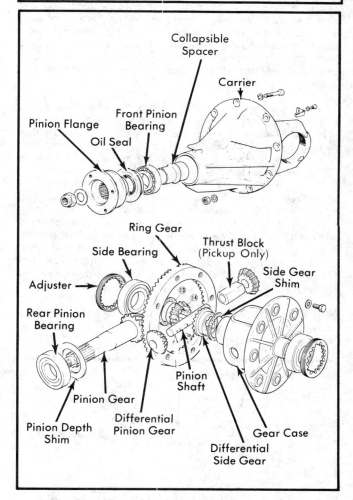

Fig. 4 Exploded View of Mazda Rear Axle Assembly

MAZDA (Cont.)

Pinion Bearing Preload — **1)** Measure collapsible spacer with micrometer. If variation of measurement exceeds ±.006" (.15 mm) of standard spacer 1.71" (43.5 mm) for GLC or 2.25" (57 mm) for all others, replace collapsible spacer. Position drive pinion in carrier and install collapsible spacer. Place front pinion bearing into position on pinion gear. Hold gear fully forward and drive bearing over pinion until seated.

2) Apply grease to pinion oil seal lip and install seal into carrier. Install flange on pinion by tapping with soft hammer. Install pinion washer and nut. Before tightening nut (when pinion preload is zero), check oil seal drag using a torque wrench, then tighten pinion nut as shown in chart.

Initial Pinion Nut Torque	
Application	**Ft. Lbs. (mkg)**
GLC	87 (12)
Pickup	145 (20)
All Others	94 (13)

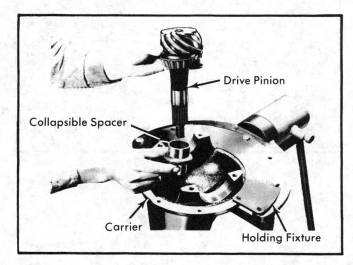

Fig. 5   Installing Drive Pinion Bearing Collapsible Spacer

3) With nut tightened to initial torque value, check preload using a torque wrench mounted on pinion nut. If preload is not as specified in specification table, continue tightening nut and checking preload until specified preload is obtained.

CAUTION — *Preload builds quickly. Nuts should be tightened a little at a time and preload checked after each slight amount of tightening.*

Case Assembly — **1)** Install a thrust washer on each differential side gear and install into case. Through openings in gear case, insert pinion gears exactly 180° opposite each other. Rotate pinion gears 90° so holes in gears line up with pinion shaft holes in gear case. Insert pinion shaft through case and pinion gears.

2) Check backlash between side gears and pinion gears. Backlash should be less than .008" (.2 mm) on pickup and less than .004" (.1 mm) on all other models. If not, install selective thrust washers to bring backlash within specifications.

NOTE — *Always use same thickness thrust washer for both side gears.*

3) If equipped with thrust block, remove pinion shaft, install thrust block and reinstall pinion shaft. On all models, install lock pin into case to secure pinion shaft. Using a punch, stake lock pin hole to prevent pin from working loose. On all models, mount ring gear on case, then install and tighten ring gear attaching bolts. If removed, install differential side bearings.

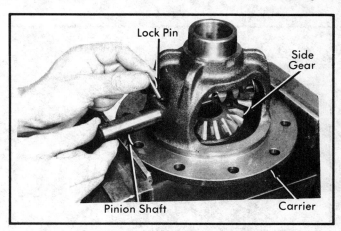

Fig. 6   Installing Pinion Shaft and Lock Pin

Backlash & Side Bearing Preload — **1)** Place differential case assembly into carrier making sure index marks on ring and pinion gears are aligned. Install bearing adjusters and bearing caps, then tighten bearing cap nuts or bolts finger tight. Turn adjusters with a suitable spanner wrench (49 0259 720) until bearing end play is eliminated and some backlash exists between ring gear and pinion. Slightly tighten one bearing cap nut or bolt on each side of carrier and measure backlash.

2) Mount a dial indicator to carrier flange so button of indicator contacts one of the ring gear teeth at a right angle, then check backlash between ring and pinion gears. Using the spanner wrench, turn both bearing adjusters equally until backlash is as specified in Axle Assembly Specifications.

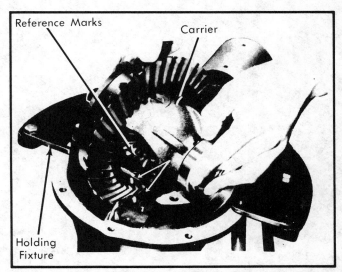

Fig. 7   Installing Differential Assembly in Housing

MAZDA (Cont.)

3) Differential bearing preload (case spread) is obtained by tightening both bearing adjusters equally. Tighten adjusters until the distance between pilot sections of side bearing caps is 6.5133-6.5158" (165.437-165.50 mm) on GLC, 7.3004-7.3033" (185.43-185.50 mm) on 626 & RX7 or 8.0485-8.0513" (204.428-204.50 mm) on pickup. Tighten bearing cap nuts or bolts, then recheck backlash adjustment. Make a gear tooth pattern check to insure correct assembly, then install adjuster lock plates on bearing caps.

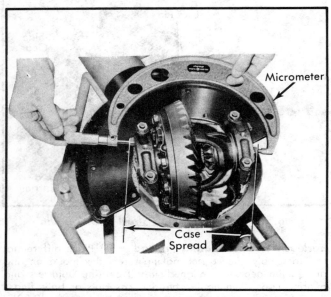

Fig. 8　Adjusting Differential Bearing Preload (Case Spread)

AXLE ASSEMBLY SPECIFICATIONS

Application	Specification
Pinion Bearing Preload①	
GLC	2.6-6.1 INCH lbs. (3-7 cmkg)
Pickup	11.3-15.6 INCH lbs. (13-18 cmkg)
All Others	7.8-12.2 INCH lbs. (9-14 cmkg)
Ring & Pinion Backlash	
GLC	.0059-.0067" (.15-.17 mm)
Pickup	.0075-.0083" (.19-.21 mm)
All Others	.0035-.0043" (.09-.11 mm)
Side Bearing Preload	
GLC	4-9 INCH lbs. (5-10 cmkg)
Pickup	4-13 INCH lbs. (5-15 cmkg)
All Others	5-18 INCH lbs. (6-21 cmkg)
Side Gear & Pinion Backlash	
Pickup	0-.008" (0-0.2 mm)
All Others	0-.004" (0-0.1 mm)

① — Without oil seal installed.

TIGHTENING SPECIFICATIONS

Application	Ft. Lbs. (mkg)
Pinion Nut	
GLC	87-130 (12-18)
Pickup	145-253 (20-35)
All Others	94-130 (13-18)
Ring Gear-to-Differential Case	
RX7	51-61 (7.0-8.5)
All Others	54-61 (7.5-8.5)
Differential Bearing Cap Bolts	
GLC	23-34 (3.2-4.7)
Pickup	41-59 (5.6-8.2)
All Others	27-38 (3.8-5.3)

Drive Axles

MERCEDES-BENZ INTEGRAL CARRIER

240D
280 Series
300 Series
450 Series

DESCRIPTION

Axle assembly is of integral carrier housing, hypoid gear type in which centerline of drive pinion is mounted below centerline of ring gear. Removable rear housing cover permits inspection and service of differential. Some models may also be equipped with limited slip differential. All adjustments, except pinion bearing preload, are performed using shims. Pinion bearing preload is set using a collapsible spacer.

AXLE RATIO & IDENTIFICATION

All of the above mentioned Mercedes-Benz models use the integral carrier rear axle with semi-trailing arm rear suspension. Some models also have limited slip differentials. To determine axle ratio, divide number of ring gear teeth by number of pinion gear teeth. Two different size center housings are also used. The small center housing, generally used on smaller vehicles, has breather mounted on end cover and side covers are secured with six bolts. The large center housing, generally used on larger vehicles, has breather located on right side of housing and side covers are secured with eight bolts.

REMOVAL & INSTALLATION

AXLE DRIVE SHAFTS

Removal — 1) Drain lubricant from rear axle. Remove brake caliper and suspend on piece of wire. Remove bolt attaching axle drive shaft to axle shaft. Force axle drive shaft out of axle shaft. If required to aid axle drive shaft removal, loosen upper shock absorber mount and lower suspension arm to stop.

2) Support axle housing and remove rubber mount from body. Lower axle housing slightly. Clean housing and remove rear cover plate. Remove "C" lock holding axle drive shaft to differential side gear. Pull shaft from gear along with spacer ring.

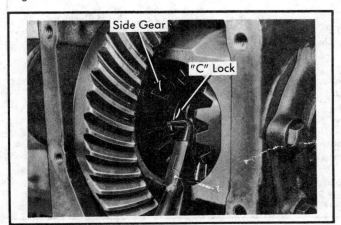

Fig. 1   Removing "C" Lock for Axle Shaft Removal

Installation — 1) Face of universal joint spider carries a stamped "R" for right or "L" for left. Make sure correct axle is used on correct side. Place old spacer ring on inner constant velocity joint. Slide axle drive shaft into differential side gear and install new "C" lock into shaft. Check end play between inner universal joint and axle housing. There should be no perceptible end play. In addition, lock ring should still turn in groove. If necessary, install a thicker or thinner lock ring to achieve desired results.

2) Completely telescope axle drive shaft and install axle shaft. Tighten securing nut. Mount end cover with suitable sealing compound and tighten bolts. Raise axle housing, install rubber mount and attach to body. Attach brake caliper using new lock washer and fill axle with lubricant.

AXLE DRIVE SHAFT RUBBER SLEEVES

Removal — Remove axle drive shaft. Cut stop sleeve of constant velocity joint on beaded edge and pull sleeve from spider. Remove spider from hub along with six balls. Remove lock ring from groove in axle drive shaft and press spider from shaft. Pull stop sleeve and rubber sleeve from shaft. Loosen hose clamps and pull second rubber sleeve across disassembled end of axle drive shaft. Carefully clean joints and check balls and other parts for wear or damage.

Installation — 1) Slide new rubber sleeve on shaft up to bead. Place suitable assembly bushing (115 589 01 63 000) on splines to protect against damage. Place new stop sleeve on shaft and press spider on axle drive shaft. Install locking ring. Assemble universal spider and 6 balls using suitable magnetic ball holders for assistance.

2) Place new sealing rings on universal spider and attach new protective sleeve. Insert complete drive axle into suitable beading tool (115 589 00 63 00) and install split supporting ring. Attach beading ring and bead edge of sleeve while tightening nuts against stop of beading tool. Remove axle from tool and fill constant velocity joint with 8.5 ozs. (241 grams) of suitable CV joint oil. Attach rubber sleeve on stop sleeve and on axle shaft with new hose clamps.

AXLE SHAFT & BEARING

Removal — 1) Unscrew bolt and force axle drive shaft out of axle shaft, tie axle drive shaft up out of way. Do not allow axle drive shaft to hang freely. Remove brake caliper and rotor and if necessary, parking brake shoes. Using suitable wrench, remove slotted nut from axle shaft while holding shaft with suitable tool (136 589 05 31 00). Remove sealing rings from support housing using screwdriver.

2) Knock axle shaft out of support housing and remove bearing inner race along with spacer sleeve. Force outer sealing ring from support housing and pull outer bearing race out of outer bearing from wheel bearing. Knock outer bearing race of inner bearing from support housing. Force outer bearing inner race from axle shaft.

Installation — 1) For identification, axle shafts have a stamped "R" for right or "L" for left. Insure that axle shafts are installed in correct sides. Press inner race of outer bearing onto axle shaft and install both bearing outer races in support housing. Coat seat for outer sealing ring on support housing with sealing compound and install seal making sure that seal rests straight against chamfer at bottom of housing. Fill cavity between two bearing races in support housing with 1.8 ozs. (50 grams) multi-purpose grease.

Drive Axles

MERCEDES-BENZ INTEGRAL CARRIER (Cont.)

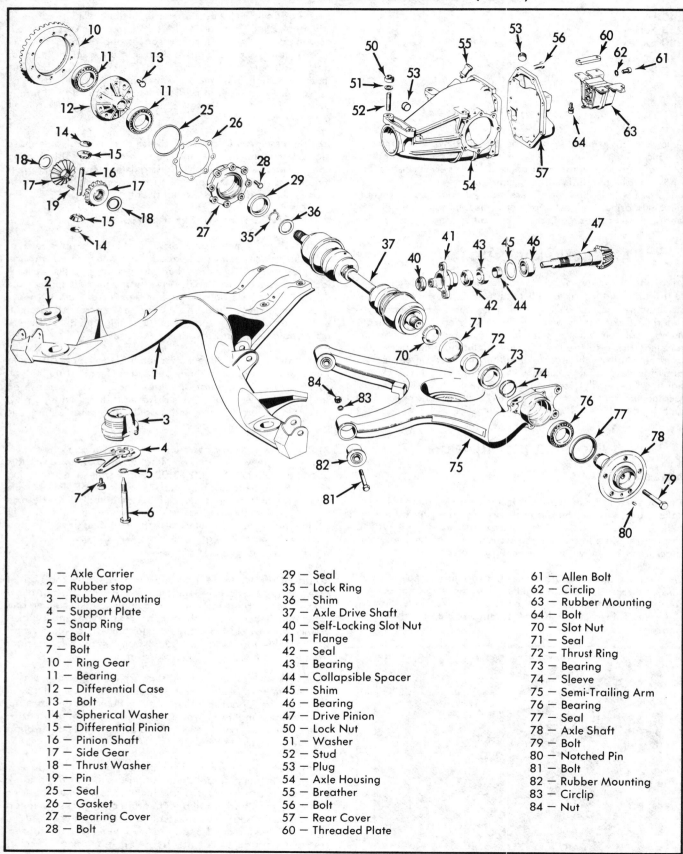

1 — Axle Carrier	29 — Seal	61 — Allen Bolt
2 — Rubber stop	35 — Lock Ring	62 — Circlip
3 — Rubber Mounting	36 — Shim	63 — Rubber Mounting
4 — Support Plate	37 — Axle Drive Shaft	64 — Bolt
5 — Snap Ring	40 — Self-Locking Slot Nut	70 — Slot Nut
6 — Bolt	41 — Flange	71 — Seal
7 — Bolt	42 — Seal	72 — Thrust Ring
10 — Ring Gear	43 — Bearing	73 — Bearing
11 — Bearing	44 — Collapsible Spacer	74 — Sleeve
12 — Differential Case	45 — Shim	75 — Semi-Trailing Arm
13 — Bolt	46 — Bearing	76 — Bearing
14 — Spherical Washer	47 — Drive Pinion	77 — Seal
15 — Differential Pinion	50 — Lock Nut	78 — Axle Shaft
16 — Pinion Shaft	51 — Washer	79 — Bolt
17 — Side Gear	52 — Stud	80 — Notched Pin
18 — Thrust Washer	53 — Plug	81 — Bolt
19 — Pin	54 — Axle Housing	82 — Rubber Mounting
25 — Seal	55 — Breather	83 — Circlip
26 — Gasket	56 — Bolt	84 — Nut
27 — Bearing Cover	57 — Rear Cover	
28 — Bolt	60 — Threaded Plate	

Fig. 2 Exploded View of Mercedes-Benz Drive Axle Assembly

MERCEDES-BENZ INTEGRAL CARRIER (Cont.)

2) Attach new spacer sleeve to axle shaft and install into carrier housing. Attach bearing inner race for inner bearing to axle shaft. Fill new sealing ring between lips with anti-friction bearing grease and coat with sealing compound on outside diameter. Press bearing inner race and sealing ring into housing. Install seal running ring and screw on new slotted nut.

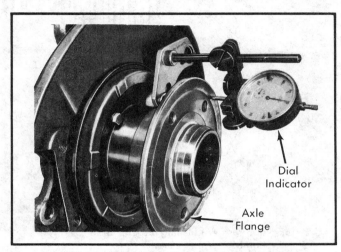

Fig. 3   Checking Axle Shaft End Play

3) Attach dial indicator holder to support housing and check end play of axle shaft while tightening slotted nut and rotating axle shaft back and forth. End play should be .0016- .0024" (.04-.06 mm). If slot nut is overtightened, reducing end play to zero, install a new spacer sleeve and retighten slot nut. Lock slot nut by bending into grooves in axle shaft at two points. Install axle drive shaft, brake components and bleed brake system.

PINION FLANGE & SEAL

Removal — 1) Remove exhaust system and shielding plate, if necessary. Loosen clamping nut and unscrew propeller shaft intermediate bearing from frame. On three-piece propeller shaft, loosen front clamping nut only. Unflange propeller shaft from axle and push forward out of centering alignment.

2) Make sure axle drive shafts are horizontal and that brakes are not dragging and check and record torque required to rotate entire rear axle assembly. Attach holding wrench to flange and loosen slotted nut with suitable wrench (115 589 01 07 00). Pull flange from pinion using puller if required. Force seal out of housing using a screwdriver. Check running surface for seal on flange and replace flange if surface is worn.

Installation — 1) Coat new seal on outside diameter with sealing compound and knock in against stop in axle housing using suitable driver (116 589 12 61 00). Attach flange and carefully tighten slotted nut until turning torque for rear axle is equal to torque measured previously. Do not overtighten or a new collapsible spacer will have to be installed on pinion.

2) Reconnect propeller shaft and lightly tighten propeller shaft intermediate bearing. Fill axle housing with oil, lower vehicle and move back and forth several times. Tighten clamping nut on universal and propeller shaft intermediate bearing. Reinstall shielding plate and exhaust system, if necessary.

AXLE ASSEMBLY

Removal — 1) Drain oil from rear axle. On vehicles without starting torque compensation, unscrew brake caliper at right and suspend out of way. On vehicles with starting torque compensation, disconnect brake cable control, unscrew holding bracket on support housing, remove rubber sleeve and push cover back. On all models, disconnect axle drive shafts from axle shaft on both sides and force axle drive shafts out of axle shafts.

2) If necessary, remove exhaust system and shielding plate. Loosen clamping nut and unscrew propeller shaft intermediate bearing on frame. On three-piece propeller shaft, loosen front clamping nut only. Disconnect propeller shaft and push forward out of way. Support axle assembly with jack and suitable holding fixture (115 589 35 63 00 for small center housing, 116 589 02 63 00 for large center housing).

3) Unscrew rear rubber mounting on frame floor, or unscrew socket bolt for rubber mounting on cover of axle housing. On 240D and 280 Series, fold back rubber mat in trunk and remove rubber plugs. Unscrew axle housing from rear axle carrier. On all models, lower rear axle and remove along with axle drive shafts. Use care not to let axle drive shafts droop. Unscrew rubber mounting from housing and replace if worn or damaged.

Installation — 1) Attach rubber mounting to axle housing and place on jack and holding fixture. Move axle up under vehicle. Mount axle housing to rear axle carrier and tighten nuts. On 240D and 280 Series, install rubber plugs and replace trunk floor mat. Install both axle drive shafts into axle shafts and tighten bolts.

2) Lift axle housing up to frame floor and attach rubber mounting to frame. Reconnect propeller shaft and lightly attach propeller shaft intermediate bearing. On vehicles without starting torque compensation, mount brake caliper using new lock washers. On vehicles with starting torque compensation, mount holding bracket for brake cable control to support housing, slide on cover and rubber sleeve, attach cable control and adjust parking brake.

3) Fill axle with oil to level of filler hole, lower vehicle. Rock back and forth several times, then tighten clamping nut on propeller shaft and tighten propeller shaft intermediate bearing. Install exhaust system and shielding plate if removed.

OVERHAUL

DISASSEMBLY

1) Clamp axle housing in suitable support so that axle drive shafts are fully supported. Remove rear cover from housing and axle drive shafts from side gears (see "Axle Drive Shafts" under REMOVAL & INSTALLATION). Remove bolts and push side bearing covers out of housing along with seal rings and shims, mark all parts for correct right and left side reassembly.

2) Tilt differential case slightly and remove from housing. Mark relative position of ring gear to differential case, remove bolts and carefully force gear from case. To disassemble case, pull roller bearings from case using suitable puller (187 589 05 33 00). Knock holding pin for pinion shaft out of case and remove pinion shaft.

MERCEDES-BENZ INTEGRAL CARRIER (Cont.)

Fig. 4   Removing Differential Assembly from Housing

3) On limited slip differentials, insert suitable assembly mandrels (116 589 18 61 00) through case and side gears. Remove pinions with spherical washers, then remove right side gear with friction discs, then repeat procedure for left side. On standard differentials, lift out side gears, thrust washers and spherical washers.

4) To remove drive pinion, remove flange nut and flange. Force pinion out of housing using tool (115 589 00 59 00). Pry seal out of housing with screwdriver. Screw suitable fixture (115 589 01 61 00) to housing and using suitable mandrel (115 589 01 61 06), press front bearing outer race out of housing. Now pull rear bearing outer race out of housing using suitable adapter (116 589 12 61 00 part 7 for small center housing or part 18 for large center housing). Press roller bearing inner race from pinion using suitable press plate (108 589 00 33 00).

REASSEMBLY & ADJUSTMENT

Case Assembly (Standard Differential) — **1)** Place thrust washers on side gears and insert in case. Insert assembly mandrels (116 589 18 61 00) into side gears and mount both pinions along with spherical washers. Insert dummy pinion shaft (115 589 03 61 00 for small center housing or 116 589 07 61 00 for large center housing) into case to locate pinion gears and spherical washers.

2) Check torque required to rotate side gears. Specified torque is 130-174 INCH lbs. (150-200 cmkg) with spot binding up to 304 INCH lbs. (350 cmkg) permitted with no end play. If necessary, change side gear thrust washers as necessary to achieve this torque value. When side gear preload is correct, insert pinion shaft in place of mandrel, install new clamping sleeve and press bearing inner races on case using suitable mandrel (115 589 04 61 00 for small center housing or 116 589 08 61 00 for large center housing).

Case Assembly (Limited Slip Differential) — **1)** Mount friction discs on side gears in correct sequence (see illustration). Install left side gear (ring gear side) with discs and insert assembly mandrel (116 589 18 61 00). Make sure disc lugs align properly in case. Repeat procedure for right side gear. Install pinions with new spherical washers.

2) Insert dummy pinion shaft (116 589 07 61 00) through case, pinions and spherical washers. Check torque required to rotate side gears. Specified torque is 217-304 INCH lbs. (250-350 cmkg) with no end play. If necessary, change side gear

thrust washers as necessary to achieve this torque value. When side gear preload is correct, insert pinion shaft in place of mandrel, install new clamping sleeve and press bearing inner races on case using suitable mandrel (116 589 08 61 00).

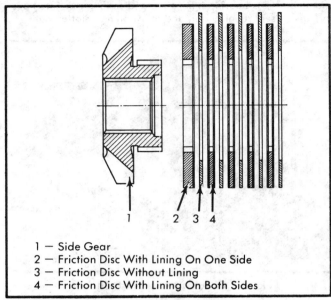

1 — Side Gear
2 — Friction Disc With Lining On One Side
3 — Friction Disc Without Lining
4 — Friction Disc With Lining On Both Sides

Fig. 5   Friction Disc Installation Sequence

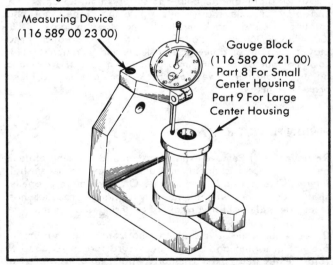

Measuring Device
(116 589 00 23 00)

Gauge Block
(116 589 07 21 00)
Part 8 For Small
Center Housing
Part 9 For Large
Center Housing

Fig. 6   Zeroing Dial Indicator for Pinion Depth Adjustment

Drive Pinion Depth — **1)** With dial indicator depressed about .12" (3 mm) by gauge block (116 589 07 21 00 part 8 for small center housing or part 9 for large center housing), zero dial indicator. Press inner tapered roller bearing on drive pinion and place bearing outer race on roller cage of bearing. Insert pinion assembly into measuring device. On pinions from large center housings, place magnetic plate (116 589 01 21 00 part 4) on top of pinion. Place indicator stem on head of pinion or plate and note reading (example: 1.50 mm).

NOTE — *On all 450 Series, the height of the pinion gear head has been increased from 1.477" (37.5 mm) to 1.535" (39 mm). This must be considered when selecting pinion depth adjusting shims. This change was made as of chassis end numbers: 0066963 (450 SLC); 017787 (450 SL); and 023515 (450 SE/SEL).*

MERCEDES-BENZ INTEGRAL CARRIER (Cont.)

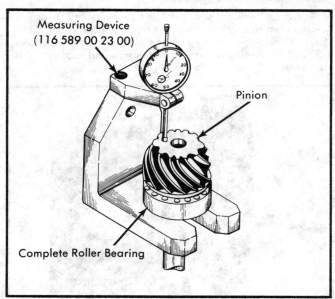

Fig. 7   Reading Pinion Height

2) Now note adjustment value engraved on pinion shaft in tenths of millimeters (example: +20 = +.20 mm). From value measured above, add adjustment value if plus and subtract value if minus. (example: 1.50 + .20 = 1.70 mm). Insert gauge block holder into axle housing and screw on appropriate gauge block. Insert dial gauge holder (111 589 08 23 00) into adjusting gauge (115 589 05 21 00) and zero indicator with stem depressed about .12" (3 mm).

3) Insert measuring device (115 589 00 21 00 part 3 for small center housing or 116 589 01 21 00 part 1 for large center housing) together with dial gauge holder into right bore of housing and screw down. Read indicator reading difference between adjusting gauge and gauge block face end. If value is plus, it must be subtracted from result obtained in step **2)** and if minus, must be added to above result (example: If measured deviation is +.16 mm, subtract this value from 1.70 mm to obtain 1.54 mm). This result is thickness of required shim.

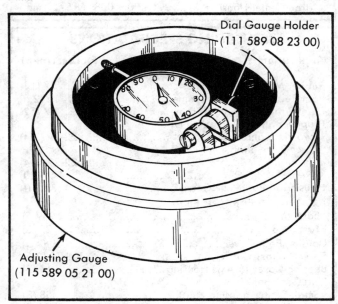

Fig. 8   Zeroing Dial Indicator

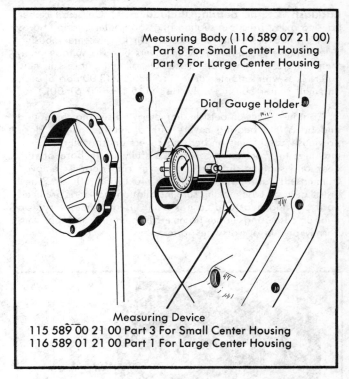

Fig. 9   Measuring Housing Depth

4) Remove all tools from axle housing. Insert shim of calculated thickness into axle housing. If necessary, a thicker washer may be ground down to required thickness. Install outer races of bearings in housing using suitable installation tool (116 589 11 61 00). Lubricate bearings on drive pinion with hypoid gear oil and insert pinion and new collapsible spacer into housing.

5) Install front bearing inner race using suitable tools. Coat new seal on circumference with sealing compound and press into cover using suitable mandrel. Coat running surface of pinion flange with molybdenum disulphide paste and slide flange on drive pinion, making sure alignment marks are lined up.

Pinion Bearing Preload — 1) Check that runout of pinion flange does not exceed .001" (.03 mm). If runout is excessive, reposition flange. Attach suitable holding wrench to flange and screw on new locking slot nut. Gradually tighten slot nut while turning pinion and applying light hammer blows to axle housing. Continue tightening nut until torque required to rotate pinion is 10.4-12.2 INCH lbs. (12-14 cmkg) with new bearings or 4.3-8.7 INCH lbs. (5-10 cmkg) with used bearings.

2) Use care not to exceed specified preload. If preload is exceeded, remove pinion from housing and replace collapsible spacer. Again insert measuring device together with dial gauge holder into right bore of housing and place magnetic measuring plate (116 589 01 21 00 part 4) on head of pinion. Dial indicator should read value engraved on pinion shaft. Maximum error is —.0008" (.02 mm). If error is higher, disassemble pinion and install correct shim.

MERCEDES-BENZ INTEGRAL CARRIER (Cont.)

Backlash & Side Bearing Preload — **1)** On small center housing axles, press out sealing rings and outer bearing bores from side covers using a mandrel. On large center housing axles remove sealing rings from covers using a suitable tool, then remove bearing outer race. On all axles, press in new outer races with suitable sleeve (116 589 04 43 00 part 5) and, on small center housing only, disc (115 589 00 61 00).

2) Coat new seals on outside diameter with sealing compound and press into bearing covers with a suitable punch. Place previously used shims on bearing covers and install new sealing rings in grooves of covers. Carefully clean bore of ring gear and seat on differential case as ring gear is removed from case. Heat ring gear to about 140-158°F (60-70°C) and install gear on case making sure installation markings are lined up if old ring gear and case is being used. If necessary, tap gear on case using rubber hammer. Tighten ring gear bolts uniformly and in a crosswise pattern.

Support
(115 589 04 21 00 Part 3)

Spread Measuring Device
115 589 04 21 00 For Small Center Housing
116 589 04 21 00 For Large Center Housing

Fig. 10   Measuring Housing Spread

3) Place differential case into housing. Place suitable assembly fixture (116 589 06 61 00) into housing. Place both bearing covers with shims on centering surface of fixture and slide into housing on same side from which they were removed. Turn both covers so that marking "bottom" ("unten") faces downwards. Remove assembly fixture and screw in bearing cover bolts but do not tighten. Mount suitable case spread measuring device (115 589 04 21 00 for small center housing or 116 589 04 21 00 for large center housing) and support (115 589 04 21 00 part 3) on housing and zero dial indicator.

4) Tighten bolts on bearing covers, crosswise, to a torque of 14.5 ft. lbs. (2 mkg). Place spread measuring device on support blocks and measure spread of axle housing. Spread should be .004-.006" (.10-.15 mm) for small center housing or .006-.008" (.15-.20 mm) for large center housing. Adjust size of shims as necessary to achieve specified case spread. Install suitable backlash measuring device (115 589 03 23 00) into right side bearing bore and clamp down.

5) Measure backlash at four points on ring gear. The lowest measured value of backlash should be .003-.0055" (.08-.14

mm). Adjust shims from side to side as necessary to achieve specified backlash. When preload and backlash is correct, install both axle drive shafts with new "C" lock rings. Clean sealing surface on end cover and axle housing and coat with sealing compound. Install cover and tighten bolts.

Axle Housing

Dial Gauge

Backlash Measuring Tool

Fig. 11   Measuring Ring-to-Pinion Gear Backlash

AXLE ASSEMBLY SPECIFICATIONS

Application	Specification
Flange Runout	.0047" (.12 mm) Max.
Wheel Bearing End Play	0-.0015" (0-.04 mm)
Axle Shaft End Play	.0016-.0024" (.04-.06 mm)
Ring Gear Runout	.0008" (.02 mm) Max.
Side Gear Turning Torque	
Standard Diff.	130-174 INCH lbs. (150-200 cmkg)
Limited Slip Diff.	217-303 INCH lbs. (250-350 cmkg)
Pinion Turning Torque	
New Bearings	10-12 INCH lbs. (12-14 cmkg)
Old Bearings	4-9 INCH lbs. (5-10 cmkg)
Ring & Pinion Backlash	.003-.0055" (.08-.14 mm)
Housing Spread	
Small Center Housing	.004-.006" (.10-.15 mm)
Large Center Housing	.006-.008" (.15-.20 mm)

TIGHTENING SPECIFICATIONS

Application	Ft. Lbs. (mkg)
Rubber Mount-to-Axle Housing	87 (12)
Rear Rubber Mount-to-Frame	18 (2.5)
Front Rubber Mount-to-Frame	87 (12)
Propeller Shaft Clamping Nut	
Two Piece Shaft	22-29 (3-4)
Three Piece Shaft	
Front	22-29 (3-4)
Rear	145 (20)
Housing-to-Rear Axle Carrier	72 (10)
Axle Drive Shaft-to-Axle Shaft	
Early (M 12)	69 (9.5)
Late (M 8)	22 (3)
Housing Rear Cover	33 (4.5)
Brake Caliper Carrier Bolt	18 (2.5)
Bearing Cover-to-Axle Housing	14 (2)
Ring Gear Bolts	
Small Center Housing	58 (8)
Large Center Housing	87 (12)

MGB

DESCRIPTION

Rear axles are hypoid design with center line of pinion set below centerline of ring gear. The axle shafts can be serviced without removing axle from vehicle. All differential adjustments are performed using shims. No adjustment for axle shaft end play is necessary. A collapsible spacer is used on drive pinion shaft.

AXLE RATIO & IDENTIFICATION

Only one basic axle design is used on these models. To determine axle ratio, divide number of ring gear teeth by number of pinion gear teeth.

REMOVAL & INSTALLATION

AXLE SHAFTS & BEARINGS

Removal — 1) Raise rear of vehicle and support just ahead of spring shackles. Remove wheel, axle nut, collar and brake drum. Remove clevis pin from parking brake cable. Disconnect and plug brake line openings.

2) Remove brake back plate, then remove oil seal collar, bearing hub cap and oil seal from axle shaft. Remove axle shaft using suitable tool and press bearing from shaft.

Installation — To install, repack bearings with grease and reverse removal procedure. Use suitable tool to drift axle shaft into position. Lubricate and install new oil seal with lip facing inwards.

PINION FLANGE & SEAL

Removal — Raise and support vehicle; remove wheels and brake drums. Drain rear axle. Mark propeller shaft and pinion flange for reassembly reference and disconnect propeller shaft. Measure and record torque required to rotate pinion. Install pinion holding tool to prevent pinion from turning and remove flange retaining nut and washer. Remove pinion flange. Remove and discard oil seal.

Installation — 1) Grease edge and sealing lip of new oil seal and install seal flush with axle housing. Install pinion flange and washer. Gradually screw on retaining nut until resistance is felt. Rotate pinion to seat bearings and measure torque required to rotate pinion.

2) If reading obtained in step **1)** is less than value recorded during removal, tighten nut very small amount, reseat bearings and recheck torque reading. Repeat this procedure until a reading equal to that at removal, but not less than 4-6 INCH lbs. (4-7 cmkg), is obtained. Continue installation in reverse of removal procedure.

CAUTION — *Preload build up is rapid, tighten nut with care. If a torque reading in excess of 6 INCH lbs. (7 cmkg) is exceeded, axle must be dismantled and a new collapsible spacer installed.*

AXLE ASSEMBLY

Removal — 1) Raise rear of vehicle and mark propeller shaft and flange for correct reassembly. Disconnect propeller shaft. Remove nuts and washers securing each end of rebound straps to anchor pins on axle and remove straps. Disconnect parking brake at operating levers and remove cable clamp from housing. Support axle with jack and remove wheels. Disconnect roll bar brackets from axle.

2) Disconnect brake hose at battery box bracket. Lower jack until full weight of axle is on springs. Remove nuts and washers from exhaust system support brackets and disconnect brackets. Place support under exhaust system. Remove "U" bolts and mounting plates holding axle to spring and withdraw assembly from right hand side of car, rotating axle as necessary.

Installation — To install, reverse removal procedure.

OVERHAUL

DISASSEMBLY

1) Drain and remove axle from vehicle. Remove axle shafts and hubs. Remove differential cover and mark each differential bearing cap before removal for reassembly reference. Remove bolts and bearing caps. Before differential assembly can be removed from axle housing, housing must be stretched with stretcher (18G-131C). DO NOT stretch housing more than is absolutely necessary or housing may be damaged. Maximum stretch is .012" (.3 mm) or 9 flats of tool (18G-131C).

2) Pry differential assembly out of stretched housing using two pry bars, one on each side of housing. Do not damage case or apply leverage on stretcher tool. Release housing stretcher. Bend back locking tabs and remove ring gear bolts and ring gear. Drive out pinion shaft pin and remove shaft. Turn differential gears by hand until pinions are opposite opening in differential cage and remove pinions and thrust washers.

3) Remove differential gears and thrust washers. If necessary, remove differential inner bearing races. Before removing pinion, measure preload. If preload is zero, install new pinion bearings. Hold pinion flange and remove pinion nut and washer. Remove flange by tapping with soft hammer. Press out pinion; do not drive out. Remove front and rear bearing outer races from axle housing. Oil seal will come out with front bearing. Remove rear bearing inner race from pinion.

REASSEMBLY & ADJUSTMENT

Drive Pinion Depth — 1) Install bearing outer races in axle housing using suitable tools. Using a dummy pinion (18G-191H), install inner race of bearing on dummy and place in housing without collapsible spacer or oil seal. Install inner race of front bearing. Install pinion flange and tighten nut gradually until a bearing preload figure of 10-20 ft. lbs. (1.4-2.8 mkg) is obtained.

2) Clean dummy pinion head and position dial indicator foot on pinion head and zero indicator. Move indicator until foot of gauge rests on center of differential bearing bore and note indicator reading. Repeat this procedure on opposite bearing bore and average the two figures. The reading shown on indicator will be amount of correction necessary from a standard spacer of .208" (5.3 mm). If indicator reading is negative, reduce spacer thickness by this amount and vise versa.

Drive Axles

MGB (Cont.)

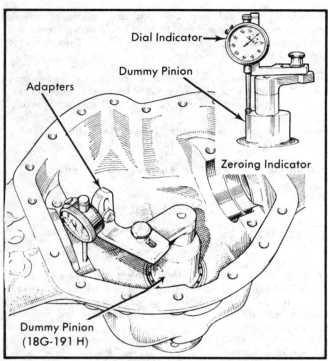

Fig. 1   Measuring Pinion Installed Depth

3) Allowance must also be made for pinion depth marked on pinion head in a rectangular bracket. If marking is positive, reduce washer thickness by equal amount and visa versa. A tolerance of .001" (.03 mm) is allowed in thickness of washer finally installed. Remove dummy pinion.

Pinion Bearing Preload -- 1) Install washer of thickness calculated above under pinion head. Install pinion inner bearing race. Insert pinion into case and install collapsible spacer with small diameter towards shoulder of pinion head. Support head of pinion and press outer bearing onto pinion using care not to compress spacer. Grease edge and sealing lip of seal and install seal flush with axle housing. Install flange, washer and nut.

2) Tighten flange nut slowly until spacer starts to collapse. Rotate pinion to settle bearings and check pinion preload. Gradually tighten in very small amounts, checking preload between each tightening, until specified preload is obtained.

CAUTION — *Bearing preload is rapid. If preload torque of 24 INCH lbs. (30 cmkg) is exceeded, pinion must be dismantled and a new collapsible spacer installed.*

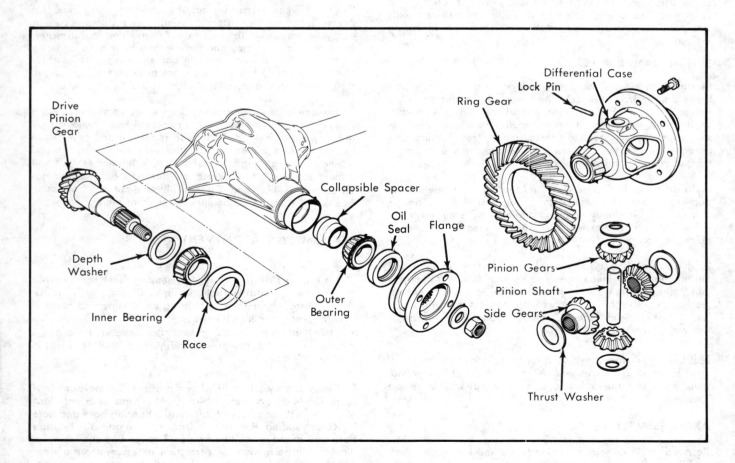

Fig. 2   Exploded View of MGB Drive Axle Assembly

MGB (Cont.)

Side Bearing Preload — 1) Assemble each inner and outer bearing race to differential assembly. Using ring gear setting tools (18G-191, 18G-191 F & 18G-191 J) place differential assembly onto jig and load ring gear assembly (see illustration). Spin unit to settle bearings. Standard measurement of bearing bores is 7.243" (183.98 mm). Any excess machined from bores will be marked "A" and "B" on axle casing. The "A" and "B" tolerances, added to standard measurement, will determine overall dimension. See example:

EXAMPLE:

Differential case standard	7.243" (183.98 mm)
PLUS value "A" stamped on case	.001" (.025 mm)
PLUS value "B" stamped on case	.002" (.038 mm)
Total distance between bores	7.246" (184.05 mm)

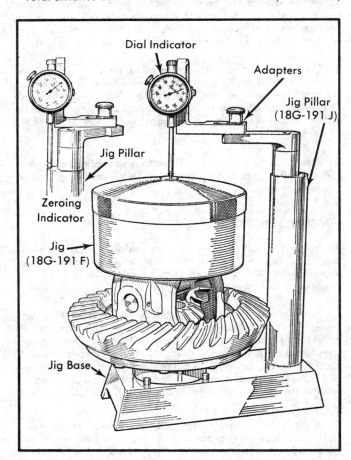

Fig. 3 Measuring Differential Side Bearing Preload

NOTE — *Pillar is standard height of differential assembly or 6.972" (177.10 mm) high.*

2) Clean head of jig pillar and place dial indicator on pillar head. Spin differential to settle bearings and move arm of dial indicator to machined face of jig and take a reading. Add this variation to the standard height to obtain total width of differential assembly. For example:

EXAMPLE:

Differential assembly standard	6.972" (177.10 mm)
PLUS indicator reading	.008" (.203 mm)
Total differential assembly	6.980" (177.30 mm)

3) Subtract total width of differential assembly, as shown in step 2), from total distance between the bores, determined in step 1). To this value, add specified bearing preload value and divide the result by 2 to obtain shim thickness of equal values for both sides of assembly.

EXAMPLE:

Total distance between bores	7.246" (184.05 mm)
MINUS total differential assembly	6.980" (177.30 mm)
Result	.266" (6.75 mm)
PLUS bearing preload	.004" (.102 mm)
Total shim thickness	.270" (6.86 mm)
Divided by 2	÷2
Shims each side	.135" (3.43 mm)

Backlash Adjustment — 1) Correct figure for backlash to be used with any particular ring and pinion is etched on rear face of ring gear. INCREASE shim thickness on opposite side of ring gear by this amount and DECREASE shim thickness on ring gear side by same amount. See example:

EXAMPLE:

Calculated shim thickness	.135" (3.43 mm)
MINUS backlash value	.008" (.203 mm)
Ring gear side shims	.127" (3.23 mm)
Calculated shim thickness	.135" (3.43 mm)
PLUS backlash value	.008" (.203 mm)
Shim thickness opposite ring gear	.143" (3.62 mm)

2) Install differential in axle housing. Replace bearing caps and tighten bolts. Set up dial indicator to accurately measure backlash of ring gear. If backlash is not at value etched on ring gear, move shims from side to side to obtain correct value. A movement of .002" (.051 mm) shim thickness from one side of differential to the other will produce a variation in backlash of about .002" (.051 mm). Ensure absolute cleanliness during above operation to ensure accuracy. Continue installation in reverse of removal procedure.

AXLE ASSEMBLY SPECIFICATIONS

Application	Specification
Pinion Bearing Preload	
New	14-24 INCH lbs. (16-28 cmkg)
Side Bearing Preload	.004" (.102 mm)
Differential Case Standard	7.243" (183.98 mm)
Differential Assembly Standard	6.972" (177.10 mm)
Oil Seal Change (Rotating Torque)	
Minimum	4-6 INCH lbs. (4-7 cmkg)
Maximum	①

① — If preload exceeds 24 INCH lbs., disassembly is required and a new collapsible spacer must be installed.

TIGHTENING SPECIFICATIONS

Application	Ft. Lbs. (mkg)
Ring Gear-to-Carrier	60-65 (8.3-9.0)
Differential Bearing Cap	53 (7.2)
Pinion Bearing Nut	
NEW Spacer Only	135-140 (18.7-19.4)
Axle Bearing Retaining Nut	150 (20.7)

PEUGEOT SPLIT HOUSING – I.R.S.

505
604

DESCRIPTION

Hypoid type differential is housed in a split case which is bolted to the rear suspension cross member. A torque tube houses the propeller shaft which is splined to the drive pinion. Ribbed aluminum alloy housing attaches to torque tube at front by flange and four nuts. Drive axle shafts are driven by differential side gears through tripod type constant velocity joints.

AXLE RATIO & IDENTIFICATION

One basic design axle housing is used on all models. To determine axle ratio, divide number of ring gear teeth by number of pinion gear teeth.

REMOVAL & INSTALLATION

AXLE SHAFTS & BEARINGS

Removal — **1)** Raise rear of vehicle and support under rear suspension arms. Remove rear wheels. Loosen but do not remove hub nut.

2) From rear brake caliper remove: anti-chatter spring, lock pin arrangement and brake disc pads. Open brake line clamp, located on lower control arm, and move brake line upward. Hang brake caliper from vehicle in such a way that brake line is not stressed.

3) Remove bolts attaching brake rotor to hub. Mark rotor-to-hub position and remove rotor. Insert socket on extension through hole in hub. Remove bolts securing axle hub bearing support to lower control arm.

4) To remove axle, complete with hub and bearing support, work from rear (*See Fig. 1*) and use two bolts and plate (special tools B1, B2 and B3 of tool set 8.0521). With plate installed between hub and bearing support, insert the two bolts, as illustrated, and alternately tighten both bolts until axle assembly is pressed free of lower control arm.

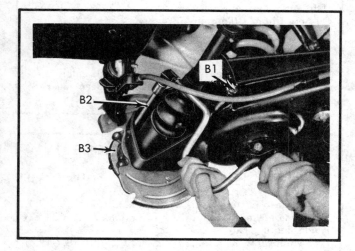

B1

B2

B3

Fig. 1   Forcing Out Front Axle Assembly

5) With axle assembly pressed out of lower control arm, remove axle assembly from rear carrier housing. Remove axle assembly through lower control arm. With axle removed, place axle assembly in press, with adapter plate located just below hub. Remove hub nut and washer. Press axle out of hub.

NOTE — *When removing axle assembly from rear carrier, take care not to damage carrier seal.*

Installation — To install, reverse removal procedures and observe the following precautions:

NOTE — *When installing hub nut, hand tighten ONLY.*

1) Before assembling hub to axle bearing support, grease spline of axle stub. Before installing axle assembly into carrier housing, make sure carrier side seal is in perfect condition. Apply grease between lips of seal and to drive axle splines.

2) Use new washer, when assembling bearing support-to-lower control arm. Tighten bolts to specifications. When installing brake caliper, use new washers and tighten bolts to specifications. When installing brake anti-chatter spring onto caliper, make sure arrow of spring is facing normal direction of rotation.

3) When installing hub nut, tighten to specifications and peen the nut. After installing road wheels, check level of grease in carrier housing.

PINION FLANGE & SEAL

Removal — **1)** Raise and support vehicle. Remove exhaust pipe assembly and allow it to rest on rear crossmember. Remove both Allen screws securing carrier housing and allow housing to rest on rear crossmember.

2) Inside vehicle, remove rear seat cushions. Loosen three nuts on "T" shaped metal bracket and remove first nut. Bend up "T" bracket and remove plastic plug from guide hole. Insert special guide pin K1 into guide hole and tighten pin with special bar K2. Leave K2 in guide pin and remove other two lock nuts. Lower crossmember until special bar K2 is resting on floorboard. Repeat operation on opposite side.

3) Remove four nuts securing carrier housing to propeller shaft tube. Move carrier housing rearward and allow it to rest on wooden block. Remove spring located inside propeller shaft. Remove seal support plate from front of carrier and place in vise. Thoroughly clean front oil seal housing and remove oil seal by using pry bar.

NOTE — *When prying out old oil seal, take care not to damage insert deflector. Any damage to oil seal deflector necessitates replacement of complete oil seal housing.*

4) Use seal driver to seat new oil seal in housing. Drive seal inward until it is flush with oil seal housing. Coat new seal in engine oil and place seal housing on carrier housing.

Installation — To install, reverse removal procedure and note the following precautions: Use all new washers and tighten all bolts to specifications.

PEUGEOT SPLIT HOUSING – I.R.S. (Cont.)

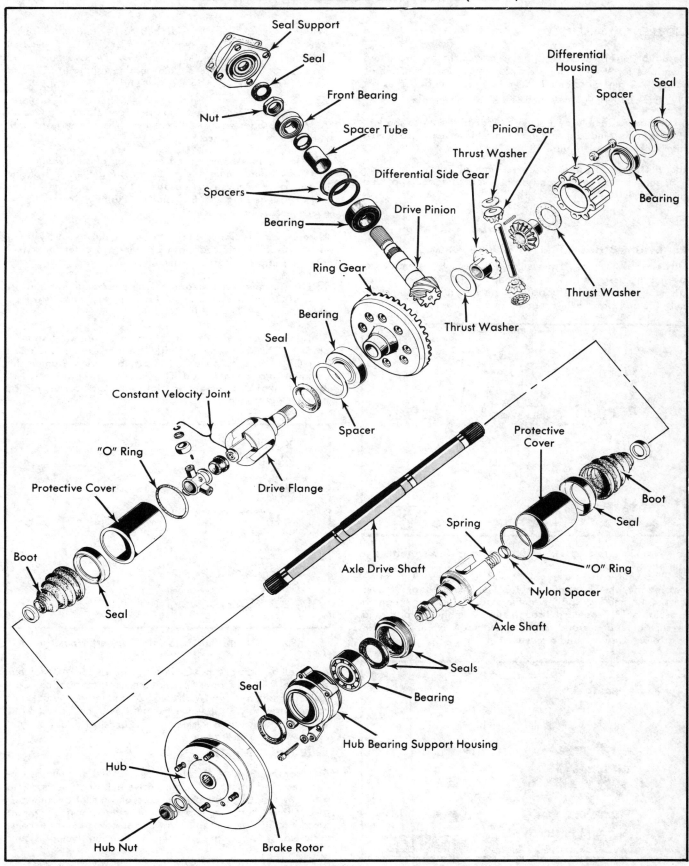

Fig. 2 Exploded View of Peugeot Independent Rear Suspension (I.R.S.) Drive Axle Assembly

Drive Axles

PEUGEOT SPLIT HOUSING — I.R.S. (Cont.)

DIFFERENTIAL ASSEMBLY

Removal — 1) With axle shafts removed, follow procedure described for *Pinion Flange & Seal* removal and continue as follows: Drain differential. Remove rear muffler flexible mounting nuts and lower heat baffle (if equipped).

2) Remove assembly by pulling to rear and then to the left. Propeller shaft must be held in position to prevent it from moving back with differential.

Installation — To install, reverse removal procedure noting that splines are greased and propeller shaft spring is placed into rear end of propeller shaft.

OVERHAUL

REAR HUBS & HUB CARRIER BEARING & SEALS

Disassembly — 1) Remove axle and hub assembly as previously described. With hub and axle removed, place assembly in press with adapter plate beneath hub. Remove hub nut and press axle assembly out of hub.

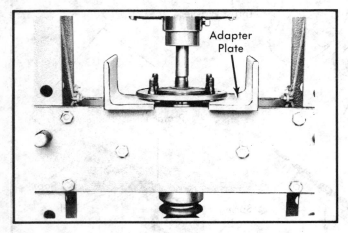

Fig. 3 Pressing Axle Shaft from Hub Assembly

2) Place hub-carrier assembly in soft jawed vise. To remove carrier nut, install spanner nut plate (special tool D) over carrier nut and lock spanner nut in place by inserting long bolt (special tool C1) upward through hub assembly. Use open end wrench on spanner and fulcrum advantage extension (see illustration). Unscrew and remove nut.

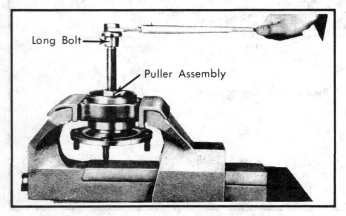

Fig. 4 Removing Double Bearing from Hub Assembly

3) Place special tool C3 inside hub carrier and install puller (special tool C4 and C1) into hub carrier. Tighten puller bolt (C4) until hub is completely withdrawn. Remove puller and thrust pad (C3). Remove double bearing using nut (C2) and press. Turn carrier over in the vise and pry out seal.

Reassembly — 1) Use suitable drift (special tool E) to install oil seal into back side of hub carrier. Drive seal inward until seal is flush with hub carrier.

NOTE — *All new bearings are fitted with plastic retainer (inside) which holds inner and outer races together. This plastic part must be removed before attempting to install new bearing. Grease bearing with Esso Multiple Purpose Grease H or its equivalent before installing.*

2) Insert double lipped seal into carrier nut assembly using same drift (E). Insert bearing, with inner and outer races held together, into hub-carrier assembly.

NOTE — *Installation of bearing must be completed with use of press or special tool. Procedure for using special tools will be only procedure described.*

3) Tighten carrier nut until it contacts the bearing. Install C4 onto nut C1. Place spanner head "D" on carrier nut and insert bolt C1 fitted with puller C4 into hub carrier. Tighten this assembly into spanner head "D". Tighten carrier nut to 181 ft. lbs. (25 mkg) and remove special tools. Lock carrier nut by peening with punch.

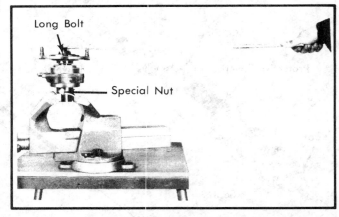

Fig. 5 Installing Hub into Support Housing

4) Install bolt C1 and nut C2 into carrier assembly. Install hub and screw down on nut C2 until nut contacts bearing. Coat splines of stub axle with Molycote 321 and insert stub axle into carrier assembly. Install washer and hub nut, hand tight. Install assembly onto vehicle in reverse order of disassembly.

AXLE DRIVE SHAFTS

Disassembly — 1) With drive axles removed and hub assemblies removed from axles, clamp drive axle shaft vertically in soft jawed vise. Place adhesive tape on oil seal bearing surface. Using pliers, uncrimp edge of metal cover. Using soft faced hammer, gently tap downward on cover to expose constant velocity joint. Place adhesive tape around velocity joint.

NOTE — *Constant velocity joint is not repairable and must be replaced as a unit.*

PEUGEOT SPLIT HOUSING — I.R.S. (Cont.)

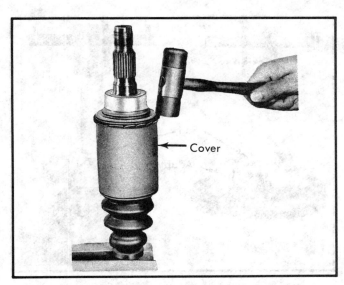

Fig. 6 Removing Axle Shaft Protective Cover

2) Remove as much grease as possible, but do not dip components in degreasing agent. Use press to remove constant velocity joint.

NOTE — *There is no need to remove 3 punch marks on end of shaft as they will disappear during removal procedure.*

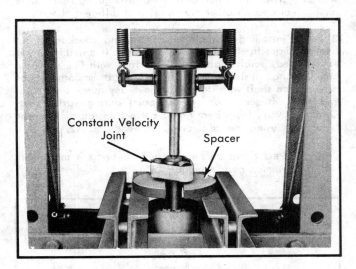

Fig. 7 Removing Constant Velocity Joint

3) Remove protective cover (metal) and rubber ring. Remove other "U" joint in same manner as previously described. From outside of CV joint housing, remove "O" ring. From inside, remove all grease. If nylon bushing on inside of CV joint housing is damaged, remove nylon with chisel

4) Remove retaining washer with screwdriver. Use small stone and drill to remove any burrs in housing. When this operation is complete, clean inside of housing and blow dry with compressed air.

Reassembly — 1) To reassemble, reverse disassembly procedure with the following precautions: When installing

metal cover, note there are 2 different sizes. The shorter one fits on differential side of axle shaft. Protective stopper must be installed on wheel side of axle shaft. After installing CV joints onto respective shafts, use punch to peen shaft at 3 equadistant places on shaft end.

2) If nylon bushing (stop) was removed, insert new bushing (stop). Insert washer over bushing and peen washer in 3 equadistant places. Before installing cover over CV joint housing, grease inside of housing and replace "O" ring. With cover over housing and assembly placed in press to hold tension, peen over cover. Install axle assembly as previously outlined.

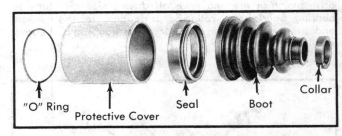

Fig. 8 Disassembled View of Axle Shaft Protective Covers

DIFFERENTIAL

Disassembly — 1) With differential removed, remove front oil seal support plate. Place carrier housing in holding fixture in vise. Loosen all bolts and nuts on rear housing. Remove front attaching screws of bearing side plates. Remove 6 bolts and 4 nuts holding housing halves together. Lift off rear half of housing. If necessary, use soft faced mallet to assist in removing rear housing half.

2) Loosen vise and rotate holding fixture to allow front of housing to be in horizontal position. Install special spanner tool N (hex sleeve with bolt tang) over end of drive pinion nut and secure to holding fixture with bolt through tang. See *Fig. 9.* Install drive pinion holder M (splined socket) over pinion spline. To loosen drive pinion nut, pinion spline is turned clockwise while holding nut steady.

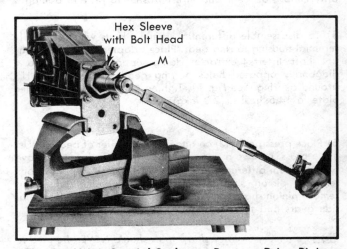

Fig. 9 Using Special Socket to Remove Drive Pinion

Drive Axles

PEUGEOT SPLIT HOUSING — I.R.S. (Cont.)

NOTE — *Catch pinion as assembly is pressed out of housing.*

3) Remove carrier housing from vise and remove holding fixture from carrier housing. Place housing in vise and press on drive end of pinion to remove drive pinion assembly. To remove drive pinion rear bearing outer race, install parts of special puller/driver (tool L). Install bolt L1, extractor L4 and support plate D. Turn bolt counterclockwise to remove outer race.

4) To remove drive pinion front outer race, install parts of special puller/driver (tool L). Install bolt L1 and extractor L3. Turn bolt clockwise to remove front outer race. Now place drive pinion in vise and press off drive pinion rear tapered bearing. Special tool (collar SZ) is designed for this purpose and fits over drive pinion gear and against rear bearing shoulder.

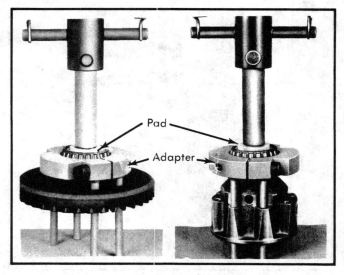

Fig. 11   Removing Differential Side Bearing

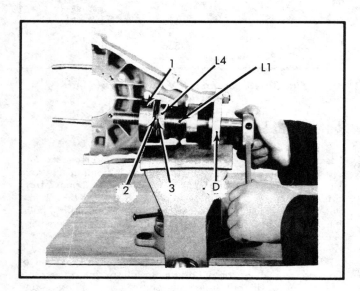

Fig. 10   Removing Pinion Rear Outer Bearing Race

CAUTION — *As parts are separated in following step, catch differential side gear and thrust washer to prevent damage.*

5) To disassemble differential, remove bolts which hold differential housing to ring gear. Place adapter C over differential shaft. Insert 4 extractor clamp support rods (H3) into 4 diagonally opposed holes of ring gear. Place adapter H1 around bearing. *See Fig. 11.* Tighten Allen screws on adapter plate to 14.5 ft. lbs. (2.0 mkg).

6) Place press pad (H2) on ring gear, in center of bearing. Using a press, remove ring gear. Use same procedure to remove bearing from differential case. Use drift punch to remove differential pinion shaft-to-pinion gear retaining pin. Then remove pinion shaft, pinion gears, spacer washers, differential side gears and thrust washers.

NOTE — *Emery cloth or sharp tools should NEVER be used to clean housing or other differential parts.*

Reassembly & Adjustment — **1)** Clean all parts in suitable solvent and blow dry with compressed air. Spray Molykote 321 into drive pinion housing. Do not heat housing. Every time ring gear and drive pinion are replaced, they must be replaced as an assembly and the following parts should also be changed: differential side bearings, drive pinion bearings, flex washers, drive pinion nut, differential assembling bolts, drive pinion seal and all other "O" rings and differential seals.

2) Before installing drive pinion rear bearing, check that front bearing slides freely on drive pinion shaft. If any difficulty is experienced, polish shaft bearing surface with fine abrasive until bearing just slides (as free fit) onto shaft. Smooth front of drive pinion shaft with stone to remove any burrs, since front end of shaft serves as contact point during various adjustments. With front bearing fit correct, install pinion rear bearing by using special sleeve C and end pad H2.

NOTE — *Press down on bearing until bearing is in contact with drive pinion gear shoulder.*

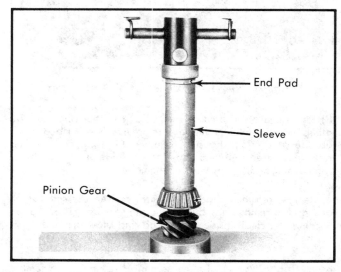

Fig. 12   Installing Drive Pinion Rear Bearing

PEUGEOT SPLIT HOUSING — I.R.S. (Cont.)

3) Place forward half of carrier housing in holding fixture in vise so that housing is in horizontal position. Using special puller-driver, install thrust washer 3, outer bearing races 4 and 5 (back to back) into housing. Use bolt L1, thrust plate L2 and nut L5. Tighten bolt head of L1 to 101 ft. lbs. (14 mkg). Oil bearings with Esso Extra Oil 20 W 30/40.

4) Install drive pinion into housing with rear bearing, long spacer, front bearing and nut. Install special spanner tool (hexagon sleeve with bolt tang) over end of drive pinion nut and secure to holding fixture with bolt through tang (see illustration). Install drive pinion holding socket M (splined socket) over pinion spline. Torque nut to 7.2 ft. lbs. (1.0 mkg). Rotate drive pinion in both directions and again tighten nut. Continue operation until nut can no longer be tightened less than torque specification.

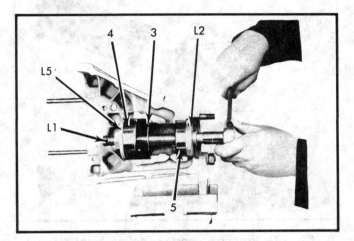

Fig. 13   Installing Drive Pinion Bearing Outer Race

5) Install special tool AZ (for measuring pinion depth) into front half of housing and hold in position by means of bridge clamp A3. *See Fig. 14.* Tighten nuts of clamp to 7.2 ft. lbs. (1.0 mkg). Equalize distance between bridge pads and housing on both sides by using feeler gauges. Free feeler assembly A2 and ensure there is no contact with drive pinion.

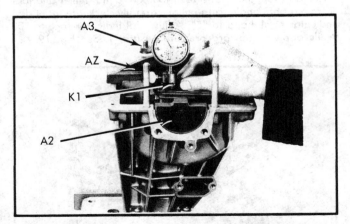

Fig. 14   Measuring Drive Pinion Installed Depth

6) Install dial indicator onto holder K1. Position latter so that dial indicator foot guide is resting on upper surface of A2. Adjust height of dial indicator so that small hand is set to "3"

(for example). Turn dial face to zero indicator. Slide support K1 to bring dial indicator foot into contact with machined surface of AZ. Movement of dial indicator indicates depth of A2. Write down value obtained.

7) There are 2 reference marks on hypoid gear end of drive pinion; 1st indicates pinion depth and 2nd corresponds with number of ring gear (matched set). Write down reference number (bottom number) marked on end of drive pinion. To this number, whether positive or negative, add + .30 mm to find corresponding guide number. Compare dial indicator reading previously obtained with guide number. The difference between 2 numbers represents thickness (in mm) of shims to be installed between drive pinion rear bearing outer race and thrust washer. To find corresponding guide number and to calculate thickness of shims, use sample calculation:

Sample Calculation

Constant Added to Determine Guide Number	.30
Number on End of Drive Pinion	−.04
Resulting Guide Number	.26
Dial Indicator Reading From Step **6)**	.67
Subtract Guide Number (Obtained Above)	−.26
Total Shim Thickness Required	①.41

① — Hundredths of a millimeter (mm).

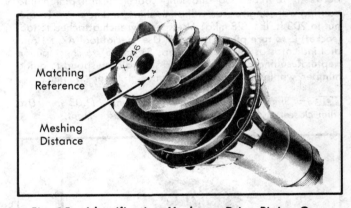

Fig. 15   Identification Marks on Drive Pinion Gear

8) Remove tool AZ and drive pinion from front housing. Use puller-driver tool to remove drive pinion rear bearing outer race from front housing. Install thrust washer and shims (previously determined) then reinstall rear bearing outer race. Torque puller-driver tool to 101 ft. lbs. (14 mkg), to seat.

9) Place drive pinion vertically on work bench and make colored chalk mark down full length of one spline (on drive pinion). Install long spacer, front bearing (fitted backward) and nut J. Place holding fixture N over nut J and use socket C to torque pinion to 203 ft. lbs. (28 mkg).

10) Screw dial indicator onto extension K2. Place dial indicator on end of drive pinion and make sure that extension K2 faces chalk mark on pinion spline and rests on machined surface of nut J. Move dial indicator to bring small hand to 1 and big hand to 0. Remove dial indicator and lay aside, making sure reading is not changed. Remove nut J and front bearing. Place pinion into front housing with long spacer and front

PEUGEOT SPLIT HOUSING — I.R.S. (Cont.)

bearing. Torque nut J to 7.2 ft. lbs.(1 mkg). Rotate pinion 10 turns counterclockwise and retorque.

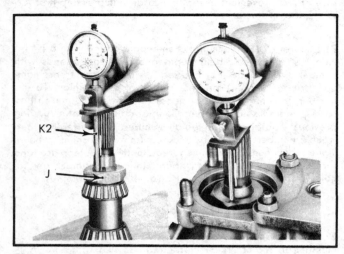

Fig. 16   Measuring Drive Pinion Depth

11) With colored chalk mark as reference, take another reading, with dial indicator between end of shaft and nut J. Find difference between two readings and subtract .06 mm. The number thus obtained is the thickness of shims necessary between front bearing and long spacer. Install pinion into housing with long spacer, adjusting shims and new nut. Torque nut to 203 ft. lbs. (28 mkg). Use speed wrench attached to tool (socket) C to turn pinion by hand. Use special tool AZ, K1 and dial indicator as described in steps **5)** and **6)** to check pinion depth. Resulting number obtained should correspond to guide number, within the following tolerance: +.05 or -.03 mm.

NOTE — *Shims are available in increments of .03 mm. Use shim closest to difference obtained in measurement.*

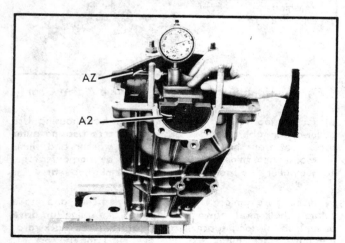

Fig. 17   Measuring Drive Pinion Depth Shim Thickness

12) Reassemble differential side gear and pinion gears into differential housing, using appropriate thrust washers. Assemble differential side gear to ring gear and assemble ring gear to differential housing, using new bolts. Clamp assembly in soft jawed vise and tighten ring gear-to-differential housing bolts. Press new bearings onto differential assembly and oil bearings with plenty of Esso Extra Motor Oil 20 W 30/40.

NOTE — *Dimples on thrust washer should face gear.*

13) With front housing held by holding fixture, place holding fixture in vise. See *Fig. 18.* Coat machined surfaces with gasket adhesive. Apply oil to bearing recesses. Install differential assembly. Install rear housing cover with 4 nuts and new washers. Tighten nuts. Install bearing left side plate with new bolts and washers. Tighten bolt. Loosen 4 nuts on rear cover and retighten by hand.

14) Now clamp assembly in vise with right side facing upward. Install special tool (clamp) P and hand tighten only. Rotate pinion spline five turns in both directions and recheck tightness of clamp P and retighten rear cover nuts.

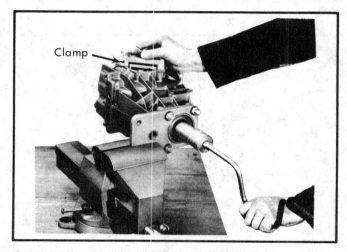

Fig. 18   Installing Tension Tool on Right Side

15) Move assembly in vise to its normal upright position. Install backlash measuring tool R horizontally. Ensure one of the radial grooves in ring gear face is in line with double quotation mark ("") of device. Lock central screw and install support rod Q2 in front upper housing. Mount dial indicator using holder Q3 so that dial indicator feeler (foot) is resting between two marks found on flat side of tool R and that feeler and tool R from a right angle. Turn pinion carefully clockwise to set dial indicator small hand to "5". Adjust dial indicator face to "0" while applying upward pressure on arm 1. See *Fig. 19.*

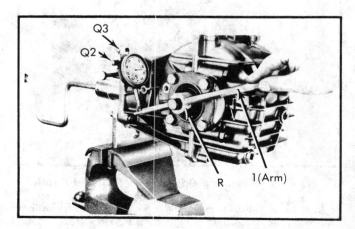

Fig. 19   Measuring Ring-to-Pinion Gear Backlash

PEUGEOT SPLIT HOUSING — I.R.S. (Cont.)

NOTE — *Before taking each reading, make sure dial indicator has been set to zero.*

16) Press downward on arm 1 until it seats. In this position, dial indicator reads backlash between drive pinion and ring gear. Note reading and repeat operation at 3 different gaps in tool R. Write down 2 extreme readings. If difference between maximum and minimum reading exceeds .10 mm, check for dirt or burrs on teeth. Subtract minimum from maximum to determine thickness of shims to be installed on left-hand side under side thrust plate.

17) Remove backlash measuring tool and clamp P. Place indicated shims into housing on bearing outer race. Install new "O" ring and thrust plate with new oil seal. Install 4 bolts which retain plate to housing. Reinstall assembly into vise with right side up. Hand tighten central screw on tool P, while turning drive pinion.

18) Place tool KZ on flat surface of right front housing with dial indicator long feeler (foot) resting on outer bearing race. Make sure dial indicator does not rest on both front and rear housings, only on front or rear. Adjust dial indicator to obtain 1 mm on hand and zero dial face. Remove dial indicator and place on machined surface to determine difference in 2 readings, which indicates depth of outer race. To obtain correct calculation, add .25 mm to difference between dial indicator reading and preset depth of 1 mm. See sample calculation:

NOTE — *Do not forget to subtract 1.0 mm upon which dial indicator was zeroed.*

Sample Calculation

Measurement On Machined Surface	7.15 mm
Measurement In Housing	−1.00 mm
Difference Between These	6.15 mm
Constant To Be Added	+ .25 mm
Total	6.40 mm

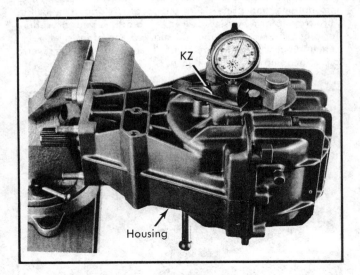

Fig. 20 Measuring Side Cover Shim Thickness

19) Place dial indicator on right-hand side plate with dial indicator-feeler (foot) on outside machined surface (see il-

lustration). Adjust dial indicator to obtain reading of "1.00" and zero face. Place dial indicator on machined surface and note reading.

NOTE — *Displacement of needle represents height of collar on plate. To calculate height, see sample calculation.*

Sample Calculation

Measurement On Machined Surface	7.29 mm
Dial Indicator Reading Before Zeroing	− 1.00 mm
Height Of Collar (Total)	6.29 mm

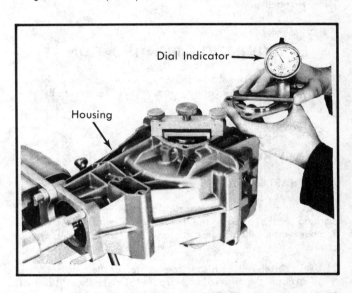

Fig. 21 Measuring Side Cover Depth

20) Subtract number obtained in step 19) from number obtained in step 18). The resulting number is correct thickness of shims to be placed between outer bearing race and side cover. Install shims and side plate. Tighten bolts.

NOTE — *Shims are available in thickness increments of .10 mm.*

21) Refer to steps 15) through 17) to determine and compensate for backlash. Install necessary shims and tighten side cover bolts. Install assembly into vehicle as previously outlined.

TIGHTENING SPECIFICATIONS

Application	Ft. Lbs. (mkg)
Hub Carrier-to-Lower Control Arm	29 (4.0)
Rear Caliper Retaining Bolts	31 (4.3)
Rear Hub Nut	189 (26)
Differential Housing-to-Sub-Frame (Allen)	27 (3.7)
Rear Brake Pad Retaining Fork Bolt	13 (1.8)
Ring Gear-to-Differential Assembly	51 (7.0)
Differential Side Plate Bolts	6 (.8)
Propeller Shaft (Torque) Tube Nuts	44 (6.0)

Drive Axles

SUBARU 4-WD

1600

(mounted on tool) into housing until seated. Fit collar to housing and press until it touches outer race of bearing.

DESCRIPTION

The rear axle assembly of all 4-WD vehicles is a hypoid type with integral carrier housing. The pinion bearing preload adjustment is made by a selective spacer and washer. The differential side bearing preload and pinion depth adjustments are made with shims. Driving power is transmitted to rear axle by ball spline type drive shafts with constant velocity (CV) joints at each end.

AXLE RATIO & IDENTIFICATION

All 4-WD vehicles use one basic type rear axle assembly. To determine axle ratio, divide number of ring gear teeth by number of pinion teeth.

REMOVAL & INSTALLATION

AXLE SHAFT & BEARINGS

Removal — 1) Raise and support the vehicle. Apply the parking brake or lock the front wheels with wheel blocks. Remove wheel, then loosen the axle nut, while applying foot brake.

2) Using chisel, relieve the staked portion of the axle nut. Apply oil around the thread and groove of axle shaft. Back off axle nut approximately .24" (6 mm), then tighten nut to original position. Repeat this operation several times so chips fall into shaft groove.

3) Disconnect drive shaft (rear) from rear axle companion flange. Apply foot brake and remove nut securing companion flange to spindle. Using a punch (or equivalent), remove spring pin connecting axle shaft to drive shaft. Take off companion flange.

NOTE — *Do not unstake companion nut. Use of a chisel will damage the spindle thread.*

4) Remove brake drum, spindle, outer seal, and bearing as a unit. Remove axle nut from spindle. Remove brake drum and outer seal. Press bearing from spindle.

5) Unlock link nut, then using suitable wrench (925350000), remove link nut and pull out inner oil seal. Using suitable press, remove inner and outer bearing race and bearing spacer from trailing arm housing.

Installation — 1) Using suitable bearing installation tool (925310000), press bearing inner race onto spindle until it reaches flange. Fit inner spacer and other bearing inner race onto spindle. Apply grease to each bearing.

2) Place outer side of trailing arm housing on a "V" block. Mount outer bearing race on suitable bearing installation tool (925310000) and press bearing into housing until seated. Fit outer spacer into housing, then press outer race of bearing

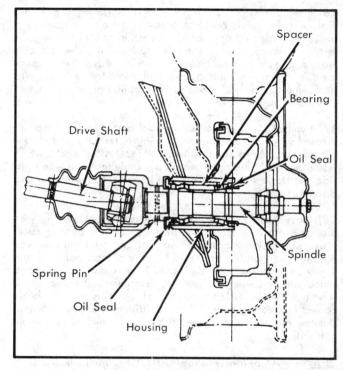

Fig. 1   Sectional View of Rear Drive Axle Assembly

3) Apply grease on outer spacer (installed in housing), then fit spindle to housing from outside. Place outer side of housing on "V" block. Use adequate means to prevent spindle from dropping.

4) Apply grease to oil seal lip and mount seal on the "I" marked side of installer (925340000). Place installer and seal into housing and press down until seal is stopped by collar. Turn trailing arm housing over in "V" block. Repeat procedure for other oil seal, using the "O" marked end of installer. Press seal into housing until seated. Install remaining parts in reverse order of removal and tighten nuts.

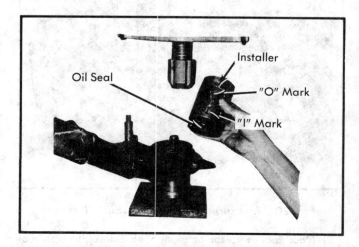

Fig. 2   Installation of Oil Seals

SUBARU 4-WD (Cont.)

NOTE – *Apply foot brake while tightening nuts. Bleed brakes.*

DRIVE AXLE SHAFTS

Removal – Raise vehicle and support on safety stands. Disconnect drive shaft from axle shaft companion flange. Remove differential side yoke attaching bolt and lift out side yoke and drive shaft as an assembly.

Installation – To install, reverse removal procedure and note the following: Use care when installing assembly to prevent damage to side yoke and oil seal. Tighten all bolts to specifications.

PINION FLANGE & OIL SEAL

Removal – Drain gear oil from differential, then raise and support rear of vehicle. Disconnect propeller shaft from pinion flange. Measure and record turning torque of pinion flange. Hold pinion flange with suitable tool (398427700), then remove pinion nut. Extract pinion flange with suitable puller. Remove oil seal.

Installation – Apply chassis grease between oil seal lips, then install oil seal using suitable drift (398417700). Install pinion flange. Hold flange with suitable tool and tighten nut until turning torque is same as recorded before removal. Install remaining components in reverse order of removal procedure.

Flange Wrench

Fig. 3   Drive Pinion Nut Removal

DIFFERENTIAL ASSEMBLY

Removal – Raise and support rear of vehicle. Drain gear oil. Remove exhaust pipe, muffler, propeller shaft and drive shafts. Support axle assembly with a jack, then remove nuts on mounting member. Remove two bolts retaining front end of differential carrier. Lower jack and remove axle assembly.

Installation – To install, reverse removal procedure and note the following: Tighten bolts to specification and fill unit with gear oil.

OVERHAUL

DRIVE AXLE SHAFT

NOTE – *Drive axle shaft should be disassembled only to lubricate ball spline.*

Disassembly – Hold drive shaft in a vise and remove rubber boot. Remove snap ring and stopper, then disassemble ball spline. Remove snap ring, needle bearing and universal joint.

Inspection – Check rubber boot and oil seals for damage and replace as necessary. Inspect drive shaft for straightness, cracks, damage and distortion. Replace drive shaft if ball spline portion is worn or damaged. Check drive shaft play at ball spline and free play of needle bearing. Maximum play of ball spline is .04" (1 mm).

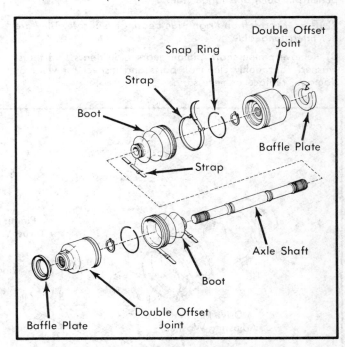

Double Offset Joint
Snap Ring
Strap
Boot
Strap
Baffle Plate
Axle Shaft
Boot
Double Offset Joint
Baffle Plate

Fig. 4   Exploded View of Drive Axle Shaft

Reassembly – To reassemble, reverse disassembly procedure and note the following: Apply grease to points shown in *Fig. 5*. Install rubber boot and adjust drive shaft length to 13.15" (334 mm). Adjust axial play to within .0008" (.02 mm) by selecting proper size snap ring. Tighten all bolts.

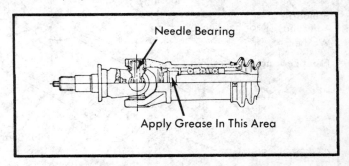

Needle Bearing
Apply Grease In This Area

Fig. 5   Drive Axle Shaft Grease Locations

DIFFERENTIAL

NOTE – *Mark side retainers for reassembly reference. Left and right retainers are not interchangeable.*

Disassembly – 1) Mount carrier on suitable holding fixture; remove cover plate. Using suitable puller, remove side

Drive Axles

SUBARU 4-WD (Cont.)

retainers. Remove differential case assembly from carrier. If side bearings are to be replaced, remove bearing outer races from side retainers with suitable puller.

2) Hold pinion flange stationary and remove pinion nut. Remove pinion flange with suitable puller. Press drive pinion from carrier and remove rear bearing inner race, bearing spacer and adjusting washer. Remove side bearings from differential case with puller. Remove ring gear by unfolding lock strap and loosening bolts. Unstake pinion shaft lock pin and punch pin out from flange side.

NOTE — *Keep left and right side bearings separate. They are not interchangeable.*

3) Remove pinion shaft, pinion gears, side gears and thrust washer. Thoroughly clean all parts and inspect for wear or damage; replace as necessary.

NOTE — *Mark gears and thrust washers for installation in their original positions.*

REASSEMBLY & ADJUSTMENT

Differential Case Assembly — 1) Assemble pinion gears, side gears and thrust washers in original positions in differential case. Fit pinion shaft to differential case so that it aligns with lock pin holes.

2) Adjust clearance between differential case and back of side gear to .004-.008″ (.1-.2 mm) by selecting proper thrust washer. Thrust washers are available in the following sizes: .030-.032″ (.75-.80 mm), .032-.034 (.80-.85 mm), and .034-.036″ (.85-.90 mm).

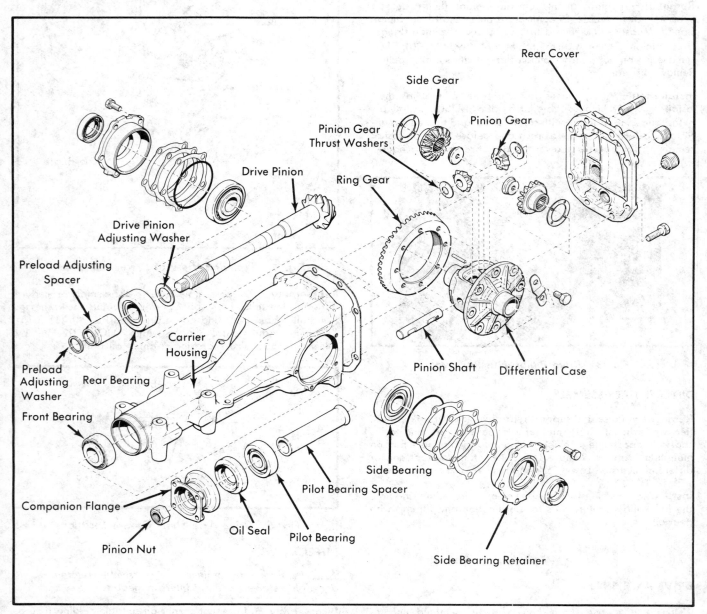

Fig. 6 Exploded View of Differential Assembly

SUBARU 4-WD (Cont.)

3) Install pinion shaft lock pin and lock in place on both sides. Apply gear oil to gear tooth surface and thrust surfaces and make sure gears rotate smoothly. Install ring gear on differential case and install bolts and new lock washers.

NOTE — *Tighten ring gear bolts diagonally while tapping around bolt heads with a hammer.*

4) When replacing side bearings, measure bearing width by using a weight block of approximately 5.5 lb. (2.5 kg). Standard bearing width is .787" (20 mm). Press side bearing inner race onto differential case and bearing outer race into side retainers. Install new oil seal on side retainer and apply grease to cavity between seal lips.

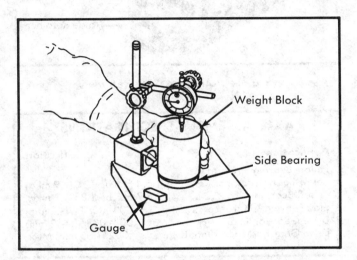

Fig. 7   Measuring Side Bearing Width

Drive Pinion Bearing Preload Adjustment — 1) Press front and rear bearing outer races into carrier. Install dummy pinion shaft (389507702) with rear bearing and pinion depth washer into the carrier.

NOTE — *If ring and pinion gear tooth contact pattern show normal pattern, reuse original washer.*

2) Install preload adjusting spacer and washer, front bearing inner race, dummy collar (398507703), companion flange and nut onto dummy shaft. Do not install oil seal. Rotate pinion by hand until it is seated.

NOTE — *Do not exceed specified preload torque during preload adjustment.*

3) Tighten nut to specified torque. Using an INCH lb. torque wrench, check rotating torque of pinion shaft. If preload is not within specification, select the correct washer and spacer so that specified preload is obtained when nut is tightened to correct torque.

NOTE — *Spacers are available in lengths from 2.213" (56.2 mm) to 2.252" (57.2 mm) in increments of .008" (.20 mm) and washers are available in thicknesses from .102" (2.59 mm) to .0909" (.231 mm) in increments of .0008" (.02 mm).*

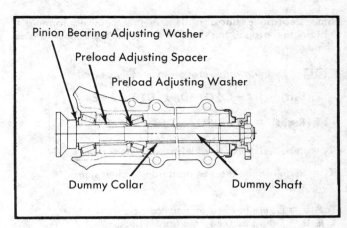

Fig. 8   Installing Dummy Shaft

Drive Pinion Gear Installed Height — 1) Leave dummy drive pinion shaft installed (*See Preload Adjustment*) and install height gauge (398507701). Measure clearance between end of pinion gear head and height gauge using feeler gauge. Determine the thickness of the pinion height adjusting washer to be installed using the following formula:

$$T = T_o + N - (H \times .01) - .20$$

NOTE — *Formula values are given in millimeters.*

T = Thickness of adjusting washer needed.
To = Thickness of washer temporarily installed.
N = Clearance between gauge and dummy shaft.
H = Figure marked on drive pinion head.

2) After determining the correct thickness of required pinion height adjusting washer, remove dummy shaft and height gauge. Install pinion height adjusting washer on drive pinion, then press rear bearing inner race into position with suitable tool (398177700).

3) Insert drive pinion into gear carrier. Install previously selected preload adjusting spacer, washer, oil seal, companion flange, and pinion nut. Tighten pinion nut to specification.

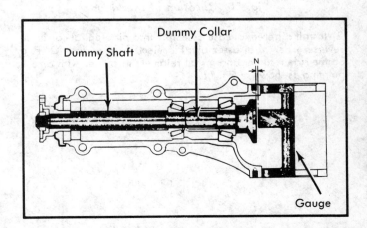

Fig. 9   Measuring Drive Pinion Gear Installed Height

SUBARU 4-WD (Cont.)

Side Bearing Preload — 1) Use the following formula to obtain the proper thickness of left and right side retainer shims.

NOTE — *Formula values are given in Millimeters.*

$$T_1(\text{Left}) = (A+C+G_1-D) \times .01+.76-E$$

$$T_2(\text{Right}) = (B+D+G_2) \times .01+.76-F$$

T_1 = Required thickness of left side retainer shim.

T_2 = Required thickness of right side retainer shim.

A & B = Figure marked on gear carrier.
C & D = Figure marked on differential case.
E & F = Difference in width of left or right bearing.
G_1 = Figure marked on left side retainer.
G_2 = Figure marked on right side retainer.

NOTE — *If the figure is not marked, regard as zero.*

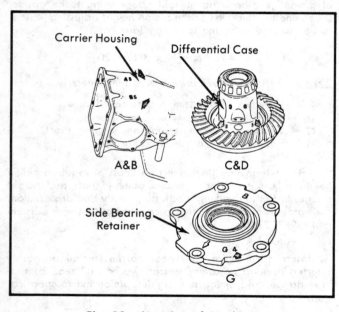

Fig. 10   Location of Markings

2) Install differential case assembly into differential carrier in reverse order of disassembly. Fit selected shims and "O" ring on the side retainer and install retainers in carrier with arrow pointing as shown in *Fig. 11*.

3) Measure drive gear-to-drive pinion backlash. If reading is not within specification, correct by decreasing the shim thickness on one side and increasing the shim thickness on other side the same amount. Total shim thickness must be the same to maintain proper preload.

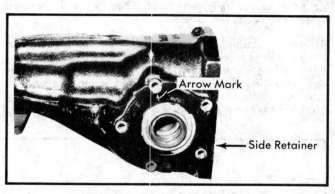

Fig. 11   Aligning Side Retainer

AXLE ASSEMBLY SPECIFICATIONS

Application	Specification
Pinion Bearing Preload	
New Bearing	4.4-6.4 Ft. Lbs. (2.0-2.9 mkg)
Used Bearing	1.9-3.7 Ft. Lbs. (.85-1.7 mkg)
Side Bearing Clearance	.004-.008" (.1-.2 mm)
Drive Gear-to-Pinion Backlash	.004-.008" (.1-.2 mm)
Drive Gear Backface Runout	.002" (.05 mm) Max.

TIGHTENING SPECIFICATIONS

Application	Ft. Lbs. (mkg)
Pinion Nut	123-145 (17-20)
Side Bearing Retaining Bolt	7-9 (.9-1.2)
Side Yoke Retaining Bolt	14-19 (1.9-2.6)
Rear Cover Bolts	14-19 (1.9-2.6)
Front Carrier Mounting Bolts	58-72 (8-10)
Rear Carrier Mounting Bolts	43-51 (6-7)
Propeller Shaft Flange Bolts	13-18 (1.8-2.5)
Companion Flange Bolts	13-18 (1.8-2.5)
Axle Nut	174 (24)
Rear Drive Shaft Spindle Ring Nut	130-160 (18-23)

TOYOTA INTEGRAL CARRIER

Celica (Exc. Limited Slip)
Corona (Exc. Limited Slip)
Supra (Exc. Limited Slip)

DESCRIPTION

Final drive assembly has hypoid type ring and pinion gear and removable rear cover. Differential carrier is retained in the sides of the housing by retaining plates and is supported by tapered roller bearings. Side bearing preload is adjusted by turning adjusting nuts on each side of carrier. Drive pinion gear is supported by roller bearings and preload is maintained by a non-collapsible spacer between the bearings.

AXLE RATIO & IDENTIFICATION

The integral carrier is identifiable by the inspection cover on the rear of the carrier housing. To determine axle ratio, divide number of ring gear teeth by number of pinion gear teeth.

REMOVAL & INSTALLATION

AXLE SHAFTS

NOTE — *Removal procedures not available for Supra.*

Removal — Raise and support vehicle. Remove tire and wheel. Working through hole in axle flange, remove bolts holding bearing retainer to axle housing flange. Using slide hammer, remove shaft from housing using care not to damage axle seal. If both axles are to be removed, be sure to index each for reinstallation in original position. If axle housing seal is being replaced, coat sealing lip with grease before installing.

Installation — To install, reverse removal procedure.

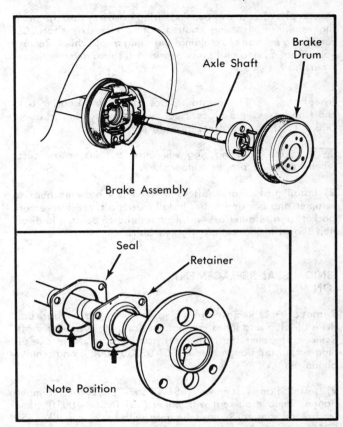

Fig. 2 Exploded View of Rear Axle Assembly (Celica & Corona Shown)

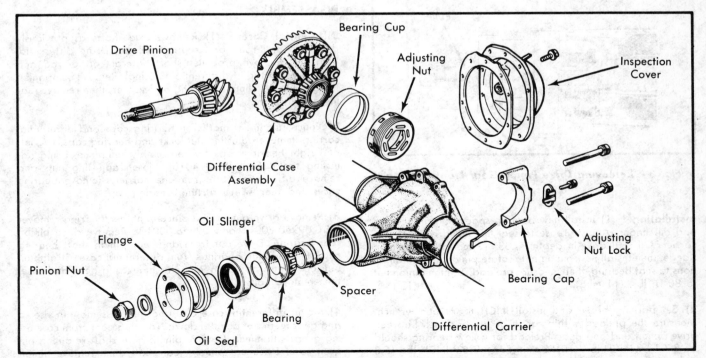

Fig. 1 Exploded View of Toyota Integral Carrier Differential

TOYOTA INTEGRAL CARRIER (Cont.)

AXLE BEARINGS

Removal — To remove bearing, grind part way through bearing retainer ring using caution not to nick axle shaft. Cut remaining portion of retaining ring using a cold chisel. Remove split retaining ring and press bearing off shaft. Remove spacer from shaft.

Installation — 1) To install, place spacer and bearing onto shaft and press into place. Heat new retaining ring to about 300°F (150°C) and press into place.

NOTE — *The retaining ring will show a faint yellow color when heated to proper temperature.*

2) Install gaskets on shaft so they will be between bearing retainer and backing plate. Install axle shaft, check to ensure gaskets and retainer are installed with notch pointed in direction shown in illustration. Tighten bolts.

PINION SEAL REPLACEMENT
(ON VEHICLE)

Removal — 1) Remove drain plug and drain carrier lubricant. Reinstall plug and index companion flange to propeller shaft. Remove propeller shaft, then set parking brake. Unstake pinion nut, install flange holder (SST 09330-00020) and remove pinion nut.

2) Install flange remover (SST 09557-22022) and remove flange. Remove oil seal with puller (SST 09308-10010), then remove oil slinger. Remove bearing with bearing puller (SST 09556-22010). Remove bearing spacer.

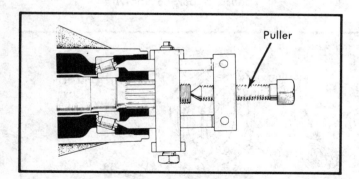

Fig. 3   Removing Drive Pinion Gear Front Bearing

Installation — 1) Install new bearing spacer. Install bearing and oil slinger. Apply grease to seal lip and drive seal into carrier. Oil seal drive-in depth is .08" (2 mm). Install pinion flange, then install new pinion nut. Rotate pinion in both directions to seat bearing, then measure preload. Tighten pinion nut to 80 ft. lbs. (11 mkg).

2) Set parking brake and install INCH lb. torque wrench. Measure the preload within range of the backlash between drive pinion and ring gear. Preload for a new bearing should be 8.7-13.9 INCH lbs. (10-16 cmkg) or 4.3-6.9 INCH lbs. (5-8 cmkg) for a reused bearing.

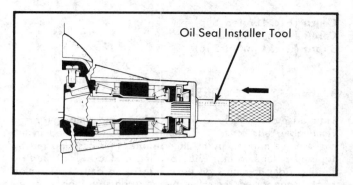

Fig. 4   Installing Oil Seal

3) If preload is greater than specification, replace bearing spacer. If preload is less than specification, retighten nut 10 ft. lbs. (1.3 mkg) at a time until specified preload is obtained. After adjustment, stake pinion nut, then align companion flange and propeller shaft index marks and install propeller shaft.

NOTE — *If maximum torque of 173 ft. lbs. (24 mkg) is exceeded, replace bearing spacer and repeat procedure. DO NOT back off pinion nut to reduce preload.*

DIFFERENTIAL CARRIER

NOTE — *Differential carrier is integral part of axle housing and can not be removed as an assembly.*

OVERHAUL

DISASSEMBLY

Differential Case — 1) Remove axle shafts as previously described and raise and support vehicle. Drain differential lubricant. Remove propeller shaft, lateral control rod and brake line (at top of differential housing). Remove companion flange, oil seal, slinger, bearing and spacer, then remove rear inspection cover.

2) Punch alignment marks on bearing caps and differential carrier. Remove adjusting nut locks and bearing caps. Tag left and right bearing caps for reassembly reference. Using adjusting tool (SST 09524-14010), loosen adjusting nuts and remove differential case from the carrier. Remove bearing races and keep with matching bearing cap.

3) Remove drive pinion and place in holder/bearing remover (SST 09950-20011 and 09956-00010). Remove drive pinion rear bearing. Drive out front and rear pinion shaft bearing cups. Remove side bearings from differential case. Straighten out lock plates on ring gear bolts, index ring gear and case, then remove bolts.

4) Mount differential case and ring gear assembly in vise so ring gear teeth are pointed down. Tap ring gear from case using a brass hammer. Remove pinion gear shaft retaining pin from case. Drive out pinion gear shaft, then remove pinion gears, side gears and thrust washers.

TOYOTA INTEGRAL CARRIER (Cont.)

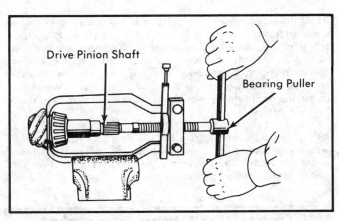

Fig. 5 Removing Drive Pinion Gear Rear Bearing

REASSEMBLY & ADJUSTMENT

Case Assembly — 1) Lubricate all components with hypoid gear lubricant. Assemble side gears and pinion gears into differential case. Make sure oil groove, if present, on side gear thrust washer faces toward gear.

2) Check backlash between side gears and pinion gears. If backlash is not .002-.008" (.05-.20 mm), install suitable selective fit thrust washers in equal thicknesses on both sides. Install pinion shaft lock pin and peen over hole.

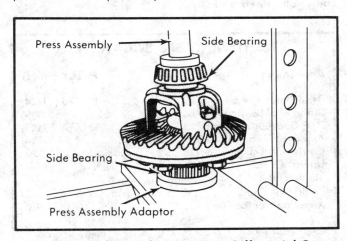

Fig. 6 Installing Side Bearing on Differential Case

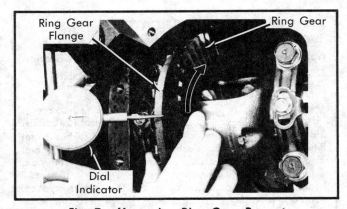

Fig. 7 Measuring Ring Gear Runout

3) Press differential side bearings onto differential case. Heat ring gear in oil bath to approximately 212°F (100°C), then quickly wipe off gear and install on differential case. Fit bolts and tighten evenly, then bend over lock tabs. Install differential case assembly in differential carrier and measure ring gear runout. If runout exceeds .003" (.07 mm), replace ring gear.

Drive Pinion Depth — 1) Remove differential case from carrier. Install drive pinion bearing cups in carrier. Install pinion shaft rear bearing onto suitable base rod, then install base rod head and bolts. Insert this assembly into carrier from rear. Install front pinion bearing into carrier from front end. Install collar and nut onto front end of base rod.

NOTE — *Tighten nut only to extent that driving pinion bearing has no play.*

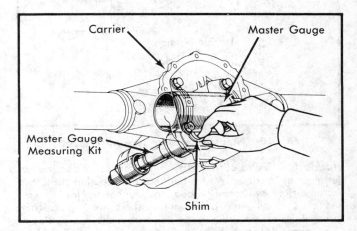

Fig. 8 Measuring Drive Pinion Installed Height

2) Install Toyota Master Gauge into differential side bearing bores, then install bearing caps and bolts. Ensure left and right bearing caps are matched with correct bore. Tighten bearing cap bolts to specification. Select a shim that snugly fits between master gauge and base rod head. One shim or none must be used: do not use more. After selecting shim, remove all components of master gauge kit. Press bearing and shim onto drive pinion, if shim has chamfered edge, install that edge toward pinion gear.

Pinion Bearing Preload — 1) Install pinion shaft assembly into carrier. Insert shims (if any) that were removed during disassembly onto pinion shaft. Install NEW bearing spacer, then install front bearing and oil slinger. Press oil seal into carrier .08" (2.0 mm). Install companion flange, washer and NEW nut. Torque pinion flange nut to 80 ft. lbs. (11 mkg).

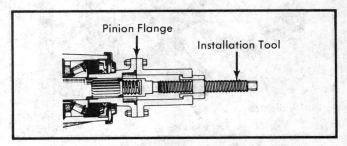

Fig. 9 Installing Pinion Flange

TOYOTA INTEGRAL CARRIER (Cont.)

2) Using an INCH lb. torque wrench, measure pinion bearing preload. If preload is excessive, replace spacer and repeat procedure. If preload is not to specification, tighten nut in small increments and recheck preload each time, until specified preload is reached. If preload is not to specification even after specified torque is reached, loosen nut and repeat procedure.

NOTE — *DO NOT exceed 173 ft. lbs. (24 mkg) during preload adjustment.*

3) Mount dial indicator to differential carrier and measure companion flange longitudinal and latitudinal deviations. If specifications are exceeded, replace companion flange and recheck.

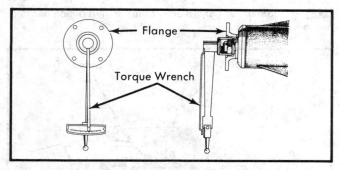

Fig. 10 Measuring Side Bearing Preload

Backlash & Side Bearing Play — 1) Install side bearing adjusting nuts in carrier. Match bearings and bearing cups, then install differential case and bearings into carrier. Install bearing caps and tighten bolts until washers are slightly compressed. Install dial indicator so plunger touches flange side of ring gear. Using bearing adjusting wrench (SST 09524-14011), tighten flange side adjusting nut so ring gear has free play of about .008" (.2 mm).

2) During adjustment procedure, rotate ring gear through several revolutions to seat side bearings. Tighten drive pinion side adjusting nut to the point where free play is eliminated. If tightening nut creates free play, loosen nut. Adjust side bearings for zero preload by tightening drive pinion adjusting nut until it feels hard to turn.

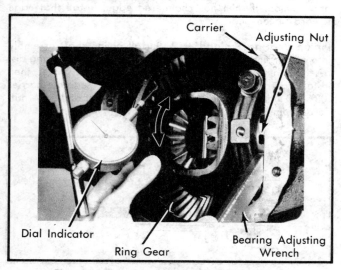

Fig. 11 Measuring Ring Gear Backlash

3) At the point where zero preload is obtained, tighten drive pinion adjusting nut an additional 1-1½ notches to preload side bearings. Mount dial indicator so plunger is perpendicular to ring gear tooth. Measure ring gear backlash. If not within specifications, turn left and right adjusting nuts to shift differential assembly in proper direction. If left side is loosened 1 notch, the right side must be tightened 1 notch to maintain side bearing preload.

4) Tighten side bearing cap bolts. Using an INCH lb. torque wrench, measure total (combined) bearing preload. If preload is not to specifications, repeat adjustment procedures for side bearings and pinion bearings.

Combined (Side & Pinion) Bearing Preload		
Application	**New INCH lbs. (cmkg)**	**Used INCH lbs. (cmkg)**
All Models	11.3-18.2 (13-21)	6.9-11.3 (8-13)

5) Install bearing adjusting nut locks. Stake drive pinion flange nut. Install inspection cover and tighten bolts. Connect brake line, install lateral control arm and align and install propeller shaft. Install axle shafts, add lubricant to differential carrier and bleed brake system.

TIGHTENING SPECIFICATIONS

Application	Ft. Lbs. (mkg)
Drive Pinion Flange Nut	80-173 (11-24)
Differential Bearing Cap Bolts	51-65 (7-9)
Ring Gear-to-Case Bolts	67-75 (9-10.5)
Axle Shaft Bearing Retainer	44-53 (6-7.4)
Carrier Inspection Cover	15-21 (2-3)
Lateral Control Arm Bolts	
Body-Side Bolt	51-65 (7-9)
Axle-Side Bolt①	26-39 (3.5-5.5)
Adjusting Nut Lock Bolt	8-11 (1-1.6)

① — Corona — 30-55 ft. lbs. (4.1-7.7 mkg).

AXLE SPECIFICATIONS

Application	Specification
Drive Pinion Bearing Preload	
New	8.7-13-9 INCH lbs. (10-16 cmkg)
Used	4.3-6.9 INCH lbs. (5-8 cmkg)
Side-to-Pinion Gear Backlash	.002-.008" (.05-.20 mm)
Pinion-to-Ring Gear Backlash	.005-.007" (.13-.18 mm)
Ring Gear Runout	.003" (.07 mm) Max.
Companion Flange Deviation	
Longitudinal	.004" (.10 mm) Max.
Latitudinal	.004" (.10 mm) Max.

Drive Axles

TOYOTA SEPARATE CARRIER

Celica (Limited Slip)   Land Cruiser
Corolla   Pickup
Corona (Limited Slip)   Supra (Limited Slip)
Cressida

DESCRIPTION

The axle assembly is hypoid gear type with a separate carrier housing. It comes in slightly different models for use in all Toyota vehicles. Two-pinion differential cases are one-piece design while four-pinion cases are two-piece design. The differential side bearing preload is set with adjusting nuts on all models. The pinion bearing preload can be set with a solid spacer and adjusting shim or with a collapsible spacer.

AXLE RATIO & IDENTIFICATION

Toyota uses only one basic type of axle assembly. Any differences in Removal & Installation or Overhaul procedures will be noted where they occur. To determine axle ratio, divide number of ring gear teeth by number of pinion gear teeth.

REMOVAL & INSTALLATION

FRONT AXLE SHAFTS & BEARINGS
(LAND CRUISER & 4-WD PICKUP)

NOTE — *On vehicles equipped with locking hubs, refer to Locking Hubs article in this Section to remove hub, then proceed with removal procedures. Ensure locking knob is set to "FREE" position before removal.*

Removal — 1) Raise and suitably support vehicle under axle housing. Remove tire and wheel. Disconnect and remove brake line at brake caliper and remove caliper assembly. Remove dust cap and snap ring. Remove axle flange lock washers with punch. Install bolts in flange bolt holes, then turn bolts equally to remove flange.

NOTE — *Tab of lock washer must be straightened with chisel to facilitate removal of outer lock nut.*

2) Remove outer lock nut with suitable wrench (SST 09607-60020). Then remove lock washer and adjusting nut. Place hand over axle shaft and carefully move axle hub/disc assembly back and forth to remove outer bearing and washer. Remove axle hub/disc assembly.

3) To remove inner wheel bearing, pry out oil seal and remove bearing. Replace outer bearing races by drifting out, then replace using bearing installer (SST 09608-35013).

4) Remove 8 dust shield retaining bolts, then remove dust seal, gasket and shield. Remove spindle assembly, tapping with a drift if necessary, then remove gasket. Align one flat of constant velocity (CV) joint so it is pointing upward, then extract axle/drive shaft assembly. Remove grease and clean assembly with suitable solvent.

CAUTION — *Do NOT attempt to remove steering knuckle. Any adjustment to specifications requires alignment of axle shaft and adjustment of knuckle bearing preload.*

Installation — To install, reverse removal procedure using the following notes: Install axle/drive shaft with one flat of constant velocity joint pointing upward. Pack steering knuckle cavity with molybdenum disulphide (lithium base grease) to about ¾ of knuckle volume. Tighten all bolts.

REAR AXLE SHAFTS

NOTE — *Land Cruiser models with semi-floating rear axles require removal of axle housing inspection cover BEFORE attempting removal of axle shaft.*

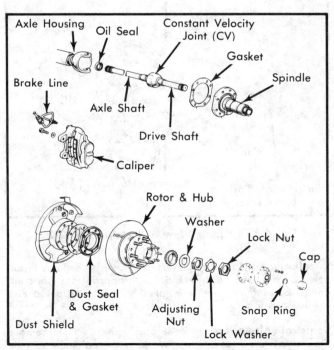

Fig. 1 Exploded View of Front Axle Shaft Assembly (4-WD Pickup and Land Cruiser)

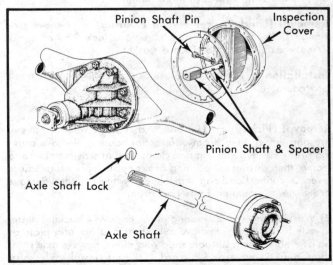

Fig. 2 Exploded View of Land Cruiser Rear Axle Shaft Assembly (Semi-Floating Axle Shafts Shown)

TOYOTA SEPARATE CARRIER (Cont.)

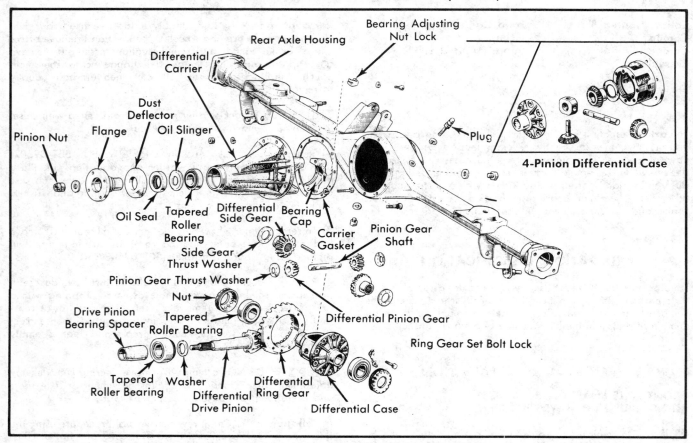

**Fig. 3   Exploded View of Typical Toyota Two Pinion Rear Differential Assembly
(Four Pinion Differential Case Shown in Inset)**

Removal (Land Cruiser — Semi-Floating) — Raise and suitably support vehicle and remove tire, wheel and brake drum. Drain axle housing and remove inspection cover. Remove pinion shaft lock pin, then remove pinion shaft and spacer. Remove axle lock circlip, then remove axle shaft.

Installation — To install, reverse removal procedure and fill differential with appropriate lubricant.

Removal (Land Cruiser — Full Floating) — Remove axle flange bolts, then using punch, remove lock washer cones. Remove axle shaft and discard gasket.

Installation — To install, replace gasket and reverse removal procedure.

Removal (Pickup) — 1) Raise and support vehicle, remove tire and wheel, then drain differential housing. Remove parking brake cable guide clip and clamp bolt at crossmember and frame, then disconnect parking brake cable from intermediate lever. Disconnect and cap brake line at wheel cylinder. Remove brake drum mounting bolts and drum.

2) Working on rear of backing plate, remove 4 backing plate-to-axle housing nuts. Remove axle shaft and backing plate as an assembly. Using suitable snap ring pliers, remove axle shaft snap ring. Remove and discard "O" ring. Install axle shaft remover (SST 09521-25011) and press out axle shaft, ensuring not to damage oil seal in housing. Remove bearing retainer.

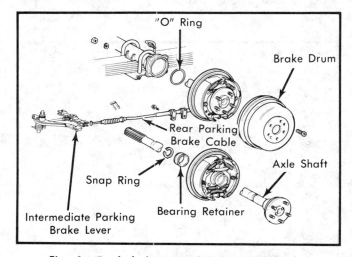

Fig. 4   Exploded View of Pickup Rear Axle

Installation — To install, reverse removal procedure, install new "O" ring and fill differential with appropriate lubricant. Ensure bearing retainer is installed with small tapered end toward bearing.

Removal (All Others) — Raise and support vehicle, remove tire, wheel and brake drum. Working through hole in axle flange, remove bearing retainer-to-axle housing bolts. Using a slide hammer, remove shaft from housing using care not to

TOYOTA SEPARATE CARRIER (Cont.)

damage axle seal. If axle housing seal is being replaced, coat sealing lip with grease before installing.

Installation — To install, reverse removal procedure.

REAR AXLE BEARINGS

Removal (Land Cruiser) — With axle shaft removed, raise and support vehicle. Remove brake drum retaining screw, then remove brake drum. Using bearing wrench (SST 09607-60020), remove lock nut. Remove retaining screw from bearing adjusting nut and remove adjusting nut and lock washer. Remove outer bearing, then remove hub assembly. Replace inner bearing after removing oil seal.

Installation — To install, coat inner walls of hub with grease and reverse removal procedure. Install adjusting nut to torque of 43 ft. lbs. (6 mkg), rotate hub back and forth 3 or 4 times and retighten adjusting nut to specification. Back off adjusting nut ⅛ to ⅕ turn. Install lock screw. Tighten lock nut to 58-72 ft. lbs. (8-10 mkg).

Removal (Pickup) — Disassemble brake assembly and remove oil seal with suitable slide hammer. Press out bearing. Index bearing case and remove by installing nuts to the bolts, knocking bolts out with hammer, then removing bearing case. Remove axle shaft oil seal from housing with suitable slide hammer.

Installation — Install axle shaft oil seal with installer (SST 09608-30011). Align bearing case index marks, position long bolts at top and short bolts at bottom and press into case and backing plate. Install bearing and oil seal. Reassemble brake assembly.

Removal (All Others) — To remove bearing, grind part way through bearing retainer ring using caution not to nick axle shaft. Cut remaining portion of retaining ring using a cold chisel. Remove split retaining ring and press bearing off shaft. Remove spacer from shaft.

Installation — 1) To install, place spacer and bearing onto shaft and press into place. Heat new retaining ring to about 300°F (150°C) and press into place.

NOTE — *The retaining ring will show a faint yellow color when heated to proper temperature.*

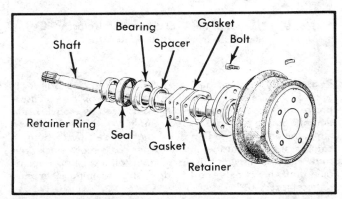

Fig. 5 Exploded View of Typical Rear Axle Assembly for All Models Except Land Cruiser & Pickup

2) On Corolla models only, measure thickness of brake backing plate and choose proper thickness selective fit gasket. Install gasket between backing plate and axle housing flange. On all other models, place gasket(s) into position so when shaft is installed, gasket(s) will be between bearing retainer and backing plate.

3) Ensure notched portion of retainer and gaskets (if equipped) are installed in the position shown in illustration. Install axle shaft, check alignment of gaskets, then tighten bolts.

PINION SEAL REPLACEMENT (ON VEHICLE)

Removal (Except Land Cruiser) — 1) Index mark propeller shaft and companion flange and set parking brake. Disconnect and remove propeller shaft.

2) On Corona and Pickup models, measure and record total pinion preload with pull scale attached to pinion flange at one of the propeller shaft bolt holes. Measurement is made within the small movement caused by the ring gear and axle shaft backlash. Axle shafts are locked by parking brake.

3) On all models, loosen stacked portion of pinion shaft nut. Install suitable holding tool to flange and remove the nut. Using flange puller, remove pinion flange. Remove oil seal using suitable puller and remove oil slinger. Remove bearing with bearing puller, then remove spacer and shim (Pickup 8" differential).

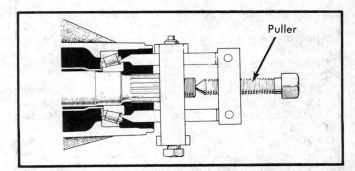

Fig. 6 Removing Drive Pinion Gear Front Bearing

NOTE — *If maximum tightening torque is exceeded during installation of oil seal, back off nut and retighten.*

NOTE — *Toyota recommends installing new spacer for Celica, Corona and Supra models whenever oil seal is replaced.*

Installation (Corolla, Cressida & Pickup) — 1) Install spacer, shim (Pickup 8" differential), bearing and oil slinger. Apply grease to seal lip and install to depth shown in "Pinion Seal Depth" chart. Using tool attached to pinion flange, install pinion flange. Remove tool and install new nut. Tighten nut to 69 ft. lbs. (9.5 mkg) on Corolla 6" differential and to 80 ft. lbs. (11 mkg) on all other models while holding companion flange stationary.

2) Rotate pinion in both directions to seat bearing, then measure bearing preload (starting torque). If preload is excessive, replace spacer and repeat procedure. If preload is insufficient, gradually tighten nut in increments of 5-10°, until preload is obtained. If preload is exceeded, replace spacer.

Drive Axles

TOYOTA SEPARATE CARRIER (Cont.)

Complete installation by reversing removal procedure. Add suitable lubricant if required.

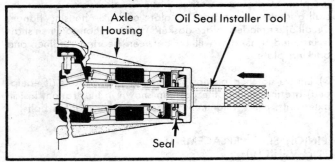

Fig. 7   Installing Oil Seal

Installation (All Others) — 1) Install spacer, bearing and oil slinger. Apply grease to seal lip and install to depth shown in "Pinion Seal Depth" chart. Using tool attached to pinion flange, install pinion flange. Remove tool and install new nut. Tighten nut to 80 ft. lbs. (11 mkg) while holding companion flange stationary.

2 Rotate pinion in both directions to seat bearing, then measure bearing preload (measured within range of backlash between drive pinion and ring gear with parking brake set). If preload is excessive, replace spacer and repeat procedure. If preload is insufficient, gradually tighten nut in increments of 5-10° until preload is obtained. If preload is exceeded, replace spacer. Complete installation by reversing removal procedure. Add suitable lubricant if required.

Pinion Seal Depth Chart

Application	Depth
Celica & Supra	.16" (4 mm)
Corolla	
6.00" Ring Gear	.04" (1 mm)
6.38" Ring Gear	To Carrier End Face
6.70" Ring Gear	.16" (4 mm)
Corona	
6.70" Ring Gear	.16" (4 mm)
7.10" Ring Gear	.04" (1 mm)
All Others	.04" (1 mm)

DIFFERENTIAL CARRIER

Removal — Drain oil from axle housing. Loosen hub nuts and remove wheels. Index propeller shaft to companion flange and remove propeller shaft. Remove axle shafts as previously described. Loosen bolts and remove differential carrier.

NOTE — *Do not damage oil seal during removal of axle shafts if it is not scheduled for replacement.*

Installation — To install, reverse removal procedure, noting the following: Coat both sides of carrier-to-housing gasket with sealer before installation. Fill axle housing with gear oil.

OVERHAUL

FRONT AXLE SHAFT & SPINDLE (LAND CRUISER & 4-WD PICKUP)

Disassembly — 1) Mount spindle in vise and remove bushing with suitable puller. Install new bushing with installing tool and

press. Inspect axle shaft for wear or damage and carefully inspect constant velocity (CV) joint for excessive looseness.

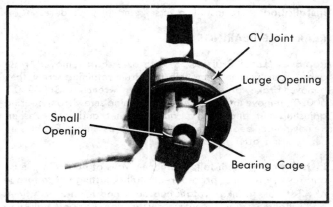

Fig. 8   Removing & Installing CV Joint Bearing Cage & Retainer

2) Mount axle shaft (inner shaft) in a vise with CV joint pointing upward. Place a brass drift against inner race and drive off drive shaft (outer shaft). Do not allow drive shaft to drop. Remove snap rings from axle shaft.

3) Tilt bearing cage and inner race outward from housing and remove 6 ball bearings. Remove each ball separately and do not drop. Turn bearing cage and retainer outward from drive shaft and align the 2 larger openings of the bearing cage with 2 protrusions of CV joint. Remove bearing retainer and cage, separate by turning retainer perpendicular to large bearing openings and pulling out.

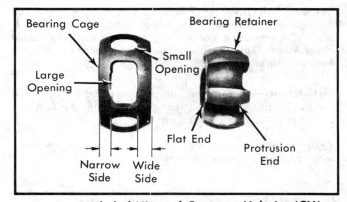

Fig. 9   Exploded View of Constant Velocity (CV) Joint Bearing Cage & Retainer

Reassembly — Coat bearing retainer, cage and balls with suitable grease and reverse disassembly procedure. Ensure protrusion end of bearing retainer is covered by the wide portion of bearing cage during reassembly. When installing bearing retainer and cage into outer shaft, wide side of bearing cage must be on outside portion. After reassembly, pack drive shaft end with lithium base grease. Install new snap rings on axle shaft, insert axle shaft to drive shaft keeping inner snap ring compressed.

NOTE — *After reassembly, ensure that axle shaft can NOT be pulled out of drive shaft CV joint.*

TOYOTA SEPARATE CARRIER (Cont.)

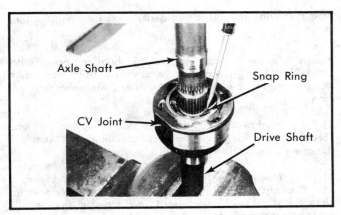

Fig. 10 Installing Axle Shaft to CV Joint

DIFFERENTIAL

NOTE — *Front differentials are overhauled using same procedures as those described for rear differentials.*

Disassembly — 1) Mount carrier on suitable work stand and perform the following pre-disassembly checks: Tooth contact pattern, ring gear backface runout, ring gear backlash and total preload. Total bearing preload is measured amount of pinion bearing preload recorded prior to disassembly PLUS 2.6-4.3 INCH lbs. (3-5 cmkg) for Celica, Corolla, Corona and Supra models and PLUS 3.5-5.2 INCH lbs. (4-6 cg) for all other models.

NOTE — *Note quantity and position of any shims.*

2) Loosen stacked portion of pinion shaft nut, install suitable holder and remove nut. Using flange puller, remove companion flange, then remove oill seal, bearing and slinger. Punch identification marks on left and right bearing caps to prevent intermixing. Remove adjusting nut lock bolt(s), then remove side bearing bolts, caps and adjusting nuts.

NOTE — *Maintain all left and right side bearing components identified for installation on correct side.*

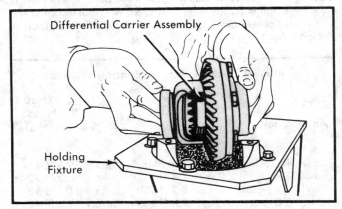

Fig. 11 Removing Differential Case

3) Remove differential case assembly with side bearings. Remove drive pinion, mount pinion in suitable holder and with suitable puller, remove rear pinion bearing. Use caution to avoid deforming shim that adjusts pinion depth. Press out front and rear pinion bearing outer races.

NOTE — *Differential case has cutaways to ease side bearing removal.*

4) Remove side bearings from differential case. Index ring gear to case and straighten ring gear bolt lock plates, then remove bolts. Mount case assembly in vise so ring gear teeth are pointed down. Tap ring gear from case using a soft faced hammer. On two-pinion differentials, remove pinion gear shaft retaining pin and drive out gear shaft. Then remove pinion gears, side gears and thrust washers.

5) On four-pinion differentials, index differential case cover to case. Remove cover attaching bolts, then drive out 3 pinion shafts. Remove pinion gears, pinion shaft holder, side gears and thrust washer(s).

NOTE — *The 3 longer differential cover bolts are used to secure pinion shafts in four-pinion differentials.*

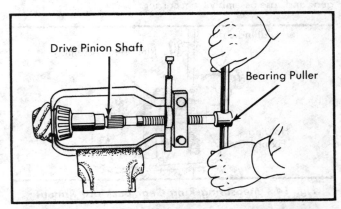

Fig. 12 Removing Drive Pinion Gear Rear Bearing

REASSEMBLY & ADJUSTMENT

Case Assembly — 1) Lubricate all components with hypoid gear lubricant. On two-pinion models, assemble side gears and pinion gears into differential case. Make sure oil groove, if present, on side gear thrust washer faces toward gear. On four-pinion types, install side gears, thrust washers, differential pinions, pinion shaft holder, differential shaft, and pinion shaft. Install differential case cover, aligning index marks and tighten bolts. Note location of 3 longer bolts (pinion shaft bolts).

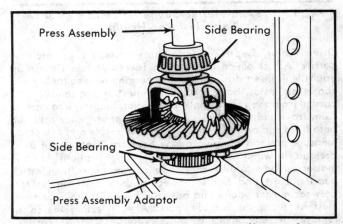

Fig. 13 Installing Side Bearing On Differential Case

TOYOTA SEPARATE CARRIER (Cont.)

2) Check backlash between side gears and pinion gears. If not within specifications, install suitable selective fit thrust washers. Install equal thickness thrust washers on each side, if possible.

3) Press differential side bearings onto differential case. Heat ring gear in oil or water bath to approximately 212°F (100 °C), then quickly wipe off gear and install on differential case. Fit bolts and tighten evenly, then bend over lock tabs. Install differential case assembly on differential carrier and measure ring gear runout.

4) If runout is within specifications, remove differential carrier and bend up on ring gear lock plate. If runout exceeds specifications, remount ring gear 180° from original position on differential case. If this fails to bring ring gear into specifications, remove ring gear from case and examine runout. If case runout is within range specified for ring gear, then ring gear is at fault and should be replaced. Remove ring gear and case assembly from carrier.

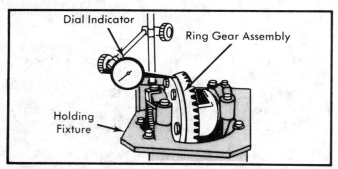

Fig. 14   Measuring Ring Gear Backface Runout

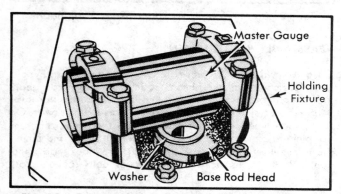

Fig. 15   Toyota Master Gauge for Measuring Drive Pinion Installed Height

Drive Pinion Depth — Install drive pinion cups into the carrier. Adjust pinion depth using Toyota Master Gauge or equivalent. Insert drive pinion rear bearing onto suitable base rod, then install base rod head. Insert this assembly into carrier from the rear. Install front pinion bearing into carrier from front end. Install collar, preload flange pulley and nut onto front end of base rod. Using a spring scale and thin cord, measure preload of drive pinion bearings. Tighten nut until preload is within specifications (see specifications). Install master gauge into differential side bearing bores, then install bearing caps and tighten. Select a shim that will just fit between master gauge and base rod head. One shim or none must be used: do not use more. After selecting the shim, remove all components of master gauge kit from carrier. Install shim onto drive pinion, if it has a chamfered edge, in-

stall that edge toward pinion gear; press rear bearing into place.

Pinion Bearing Preload — **1)** Install bearing spacer onto pinion shaft and insert assembly into carrier from rear. Insert shims (if any) that were removed during disassembly onto pinion shaft.

2) Install front bearing, oil deflector, flange, washer and nut. Torque pinion flange nut to specifications. Install preload flange onto pinion flange.

3) Using a torque wrench, measure pinion bearing preload. If not to specifications, shims in front of preload spacer must be changed. If preload is too great, increase shim thickness: if preload is too small, decrease shim thickness.

4) Use either two shims or none for adjustment. If thicker shim pack is needed, use thicker shims, not more shims. When preload is correct, remove flange, install oil seal and reassemble.

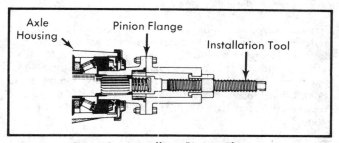

Fig. 16   Installing Pinion Flange

Backlash & Side Bearing Play — **1)** Assemble bearings in cups and install onto carrier. Install differential assembly into carrier, then fit adjusting nuts. Put bearing caps on in original position. Tighten bolts carefully, while checking that adjusting nuts are aligned in bearing bore threads. Install dial gauge so plunger touches flange side of ring gear. Tighten flange side adjusting nut until a slight backlash remains. During operation, rotate ring gear through several revolutions to seat side bearings. Tighten tooth side nut just to the point where there is no differential end play when measured with dial indicator. At this point tighten tooth side nut an additional 1-1½ notches to preload side bearings.

	Combined (Side & Pinion) Bearing Preload	
Application	New INCH Lbs. (cmkg)	Used INCH Lbs. (cmkg)
Corolla		
6.00" Ring Gear	7.4-14.3 (8.5-16.5)	5.2-9.5 (6-11)
6.38" Ring Gear	10.4-17.4 (12-20)	6.0-10.4 (7-12)
6.70" Ring Gear	11.3-18.2 (13-21)	6.9-11.3 (8-13)
Celica & Supra	11.3-18.2 (13-21)	6.9-11.3 (8-13)
Corona		
6.7" Ring Gear	11.3-18.2 (13-21)	6.9-11.3 (8-13)
7.1" Ring Gear	17.4-18.2 (20-28)	10.4-14.7 (12-17)
Cressida	17.3-24.2 (20-28)	10.4-14.7 (12-17)
Pickup	20-27.8 (23-32)	11.3-16.5 (13-19)
Land Cruiser	20-27.8 (23-32)	11.3-16.5 (13-19)

TOYOTA SEPARATE CARRIER (Cont.)

2) Confirm that some backlash is still present. Install the preload flange onto the pinion shaft flange and measure preload. If within specifications go on to next step; if not, tighten tooth side adjusting nut one more notch and recheck.

3) Install dial gauge so that plunger is perpendicular to ring gear tooth. Measure ring gear backlash. If not within specifications, turn left and right adjusting nuts to shift differential assembly in proper direction. If left side is loosened one notch, the right side must be tightened one notch to maintain side bearing preload. Continue procedure until backlash is within specifications. One notch will change backlash .002" (.05 mm). Tighten side bearing cap bolts. Check gear tooth contact pattern. *See Gear Tooth Contact Pattern at beginning of this section.* Install differential carrier.

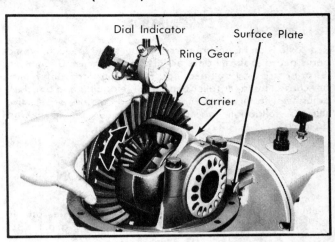

Fig. 18   Measuring Ring Gear Backlash

AXLE SPECIFICATIONS

Application	New INCH lbs. (cmkg)	Used INCH lbs. (cmkg)
Drive Pinion Bearing Preload		
Celica & Supra	8.7-13.9 (10-16)	4.3-6.9 (5-8)
Corolla		
6.00" Ring Gear	5.7-10.8 (6.5-12.5)	3.5-6.1 (4-7)
6.38" Ring Gear	8.7-13.9 (10-16)	4.3-6.9 (5-8)
6.70" Ring Gear	8.7-13.9 (10-16)	4.3-6.9 (5-8)
Corona		
6.70" Ring Gear	8.7-13.9 (10-16)	4.3-6.9 (5-8)
7.10" Ring Gear	14-19 (16-22)	7.0-9.5 (8-11)
Cressida	13.8-19.0 (16-22)	7.0-9.5 (8-11)
Pickup	16.5-22.6 (19-26)	7.8-11.3 (9-13)
Land Cruiser	16.5-22.6 (19-26)	7.8-11.3 (9-13)

Application	Specification In. (mm)
Side-to-Pinion Gear Backlash	
Corolla	
6.00" Ring Gear	.0008-.006 (.02-.15)
6.38" Ring Gear	.0008-.008 (.02-.20)
6.70" Ring Gear	.002-.008 (.05-.20)
Land Cruiser	.0008-.008 (.02-.20)
All Others	.002-.008 (.05-.20)
Drive Pinion-to-Ring Gear Backlash	
Corolla	
6.00" Ring Gear	.004-.006 (.10-.15)
6.38 & 6.70" Ring Gear	.005-.007 (.13-.18)
Land Cruiser	.006-.008 (.15-.20)
All Others	.005-.007 (.13-.18)
Ring Gear Backface Runout	
Pickup & Land Cruiser	.004 (.10) Max.
All Others	.003 (.07) Max.

TIGHTENING SPECIFICATIONS

Application	Ft. Lbs. (mkg)
Drive Pinion Flange Nut	
Corolla	
6.00" Ring Gear	69-145 (9.5-20.0)
6.38 & 6.70" Ring Gear	80-174 (11.0-24.0)
Celica, Corona, Cressida, Supra	80-174 (11.0-24.0)
Pickup	
7.50" Ring Gear	80-174 (11.0-24.0)
8.00" Ring Gear	123-152 (17.0-21.0)
Land Cruiser	145-174 (20.0-24.0)
Differential Bearing Cap Bolts	
Corolla	
6.00" Ring Gear	40-47 (5.5-6.5)
6.38" Ring Gear	36-51 (5.0-7.0)
6.70" Ring Gear	51-65 (7.0-9.0)
Celica, Corona, Cressida, Supra & Pickup	51-65 (7.0-9.0)
Land Cruiser	65-80 (9.0-11.0)
Ring Gear-to-Case Bolts	
Corolla	
6.00" Ring Gear	65-76 (9.0-10.5)
6.38" Ring Gear	51-58 (7.0-8.0)
6.70" Ring Gear	65-76 (9.0-10.5)
Celica, Corona, Cressida, Supra & Pickup	65-76 (9.0-10.5)
Land Cruiser	76-87 (10-5-12.0)
Carrier-to-Axle Housing	
Corona	18-25 (2.5-3.5)
Pickup	14-22 (2.0-3.0)
Backing Plate & Axle Retainer Flange Bolts	
Celica, Supra	18-25 (2.5-3.5)
Corolla, Corona, Cressida	43-54 (6.0-7.4)
Pickup	43-58 (6.0-8.0)
Land Cruiser	29-40 (4.0-5.5)
Pickup 4-WD & Land Cruiser ONLY	
Front Hub-to-Flange	20-25 (2.8-3.5)
Adjusting Nut	58-72 (8.0-10.0)
Wheel Nut	65-87 (9.0-12.0)

Drive Axles

TRIUMPH SPITFIRE

DESCRIPTION

Rear axle is an independent rear suspension type with hypoid gears and a separate differential carrier. Inner and outer axles are carried by ball bearings. Pinion shaft and differential are carried by taper roller bearings. Preloading and backlash adjustment to these bearings is made by the use of selective shims. A collapsible spacer is used to adjust pinion bearing preload.

AXLE RATIO & IDENTIFICATION

Triumph uses only 1 rear axle assembly. The axle ratio is 3.89:1; a 9-tooth pinion gear and 35-tooth ring gear.

REMOVAL & INSTALLATION

AXLE SHAFTS & BEARINGS

Removal (Outer Axle) — 1) Jack up rear of vehicle and support on floor stands. Remove wheel and brake drum.

Disconnect brake line at chassis and wheel cylinder. Disconnect parking brake cable at backing plate and release return spring. Using a jack under vertical link to relieve shock absorber load, remove bolt attaching radius arm to link bracket.

2) At inner drive axle flange, disconnect "U" joint by removing four bolts. Disconnect lower shock mount at vertical link. Remove jack while supporting axle assembly by hand. Remove bolt attaching road spring to vertical link and withdraw axle assembly and link.

3) Remove wheel hub flange nut from axle. Using suitable puller (S109C), remove hub flange and Woodruff key. Remove bolt attaching vertical link to bearing housing. Remove four bolts attaching grease trap, backing plate and seal holder.

4) Using suitable tool (S4221A & -14), press axle shaft from bearing housing. With a drift or press, drive out oil seal and needle bearing, noting direction seal and needle bearing are facing. Drive out ball bearing at opposite end of housing.

Installation — 1) Using suitable tool (S300A), press needle bearing into housing to a depth of .50" (12.7 mm) below housing face. Press seal into housing. Pack needle bearing with grease and slide housing onto axle shaft.

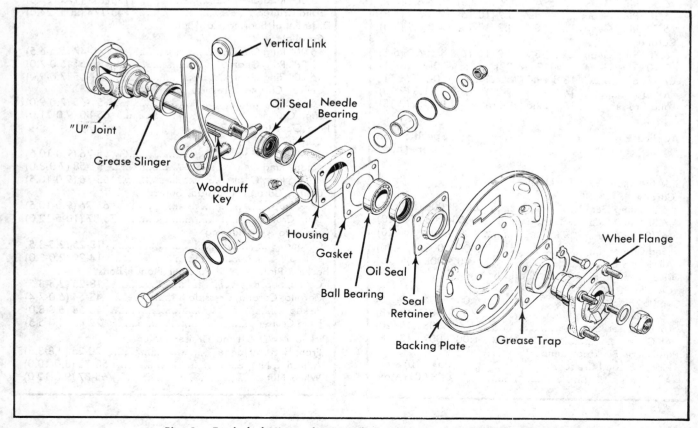

Fig. 1   Exploded View of Triumph Spitfire Outer Axle Assembly

TRIUMPH SPITFIRE (Cont.)

2) Holding axle in a soft jawed vice, drive ball bearing onto axle shaft using suitable tool (S304). Pack ball bearing and housing with grease and tap bearing into housing. Install gasket, seal, seal housing, backing plate and grease trap and tighten attaching bolts.

3) Install Woodruff key and wheel flange. Using a plain washer and a new locknut, tighten nut to specifications. Bolt axle assembly to vertical link with nut to the rear. Fit vertical link and axle assembly to spring eye with nut to the rear (Do not tighten).

4) Jack up assembly and attach shock absorber. Connect radius arm to vertical link. Using new lock nuts, attach "U" joint to inner axle flange. Attach parking brake cable and reconnect return spring. Connect brake line and bleed hydraulic system. Install brake drum and wheel. Remove floor stands and roll vehicle to settle suspension. Finally tighten spring eye bolt.

Removal (Inner Axle) — 1) With outer axle assembly removed remove Allen screws retaining seal housing plate. If both inner axle shafts are to be removed, mark shafts for correct reassembly. Place a pan under differential case to catch grease. Withdraw axle shaft complete with bearing and oil seal housing.

2) Remove circlip locating bearing. Using suitable tools (S4221A & -7B), press axle shaft from bearing. Remove seal housing plate and drive out seal.

Installation — 1) Press oil seal into seal housing plate so seal lip will face differential case when assembled. Carefully slide seal and housing over axle shaft. Using suitable tool (S4221A), press axle shaft through bearing until circlip groove is completely exposed.

2) Install circlip in axle groove. Lubricate shaft splines and bearing. Apply suitable joint compound to seal plate. Slide axle shaft into differential case and make sure shaft splines engage with differential side gear splines. Install and tighten Allen screws.

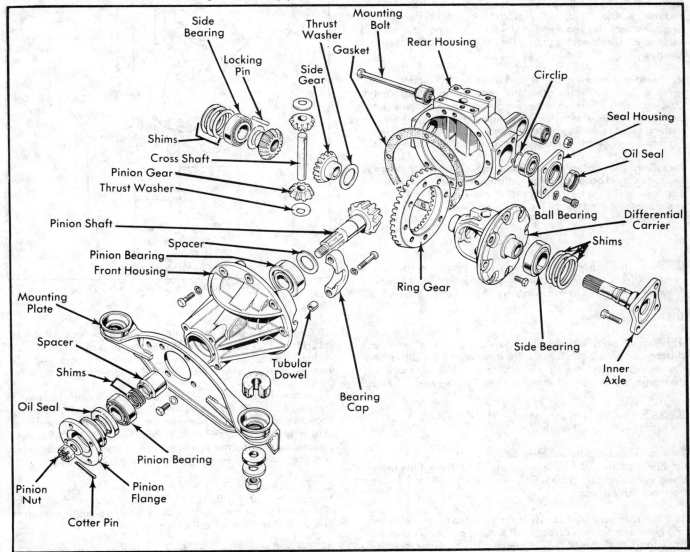

Fig. 2 Exploded View of Inner Axles and Differential Assembly

TRIUMPH SPITFIRE (Cont.)

PINION FLANGE & SEAL

Removal — Raise vehicle on a hoist and remove muffler. Mark propeller shaft and pinion flange for correct reassembly. Disconnect propeller shaft and place aside. Remove cotter pin and install suitable flange holder tool (S337 or RG421). Place a pan under differential case to catch grease and remove pinion nut and flange. Pry out old seal.

Installation — Soak oil seal in light oil for approximately an hour. With seal lip facing pinion bearing, drive seal into housing. Install pinion flange and tighten pinion nut. Install new cotter pin and connect propeller shaft, making sure marks are aligned. Replace muffler, add lubricant and remove vehicle from hoist.

AXLE ASSEMBLY

NOTE — *The following removal procedure is for inner axles and differential assembly only. For outer axle assemblies, see Axle Shafts & Bearings.*

Removal — 1) Jack up vehicle and place on floor stands. Remove muffler and tail pipe. Mark pinion flange and propeller shaft for reassembly. Disconnect propeller shaft and set aside. Disconnect outer axle "U" joints at inner axle flanges.

2) Remove rear trim panel and rear spring access cover. Remove nuts and studs attaching rear spring to differential case assembly. Remove differential case rear mounting nut and bolt. While supporting assembly, remove two nuts attaching front mounting plate to chassis. Holding assembly upright to avoid grease spillage, remove assembly from vehicle.

Installation — To install, reverse removal procedures noting the following: Locate dowel pin in bottom spring leaf so that it engages hole in differential case. Make sure rubber washers are mounted on outside of rear mounting lugs.

OVERHAUL

NOTE — *This procedure assumes inner and outer axles are removed from differential assembly and assembly is removed from vehicle. For axle removal, see Axle Shafts & Bearings.*

DISASSEMBLY

1) Remove bolts and lock washers joining front and rear differential housings. Remove front housing and differential Carrier from rear housing. Place differential housing in a vise and mark bearing caps for reassembly. Remove bearing caps.

CAUTION — *Case damage may occur if housing is spread more than .008" (.20 mm).*

2) Install suitable differential spreader (S101 & -1) to differential housing. Spread housing and pry out differential carrier. Using suitable tools (18G47C & -BD), press carrier bearings from carrier assembly.

3) Mark ring gear and carrier for proper reassembly. Remove ring gear and drive out cross shaft locking pin. Push out pinion cross shaft and rotate pinion gears 90° to carrier opening. Remove pinion gears and side gears with their thrust washers.

4) Remove cotter pin from pinion shaft. Using suitable flange holder (RG421 or S337), remove pinion shaft nut and flange. Press out pinion shaft and remove shims and spacer. Using suitable tools (S4221A & -17), press bearing from pinion shaft. With a drift, drive out bearing races and oil seal from pinion housing.

NOTE — *Ring and pinion gears are replaced as a matched set only. Numbers etched on each gear must be the same.*

REASSEMBLY & ADJUSTMENT

Drive Pinion Depth — 1) Press inner and outer bearing races into pinion housing. Place inner pinion bearing on dummy pinion shaft (18G191M). Oil bearings and install dummy pinion, outer bearing, tool spacer, washer and nut into pinion housing.

NOTE — *Standard pinion bearing spacer is .077" (1.95 mm) and is incorporated into dummy pinion.*

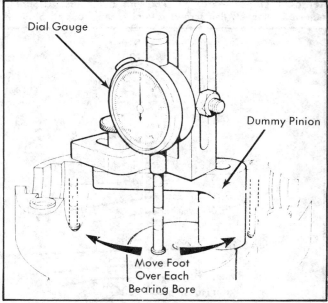

Fig. 3   Measuring Drive Pinion Depth

2) Gradually tighten nut until a bearing preload of 15-18 INCH lbs. (17.3-20.8 cmkg) rotating torque is obtained. Mount a dial indicator on pinion housing so foot of indicator will contact head of dummy pinion. Zero dial indicator.

3) Move indicator foot over center of each differential bearing bore and take a dial reading. Add two dial readings together and divide by two. The result will either be added or subtracted to standard spacer thickness, .077" (1.95 mm), depending on whether pinion is high or low in housing. Select a spacer washer of correct thickness for pinion assembly.

NOTE — *There are 22 pinion head washers available in sizes ranging from .075-.096" (1.91-2.44 mm). Ignore "+", "−" or "N" markings on pinion, they are taken into consideration in design and method of using dummy pinion.*

4) Remove dummy pinion from pinion housing. Press inner bearing from dummy pinion.

TRIUMPH SPITFIRE (Cont.)

Pinion Bearing Preload — **1)** Place selected pinion depth washer on pinion and install inner bearing onto pinion. Oil bearing and install drive pinion gear in housing.

2) Install collapsible spacer and outer pinion bearing on pinion shaft. Install oil seal with lips of seal towards pinion gear head. Install flange, washer, and nut, but do not tighten nut.

3) While gradually tightening nut, keep checking the pinion bearing preload using an inch pound torque wrench. Tighten nut as required to obtain specified pinion bearing preload. Initial preload is 15-18 INCH lbs (17.3-20.8 cmkg).

CAUTION — *If pinion bearing preload torque specification is exceeded, a new collapsible spacer will be required and this procedure repeated.*

Case Assembly — **1)** Using suitable tool (550 and 18G134-DH), press differential bearings onto carrier housing. Install thrust washers and side gears into carrier. Place pinion gears in carrier meshed with side gears. Using an axle shaft, rotate side gears until cross shaft can be inserted through carrier and pinion gears.

2) Press pinion gears fully into mesh with side gears. Using a dial indicator, measure for run out to determine needed thrust washer thickness. Remove cross shaft and pinion gears.

3) Install thrust washers (22 sizes available), pinion gears and cross shaft. Gear backlash should be "0". If required, adjust thrust washers until pinion gear end play results in "0" gear backlash. Install cross shaft locking pin and peen over edge of pin hole.

Backlash & Side Bearing Preload — **1)** After checking for burrs, mount ring gear to carrier, using Loctite on the bolts. Install bearing caps and measure ring gear runout.

2) Before installing pinion shaft, measure "Total End Play" of carrier assembly as follows: Mount a dial indicator so foot will touch rear side of ring gear. With bearing caps removed, push carrier fully to one side of case and zero dial indicator. Move carrier fully in the opposite direction and note total end play measurement for further use.

3) With pinion shaft installed, fully move ring gear into mesh with pinion gear and zero dial indicator. Move carrier assembly fully in opposite direction until ring gear side bearing is butted in housing. Note "In-Out" mesh clearance for ring gear backlash calculations.

4) To determine ring gear backlash, subtract backlash specification from "In-Out" reading obtained in step **3)** to determine correct ring gear side shim pack thickness. Subtract ring gear side shim pack thickness from the total end play figure obtained in step **2)** to determine caged side shim pack thickness.

NOTE — *For preload, add .002" (.05 mm) to each shim pack.*

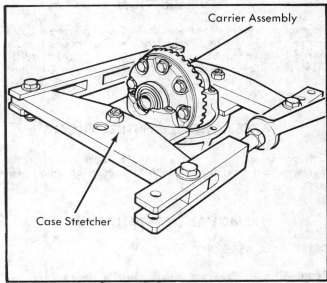

Fig. 4   Using Case Stretcher to Install Carrier Assembly

5) Install case stretcher (S101 & -1) and spread case just enough to install carrier assembly and proper shim packs. Remove case stretcher, install bearing caps to original positions and tighten bolts. With a dial indicator, measure ring gear backlash at several points. If backlash is not to specifications, remove shims from one side and add to opposite side until correct backlash is achieved.

NOTE — *Moving a .002" (.05 mm) shim from one differential bearing to the other will vary backlash about .002" (.05 mm).*

Final Inspection & Assembly — Make a tooth contact pattern check to assure proper running mesh. Using a suitable gasket compound, install gasket and front housing on rear housing and tighten attaching bolts.

AXLE ASSEMBLY SPECIFICATIONS

Application	Specification
Pinion Bearing Preload ...	13-20 INCH Lbs. (15-23 cmkg)
Differential Gear Backlash	"0"
Ring Gear Backlash	.004-.006" (.10-.15 mm)
Ring Gear Runout	.003" (.076 mm) max.

TIGHTENING SPECIFICATIONS

Application	Ft. Lbs. (mkg)
Pinion Shaft Nut	90 (12.4)
Axle Shaft Flange Nut	90-120 (12.4-16.6)
Front-to-Rear Axle Housing	15-20 (2.1-2.8)
Spring-to-Axle Housing	26-34 (3.6-4.7)
Front Mount-to-Chassis	26-34 (3.6-4.7)
Axle Assembly-to-Vertical Link	38-48 (5.2-6.6)
Radius Arm-to-Vertical Link	24-32 (3.3-4.4)
Spring Eye Bolt	38-48 (5.2-6.6)

Drive Axles

TRIUMPH TR7 & TR8

DESCRIPTION

Rear axle is hypoid design with centerline of pinion set below centerline of ring gear. Drive pinion bearing preload is maintained by a collapsible spacer. All other differential adjustments are made using selected shims. Adjustment of axle shaft end play is not required.

AXLE RATIO & IDENTIFICATION

Only one basic axle design is used. To determine axle ratio, divide number of ring gear teeth by number of pinion gear teeth.

REMOVAL & INSTALLATION

DRIVE AXLE ASSEMBLY

Removal — 1) Place jack under rear axle, raise vehicle, and support body securely on stands.

2) Remove rear wheels. Disconnect propeller shaft at rear axle and disconnect forward end of flexible rear brake hose. Disconnect handbrake cable at backplate, then remove bolt and nut securing handbrake adjusting cable compensator to rear axle housing.

3) Disconnect rear shock absorbers at axle housing bracket. Lower jack and remove rear springs. Remove bolts and nuts securing radius rods to axle and detach handbrake cable bracket from left side.

4) Release radius rods from axle brackets, then lift axle clear of suspension arms and anti-roll bar and remove from vehicle.

Installation — To install, reverse removal procedure and bleed brakes.

AXLE SHAFTS & BEARINGS

Removal — Raise and support rear of vehicle. Remove wheels. Release emergency brake and remove brake drum. Remove retaining plate-to-differential housing bolts. Using a puller, remove axle shaft with seal, bearing and retaining collar.

Installation — To install, reverse removal procedure and note the following: Grease bearing, seal and differential housing bearing area with lithium base grease.

PINION FLANGE & SEAL

Removal — Raise and support rear of vehicle. Remove propeller shaft-to-pinion flange bolts. Remove pinion flange nut and pinion flange. Remove pinion seal cover bolts and pinion seal cover. Remove seal.

Installation — To avoid damaging seal lip, wrap a piece of tape around machined step of pinion. Grease seal lip and tape. Install seal with lip facing away from differential housing. Tap seal into place and install pinion seal cover. Install pinion flange and nut, then attach propeller shaft.

OVERHAUL

DISASSEMBLY

1) With rear axle assembly removed from vehicle, remove axle shafts. Place container under differential housing assembly to catch lubricant. Remove differential cover, pinion flange and pinion flange seal cover. Mark differential case bearing caps so they can be installed in original positions. Remove bearing cap bolts and bearing caps. Remove differential case from axle housing assembly. If differential case is difficult to remove, use spreader tool (S101 and S101-1) to ease removal.

NOTE — *Bearing caps MUST be installed in original positions.*

2) Using a press and adapters, remove differential bearings. Remove ring gear bolts and ring gear. Remove pinion shaft locating ball, then remove pinion shaft.

3) Rotate side gears until pinion gears, with thrust washers, are clear of differential case. Remove pinion gears with their thrust washers, then remove side gears and their thrust washers.

4) Remove pinion nut, then tap pinion out of differential housing assembly with a wooden block. Pinion is removed with selective spacer, pinion inner bearing and collapsible spacer.

5) Using a drift, drive pinion bearing outer races from differential housing, being careful not to damage differential housing. Remove collapsible spacer from pinion, then use a press and adaptors to remove pinion bearings from pinion.

INSPECTION

Clean and inspect all components for wear or damage. Ring and pinion gears, differential bearings and pinion bearings must be replaced as matched sets.

REASSEMBLY & ADJUSTMENT

Drive Pinion Depth — 1) Install inner and outer pinion bearing cups to axle housing. Install pinion inner bearing to dummy pinion (18G-191-1). Oil bearing and install dummy pinion, outer bearing, tool spacer, washer and nut. Tighten nut gradually until bearing preload of 15-18 INCH lbs. (.17-.21 cmkg) is obtained. Clean dummy pinion head and position dial indicator gauge foot (of tool 18G-191) on dummy head and zero indicator.

NOTE — *Dummy pinion incorporates the maximum allowance for pinion head bearing spacer available, .0492" (1.25 mm) thickness.*

2) Move dial indicator over center of one differential bearing bore and note reading. Repeat for opposite bearing bore. Average these 2 measurements and perform the following calculation:

EXAMPLE:
Average of bore measurements .... .002" (.051 mm)
Plus dummy pinion spacer allowance ...... .0492" (1.25 mm)
Required size of pinion spacer .... .051" (1.301 mm)

TRIUMPH TR7 & TR8 (Cont.)

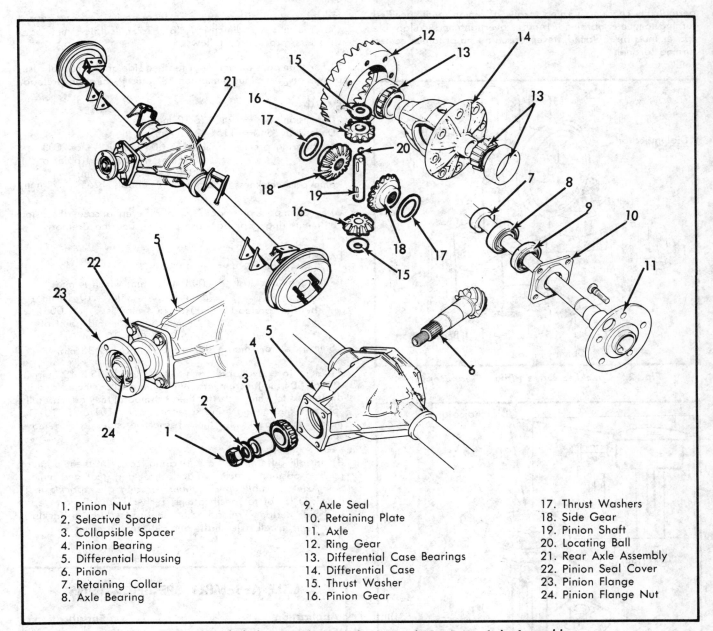

Fig. 1   Exploded View of Triumph TR7 and TR8 Drive Axle Assembly

1. Pinion Nut	9. Axle Seal	17. Thrust Washers
2. Selective Spacer	10. Retaining Plate	18. Side Gear
3. Collapsible Spacer	11. Axle	19. Pinion Shaft
4. Pinion Bearing	12. Ring Gear	20. Locating Ball
5. Differential Housing	13. Differential Case Bearings	21. Rear Axle Assembly
6. Pinion	14. Differential Case	22. Pinion Seal Cover
7. Retaining Collar	15. Thrust Washer	23. Pinion Flange
8. Axle Bearing	16. Pinion Gear	24. Pinion Flange Nut

3) There are 3 sets of numbers stamped on pinion head; the first is a 4 digit number indicating pinion and ring gear matching sets (this same number will be stamped on ring gear). The second number will be preceded by a plus or minus, this indicates variation of pinion head nominal thickness in thousandths of an inch (+2 equals plus .002"). The third number is boxed and indicates the variation from nominal position for best running position. If boxed number is a "+", subtract this value from calculated pinion spacer size (.051" minus .003 is .048" spacer). If boxed number is a "−", add this value to calculated pinion spacer size (.051" plus .003 is .054").

4) Zero dial indicator with differential case pushed to one side, then push differential case to opposite side and record reading as dimension "A". This will be used later to determine preload shim pack. Remove differential case and bearings.

Lubricate side gears, pinion gears and thrust washers. Install side gears, with thrust washers, to differential case. Install pinion gears to side gears (1 each side) and rotate side gears to align pinion gears to pinion shaft holes in differential case. Install pinion shaft.

5) After performing above calculations, remove all measuring devices and dummy pinion. Install spacer of calculated thickness to pinion. Install pinion inner bearing collapsible spacer to pinion. Install pinion to axle housing. Install outer bearing, washer and nut to pinion. Carefully tighten nut, while

Side Bearing Preload — 1) Preload should be .002-.004" (.05-.10 mm), to obtain this proceed as follows: install differential case bearings (lubricated) to differential case. Install differential case to axle housing and rotate differential case to

TRIUMPH TR7 & TR8 (Cont.)

periodically checking turning torque of pinion, until specified turning torque is obtained. If nut is overtightened, collapsible spacer must be replaced; never loosen nut to obtain specified turning torque.

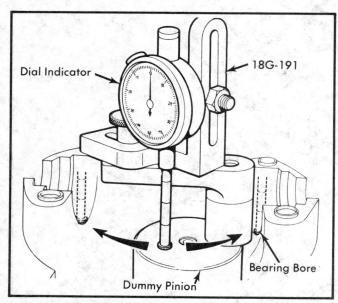

Fig. 2   Checking Drive Pinion Gear Depth

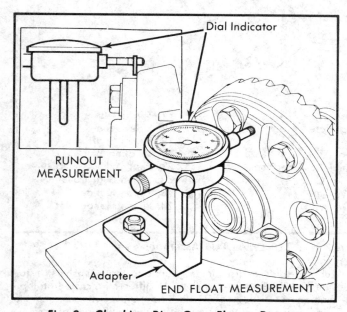

Fig. 3   Checking Ring Gear Flange Runout

3) Press each pinion gear firmly into mesh with side gears and determine pinion gear thrust washer thickness to give a "O" backlash. Remove pinion shaft and pinion gears, then install lubricated pinion gears with selected thrust washers to differential case. Install pinion shaft, with groove aligned with locating hole (for locating ball), in differential case. Recheck for "O" backlash. Install ring gear. Install locating ball to pinion shaft.

4) Install the assembled differential case into axle housing assembly. Lower case until ring gear is fully meshed with pinion. Push differential case to one side. Install and zero a dial

indicator. Push differential case to opposite side and record this reading as dimension "B". To calculate shim pack thickness, proceed as follows:

5) For shim pack on ring gear toothed side of differential case; dimension "A" minus dimension "B" plus ½ bearing preload.

EXAMPLE:
Dimension "A" — .240" (6.10 mm)
Dimension "B" — .115" (2.92 mm)
½ bearing preload — .0015" (.04 mm) is ½ of .003"
                   (.08 mm) which is mid point of
                   .002-.004" (.05-.10 mm)
Shim pack thickness for toothed side equals .1265" (3.21 mm)

6) For shim pack on smooth side of differential case; dimension "B" minus ring gear backlash plus ½ bearing preload.

EXAMPLE:
Dimension "B" — .115" (2.92 mm)
Ring gear backlash — .005" (.13 mm) which is mid
                   point of .004-.006" (.10-.15 mm)
½ bearing preload — .0015" (.04 mm) is ½ of .003"
                   (.08 mm) which is mid point of
                   .002-.004" (.05-.10 mm)
Shim pack for smooth side equals .1115" (2.83 mm)

7) Shims are available from .112-.136" (2.85-3.45 mm) in .0016" (.04 mm) increments. With shim packs selected and indicated as to which side (toothed or smooth) they go, carefully spread axle housing using spreader tool (S101 and S101-1). Install shim packs to their respective sides and remove spreader tool.

8) Install differential case bearing caps in their original marked positions. Recheck backlash of ring gear and pinion. *See Axle Assembly specifications for ring gear backlash.* If backlash is not to specifications, recheck Drive Pinion Depth and Side Bearing Preload adjustment procedures. If backlash is correct, install axle shafts and differential cover.

AXLE ASSEMBLY SPECIFICATIONS

Application	Specification
Ring Gear Runout	.003" (.076 mm)
Pinion Bearing Preload	13-20 INCH lbs. (15-23 cmkg)
Ring Gear Backlash	.004-.006" (.10-.15 mm)

TIGHTENING SPECIFICATIONS

Application	Ft. Lbs. (mkg)
Rear Cover-to-Axle Case	16-21 (2.2-2.9)
Pinion Housing-to-Axle Case	30-37 (4.1-5.1)
Differential Bearing Caps	60-75 (8.3-10.4)
Ring Gear-to-Differential	80-90 (11-12.4)
Pinion Flange-to-Pinion	90-120 (12.4-16.6)
Axle Shafts-to-Axle Casing	35-40 (4.8-5.5)

VOLVO

DL	GLE
GL	Coupe
GT	Diesel

DESCRIPTION

Rear axle assembly uses a hypoid type ring and pinion gear set. Semi-floating axle shafts are retained in housing by tapered roller bearings and a bearing retainer at housing outer ends. Bearing clearance is not adjustable and is determined by bearing design. Differential adjustment is accomplished by the use of shims.

AXLE RATIO & IDENTIFICATION

A plate attached on left side of axle housing gives axle ratio, part number, and serial number.

REMOVAL & INSTALLATION

AXLE SHAFTS & BEARINGS

Removal — 1) With vehicle raised and wheels removed, disconnect brake line from caliper. Remove disc and caliper. Loosen bolts for thrust washer through holes in axle flange.

2) Pull out axle shaft using suitable puller. Remove inner sealing ring using a puller or by prying it out with a screwdriver. Press bearing and lock ring off axle shaft using suitable tools. Remove oil seal.

Installation — 1) Fill space between new seal lips with grease, then install seal on axle shaft. Install bearing and new lock ring by pressing on axle shaft. Always use a new lock ring and insure that bearing is installed with taper away from axle shaft flange.

2) Use a suitable seal installing tool and install inner seal ring. Fill bearing with good quality grease. Also fill space between seals and between seal lips with grease. Install axle shaft and tighten thrust washer bolts. Install brake disc and caliper, reconnect brake lines, bleed and adjust brakes. Install road wheels and lower vehicle.

PINION FLANGES & SEAL

Removal — Disconnect rear section of propeller shaft from pinion flange. Check for looseness of pinion in its bearing. If it is loose, this must be corrected before a new seal is installed. Remove nut from flange using a suitable flange holding tool. Pull off flange using suitable puller. Pull out old oil seal.

Installation — Coat seal lips of new ring with grease. Also lubricate the spring coil so it does not jump off during installation. Install oil seal using suitable seal installing tool. Press on flange using suitable pressing tool. Install flange washer and nut and tighten. Reconnect propeller shaft.

AXLE ASSEMBLY

Removal — 1) With rear of vehicle raised and supported and wheels removed, support rear axle with suitable jack and holding fixture. Remove upper attaching bolts for shock absorber and parking brake cables from levers and brackets on brake backing plate. Remove brake pipe union from rear axle housing and propeller shaft from pinion.

2) Disconnect Panhard rod from bracket on rear axle housing and remove lower attaching bolts for spring. Lower jack until trailing arms release from spring. Loosen bolts holding rear axle housing to trailing arms. Lower jack and pull rear axle assembly forward.

Installation — To install, move axle under vehicle and install bolts for support arms and torque rod. Raise jack until Panhard rod can be installed. Install attaching bolts for spring and tighten nuts for support rods and trailing arms. Install bracket, union, and brake hoses. Reconnect propeller shaft to pinion flange. Install upper bolt for shock absorbers and reconnect parking brake cable. Adjust parking brake and bleed brakes. Install wheels and lower vehicle.

OVERHAUL

DISASSEMBLY

1) Place axle assembly in suitable holding fixture with pinion flange pointing downward. Remove brake lines and axle shafts. Remove inspection cover. If final drive is being reconditioned because of noise, run a tooth contact pattern check before disassembly as this may assist in locating fault.

2) Check alignment markings on bearing caps and carrier. If there are no markings, or if they are difficult to see, mark one side with a punch. Remove cap. Using a suitable case stretching tool, lift out carrier with ring gear. Turn final drive over and drain oil. Remove pinion flange and press out pinion. Remove pinion front bearing, washer and oil seal with suitable driver.

3) If necessary, drive out rear pinion bearing from case using a suitable drift. Clean axle case gasket surface and remove any burrs present. If necessary, pull off rear bearing from pinion using a suitable puller. Pull off differential carrier bearing with suitable puller and retain shims. Remove lock plate for ring gear bolts, remove bolts and ring gear. Drive out lock pin securing differential gear shafts and remove shaft, gears and thrust washers.

INSPECTION

Inspect all parts for wear or damage. Also, install differential gear into carrier together with shaft and thrust washers. Use no lubricant. Now, check play of differential side gears. If play exceeds specifications when gears have been rotated to maximum play, replace thrust washers with thicker ones.

VOLVO (Cont.)

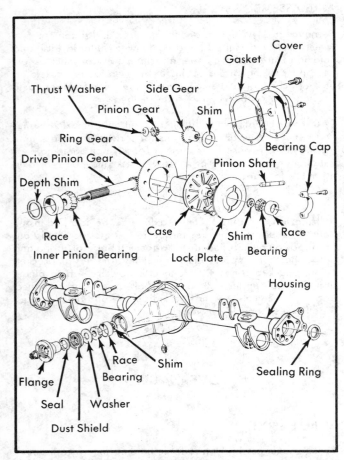

Fig. 1   Exploded View of Volvo Drive Axle Assembly

REASSEMBLY & ADJUSTMENT

Case Assembly — Place differential side gears together with thrust washers in differential carrier. "Roll" in both side pinions simultaneously with dished thrust washers, then drive in shaft. Install ring gear, making sure that contact surfaces are clean and without any burrs. Install new ring gear bolts and tighten.

Drive Pinion Depth & Bearing Preload — 1) Clean marking surface on drive pinion. Install adjusting ring tool (2685) and (2841) on pinion and place this assembly into housing. Place pinion on carrier so bolt on adjusting ring faces large side of carrier.

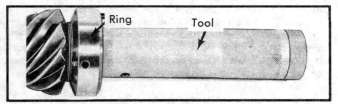

Fig. 2   Pinion Adjusting Ring and Tool

2) The pinion should have a certain nominal measurement to the center line of the ring gear. Due to manufacturing tolerances, there are deviations from this nominal measurement. On rear axles made by Volvo, the deviation is always positive and is indicated in hundredths of a millimeter. The plus sign is excluded.

3) Place pinion gauge (2393) on ground surface of pinion and adjusting jig (2393) in differential bearing positions. Place dial indicator retainer (2284) with dial indicator on gasket face of axle housing with dial indicator foot touching adjusting ring. Zero dial indicator. Now move indicator over until

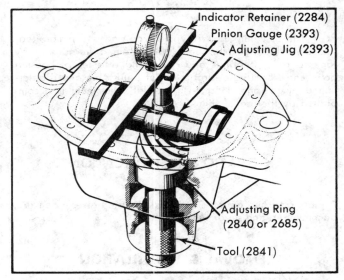

Fig. 3   Measuring Drive Pinion Gear Installed Height

it touches pinion gauge. If the pinion is, for example, marked 33, the pinion gauge should lie .013" (.33 mm) under adjusting fixture. The setting is adjusted by turning cam on pinion until dial indicator shows correct value, then lock adjusting ring with set screw.

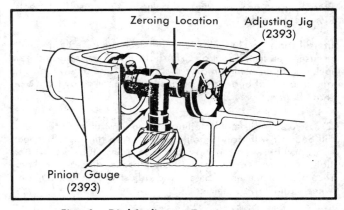

Fig. 4   Dial Indicator Zeroing Location
(Indicator Retainer Not Installed)

4) Remove measuring tool and pinion. Place complete rear pinion bearing with outer ring in measuring fixture (tool 2600). Put on plate, spring and nut with flat side of nut facing up. Rotate plate and bearing several times so that rollers take up correct set. Place adjusting ring in retainer (tool 2284) and dial indicator opposite adjusting ring, zero indicator. Set pointer of indicator to outer ring of bearing. The indicator will now show directly thickness shims should have. Measure shims for correct thickness with micrometer. Since it is unlikely to find a shim with exact thickness required, shim may be .0012" (.03 mm) thicker or .002" (.05 mm) thinner than measured value.

VOLVO (Cont.)

Fig. 5 Measuring Installed Depth of Pinion Gear

5) Press rear bearing on pinion with suitable sleeve. The washer under rear bearing inner ring must NOT be installed when overhauling. Place measured shims in axle housing and press in both outer rings of bearings using suitable tool. Insert pinion in housing and install three .03" (.75 mm) thick shims and front pinion bearing. Pull pinion into housing using suitable tools. Install washer and nut on pinion shaft and tighten to specifications.

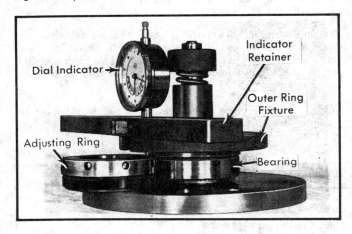

Fig. 6 Determining Pinion Depth Shim Thickness

6) Install pinion gauge and dial indicator retainer. Pull down pinion while rotating it backwards and forwards. Set dial indicator to zero. Press pinion upwards while rotating it forwards and backwards. Dial indicator will read clearance. Remove pinion and remove shims corresponding to the measured clearance plus .003" (.07 mm). Reinstall pinion. Now use torque gauge to check pinion bearing torque. Adjust shim thickness if required to obtain specified torque. Recheck pinion depth using measuring tools as described in step **3)**.

Backlash & Side Bearing Preload — 1) Lubricate inside of adjustment rings (tool 2595) and install them on differential carrier. Ring with black oxidized adjustment ring should be placed on ring gear side. Also lubricate bearing bores in carrier. Install carrier and adjustment rings in axle housing.

2) Use dial indicator and adjust rings so that specified backlash is obtained. Backlash may vary within backlash range but get as close to specified backlash as possible.

NOTE — Due to altered manufacturing and test procedures, it is no longer possible to determine correct installation of gears by means of a contact pattern test. The pinion gear should always be installed in its marked position regardless of the contact pattern.

3) If the gear set is correctly installed, but still causes noise, try re-positioning pinion gear .002" (.05 mm) "plus" or "minus" (try "plus" first). This may help if pinion gear has been incorrectly marked.

4) After correct backlash is obtained, remove carrier and adjustment ring. Place adjusting ring and bearing into measurement fixture with flat side of nut facing downwards. Rotate plate several times. Install dial indicator and retainer (tool 2284) and zero indicator on adjusting ring. Place measuring point of indicator facing bearing and read off indicator.

5) Use a micrometer to form a shim pack equal in thickness to clearance indicated by dial indicator plus .003" (.07 mm). Place shims together with measured bearing to one side. Repeat this procedure with the other bearing. Install shims on differential carrier, making sure which side respective bearing and shims are installed on, and press on bearings using suitable drift. When installing second bearing, use suitable support so as not to damage first bearing.

NOTE — Do not forget to lock cover for ring gear bolt.

6) Install tool (2394) on pinion carrier and expand tool until pins are flush against hole edges in carrier, then tighten screws an additional 3 ½ turns. Install differential carrier and outer rings. Install bearing caps and tighten bolts to specification.

7) Install pinion oil seal and flange, inspection cover and gasket. If inner oil seals for axle shafts were removed, drive them in with suitable tool. Reinstall axle shafts and adjust end play if necessary. Install brake discs, caliper and brake pipes. Bleed and adjust brakes.

AXLE ASSEMBLY SPECIFICATIONS

Application	Specification
Side Gear Play	.0024" (.06 mm) Max.
Pinion Bearing Preload Torque	
Used Bearing	5-10 INCH lbs (6-11 cmkg)
New Bearing	13-30 INCH lbs (15-35 cmkg)
Preferred Backlash (Pinion-to-Ring Gear)	.006" (.15 mm)
Backlash Range	.005-.007" (.13-.18 mm)
Differential Bearing Preload	.005-.008" (.13-.20 mm)
Nominal Pinion Depth (DL,GL,GT)	2.55" (64.7 mm)

TIGHTENING SPECIFICATIONS

Application	Ft. Lbs. (mkg)
Pinion Flange Nut	
Without Integral Washer	200-220 (28-30)
With Integral Washer	145-180 (20-25)
Bearing Cap Bolts	36-50 (5-7)
Ring Gear Bolts	45-60 (6-8)
Axle Shaft Thrust Washer Bolts	36 (5.0)

Locking Hubs

DATSUN, LUV & TOYOTA

Datsun 4-WD Pickup
LUV 4-WD Pickup
Toyota
  Land Cruiser
  4-WD Pickup

DESCRIPTION

Locking hubs provide means of engagement of front wheels on vehicles equipped with front driving axles. When hubs are engaged, full power is transmitted to both front wheels. When hubs are disengaged, front wheels are free to turn, but axle shafts and differential will remain idle. Engagement is accomplished through action of gears within hub. With hub in engaged position, inner clutch ring and axle shaft sleeve act as one piece to connect axle shaft to wheel hub.

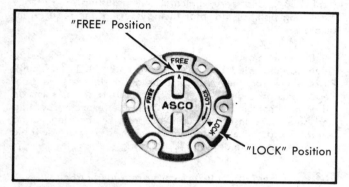

Fig. 1   Front View of ASCO Locking Hub

IDENTIFICATION

ASCO internal locking hubs are used on LUV and Toyota models. ASCO hubs are identified externally by the word "ASCO" stamped on the metal control knob used to engage and disengage hub. Datsun locking hub is not stamped with any markings, but is of similar configuration as locking hub used on LUV.

NOTE — *Land Cruiser may not be stamped with "ASCO".*

REMOVAL & INSTALLATION

Removal — With control knob set to "FREE" ("LOCK" on Datsun) position and transfer shift lever set in "2H" position, remove cover attaching bolts. Remove cover assembly and gasket. Remove snap ring, shims (if equipped) and inner clutch from axle shaft. On Toyota models, remove 6 hub body retaining nuts and cone-shaped lock washers. On all models, remove hub body.

Installation — 1) To install, reverse removal procedure and ensure axle shaft is properly seated. On LUV pickup, place a bolt in end of axle shaft and pull out with hand pressure, then install snap ring. Measure and set clearance between inner clutch and snap ring to 0-.01" (0-.25 mm) with proper shim. On LUV and Toyota, ensure control knob is set to "FREE" position and control knob operates smoothly after installation.

NOTE — *Shims are available in thicknesses of .008" (.20 mm), .01" (.25 mm), .02" (.50 mm) and .04" (1 mm) for LUV.*

2) On Datsun, install inner clutch and measure axle shaft end play with dial indicator. Adjust end play to .004-.012" (.1-.3 mm) with snap ring of proper thickness. Ensure control knob is set to "LOCK" position and control knob operates smoothly after installation.

NOTE — *Datsun snap rings are available in 5 thicknesses ranging from .043-.075" (1.1-1.9 mm) in increments of .008" (.2 mm).*

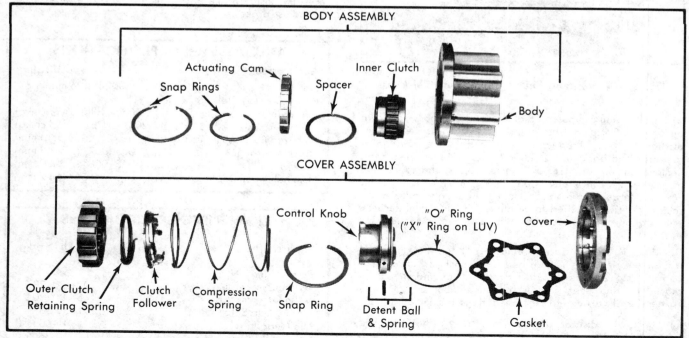

Fig. 2   Exploded View of Toyota Locking Hub — LUV and Datsun Similar

Locking Hubs

DATSUN, LUV & TOYOTA (Cont.)

OVERHAUL

Disassembly — 1) On LUV and Toyota, separate cover and outer clutch assemblies by pushing follower toward control knob and turning clutch assembly clockwise. Remove clutch assembly from control knob. Remove control knob snap ring and control knob. DO NOT lose detent ball and spring. Remove "O" ring.

NOTE — *Datsun outer clutch is removed in similar manner. However, a pin is used instead of detent ball and spring. Use a magnet to assist in removing outer clutch. See Fig. 3.*

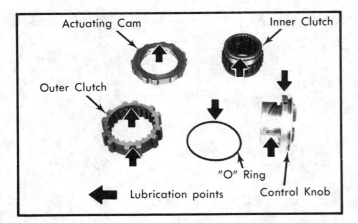

Fig. 3   Using a Magnet to Remove Datsun Outer Clutch

2) Remove compression spring from outer clutch assembly. Disengage clutch retaining spring from clutch follower, then remove clutch follower from outer clutch. Remove the retaining spring from clutch by turning counterclockwise.

3) Remove snap ring from rear of body assembly and remove inner clutch assembly. Remove snap ring from rear of inner clutch assembly and remove actuating cam and spacer.

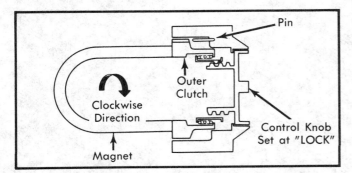

Fig. 4   View Showing Parts and Lubrication Points

Cleaning & Inspection — 1) Clean and wash all parts in suitable cleaning solvent and blow dry. Inspect all parts for excessive wear or damage and replace as required. Before assembling parts, coat those shown in *Fig. 4* with multipurpose grease as indicated.

2) On Toyota models only, measure inside diameter of actuating cam. Measure outside diameter of inner clutch and subtract this measurement from that of actuating cam. Difference is oil clearance. If clearance is not .012" (.3 mm), replace inner clutch assembly.

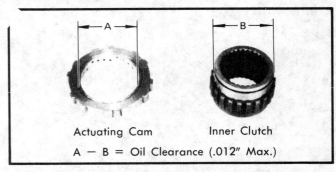

Fig. 5   Measuring Toyota Inner Clutch Oil Clearance

Reassembly — 1) Install actuating cam and spacer, then fit snap ring to rear of inner clutch. Insert inner clutch assembly to body and install snap ring. Reassemble outer clutch assembly, ensuring retaining spring is seated. Install compression spring. See Fig. 6.

NOTE — *Ensure inner clutch is installed with tooth end on outer side of hub.*

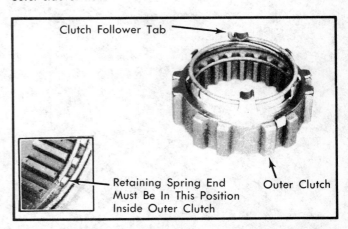

Fig. 6   Installing Retaining Spring and Clutch Follower to Outer Clutch With Inset Showing Inner Spring End

2) Install detent ball and spring (pin on Datsun) and ensure control knob is set to "FREE" ("LOCK" on Datsun) position. Insert control knob in cover and install snap ring. Assemble clutch assembly to cover assembly by pressing and rotating counterclockwise.

NOTE — *On Datsun, after clutch assembly is seated, rotate clutch assembly clockwise to align bolt holes.*

TIGHTENING SPECIFICATIONS

Application	Ft. Lbs. (mkg)
Hub Body-to-Hub	
Toyota 4-WD Pickup	21-25 (2.8-3.5)
Toyota Land Cruiser	18-25 (2.5-3.5)
Cover Assembly-to-Hub	
Datsun	18-25 (2.5-3.5)
LUV	14.5 (2.0)
Toyota Land Cruiser	3-5 (.5-.7)
Toyota 4-WD Pickup	6-8 (.8-1.2)

Latest Changes & Corrections

FOR 1980 AND PREVIOUS MODELS

▶ NOTE — *Changes which arrived too late to be included in the regular data pages are printed on these sheets and are arranged alphabetically by vehicle manufacturer. These items have been numbered to assist you in relating them to the general text. To prevent overlooking these last-minute changes, simply write the number of the item on the appropriate page.*

AUDI

▶ **1980 AUDI 5000 WITH DIESEL ENGINE AND 5-SPEED TRANSMISSION: MODIFICATIONS TO SELECTOR SHAFT** — **[1]** On subject models with 016 5-speed transmissions, the following modifications have been made after transmission number 14 07 0.

- The selector shaft bearing is now located in transmission housing.

- Spring and thrust washers that press shift lever into third and fourth gear and prevent shifting from fifth to reverse, have been changed.

- Selector shaft lever is now held by center screw on selector shaft, fixed by recess in shaft.

- Selector shaft is available only as an assembled part.

▶ **1980 AUDI 5000 MODELS WITH 087 AUTOMATIC TRANSMISSIONS: STRAINER DELETED** — **[2]** Beginning with transmission number 21040, the strainer in the pressure channel has been deleted from production. During repairs to transmissions built prior to number 21040, do not reinstall the strainer.

▶ **1980 AUDI 4000 MODELS WITH 014 4-SPEED TRANSMISSIONS: TRANSMISSION BREATHER MODIFIED** — The **[3]** breather on these transmissions has been relocated onto the final drive housing. When installing a new housing on 014

transmissions, drive the breather into the housing to a depth of $^{27}/_{32}$" (21 mm). When re-using gear shift housings, the old breather hole must be plugged with an $^1/_8$" (3 mm) pop rivet. Gear shift housings with and without breather holes are available as spare parts, however, only install housings with breather hole in transmissions up to number 21 01 0.

▶ **AUDI 5000 WITH AUTOMATIC TRANSMISSION: SLIPPING IN DRIVE RANGES** — Slippage in various drive ranges may be **[4]** caused by radiator coolant leaking into automatic transmission fluid through ATF cooler. Check and repair, if necessary, as follows:

1. Check ATF level on dipstick with engine warm and idling, selector lever in neutral and parking brake applied.

2. If level is above full mark, check color. If it appears milky, proceed as follows:

3. Install new oil cooler. Install new torque converter. Drain ATF from cooler.

4. Refill transmission with prescribed amount of ATF.

5. Run engine until warm to flush contaminated fluid from transmission parts. Drain ATF from transmission.

6. Refill with proper amount of ATF. Start engine and check operation of transmission.

BMW

▶ **1975-78 BMW 3.0 & 530i MODELS WITH BORG-WARNER MODEL 65 TRANSMISSION: GOVERNOR AND OIL TUBES [5] REMOVAL ILLUSTRATION** — The governor and oil tubes removal illustration provided by the manufacturer was incorrect. The correct governor tube locations are shown in the accompanying illustration. The incorrect illustration appears in the 1975 through 1978 editions of Mitchell's Transmission Manual as indicated in the following table:

Year of Edition	Page Number	Fig. Number
1975	2-31	7
1976	2-34	7
1977	2-34	5
1978	2-21	5

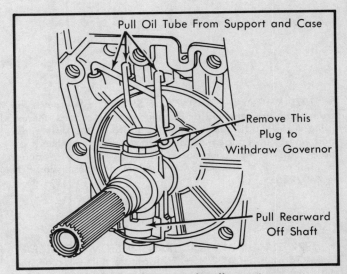

Pull Oil Tube From Support and Case

Remove This Plug to Withdraw Governor

Pull Rearward Off Shaft

Correct Governor Tube Illustration
Borg-Warner Model 65 Transmission

FOR 1980 AND PREVIOUS MODELS

CHRYSLER CORP. IMPORTS

[6] ► *1979-80 CHRYSLER CORP. ARROW AND D50 PICKUPS WITH 4-SPEED KM 130 MANUAL TRANSMISSIONS: HARD SHIFTING INTO REVERSE* — If a high effort, or slipping of the clutch is required to engage reverse gear, the following items should be used to correct this problem. The reverse gear and reverse idler gear must be replaced with new style gears. The new reverse gear (Chrysler Part No. MD703715) has improved chamfering on the gear teeth. The new reverse idler gear (Chrysler Part No. MD703716) has tapered teeth surfaces to prevent gear disengagement. When replacing these gears, both new gears must be replaced together.

[7] ► *1978-80 CHRYSLER CORP. IMPORT VEHICLES WITH KM 130 AND KM 132 MANUAL TRANSMISSIONS: NEW CLUTCH RELEASE BEARING* — A new style clutch release bearing with an integral carrier has been released for servicing these vehicles. The new style release bearing is self-aligning and replaces the separate release bearing and carrier set. The appropriate part numbers are listed below.

Application	Part No.
KM 130	MD700257
KM 132	MD703270

DATSUN

[8] ► *1978-79 B210 AND 210 AUTOMATIC TRANSMISSION 3N71B: FRONT OIL PUMP OIL SEAL* — The oil seal for the torque converter in the front extension of the oil pump on 3N71B transmissions, has been changed from a plain lip type seal to a threaded lip type seal. The new seal part number is 31344X-0101.

[9] ► *1978 510 AUTOMATIC TRANSMISSION: BAND SERVO CONTROL VALVE AND BRAKE BAND* — To improve shifting performance, the diameter of the band servo piston has been decreased and the old rigid brake band has been replaced by a flexible band. Also, the orifice check valve in the control assembly has been redesigned. The old servo piston diameter was 2.52" (64 mm) and the new piston diameter is 2.36" (60 mm).

[10] ► *1978 810 STATION WAGON: PRODUCTION CHANGE IN H190 TYPE DIFFERENTIAL CARRIER* — To insure quiet operation, the tooth height of ring gear and pinion gear have been increased. The inner space of the carrier has also been increased. Change became effective beginning with serial number WHLD810-826822.

[11] ► *1978 210 AND 810 AUTOMATIC TRANSMISSION 3N71B: PRODUCTION CHANGE IN BRAKE BAND* — The brake band for the 3N71B transmission has been changed to a flexible type. When out of the transmission, care must be taken to prevent the brake band from being damaged by unrolling. Change begins with serial numbers; HLB210-245998, HLG810-107189, HLB210-390270 and WHLD810-82775.

FIAT

[12] ► *1979 X1/9 AND STRADA: AXLE SHAFTS* — Whenever the axle shafts are removed or disconnected for repairs, the existing Allen head bolts securing the shafts to the differential and wheel hub flange must be replaced. The new Allen head bolts must be tightened to 31 ft. lbs. (4.3 mkg). Manual transmission P/N is 4393157 and automatic transmission P/N is 4402236.

[13] ► *1979 STRADA MANUAL TRANSMISSION: GEAR SHIFT LINKAGE MODIFICATION* — To facilitate shift selection, the shift rod has been modified. Vehicles after serial number 2207149 have been affected.

[14] ► *1978 & EARLIER FIAT 128 & X1/9 MODELS: NEW BELL HOUSING GASKET* — A new gasket (Part No. 4390609) between the bell housing and transmission case ensures proper positioning of the gasket during installation. Replacing gasket No. 4186529, the new gasket is wider and may be installed on earlier production vehicles.

[15] ► *1979 STRADA MANUAL TRANSMISSION: SHIFT LINKAGE ANTI-VIBRATION BRACKET* — To prevent the plastic sleeve from sliding off the arm of the shift linkage anti-vibration bracket, install a 5/16" (8 mm) push nut on the end of the bracket swing arm.

FOR 1980 AND PREVIOUS MODELS

FIESTA

▶ **1978-1979 FIESTA TRANSAXLE: TRANSAXLE CASE —**
16 Some transaxle housings, both production and replacement, do not have a recess for the differential housing cup and cup springs machined in the small section. Equal size cup springs must be used if there is no recess in the transaxle housing. Install bearing cup and secure with a light blow to prevent cup from dropping out when housing section is assembled.

▶ **1978-79 FORD FIESTA WITH MANUAL TRANSMISSIONS:**
17 **CLUTCH RELEASE FORK ATTACHING BOLT BREAKAGE —** If clutch pedal feels spongy and the friction point for clutch engagement moves toward lower end of pedal travel causing difficult noisy gear changes, it may be caused by the release fork bolt breaking.

The bolt breaking can be caused by one of the following: If bolt is insufficiently tightened, or bolt shank is not flush to release fork mating surface. If there is a misalignment of shaft threaded hole-to-fork counterbore. If bolt bottoms in fork due to insufficient thread depth. If any of these conditions exist, the following procedure can be used to correct it.

1. Remove transaxle assembly from vehicle.

2. Drill out and remove broken bolt. Dismantle fork, shaft and lever assembly.

3. Hand check new bolt into fork prior to assembly on shaft and lever. Verify that threaded hole is not misaligned with counterbore.

4. Hand start new bolt until shank is fully seated in counterbore. If bolts fails to seat by hand, replace shaft and lever assembly.

5. Insure that bolt is fully seated and properly tightened to 19-24 ft. lbs. (2.6-3.3 mkg).

▶ **1980 FIESTA: REVISED DESIGN TRANSAXLE BREATHER**
18 **ASSEMBLY —** A transaxle assembly with a revised design breather assembly was introduced into production in June, 1980. The revision involved a light-alloy transmission housing cover, a new breather tube and an input shaft with a deeper bore to accomodate the new breather tube. The light-alloy cover can be recognized by reinforcing ribs between bolt holes, as opposed to earlier level pressed steel cover which is recessed in area of bolt holes.

The original level breather tube assembly can be fitted to transaxles with either long or short bore input shaft, therefore only original pressed steel cover, bolts and breather hose will be available as service replacement parts. The original design breather and cover should be used to service both types of breather, if replacement is necessary.

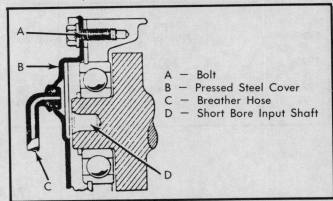

A — Bolt
B — Pressed Steel Cover
C — Breather Hose
D — Short Bore Input Shaft

Ford Fiesta Original Transaxle Breather Assembly

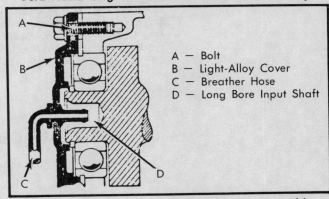

A — Bolt
B — Light-Alloy Cover
C — Breather Hose
D — Long Bore Input Shaft

Ford Fiesta Revised Transaxle Breather Assembly

HONDA

▶ **1973-75 HONDA MODELS WITH 4- OR 5-SPEED MANUAL**
19 **TRANSMISSIONS, CREEPING FORWARD IN 1ST GEAR WITH**
CLUTCH PEDAL FULLY DEPRESSED — Condition may be due to failure of clutch disc to fully disengage. Check clutch pedal free play. Depress clutch pedal fully and shift transmission into 1st gear. Start engine and run at 2500 RPM. If vehicle moves forward slowly, shut off engine and replace clutch disc with 1976 type disc, which has relief slots cut across the rivets on pressure plate side.

▶ **1977 & EARLIER HONDA MODELS WITH HONDAMATIC**
20 **TRANSMISSION, SPEEDOMETER DRIVEN GEAR DAMAGE —**
Gear damage can result if transmission countershaft lock nut is insufficiently torqued and inadequately staked. Nut then can back off, cutting speedometer driven gear teeth. In such cases it is not enough to just replace the driven gear. It is imperative that the transmission be disassembled, inspected and thoroughly cleaned. There could be damage to the low gear/low gear clutch pack, valve body or torque converter. Disassembly should include sub-assemblies. Make sure all oil passages are free of debris.

JAGUAR

21 ► *1975-78 JAGUAR XJ6 MODELS WITH BORG-WARNER MODEL 65 TRANSMISSION: GOVERNOR AND OIL TUBES REMOVAL ILLUSTRATION* — The governor and oil tubes removal illustration provided by the manufacturer was incorrect. The correct governor tube locations are shown in the accompanying illustration. The incorrect illustration appears in the 1975 through 1978 editions of Mitchell's Transmission Manual as indicated in the following table:

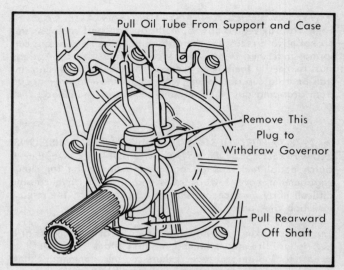

Pull Oil Tube From Support and Case

Remove This Plug to Withdraw Governor

Pull Rearward Off Shaft

*Correct Governor Tube Illustration
Borg-Warner Model 65 Transmission*

Year of Edition	Page Number	Fig. Number
1975	2-31	7
1976	2-34	7
1977	2-34	5
1978	2-21	5

MAZDA

22 ► *1979 MAZDA MANUAL TRANSMISSION: CLUTCH CHATTER* — Clutch chatter is caused by disc material which is slow to "seat-in" on the flywheel and pressure plate. If after initial 5000 miles of driving the clutch still chatters, a new clutch disc P/N 1246224600 which has softer material should be used.

MERCEDES-BENZ

23 ► *MERCEDES-BENZ VEHICLES WITH 716.005/006 TRANSMISSIONS: MODIFIED COUNTERSHAFT* — Since August, 1979, this transmission is equipped with a countershaft on which constant-mesh and third gear are assembled by shrink fitting. In case of repair, the complete countershaft must be replaced. On modified countershaft, constant-mesh, third and reverse gears are secured with one circlip each. Previously these gears were secured with one hex nut. In addition, on modified countershafts no spacer shim will be fitted between ball bearing and constant-mesh gear. Replacement countershaft assemblies can be ordered by MB Part No. 115 260 30 24.

24 ► *MERCEDES-BENZ 240D AND ALL 300 SERIES MODELS WITH AUTOMATIC TRANSMISSIONS: MODIFIED CLUTCH DISCS FOR K2 CLUTCH* — Since September of 1979, clutch discs without grooves have been installed in 722.117/118/120 transmissions. At the same time, the number of pressure springs for clutch piston was reduced from 20 to 16. The modified clutch discs possess a greater coefficient of friction, resulting in prevention of occasional slippage on 3rd to 4th upshifts. When rebuilding transmissions, it is possible to install new clutch discs on transmissions which do not have them. In addition, the number of pressure springs should be reduced to 16, from 20. The modified clutch discs were placed in production after the following transmission numbers.

Application	Transmission No.
300SD	14921
240D	30916
300D, CD & TD	86933

FOR 1980 AND PREVIOUS MODELS

MERCEDES-BENZ (Cont.)

25 ▶ *1980 MERCEDES-BENZ DIESEL ENGINE MODELS EXCEPT TURBOCHARGED ENGINES: ADJUSTMENT OF VACUUM MODULATING VALVE* — Since December, 1979, a modified vacuum modulating valve was installed on the transmission. Shifting complaints such as hard, delayed or light slipping, and premature up-shifting at partial load can be corrected by adjusting vacuum modulating valve individually. Vehicles which do not have the modified valve and have the complaints listed, must have the valve installed in conjunction with a push rod and plastic connector. The modified vacuum valve has a full throttle stop and an idle stop. This stop prevents the deviation of the predetermined tensioned spring in modulating valve, due to overexertion of actuating lever against spring. Adjustment is as follows:

1. Basic adjustment requires that push rod be adjusted to a length of 4-13/16" (122 mm). Compensating adjustment is made with ball head at regulating lever.

2. Apply full throttle, causing actuating lever to touch full throttle stop. Loosen and slide adjustable ball head in order to gain a clearance of .020" (.5 mm) between actuating lever and full throttle stop. Lock ball head.

Hard & Delayed Upshifting Adjustment

1. Loosen adjustable ball head and slide downward. Lock ball head. Loosen lock nut and disconnect ball joint.

2. Lengthen push rod via ball joint to gain a clearance of .020" (.5 mm) between actuating lever and full throttle stop in full throttle position. Connect ball joint and tighten lock nut.

Slippage & Early Upshifting Adjustment

Loosen adjustable ball head and slide upward, and lock ball head. If necessary, push rod length can be shortened by cutting threaded end of rod by approximately 3/16" (5 mm).

NOTE — *After adjustments of vacuum modulating valve, the EGR vacuum control valve must be tested and corrected if required.*

26 ▶ *MERCEDES-BENZ 240D AND 300 SERIES MODELS WITH AUTOMATIC TRANSMISSION: MODIFICATION OF SHIFT VALVE HOUSING FOR MODIFIED PARTIAL LOAD SHIFT POINTS* — Since June, 1980, the large intermediate steel plate with a larger restricting bore of .1811" (3 mm) was installed in transmissions on these vehicles. In addition, a modified control pressure increase valve with corresponding spring, as well as modified springs on 1st and 2nd gear shift control valve and control pressure regulating valve were installed. These changes will prevent rapid successive upshifts and spread partial load downshifts to high side.

If complaints of this nature exist on earlier production vehicles, the restricting bore of large intermediate plate can be enlarged using the following procedure.

1. Remove valve body from transmission. Disassemble valve body.

2. Enlarge restricting bore in large intermediate plate to diameter of .1181" (3 mm).

NOTE — *240D models use a different intermediate plate than 300 series models. Be sure that proper hole is enlarged on correct plate.*

3. Remove any burrs from enlarged hole. Loosen fastening screws on end plate and remove all except one.

4. Swing out end plate far enough to allow for removal of plug, control pressure regulating valve and both springs.

5. Replace heavier spring with new spring (MB Part No. 123 993 41 01). Reinsert lighter spring, regulating valve and plug. Tighten end plate screws.

6. Loosen fastening screws on opposite side on end plate and remove all screws except one. Swing out end plate far enough to allow removal of control pressure increase valve and 1-2 shift valve with piston and spring.

7. Replace increase valve and spring with new valve (MB Part No. 123 277 07 31) and spring (MB Part No. 123 993 40 01). Insert 1-2 shift valve with piston and spring in valve body. Tighten screws and assemble valve body and install in transmission.

8. Check and replenish fluid level.

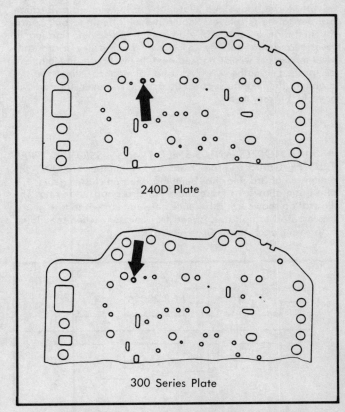

240D Plate

300 Series Plate

Mercedes-Benz Intermediate Plate Restricting Bores

FOR 1980 AND PREVIOUS MODELS

PEUGEOT

27 ▶ *1980 PEUGEOT 505 AND 604 MODELS WITH 5-SPEED TRANSMISSION: REAR HOUSING BREAKAGE* — When reinstalling the 5-speed gearbox rear housing with the transmission in the vehicle, mispositioning of the ring shown in the illustration can cause the rear housing to break. When the rear housing is removed and replaced, the following items should be noted.

- Be sure the ring is properly positioned on its flats as shown in the illustration.

- Use multi-purpose grease to hold ring in place while housing is being installed. This will help to prevent the ring from moving off its flats during installation.

- If the procedure is performed with transmission off vehicle, place transmission in a vertical position to ease installation of the ring and housing.

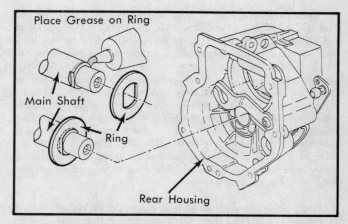

Installing Ring in Peugeot Gearbox Housing

SAAB

28 ▶ *SAAB MODELS WITH MANUAL TRANSMISSION: HARD SHIFTING AND/OR IGNITION KEY WILL NOT RELEASE* — If complaints of hard shifting and ignition keys not being released from the switch are encountered, check the rubber damper bushing in the shift rod to the transmission. The rubber damper forms a moulded joint in the rod to eliminate vibration transfer to the shift lever. Should the joint begin to pull apart, the first sign is a loss of adjustment, preventing locking in reverse and the inability to remove ignition key. Hard shift lever movement will be noticed next. In most cases the joint can be pushed together, drilled and pinned to eliminate the problem. If complete separation occurs, however, the rod will have to be replaced.

29 ▶ *SAAB MODELS WITH 5-SPEED TRANSMISSION: ALTERED CLUSTER GEAR* — From transmission number 408097, the dimension of 3rd gear has been modified on cluster gears. The alteration allows for more space for 3rd gear guide ring. The illustration shows size difference between early and late gears. It is advised to update 5-speed transmissions when rebuilding to prevent damage to 3rd gear guide ring.

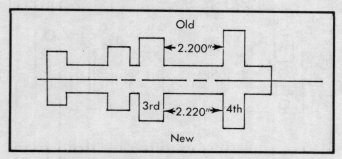

Saab 5-Speed Transmission Dimension Change

30 ▶ *SAAB MODELS WITH MANUAL TRANSMISSION: BRASS PARTICLES IN CASE* — When rebuilding manual transmissions which have a damaged synchro ring, it is very important that all brass particles be removed from the case. Places often neglected during such cleaning are the front primary gear cover oil collector and differential side cover oil dam. Both areas can fill with brass particles. If not removed, these particles will be circulated and coat the new synchro ring, which results in a synchro ring failure in a very short time.

31 ▶ *SAAB MODELS WITH 5-SPEED TRANSMISSIONS: DIFFICULT ENGAGEMENT OF FIRST AND SECOND GEARS* — Whenever difficult engagement of 1st and 2nd gear is noticed, the gear shift lever should be adjusted according to procedures in *Manual Transmission Servicing Section.* If this fails to correct the difficult engagement, the following procedure should be used.

1. Select either 1st or 2nd gear position and check side play of shift lever.

2. If no side play with 1st or 2nd engaged, shift lever housing should be repositioned by placing a .118" (3 mm) shim (Saab Part No. 7061328) under left front mounting flange.

3. If selection of other gears becomes difficult after installing shim, replace shim with a .039" (1 mm) shim (Saab Part No. 7311764) to reduce angle of housing.

4. After installation, side play in 1st and 2nd gear should be about the same as that in 3rd and 4th gears. Road test to verify adequate shifting.

NOTE — *After VIN 90801020095, shift rod taper pin holes are offset 3°, which has the same effect as the above procedure.*

Latest Changes & Corrections

FOR 1980 AND PREVIOUS MODELS

SAAB (Cont.)

32 ▶ SAAB MODELS WITH 4-SPEED MANUAL TRANSMISSION: JUMPING OUT OF THIRD GEAR UNDER LOAD — The problem of 3rd gear jump out began appearing with the introduction of synchro hub (Saab Part No. 8712283). Although the hub is correctly designed, machining tolerances could create a condition that prevents operating sleeve from accomplishing a complete engagement of 3rd gear. New parts have been corrected, and to eliminate this condition, synchro hubs should be replaced with parts from the new inventory.

33 ▶ SAAB VEHICLES WITH TYPE 35 AUTOMATIC TRANSMISSIONS: NEW PINION SEAL SHAFT OIL SEAL — An improved pinion shaft seal (Saab Part No. 9346602) is available for use on Saab 99 and 900 models with type 35 automatic transmissions. The seal is a "V" ring design and replaces one of two seals previously used.

A new distance spacer (Saab Part No.8791022) must be used with installing tool (Saab Part No. 8790164) to properly position seal (Saab Part No. 8707176) so new seal will seat against it properly. The following procedure should be used to install the seal.

1. Press seal 8707176 into pinion housing installing tool and distance spacer. Be sure seal lip faces toward transmission.

2. Place seal protector (Saab Part No. 8791006) on pinion shaft. Lubricate new seal and slide onto pinion shaft with thick portion against pinion bearing.

3. Reassemble pinion shaft, housing and governor following standard reassembling procedures.

VOLKSWAGEN

34 ▶ NEW MAINSHAFT OIL SEAL INSTALLATION ON MANUAL TRANSMISSIONS — On Rabbit and Scirocco models, a new oil seal mounting groove has been machined into transmission case. With the new type of case no sealer is used when installing oil seal, instead lubricate seal lightly with oil before installation.

35 ▶ 1979 RABBIT & SCIROCCO WITH AUTOMATIC TRANSMISSION: TRANSMISSION CASES NOT INTERCHANGEABLE — New transmission case housing does not have mounting stud as did earlier case. Mounting stud has been replaced with a bolt. This change requires that transmission be supported during removal procedures BEFORE removing last mounting bolt. If final drive assembly is being replaced, install new housing (without mounting stud) and new gravel guard.

36 ▶ 1979 RABBIT & SCIROCCO WITH 4-SPEED MANUAL TRANSMISSION (020): MODIFIED PINION SHAFT BEARING — Pinion shaft bearing is now seated in housing with retaining screw. When installing new, modified transmission housing in early models, use new bearing and retaining screw. Remove and discard pinion shaft stop. Warm transmission housing to 176°F (80°C) and pull out and discard old bearing. Bearings are still available for use in early transmission housings. Modification began on limited basis with transmission number GC08109 and full modification of transmissions from GC20019.

37 ▶ SELF-LOCKING SCREW FOR SHIFT CONTROL ROD — 8mm square headed shift rod lock screw has been replaced with a 10mm hex headed self-locking screw. Do not reuse new type screw as self-locking adhesive is destroyed upon removal, always replace screw when installing shift rod.

VOLVO

38 ▶ VOLVO MODELS WITH M45 AND M46 MANUAL TRANSMISSIONS: REPLACING PULL ROD INTERLOCK SLEEVE — Replacement of the pull rod for reverse lockout does not require replacement of the complete gearshift lever. Only pull rod requires replacement. Rod can be replaced by disconnecting and removing upper section of shift lever. When replacing pull rod, early type interlock sleeve should also be replaced with a new type sleeve (Volvo Part No. 1232687-2). New sleeve has a locating notch which prevents it from

rotating on shift lever, and a groove in which pull rod is fitted. This prevents pull rod from wearing against interlock plate.

When fitting older type gear lever with new interlock sleeve, place a .078" (2 mm) by ½" (13 mm) O.D. washer to act as a spacer on knob before pressing it onto lever. This is necessary since new interlock sleeve is .078" (2 mm) longer and it must be able to lift above interlock plate. If screw is worn, it must be replaced at same time with a new, harder type screw (Volvo Part No. 1232688-0).

Latest Changes & Corrections

VOLVO (Cont.)

▶ *VOLVO MODELS WITH BORG-WARNER 55 TRANSMISSIONS: PUMP OIL SEAL* — The green pump oil seal for BW55 transmissions can in extreme cases cause an oil leakage. This will only occur when towing a heavy trailer, driving in mountainous terrain or after prolonged high speed driving in hot temperatures. This can be corrected by replacing the green seal with a red Koyo seal with same part number. Red seal has been put into production in transmissions after the following numbers, 014-24256, 019-5155, 020-3549 and 023-7027.

▶ *1979 VOLVO 240 & 260 MODELS WITH OVERDRIVE: REVISED REMOVAL PROCEDURES OF OVERDRIVE ONE-WAY CLUTCH* — The overdrive one-way clutch can be removed without removing transmission from vehicle. With vehicle suitably supported on a hoist, remove overdrive one-way clutch as follows:

1) Unload overdrive by starting engine and engaging overdrive, then depress clutch pedal and stop engine. Disconnect propeller shaft and speedometer cable from overdrive. Disconnect ground cable at solenoid. Remove rear overdrive housing retaining bolts and washers. Remove overdrive rear assembly.

2) Mount rear housing in soft-jawed vise. Remove circlip and oil slinger, then carefully remove one-way clutch. The rollers of the one-way clutch are loose. Remove roller cage, rollers and spring from clutch. Clean all parts and ensure modified clutch is installed. Newer clutch has higher lobes than early production clutch. Check cage for wear or damage.

3) Install spring and roller cage. Rotate cage clockwise, and lock in farthest position of rotation. Insert rollers and hold in place by using a rubber band or string. Ensure correct thrust washer is installed in overdrive output shaft. Install one-way clutch and remove rubber band or string used to secure rollers.

4) Install oil slinger and circlip. Check all gaskets and replace those which show damage. Reverse removal procedure and install overdrive rear assembly. Fill transmission with ATF, start engine and engage overdrive. Stop engine and check fluid level.

▶ *VOLVO MODELS WITH MANUAL TRANSMISSIONS: PRESSURE PLATES AND RELEASE BEARINGS* — Two different designs of pressure plates and release bearings are used on Volvo 240 and 260 models. The two designs are easily recognizable by the fingers of the pressure plate. Plates for 260 models have fingers that are raised approximately $9/32"$ (7 mm) at the center. Plate fingers on 240 model plates are straight. Because of the finger difference, there are two different release bearings for these models. Release bearings for 260 models are approximately $1-7/16"$ (36.5 mm) long. Release bearings for 240 models are approximately $1-11/16"$ (43 mm) long. Pressure plates and release bearings must be used in the correct combination and should never be mixed.

"WE LISTEN"

We will greatly appreciate receiving your comments or corrections so that we may continue to publish the world's best automotive manuals. **Mail this card today. We'd like to hear from you!**

☐ Domestic   ☐ Imported   ☐ Trucks
☐ A/C Service   ☐ Tune-Up   ☐ Mechanical   ☐ Transmissions   ☐ Emission Control

Section No._____ Page No._____ Vehicle Model, year _____

Comments: _____

_____

_____

Company Name _____ Phone __(____)_____

Address _____ Zip _____

"WE LISTEN"

We will greatly appreciate receiving your comments or corrections so that we may continue to publish the world's best automotive manuals. **Mail this card today. We'd like to hear from you!**

☐ Domestic   ☐ Imported   ☐ Trucks
☐ A/C Service   ☐ Tune-Up   ☐ Mechanical   ☐ Transmissions   ☐ Emission Control

Section No._____ Page No._____ Vehicle Model, year _____

Comments: _____

_____

_____

Company Name _____ Phone __(____)_____

Address _____ Zip _____

"WE LISTEN"

We will greatly appreciate receiving your comments or corrections so that we may continue to publish the world's best automotive manuals. **Mail this card today. We'd like to hear from you!**

☐ Domestic   ☐ Imported   ☐ Trucks
☐ A/C Service   ☐ Tune-Up   ☐ Mechanical   ☐ Transmissions   ☐ Emission Control

Section No._____ Page No._____ Vehicle Model, year _____

Comments: _____

_____

_____

Company Name _____ Phone __(____)_____

Address _____ Zip _____

BUSINESS REPLY CARD

| FIRST CLASS | PERMIT NO. 3701 | SAN DIEGO, CA |

POSTAGE WILL BE PAID BY ADDRESSEE

MITCHELL MANUALS, INC.

P.O. BOX 26260
San Diego, California 92126

BUSINESS REPLY CARD

| FIRST CLASS | PERMIT NO. 3701 | SAN DIEGO, CA |

POSTAGE WILL BE PAID BY ADDRESSEE

MITCHELL MANUALS, INC.

P.O. BOX 26260
San Diego, California 92126

BUSINESS REPLY CARD

| FIRST CLASS | PERMIT NO. 3701 | SAN DIEGO, CA |

POSTAGE WILL BE PAID BY ADDRESSEE

MITCHELL MANUALS, INC.

P.O. BOX 26260
San Diego, California 92126